vhf/uhf manual

FOURTH EDITION

Editor: G. R. Jessop, CEng, MIERE, G6JP

RADIO SOCIETY OF GREAT BRITAIN

Published by the Radio Society of Great Britain, Lambda House, Cranborne Road, Potters Bar, Hertfordshire EN6 3JE

First published 1969
Fourth edition 1983, reprinted 1985, 1987, 1989, 1990 (twice), 1991, 1992

ISBN 0 900612 92 4

Printed in Great Britain at The Bath Press, Avon

Contents

Foreword

The 1979 World Administrative Radio Conference of the International Telecommunication Union re-defined the amateur service as "A radiocommunication service for the purpose of self-training, intercommunication and technical investigation carried out by amateurs, that is, by duly authorized persons interested in radio technique solely with a personal aim and without pecuniary interest".

The conference, which was a world assembly of national governments acting in concert, like its predecessors, acknowledged the importance of the amateur service and the amateur-satellite service by confirming existing allocations and making new ones, particularly above 40GHz. The ITU has always taken note of the contribution made by the amateur service in the propagation field and in the development of effective equipment to exploit the full potential of the various frequency bands allocated to it.

During the six years that have passed since the last edition of this manual appeared, there have been many technical advances enabling higher-performance equipment to be constructed by the experienced amateur. One example is the achievement of low-power long-distance communication in the 10GHz band over ranges in excess of 1,000km. The establishment of beacons in the various bands has considerably assisted regular observation work. The development of networks of repeaters on 144 and 432MHz has enabled large numbers of low-power mobile units to communicate with one another using a minimum of spectrum space.

Self-training in the amateur service in the multitude of processes involved in communication cannot be undertaken without suitable material for study being made available. The success of the *VHF/UHF Manual* in its past editions bears witness to the outstanding contribution that it has made in filling this need. I have no doubt that this new edition, which is even larger than its predecessors, will prove a worthy successor. A debt of gratitude is owed to George Jessop, who has master-minded this work, and to those who have contributed material.

D. E. Baptiste, CBE
RSGB President 1983

Preface

The continued considerable increase of interest in the amateur vhf/uhf bands has been clearly demonstrated by the exceptional number of new licences being issued in this country and abroad, together with the quantity of articles being published in national society journals and in popular magazines.

There is an undoubted need for an updated manual for amateur operators, covering the spectrum above 30MHz and providing material that is directly useful to all who wish to have a better understanding of the subject, and who may wish to construct some of their own equipment or accessories. It is hoped that the present volume amply fulfils these requirements. Those who may be called "black box" operators will find a considerable amount of the content devoted to matters of general interest, such as antennas, propagation and test equipment etc.

In preparing this, the fourth edition, opportunity has been taken to revise extensively the various chapters, replacing earlier designs with more modern versions. In certain cases, however, generic circuits for valves have been included, together with valve power amplifiers, and no apology is made for this action. Although valve receiver designs have largely been replaced by those using semiconductors, it is worth noting that valves are about 100 times less susceptible to damage from emp radiations of one sort or another, including lightning. However, due to higher noise, their use is limited above about 100MHz.

The popularity of operation through satellites and on microwaves has grown considerably, and the microwave activity pioneered by UK amateurs is growing in other parts of the world. The relevant chapters on these subjects have been significantly improved and extended.

G.R.J.

Acknowledgements
The editor wishes to express his thanks to the following, who have contributed complete chapters:

D. S. Evans, G3RPE (Microwaves)
R. G. Flavell, G3LTP (Propagation)
R. J. Phillips, G4IQQ (Space communications)
R. G. Powers, G8CKN (Antennas)

He is also grateful to T. G. Giles, G4CDY, P. J. Hart, G3SJX, and R. S. Hewes, G3TDR, for various contributions to the chapters on transmitters and receivers; to R. S. Roberts, G6NR, for his revision of the television transmission material; to R. W. Addie, G8LT, P. Edwards, GW4BXE, and N. G. Hyde, G2AIH, for constructional projects; to R. J. Eckersley, G4FTJ, the Society's book editor, for considerable assistance and many helpful suggestions made during the preparation of the final copy; to J. N. Gannaway, G3YGF, for reviewing the page proofs; to other contributors to previous editions whose material has been retained; and to those whose material has been extracted from *Radio Communication* and other magazines. In this connection, thanks are due to the publishers of *Ham Radio, Practical Wireless* and *VHF Communications* for their permission to reproduce copyright material. Acknowledgement is also due to Jaybeam Engineering Ltd for permission to reproduce certain charts appearing in Chapter 8.

CHAPTER 1

Historical perspectives

Even today, many radio amateurs tend to regard vhf/uhf techniques as something "new fangled", and necessarily more complex than those used on the hf bands.

Nothing could be further from the truth; indeed some of the pioneering radio experiments were carried out on these frequencies. Hertz used 800MHz for some of his earliest tests before the beginning of this century, while much of Marconi's work was concerned with vhf. Just after the first world war, he built a 150MHz a.m. transmitter using a V24 valve with a dipole antenna and parabolic reflector. The matching receiver used a semiconductor diode (crystal) detector.

This frequency was very close to the limit at which the valves of that era would function normally, but in 1919 Barkhausen and Kury discovered that ordinary cylindrical-electrode triodes would oscillate at up to 900MHz if the grid was made very positive and the anode negative. In 1920 Hull invented the magnetron, a cylindrical diode with a magnetic field coil wound round the anode. This was developed into the split-anode magnetron by 1924 and, although mainly used for longer waves, 900MHz oscillation was possible. A commercial magnetron was produced which gave 50W around 144MHz. These devices were cumbersome, however, due to the large field coil, and fell out of favour until much later in 1940 when Randall and Boot developed the resonant-cavity magnetron used in radar.

In the 'twenties most amateur experimenters were devoting their time to proving that short waves could be used for long-range communciation and this historic development tended to overshadow progress in the vhf field, particularly as it was thought that frequencies above 30MHz could only follow line-of-sight paths. Such experiments as were carried out tended to use frequencies in the 50–70MHz range, as valves for this band were more readily available. A popular transmitter circuit of that period used two valves in push-pull with a tuned anode circuit and a broadly resonant, untuned grid circuit, and was therefore known as the "TNT" circuit. Most vhf receivers in those days used the super-regenerative principle proposed by Armstrong in 1922, which had the advantages of simplicity and high gain.

The first vhf antennas were of the inverted "L" type but resonant antennas were later introduced with much improved results. In 1928 Yagi and Uda developed the famous beam antenna using directors which was to have such an influence on vhf and uhf where it was not easy to generate large rf powers. They carried out experiments using frequencies of up to 6GHz, obtaining telephony contacts over 10–30km.

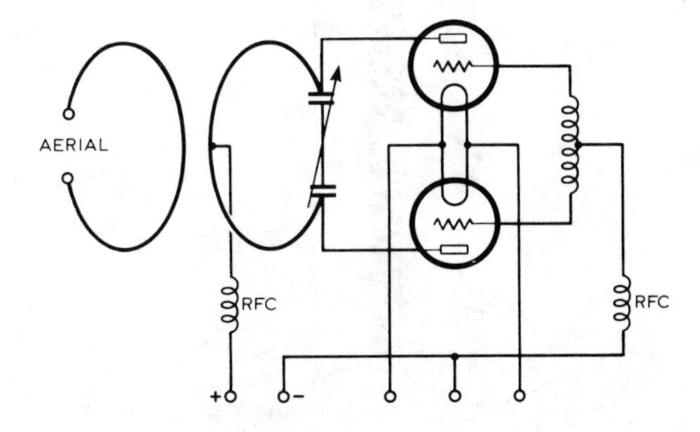

The "TNT" circuit used for 2½ and 5m

A couple of years later, Marconi used improved valves and beam antennas to demonstrate communication up to 168 miles over a sea path at frequencies over 500MHz. This was perhaps the first real indication that communication far beyond the visible range was possible, and stimulated growing interest in

V24 early short-wave triode

CW11 split-anode magnetron originally made for operation at 2m

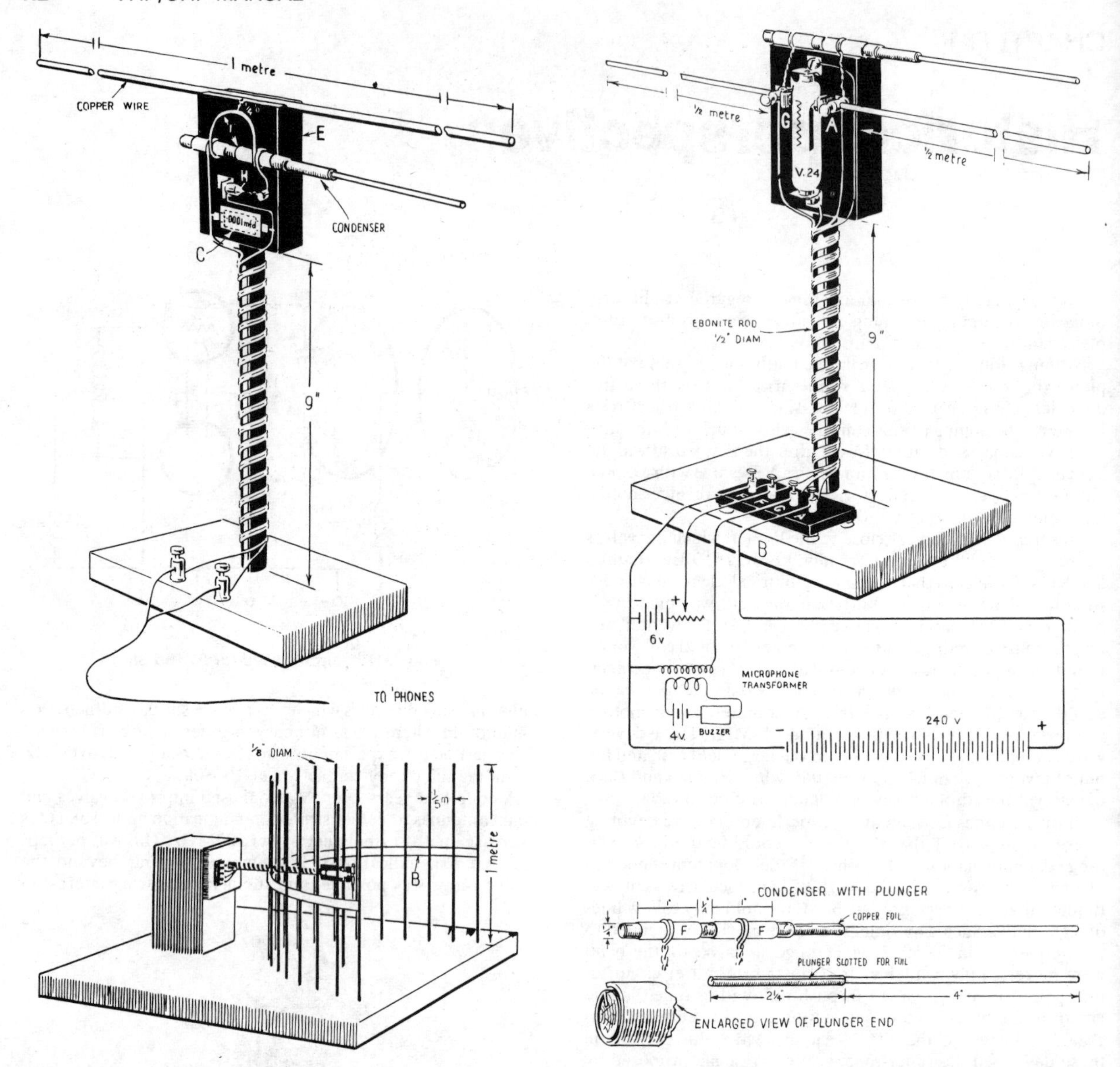

Marconi's 2m transmitter and receiver made in 1919 which demonstrated the production of a beam using a parabolic reflector

these hitherto "quasi-optical" bands. In the early 'thirties experiments by UK amateurs on 60MHz included airborne communication, and in 1935 an attempt at long-distance communication from the summit of Snowdon, which resulted in signals being received at Romford, 207 miles away.

By then, 50–70MHz was not the only band in use. Some experimenters were active on 112MHz using "organ pipe" tuned circuits to overcome stability problems, while others tested the newly-developed acorn valves at 500MHz using lecher line circuits.

By the end of the 'thirties most of the basic techniques of vhf transmission and reception described in this book had been mastered, and some amateurs were using beam antennas, crystal-controlled transmitters and superheterodyne receivers. DX was already being worked, and a sunspot peak at the end of the decade enabled USA amateurs to achieve a contact across their continent on 56MHz.

The years following the second world war saw a large amount of surplus electronic equipment appear on the amateur market. The 28MHz band had lost something of its novelty by then and, when the new 144MHz and 432MHz bands were allocated in the late 'forties, many experimenters moved in.

It was in this period that auroral and meteor-scatter contacts began to be seriously explored, and in 1953 the first amateur moonbounce contact was made between two USA stations. An important development took place in 1957 in the UK—the establishment of a temporary 144MHz beacon for propagation studies linked with the International Geophysical Year.

Electron oscillation receiver made in March 1931 by E. Megaw, G6MU. It used a dull emitter valve (V24) as the oscillating detector

A 112MHz "organ-pipe" oscillator

GB3IGY proved the value of such beacons and four years later GB3VHF was commissioned as the first in a national (and now international) network which has done much to assist propagation studies and alert operators to "openings" over the years.

And openings there were. In 1959 Italian stations were worked for the first time from the UK on 144MHz via sporadic-E, a distance of over 1,000 miles. On the same day, 14 June, two USA amateurs set a new world record of 400 miles on 1·3GHz; a couple of days earlier the world record on 420MHz had been pushed up to 651 miles by a contact between the UK and Sweden. The world records for 144MHz and 220MHz were then the 2,540-mile path between Hawaii and California, which has subsequently seen some spectacular openings.

The concept of the vhf transceiver was still to appear at this time. Most transmitters were crystal controlled with a frequency multiplier chain and used a.m., and receivers often consisted of a vhf converter ahead of a hf communication receiver. A common operating procedure was therefore to call CQ and announce that one was "tuning the band". The receiver would be used to search out any replies, the contact being conducted on the two fixed frequencies to suit the operators. The UK had until the 'seventies a geographical band plan for the 144 and 432MHz bands. Each zone of the country had its own frequency segment and it was thus possible to listen out for amateurs in a particular part of the UK, which was helpful for inter-UK working. However, distances worked on 144MHz were continuing to increase as ssb equipment became available, and a more international band plan became necessary.

Other developments taking place, particularly in the USA, were soon to hasten this pattern of change. The late 'sixties and early 'seventies saw the introduction of commercial mobile transceivers which were compact enough to fit underneath the

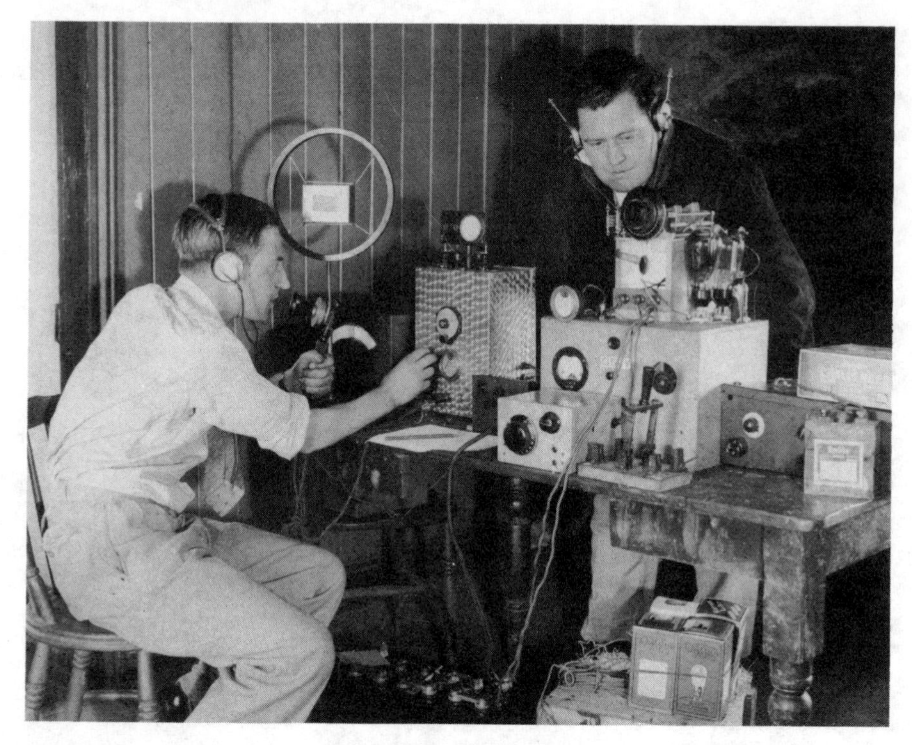

The 5m station G5CV at the top of Snowdon, North Wales, in July 1935. Signals were received at Romford in Essex (photo courtesy of the National Portrait Gallery)

dashboard of a car. These steadily reduced in size as semiconductors replaced valves, and in price in real terms as the Japanese began mass production for the American market. A tremendous upsurge in mobile activity was the result. At first a.m. was used but increasingly fm became the preferred mode, for reception was less affected by automotive interference; fm was also more suited to the capabilities of the earlier rf power transistors coming into use.

Mobile operation was still at this time a "patchy" affair, with communication often restricted by tall buildings or other obstructions, often due to the poor weak-signal characteristics of fm reception. Similar problems had been experienced by the authorities with police, ambulance and fire service communications, and amateurs adopted the same solution: repeater stations which automatically rebroadcast the original signal from a high and advantageous location. This cuts out a great deal of "flutter" and effectively increases the mobile–mobile range.

Introduced in the late 'sixties in the USA and early 'seventies in Europe, repeaters and the availability of low-cost channelized transceivers, together with the increasing amount of dx being worked on ssb, reinforced the need for a re-think of band plans and operating habits. In 1972 an IARU Region 1 conference adopted vhf and uhf bandplans which effectively split the bands into sections to separate the two largely incompatible types of operation: vfo-controlled cw/ssb dx working and channelized fm local operation. The old UK geographical band plan was abandoned, and in 1973 the first UK repeater, GB3PI,

An early 2·3GHz klystron oscillator and radiator

Two 420MHz beam arrays in use at G2FKZ in the 'fifties

commenced operation on an experimental basis. A great success, it was soon followed by the establishment of many others throughout the country, often using complex logic techniques and representing a considerable technical team effort on the part of the groups which built them.

The influx of compact factory-made equipment for the vhf/uhf bands had another effect, particularly in Europe. Just as experimenters had moved off the 28MHz band into vhf to see what could be achieved, so many decided to move up into the microwave region in the 'sixties and 'seventies, undoubtedly assisted by a regular feature in *Radio Communication* which began in 1970. In the UK the 10GHz band received much attention and the Gunn diode, which was then becoming available on the surplus market, formed the basis of low-cost wideband transceivers. Experiments were carried out over optical and obstructed paths and several remarkable contacts were made over hundreds of kilometres. These used super-refraction and other ducting modes and demonstrated the potential of this band.

Other experimenters were turning their eyes skywards. In 1961 the first amateur satellite, Oscar 1, was launched, carrying a 100mW telemetry beacon in the 144MHz band. A number of other amateur satellites were launched in the 'sixties, some of which provided two-way communication for limited periods, but the first really useful one was Oscar 6, launched in 1972, which provided vhf dx communication for over four years and established satellite communication as an important part of the amateur scene.

Moonbounce, while still a considerable technical achievement, has recently been shown to be possible with backyard antennas, and all continents have been worked using this mode. Auroral working in Europe was facilitated by the establishment of an early-warning net of operators who constantly monitor conditions and alert others if necessary. Meteor-scatter has become a popular dx mode, assisted by the availability of computer predictions of the best times and directions of the optimum paths.

Years of amateur research into transequatorial propagation are leading to a better understanding of this phenomenon, and also providing spectacular long-distance contacts in the 50, 144 and 432MHz bands.

In the microwave region, efforts are being made to introduce narrow-band communication modes, such as ssb, with great success, while the six new amateur microwave bands allocated at the 1979 World Administrative Radio Conference should provide an interesting area for experimentation during this decade and beyond.

The present day has seen the introduction by manufacturers of complex microprocessor-controlled equipment capable of

A challenge for the 'eighties: the 6·2m 1·3GHz moonbounce dish at GW3XYW

Amateur service frequency allocations above 30MHz (WARC 79)

Region 1	Region 2	Region 3
47–68MHz **Broadcasting**	50–54 **Amateur**	
144–146	**Amateur, Amateur-Satellite**	
146–149·9 **Fixed, Mobile** except aeronautical mobile (R)	146–148 **Amateur**	146–148 **Amateur, Fixed, Mobile**
223–230 **Broadcasting,** Fixed, Mobile	220–225 **Amateur, Fixed, Mobile**, Radiolocation	223–230 **Fixed, Mobile, Broadcasting, Aeronautical Radionavigation,** Radiolocation
430–440 **Amateur, Radiolocation**	430–440 **Radiolocation**, Amateur	
890–942 **Fixed, Mobile** except aeronautical mobile, **Broadcasting,** Radiolocation	902–928 **Fixed**, Amateur, Mobile except aeronautical mobile, Radiolocation	890–942 **Fixed, Mobile, Broadcasting,** Radiolocation
1,240–1,260	**Radiolocation, Radionavigation-Satellite** (space-to-earth), Amateur	
1,260–1,300	**Radiolocation**, Amateur	
2,300–2,450 **Fixed**, Amateur, Mobile, Radiolocation	2,300–2,450 **Fixed, Mobile, Radiolocation**, Amateur	
3,300–3,400 **Radiolocation**	3,300–3,400 **Radiolocation,** Amateur, Fixed, Mobile	3,300–3,400 **Radiolocation,** Amateur

Region 1	Region 2	Region 3
3,400–3,600 **Fixed, Fixed-Satellite** (space-to-earth), Mobile, Radiolocation	3,400–3,500 **Fixed, Fixed-Satellite** (space-to-earth), Amateur, Mobile, Radiolocation	
5,650–5,725	**Radiolocation**, Amateur, Space Research (deep space)	
5,725–5,850 **Fixed-Satellite** (earth-to-space), **Radiolocation,** Amateur	5,725–5,850 **Radiolocation,** Amateur	
5,850–5,925 **Fixed, Fixed-Satellite** (earth-to-space), **Mobile**	5,850–5,925 **Fixed, Fixed-Satellite** (earth-to-space), **Mobile**, Amateur, Radiolocation	5,850–5,925 **Fixed, Fixed-Satellite** (earth-to-space), Mobile, Radiolocation
10–10·45GHz **Fixed, Mobile, Radiolocation,** Amateur	10–10·45 **Radiolocation,** Amateur	10–10·45 **Fixed, Mobile, Radiolocation,** Amateur
10·45–10·5	**Radiolocation**, Amateur, Amateur-Satellite	
24–24·05	**Amateur, Amateur-Satellite**	
24·05–24·25	**Radiolocation**, Amateur, Earth Exploration-Satellite (active)	
47–47·2	**Amateur, Amateur-Satellite**	
75·5–76	**Amateur, Amateur-Satellite**	
76–81	**Radiolocation**, Amateur, Amateur-Satellite	
142–144	**Amateur, Amateur-Satellite**	
144–149	**Radiolocation**, Amateur, Amateur-Satellite	
241–248	**Radiolocation**, Amateur, Amateur-Satellite	
248–250	**Amateur, Amateur-Satellite**	

The band 119·98–120·02GHz is also allocated to the amateur service on a secondary basis.

all-mode operation, sometimes on more than one band; it is difficult for the average amateur to build equipment which is equivalent to that available today commercially, and indeed some amateurs regard 144MHz as a "black box" band.

However, many enthusiasts do continue to build their own equipment, for sometimes commercial items are not up to the required standards of performance or are simply unavailable. For example, commercial transceivers are often fitted with home-made preamplifiers to increase their sensitivity. Others find that construction of a simple fm transmitter gives great satisfaction. Then again, there is scope for ingenuity in devising different antennas.

The designs featured in this book should assist the reader but it should equally be remembered that no such collection can be definitive; experimentation is a tradition in the vhf field, and the hobby is all the richer for it.

CHAPTER 2

Propagation

Introduction

Today it is recognized that the troposphere, the ionosphere and even objects in space all contribute in their various ways to propagation above 30MHz. Yet, even now, much still remains to be explained about the mechanisms concerned and radio amateurs are in a very strong position to help provide some of the answers.

For many years the amateur service has enjoyed direct representation on the two CCIR Study Groups concerned with radio propagation. (The letters "CCIR" represent the French initials of an organization known as the International Radio Consultative Committee, a part of the Geneva-based International Telecommunication Union.) With growing momentum an awareness of the potential research capabilities of the amateur service has been brought about and it has now been acknowledged that an organized network of amateur operators and observers provides a powerful research tool, capable of undertaking investigations on a scale impossible to achieve by any other means. Considerable encouragement to use this strength has been given in order that contributions may be made to a number of very important projects.

In an attempt to make the most of these opportunities this propagation chapter has been revised and almost entirely rewritten for this edition in a form which, it is hoped, will lead eventually to a number of useful inputs to CCIR. Each section contains the sort of information required to begin an analysis of observations made "in house", or obtained from one of the amateur collecting centres, such as the DUBUS organization in Germany, or through the Propagation Studies Committee of the RSGB.

To make the most effective use of the space available in this book it has been assumed that the reader will have access to the propagation chapter of the RSGB *Radio Communication Handbook*, which contains a number of fundamental truths and mathematical expressions which supplement the information given here.

At a time when considerable pressures are being directed towards a future erosion of amateur bands in favour of commercial interests, it is important that amateurs should at all times seek to present their case for survival in the best possible light. There is no doubt at all that any amateur contributions to propagation research will always be seen as a powerful argument in favour of retaining bands allocated to the amateur service.

Recognizing vhf/uhf modes of propagation

At frequencies above 30MHz (following the definition of the terms vhf and uhf) propagation by the regular layers of the ionosphere takes place but rarely and then generally only around times of maximum sunspot activity.

The most usual mechanism governing the day-to-day performance between two earth-based stations has its origin in the lower part of the atmosphere, at rarely more than 4–5km above the ground. *Tropospheric propagation* is descriptive of this mode and the fundamental properties of the air which have the most influence are the vertical distributions of temperature and water vapour, both of which tend to decrease with height and, in so doing, cause elevated radio rays, such as might otherwise escape into space, to bend back down towards the ground, and to reach it beyond the normal visible horizon. At times, usually in the presence of an anticyclone, when dry warm air overlays cool moist air, ranges extend dramatically and signals from up to about 2,000km may be expected. At the same time the strength of less-distant signals may be enhanced, effects which extend throughout the vhf and uhf parts of the radio spectrum. During a "tropo opening", as it is often called, signals generally rise slowly, with a progressively slower rate of fading. At peak, fading may be absent altogether. A long period of enhancement generally ends when a cold front reaches one end of the transmission path.

Tropospheric scatter depends on the presence of small-scale refractive index irregularities and dust or cloud particles in a volume of the atmosphere towards which both the transmitting and the receiving antennas are directed. High power is required at the transmitter and good signal-to-noise performance at the receiver. Scattered signals are weak, spread in frequency by up to 1kHz either side of an unmodulated carrier, due to the various motions of the scattering particles, and several rates of fading may co-exist, often giving the impression of a rough modulation. The rate at which intelligence may be sent is limited by "blurring", introduced by the range of signal path transit times possible within the upper and lower limits of the scattering volume.

At the top end of the uhf band *atmospheric absorption* effects begin to become noticeable and beyond 3,000MHz, in the shf part of the radio spectrum, *attenuations* due to oxygen, water vapour and precipitation (rain, snow etc) become increasingly important. These affect not only transmission paths that are wholly within the troposphere, but paths originating within and terminating without—ground to satellite, eme etc—although there the effects tend to diminish with increase of beam elevation as the length of path containing the absorbers and attenuators decreases.

Although many textbooks still imply that the ionosphere has little, if any, effect at 70MHz and above, a number of very important events have their origin there. Nearly all of them are associated in some way with the level around 100km above the ground, which is generally occupied during the day by the regular E-layer. Of these the most important is *sporadic-E*, which radio amateurs have studied at 144MHz for many years, despite the fact that its presence there, according to our professional colleagues, is impossible. In 1980 the amateur service was invited to contribute to a symposium on sporadic-E held at the Appleton Laboratory, and it was clear the amateur activities in this mode of propagation came as a surprise to many of the distinguished authorities present. It is now acknowledged by them that such a mode does exist at frequencies that may exceed 200MHz for short intervals of time, but the feeling is that it may not be sporadic-E at all, but an entirely different mechanism as yet unidentified. Here, it will still be referred to as sporadic-E (or E_s) until such time as its true identity is discovered. Sporadic-E signals generally begin suddenly and unpredictably (hence their name), bring in stations from distances of 1,000–2,000km at excellent strength and clarity for periods of up to several hours, and then, with a rapid decline, they cease. The duration of an opening decreases with increasing radio frequency, the higher frequencies starting later and finishing sooner than the lower ones. During the event the locations heard gradually progress from one area to another. Sporadic-E events at vhf are generally confined to the months of May to August.

Another ionospheric mode is associated with the appearance in the northern sky of the aurora borealis (or "Northern Lights"), which is caused by the interaction of streams of charged particles from the sun with the earth's magnetic field. Signals reflected from the very mobile *auroral-E* curtains, which usually accompany visual displays often seen in the Northern Isles and the north of Scotland but less frequently further south, are readily recognizable with their characteristic tone, variously described as "rasping", "ringing" or "watery", and the fact that beam headings for optimum signal strength are commonly well to the north of the great circle path joining the two stations in contact.

Short-lived trails of ionization due to the entry into the earth's atmosphere of small particles of solid matter (seen at night as shooting stars) can be responsible for *meteor scatter*, where two stations, usually widely spaced, can establish contact in intermittent bursts ranging in duration from several seconds down to periods which afford little more than occasional "pings" of signal. Meteor-scatter signals should be looked for at times of meteor showers, which are listed later in this chapter. Duration of meteor reflections and their frequency of occurrence decline with increasing frequency. Meteor-scatter propagation is used professionally at operating frequencies of between 30 to 40MHz.

Trans-equatorial propagation is usually confined to paths in which transmitter and receiver are situated approximately equal distances either side of the magnetic equator (eg the Mediterranean area and Zimbabwe). 144MHz openings seem to require high solar flux and low geomagnetic index; frequency spreading is apparent at 144 and 432MHz, with flutter fading, often giving the signals a quality similar to that of signals reflected from the aurora. On the Zimbabwe–Cyprus path openings were centred on 2000 local time at Cyprus. It is believed that extensions to tep via E_s or tropo may be possible.

At the time of writing there have been no definite instances of *F2 level* involvement at vhf, although it has been suggested that it may have been the mode responsible for 70MHz signals from ZB2BL, Gibraltar, being heard by VE1ASJ in St John on 17 November 1980, and from G4BPY in the UK to St John on the following day. These are distances of the order of 5,000 miles. Some of the time-delay measurements carried out on the tep path between Zimbabwe and Cyprus are consistent with two-hop propagation via the F2 layer, but others have indicated that an even longer path may have been involved.

Tropospheric propagation

The propagation of light

It may be found helpful to begin this study of tropospheric propagation by considering first some comparable aspects of the propagation of light. In most cases the analogy is a close one because radio and light are both forms of electro-magnetic radiation differing only in wavelength (or its inverse, frequency). However, light has the advantage of being readily detectable by its direct action on one of our senses, and most of us have had many years of experience working with it. We do not usually think of a torch bulb as being a transmitter, nor our eyes as being receivers, but they are, nevertheless, and all the perturbing effects to which a radio wave is subjected within the troposphere have their visual counterparts, with which we are very familiar already.

A beam of light normally travels in a straight line unless something is done to alter it. This can be by *reflection*, as in a mirror or from the surface of a still pond, *refraction*, when light passes from one medium to another so that a straight rod in water appears to be bent, or by *scattering* as from the dust in a shaft of sunlight. Certain frequencies can be made to suffer *attenuation* by inserting one or more filters in the path of the beam, and a very important filter which occurs naturally is provided by a layer of ozone in the upper atmosphere which prevents harmful amounts of ultra-violet light from destroying life on earth.

It will be seen later that most tropospheric radio events of any importance are manifestations of refraction. In terms of light it is refraction which provides the lens with its well-known properties, whereby light leaving one medium, such as air, and entering another, such as glass, suffers a deflection. A Dutch scientist named Willebrord Snell discovered in 1621 that the sine of the angle made by the incident ray with respect to the normal, divided by the sine of the angle made by the refracted ray, was a constant for a given pair of media. The property possessed by each of the materials involved is known as the *refractive index*, and Snell's constant ($\sin i / \sin r$) is equal to the inverse ratio of the refractive indices of the two media.

Changes in refractive index also occur in the atmosphere, due to variations in density, usually as a result of the juxtaposition of two unmixed layers differing greatly in temperature, or due to the presence of a sharp gradient of temperature within a single layer. Thus the origin of the *mirage*. When air near the ground is heated, as over hot sand in the desert or sometimes beside the sea, a line of sight directed downwards is refracted upwards, giving an unexpected (and usually unsuspected) view of the sky which appears as a shimmering pool on the land. Conversely, where cool air underlies warm air a line of sight directed slightly upwards is bent down, so that objects which are, in reality, well beyond the normal horizon appear to be on it, or even above. There was a famous occasion in 1798 when the whole of the French coast from Calais to Dieppe became visible one afternoon from the cliffs near Hastings.

Effects such as these are even more pronounced at radio frequencies because the radio refractive index contains a term which is dependent upon the amount of water vapour present, and this is a parameter which is subject to considerable change in the lower atmosphere in both space and time.

The radio refractive index of air

There are two basic methods used to determine the refractive index of air; one is to measure it more or less directly using a device called a *refractometer*, the other is to derive it from other, more readily accessible, functions of the atmosphere.

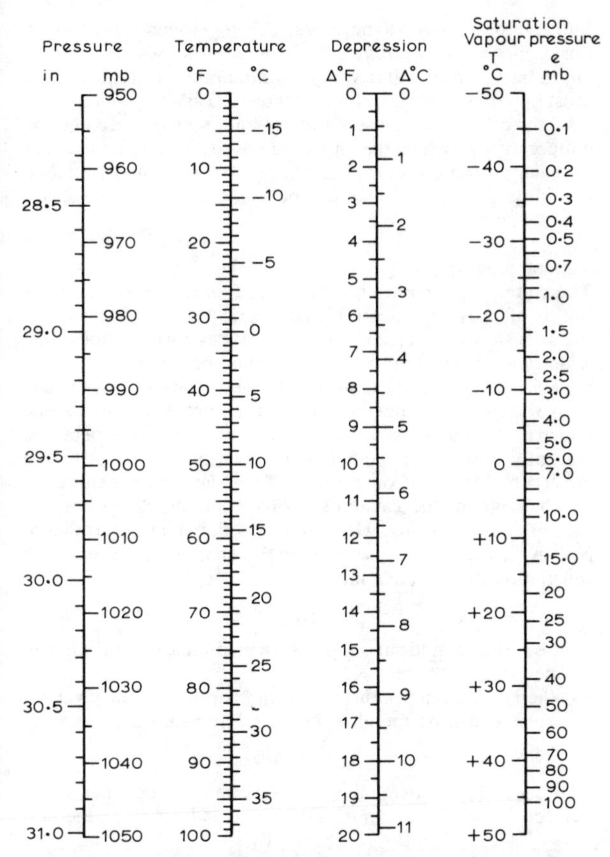

Fig 1. Conversion scales for various meteorological functions. (a) Atmospheric pressure, inches of mercury to millibars. (b) Temperature, degrees Fahrenheit to Celsius (or Centigrade) (add 273 to degrees C for absolute or Kelvin). (c) Depression of wet-bulb or dew point from degrees Fahrenheit to either Celsius or Absolute. (d) Values of saturated vapour pressure (mb), given temperature in degrees C

Refractometers are beyond the scope of the radio amateur. They are usually airborne or tethered balloon-borne devices constructed and operated by large research organizations. They depend on the fact that the resonant frequency of an open microwave cavity is a function of the dielectric constant of the air within it, and that this is also a function of refractive index.

The more common method is to use upper-air soundings of pressure, temperature and humidity provided by meteorological services all over the world, generally on a twice-daily basis, at midnight and midday, gmt. This information is obtained from cheap and simple balloon-borne telemetry devices called *radiosondes*, which have been in regular use since shortly before the second world war.

The radio refractive index of the air, symbol n, is a quantity which is only very slightly higher than unity, but the difference between, say, 1·000345 and 1·000300 is all-important in propagation studies and may have a profound effect on the destination of a radio wave. To bring out this importance, and to simplify subsequent calculations, it is usual to subtract 1 from the refractive index value and then multiply the remainder by one million. This quantity is given the symbol N; in mathematical terms $N = 10^6(n-1)$.

Before demonstrating how N values can be calculated from meteorological data it will be advisable to define the units involved, and, in some cases, to show how they can be obtained from measurements made at home.

Meteorological units

Pressure

The current unit of pressure is the millibar (mb), equivalent to a force of 100N/m^2. Many home barometers carry calibrations in inches, a relic of the days when pressure was measured by balancing the weight of air above against a column of mercury. The conversion between the two units can be made on a slide-rule, knowing that 29·53in = 1,000mb, or by the use of the scale in Fig 1(a). Whole millibars will be found accurate enough for most refractive index calculations. The mean value of surface pressure at sea level is about 1,012mb.

Pressure decreases with height in an approximately logarithmic manner. Near the ground the rate of change is about 1mb in 10m, but this should not be presumed to extend over too great an interval as the relationship is actually a function of temperature also.

In meteorological studies it is customary to use pressure as a measure of vertical displacement, rather than height, and it will be found very convenient to carry over this practice into propagation work, because the physical processes of the atmosphere are a function of pressure, not of height, and any attempt to make them otherwise will complicate normally convenient relationships beyond belief. It requires some adjustment of ideas, not the least being that height is traditionally measured upwards from the ground, whereas pressure is measured from the top of the atmosphere downwards. But the radio wave, once launched on its way from the transmitting antenna, encounters nothing that can be identified directly with height. It "sees" changes in air density and refractive index, which are themselves functions of pressure, temperature and water vapour content. Height, as such, is not one of the natural properties of the atmosphere, and that is why aircraft altimeters, which appear to measure it, have to be set to read zero at sea level before the pilot attempts to land, for they are really barometers carrying an approximate scale of feet or metres instead of an accurate one in millibars.

As a simple rule of thumb it is worth remembering that a pressure of 900mb is roughly equivalent to a height of 1km, and 700mb is approximately 3km. The exact relationship relating to a particular radiosonde ascent is always given as part of the basic information, so that general rules for height calculations are unnecessary here.

Temperature

In scientific work it is usually necessary to have temperatures expressed in degrees Celsius (or Centigrade to give the more popular name). Not everyone has a suitably calibrated thermometer in the house, so the scale of Fig 1(b) has been provided to make the necessary conversion. For degrees Absolute (°A) or Kelvin (K) add 273 to the Celsius value; they are not identical, but the slight difference is of no consequence here.

Relative humidity

This is a measure of the amount of moisture actually present in a sample of air, expressed as a percentage of the total amount which could be contained at the given temperature. It can be obtained from the readings of two identical thermometers, one of which has its bulb surrounded by a moistened muslin wick.

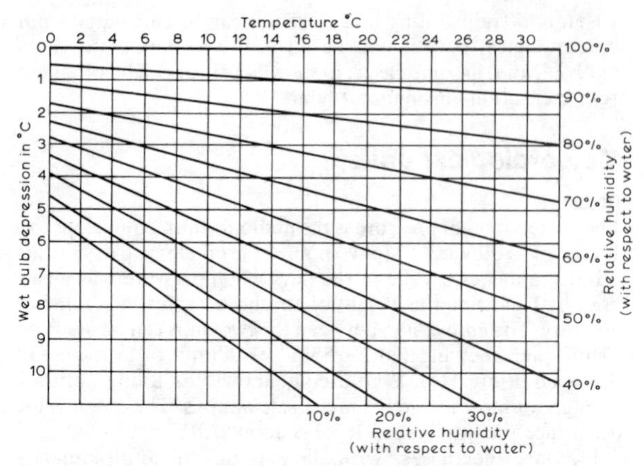

Fig 2. Percentage relative humidity as a function of temperature and wet-bulb depression

They should be well-sited in the shade, and preferably enclosed in a properly ventilated screen. The difference between the two readings is the *depression of the wet bulb*, and the percentage relative humidity can be found from the diagram, Fig 2. If the thermometers are calibrated in degrees Fahrenheit it is more accurate to subtract the two readings first and convert their difference using the scale of Fig 1(c).

Dew point

If a sample of air containing a given amount of moisture is allowed to cool it will be found that the wet-bulb depression decreases until eventually both wet and dry bulb thermometers read the same. The relative humidity will have become 100 per cent and the air is said to be *saturated*. The temperature at which this occurs, the *dew point*, is therefore another way of expressing the amount of water vapour contained in a sample of air. Most upper air reports nowadays show this as *dew point depression*, the difference between the dry-bulb temperature and the temperature to which the air would have to be cooled in order to reach saturation, but some still refer to percentage relative humidity. The chart, Fig 3, can be used to make a conversion either way.

Vapour pressure

The water vapour present in a sample of air exerts a contribution of its own to the total atmospheric pressure. The scale of Fig 1(d) shows saturation vapour pressures corresponding to a wide range of temperatures, but it must be admitted that the scale is a difficult one to interpolate. The relationship between temperature and saturation vapour pressure is a complex one and in the past most calculations have involved the use of tables. Recently, however, a number of organizations have tried to find an acceptable approximation, making use of an expression which is within the capabilities of a "scientific" pocket calculator. The following, which is due to Parish and Purtnam of NASA, has been used elsewhere in this chapter for the machine calculation of refractive index:

$$e_s = T^{-4\cdot 9283} \,.\, 10^{(23\cdot 5518 - (2937\cdot 4/T))}$$

where e_s is saturated vapour pressure in millibars and T is the air temperature in degrees K.

When the air is not saturated the appropriate value of vapour pressure, e, can be found from the relationship

$$e = e_s \,.\, u$$

where u is the relative humidity expressed as a decimal (eg 72 per cent = 0·72), or, more usually nowadays, from the dew

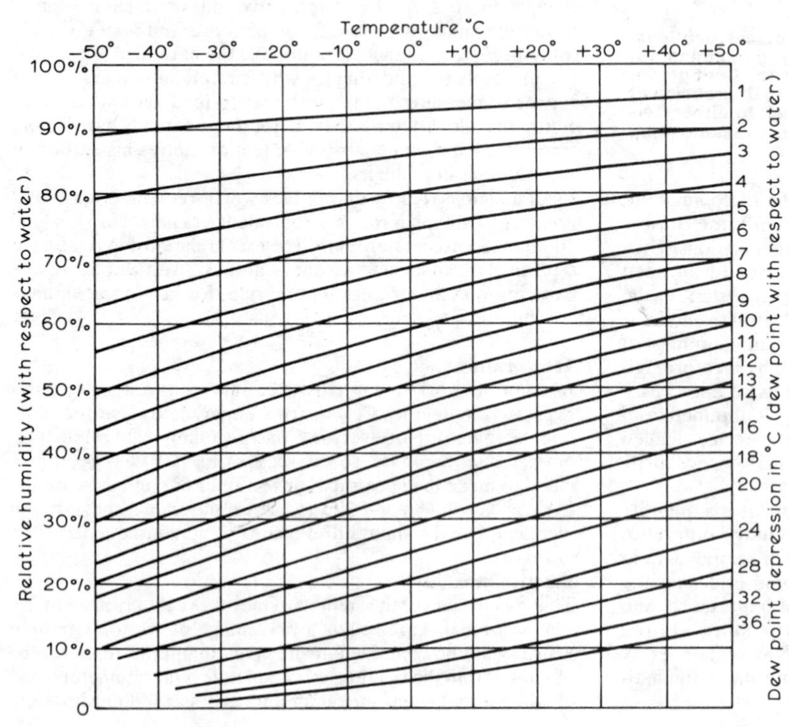

Fig 3. Percentage relative humidity as a function of temperature and dew-point depression. (May be used to convert radiosonde data published in the "wrong units".)

Table 1. TI58/59 program: radio refractive index, *N*, from basic meteorological data

Working stores		Data inputs
STO–01	p	p Pressure (millibars)
STO–02	T	T Temperature (°C)
STO–03	D	D Dew point depression (°C)

Load stores as follows:

273	STO–04	23·5518	STO–07
2937·4	STO–05	77·6	STO–08
–4·9283	STO–06	4810	STO–09

Program

(Enter p)		03	013–03	×	034–65
		1	014–01	RCL	035–43
STO	000–42	0	015–00	09	036–09
01	001–01	y^x	016–45	÷	037–55
R/S	002–91	(	017–53	RCL	038–43
		RCL	018–43	02	039–02
(Enter T)		07	019–07	+	040–85
		−	020–75	RCL	041–43
+	003–85	RCL	021–43	01	042–01
RCL	004–43	05	022–05	=	043–95
04	005–04	÷	023–55	×	044–65
=	006–95	RCL	024–43	RCL	045–43
STO	007–42	03	025–03	08	046–08
02	008–02	)	026–54	÷	047–55
−	009–75	×	027–65	RCL	048–43
R/S	010–91	RCL	028–43	02	049–02
		03	029–03	=	050–95
(Enter D)		y^x	030–45	*FIX	051–58
		RCL	031–43	0	052–00
=	011–95	06	032–06	R/S	
STO	012–42	=	033–95		

Test
p = 900
T = −3·0
D = 8
N = 272

* = 2nd function key

point T_d or the dew-point depression, D (where $T_d = T - D$), using the expression

$$e = T_d^{\,-4\cdot9283} \,.\, 10^{(23\cdot5518 - (2937\cdot4/T_d))}$$

which will be found to be the most practical form for use with a calculator. Of course, the same trick of using the dew point to find the actual vapour pressure as if it was a saturated vapour pressure may be performed on the scale of Fig 1(d) to provide the required value of *e*.

The calculation of *N*

The basic equation is

$$N = \frac{77\cdot6}{T}\left(p + \frac{4{,}810\,.\,e}{T}\right)$$

where *p* is the atmospheric pressure in millibars, *e* is the water vapour pressure in millibars and *T* is the air temperature in degrees K. It is often more convenient to expand this into

$$N = \frac{77\cdot6\,p}{T} + \frac{3\cdot733 \times 10^5\,.\,e}{T^2}$$

because it then separates conveniently into a "dry" term, corresponding approximately to the optical value of refractive index, and a "wet" term which contains all the contribution due to the presence of water vapour. The values which result from these expressions are known as *refractivities*, but they are often referred to simply as *N-units*.

The degree of ray bending which results from refractive index changes can be assessed by calculating the decrease over unit height change. The normal gradient from the ground may be regarded as being approximately −40*N*-units/km. Should it become −157*N*/km the curvature of the ray becomes the same as that of the earth, while gradients greater (ie more negative) than −157*N*/km result in *ducting*, where the waves travel for great distances, confined within a relatively shallow range of heights, suffering alternate refractions at the steep-lapse layer and reflections from the ground.

The following example of a calculation directly from basic meteorological data may be found useful:

p = 900mb, T = −3°C (= 270K), dew point depression = 8°C.

From this the dew point must be −11°C and the corresponding vapour pressure from Fig 1(d) is 2·6mb. Hence

$$N = \frac{77\cdot6 \times 900}{270} + \frac{3\cdot733 \times 10^5 \times 2\cdot6}{270 \times 270} = 259 + 13 = 272$$

A pocket calculator program has been prepared, providing *N* values from a single entry of pressure, temperature and dew-point depression, the form in which the information will be obtained in the majority of cases. The program was produced originally for the Texas Instruments SR56, which was widely used at the time, and both it and the equations involved in its preparation have been discussed in a paper presented at the IARU Region 1 Conference in Hungary, 1978. In Table 1 the method has been adapted for the Texas Instruments TI58 and the card-programmable TI59, both of them likely to remain popular for many years to come, but it will not be found difficult to adapt the sequence to suit a different machine. It is advisable to make a practice of performing the check sequence before starting with fresh data.

Causes of tropo dx

Having established a method of obtaining refractive index values from standard meteorological upper-air observations it is a natural progression to apply that knowledge to a study of the atmosphere during a well-marked tropospheric "opening"—probably the main reason why radio amateurs take an active interest in this mode of radio propagation. For that purpose, consider the situation late in the evening of 20 January 1974, when Europe was "wide-open" to the UK; this is still thought of by many operators as one of the best-ever events.

Fig 4 shows a cross-section of the atmosphere up to 700mb (about 3km in terms of height), from Camborne in SW England to Berlin. The *isopleths* join levels having equal values of refractivity, scaled in *N*-units. There is no mistaking the concentration formed in the lower part of the diagram. This indicates a steep fall of refractive index with height and is in the correct sense to cause the return to earth of rays which would otherwise have been lost in space above the horizon. Super-refraction of this sort produces bending towards the earth in the case of both ascending and descending rays. Because there is a normal tendency for refractive index to decrease with height, this effect is nearly always present in some degree and this accounts for the fact that radio communication at vhf and uhf is usually possible beyond the visible horizon. The presence in the lower atmosphere of a layer in which refractivity decreases very rapidly with height, as in the case being considered, is always accompanied by enhancement of signal strengths and an

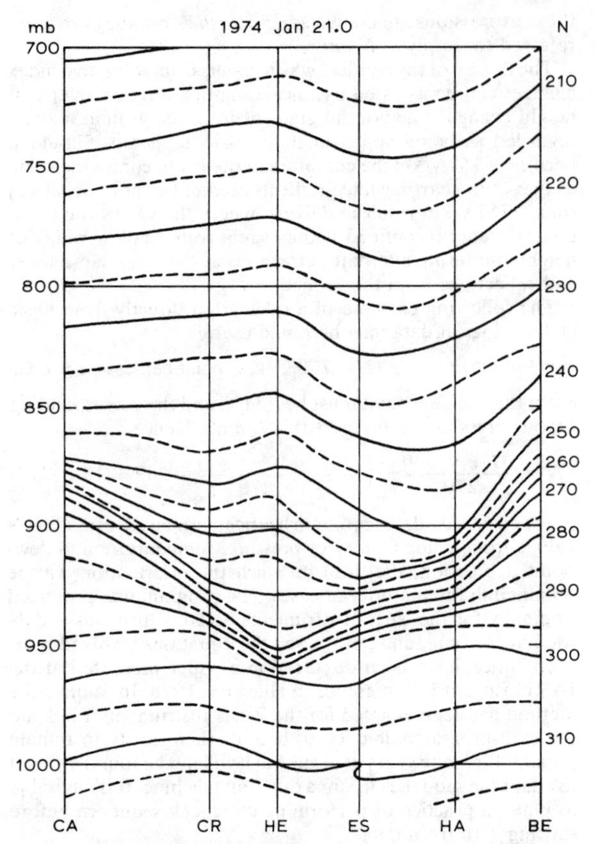

Fig 4. Cross-section from SW England to Central Europe, at midnight (0000gmt) 21 January 1974, drawn in terms of conventional refractive index *N*. The vertical scale is in terms of pressure, 700mb=3km approx. CA=Camborne, CR=Crawley, HE = Hemsby, ES = Essen, HA = Hannover, BE = Berlin

increase in working range. However, in the case where very narrow beamwidth antennas are used at both ends of the path, received signal strengths may fall, due to energy being deflected away from a path which has been optimized under conditions of normal refractivity.

From a cross-section, such as Fig 4, it would be quite possible to calculate the probable paths of rays leaving a transmitting antenna at various angles of take-off, using Snell's law, as with optical ray-tracing, but this is an exercise which is probably outside the needs of most amateurs. It should be noted that the values of refractivity at ground level reveal little of the situation above. For that reason the only really effective study of tropospheric propagation phenomena involves the acquisition of upper-air meteorological data.

The atmosphere in motion

It does not require a great deal of experience on the vhf and uhf bands to realize that all the big "openings" to the Continent occur during periods of high atmospheric pressure. Indeed, some amateurs look upon an aneroid barometer in the home as being their guide to the state of the bands. But, whereas good conditions are accompanied by high-pressure readings, high pressure is not always accompanied by good conditions. Why should that be? The answer lies in an appreciation of the role played by vertical motions in the atmosphere.

In general, rising air becomes cooler and moister, while descending air warms and becomes more dry. Air is sometimes forced into vertical motion by the topography in its path; it rises when it flows over hills and it descends into valleys. However, the present context mainly concerns vertical motion associated with the two main types of pressure system.

Consider first a low-pressure system, or "depression". Air circulates around it in an anticlockwise direction (in the northern hemisphere), with a slight inclination towards the centre, creating an inward spiral which leaves progressively less room for the volume of air in motion. There is only one escape route available, and that is upwards. So low-pressure systems are associated with rising air.

On the other hand, anticyclones (high-pressure systems) are characterized by light winds blowing clockwise around the centre but with a slight deflection outwards. As the air spirals outwards fresh quantities must be available to maintain the supply and the only source is from aloft, resulting this time in a downward flow. So high-pressure systems have descending air associated with them.

Adiabatic changes

Air in vertical motion changes in both volume and pressure (they are directly related) and in temperature also, although there need be no gain or loss of heat. This may appear at first to be a contradiction in terms, for heat and temperature might be thought to be alternative names for the same thing. In fact, heat is a quantity which can be distributed either over a small volume to provide a large increase in temperature, or spread over a large volume to appear as a small increase in temperature. Thus 1kg of air descending from a height of 3km may begin with a pressure of 700mb and a temperature of −5°C, to arrive at 1·5km with a pressure of 850mb and a temperature of 10°C with no change of heat being involved. Such a process is *adiabatic*, and it is an important principle in meteorology. A homely demonstration of it at work may be found in the case of the bicycle pump, the barrel of which gets hot in use due to the air inside having been compressed.

When the air is anything other than dry another apparent paradox links the amount of water vapour and the corresponding humidity during the adiabatic process. Going back to the example, at 700mb 3·78g of water vapour would have been sufficient to produce saturation (100 per cent relative humidity) in the 1kg sample of air, whereas at 850mb the same amount would give only 41·5 per cent relative humidity because air at 10°C could hold 9·1g of water vapour. So, air descending adiabatically gets warmer and drier, although the actual amounts of heat and water vapour remain unchanged.

The action is reversible up to a point. Ascending air is accompanied by increasing relative humidity, which at some stage will reach 100 per cent. Any further lifting will result in the appearance of liquid water, which will appear either as cloud or as larger droplets, which are likely to fall out of suspension as rain. When condensation occurs, the rate of cooling is altered by the appearance of latent heat, and the precipitation will alter the amount of moisture in the sample of air.

No such considerations affect descending air once its relative humidity has fallen below 100 per cent, although there will have been alterations to the rate of change of temperature if liquid droplets of water have been evaporating, again on account of latent heat. If the sample of air is taken adiabatically to a standard pressure of 1,000mb the temperature it assumes is known as the *potential temperature* of the sample. It follows from this that potential temperature is a quantity which remains constant during any adiabatic change: conversely, a change is an adiabatic one if it is associated with constant potential temperature.

Potential refractive index

Referring back to Fig 4 it will be seen that, quite apart from the region of interest referred to earlier, there is a general background of fairly regularly spaced isopleths which represent the normal fall-off of refractive index with height. A number of modifications to the standard procedure for calculating refractive index have been proposed from time to time, all with the intention of minimizing this effect, leaving emphasis on the features that are of most interest to the propagation engineer.

Opinions have varied on the best way to do this. Most methods proposed have involved some form of model atmosphere, and the calculation of departures from it, resulting in complex exercises for which a computer is advisable. Another disadvantage has been the difficulty of recovering the original values of refractive index from the final data (should they be required elsewhere, or at a later date). The method to be described was first proposed in 1959 by Dr K. H. Jehn of the University of Texas, who does not seem to have taken advantage of the full potential of his suggestion. Curiously, little has been done outside amateur circles to exploit its usefulness; it involves a unit known as *potential refractive index* (K).

It may be obtained from upper-air meteorological sounding data in just the same way as has been described for N-units, the only difference being that each sample of air, whatever its true level may be, is presumed to have been transported adiabatically to a pressure of 1,000mb before the calculations are made.

The advantages of this form of normalization are considerable. By adopting a procedure which imitates the natural process of the atmosphere, applying, for example, to the large mass of air which subsides from aloft over an anticyclone, each level of air is effectively labelled with a value of potential refractive index which remains with it during any adiabatic change.

The effect may be seen particularly well in time-sections, such as that of Fig 5(a), which shows how the potential refractive index pattern varied from day to day at a single station, Crawley, over a period which included that eventful evening of 20 January 1974. There is no mistaking the extensive tongue of warm, dry, subsiding air associated with an anticyclone and the steep-lapse refractive index layer built up where it meets the opposing cool, moist air underneath.

Towards the right and left edges of the diagram may be seen evidence of rising air which is associated with two depressions, which preceded and followed the period of high pressure. These potential refractive index isopleths are very sensitive indicators of vertical motion in the atmosphere, and the patterns on cross-sections and time-sections take on an interesting three-dimensional aspect when viewed in conjunction with surface weather charts.

It is interesting to compare the potential refractive index time-section of Fig 5(a) with the corresponding section drawn in terms of conventional radio refractive index, N, Fig 5(b). Note first that there are fewer lines on the potential refractive index diagram, indicating that the normal fall-off of refractive index with height has been considerably reduced. At the steep-lapse layer, the concentration of isopleths has been greatly emphasized in Fig 5(a) but it is important to notice that this has not been at the expense of accuracy in indicating either the height at which the effect occurred or its vertical extent.

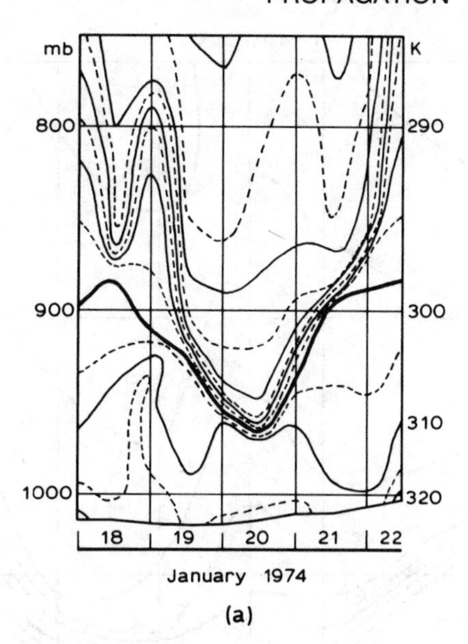

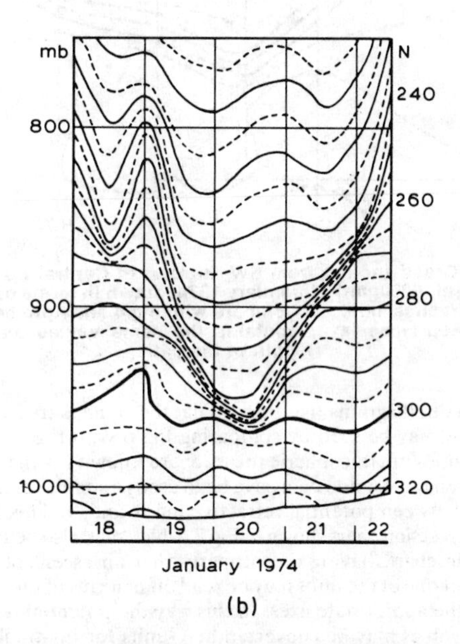

Fig 5. (a) Time section showing isopleths of potential refractive index, *K*. Crawley, 18–22 January 1974. (b) Time section showing isopleths of radio refractive index, *N*. Crawley, 18–22 January 1974

Because air undergoing adiabatic changes has been shown to carry its value of potential refractive index along with it, no matter what its level, it should not be surprising that the boundary layer across the whole of Fig 5(a) is formed of basically the same set of K-values irrespective of changes in pressure (or height). Fig 5(b) shows that the same is not true for conventional refractive index. This is not to suggest that the N-values are wrong, but rather to point out that they do not share this very useful attribute of coherence independent of height which

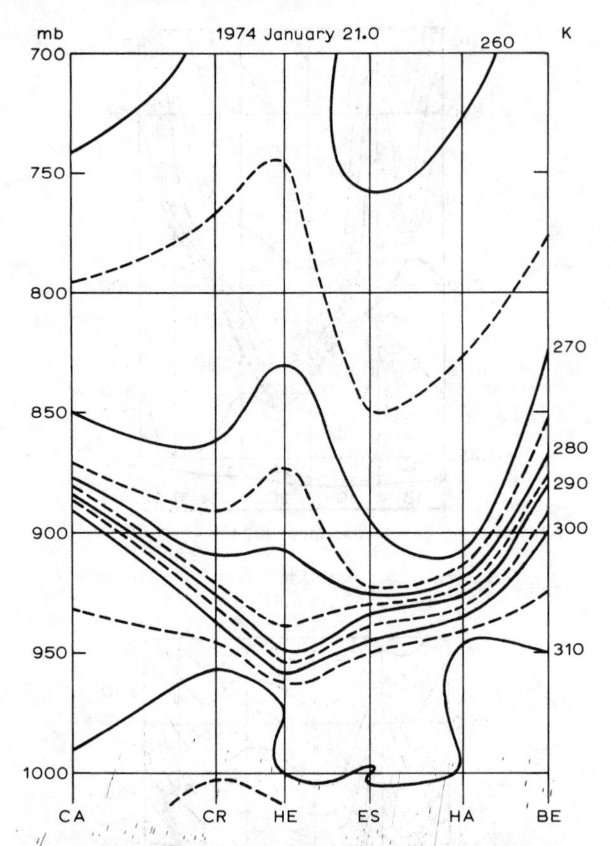

Fig 6. Cross-section from SW England to Central Europe, at midnight (0000gmt) 21 January 1974, drawn in terms of potential refractive index, *K*. Compare with Fig 4 and note here how the steep-lapse layer contains the same values along the length of the path

appears in diagrams like these. That the same is true of cross-sections may be seen by comparing Fig 6 with Fig 4.

If values of atmospheric pressure are known (as they always are when radiosonde data have been used) a simple relationship exists between potential refractive index and N. This leads to the conversion chart shown in Fig 7, which may also be used as a plotting chart, having the property that an ascent plotted in terms of one of the units may be read off in terms of the other by using the appropriate axes. In this way the potential refractive index values may be converted to N-units for ray-tracing purposes, or compared with N-unit profiles produced elsewhere.

Alternatively, use may be made of the following expressions

$$N = 0{\cdot}00731 \,.\, p^{0.712} \,.\, K$$

and

$$K = 136{\cdot}8 \,.\, p^{-0.712} \,.\, N$$

which may be performed without difficulty on a scientific pocket calculator.

Acquiring meteorological data

There are three ways of acquiring meteorological data of the sort needed for the study of upper-air refractive index distributions. They are:

(i) by using tabulated data published by national weather services,
(ii) by the reception of radio-teleprinter (rtty) broadcasts,
(iii) by the reception of radio-facsimile (fax) broadcasts.

As most analyses are carried out retrospectively, published information is the most convenient. Until 31 December 1980, the source of data from the nine regular British and Irish upper-air stations was the *Daily Aerological Record*, published by the Meteorological Office, London Road, Bracknell, Berkshire. A companion series, called the *Daily Weather Report*, gave six-hourly surface observations in coded form from about 50 meteorological stations in various parts of the British Isles, and provided a weather chart for each of the periods, the one for 1200 gmt covering a large part of the northern hemisphere.

Unfortunately, cuts and economies have halted both these publications. In this country there is nothing that can take the place of the *Daily Aerological Record*, but there are several alternatives providing outline surface weather maps. London Weather Centre in High Holborn (and certain other weather centres) can provide current locally-produced maps, either sold

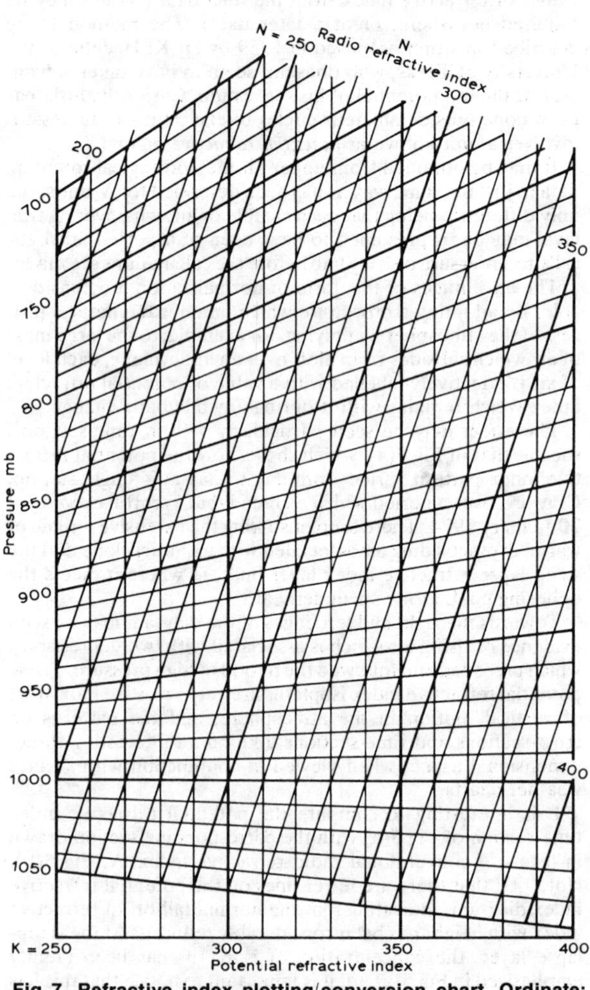

Fig 7. Refractive index plotting/conversion chart. Ordinate: pressure (mb). Abscissae: (vertical) potential refractive index, *K*; (slant) radio refractive index, *N*

Table 2. Some broadcasts carrying meteorological data

RADIO-TELEPRINTER (RTTY)

Station name	Callsign	Power (kW)	Operating frequencies (kHz)
Bracknell	GFL	10	4,489, 6,835 (n), 9,886·5, 14,356, 18,230 (d)
Paris	HXX	10	4,013·5 (n), 8,163, 14,980 (d), 17,455 (d)
Potsdam	Y3K	5	4,057, 7,980
Warszawa	SOE	10	4,497
	SOH	5	7,997
Rome	IMB	5	3,172·5, 5,887·5, 11,453
Oslo	LMO	2·5	3,869, 5,768, 7,947·5, 16,087·5
Sofia	LZA	5	4,813 (d),
	LZF	5	3,253

n=night, d=day.

FACSIMILE (FAX)

Station name	Callsign	Power (kW)	Operating frequencies (kHz)
Offenbach/ Main	DCF54	50	134·2 Programme A
	DCF37	50	117·4 Programme B
Bracknell	GFA	10	3,289·5, 4,610 (n), 8,040, 11,086·5, 14,582 (d)
Paris	FYA	100	131·8

Notes

1. The designations "Programme A" and "Programme B" relate to entries in Table 3.
2. White/black shifts are +150/−150Hz for Offenbach and Paris, +400/−400 for Bracknell.

over the counter or dispatched by post, but they normally would not supply "back-numbers" unless arrangements had been made to save them. A subscription to the magazine *Weather* (published by the Royal Meteorological Society, James Glaisher House, Grenville Place, Bracknell, Berkshire) includes receipt of a monthly supplement containing daily weather maps for 1200gmt (Europe and the North Atlantic area) two months in arrears, eg January maps appear with the March issue of the magazine.

The most up-to-date charts are those displayed and discussed by the BBC television "weathermen" at regular times during the day. A suitable camera, loaded with an inexpensive black-and-white film, is an effective way of obtaining "hard copy" for study at a later date. Even the super-convenient "instant picture" film is cheaper than a radio facsimile installation if relatively few charts a year are likely to be required.

In published form the current most-important source of European data (including some British) is the *European Meteorological Bulletin*, published daily by the Deutscher Wetterdienst, Zentralamt, D-6050, Offenbach am Main, Frankfurterstrasse 135, Federal Republic of Germany, and obtainable by monthly or annual subscription. Each issue consists of eight A3-size pages containing surface and upper-air maps, some of Europe and the North Atlantic, but four of them covering most of the land areas of the northern hemisphere.

For propagation studies the main attraction is a set of 36 plotted upper-air ascents showing, though for midnight gmt only, the respective profiles of temperature and dew point against pressure. If care is taken, it is possible to recover the original values with sufficient accuracy to produce extremely useful refractive index cross-sections. One's ability to interpolate the scales may be tested by comparing read-off values for the German stations against the tabulated data for them, which appears in an insert (which may have to be requested or ordered separately). The stations for which midnight soundings are given are those indicated in Table 3 by an asterisk in the column headed "EMB". A "T" in the same column indicates that tabulated data for both 0000 and 1200gmt are available.

Published reports from other countries in Europe are becoming fewer each year, but notable exceptions are those from Belgium and the Netherlands: both are of interest in connection with propagation studies involving the United Kingdom.

Any of these publications may be consulted at the National Meteorological Library, London Road, Bracknell, but it is advisable to make a prior enquiry before planning a visit to make sure that the information required is already on the shelves.

Those with rtty or fax reception facilities are in the happy position of having access to a continuous and inexhaustible supply of meteorological data, all transmitted within a short time of the observations being made. Table 2 gives details of some of the most useful broadcasts for radio propagation study material; there are many others. It should be noted that a licence is now required for the reception of meteorological broadcasts. Application should be made to the Home Office, Radio Regulatory Branch (R1), Waterloo Bridge House, Waterloo Road, London SE1 8UA.

Fig 8 shows the location of all the upper-air (radiosonde) meteorological stations making regular soundings within the area shown. They are identified in terms of the QTH locator lettered squares in which they lie. This map may be used to select those stations for which data are required to investigate a particular path, say, squares WO, YN, AM, DL and FK. By reference to Table 3 these are found to refer to the meteorological stations of Long Kesh, Aughton, Hemsby, Essen and Meiningen. The table also indicates which broadcast transmissions carry the information, and shows the indicator letters and station numbers required to identify the particular messages concerned. In this instance no one broadcast carries all the data; the three UK stations may be received from either GFL Bracknell or HXX Paris, but only Y3K Potsdam has the observations for both the stations in Germany.

The GFL Bracknell rtty transmissions carry coded upper-air data for all the British Isles stations in blocks beginning at 0105gmt for the 0000gmt soundings and 1305gmt for the ones at 1200gmt. Data for certain other countries begin at 0205 and 1405gmt.

The Paris HXX broadcast is particularly useful because it includes, between 0100–0200 and 1300–1400gmt, the French, British, Belgian, Irish and Dutch ascents in good time to be useful. The German, Central and East European ascents are dealt with by Potsdam at approximately 0200 and 1400gmt. The ascents broadcasts by Warszawa are at approximately 0315 and 1515gmt.

Offenbach carries by far the best facsimile broadcasts for radio propagation studies and it is suggested that the two transmissions labelled A and B in Tables 2 and 3 will probably meet all the most likely requirements. The presentation is in the form of plotted diagrams of temperature and dew point against pressure, from which the approximate values at the turning points of the traces may be read. The stations in Germany and neighbouring countries are included in a batch in Programme A sent at 0230 (1430 for 1200gmt data); the UK, French and

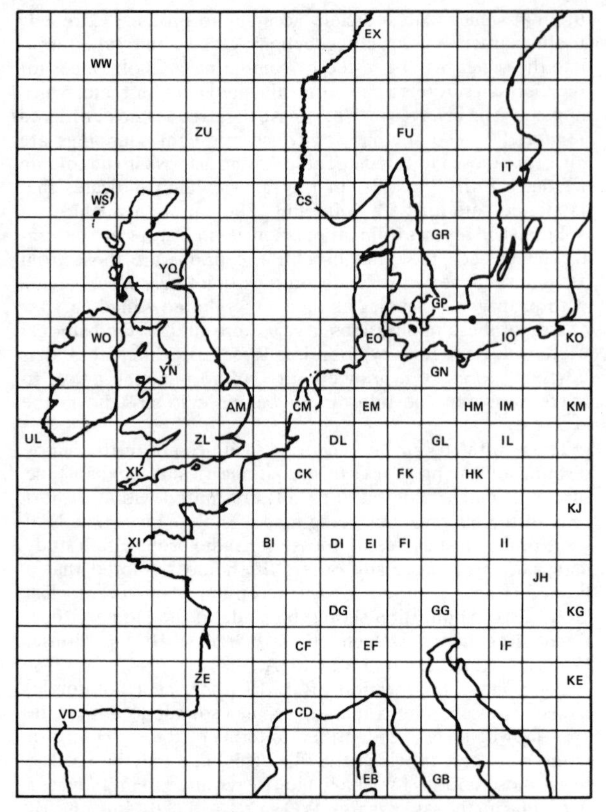

Fig 8. Chart showing the positions of meteorological upper-air stations relative to QTH locator squares. The stations may be identified by reference to Table 3

Belgian reports are sent at 0310 (1444). The transmissions on Programme B occur at 0500 and 1700gmt, with, at 0941, a repeat of a selection of German stations sent earlier on Programme A.

The French facsimile stations transmit upper-air diagrams at 0250 and 1445gmt. The facsimile service from Bracknell consists mainly of analytical charts for various levels which are of limited interest in the context under consideration.

Full details of meteorological broadcasts are published by the World Meteorological Organization in a set of books identified as WMO/OMM No 9 TP4. Much of the information in this section was obtained from Volume C (Transmissions), where the various programmes are outlined in full.

Extracting the data

In rtty broadcasts the data are transmitted in two parts, identified by the letters and station numbers shown in Table 3 and the notes which follow in this section of the text. The approximate locations, shown in QTH locator code as this is now familiar to most vhf/uhf operators, may be found in Fig 8.

The first message, headed with a prefix beginning "US" (eg USUK for British stations, USFR for French stations etc) and/or by the group "TTAA", relates to observations at specific levels of pressure. The station number is generally the second of the numerical groups.

Next, look for a group beginning 99. This and the one following are in the form

99ppp TTTDD

where "99" indicates that ground level data follows. "ppp" is the pressure in whole millibars, with the initial 1 omitted for 1,000mb and over. "TTT" is the air temperature in degrees Celsius. If the tenths figure, the third one, is odd, the whole number is negative (ie 046 = 4·6°C, but 045 = −4·5°C). "DD" is the dew-point depression in tenths of a degree up to 5°, then in whole degrees with 50 added (eg 46 = dew-point 4·6° below air temperature; 66 = 16° below). Codes 51–55 are not used.

At regularly spaced intervals there will be further groups beginning 00, 85 and 70, indicators showing that the data which follows are for 1,000, 850 and 700mb respectively. These groups and the ones which follow immediately have the form

00hhh TTTDD . . . 85hhh TTTDD . . . 70hhh TTTDD

"hhh" is the height above sea level of the pressure level in metres, omitting the thousands figure. For 1,000mb this becomes a negative number when the pressure at sea level is below that value, and this is indicated by adding 500 to the code figure (ie 675 = −175m). The missing first figure is 1 for 850mb and either 2 or 3 for 700mb, generally whichever puts the value closer to 3,000m. "TTTDD" has the same significance as before.

The second message is headed with an indicator beginning "UK" (eg UKUK, UKFR etc) and/or the group "TTBB", signifying that it relates to turning points in the temperature and dew-point profiles. It is the more useful of the two because it contains everything necessary for propagation studies, apart from the relationship between pressure and height for the particular ascent. Table 3 presumes that only the second message is required. As before, the station number is generally second of the five-figure groups in the message. To decode the remainder, point off succeeding groups in pairs that begin with the figures 00, 11, 22, 33 etc. The pairs have the form

NNppp TTTDD

where "NN" enumerates the data points, 00 always signifies local ground-level. "ppp" is the pressure, in millibars, at the level of the observation, with the initial 1 omitted if the value exceeds 1,000. "TTTDD" contain the temperature in degrees and tenths and the dew-point depression, coded as before.

For most tropospheric propagation studies there is little point in going beyond the level at which the pressure has fallen to 700mb, unless it is to interpolate a refractive index value for 700mb in order to provide a uniform "top" to a cross-section.

In a radiometeorological study it is quite likely that all the work will be carried out in terms of pressure rather than height, not only for convenience because that is the form adopted in the radiosonde messages, but because the radio wave, once launched, does not "see" changes in height but rather changes in air density, a quantity closely related to pressure. In the atmosphere, height, which seems so easy to understand on the ground, becomes a complex function of the integrated effects of temperature and humidity, and of the value of pressure at station height.

There are two ways of finding the heights corresponding to the various pressure levels reported in the Part 2 message. The more accurate, though time-consuming, way is to plot the ascent data on a standard tephigram (obtainable from HMSO, where it is known at Metform 2810B) and then to follow the

Table 3. Identification data for upper-air sounding stations

QTH locator	Radiosonde station No	Radiosonde station Name	Metres asl	EMB	Fax broadcast	RTTY broadcasts Indicator	RTTY broadcasts Transmissions
UL09c	03953	Valentia	14		—	UKIE1	GFL, HXX
VD58b	08001	La Coruna	67		—	UKSP1	HXX
WO50a	03920	Long Kesh	37	*	A	UKUK1	GFL, HXX
WS69a	03026	Stornoway	13		—	UKUK1	GFL, HXX
WW74d	06011	Thorshavn	55		—	UKFA1	GFL
XI48c	07110	Brest	103	*	A	UKFR1	HXX
XK64a	03808	Camborne	88	*	A	UKUK1	GFL, HXX
YN36j	03322	Aughton	56		—	UKUK1	GFL, HXX
YQ46j	03170	Shanwell	5	*	A	UKUK1	GFL, HXX
ZE17a	07510	Bordeaux	51	*	A	UKFR1	HXX
ZL79b	03774	Crawley	144	*	A	UKUK1	GFL, HXX
ZU65f	03005	Lerwick	82	*	A	UKUK1	GFL, HXX
AM29j	03496	Hemsby	13	*	A	UKUK1	GFL, HXX
BI11f	07145	Trappes	168	*	A	UKFR1	HXX
CD13h	07645	Nimes	62	*	A	UKFR1	HXX
CF26a	07481	Lyon	240	*	A	UKFR1	HXX
CK12c	06447	Uccle	104	*	A	UKBX1	HXX
CM76b	06260	De Bilt	4	*	A	UKNL1	GFL, HXX
CS19a	01415	Stavanger	33	*	B	UKNO11	GFL, LMO
DG15c	06610	Payerne	491	*	A	USSW1	HXX (part A only)
						USEU22	GFL (part A only)
DI22g	07180	Nancy	217		—	UKFR1	HXX (12 gmt only)
DL45d	10410	Essen	161	*T	A	ULDL1	Y3K, SOE/SOH
EB05g	07761	Ajaccio	9		—	UKFR1	HXX
EF47j	16080	Milano	138	*	B	UKIY1	IMB
EI17h	10739	Stuttgart	315	*T	A	UKDL1	Y3K, SOE/SOH
EM49a	10338	Hannover	56	*T	A	UKDL1	Y3K, SOE/SOH
EO38d	10035	Schleswig	48	*T	A	UKDL1	Y3K, SOE/SOH
EX29g	01241	Ørland	10	*	A	UKNO13	GFL
FI58d	10868	München	484	*T	A	UKDL1	Y3K
FK32c	09548	Meiningen	453	*	A	UKDD1	Y3K
FU66j	01384	Oslo	201	*	B	UKNO11	LMO
GB12g	16242	Roma	3	*	B	UKIY1	LZA/LZF, IMB
GG76d	16044	Udine	94	*	B	UKIY1	LZA/LZF, IMB
GL79a	09486	Wahnsdorf	232		—	UKDD23	Y3K
GN78h	09184	Griefswald	6	*	A	UKDD1	Y3K
GP13e	06181	København	40	*	A	UKDN1	GFL, Y3K
GR22j	02527	Goteborg	155	*	B	UKSN5	GFI
HK73f	11520	Praha	304	*	B	UKCZ1	Y3K, SOE/SOH
HM61a	09393	Lindenberg	115	*	A	UKDD1	Y3K
IF11f	13130	Zagreb	128		—	UKYG2	LZA/LZF
II52d	11035	Wien	209	*	A	UKOS21	LZA/LZF, Y3K
IL65d	12425	Wrocklaw	116		—	UKPL1	Y3K, SOE/SOH
IM45g	12330	Poznan	92		—	UKPL1	Y3K, SOE/SOH
IO18d	12120	Leba	2		—	UKPL1	Y3K, SOE/SOH
IT55b	02465	Stockholm	22	*	B	UKSN4	GFL
JH46c	12843	Budapest	140	*	B	UKHU1	LZA/LZF, Y3K
KE13d	13275	Beograd	243	*	B	UKYG1	LZA/LZF
KG51e	12982	Szeged	84		—	UKHU2	LZA/LZF
KJ72e	11952	Poprad	706		—	USCZ2	IMB (Part A only)
KM45d	12374	Legionowo	96	*	B	UKPL1	Y3K, SOE/SOH

instructions given on the form. Alternatively, and this may well be accurate enough for the present purpose, refer to Fig 9, which assumes an average vertical distribution of temperature and dew point, leaving the height a function only of surface pressure. The diagram is used as follows:

(a) Find the station height from Table 3 and draw a vertical line at the corresponding value on the horizontal scale. (Crawley, at 144m, has been used as an example.)

(b) Find the point where that vertical line intersects a horizontal line appropriate to the reported value of ground-level pressure.

(c) Through that point lay off a line which maintains a constant proportion of the space between the two sloping lines. (An overlay of tracing paper is useful here.)

(d) Approximate heights corresponding to given pressures may now be read from the horizontal scale.

This diagram may be used also to interpolate between the height values reported in the standard-level message.

Full details of all the codes used in meteorological broadcasts will be found in *Met O 920b: Handbook of Weather Messages, Part II, Codes and Specifications*, published by HMSO, London.

The tephigram

Meteorologists usually plot radiosonde ascent data on a rather complex thermodynamic chart known as a *tephigram*, (which may be used as a means of calculating potential refractive

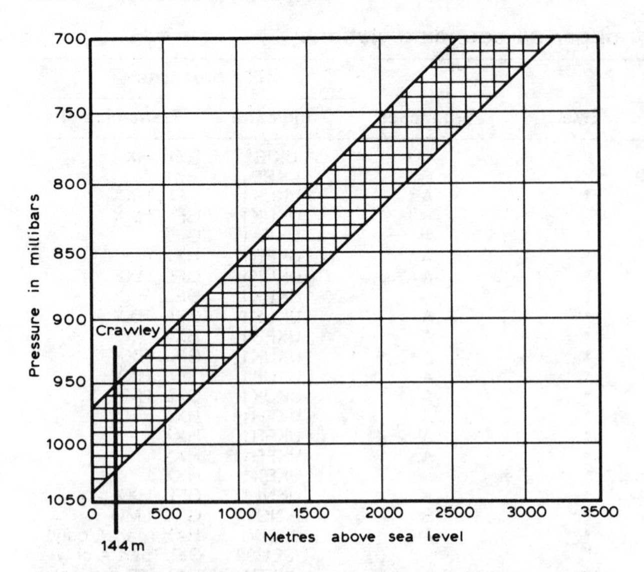

Fig 9. Relationship between pressure and height between the surface and 700mb, assuming an average contribution from temperature and humidity

index) and a knowledge of its properties will help to achieve an understanding of the processes involved in the atmospheric movements we have been considering. Fig 10 shows an outline diagram, including a set of *K*-lines which will be explained in the next section. Reference should be made to the small inset diagram which identifies the various axes as they appear at the 1,000mb, 0°C intersection:

- P—P are isobars, or lines of constant pressure.
- T—T are isotherms, or lines of constant temperature.
- D—D are lines of constant moisture content, which are followed by the dew point as the pressure alters during adiabatic changes.
- A—A are lines of constant potential temperature, followed by the air temperature during an adiabatic change.
- W—W is a saturated adiabatic, which marks the temperature changes followed by ascending saturated air (only one is shown here in order to simplify the diagram as much as possible).

Both temperature and dew point are plotted with reference to the T—T lines.

An example of the use of the tephigram will help to emphasize the points which have been made earlier in the text. Consider Fig 11(a), which shows two points on the 900mb line,

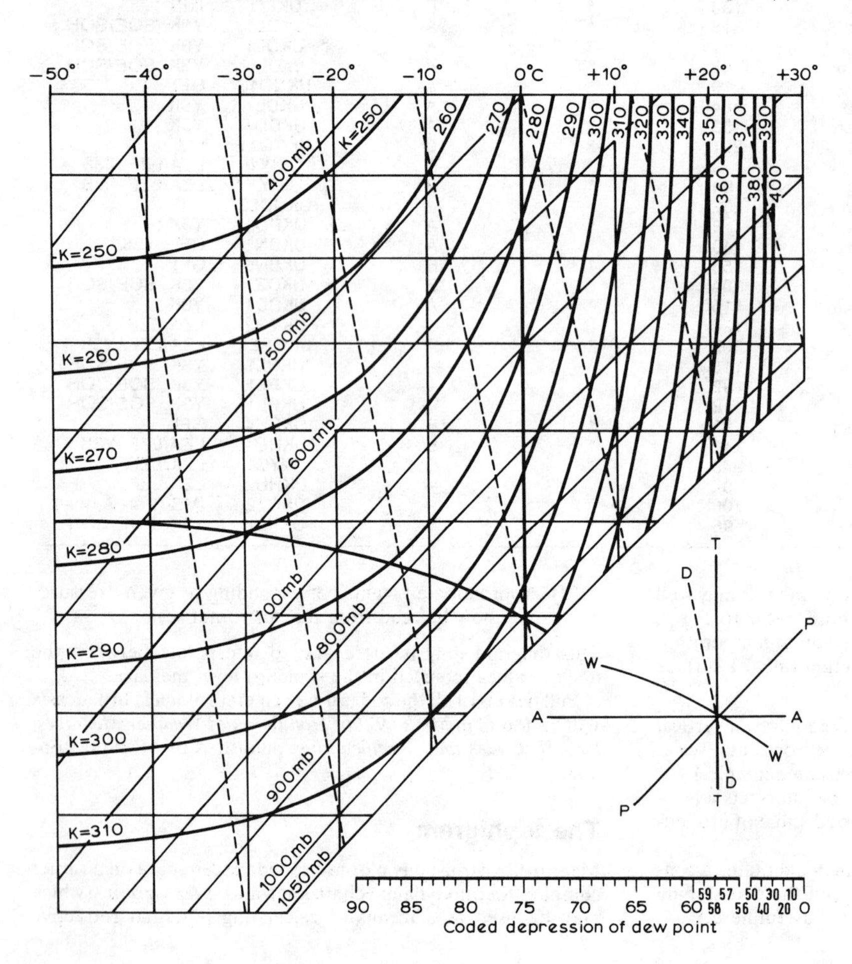

Fig 10. Skeleton tephigram (a meteorological temperature-entropy diagram) showing the positions of additional curves, labelled *K* = 250 to 450, used for direct graphical calculation of potential refractive index values from published radiosonde measurements. For practical use it is recommended that the curves should be transferred to a standard full-sized tephigram, available from HMSO as Metform 2810B

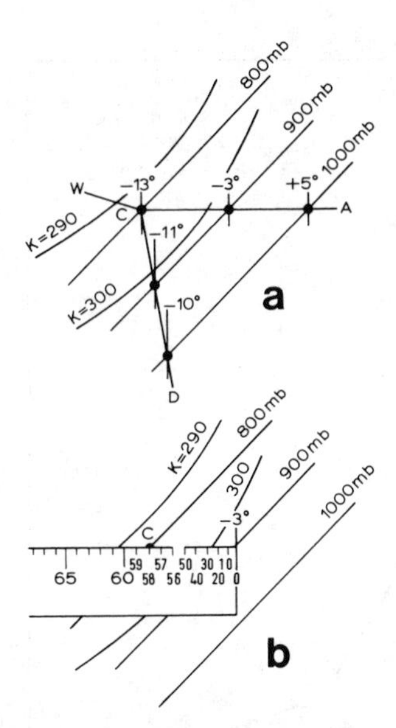

Fig 11. Alternative methods of determining values of potential refractive index from reported measurements of pressure, temperature and dew-point depression, using the tephigram modified as in Fig 10. (a) Intersection method. (b) Using scale of coded dew-point depression values

representing a temperature of −3°C and a dew point of −11°C. If that sample of air is taken to a pressure of 1,000mb adiabatically, the temperature will follow the horizontal line CA, and the dew point will follow CD. At 1,000mb the temperature becomes +5°C (by definition the potential temperature), and the dew point becomes −10°C. Lifting would cause the temperature and the dew point to come closer together, and they would become coincident at the point C, which is known as the *condensation level*, where condensed droplets of water begin to appear as cloud. Further lifting will cause the temperature to follow one of the saturated adiabatics such as CW, instead of an extension of AC, due to the liberation of latent heat.

Obtaining potential refractive index values

Potential refractive index values may be obtained in one of four ways, the method to be used depending on the resources available.

1. From the expression

$$K = \frac{77\cdot6}{\theta}\left(1{,}000 + \frac{4{,}810{,}000\,.\,e}{p\theta}\right)$$

where p is the pressure in millibars at the level of observation. θ is the potential temperature in degrees Kelvin.

$$= (T_{(°C)} + 273) \times \left(\frac{1{,}000}{p}\right)^{0\cdot288}$$

e is the saturation vapour pressure at the dew-point temperature.

Example: p = 900mb, T = −3·0°C, dew-point depression = code 58 = 8°C below −3·0°C = −11·0°C, then

$$\theta = 270 \times \left(\frac{1{,}000}{900}\right)^{0\cdot288} = 278\cdot3$$

and from Fig 1(d)

$$e = 2\cdot6\text{mb (at } -11°\text{C)}$$

whence K = 292·8

2. Using a programmable calculator. Table 4 outlines a TI58/59 (Texas Instruments) program which provides k values directly from pressure, temperature and dew-point depression.

3. Using a full-sized tephigram based on Fig 10 and a two-line construction. The curved potential refractive index lines labelled K= 290, K = 300 etc are so placed that the required value of K may be read at the intersection of the dry adiabat through the temperature point and the moisture content line through the dew point, plotted on the appropriate isobar. These points are shown on Fig 11(a) at −3°C and −11°C (900mb), as in the previous example. The lines drawn as indicated intersect at the point C which, when referred to the K lines, gives the answer directly: K = 293.

4. Alternatively, the scale labelled "coded depression of the dew point" may be transferred to the edge of a card and used horizontally on the diagram as shown in Fig 11(b), with the right-hand index against the point on the diagram defined by the temperature and pressure. The required K value is read against the coded dew-point depression (58, signifying 8° depression). The scale is the projection on to a horizontal of depressions along an isobar, using the slope of the moisture content lines. This method is strictly correct only on the right-hand side of the diagram and the method would suffer a progressive loss of accuracy towards the left (because the moisture content lines are not parallel), were it not for the fact that the dependence of K on dew point diminishes at low temperatures.

From profile to section

Once the calculations have been made all the information necessary to draw a profile will be to hand,

A profile, such as the one shown in Fig 12, reveals immediately the presence of warm, dry, low-refractivity air overlying a ground-based layer of air which is cool, moist, and of high refractive index. The more abrupt the boundary between them, the more nearly horizontal will the transition appear on the diagram, and the more pronounced the bending experienced by the radio wave. Some of the occasions when conditions have been most favourable for dx have occurred during periods when there has been anticyclonic subsidence aloft with a contrasting depth of wet fog at the ground.

In some cases the refractive index profile is all that is required. It is much more rewarding, however, to combine it with others in order to make a section.

The first step is to project the pressures at which regular values of K occur across to a vertical line, as shown in the diagram. The spacings which result can then be transferred to form part of a time-section for the station in question (Fig 5), or a cross-section for a given path (Fig 6)—the one profile forms part of both diagrams.

The additional work involved in this type of exercise is amply justified by the sense of continuity which results. Thus the time-section shown in Fig 5 reveals in a single glance far more about the formation and eventual dissipation of a subsidence boundary layer than could be gained by a prolonged study of the 10 separate profiles which were combined in its construction.

Table 4. TI58/59 program: potential refractive index, *K*, from basic meteorological data

0·288	STO–04	77·6	STO–08
2937·4	STO–05	4810000	STO–09
−4·9283	STO–06	273	STO–10
23·5518	STO–07	1000	STO–11

Form A—Humidity as dew-point depression

(Enter P)		y^x	028–45	×	061–65
STO	000–42	RCL	029–43	RCL	062–43
01	001–01	04	030–04	09	063–09
R/S	002–91	=	031–95	÷	064–55
(Enter T°C)		STO	032–42	RCL	065–43
+	003–85	12	033–12	12	066–12
RCL	004–43	(	034–53	÷	067–55
10	005–10	(	035–53	RCL	068–43
=	006–95	1	036–01	01	069–01
STO	007–42	0	037–00	)	070–54
02	008–02	y^x	038–45	+	071–85
−	*099*–75	(	039–53	3	072–03
R/S	010–91	RCL	040–43	INV	073–22
(Enter D°C)		07	041–07	*Log	074–28
*NOP	*011*–68	−	042–75	)	075–54
*NOP	*012*–68	RCL	043–43	×	076–65
*NOP	*013*–68	05	044–05	RCL	077–43
*NOP	*014*–68	÷	045–55	08	078–08
=	015–95	RCL	046–43	÷	079–55
STO	016–42	03	*047*–03	RCL	080–43
03	017–03	)	048–54	12	081–12
RCL	018–43	×	049–65	=	082–95
02	019–02	RCL	050–43	*FIX	083–58
×	020–65	03	*051*–03	0	084–00
(	021–53	y^x	052–45	R/S	085–91
RCL	022–43	RCL	053–43		
11	023–11	06	054–06	**Test:**	
÷	024–55	*NOP	*055*–68	P = 900,	
RCL	025–43	*NOP	*056*–68	T = −3·0	
01	026–01	*NOP	*057*–68	D = 8	
)	027–54	*NOP	*058*–68	K = 293	
		=	059–95		
		Pause	060–66		

Vapour pressure flashes up at step 60. To hold, replace with R/S 060–91.
* = 2nd function key.

Form B—Humidity as dew point, T_d°C
Program as for Form A, except:

Enter T_d°C after step 10. Substitute the following at the steps in italics:

*NOP	009–68	*NOP	055–68	**Test:**
÷	011–85	*NOP	056–68	P = 900
RCL	012–43	*NOP	057–68	T = −3·0
10	013–10	*NOP	058–68	T_d = −11·0
*NOP	014–68			K = 293

Form C—Humidity as RH per cent
Program as for Form A, except:

Enter RH per cent after step 10. Substitute the following at the steps in italics:

*NOP	009–68	03	051–03	**Test:**
÷	011–55	)	055–54	P = 900
2	012–02	×	056–65	T = −3·0
INV	013–22	RCL	057–43	RH = 53%
*Log	014–28	03	058–03	K = 293
02	047–02			

"Normal" values of *N* and *K*

In studies of this nature it is of interest to know how a particular example compares with so-called "normal" conditions. The

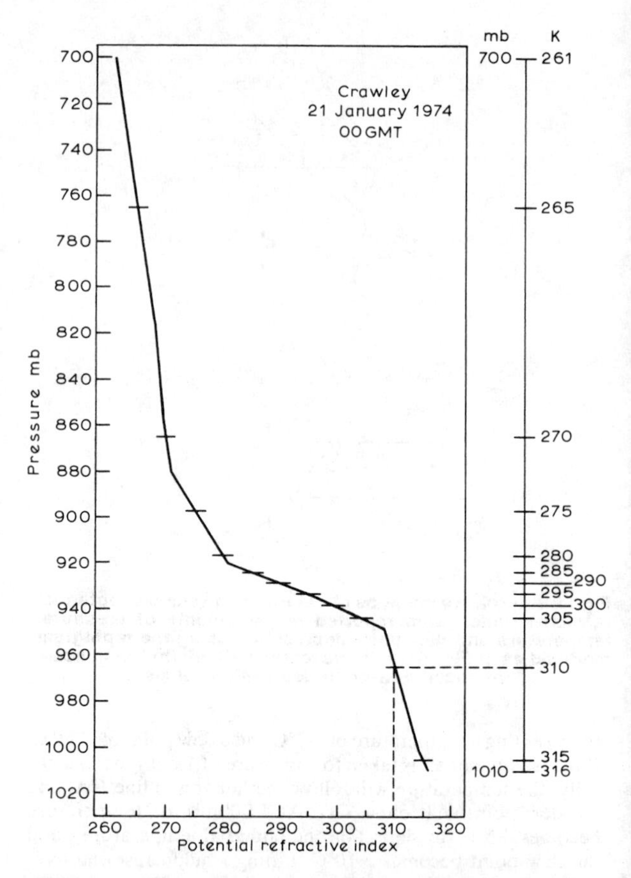

Fig 12. Potential refractive index profile from Crawley, 21 January 1974, at 0000gmt. The spaced values along the vertical line on the right have been used in the construction of both Fig 5 and Fig 6

RSGB has carried out a long-term study of refractive index distributions in the lower troposphere over Southern England and Tables 5 and 6 summarize mean values of *N*, *K* and height at intervals of 50mb pressure and half a month period throughout the year. These results are based on 4,380 consecutive radiosonde ascents at Crawley, Sussex, reduced to refractive index and meaned arithmetically. They appeared first in *IERE Conference Proceedings* No 40 (July 1978), to which reference should be made for further details and other results of the six-year study concerned.

Signal strengths and ranges attainable

For a final look at tropospheric propagation let us briefly examine the signal variations of tv sound transmissions on 174MHz, coming from Lille in northern France, taken from pen recordings made by G3BGL at a site just west of Reading, a transmission path of some 300km (Fig 13). The broadcasts were by no means continuous, but enough time was available each day to show that the strongest signals occurred when the subsidence boundary layer above Crawley (which was along the path) was low and intense and that the end of the period of enhancement coincided with the break-up of the anticyclonic conditions on 29 September, which was brought about by the

Table 5. Seasonal variation of radio refractive index *N* at Crawley. Six years combined data, 1972–7

Half-month period		Sfc *N*	Sfc *P*	950 *N*	900 *N*	850 *N*	850 *H*	800 *N*	750 *N*	700 *N*	700 *H*
JA	A	318	1,001	297	278	260	1,465	244	227	213	3,001
	B	314	995	296	278	261	1,407	244	228	213	2,929
FE	C	313	991	296	278	261	1,381	245	228	214	2,909
	D	315	1,002	294	276	259	1,468	244	228	213	2,995
MR	E	313	999	294	276	259	1,444	243	227	213	2,966
	F	313	1,000	294	276	259	1,455	243	228	213	2,984
AP	G	312	997	294	277	262	1,434	245	229	214	2,958
	H	313	1,002	294	278	261	1,480	244	227	212	3,014
MY	J	316	997	297	280	263	1,443	246	229	214	2,979
	K	319	1,000	298	281	262	1,483	244	228	213	3,035
JE	L	321	1,001	300	282	263	1,497	245	228	213	3,059
	M	326	1,001	304	285	265	1,510	247	230	213	3,091
JL	N	330	1,001	306	287	267	1,513	247	230	213	3,098
	P	331	1,000	308	288	269	1,503	249	231	214	3,096
AU	Q	331	1,001	307	288	268	1,519	248	229	213	3,102
	R	330	1,001	306	287	266	1,518	246	228	212	3,098
SE	S	327	1,000	305	285	265	1,495	246	229	213	3,067
	T	327	999	304	284	265	1,479	246	228	213	3,041
OC	U	323	997	302	282	262	1,455	244	227	213	3,014
	V	323	1,000	300	280	260	1,475	244	227	212	3,030
NV	W	320	998	299	281	262	1,448	245	228	213	2,990
	X	315	998	295	277	260	1,439	243	227	213	2,968
DE	Y	316	998	296	278	261	1,441	244	227	213	2,973
	Z	318	1,002	296	278	261	1,469	243	227	212	3,006
Overall six-year mean		320	999	299	281	263	1,468	245	228	213	3,015

arrival of a cold front. The rising dome of air within the associated depression is clearly evident. On sections such as these, anticyclones reveal themselves by downward departures of the isopleths from the top of the chart, while depressions appear as a rise from the lower boundary, which is, of course, a graph of surface pressure taken at 12h intervals.

The subsidence boundary layer is really a balance between the descending dry air and the turbulent moist air underneath. If the strength of the turbulence weakens the boundary falls; if it ceases altogether the subsiding air may well continue right on down to ground level. There was a tendency for this to happen on 27/28 September in the diagram but in this instance enough of the layer remained around 850mb to maintain the enhanced signals.

When the subsidence does reach the ground the antennas emerge into air which has a refractive index lapse rate considerably less than normal, and the result of this is a mysterious drop-out, just after signal strengths from distant stations have been at their highest. This sometimes occurs during field day events, when operators who have taken their equipment to the top of a hill may find that they have lost contact with the dx, while they can hear their colleagues lower down still enjoying the good conditions. The reason for this effect should now be clear; it is not the subsiding air alone (nor the fact that pressure is high) which brings in the dx, but the steep-lapse boundary formed where the dry air is met by moist air underneath. This also explains why signal paths over the sea, where there is an almost inexhaustible supply of cool, moist air at low levels, are always more effective than those of comparable distances over land.

At their best, tropospheric "openings" are productive of ranges considerably in excess of the expectations of our professional colleagues. Using an analysis of extreme-range signal reports it has been shown that if 1,000km can be exceeded at 144MHz there is a strong probability that 1,500km will be reached, for there is a pronounced peak in the distribution at that range. Similarly, if 750km can be exceeded at 432MHz, there is a good probability that 1,200km will be reached. Histograms showing these findings are included in an RSGB paper in *IEE Conference Publication 195*, Part 2, pp 163–167 ("The use of a dense network of amateur radio stations to determine the limits of long-range tropospheric propagation within an anticyclone", by R. G. Flavell.)

At the time of writing the maximum confirmed range by tropospheric propagation at 144MHz from the European area has been 2,625km , SW England to the Canary Islands, by G3CHN (locator YK61b) and EA8XS (SO73d), 6 August 1980, an event which is analysed in terms of potential refractive index in the work cited.

At 432MHz the European record is currently 1,608km, NW Germany to northern Spain, 29 November 1979, set up by DK2NH (FN31a) and EA1CR (XD32d). In this part of the

Table 6. Seasonal variation of potential refractive index K at Crawley. Six years combined data, 1972–7

Half-month period		Sfc K	Sfc P	950 K	900 K	850 K	850 H	800 K	750 K	700 K	700 H
JA	A	318	1,001	308	300	292	1,465	286	279	275	3,001
	B	315	995	307	300	293	1,407	286	280	275	2,929
FE	C	315	991	307	300	293	1,381	287	280	276	2,909
	D	315	1,002	305	298	291	1,468	286	280	275	2,995
MR	E	313	999	305	298	291	1,444	285	279	275	2,966
	F	313	1,000	305	298	291	1,455	285	280	275	2,984
AP	G	313	997	305	299	294	1,434	287	281	276	2,958
	H	313	1,002	305	300	293	1,480	286	279	273	3,014
MY	J	317	997	308	302	295	1,443	288	281	276	2,979
	K	319	1,000	309	303	294	1,483	286	280	274	3,035
JE	L	321	1,001	311	304	295	1,497	287	280	274	3,059
	M	326	1,001	315	307	298	1,510	290	282	275	3,091
JL	N	330	1,001	317	309	300	1,513	290	282	275	3,098
	P	331	1,000	320	311	302	1,503	292	283	276	3,096
AU	Q	331	1,001	318	310	301	1,519	291	281	274	3,102
	R	330	1,001	317	309	299	1,518	289	280	273	3,098
SE	S	327	1,000	316	307	298	1,495	289	281	274	3,067
	T	327	999	315	306	298	1,479	288	280	274	3,041
OC	U	324	997	313	304	294	1,455	286	279	274	3,014
	V	323	1,000	311	302	292	1,475	286	279	273	3,030
NV	W	321	998	310	303	294	1,448	287	280	274	2,990
	X	316	998	306	299	292	1,439	285	279	275	2,968
DE	Y	317	998	307	300	293	1,441	286	279	274	2,973
	Z	318	1,002	307	300	293	1,469	285	279	273	3,006
Overall 6-year mean		321	999	310	303	295	1,468	287	280	275	3,017

world we are still a long way from the 432MHz performance of WB6NMT, California, and KH6HME, Hawaii, who spanned 4,080km to greet one another on 18 July 1979.

Free-space attenuation

The concept of *free-space attenuation* between isotropic antennas, or *basic transmission loss*, L_b, provides a useful yardstick against which other modes of propagation may be compared. It is a function of frequency and distance, such that

$$L_b = 32{\cdot}45 + 20 \log f + 20 \log d$$

where f and d are expressed in megahertz and kilometres respectively.

Table 7 provides a representative range of values against distance for various amateur bands above 30MHz.

Tropospheric scatter propagation

Tropospheric scatter propagation depends on the presence of dust, particles, cloud droplets and small-scale irregularities in radio refractive index within a volume of the atmosphere which is common to both the transmitting and receiving antenna beam cones. The height of the bottom of this common volume is a

Table 7. Free-space attenuation

Frequency (MHz)	Distance (km) 50	100	150	200	300	400	500	750	1,000
50	100	106	110	112	116	118	120	124	126
70	103	109	113	115	119	121	123	127	129
144	110	116	119	122	125	128	130	133	136
432	119	125	129	131	135	137	139	143	145
1,296	129	135	138	141	144	147	149	152	155
2,300	134	140	143	146	149	152	154	157	160
3,400	137	143	147	149	153	155	157	161	163
5,600	141	147	151	153	157	159	161	165	167
10,000	146	152	156	158	162	164	166	170	172
24,000	154	160	164	166	170	172	174	178	180

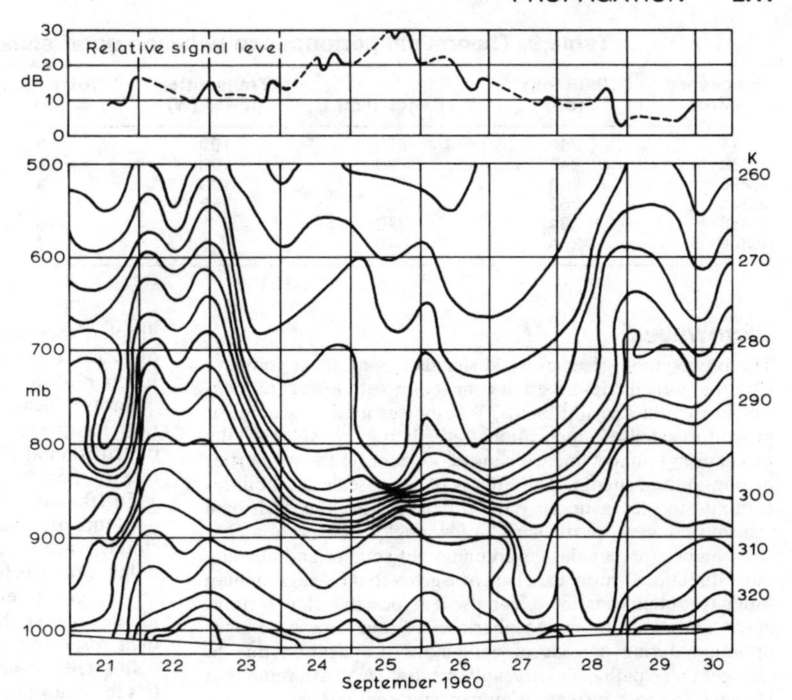

Fig 13. Potential refractive index time section, Crawley, 21–30 September 1960, together with a record of signal strengths, obtained on a chart recorder located near Reading, from vhf tv transmissions originating at Lille in France. Note that the highest signals occur when the steep-lapse layer is most pronounced, and a sudden drop occurs as the anticyclone is replaced by a low-pressure system. With acknowledgements to *J Atmos Terr Phys*, Pergamon Press

function of distance between the stations concerned owing to the effect of the curvature of the earth. Typical heights are 600m for a 100km path, 9,000m for a 500km path. Path losses increase by about 10dB for every degree of horizon angle at each station so that a site with an unobstructed take-off is an important consideration.

Only a very small proportion of the signal energy passing through the common volume will be scattered, and only a small proportion of that will be directed towards the receiving station. Therefore the loss in the scattering process is extremely large and the angle through which the signal ray has to be deflected is an important characteristic of a troposcatter path; for best results it should be no more than a few degrees.

J. N. Gannaway, G3YGF, has made a critical study of the losses in tropospheric scatter propagation, which appeared in *Radio Communication* August 1981, pp710–714, 717, and which should be consulted for a fuller discussion of the mode than can be given here.

Table 8 shows the path losses between two stations on a smooth earth, expressed as decibels below the free-space values, for the vhf, uhf and shf amateur bands. (Free-space losses have been given earlier in Table 7.) To these values must be added losses depending on characteristics of the sites—height, distance to the first obstruction, antenna coupling losses etc—and variables depending on seasonal and weather factors.

Table 9, which is taken directly from the work cited, shows the theoretical range that could be expected under flat conditions and from good sites, with the equipments shown against each of the amateur bands. The ranges are for a 0dB signal-to-noise ratio in a bandwidth of 100Hz, representing a weak cw signal; for ssb these ranges should be reduced by 130km on each band.

For distances approaching 1,000km the equipment requirements are comparable to those needed for propagation by moonbounce.

Because signal-path transit times vary with height of scatter within the common volume a "blurring" occurs which limits the maximum speed of transmission of intelligence; narrow beams have the faster capabilities.

Table 8. Troposcatter path losses on a smooth earth

Band (MHz)	Distance (km) 50	100	150	200	300	400	500	750	1,000
70	47	49	53	55	61	69	75	91	109
144	50	52	55	58	64	72	78	94	112
432	55	56	60	62	69	76	82	99	116
1,296	59	61	65	67	74	81	87	104	121
2,300	60	63	67	70	76	83	90	106	
3,400	62	65	68	72	78	84	91	108	
5,600	64	68	71	74	81	87	94		
10,000	68	71	74	78	84	90	98		
24,000*	71	74	78	82	88	94	101		

* Neglecting absorption due to water vapour.

Table 9. Theoretical performance between good sites under flat conditions

Frequency (MHz)	Path loss (dB)	Range (km)	Transmitter power (W)	Noise figure (dB)	Antenna	Antenna gain (dBi)
144	240	870	100	3	2 × 16-el Yagi	18
432	247	790	100	3	2 × 25-el loop Yagi	22
1,296	258	760	100	3	2 × 25-el loop Yagi	24
2,304	262	720	50	3	6ft dish	31
10,368	234	240	0·1	10	4ft dish	39
10,368	254	440	1	3	4ft dish	39

Microwaves

The propagation of microwave signals has much in common with that already described in connection with lower frequencies in the vhf and uhf bands. Whether ground-to-ground or ground-to-satellite applications are being considered the mechanism remains one which is dependent on the properties of non-ionized media. The effects of large-scale variabilities continue to play a major part in determining the path of a transmitted wave, particularly at low angles of elevation.

At higher frequencies, as antennas get smaller and become more directional, more care has to be given to their alignment in order to obtain maximum signals. It is possible that settings made under normal atmospheric conditions are no longer optimum during periods of anomalous propagation due to changes in the path geometry, and this could lead to a reduction in signal strength instead of an expected increase.

Small-scale variations in refractive index (known as *scintillations*) lead to rapid and irregular fluctuations in amplitude, phase, angle of arrival and polarization. Further losses can result from beam scattering, which may cause large antennas to have lower gains than expected, and there may be disappointing results at very low elevation angles due to spreading of the beam if conditions are such that the refraction varies considerably over the first few degrees of take-off.

Above about 1GHz the attenuation due to precipitation, cloud and atmospheric gases becomes an important consideration. Absorption from this cause is extremely high at 22–23GHz on account of water vapour, and again at about 60GHz due to oxygen. When the limits of technology have been pushed back that far, there are further stop-bands to be encountered beyond.

If the transmission path passes right through the atmosphere, as it will when working earth-satellite or satellite-earth, the distance which is subject to absorption will depend on the angle between the path direction and the horizontal. In order to simplify the calculations, the effective distance for oxygen absorption is usually taken as the distance the radio wave would have to travel if the atmosphere were replaced by one having constant density reaching upwards from the ground to a height of 4km, with a vacuum above. The corresponding height for water vapour is taken as 2km. This gives a theoretical total one-way attenuation due to the combined effects of oxygen and water vapour somewhere in the region of 1·5dB at 1GHz, 2dB at 5GHz, 6dB at 15GHz and 10dB at 18GHz, for a horizontal path (ie tangential to the earth's surface). These values reduce as the elevation angle increases, to become in the limit, when the signal take-off direction is vertical, about 0·1dB at about 15GHz, with only 1dB at the 22GHz peak.

The attenuation due to rain increases rapidly with frequency and is likely to exceed the combined effects of water vapour and oxygen absorption at the frequencies likely to interest the radio amateur. It is caused mainly by the absorption of energy in the droplets themselves, but there is also some loss due to scatter outside the beam. The degree of attenuation is therefore a function of the integrated rainfall along the path and this is a quantity which cannot be known unless extensive instrumentation has been set up to measure it. Typical figures are 0·01dB/km at 3GHz and 0·5dB/km at 10GHz for a rainfall rate of 25mm/h, increasing to 0·025dB/km at 3GHz and 1·5dB/km at 10GHz for 50mm/h.

Clouds attenuate according to their liquid water content. Ice clouds, such as cirrus ("mare's tails") and cirrostratus (the milky veil which often produces haloes around the sun or moon), give attenuations which are about two orders of magnitude smaller than water clouds, owing to the difference in their respective dielectric properties.

In satellite work abnormal ray-bending may lead to difficulties in acquisition or holding. Most of the curvature of a radio ray takes place in the dense and variable part of the atmosphere near the ground. For that reason errors due to refraction are greatest at very low angles and they diminish rapidly as the satellite moves towards the zenith. With high values of refractivity near the ground these errors can amount to as much as 2° at the horizon, but they have decreased to less than ½° at 3° above. There is some advantage in siting earth stations high on mountains in order to get outside the densest and most troublesome part of the atmosphere.

As regards the calculation of transmission loss at microwaves, there is a certain lack of agreement between the various authorities as to which is the best method. Alternative theories may differ by several tens of decibels and for that reason records of signal strength (preferably autographic rather than manual) extending over long periods of time are urgently required in order to improve empirical predictions. This is therefore a field in which interested amateurs could make a very useful contribution.

Table 10 lists all the amateur-band microwave beacons authorized at the time of writing, together with their positions in terms of both QTH locator and National Grid co-ordinates. Regular observations of any of these beacons, but especially the 10GHz ones, extending over a long period of time, are urgently required by CCIR. This is an activity in which club stations might be able to share their resources and their expertise in a very worthwhile project. It must be stressed that high standards of equipment performance, particularly as regards frequency stability and regularly calibrated outputs, are essential, and advice should be sought from the RSGB before any recordings are begun in earnest.

Ionospheric propagation at vhf and uhf

Regular layers

The regular layers of the ionosphere play little part in the properties of the vhf bands and, according to present thought at

Table 10. Some microwave beacons in the UK

Frequency (MHz)	Callsign	QTH locator	National Grid Reference
1,296·83	GB3BPO	AM77j	TM 251 448
1,296·87	GB3AND	ZL63b	SU 379 467
1,296·89	GB3DUN	ZL08e	TL 044 210
1,296·90	GB3IOW	ZK34a	SZ 494 772
1,296·91	GB3CLE	YM48h	SO 593 866
1,296·99	GB3EDN	YP05g	NT 268 706
2,304·01	GB3NEW	ZL63b	SU 379 467
2,304·05	GB3LDN	AL41a	TQ 435 767
3,456	GB3UOS	ZN42c	SK 278 929
10,100	GB3IOW	ZK34a	SZ 494 772
10,120	GB3ALD	YJ30a	CI 865 798
10,400	GB3LEX	ZM24d	SK 485 108
10,400	GB3XGH	YN57d	SJ 567 721

Notes:

1. These details are subject to change—an up-to-date list of all UK beacons can be obtained from RSGB HQ.
2. There is a transmitter on the moon, left behind by the last Apollo mission, on 2,276·0MHz, right-hand circular polarization, fm with 1·06kb/s data, audible on an ssb receiver as two modulated sidebands plus central carrier. This might be a useful source by which to gauge system performance, compare antenna gains etc.

least, none at all at uhf and above. Around the time of sunspot maximum and for perhaps a year or two after, there are occasions when maximum usable frequencies exceed 50MHz and cross-band working with North American amateurs becomes possible. The most favourable times for transatlantic contacts at 50MHz occur when the solar flux is high and the magnetic index is low, but the required conditions do not persist for long. On 8 February 1979 G3COJ and WB2RLK/VE made the first 28/50MHz transatlantic contact since 1958. On the other hand, when conditions are good, they are often very good. EI2W, the only 50MHz licensed amateur in northern Europe, succeeded in working 40 states of the USA on 50MHz during 1979–80. Such contacts are made via the F˜ layer. It is unlikely that transmissions above 30MHz would ever by propagated by the regular E layer. In the tropics some occasional periods of activity around noon in maximum sunspot years may be possible, using the F1 layer.

Any propagation at vhf which may take place via the regular layers of the ionosphere will have a very strong dependence on the solar cycle.

Non-regular ionization

Contacts at vhf and uhf are occasionally possible via ionization which may take the form of sheets, clouds, mobile curtains or long narrow cylinders. Most of these forms are active around E-layer height, but they are not directly associated with the regular layers. Some effects, those involving the equatorial ionosphere, for example, may take place at F-layer levels. The varieties which will be dealt with here are sporadic-E, auroral-E, trans-equatorial propagation and meteor scatter.

Sporadic-E

As has been noted before, there is currently some doubt as to whether what radio amateurs refer to as "sporadic-E" at vhf is the same mechanism as that which has long been known by that name in connection with hf. According to present theory sporadic-E is impossible at frequencies as high as 144MHz, and a growing number of professionals are beginning to take a great interest in amateur observations in an effort to establish just what it is being used! The position is an interesting one because it has been established that amateurs are in the best position to provide the basic raw material for this investigation.

In its conventional form sporadic-E consists of horizontal sheets about 1km thick and some 100km across, usually at a height of 100–130km. Clouds form in an apparently random manner, although there is an obvious preference for certain times and seasons. They do not behave consistently, for whereas some sheets may travel across continents for several hundreds of kilometres others remain almost stationary. It has been claimed that there is a general tendency for them to drift towards the equator at about 80m/s. Both scattering and reflection modes are possible in the sporadic-E layers.

Above 30MHz, paths via E_s ionization are rarely less than 500km. The maximum single-hop range is limited by the geometry of the system to about 2,000km and double-hop from a single sheet is relatively rare because it would have to exceed 500km across in order to be able to accommodate the two points of reflection. Two-hop E_s propagation is more likely from two separate sheets, separated by less than 2,000km, when the possible maximum range is extended to 4,000km.

A study of amateur observations has suggested that multi-hop modes, which are known to be quite frequent at Band I tv frequencies, are almost non-existent at frequencies above 100MHz. However, it should be noted that the longest range so far claimed for 144MHz E_s (and is is difficult to account for it otherwise) is 3,864km, between CT1WW (at WB63b) and OD5MR (at 33·9°N 35·8°E) on 28 June 1979, using ssb.

Amateur studies of vhf sporadic-E are organized as an International Amateur Radio Union project and at the time of writing the co-ordinator for Region 1 is Serge Canivenc, F8SH, to whom all such observations eventually go after their value as news items to national societies or to the vhf correspondents of amateur radio magazines has passed. There are other collecting centres, notably the DUBUS organization in Germany, which publishes a large amount of observational material for research purposes, but the ultimate destination of this is, similarly, F8SH, in Brittany, who has devised a computer program to handle the massive input of data. At the end of each year F8SH produces for the IARU a survey of activity day-by-day; his report for 1980 consisted of 400 pages, A4 size, closely typed. He also produces detailed analyses of individual events for which he obtains a considerable amount of supporting data from ionospheric observatories and other organizations that are able to supply relevant material.

Sporadic-E at vhf is seasonal, nearly all of it (in Europe) occurring between May and August, although events outside that period are not unknown. The times of maximum activity are generally within the periods of 0700–1300gmt and 1500–2200gmt. The duration of events is an inverse function of frequency: that is, for a particular occasion the event will begin later and finish earlier at the higher of two given frequencies.

John Branegan, GM4IHJ, has given a very interesting analysis of the vhf sporadic-E event of 10 June 1980, as observed from Saline, Fife (Fig 14). This demonstrates very clearly how the longest opening—over 4½h—appeared on a 48–49MHz monitor, with progressively shorter periods on each of the other frequency bands checked. At 144MHz the event was confined, for the most part, to half an hour either side of 1800gmt. GM4IHJ has also produced a map showing the location of stations which have been positively identified during E_s openings (Fig 15). The symbols "FM" and "fm" indicate stations in the 70MHz and 100MHz fm broadcast bands respectively, while black dots are Band I tv stations. It may be seen

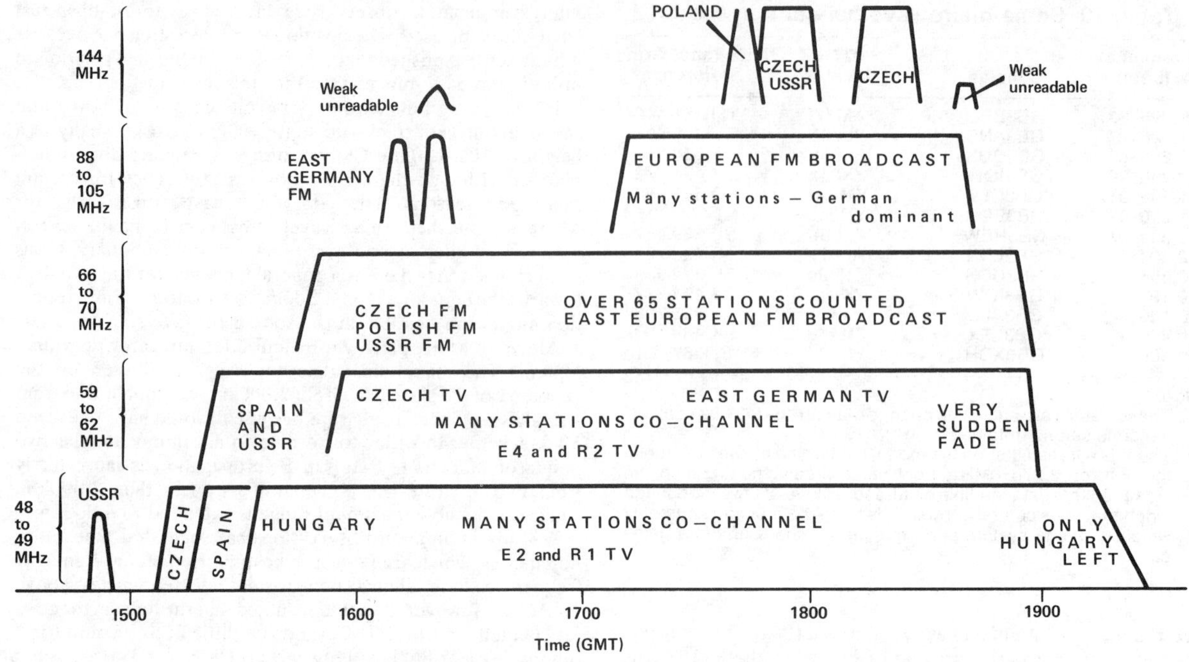

Fig 14. Frequency v time for a major sporadic-E event recorded on 10 June 1980 at GM4IHJ, Saline, Fife

that all the stations received were between 1,000 and 2,000km distant.

The maximum frequency at which these sporadic-E effects occur may be in excess of 200MHz for short periods (see Fig 16, which was produced by F8SH after studying all the reports received for 1979). The highest frequency at which E_s-type effects have been observed in the European area has been 203MHz, reached on 9 July 1974.

Several sporadic-E warning nets—some radio, some making use of telephone "chains"—are in operation in various parts of Europe, including the UK. With their help a random network of several hundred amateur stations may be got on the air in a very short time, and a careful computer analysis of their collected reports, which need consist of no more than time, band, callsigns and QTH locators, is sufficient to provide details of the size, shape and movement of the areas of ionization responsible.

Amateur auroral studies

The radio aurora at vhf probably represents the field in which radio amateurs can do most to contribute to present knowledge of radio propagation and the behaviour of the high atmosphere under the influence of solar emissions. A co-ordinated network of stations extending over a continent, each station equipped with nothing more complicated than a well-maintained receiver and operated by a person able to read and log callsigns, QTH locators and accurate times, can establish the existence and movement of areas of auroral ionization on a scale that is impossible to achieve by any other means. The addition of steerable antennas and two-way communications increase the value of the observations still further, for these enable the location of the auroral reflection point to be established.

The geometry of the path is such that no two pairs of stations will reflect off exactly the same point on the radio auroral curtain so a number of near-simultaneous observations from a random network of stations can yield detail of an *area* of ionization—its position relative to the earth's surface and the direction of its main axis—and, if the process is continued throughout an auroral event, analysis of successive periods will reveal the motion of the ionization in both space and time.

Unfortunately the aurora does not present itself as a perfect reflector placed perpendicularly to the surface of the earth. Its vertical alignment tends to follow the curvature of the geomagnetic field so that a reflection from a relatively low altitude will appear to be above a point on the ground further north than a reflection at a greater height. The reflection height is a function of the position of the two stations relative to the surface of ionization, but the vertical and horizontal beamwidths of most vhf antennas are such that a large number of alternative paths are possible without change of beam heading, although not necessarily at maximum strength. There is much to be learned from a study of accurate times and bearings for maximum signal taken as near simultaneously as possible from the two ends of a transmission path. Those stations equipped with two-axis rotators, such as are used for satellite working, can contribute further by rotating in both azimuth and elevation for maximum signal.

From the foregoing it will be clear that, in general, the beam headings in the horizontal plane depart considerably from the great-circle directions between the stations. When amateur auroral studies began in earnest in the 'fifties it was commonly supposed that all stations had to beam their signals towards the north in order to make auroral contacts. During the International Quiet Sun Years (1963–4), when the GB3LER experimental beacon station was first set up beside the magnetic observatory at Lerwick, the beam direction for auroral studies was set at first towards 10° west of true north and nearly all reports of reception via the aurora came from Scottish stations.

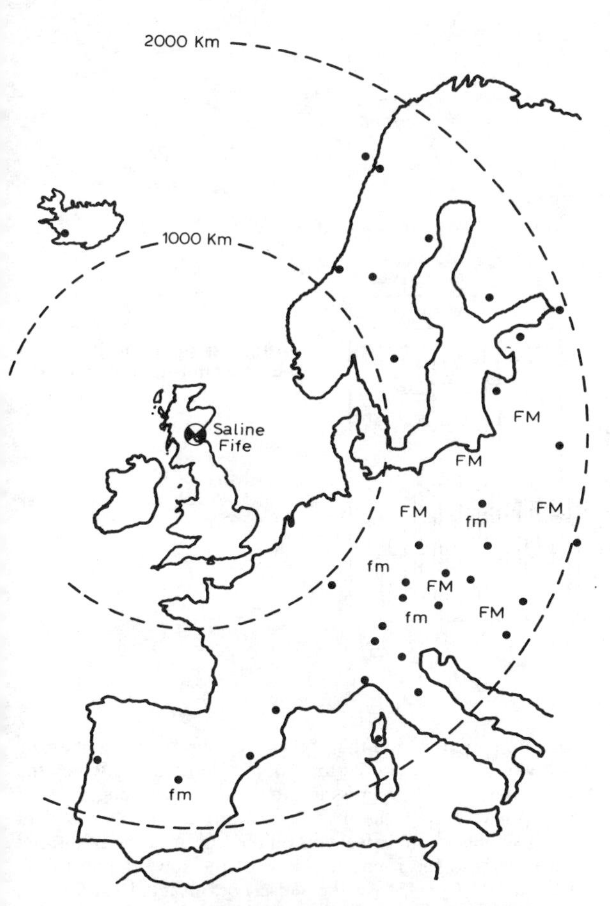

Fig 15. Stations received via sporadic-E at GM4IHJ

A change was made to 25° east of true north, and this brought in reports from many parts of the Continent. That is not to say that 25° east of true north is an optimum direction, even for Lerwick. It is now known that beam headings can vary considerably during an aurora, and from one aurora to the next. No hard and fast advice can be given on this point, other than to suggest that an occasional complete 360° beam swing during an auroral event may produce results from an unexpected quarter, even when much of the activity appears to be concentrated in one fairly constant direction (Fig 17).

Charlie Newton, G2FKZ, who is at present the IARU coordinator for amateur radio auroral studies, has established that, for any given station, there is a well-defined area within which auroral contacts are possible, and he has shown that that area is a function of the magnetic field surrounding the earth. He has called the perimeter of this area the "boundary fence" and has demonstrated that its shape and extent varies as different locations are considered as origin. As an example, Fig 18 shows the boundary fence calculated for SM4IVE (at HT68d); it is approximately elliptical, 2,000km from east to west, 1,000km from north to south. The large dots on the map indicate the centres of QTH locator lettered squares containing stations heard or worked by SM4IVE via the aurora—the lines are not signal paths, they serve only to indicate the line-of-sight directions and distances to some of the more distant stations. At any particular time during an event only a small part of the area shown will be accessible to SM4IVE, but the audible "patch" will move during the progress of an aurora and may differ considerably from one aurora to the next, although all the stations worked will lie within the boundary fence. For stations further east the area of accessibility is larger; for stations to the west and south it is smaller. Stations in Great Britain suffer from the disadvantage that there are no stations within the western half of the boundary fence.

There is a fairly close correlation between the occurrence of radio aurora and the three-hourly indices of geomagnetic activity; the greater the magnetic field is disturbed the further south the event extends. During the International Quiet Sun Years attempts were made to relate motions of the visual aurora at Lerwick to aurorally reflected signals from GB3LER as received on the Scottish mainland, but the results suggested that, on a short time-scale, the two phenomena behave almost independently, although they must stem from a common cause. At times the visual aurora appeared to the south of Lerwick and forward-scatter off the back of the beam was suspected on more than one occasion, although the point was never proved by turning the antenna because it was not accessible enough to be moved at short notice.

A study of pen recordings of signals from GB3LER, via the aurora, to Thurso on the Scottish mainland suggested that it was not the peaks of a geomagnetic disturbance that gave the strongest reflections, but rather the fastest rate of change in the components describing the instantaneous field, as recorded by the observatory magnetometers.

Every radio auroral event seems to be unique in some respect but there are characteristic patterns that regularly recur. The weaker or diffuse events, which are often only detected by northern stations, move little and slowly. They are often found to relate to minor irregularities on the magnetometer trace, known as *bays*, when the geomagnetic field deflects for a short while and then gradually resumes its normal diurnal pattern. An intense auroral event typically opens suddenly with the appearance of signals having a characteristic "flutter" tone from stations situated to the north or north-east. This often occurs in the early afternoon and contacts from European stations 1,000km or more distant are likely. After perhaps 2–3h of activity it ceases and many operators, unused to the mode, may conclude that the event is over. The more knowledgeable stay on watch, and frequently their patience is rewarded by the appearance of a second phase, usually more rewarding than the first. The motion of the active region often follows the same general movement as the first phase, but reaching several hundred kilometres further south. Finally, when the event seems to have reached a peak, perhaps by late evening, all the activity suddenly ceases as though somebody, somewhere, has "pulled the big switch" and gone off to bed (Fig 19).

There is a tendency for a major radio auroral event to recur after an interval of slightly more than 27 days. That is because the event has come about as a result of a disturbance on the sun, and in that interval an active region has made a complete circuit of the sun as seen from the earth, and is in more-or-less the same position again. That position, at the time of the event, is generally about one day past central meridian passage (cmp), or, say, 13° west of the centre of the visible disc.

It is convenient to record the dates of radio auroral events on a solar rotation base map, as shown in Fig 20. These charts have been produced for each year since 1970 by the RSGB Propagation Studies Committee, and a copy of the current one is available at any time by writing to the Membership Services Officer at RSGB headquarters. The vertical axis is scaled in degrees,

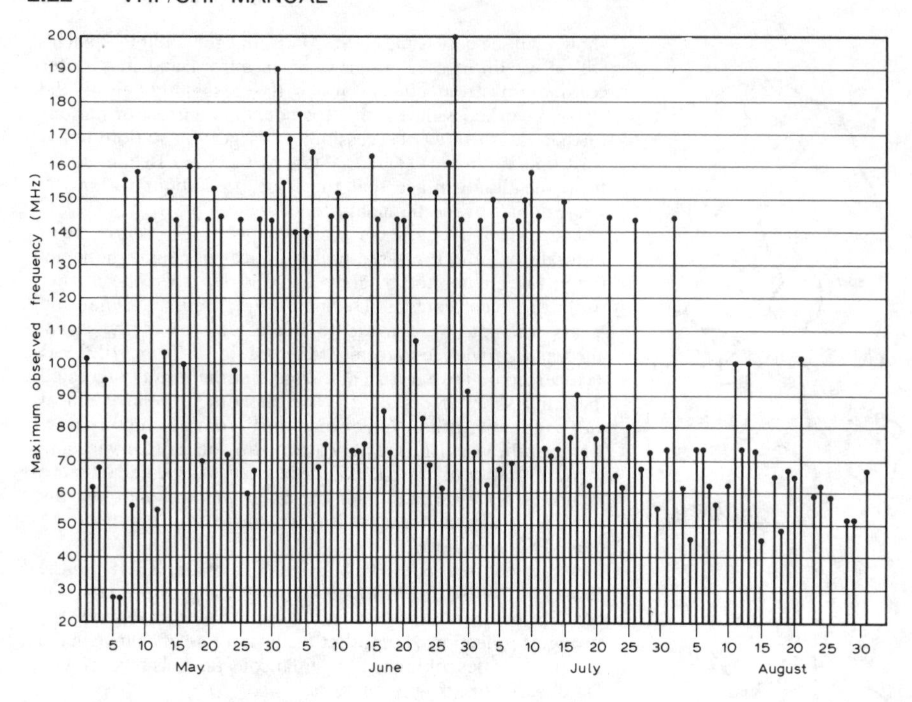

Fig 16. VHF sporadic-E activity in Europe during summer 1979

showing the longitude at the centre of the solar disk, a quantity known as L_0; this follows a sequence originated over 100 years ago at Greenwich Observatory, and that also determines the numbering of the rotations. The horizontal scale represents degrees of the sun's true longitude, a measure of the progress of the earth along its orbit. The value of each of these two functions at 1200gmt each day is represented by a point on the diagram and, as time goes on, the sequence of points forms a raster. It may be seen that the lower and upper edges of the chart are common, and that if they were brought together the chart would then be in the form of a cylinder along which the daily points would progress in the manner of a helix.

The chart may be used to record any event suspected of having a connection with events on the sun. A horizontal trend corresponds to the rotation period of the sun relative to the earth; a trend of 45° (in the sense bottom left to top right) corresponds to the rotation period of the sun relative to the stars. Known dates of radio auroral events are currently included in the propagation news section of the GB2RS news bulletin service of the RSGB, and the patterns which emerge provide a useful guide to probable active and quiet periods up to about a month ahead. Fig 20, which shows the days when radio aurora was reported by UK stations during 1981–2, should be compared with Fig 21, which shows the days when the magnetometers at Lerwick recorded a disturbance of 5 or more on the conventional scale of geomagnetic K-units. It will be seen that there is a close relationship between the two patterns and this confirms the usefulness of the Lerwick data when dealing with the analysis of radio auroral events taking place in the region of north-west Europe.

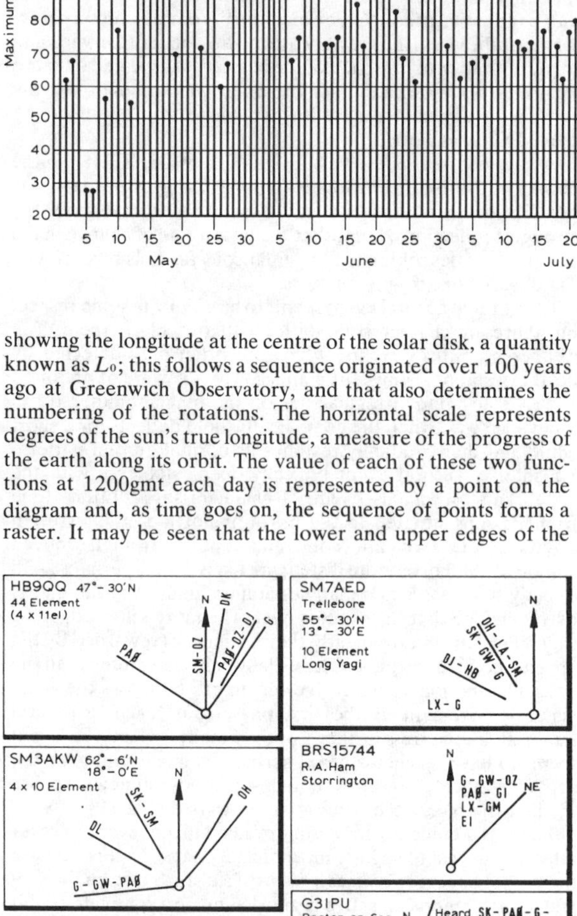

HB9QQ 47°-30'N
44 Element
(4 x 11el)
N
DK
PAØ-OZ-DJ
G
SM-OZ
PAØ

SM7AED
Trelleborg
55°-30'N
13°-30'E
10 Element
Long Yagi
N
OH-LA-SM
SK-GW-G
DJ-HB
LX-G

SM3AKW 62°-6'N
18°-0'E
4 x 10 Element
N
SK-SM
OH
DL
G-GW-PAØ

BRS15744
R.A.Ham
Storrington
N
G-GW-OZ
PAØ-GI
LX-GM
EI
NE

G3USF
Keele, Staffs
N
EI

G3IPU
Bacton-on-Sea
Norwich
14E Para Beam
N
Heard SK-PAØ-G-SM-OZ-ON-EI
Worked GW-LA

G3JYP
Appleby
Westmorland
6 over 6
N
Worked G-GW-PAØ-F-EI-GM-OZ-OK-DJ
Heard HB-SM-LX

Fig 17. Beam headings recorded by certain operators during the aurora of 8 March 1970

Monitoring auroral propagation

In a contribution to the March 1977 issue of *Radio Communication*, Peter Blair, G3LTF, gave practical advice on monitoring distant vhf transmissions, which can be used as a guide to the onset of auroral propagation events on the amateur bands. Many of his remarks were directed towards observers living in the south of England, but his methods are applicable to other locations, provided that suitably placed transmitters can be found. What is required is a signal from a northerly direction in the low vhf region, for this will go auroral before the effects reach 144MHz. For many observers these requirements will be met by one of the Band I BBC-TV sound transmitters, which

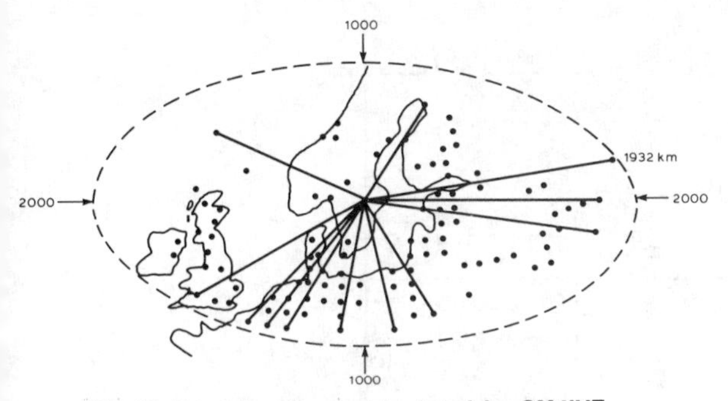

Fig 18. Boundary fence calculated for SM4IVE

are slightly offset from one another on shared channels and can be separated and monitored.

For southern England the most convenient transmission is Meldrum, near Aberdeen, on Channel 4, nominally 58·25MHz. On this channel the dominant signal is that from Sutton Coldfield; Meldrum will be found 35kHz lower. Another, but less satisfactory, station is Sandale, near Carlisle, which will be found 19kHz higher than Sutton Coldfield. The normal signals from these two stations over a path of some 300–350 miles is mainly troposcatter with aircraft reflections, superimposed with occasional meteor pings and bursts. The average level is about 5dB over noise to G3LTF. When aurora occurs the level increases by anything up to 40dB, with an unmistakeable rasping growl that spreads the signal 10kHz or more.

The suggested equipment for the aurora monitor is relatively simple. The antenna consists of two elements, radiator 95in by $\frac{3}{8}$in, reflector 105in by $\frac{3}{8}$in, spacing 30in, mounted 18 to 20ft off the ground, pointing north. This feeds a crystal-controlled converter, such as the one shown in Fig 22, which uses any convenient crystal which will produce an i.f. of around 7MHz. After alignment in the usual way the circuits should be peaked on the desired signal when the opportunity arises. The two outputs are at around 7MHz; one is intended for a simple fixed-frequency receiver, the agc voltage of which drives a recording meter through a suitable dc amplifier. When correctly tuned the

Table 11. Components list for converter

C1, C4	6·8pF ceramic	**R1**	5·6kΩ
C2, C5, C11, C24	12pF tubular trimmers	**R2**	18kΩ
C3, C16	0·5pF ceramic	**R3, R5**	100Ω
C6	390pF ceramic	**R4, R9**	1kΩ
C7	1-10pF tubular trimmer	**R6**	82kΩ
C8, C10, C18, C22	1,000pF feedthrough capacitors	**R7**	2·2kΩ
C9, C21	1,000pF ceramic	**R8**	68Ω
C12	4·7pF ceramic	**R10**	4·7kΩ
C13	33pF ceramic	**R11**	6·8kΩ
C14	22pF (to suit ift L4)	all $\frac{1}{4}$ or $\frac{1}{10}$W carbon	
C15	3,300pF disc ceramic		
C17	0·01pF 15V	**TR1**	GMO290 or similar low noise— AF139, AF239
C19	180pF ceramic		
C20	18pF ceramic		
C23	0·22μF 15V	**TR2**	2N3819
		TR3	2N3904
L1	10 turns $\frac{3}{8}$in i.d. 18g enam close-wound tapped 2t up		
L2	As L1 but tapped 4t up		
L3	11 turns $\frac{3}{8}$in i.d. 18g enam close-wound tapped at one turn and five turns from cold end		
L4	I.F. transformer appropriate to crystal chosen		
L5	Six turns 20g on $\frac{1}{4}$in slug tuned form (for 65MHz crystal		
L6	Nine turns $\frac{1}{4}$in i.d. spaced wire diameter		

144MHz trap prevents the converter from being blocked in the presence of a local transmission.

Fig 23 shows the appearance of some typical auroral signal recordings. According to G3LTF a sudden (say within 2min) onset of the auroral enhancement usually indicates that the effects will reach 144MHz within 10–15min. A more gradual onset might herald a delay of up to about 30min. It is rare for the effect not to reach 144MHz at all once it has been detected on the monitor. The equipment may also be used as an indicator for 70MHz; but the respective time delays are considerably reduced.

The monitor should be left running during the day from about midday onwards. If the operator is unable to attend during the afternoon he or she may come home to find evidence of earlier activity. This should alert him to expect a second phase, and perhaps a third, later on. Where a more-or-less

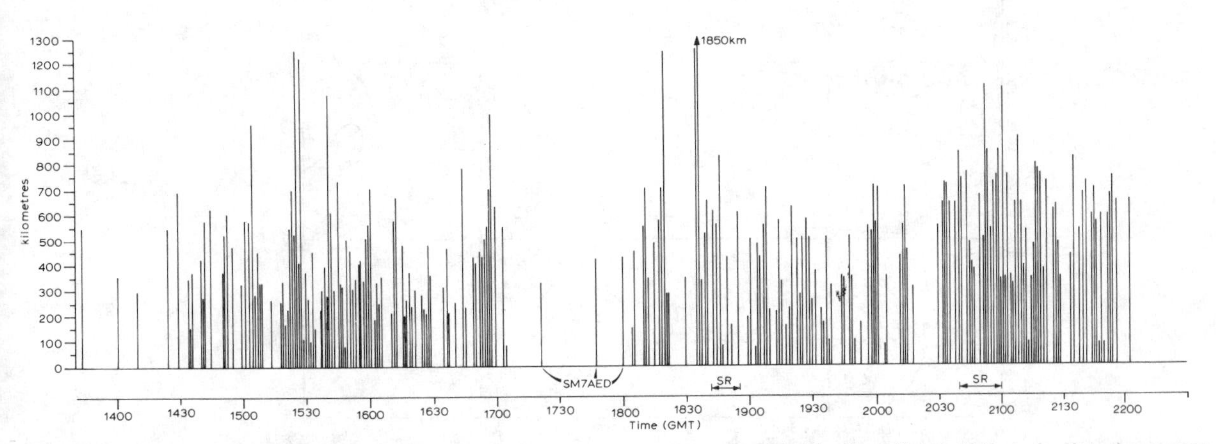

Fig 19. Times and distances for all stations heard or worked, based on logs submitted for the 8 March 1970 study. Note the pauses and the bunching of the longer-range contacts. The periods marked "SR" indicate when a radar at Sheffield University recorded radio aurora to the north west

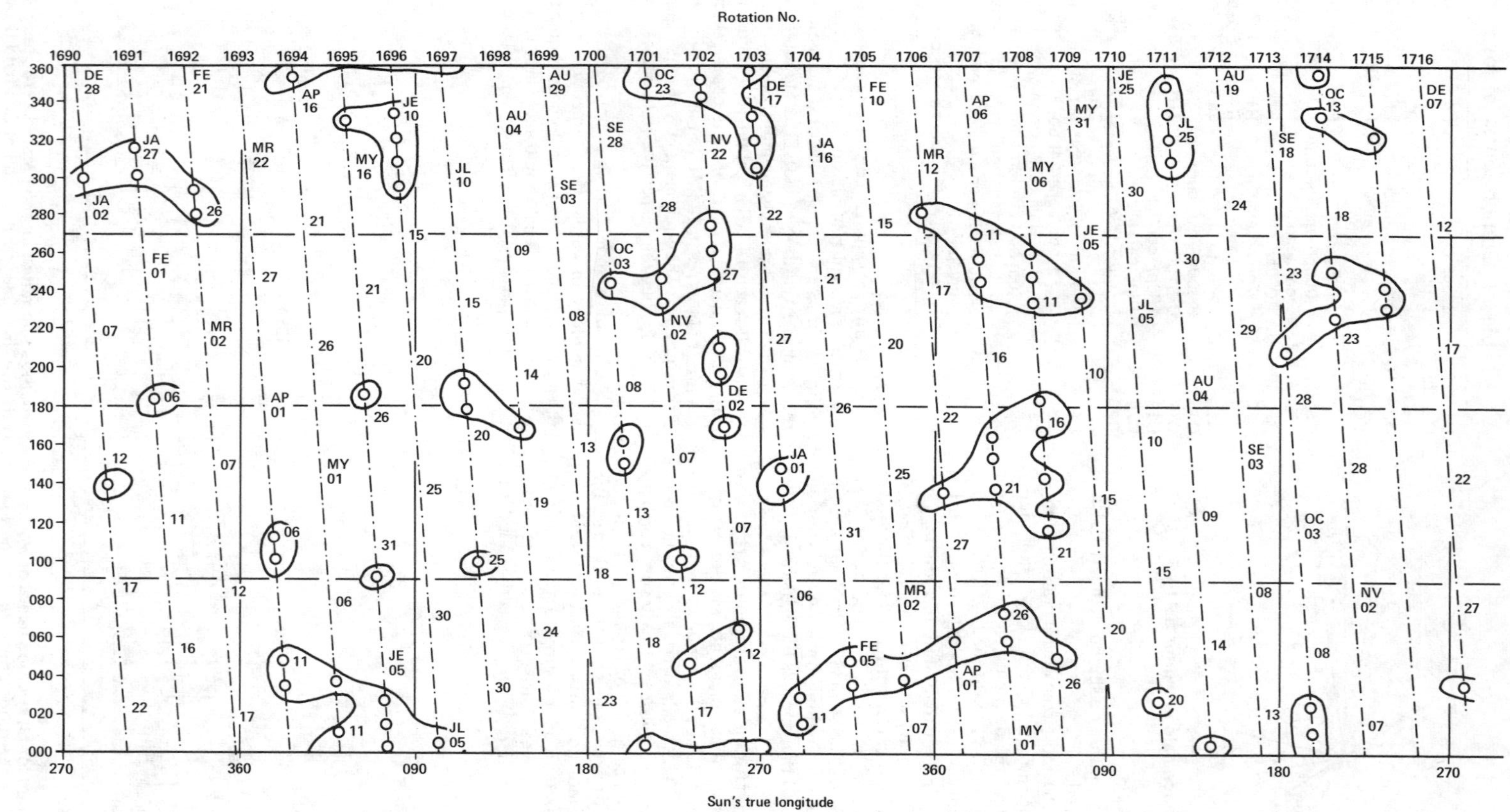

Fig 20. Days with reported radio aurora during 1981–2

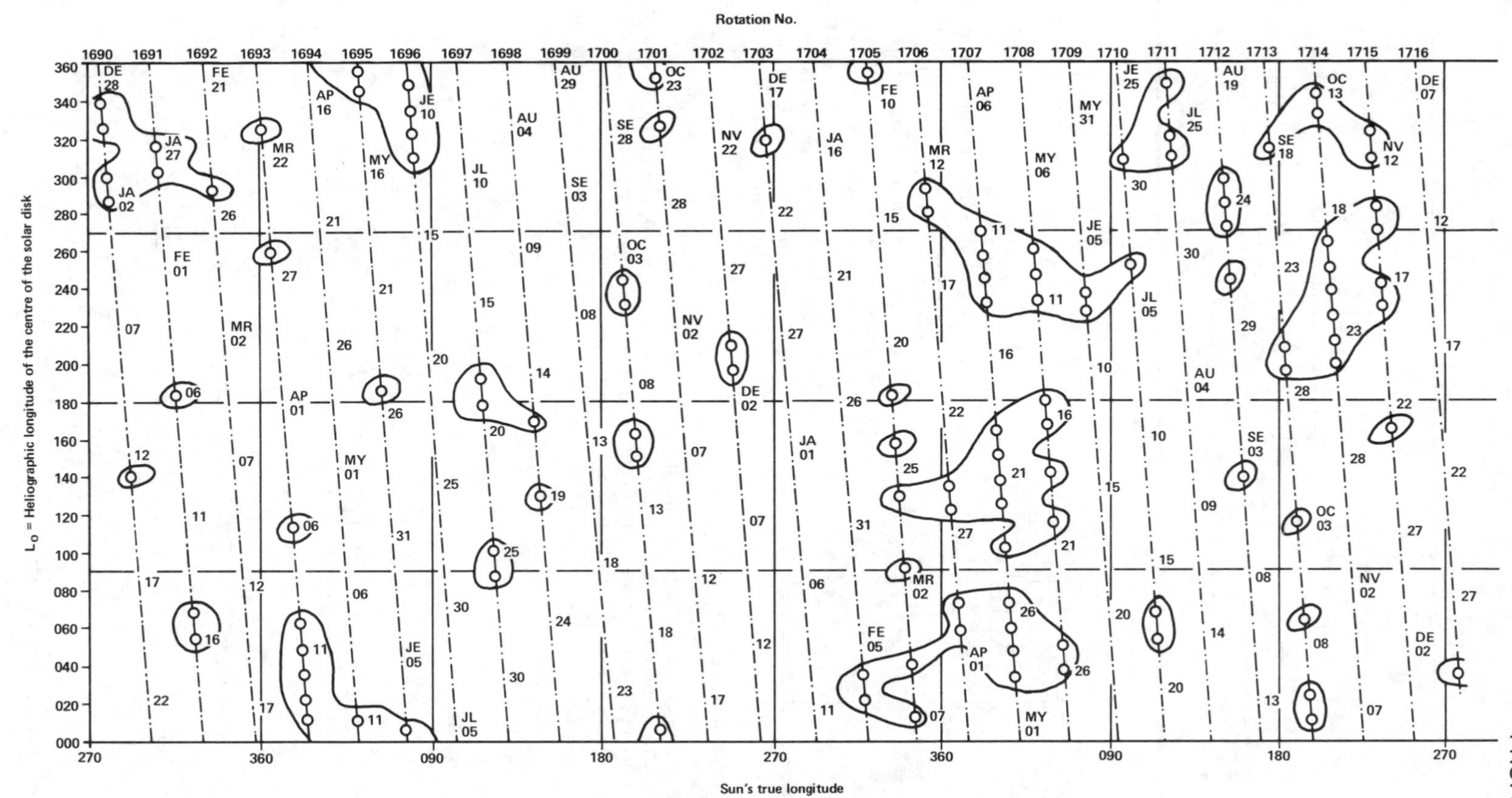

Fig 21. Days when Lerwick *K*-figure was five or greater during 1981–2

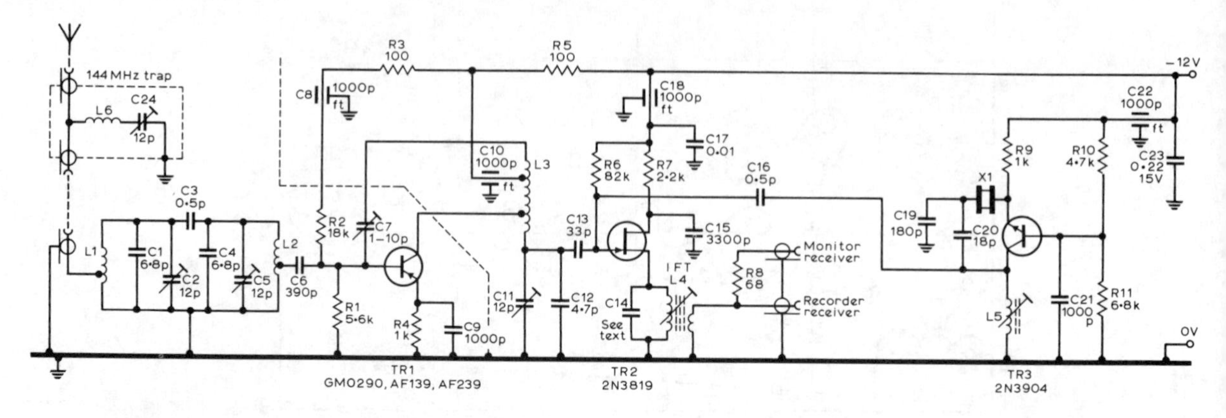

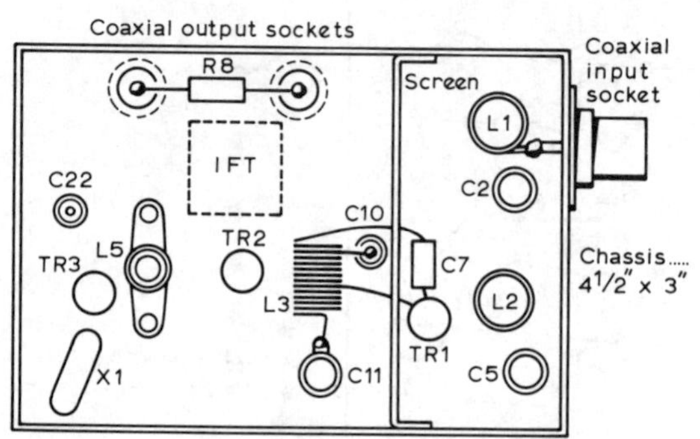

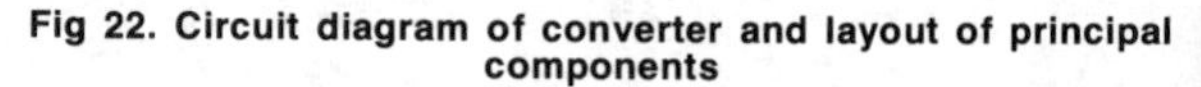
Fig 22. Circuit diagram of converter and layout of principal components

continuous watch is impracticable, the most fruitful times for checking the monitor are mid-afternoon, early evening and around 2200 local time. It should not be forgotten that the transmitter being monitored will close down each day at the end of the day's programmes, but this is no real disadvantage of the method as it is unusual for an aurora to make its first appearance after midnight.

Auroral warning network

Monitoring a northern tv station in order to obtain advance warning of the onset of an auroral propagation event on the vhf amateur bands is a very effective method, but unfortunately it can be costly in both operator's time and equipment expenses.

Because auroral events generally affect northern stations before southern, and eastern stations before western, it follows that observers situated in the north-east of Europe should be in a position to alert their colleagues elsewhere when they observe the first signs of an opening. From this line of reasoning there developed a large-scale warning network, extending from Scandinavia down into Central Europe, using the cheap direct-dialling telephone facility now provided on an international scale in this country and similar arrangements abroad. The continental network was established by a German group, DUBUS, and the UK network, which essentially forms part of it, has been organized by the RSGB, with G2FKZ as co-ordinator.

There is a Swedish link into Scotland and another into the

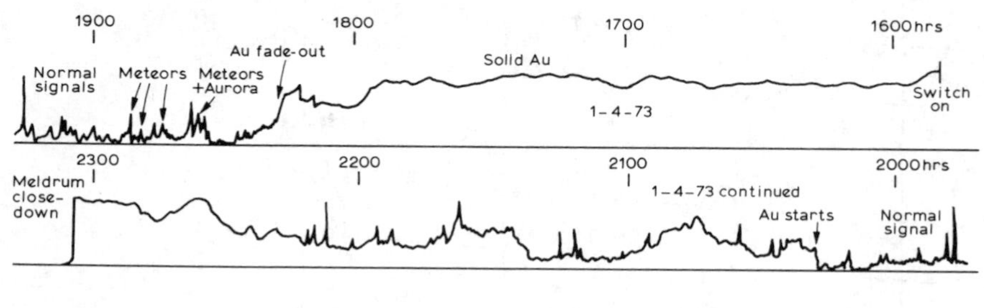

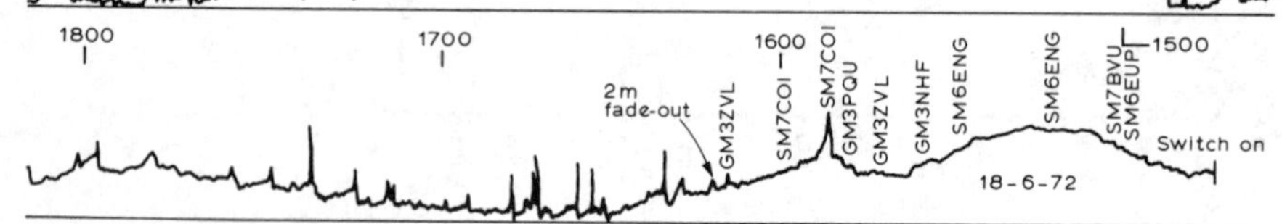

Fig 23. Some typical auroral signal recordings

Continent from South Wales. A warning received in Scotland is only passed south through the chain of co-operating stations when local observations have confirmed it. Most of the successive key stations have arrangements to alert others in their area and, by these means, a rapid mobilization of effort can be achieved in time to observe the early stages of the aurora. This serves to attract the attention of others already active on the band, who may be encouraged to take part themselves or pass the news on to someone else. Whether these other stations take part in the auroral project themselves is immaterial; the more stations there are active the more paths are open for observation.

Details of the current make-up of the network and advice on how best to link up with it may be obtained from the RSGB co-ordinator, G2FKZ, who would also welcome auroral observations at any time, particularly those which have been accurately timed, with, if possible, peaked beam headings from both ends of the transmission path. (A recommended method of asking for the other stations's direction of reception is to send QTF/A, meaning "What is your auroral beam heading?")

The UK network has both primary and secondary warning routes so that it can continue to work even when some of the key stations are unobtainable. Also it has been designed to eliminate false alarms, as far as possible, by having certain stations wait for confirmation of a radio aurora before passing the word further south.

The present capabilities of the system are such that a large-scale aurora can stimulate a level of activity amounting to several hundred transmitters being brought on the air during the early stages of the event. This cannot be matched anywhere outside the amateur service and offers a unique opportunity to put the service's talents to good use by doing no more than reporting its successes as soon as possible after the event.

Trans-equatorial propagation

An aspect of research in which radio amateurs can justifiably claim to have played a major part is in the field of trans-equatorial propagation, te or tep for short. From its discovery just after the second world war (between stations in Mexico and Argentina, reported in *QST* for October 1947), to the present day, amateurs have provided almost all the raw material for subsequent study. Some dedicated operators have spent 20 years or more setting up series of carefully-controlled experiments designed to test theories proposed or to provide fresh material for consideration. For a particularly useful survey of progress to date of circuits between Europe and southern Africa, reference should be made to an article by ZE2JV and 5B4WR entitled "Twenty-one years of te", which appeared in *Radio Communication* June/July, August 1980, pp626–634, 785–788. Some of the areas of the world which have contributed to the present knowledge of the mode are shown in Fig 24, where it will be seen that a prime requirement appears to be that the transmission path shall have the magnetic zero-dip equator (a) approximately at its mid-point and (b) nearly normal to it. The placing of the KP4/ZD8 path with respect to the change of direction of the zero-dip line over the Atlantic Ocean area is particularly interesting evidence in support of requirement (b).

The mode was first observed on 50MHz. Subsequent work has used 28, 50, 144 and 432MHz. During years of high sunspot activity the reliability of a te path is considerable. On 50MHz the peak time during an opening was found to be 1845–1900. At 144MHz, using 100W rf into 16-element long Yagis,

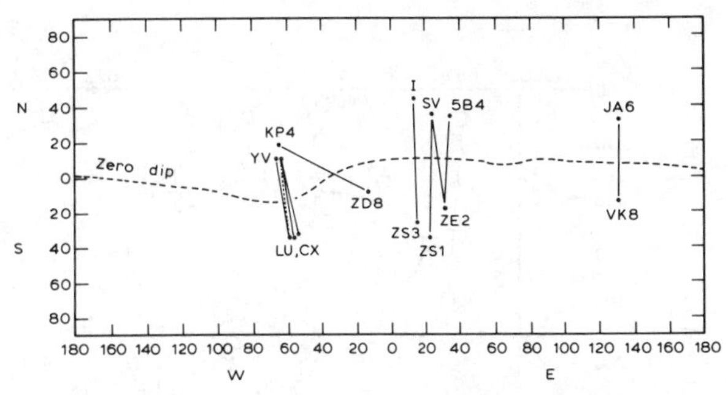

Fig 24. Areas of the world where trans-equatorial propagation has been observed

openings between Europe and southern Africa have lasted for up to 2h, centred on 2000 local time in Cyprus; high solar flux and low geomagnetic activity seem essential. Detrimental effects of geomagnetic storms are less evident at 50 and 28MHz than at 144MHz. Fig 25 shows the days on which te signals were observed at 144MHz, plotted on a solar rotation base map, which reveals some tendency towards 27-day recurrences, particularly around the time of the equinoxes. On the American paths, peak occurrences at the equinoxes were noted.

On the Zimbabwe/Cyprus path there was a decline at that time, thought by ZE2JV and 5B4WR to be a peculiarity of the path connected in some way with the southern Africa magnetic anomaly which gives rise to high dip angles at the southern end.

In February 1979, ZS6DN, Pretoria, and SV1AB, Athens, held the world record for a 144MHz contact by the ionosphere, but at time of writing the current holders are ZS3B and I4EAT, who, on 31 March 1979, established transmission and reception in both directions over a distance in excess of 8,000km.

Fading and chopping occur on the signals at rates which increase with transmission frequency. Slow chopping on 28 and 50MHz sometimes makes it almost impossible to read morse code. At 144MHz the chopping rate is much faster, making the signal sound rough with an apparent raw ac note. Frequency spreading has been observed to 2kHz or more. The character of the signals may change considerably from day to day and from hour to hour in a random manner. Under the best of conditions 144MHz ssb is just intelligible. At other times the spread is so wide and the flutter is so rapid that no beat note can be obtained with the received signal, which then appears merely as a change in the background noise. At 432MHz the Zimbabwe beacon operated by ZE2JV was heard in Athens by SV1DH and SV1AB between 1816 and 1830gmt on 20 March 1979, and on 13 May 1979 by 5B4WR. Their comments were that the signals were rougher than on 144MHz and spreading more in frequency.

Time-delay measurements made in both directions along the Zimbabwe/Cyprus circuit showed afternoon intervals which at times corresponded with two-hop F2-layer propagation, but evening delays took about 10 per cent longer, which may have been due to an extra ray-path distance of some 600km each way, or was in some way a function of the propagation mechanism. There appears to be no difference in delay time between 28MHz and 144MHz te; although the character of the received signals differ on account of differences in fading rate.

Meteor trail propagation

Propagation is also possible on an intermittent basis by means of scatter from short-lived trails of ionization which appear as a

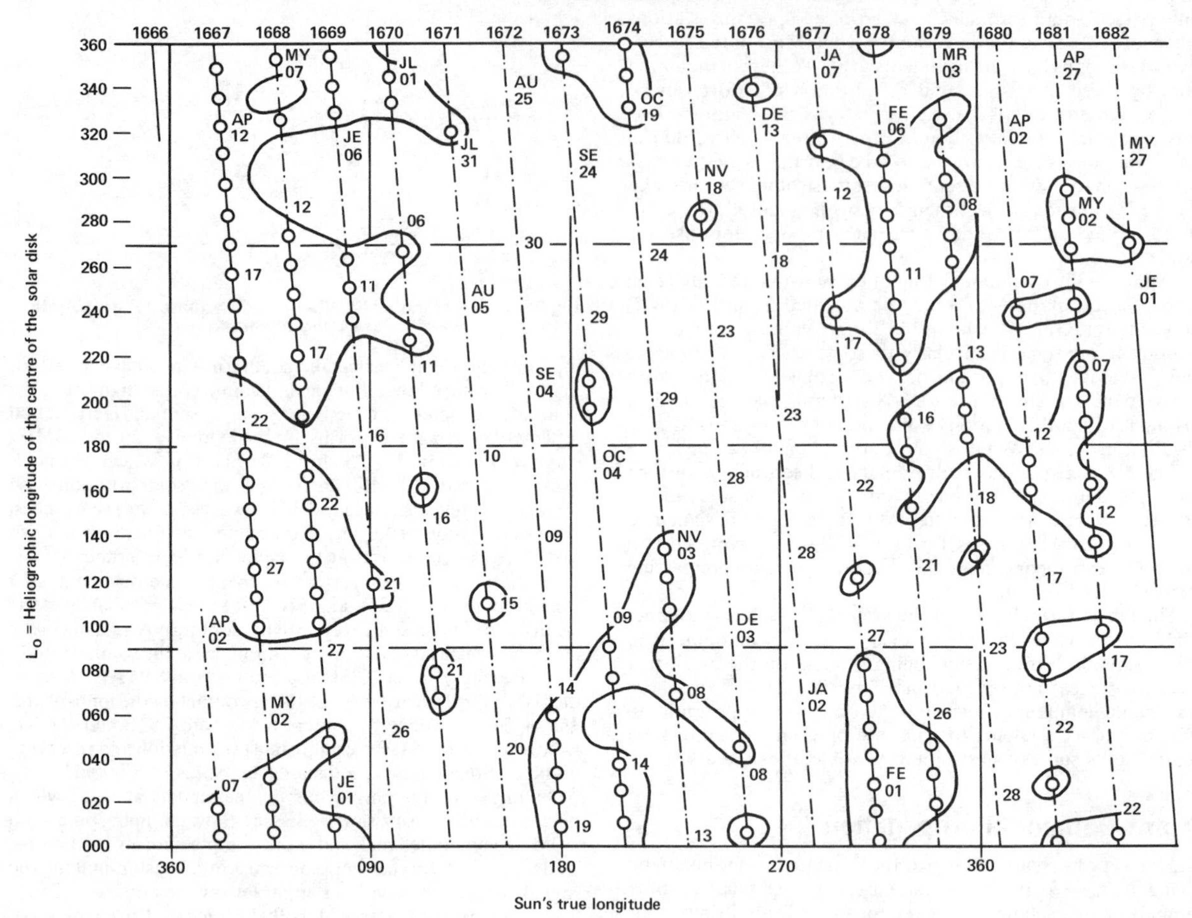

Fig 25. Trans-equatorial propagation. Reception of ZE2JV by 5B4WR (144·16MHz), 1630–1900gmt between 1 April 1978 and 31 May 1979

result of small particles of solid matter entering the earth's atmosphere and becoming heated to incandescence by friction. They are usually accompanied by streaks of light, popularly known as "shooting stars". These *meteors* (strictly the term applies only to the visible streak, although most writers use it as though it refers to the object itself) fall into two general classes, *shower meteors*, which follow definite and predictable orbits, and *sporadic meteors*, which follow individual paths and are present at all times.

Both the ionization and the visual display occur simultaneously at heights of around 85 to 120km. Most of the objects responsible are no bigger than a grain of sand and they burn up completely in the upper atmosphere. Occasionally larger ones survive the descent and examples of some which have reached the ground are to be seen in museums, where they are referred to as *meteorites.*

Numbers vary during the year from a maximum in July to a minimum in February, with a ratio of about 4:1. There is a marked diurnal variation, due to the combined motions of the earth's rotation and its movement around the sun, leading to a maximum at 0600 local time and a minimum at 1800.

The initial trail of ionization is in the form of a long, thin, pencil-like cylinder, perhaps 15 to 20km in length. As soon as it is formed it begins to expand radially and to move with the various motions of the air through which it passes. The length of time when the trail is capable of supporting communication is generally very short, often less than a second, although longer persistences of a minute or more occur from time to time. The durations (and the frequency of occurrence) decrease with increase in signal frequency.

Considerations of phase coherence lead to an aspect sensitivity which favours radiation meeting the trail axis at right-angles. Because of this only a small part of any trail acts as a reflector, and the orientation of the trail relative to the antennas is of considerable importance because it determines the height and position of the main reflection point. Meeting the right-angle requirement from both ends of a transmission path demands that the trail must lie in such a way that it is tangential to an ellipsoid of revolution having transmitter and receiver antennas at the focal points, and if ionization is to result this condition has to be met at a level which is within 80 and 120km above the ground. It follows that large numbers of meteors enter the earth's atmosphere along paths which can never satisfy the tangent condition within the prescribed limits of height and in consequence do not contribute to propagation along a given path.

Table 12. Calendar of the main meteor showers

Start	Dates of Maximum	End	Name	Comparative rate*	Transit Time	Elev
Jan 01	Jan 03	Jan 06	Quadrantids	6	09	90
Apr 19	Apr 21	Apr 24	April Lyrids	3	04	70
May 01	May 05	May 08	Eta Aquarids	3	08	40
Jun 10	Jun 16	Jun 21	June Lyrids	2	01	70
Jun 17	Jun 20	Jun 26	Ophiuchids	2	23	20
Jul 10	Jul 26	Aug 15	Capricornids	2	01	20
Jul 15	Jul 27	Aug 15	Delta Aquarids	4	02	30
Jul 15	Jul 31	Aug 20	Pisces Australids	2	02	10
Jul 15	Jul 30	Aug 25	Alpha Capricornids	2	00	30
Jul 15	Aug 06	Aug 25	Iota Aquarids	2	01	30
Jul 25	Aug 12	Aug 18	Perseids	5	06	80†
Aug 19	Aug 21	Aug 22	Chi Cygnids	1	21	90
Oct 16	Oct 21	Oct 26	Orionids	4	04	50
Oct 20	Nov 08	Nov 30	Taurids	3	01	60
Nov 07	Nov 09	Nov 11	Cepheids	2	20	80†
Nov 15	Nov 17	Nov 19	Leonids	2	06	60
Dec 07	Dec 14	Dec 15	Geminids	5	02	70
Dec 17	Dec 22	Dec 24	Ursids	1	08	60†

*Each step on the comparative rate scale represents a factor of 2.
†Above northern horizon.

These requirements suggest that it is unwise to direct very narrow-beam transmitting and receiving antennas (to be used for meteor-scatter work) along the strict line-of-sight between the stations. The only trails which can be tangential to the ellipsoid of revolution in that direction are those lying parallel to the ground, and this is an unlikely attitude to be taken up by a solid body entering the earth's atmosphere from interplanetary space. The most likely beam directions lie a few degrees to one side or the other of the direct transmission path (both antennas must be deflected towards the same side, of course), and the optimum headings may have to be determined by careful experiment. Where the antennas are less directional the great-circle path between stations may be found to give best results, however, because, although little is likely to be received along the direct path heading, the acceptance angles of the antennas may be wide enough to include the longer, but more likely paths on both sides.

The short bursts of signal which result from ms (meteor scatter) can best be observed on stations situated 1,000 to 2,000km away. In southern England several hundred examples per hour can be heard carrying signals from the 40kW fm broadcast transmitter at Gdansk, Poland on 70·31MHz.

A very detailed treatment of the subject was published in the February 1975 issue of *Radio Communication*, under the title "VHF meteor scatter propagation". In it J. D. V. Ludlow, GW3ZTH, has given details of suitable equipments for receiving and recording signals propagated by this mode, and has provided a practical method of calculating beam headings and optimum times in respect of particular showers. For those wishing to follow up the relevant theory there is a very useful list of 25 references. Details of the current IARU Region 1 QSO procedure are given in *Radio Communication* August 1981, p729.

Table 12 gives a summary of the main meteor showers likely to be of use to stations in the northern hemisphere. Full details, including times of transit and the directions from which the trails appear to radiate (an effect of perspective) appear each year in the current *Handbook of the British Astronomical Association* (see the Bibliography at the end of this chapter).

Commercial use is made of meteor-scatter propagation, particularly at high latitudes where it provides a hedge against the effects of polar cap absorption. The best-known system is the Janet Project of the Canadian Defence Research Board, which is described by G. W. L. Davis and others in *Proceedings of the IRE* December 1957. Another, and more recent, application of the technique is seen in the "Snonet" meteorological meteor-burst system for collecting observations from remote sensors. Information recorded on magnetic tape at normal speed is played back (and transmitted) in the form of high-speed bursts when a monitor on a slightly different frequency shows that a path is open.

On the amateur bands meteor scatter has been used to provide communication over distances up to about 3,000km. At time of writing the record is 3,099km at 144MHz, made by GW4CQT (QTH locator YL25d) and UW6MA (TH69c) on 12 August 1977, using cw. The furthest distance at 432MHz, 1,033km, was achieved on the same day by SK6AB (FR30c) and SM2AID (IZ32h), also using cw. These were achieved during the Perseids shower, which is notable for its high-elevation meridian transits.

Satellite propagation experiments

A number of amateurs have suggested propagation experiments using satellites in ways that were not envisaged as part of the basic projects.

Pat Gowen, G3IOR, has made use of Oscar 7 and Oscar 8 in its Mode A transponder configuration (145MHz up, 29MHz down) as a guide to conditions on 144MHz. Good tropospheric conditions are indicated by severe attenuation of one's own returned signal, with deep and rapid fading when the satellite is just above the horizon. Brief and rapid "pop-ups" of signal before and after predicted times of access are caused by scintillation of 144MHz uplink as it passes through tropospheric ducts. Sporadic-E effects are similar, but they may take place at quite high elevations. Fading suggests the presence of multiple diffraction paths in the ionosphere. Aurora causes marked degradation of tone on returned signals from some of the northern stations, often specific to small areas.

John Branegan, GM4IHJ, keeps a regular check on where satellite scintillation occurs on polar paths and uses it to define the instantaneous location of the auroral oval and to provide an

Table 13. Solar rotation calendar 1979–1990

1979	1980	1981	1982	1983	1984
1677 JA07	1691−JA24	1704 JA12	1717 JA02	1731−JA19	1744 JA08
1678 FE03	1692 FE15	1705−FE09	1718 JA29	1732 FE15	1745−FE05
1679+MR02	1693+MR18	1706 MR08	1719+FE25	1733+MR14	1746 MR03
1680 MR30	1694−AP15	1707 AP04	1720 MR25	1734−AP11	1747 MR30
1681 AP26	1695 MY12	1708+MY01	1721 AP21	1735 MY08	1748+AP26
1682+MY23	1696 JE08	1709−MY29	1722+MY18	1736 JE04	1749−MY24
1683+JE09	1697+JL05	1710 JE25	1723+JE14	1737+JL01	1750 JE20
1684−JL17	1698+AU01	1711 JL22	1724−JL12	1738−JL29	1751 JL17
1685 AU13	1699−AU29	1712+AU18	1725 AU08	1739−AU25	1752+AU13
1686 SE09	1700 SE25	1713−SE15	1726 SE04	1740 SE21	1753−SE10
1687+OC06	1701+OC22	1714 0C12	1727+OC01	1741+OC18	1754 OC07
1688−NV03	1702−NV19	1715 NV08	1728−OC19	1742−NV15	1755 NV03
1689 NV30	1703 DE16	1716+DE05	1729 NV25	1743 DE12	1756+NV30
1690+DE27			1730+DE22		1757 DE28

1985	1986	1987	1988	1989	1990
1758 JA24	1771−JA14	1784 JA03	1798 JA20	1811−JA09	1825−JA26
1759+FE20	1772 FE10	1785−JA31	1799+FE16	1812 FE05	1826 FE22
1760 MR20	1773+MR09	1786 FE27	1800 MR15	1813 MR04	1827 MR21
1761 AP16	1774−AP06	1787 MR26	1801 AP11	1814−AP01	1828−AP18
1762+MY13	1775 MY03	1788−AP23	1802+MY08	1815 AP28	1829 MY15
1763−JE10	1776 MY30	1789−MY20	1803−JE05	1816 MY25	1830 JE11
1764−JL07	1777+JE26	1790 JE16	1804 JL02	1817 JE21	1831 JL08
1765 AU03	1778−JL24	1791 JL13	1805 JL29	1818+JL18	1832+AU04
1766 AU30	1779 AU20	1792+AU09	1806 AU25	1819 AU15	1833−SE01
1767+SE26	1780 SE16	1793−SE06	1807+SE21	1820 SE11	1834 SE28
1768−OC24	1781+OC13	1794 OC03	1808−OC19	1821 OC08	1835 OC25
1769 NV20	1782−NV10	1795 OC30	1809 NV15	1822+NV04	1836+NV21
1770+DE17	1783 DE07	1796+NV26	1810+DE12	1823 DE02	1837 DE19
		1797 DE24			

− = Commencement before 0600gmt; + = commencement after 1800gmt. Rotation numbers follow Carrington's series.

estimate of the total electron content along the satellite line of sight. In this way, very high electron densities have been observed at heights above the normal 110km auroral reflection zone, considered capable of scattering frequencies of up to at least 250MHz. GM4IHJ, G3IOR and several Alaskan stations have all heard double signals on 144MHz satellite transmissions, the second signal some 750Hz from the nominal frequency, sometimes with an auroral tone.

G4DGU and SM6CKU have investigated the idea of using a large low-orbit satellite as a passive reflector. The relevant theory suggests that the total path length loss might be about 10dB better than moonbounce. There are problems—low-orbit satellites are decaying and their orbits cannot be predicted with accuracy, and there are very high Doppler shifts involved. At 432MHz signals are likely to appear first 12kHz high, shifting down at about 4kHz per second to become 12kHz low, 6–8s later, when signals would disappear. Despite these difficulties, however, a 4s burst of ssb from G4DGU has been received by SM6CKU, 10dB over noise, off a Cosmos third-stage launcher. The transmitter used was of 400W p.e.p. into an array of eight 17-element Yagis. The receiver was coupled to an 8m dish.

Solar/geophysical connections

Precursors

The relationship between events on the sun and the associated effects in the earths's ionosphere has been dealt with at length in the propagation chapter of the *Radio Communication Handbook*. Suffice it to record here that the main solar events of interest to vhf and uhf operators are solar flares, radio bursts and emissions of high-energy protons. Solar flare effects appear in three time scales. Within about 8min of a major flare suitably placed on the sun, electromagnetic radiation brings about increased D-region ionization, sudden cosmic noise absorption (scna), short-wave fadeout phenomena (swf), sudden phase anomaly of elf signals (spa), sudden enhancement of atmospherics at lf (s.e.a.), sudden frequency deviation at lf (sfd), and noise bursts (not all of these will be detected in one particular event). Within an hour of the appearance of the flare, high-energy corpuscular radiation is likely to cause polar cap absorption (pca) of anything from 20mins to 20h duration, which may extend to vhf. Some 20–40h after the flare, low-energy corpuscular radiation brings about magnetic storms, ionospheric storms and auroras, which may persist for more than a day.

The probability that this chain of events will lead to a magnetic storm and an aurora is greatest when the solar activity occurs when the region concerned is near, but slightly beyond, the central meridian.

There is a tendency for solar events to recur after periods of approximately 27 days, as has been discussed in connection with auroral propagation. Table 13 shows the starting dates of all solar rotations between 1979 and 1990 calculated in continuation of Carrington's photo-heliographic series, using a method described by the Belgian amateur astronomer Jean Meeus in the journal *Ciel et Terre*. This basic information is expanded in the solar rotation base map format shown in Figs 20, 21 and 25 about October of each year, relating to the year following.

Solar and geophysical data

There still remains much to be learned about the relationship between events on the sun, their corresponding effect on the earth's magnetic field and vhf/uhf radio propagation via the ionosphere as in sporadic-E, auroral-E and other similar "openings" on the amateur bands. This is an interesting field for individual research but it requires access to basic solar and geophysical data. Three useful sources are suggested here.

The first, the easiest to obtain but of necessity the least detailed in content, is supplied by the brief summary of solar and magnetic trends over the previous week, together with a forecast covering the week to come, which is compiled from authoritative sources and included each week in the RSGB GB2RS news bulletin. This is transmitted according to a schedule published regularly in the Society's journal *Radio Communication.*

The second source offers virtually current data at the expense of the time taken to copy a daily morse message from Paris. This facility is provided by the International Ursigram and World Days Service (IUWDS), an organization specifically set up to collect and distribute scientific reports from observatories and research establishments all over the world. Most of the exchanges are made by teleprinter on a point-to-point basis between observing centres but summary bulletins which are transmitted once or twice a day spread the information further. In the United Kingdom we have ready access to regular radio broadcasts from France, prepared at Meudon Observatory and transmitted according to the following schedule:

1208Z	FTA91	91·15kHz	FTK77	10,775kHz
1308Z	FTA91	91·15kHz	FTN87	13,873kHz
2008Z	FTA91	91·15kHz	FTH42	7,428kHz
			FTK77	10,775kHz
2108Z	FTA91	91·15kHz	FTH42	7,428kHz

The messages are sent daily, with the exception of Sundays and French public holidays. They are addressed CQ, so that they may be copied and acted upon without infringing any regulations. The mode is A1A, machine morse, generally about 12–15wpm. The schedule is prepared for two messages, each the subject of two transmissions. The full texts are often lengthy and very specialized but the first part contains a useful summary, headed "GEOALERT" which probably contains all the information most observers will need in connection with amateur radio propagation studies. Table 14 contains sufficient detail to extract the data from the GEOALERT message; further information about any of the Ursigram messages may be obtained from the RSGB Propagation Studies Committee via the Society's headquarters.

The third source of information is by far the most detailed, but it is subject to three to seven months' delay, which can seem a long time when waiting to analyse a particular period of observation. The material is to be found in the publication *Solar Geophysical Data*, produced in the USA by the Environmental Data Service of the National Oceanic and Atmospheric Administration (NOAA), of Ashville, NC. This appears in two parts each month—Part 1 (Prompt Reports) containing preliminary data covering the two months prior to the date of issue, and Part 2 (Comprehensive Reports) containing more-detailed data centred about six months prior to the date of issue. In this country the monthly parts arrive by post about the middle of the month following that shown on the cover.

For a trial inspection it is suggested that the most recent February issue (consisting of Part 1, Part 2 and a very detailed explanation booklet distributed annually at that time) should be requested through a library. In case of difficulty an approach should be made to a library specializing in science subjects. The explanatory booklet will also be found to be a valuable guide to the content of the Ursigram messages, once they have been decoded.

Table 14. Format of a typical GEOALERT message

GEOALERT CCCNN DDHHMMZ
9HHDD 1SSSG 2FFFB 3AAAE 4//// 5MMXX
QXXYY nnijk (QXXYY nnijk . . .)
(Plain-language details of major optical flares and tenflares)
8hhdd 7777C QXXYY degree of activity . . .
(Plain-language forecast of activity)
SOLALERT JJ/KK MAGALERT JJ/KK

Note: There is no fixed length to a GEOALERT message, groups being repeated as often as necessary.

Key

CCCNN	Originating centre (MEU=Meudon, WWA=Boulder); serial number of message
DDHHMMZ	Date and time of origin of message; Z = gmt.
9HHDD	Indicates that various daily indices follow, for 24h ending at HH hours on DD day of month.
1SSSG	Indicates sunspot number, SSS, and number of new groups observed, G.
2FFFB	Indicates 2,800MHz solar flux value SSS, and number of important bursts.
3AAAE	Indicates geomagnetic activity, AAA=A_k value; E= events (0=no events, 1=end of magnetic storm, 2=storm in progress, 6=gradual storm commencement, 7=sudden storm commencement, 8=very pronounced sudden storm commencement).
4////	Indicates cosmic ray data (not used on Meudon message).
5MMXX	Indicates flare counts; MM=daily total of M flares, XX=daily total of X flares.
	Then follow groups identifying active regions on the sun:
QXXYY	Q=Quadrant of the sun (1=NE, 2=SE, 3=SW, 4=NW); XX=degrees of longitude, YY=degrees of latitude, relative to the centre of the sun's visible disk.
nnijk	nn=total number of flares in active region indicated; i=number of flares greater than importance 1; j=number of M flares; k=number of X flares (in region QXXYY).
8hhdd	Indicates 24h forecast follows, starting at hh hours on dd day of month.
7777C	Indicator; C=types of observation used in forecast (1=solar radio, 2=partial solar optical, 3=optical and radio, 4=all, plus solar magnetic measurements).
QXXYY	Positions on the sun, coded as before.
JJ/KK	Days of month between which the solar or magnetic alerts apply

Daily values of K_p, C_i, C_p, A_p and other magnetic data, including an inferred interplanetary magnetic field indication derived from satellite observations, appear after a delay of about four months in the American publication *Journal of Geophysical Research (Space Physics).*

Amateur radio-astronomical observations are co-ordinated by the British Astronomical Association and an edited summary appears as a regular feature in their *Journal.*

Geomagnetic data

Solar events and associated ionospheric disturbances are of less direct interest to the vhf/uhf operator than are geomagnetic variations, which correlate well with auroral events and, though to a lesser extent, with E_s and te.

These are comparisons which fall within the scope and capabilities of interested radio amateurs, but many find it difficult to extract the necessary, elementary information from conventional manuals on the subject.

In the studies carried out on auroral propagation by the

Table 15. *K*-figures for Lerwick

0	0 to 10	5	140 to 240
1	10 to 20	6	240 to 400
2	20 to 40	7	400 to 640
3	40 to 80	8	640 to 1,000
4	80 to 140	9	1,000 or more

RSGB the region of interest is admirably represented by a knowledge of the performance of the magnetometers at Lerwick Observatory, Shetland, which location, at over 60° north latitude, often experiences spectacular displays of visual aurora. Valuable experience was gained there during the International Quiet Sun Years, 1963–4, when the GB3LER beacon transmitters were set up nearby and direct comparison of results against the magnetometer records became possible. Although this phase of the work has ceased, analysis using the data continues, thanks to monthly returns made available to the RSGB by the Institute of Geological Sciences in Edinburgh, whose help is gratefully acknowledged. The remainder of this section is intended to provide an introduction to the subject to those who take part in the Society's auroral observation work, which forms an important part of its Propagation Studies programme.

The terrestrial magnetic field at the earth's surface is not constant, but is subject to both long-term and short-term variations in intensity ranging from periods of centuries or more to hours, minutes or even less. The transient variations are small in comparison to the total field; they are measured in gammas, which are equal to 10^{-5} gauss, the force being determined in terms of three components mutually at right-angles, either in the directions X (geographic north), Y (east) and Z (vertically downward), or H (horizontal intensity), D (declination) and Z.

The main variometers at Lerwick record H, D and Z photographically on a sheet of sensitized paper approximately 40cm by 30cm, on which all three traces appear side-by-side, together with timing marks every 5min, and suitable baselines. The present sensitivities are such that H changes of 3·45 gamma, D changes of 0·94min of arc (corresponding to 4 gamma at right-angles to the meridian) and Z changes of 4·35 gamma move their respective traces by 1mm. A system of prisms ensures that any trace which approaches the edge of its section of the chart appears again from the other side, thereby extending the effective width so as to be able to handle the widest excursions.

The traces exhibit two features, one a fairly regular diurnal "background" change due to solar and lunar effects, the other a superimposed irregular, and often violent, variation, the extent of which depends on particle radiation from the sun. It is necessary to examine initially a large number of traces obtained during magnetically quiet periods in order to be able to assess the appearance of the "normal" diurnal curve, which has the form of a shallow letter "S" on its side, and allowance has to be made for season, solar flare effects and certain decreases which follow a magnetic storm. The sum of the highest positive and negative departures from the "normal" curve are converted into a quasi-logarithmic scale of *K*-figures, where the actual values for the lower limit of each number vary from one observatory to another depending on the magnetic latitude. For Lerwick the scale is given in Table 15.

At other observatories the ranges are proportional, and may be found from the value assigned for the lower limit of $K = 9$, which will be quoted as being either 300, 350, 500, 600, 750, 1,000, 1,200, 1,500 or 2,000 gamma.

Using this *K*-scale, the degree of activity is described for each directional component of the force during eight three-hourly periods of each day, and the highest of the three numbers for each period are grouped in two sets of four digits, separated by Greenwich noon, beginning with the period 0000 to 0300gmt.

A combination of *K*-figures from 12 widely-spaced observatories (of which Lerwick is one) results in the planetary *K*-index, K_p, prepared monthly by the Committee on Characterization of Magnetic Disturbances, at the University of Göttingen, Germany, which is often preferred to single-station data in analytical work, particularly in connection with the ionosphere or when purely local effects are unwanted. The normal 0 to 9 scale is expanded into one of thirds by the addition of suffixes, eg . . . 2 −, 2o, 2+, 3 −, 3o, 3+ . . . .

A daily magnetic character figure, *C*, has been in use for over half a century, each observatory subscribing a figure descriptive of their assessment of the day's activity, 0 if it was judged quiet, 1 if it was moderately disturbed, or 2 if it was very disturbed. The individual figures are rarely used, but an index C_i, the average to one decimal place of *C*-figures from a world-wide network of collaborating observatories, provides a convenient classification of daily activity. Another, apparently similar, character figure, C_p, is prepared directly from the K_p indices, but, although its derivation is so different, it rarely differs from C_i by more than 0·2. To simplify machine tabulation the scales are sometimes expressed in terms of yet another, known as C_9, which uses whole numbers from 0 to 9 in place of the decimal range from 0·0 to 2·5.

The sum and arithmetic mean of the eight three-hourly *K*-figures provide further expressions of daily activity which are simple and convenient to obtain. They are not ideal, however, because the *K*-scale is a logarithmic one (as is the decibel scale), and the arithmetic average gives the logarithm of the geometric mean and not the logarithm of the arithmetic mean. To take an extreme example, consider the two series 1111 1111 and 0000 0008, both of which give a sum of 8 and a mean of 1; the first would be representative of a quiet day, whereas the second would be considered a highly disturbed day. For this reason it is preferable to turn each *K*-index back into an equivalent range, a_k, on a linear scale, by using the corresponding values:

K	0	1	2	3	4	5	6	7	8	9
a_k	0	3	7	15	27	48	80	140	240	400

which may be summed and meaned arithmetically to represent activity over a period. It should be noted that the same table is used for all observatories, irrespective of their actual *K*-scales, so that the resulting standardized figures are not the true gamma ranges, although those may be approximated from them, if required, by the use of a factor (which in the case of Lerwick is 4). The *daily amplitude* A_k is the average of the eight values of a_k for the day. In the case of the two examples cited above as leading to the same *K*-figure sum, the first, 1111 1111, gives an A_k of 3, whereas the second, 0000 0008, produces an A_k of 30, thereby reflecting the vastly differing states of activity.

A similar, but expanded, scale relates the planetary three-hour index, K_p, to the three-hourly *equivalent planetary amplitude*, a_p:

K_p	0o	0+	1 −	1o	1+	2 −	2o	2+	3 −	3o	3+	4 −	4o	4+	5 −
a_p	0	2	3	4	5	6	7	9	12	15	18	22	27	32	39

K_p	5o	5+	6 −	6o	6+	7 −	7o	7+	8 −	8o	8+	9 −	9o
a_p	48	56	67	80	94	111	132	154	179	207	236	300	400

The *daily equivalent planetary amplitude*, A_p, is the average of the eight values of a_p for the day.

Accurate time recording

When selected frequencies need to be monitored for propagation studies, some form of recording is essential so that the operator can attend to more productive things. It also results in a semi-permanent set of observations which can be transcribed and analysed as and when convenient.

Stereo cassette recorders provide a useful method of recording. The machines are relatively cheap because they are mass-produced and, as the tapes may be used again and again, running costs are low, particularly when compared with pen recorders using paper charts. The stereo facility provides the user with two synchronized (but entirely independent) channels, one of which may be used for signal data, the other for timing signals originating from one of the standard time and frequency radio transmissions.

For some purposes it is sufficient to record no more than the presence of the selected signal at a known time and for this the recorder may be connected to the output of the receiver in the conventional way. When an indication of the signal strength is required it is advisable to use some form of voltage-to-frequency or analogue-to-digital conversion before recording from either the agc line or a special detector giving a suitable time-constant. This avoids the effects of differences between recording and playback, including the quality of the tape, from affecting the measurements.

Sometimes, to make more effective use of tape and to simplify the task of data reduction, discontinuous recording may be adopted. This can take the form of sampling, where, say, 5min in every hour are transferred to tape and the transport mechanism is halted between-times, or by causing the tape to stop automatically in the absence of signals for more than a selected period. Both of these practices complicate the provision of radio time signals from the best-known sources, such as those which share 2·5, 5, 10 and 15MHz, because only minute and second intervals are available with no indication of absolute time.

MSF, Rugby, on 60kHz carries time every minute in the form of a 0·5s burst of pulse-code modulation immediately before the minute indicator to which it refers, but special equipment is required to resolve it and, in any case, the frequency is outside the range of most receivers likely to be used nowadays by amateurs (the war-surplus Marconi receiver known variously as CR100, R1297 and B28 was a notable exception).

For most purposes the transmissions from DIZ, Nauen, East Germany, on 4,525kHz, provide a much more practical solution. Apart from a short break between 0815 and 0845 it gives standard times throughout the day and night, including a positive indication of the time (gmt) once a minute in a form which needs nothing more from the operator than the ability to count in order to decode. For some reason this very useful feature is never mentioned in publications that list the station, but fortunately it is not difficult to recognize what is being offered and then to "crack the code".

The exact minute is indicated in the usual way by a longer-than-normal "pip". Then follow 59 "ticks", at 1s intervals, some single, some double.

To find the time begin counting seconds from the minute mark. No 40 is always a double, forming a useful marker which can be used to avoid counting the previous 39 once the method is known. Note the number of seconds which have elapsed as each double tick is heard until No 55 is reached. Then refer to Table 16 and add the times equivalent to the numbers. The result refers to the minute which begins a few seconds after the last of the "doubles".

Table 16. DIZ time decode table

40	0000	49	+0100
41	+0001	50	+0200
42	+0002	51	+0400
43	+0004	52	+0800
44	+0008	53	+1000
45	+0010	54	+2000
46	+0020	55	
47	+0040		
48			

Example:
Double "ticks" noted at the following seconds: 40, 42, 43, 45, 47, 48, 49, 51, 53. Time at next whole minute is 0000 + 0002 + 0004 + 0010 + 0040 + 0100 + 0400 + 1000 = 1556gmt.

Those familiar with binary-coded decimal notation will have no difficulty in recognizing the basis of the table or in reconstructing it when necessary. Note, however, that the normal order is reversed, with the lsd of the minutes appearing first. Second No 48 provides a parity bit making an odd number of "doubles" for the minute identifiers appearing between seconds Nos 41 and 48 inclusive. No 55 does the same for the hours identifiers between seconds Nos 49 and 55.

Once the method has been understood it will be found a simple and effective way of marking the time in applications such as has been described. Its availability deserves to be more widely known.

Amateur networks and further research

It is hoped that the preceding pages of this chapter will have left the reader with the feeling that there is still much to be learned about radio propagation at vhf and uhf and that organized groups of amateurs are particularly well placed to further man's understanding of the physical processes involved in almost every mode other than direct line of sight.

There may never have been such an opportune time to put forward fresh evidence of the extent to which guidance given by such authorities as CCIR and URSI to intending users of frequencies above 30MHz seriously underestimate the range and frequency coverage of the various modes in this part of the spectrum. The professionals acknowledge that such discrepancies exist and are looking to the amateur service for raw material that will help to bring present theory more into line with what is happening in the world outside.

There is a continuing need for long-term studies of over-the-horizon transmission paths, particularly those involving the beacons that were listed in Table 10. This type of work demands a degree of involvement that can be expected from only a very few individual amateurs, although it provides a very interesting project for a club, particularly one associated with an educational establishment, provided that continuity may be assured over long holiday periods and there is sufficient overall supervision to maintain the stability and calibration of the equipment.

Enough has been written already to show the value of studies which make use of a very high volume of simple reports from stations covering a large area. The mere fact that contact was made on a specified band, at a certain time, between two stations identified by callsign and QTH locator, is of little more than passing interest to either of the operators concerned. But when hundreds of such reports are collected and processed a powerful research tool emerges, and one, moreover, that is peculiar to the amateur service.

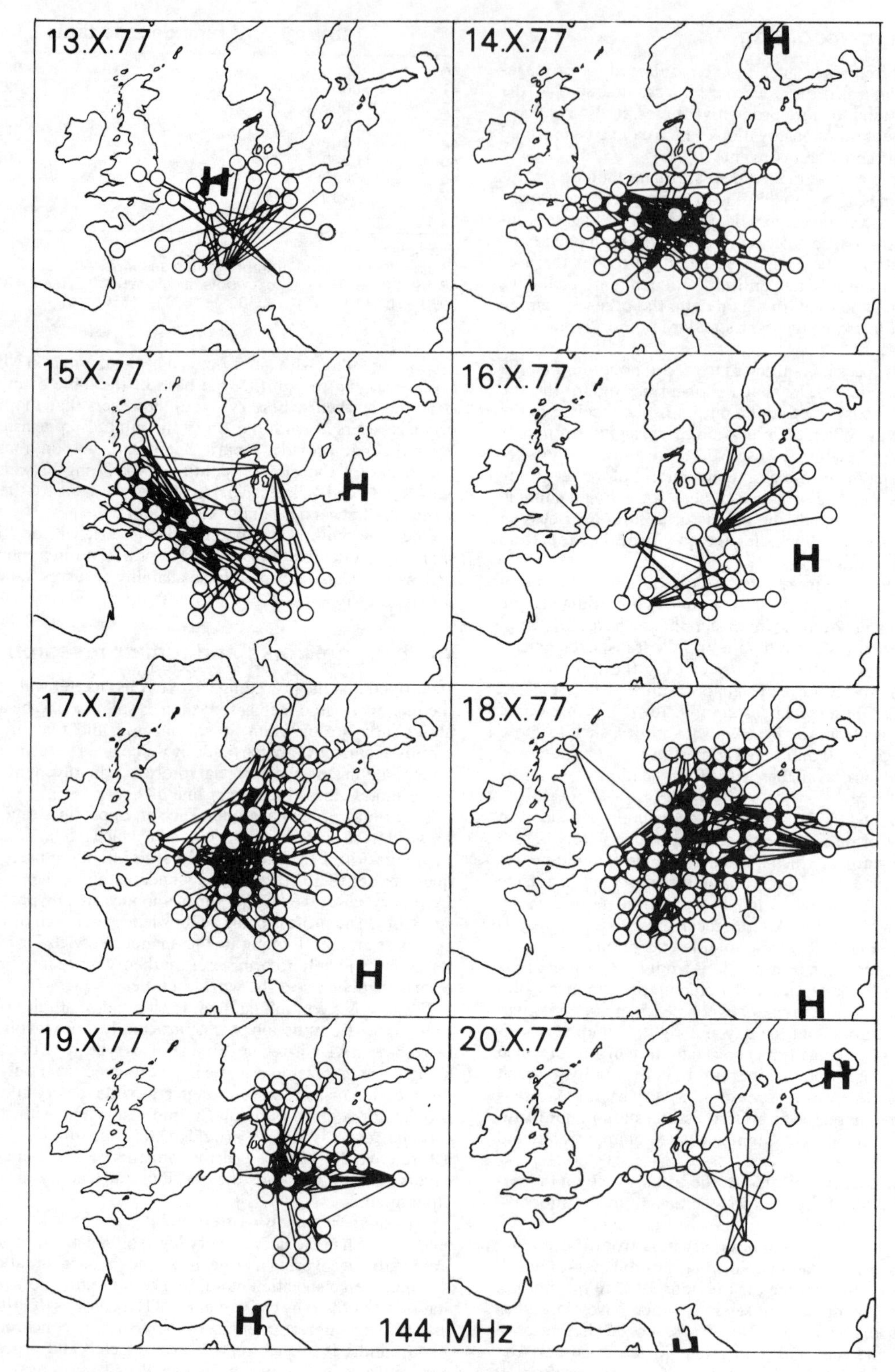

Fig 26(a) Analysis of 144MHz reports

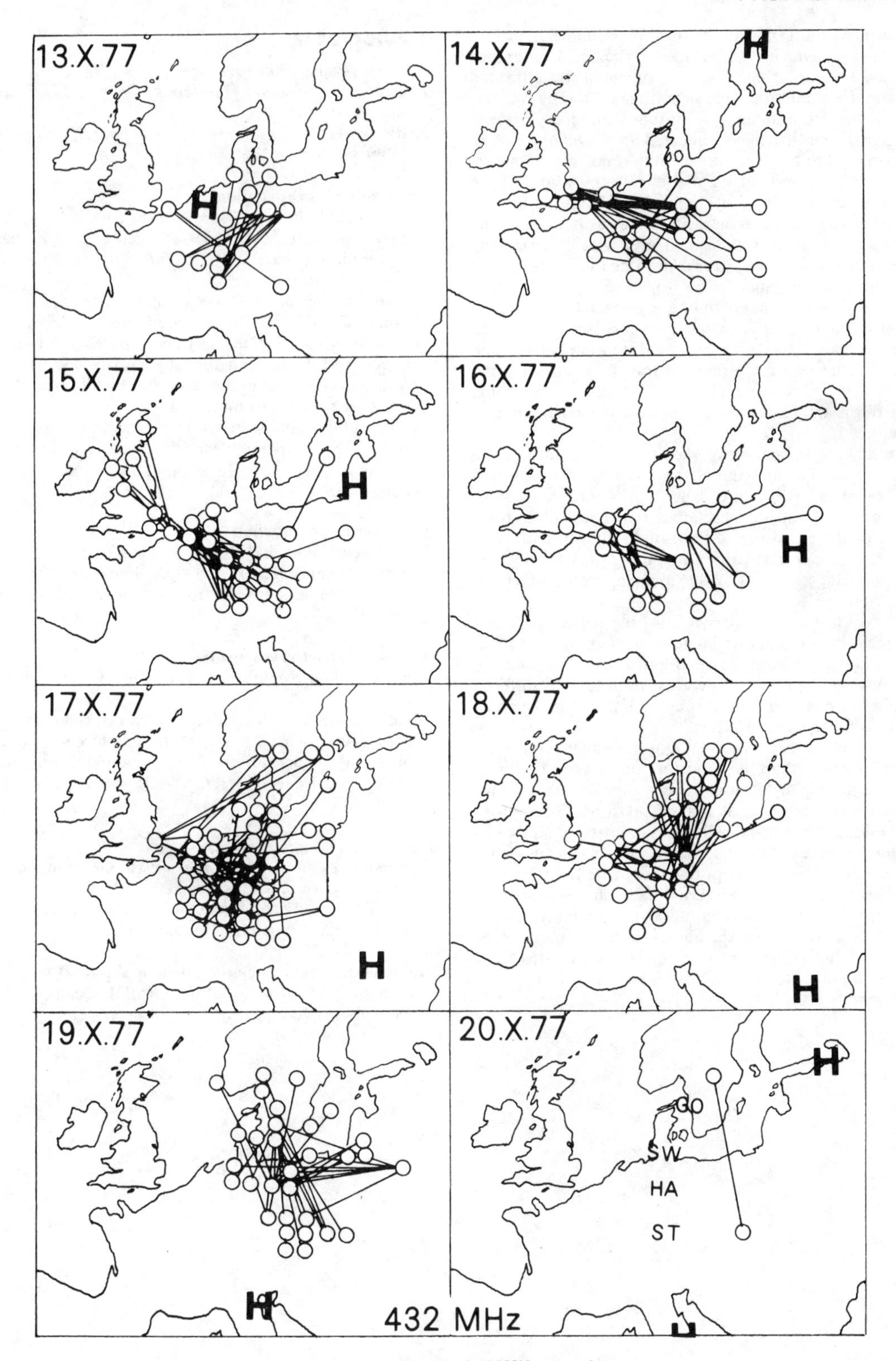

Fig 26(b). Analysis of 432MHz reports

As an example of the capabilities of this technique, consider Figs 26(a) and (b), which were included in the IEE Conference paper referred to earlier in the section of signal strengths and ranges attainable using tropospheric propagation. The two sets of maps resulted from an analysis of many hundreds of individual reports, most of them collected in Germany by the DUBUS organization. It is known that reporting amateurs were active in most parts of Europe during the whole of the period shown, and nearly all of them were within the boundaries of a very large anticyclone for a large proportion of the time, yet only a certain well-defined area was experiencing long-range anomalous propagation at any one time. That area is shown in the original paper to be where the steep-gradient boundary has formed between air of low refractive index, over air of high refractive index. Although subsidence is present elsewhere the sharp boundary is not present either because the turbulence in the lower atmosphere is too weak, allowing the low-refractive index air to reach ground level, or too strong, causing mixing at the interface and a consequent weakening of the gradient.

Observe how, in the course of the event, the centre of the anticyclone, marked with a letter H, moves from day to day, and how the axis of the really long-range paths rotates so as to maintain a broadside-on aspect relative to it. These paths form a chord across the curvature of the isobars (which had to be omitted from the diagrams in order to simplify them). In the last two maps the change in direction due to the approach of a fresh centre is of interest.

Another conclusion to be drawn from the maps is that the area of enhancement is approximately the same at both frequencies, although the two sets of reports used are entirely independent of one another. Individual path lengths differed within the area, however, being roughly half as far again at 144MHz as compared to 432MHz.

It should be clear that these techniques, which require no more from operators than the reporting of contacts that may well have had nothing to do with propagation research in themselves, have enormous potential, not only in tropospheric propagation studies, but in vhf sporadic-E and auroral-E studies as well. It should be noted, however, that reports of bearings from both ends of the path are an important requisite of the latter.

It is only because of the truly international nature of amateur radio and the seemingly tireless enthusiasm of so many people, not the least those who collect the observations and make them available for studies such as the one described, that this technique can be employed to the full. *Your* reports may be the ones needed to complete the task.

Bibliography

General propagation coverage

Radio Communication Handbook, Chapter 11 (Propagation), RSGB, 1977.

Radio Wave Propagation, A. Picquenard, Philips Technical Library, 1974.

Tropospheric propagation

Recommendations and Reports of the CCIR, 1978, XIVth Plenary Assembly, Kyoto, 1978, Volume V: "Propagation in non-ionized media", CCIR (International Radio Consultative Committee).

Handbook of Weather Messages, Part II, "Codes and specifications", 7th edn, 1979, amended 1982, HMSO.

Government Publications Sectional List No 37: Meteorological Office, HMSO, revised annually. (A free booklet, obtainable from HMSO, containing details of handbooks, charts, diagrams etc relating to meteorology.)

"Effects of the troposphere on radiocommunication", M. P. M. Hall, *IEE Electromagnetic Waves* series 8, London, 1980.

Handbook of Aviation Meteorology (Met O818/AP3340), 2nd edn, HMSO, 1971.

Ionospheric propagation

Recommendations and Reports of the CCIR, 1978, XIVth Plenary Assembly, Kyoto, 1978, Volume VI: "Propagation in ionized media", CCIR (International Radio Consultative Committee).

Solar-terrestrial relationships and data

Sun, Earth and Radio, J. A. Ratcliffe, World University Library, 1970.

Solar-Geophysical Data, Part 1 (Prompt reports) and Part 2 (Comprehensive reports), National Oceanic and Atmospheric Administration, Environmental Data and Information Service, Boulder, Colorado, USA. (Available on subscription.)

Amateur radio observations

Informationen für UKW Amateure (in German and English), DUBUS Group. (Claus Neie, DL7QY, D-7181 Rudolfsberg 24, W Germany. Available on subscription. UK distributor: G3NSM, 26 Charlbury Road, Oxford.)

Astronomical data (including meteor showers)

Handbook of the British Astronomical Association. (Published annually in October, for the following year.)

CHAPTER 3

Tuned circuits

The choice of type and construction of a tuned circuit will of course depend very much on the resonant frequency, and will vary from a lumped circuit (conventional inductor and capacitor) at 70, 144 and possibly 432MHz, to linear circuit (tuned line) and on to cavity resonators.

Also, the choice on 144, 432 and 1,296MHz will to some extent depend on the power level at which the circuit is to be used, and if it is required for a power amplifier where efficiency is of prime importance, then a more elaborate circuit is justified. While this may be true for the two higher bands, there is little point in using a linear circuit at 144MHz because the increase in power output resulting from higher efficiency is not really worthwhile.

Sometimes the linear circuit is more convenient on account of better mechanical construction, and this is usually the case where higher-power valves or transistors are being used. In such cases quite often the output capacitance is quite high, so that with a lumped type of circuit (coil) it would be quite difficult to get good circuit efficiency. Here the linear circuit is useful, as with certain air-cooled valves where the use of a large diameter tube for the anode line enables the proper air flow conditions to be met.

Another advantage of this type of circuit is that it can become part of the cooling system and this is of considerable importance in types where conduction cooling of the anode is employed.

In the linear type of circuit it is often an advantage to use a half wavelength ($\lambda/2$) instead of the more usual quarter-wave ($\lambda/4$). This is particularly useful when the amplifier device has a high output capacitance necessitating significant shortening of the line. In the $\lambda/2$ line it is usual to tune the end remote from the amplifier and to feed the ht in at a point approximately $\lambda/4$ from the open end. Fig 1 illustrates these circuits.

There are, of course, some cases when compromise is necessary between the parallel-tuned lumped constant circuit and the linear type. In these cases series-tuned circuits may be resorted to as means of getting an efficient tuned circuit.

Push-pull configuration has been shown in the above circuits but they are equally applicable to single-ended use. In this case the circuits become half that shown, as indicated by the dotted lines.

Another form of circuit which is generally used in the higher frequencies, 400MHz upwards, is the resonant cavity. Fig 2 illustrates the development from a lumped-constant circuit, through the linear circuit into a cavity.

Another circuit which is similar to the cavity is the trough line. This has the advantage that it is very much easier to construct and, if closed in on the open side, becomes in effect a square-section cavity.

At the higher frequencies, conventional tuning capacitors are either inconvenient or too large mechanically, or both, and it is better to use simple disc capacitors. The size will depend on the value required, and this can be ascertained from Fig 4.

Series-tuned circuits are suitable for use where the driving source has a relatively high capacitance, such as is obtained from an anode output. They can be used conveniently to feed a push-pull or balanced output if the series tuning capacitor is of similar value to that of the source.

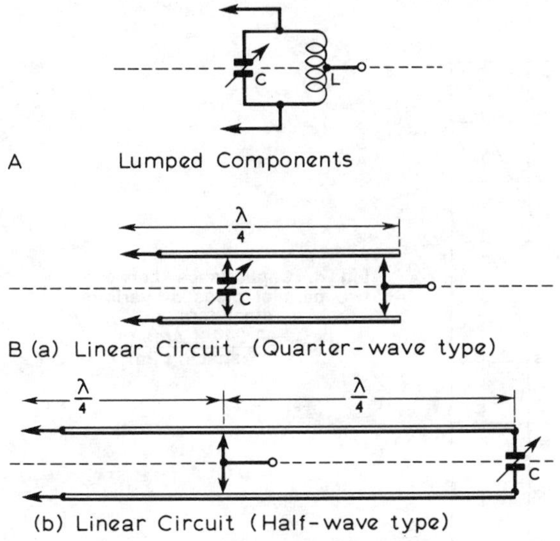

A Lumped Components

B (a) Linear Circuit (Quarter-wave type)

(b) Linear Circuit (Half-wave type)

Fig 1. Three examples of tuned circuits

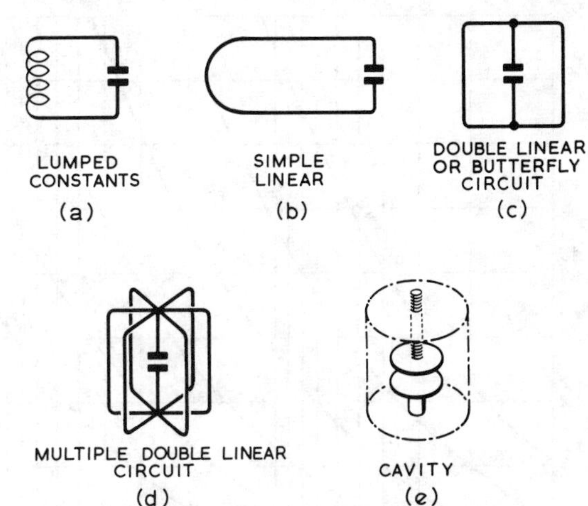

Fig 2. Illustrating the development of the cavity from the original lumped-constant circuit

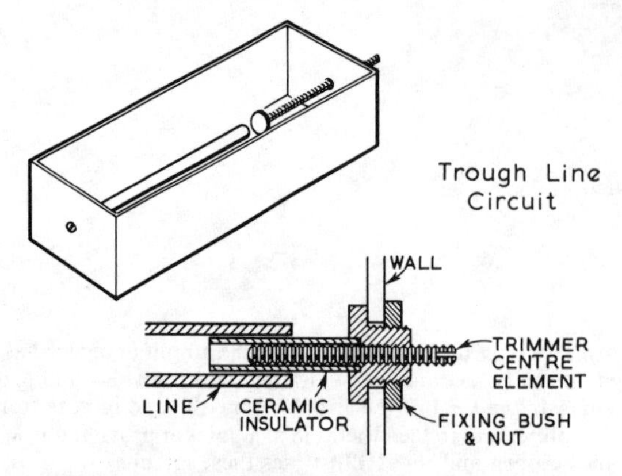

Fig 3. Trough-line circuits. The tuning capacitor may be either in line with the inner conductor (resonant line) or attached to the side wall of the trough. Another convenient method is to use a tube for the line and to fit into the end of it a ceramic trimmer centre element. In this case the outer element can be removed or connected to the line as required

As shown in Fig 5, C_0 (out) should be equal to C_T. In this case resonance must be obtained by adjustment of the inductor or an additional resonating capacitor across it. The actual value of C_T will have to be equal to the hot capacitance (working condition) of the valve or transistor. It will need to be adjustable to enable it to be set for proper balance.

Coupling to these various types of circuit should be arranged so as to transfer the maximum amount of energy either into it or out from it to the load or following stage.

Both in the lumped constant and linear circuits, coupling follows conventional means, either with a suitable inductor or tapping point that will provide a satisfactory impedance match. In the case of cavity or trough-line circuits the method is the same, but because of the different mechanical construction may appear to be unusual. The diagrams in Fig 6 illustrate these points.

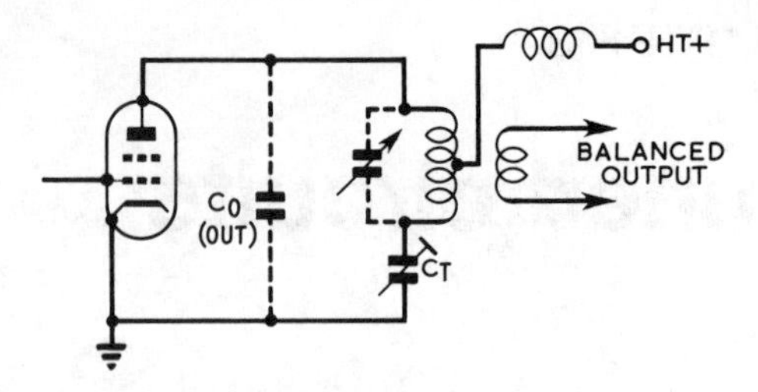

Fig 5. Illustrating a series-tuned circuit

Cavities and trough lines

The diagrams of Fig 7 show the various methods of coupling, and tuning, cavities or trough lines.

Fig 7(a) shows input and output coupling using direct connection to the tuned central line; (b) shows capacitative coupling; (c) illustrates inductive coupling; and (d) shows mixed capacitative and inductive coupling.

In all these the central line is tuned by end capacitance, and there are occasions when it is convenient to cut the line to a slightly higher frequency than that of operation and resonate by a trimming capacitance. In this case the line is connected directly to the cavity or trough at both ends. This is shown in Fig 7(e) and any of the coupling methods shown in the other diagrams may be used.

In these circuits there will be considerable circulating currents on the inside surface and for this reason the various parts shoud be a good fit. If plating is used (such as silver), it should be applied to the inside surface. Plating on the outside is unimportant other than to prevent corrosion or improve appearance.

Design of transmission-line resonators

When designing a resonator to be used as a tank circuit it is necessary to know first how long to make the lines. The resonant frequency of a capacitatively loaded shorted line, open-wire or coaxial, is given by the following well-known expression:

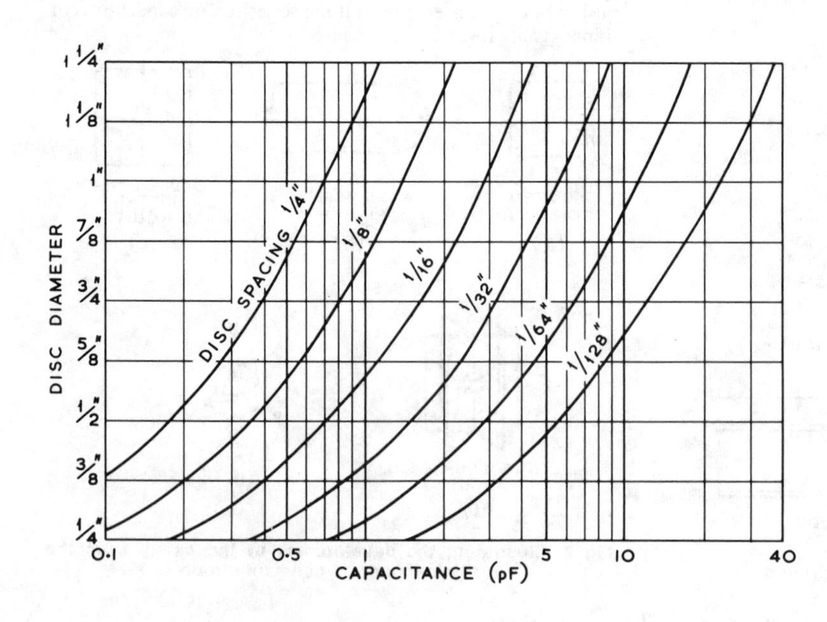

Fig 4. Capacitance between two parallel discs of various diameters

$$C(\text{pF}) = \frac{0{\cdot}244 \times \text{area (in)}}{\text{spacing (in)}}$$

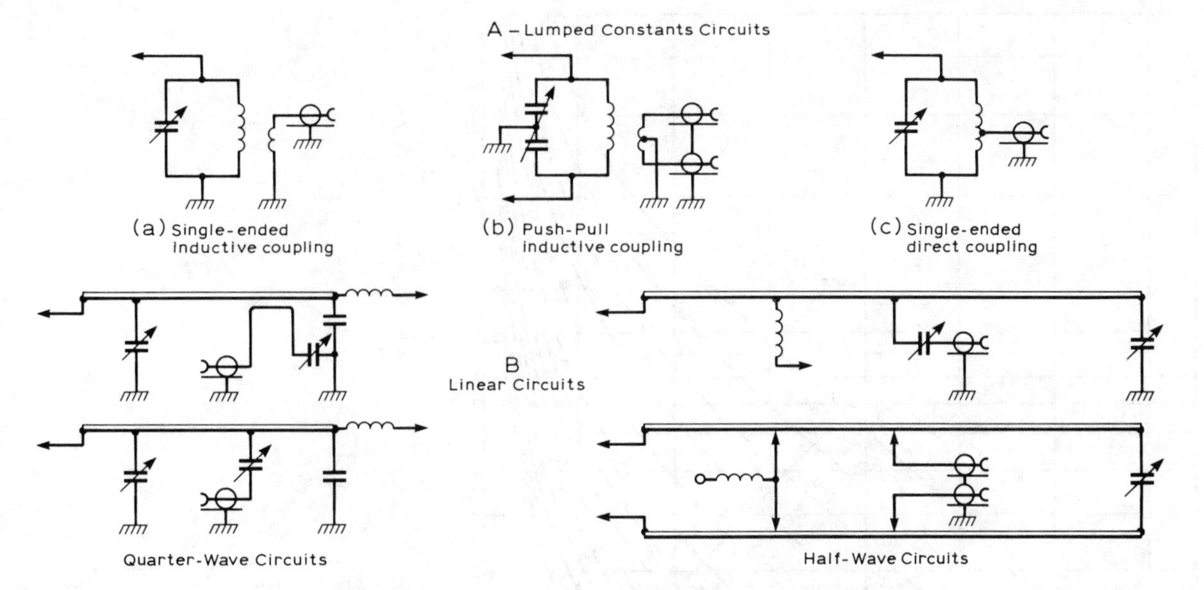

Fig 6. Methods of coupling to the various types of circuit discussed

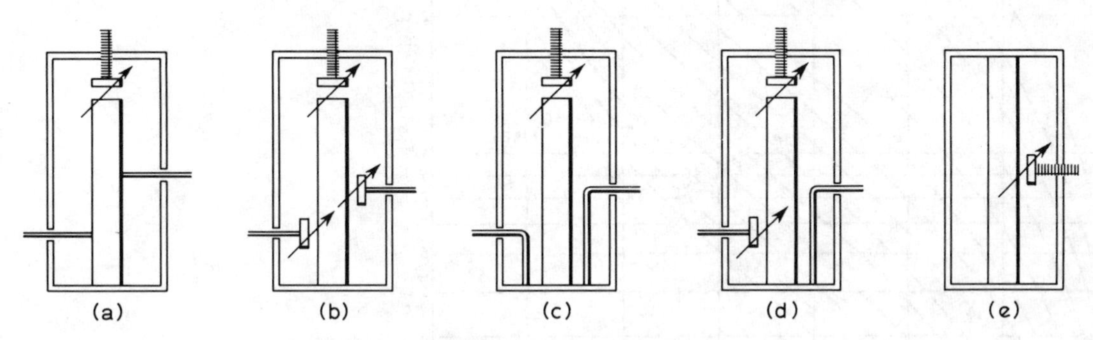

Fig 7. Methods of coupling to a trough line or cavity

$$\frac{1}{2\pi fC} = Z_o \tan \frac{2\pi L}{\lambda}$$

where f is the frequency
C is the loading capacitance
λ is the wavelength
L is the line length
Z_o is the characteristic impedance of the line.
The characteristic impedance is given by

$$Z_o = 138 \log_{10} \frac{D}{d}$$

for a coaxial line with inside radius of the outer D and outside radius of the inner conductor d.

$$\text{or } Z_o = 276 \log_{10} \frac{2D}{d}$$

for an open-wire line with conductor diameter d and centre-to-centre spacing D.

The results obtained from these expressions have been put into the form of the simple set of curves shown in Fig 8.

In the graphs fL has been plotted against fC for different values of Z_o with f in megahertz, C in picofarads and L in centimetres.

In the case of coaxial lines (the left-hand set of curves) r is the ratio of conductor diameters or radii and for open-wire lines (the right-hand set of curves) r is the ratio of centre-to-centre spacing to conductor diameter.

The following examples should make the use of the graphs quite clear:

Example 1

How long must a shorted parallel wire line of conductor diameter 0·3in and centre-to-centre spacing 1·5in be made to resonate at 435MHz with an end loading capacitance of 2pF (the approximate output capacitance, in practice, of a QQV03-20 (6252) push-pull arrangement)?

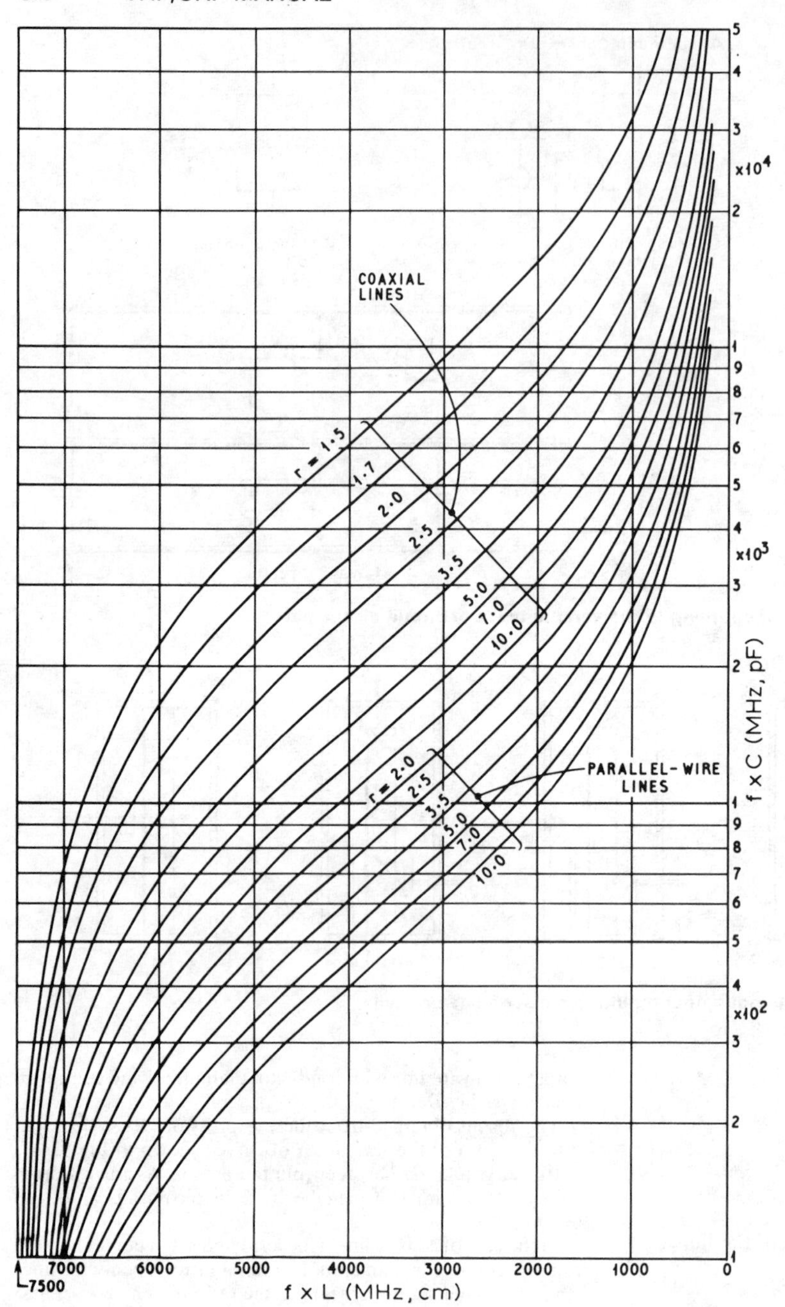

Fig 8. Resonance curves for capacitively loaded transmission-line resonators

First, work out $f \times C$, in megahertz and picofarads

$$fC = 435 \times 2$$
$$= 870$$
$$= 8 \cdot 7 \times 10^2$$

The ratio, r, of line spacing to diameter is:

$$r = \frac{1 \cdot 5}{0 \cdot 3} = 5 \cdot 0$$

Then, using the curve marked "parallel-wire lines $r = 5 \cdot 0$" in Fig 8, project upwards from $8 \cdot 7 \times 10^2$ on the vertical $f \times C$ scale to the graph and project across from the point on the graph so found to the horizontal $f \times L$ scale, obtaining:

$$fL = 2{,}800$$

therefore, $L = \dfrac{2{,}800}{435} = 6 \cdot 45$cm approximately

The anode pins would obviously absorb quite a good deal of

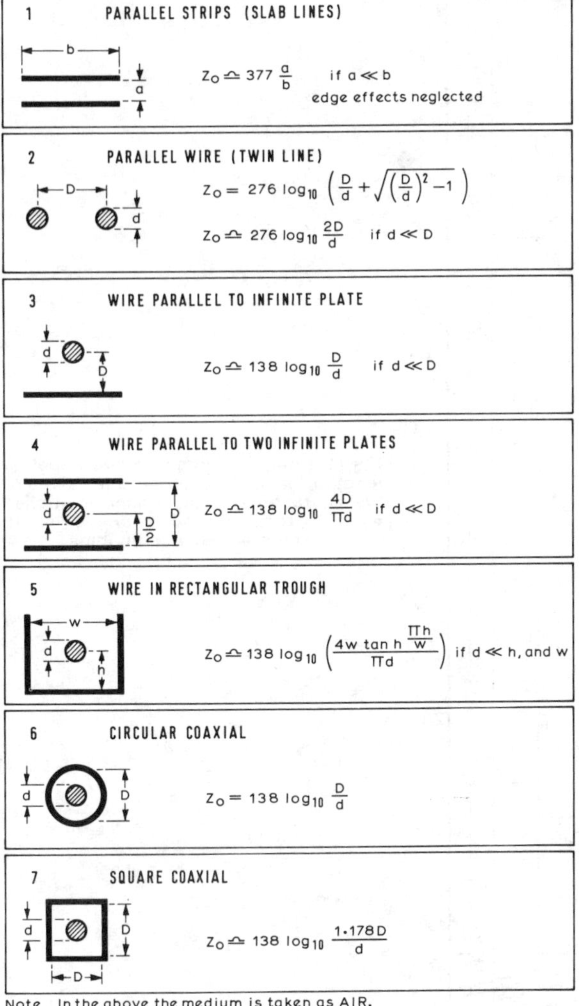

1 PARALLEL STRIPS (SLAB LINES)
$Z_0 \simeq 377 \frac{a}{b}$ if a ≪ b
edge effects neglected
2 PARALLEL WIRE (TWIN LINE)
$Z_0 = 276 \log_{10} \left(\frac{D}{d} + \sqrt{\left(\frac{D}{d}\right)^2 - 1} \right)$
$Z_0 \simeq 276 \log_{10} \frac{2D}{d}$ if d ≪ D
3 WIRE PARALLEL TO INFINITE PLATE
$Z_0 \simeq 138 \log_{10} \frac{D}{d}$ if d ≪ D
4 WIRE PARALLEL TO TWO INFINITE PLATES
$Z_0 \simeq 138 \log_{10} \frac{4D}{\pi d}$ if d ≪ D
5 WIRE IN RECTANGULAR TROUGH
$Z_0 \simeq 138 \log_{10} \left(\frac{4w \tanh \frac{\pi h}{w}}{\pi d} \right)$ if d ≪ h, and w
6 CIRCULAR COAXIAL
$Z_0 = 138 \log_{10} \frac{D}{d}$
7 SQUARE COAXIAL
$Z_0 \simeq 138 \log_{10} \frac{1 \cdot 178 D}{d}$
Note.... In the above the medium is taken as AIR.
For other medium, the resulting value of Z_0 should be multiplied by $\frac{1}{\sqrt{K}}$ where K is the dielectric constant

Fig 9. Various forms of transmission line

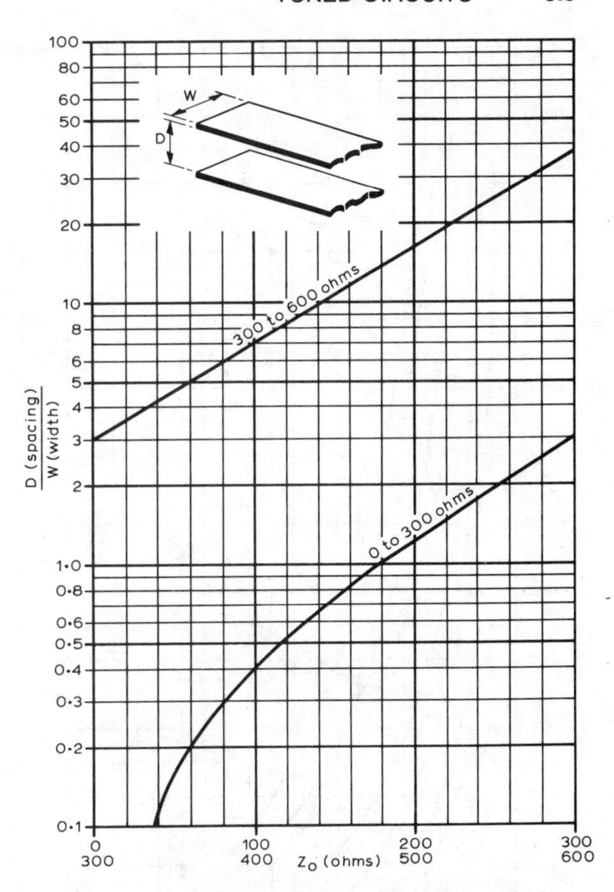

Fig 10. Characteristic impedance of balanced strip transmission line

this line length but, if the lines were made 6cm long, with an adjustable shorting bar they would be certain to be long enough.

Example 2

A transmission line consisting of a pair of 10swg copper wires spaced 1in apart and 10cm long is to be used as part of the anode tank circuit of a QQV06-40A (5894) pa at 145MHz. How much extra capacitance must be added at the valve end of the line to accomplish this?

For a pair of wires approximately $\frac{1}{8}$in diameter, spaced 1in, r is about 8. Also $f \times L$ is equal to 145×10, ie 1,450. Estimating the position of the $r = 8$ curve for a parallel wire between $r = 10$ and $r = 7$, $f \times C$ is found to be about $1 \cdot 55 \times 10^3$, ie 1,550. Hence the total capacitance C required is given by:

$$145 \times C = 1{,}550$$
$$C = 1{,}550 \div 145$$
$$= 10 \cdot 7\text{pF}.$$

Now the output capacitance of a QQV06-40 (5894) push-pull stage is around 4pF in practice, so about 7pF is required in addition. A 25 + 25pF split stator capacitor should therefore be quite satisfactory, giving 12 to 15pF extra at maximum capacitance.

Example 3

A coaxial line with outer and inner radii of 5·0 and 2·0cm, respectively, is to be used as the resonant tank circuit (short-circuited at one end of course) for a 4X150A or 4CX250B power amplifier on the 432MHz amateur band. What length of line is required?

In this case:

$$f \times C = 435 \times 4 \cdot 6$$
$$= 2{,}001$$

using the $r = 2 \cdot 5$ curve for coaxial lines,

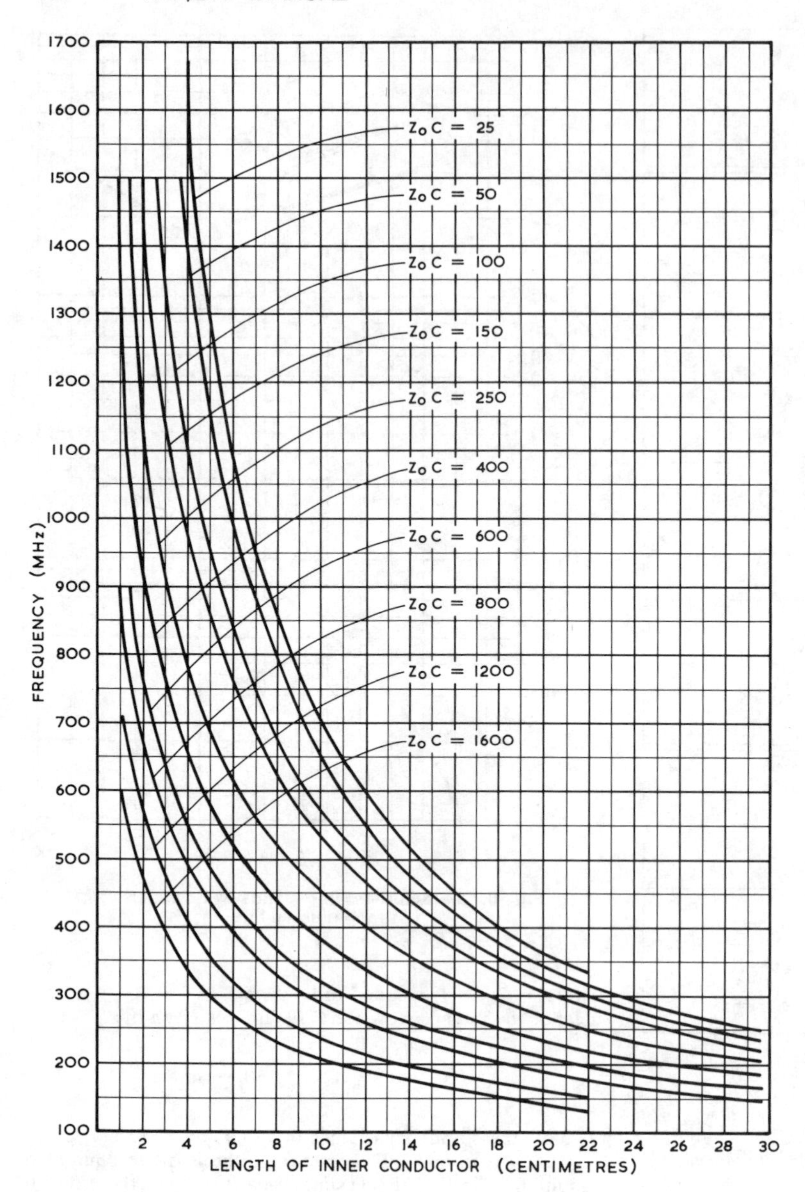

Fig 11. Chart showing frequency against length of inner line for various values of the characteristic impedance multiplied by the total capacitance. *C* is in picofarads and Z_0 in ohms

$$f \times L = 4{,}620$$
$$L = 4{,}620 \div 435$$
$$= 10{\cdot}6\text{cm approximately.}$$

This length would include the length of the anode and cooler of the 4X150A of course, but, as in Example 1, a line 10cm long would be certain to be long enough, especially as the output capacitance used in the calculations is that quoted by the manufacturers for the valve, the effective capacitance being somewhat greater in practical circuits. A shorting bridge or disc capacitor should be used for tuning the line to resonance.

Designing for maximum unloaded *Q*

The anode circuit efficiency is given by:

$$\text{Efficiency (\%)} = \frac{\text{Unloaded } Q - \text{loaded } Q}{\text{unloaded } Q} \times 100$$

It is obvious that the highest possible unloaded Q is needed to get the greatest anode circuit efficiency. The Q is greater for radial and coaxial resonators than for comparable parallel wire circuits, so the former types should always be used where possible. It should perhaps be explained that unloaded Q is the Q of the anode circuit with the valve in position and all voltages and drive power applied, but with no load coupled up to it. The loaded Q is, of course, that measured when the load is correctly coupled to the anode circuit.

The losses due to radiation which are likely with open-line circuits are appreciable and screening should be used where the maximum efficiency is required. In fitting such screening, care

Table 1. UHF resonators

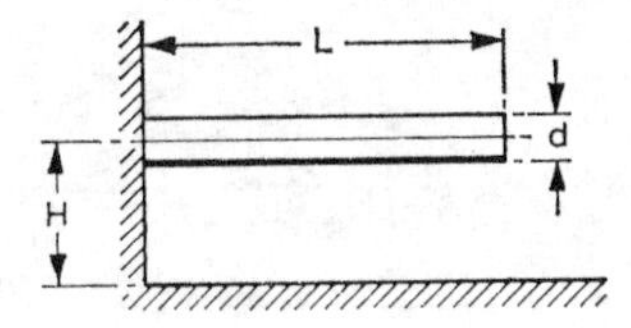

The table shows the inductance (nH) self-capacitance (pF) and self-resonance of the circuit shown for various values of D, H and L.

Height *H* above ground plane (in)	Diameter *D* (in)	Length *L* (in) 1·0	1·5	2	2·5	3·0	3·5	4·0	4·5	5·0
		5	9	12	15	19	22	26	29	33nH
1/4	1/4	0·7	1·1	1·5	1·8	2·2	2·5	2·9	3·3	3·6pF
		2·4	1·5	1·1	0·9	0·7	0·6	0·5	0·45	0·4GHz
		9	14	19	24	29	34	40	45	50
	1/8	0·4	0·6	0·8	1	1·2	1·4	1·6	1·8	2·0
		2·5	1·6	1·2	0·95	0·8	0·7	0·6	0·55	0·5
		12	19	26	33	40	47	54	61	67
	1/16	0·3	0·4	0·6	0·7	0·9	1	1·1	1·3	1·4
		2·5	1·6	1·2	1	0·8	0·7	0·6	0·55	0·5
		7	12	17	22	27	32	38	43	48
1/2	1/4	0·4	0·6	0·8	1	1·2	1·4	1·6	1·8	2·0
		2·7	1·7	1·3	1	0·8	0·7	0·6	0·55	0·5
		10	17	24	31	37	44	51	58	65
	1/8	0·3	0·4	0·5	0·6	0·7	0·9	1·1	1·2	1·3
		2·7	1·7	1·3	1	0·8	0·7	0·6	0·55	0·5
		14	22	31	39	48	57	65	74	83
	1/16	0·2	0·3	0·5	0·6	0·7	0·8	0·9	1	1·1
		2·6	1·7	1·2	1	0·8	0·7	0·6	0·55	0·5
		8	14	21	27	34	41	47	54	61
1	1/4	0·3	0·4	0·6	0·7	0·9	1	1·1	1·3	1·4
		3	1·9	1·3	1	0·9	0·7	0·65	0·6	0·5
		11	19	27	36	44	63	61	70	78
	1/8	0·2	0·3	0·5	0·6	0·7	0·8	0·9	1	1·1
		2·9	1·8	1·3	1	0·8	0·7	0·6	0·55	0·5
		15	24	34	44	55	65	75	86	96
	1/16	0·2	0·3	0·4	0·5	0·6	0·7	0·7	0·8	0·9
		2·8	1·8	1·3	1	0·8	0·7	0·6	0·55	0·5

must be taken to ensure that there is an adequate flow of air to cool the valve envelope, and that the screen is not too close to the tuned lines.

Helical resonators

This is a high-Q circuit which in effect combines the lumped-constants circuit with the cavity. It has not been used to any extent in amateur applications but offers mechanical advantages which justify its consideration, especially for filters. It consists of an inductor in a closed screen, as shown in Fig 12, and is suitable for use at all frequencies in the vhf and uhf bands.

The screen may have either a circular or square cross-section, allowance being made for the latter. The unloaded $Q = 50Df^{\frac{1}{2}}$ where D is the diameter of the screen, and f is the resonant frequency in megahertz. For a square screen use $1 \cdot 2D$ in the formula.

The number of turns required $n = \dfrac{1{,}900}{fD}$ turns

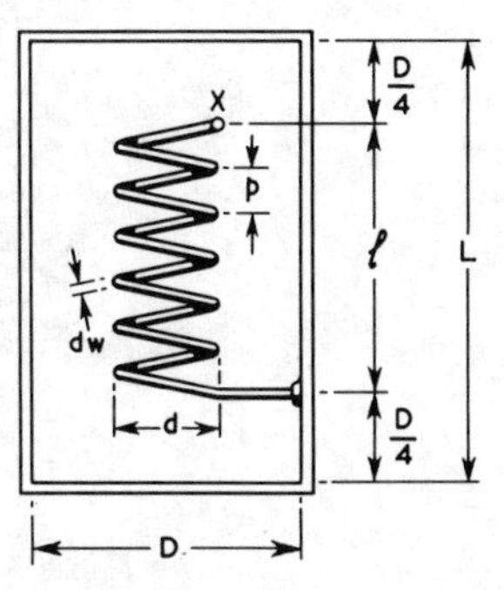

Fig 12. A helical resonator which can be used at vhf and uhf

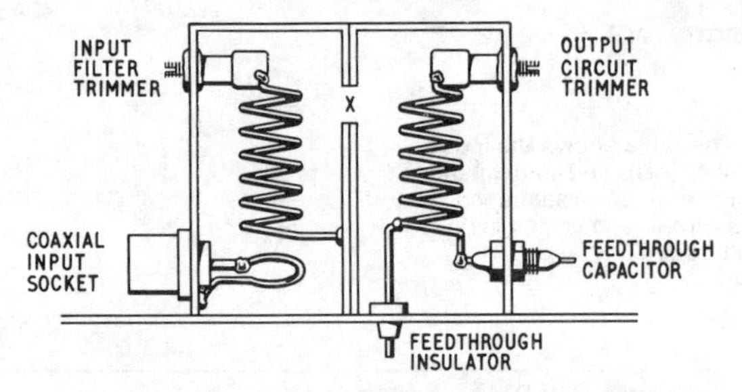

Fig 13. A typical arrangement of helical resonators

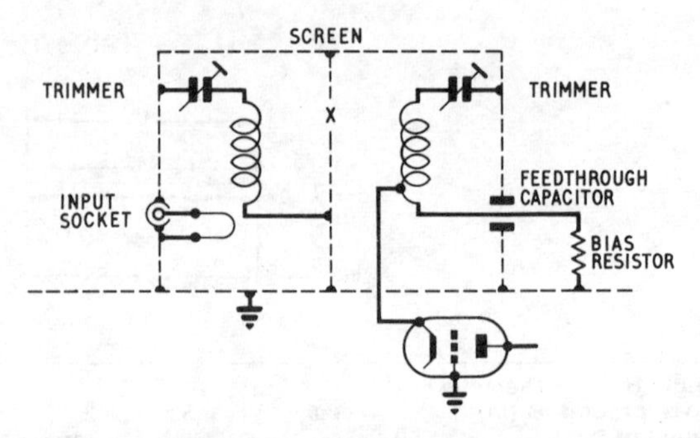

Fig 14. The equivalent circuit. This arrangement shows two tuned circuits as the input filter and input circuit to a grounded grid amplifier. Coupling between the filter and input circuits is provided by an aperture in the screen (X). Alternatively, a normal coupling method can be used, such as a link, taps or probe

Pitch (spacing between turns) $p = \dfrac{D^2 f}{2{,}300}$ in

Characteristic impedance $Z_0 = \dfrac{9{,}800}{fD}\ \Omega$

These formulae assume that $\dfrac{d}{D} = 0{\cdot}55$ and $\dfrac{L}{D} = 1{\cdot}5$

From the general arrangement it will be seen that the helix is terminated at the lower end, on the side of the screen and the free end (X) is normally connected to a low-loss tuning capacitor.

The actual value of the tuning capacitor will depend on the operating frequency and the range over which it is required to resonate the circuits. Probably the most suitable type to use would be one of the ptfe neutralizing capacitors, or another concentric type.

The equivalent electrical length of the circuit should be about 95 per cent of a free space length, and the actual conductor length is in the region of 28 per cent of the free space length. Stray capacitance is approximately equal to $0{\cdot}15D$ pF.

Design examples

(a) *70MHz filter.* Fixed frequency
Screen $1\frac{5}{8}$in × $1\frac{5}{8}$in (inside);
No of turns 14;
Diam of helix 0·9in;
Wire of helix 16swg;

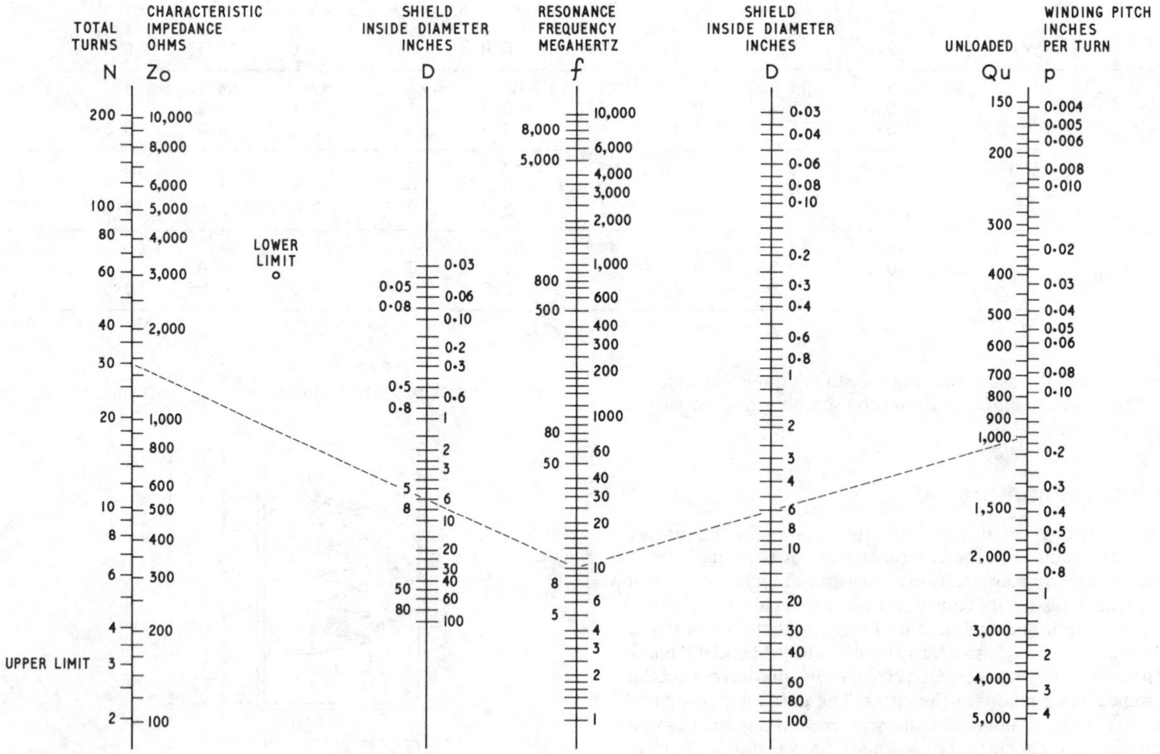

TOTAL TURNS N — CHARACTERISTIC IMPEDANCE OHMS Z_0 — SHIELD INSIDE DIAMETER INCHES D — RESONANCE FREQUENCY MEGAHERTZ f — SHIELD INSIDE DIAMETER INCHES D — UNLOADED Qu — WINDING PITCH INCHES PER TURN p

LOWER LIMIT

UPPER LIMIT

Fig 15. Design chart for λ/4 helical resonators. Lines indicate example

Helix length 2in with no end trimmer, and with silver plating on the inner surface and helix, an unloaded Q of between 850 and 1,000 can be obtained.

(b) *148 to 174MHz resonator* (suitable for 144MHz with slight increase of trimmer capacitance)

Screen 1in × 1in (inside);
Resonant frequency with end trimmer 240MHz;
No of turns 7;
Diameter of helix ⅜in;
Length of helix 1in;
Capacitance to resonate at 174MHz is 1·4pF
148MHz is 2·4pF
Unloaded Q approximately 750.

The high unloaded Q of these resonators requires that precautions are taken to avoid the introduction of losses. Where a former is needed for the helix it must be of low-loss material, but as a general rule it is better to utilize air spacing wherever possible.

Silver plating of the inside of the screen and the helix is desirable, certainly above 100MHz. Silver plating of adequate thickness would give a Q about 3 per cent higher than plain copper.

The lower termination of the helix should be as short as possible and fixed to the side of the screen. As shown in Fig 12 the coil should be fixed a distance $D/4$ from each end of the screen.

As mentioned earlier, coupling to or from the resonator can be by any of the usual means, such as tap, loop, probe or aperture. When loop is used it should be approximately perpendicular to the axis of the helix and relatively close to the bottom turn of the helix, preferably parallel to it.

Material for tuned circuits

In the case of simple tuned circuits, copper wire is normally used, either bare or enamelled, and is usually quite adequate. There is little advantage in silver plating except at the highest frequencies or as a protective surface. The largest convenient size should be used since in most cases the inductor will be self-supporting and should therefore be mechanically stable. Tinned copper wire is not satisfactory due to its high rf resistivity.

Linear circuits

These may be made from copper or brass, or even aluminium when there are weight considerations.

As these materials are subject to corrosion in moist atmospheres, silver plating (gold in special cases) should be used as a protective coating, although there is little advantage from an efficiency point of view. Chromium plating should not be used for rf circuits.

Cavities and trough lines

Here again, copper or brass are the most suitable materials, plated as indicated above. Any joints should be soldered or at least close fitting, since significant currents flow around the inside of these units and resistive losses must be kept to a minimum.

Corrosion

As mentioned earlier, copper and brass will readily corrode in moist atmospheres, and a protective coating, usually silver plating, should be used.

In connection with corrosion, it is important to avoid the use as far as possible of dissimilar metals, because in the presence of moisture (water vapour) electrolytic corrosion can be quite extensive. As an example, brass screws used to fix aluminium will show considerable corrosion after only a few weeks in the average atmosphere. It is therefore advisable to use plated fixing screws where possible, although stainless steel is also quite suitable.

Further notes on corrosion will be found at the end of Chapter 8.

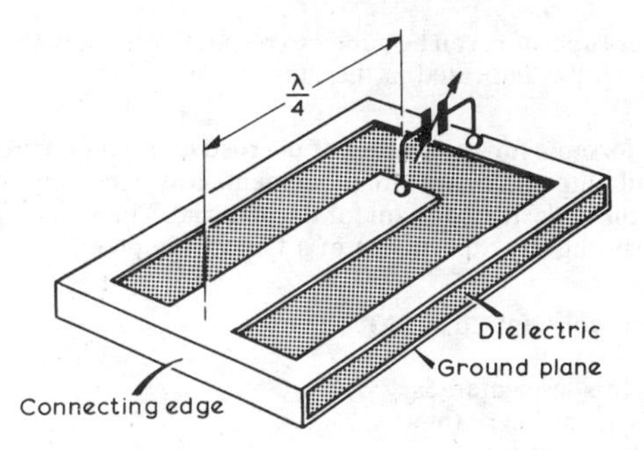

Fig 16. General arrangement of a λ/4 microstripline circuit

Microstripline circuits

At frequencies above about 300MHz, microstripline circuits are useful, offering small and stable circuit elements.

These circuits are constructed from double-clad board, the upper side being etched to form the inductor(s) required, with the lower side remaining a continuous sheet (except where clearance holes are needed). The two sides are for most purposes connected together along the edges of the board as illustrated in Figs 16 and 17.

So that the circuit has a reasonably high Q, and the losses are kept low, only high-grade material such as glass fibre pcb should be used.

Calculation of the length of a stripline inductor is fairly complex and is significantly affected both by the space (thickness of insulator) between the strip and the ground plane, and the dielectric characteristic of the particular material being used.

Within reason, the thinner the dielectric the better, because it will keep down stray fields. For most amateur purposes, board material 0·0625in or 1·5mm thick will be found suitable.

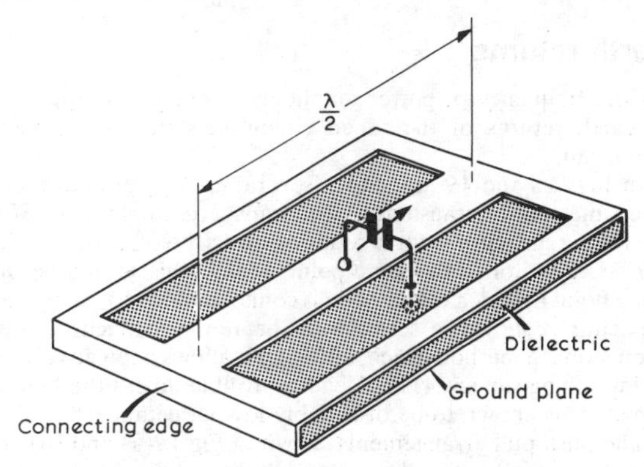

Fig 17. General arrangement of a λ/2 microstripline circuit

Trimmer capacitors can be added to resonate precisely the line ($\lambda/4$ or $\lambda/2$) as indicated in the illustrations.

Design formula for calculation of microstrip circuit elements
In calculating microstrip circuit elements it is necessary to establish the dielectric constant for the material. This can be done by measuring the capacitance of a typical sample.

Dielectric constant $e = 113 \times C \times \frac{t}{a}$

where C is in picofarads
t is thickness (mm)
a is area (mm²)

Having found the dielectric constant it is next necessary to calculate the width of the circuit element for the design impedance.

Width of element
$\mathrm{Log}_{10} W = 0 \cdot 8736 + \log_{10} t - 0 \cdot 004992 \times Z \times \sqrt{e} + 1 \cdot 14$

where t is the thickness of dielectric (mm)
Z is design impedance (Ω)
e is dielectric constant
W is in millimetres

With $\frac{1}{16}$in material, typical widths for a dielectric constant 5·0 are:

2·77mm for 50Ω
1·55mm for 75Ω
0·65mm for 100Ω

In order to calculate the circuit element length it is next necessary to calculate the velocity factor.

$$\text{Velocity factor} = \frac{1}{\sqrt{(0 \cdot 475 \times e + 0 \cdot 67)}}$$

A typical value of velocity factor for material of dielectric constant (e) of 5·0 is 0·573.

From this the circuit element length is found by multiplying the free space length by the velocity factor.

For example in air $\cdot \frac{\lambda}{4}$ for 1,297MHz = 57·8mm

for microstrip $\frac{\lambda}{4}$ for 1,297MHz = 57·8mm × velocity factor

= 33mm

Earth returns

As the frequency of power amplifiers is raised, the question of earth returns of the tuned circuit becomes increasingly important.

In Figs 18 and 19 are shown several circuit configurations often met in vhf transmitters (or transverters). In Fig 18(a) the tuning capacitor rotor is returned directly to chassis and the bypass capacitor to the same point. Ideally this should be the same point to which the cathode is connected. In (b) the bypass capacitor is shown in series with the tuning capacitor rotor connection, a method which, although it allows a lower voltage rating tuning capacitor, may lead to trouble unless the bypass capacitor is known to be of suitably low inductance.

The push-pull arrangements shown in Fig 19(a) and (b) are electrically similar though mechanically very different. In either case the tuning capacitor, often a split stator type, may be

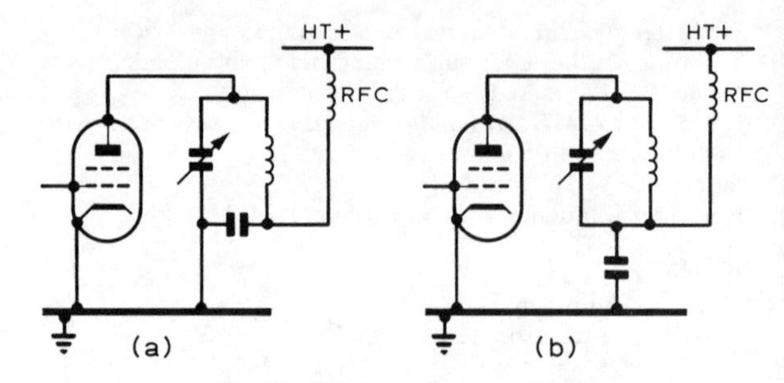

Fig 18. Single-ended amplifiers

earthed or not as required, although in many cases lack of balance can be caused by earthing. It is usually undesirable to earth the rotor in the circuit of Fig 19(b) when the use of tuned lines is intended to obtain the largest inductance for the particular frequency.

If an earthed rotor is used, then no bypass capacitor should be used at the point to which the rf choke is connected, as the multiple earth thus created will cause chassis circulating currents and consequent losses.

Table 2. Self-resonance frequencies of some commonly used capacitors

Capacitance (pF)	Frequency in MHz with 1/4 in. leads	1/2 in. leads	ERIE Type
330	85	62	831 (10mm, A, lead)
220	120	82	
100	145	120	
47	240	180	
33	250	210	
22	280	235	
15	400	300	
10	530	390	
6·8	600	470	
1000	75	42	811 (lead, 7mm dia)
10,000	14	12	701B (lead, 15mm dia)
1000 (feed through) (18swg single lead)	—	40	CDFT 100–107
1000 (discoidal) (18 swg single lead)	200	125	

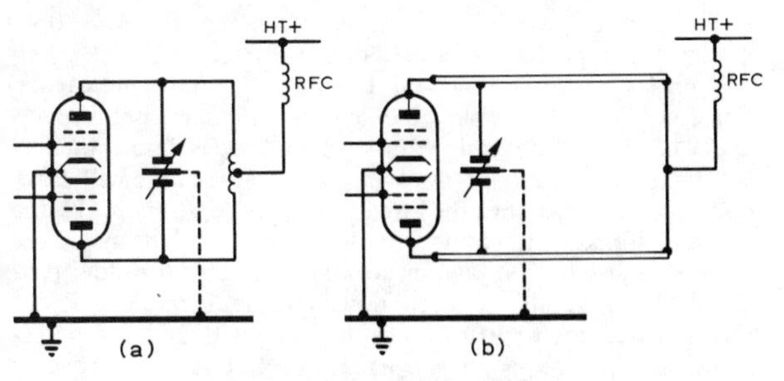

Fig 19. Push-pull amplifiers

In these circuits the rf chokes may be either a quarter or one-third wavelength of wire, but for most purposes low-value wire-wound resistors will be found very effective. Vitreous enamelled types of 2 to 5W rating and with a resistance between 25 and 100Ω are mechanically very suitable for this purpose.

In the circuit of Fig 19(b) the rf choke should always be assembled outside the loop formed by the tuned circuit and mounted at right-angles to the lines.

Varicap diodes

The varicap diode is a diode which exhibits a change of capacitance when a change of reverse voltage is applied to it. Modern varicap diodes are made by diffusing pn junctions on to a silicon slice, and by special treatment of the junction different capacitances are obtained. A diode with a small capacitance change (2·5:1) has an abrupt junction, while a diode with a large capacitance change (25:1) has a hyper-abrupt junction. Varicaps used at vhf/uhf fall in the category of abrupt-junction types and have a high value of Q at these frequencies, although the capacitance swing is small.

The relationship between V, f and C, where V is the applied reverse voltage, f is the frequency, and C the capacitance is as follows:

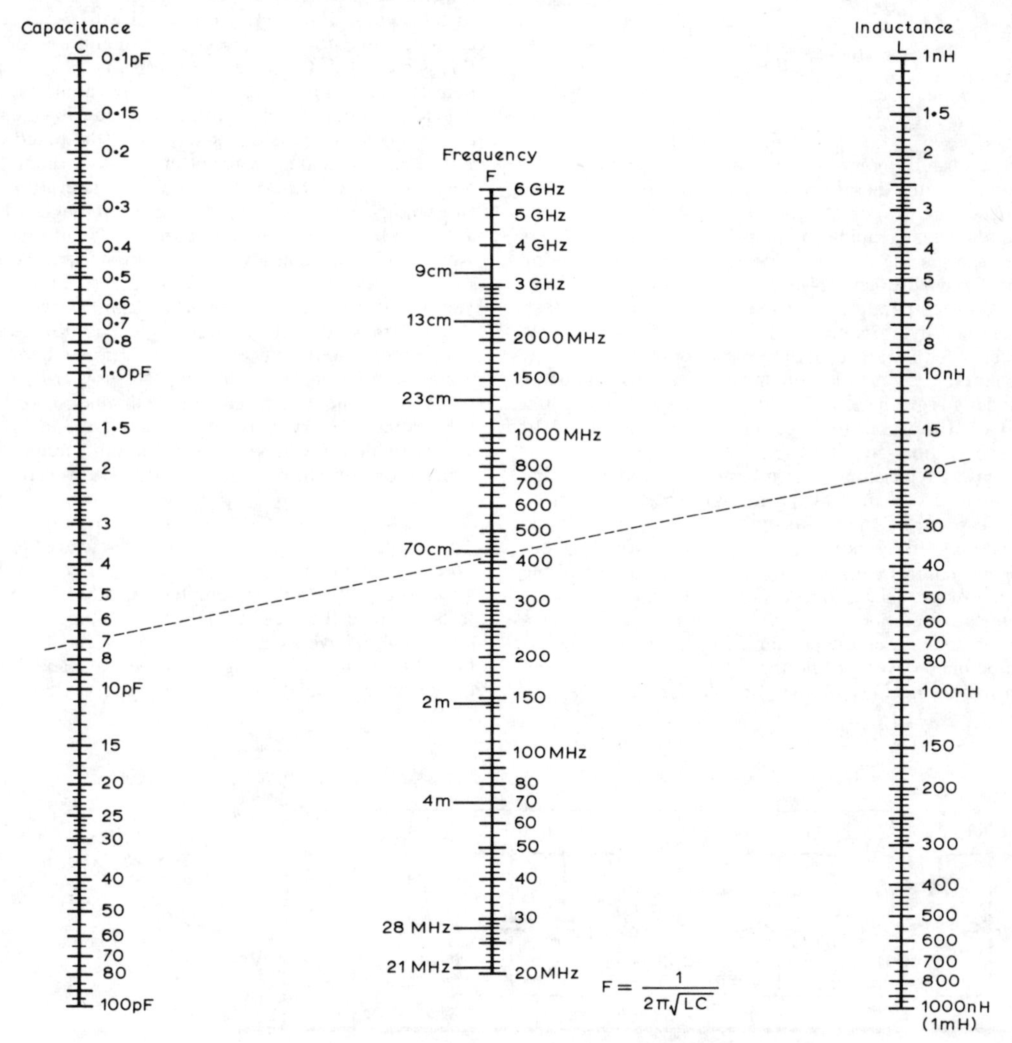

Fig 20. Resonant frequency chart for 20 to 6,000MHz

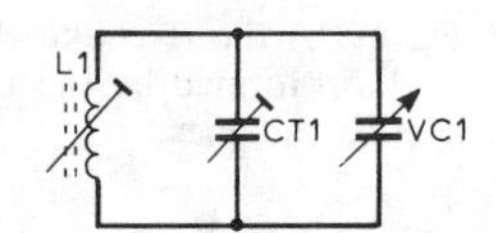

Fig 21. Standard tuned circuit

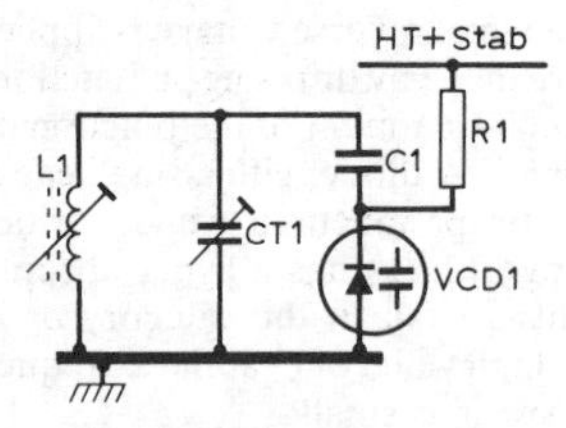

Fig 22. Varicap as tuner

Given that $f \simeq \frac{1}{\sqrt{C}}$ as $V = \frac{1}{\sqrt{C}}$

then $f^2 \simeq \frac{1}{C}$ therefore $V^2 = \frac{1}{C}$

so $f^2 \simeq V^2$.

This relationship shows that for a given ΔV there is a proportional Δf and therefore a straight-line frequency law characteristic.

Varicap diodes are rapidly finding their way into receivers and exciters, replacing the air and solid dielectric type tuning capacitors. Physically, they are very small and robust, will operate under large temperature variations, are immune from dust, dirt and are non-hydroscopic.

As will be seen they are ideal for remote control applications in fixed, portable or mobile equipment. The semiconductor front-end designs given are in fact ideal for the practical application of the varicap diode in single-tuned circuits or ganged for tracking two or more circuits.

Fig 21 shows a typical tuned circuit using an orthodox tuning capacitor. In Fig 22 the tuning capacitor is replaced by a varicap diode. The capacitor C1 prevents the dc control voltage to the diode being shorted by inductor L1 to chassis. Note that this positive-going control voltage is applied to the cathode of the diode, ie it is reverse biased, this condition being necessary for correct varicap operation.

The swing of the variable capacitor in Fig 21 is determined by the required band coverage and the total stray circuit capacitance (including the C_{min} of the variable capacitor). As an example take the case where $C_{min} = 20$pF and $C_{max} = 50$pF. This represents a capacitance ratio of 2·5:1.

With VC1 replaced by VCD1 as in Fig 22 the same capacitance ratio must be employed to maintain the same band coverage. The capacitance swing of a varicap diode is determined by two factors. When V_R approaches 0 (C_{max}) the diode will introduce non-linearity into the circuit. V_R max (C_{min}) is set by the reverse breakdown voltage of the diode, so that the range between these two voltages is normally 2 to 20V for older type diodes. However, higher breakdown voltages in modern diodes give an extension to 30V for C_{min} together with an improved Q factor at high frequencies. Furthermore, at very low reverse voltages a tolerance of capacitance between similar varicaps becomes apparent: up to ± 10 per cent of the nominal value, accompanied by a fall in Q factor.

A practical front-end circuit using varicaps is illustrated in Fig 23. As in Fig 22, C1, C2 and C3 prevent shorting out of the control voltage. The capacitive value should be calculated to present very low reactance at the frequency of operation. Preset inductors L1, L2 and L3 with trimmers C1, C2 and C3 are used to set band coverage; C4 in parallel with the oscillator tank circuit is used for any necessary temperature compensation. R1, R2 and R3, the series feed resistors, provide rf isolation between each tuned circuit. The value should be sufficiently high to prevent parallel damping, thus reducing the working Q, as at rf these resistors effectively shunt the tuned circuit.

The reverse leakage current of a varicap diode is normally very low (less than 1μA at an ambient temperature of 25°C) so the voltage drop across the resistors is negligible. Resistor values of between 50 to 100kΩ are usually satisfactory for vhf, while at uhf values as low as 10kΩ are normal. Potentiometer RV1 effectively becomes the tuning control for the receiver by varying the control voltage to the varicaps, and can be of carbon sprayed track or moulded carbon type. Accurate resettability is of paramount importance, particularly in an ssb receiver where a helical potentiometer requiring 10 turns from minimum to maximum value, and fitted with a suitable slow-motion drive will provide a very satisfactory means of tuning. Note that simple small wirewound controls are not suitable for varicap applications due to the relatively large turn-to-turn voltage.

Capacitor C4 (1·0μF) provides af decoupling, minimizing hum pick-up, and should be a tantalum or polyester capacitor. These types have negligible leakage characteristics. The preset potentiometer controls V_R min (normally 2 to 3V) and must be set before calibration is attempted. Another factor which controls V_R min is the oscillator tank voltage amplitude. A varicap diode will behave as an ordinary silicon diode when forward biased (Normal "on voltage" between 0·7 and 1·0V).

During the oscillatory cycle the tank voltage (say 1·5Vrms)

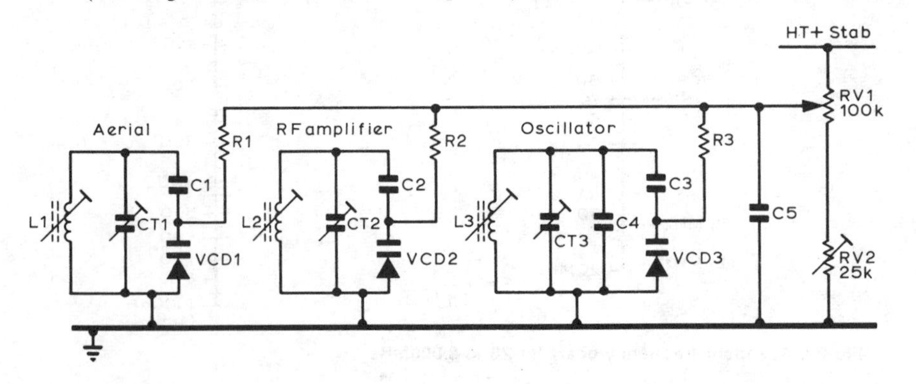

Fig 23. The use of varicap diodes for tuning a front end of a receiver

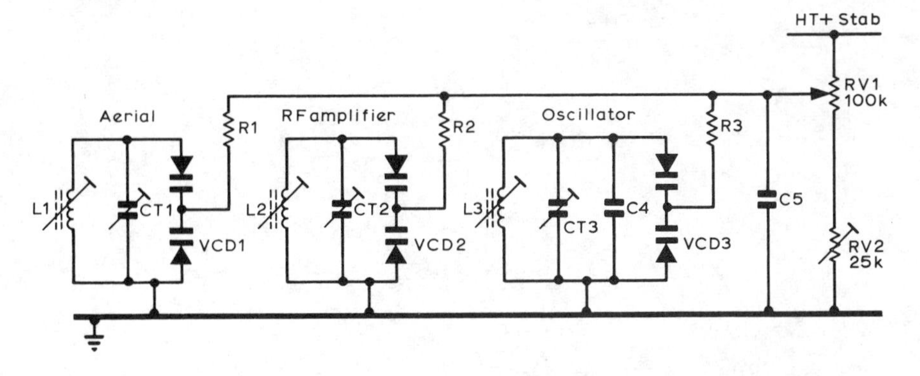

Fig 24. An alternative tuning circuit using dual varicaps

Table 3. Characteristics of some commercially available diodes

Type	Model no	C_T at 1MHz	Q min	C_R min/max at 1MHz	I_R max at ambient = 25°C
Dual*	MV104	37–43pF, V_R = 3V	100 at 100MHz	2·5/2·8	50mA
Single*	MV109	26–32pF, V_R = 3V	280 at 50MHz	5·0/5·6	100mA
Single†	BB105A	3·3–2·8pF, V_R = 25V	225 at 100MHz	4·0/5·0	50mA
Single†	BB105B	2·3–2·8pF, V_R = 25V	225 at 100MHz	4·5/6·0	50mA
Single†	BB105G	1·8–2·3pF, V_R = 25V	150 at 100MHz	4·0/6·0	50mA

All these types are available from Motorola Semiconductors, although exact equivalents are produced by Siemens.
* vhf type. † vhf/uhf type.

will be alternately positive and negative about the tuned circuit. Thus if $V_R = 0$ the varicap diode will be forward biased during the cycle where the anode is positive with respect to its cathode. In this event, rectification will take place, degrading linearity and increasing the harmonic content relative to the fundamental frequency amplitude. V_R min is set to prevent forward biasing, the voltage being dependent on the tank voltage. The diode must be reverse biased during the complete oscillatory cycle. These factors also relate to the antenna and rf circuits, particularly when strong signals are present at the receiver antenna socket. Cross-modulation and intermodulation can occur due to varicap rectification with consequent degradation of receiver performance.

The problems associated with single-ended varicap diodes, particularly when used with voltage-operated semiconductor amplifiers, mixers and oscillators, can be overcome by using the back-to-back (hereafter referred to as dual) varicap diode. This diode is formed by diffusing two junctions on the same silicon wafer (monolithic chip construction) with the cathode being common to each anode. Signal rectification is virtually eliminated, as during any part of an rf waveform cycle, when one diode is forward biased the other diode is reverse biased. A disadvantage of the dual diode is that the effective capacitances of each diode are in series, thus a dual varicap of $2 \times C$ pF is required to replace the single varicap.

However, in modern dual diodes this problem is overcome by advanced diffusion techniques, and capacitance ratios of 2·5:1 are common. In Fig 24 the dual diodes replace the single diode and the dc blocking capacitors. Although dual diodes are more expensive there will be some cost saving as these capacitors are no longer required. Where possible, dual diodes are preferred to the single-ended type. A list of both types for vhf and uhf together with the manufacturer's name is set out in Table 3.

The control voltage for varicap diodes must be derived from a very high stability supply, not only in terms of voltage but also temperature. A simple zener stabilized supply will not meet either requirement, but the addition of a transistor to form a series or shunt voltage stabilizer will improve these characteristics. Semiconductor manufacturers, realizing the requirements, have produced stabilizers with excellent voltage stability and negligible temperature coefficient. These stabilizers are of ic construction in either glass or moulded encapsulation, and offer the constructor an ideal, if not cheap, solution to voltage and temperature stabilization. A list of suitable types is given in Table 4.

Table 4. Suitable voltage stabilizers for use with varicap diodes

Type ITT/STC	Reference voltage (V)	Dynamic resistance (Ω)
2TK9	8–10	10
2TK11	10–12	10
2TK18	16–20	11
2TK22	20–24	11
2TK27	24–30	12
2TK33	30–36	12

Temperature coefficient of reference voltage at I_z = 50mA is −2 (−10. . . . +5) × 10^{-5}/°C. There are of course other manufacturers with equivalent devices.

CHAPTER 4

Receivers

The receiver required for satisfactory reception of vhf or uhf signals is generally similar to that used on the hf bands, except that more care is required with the overall noise performance in order to take advantage of the lower external noise above 30MHz. There is also the problem of achieving satisfactory vfo stability if a single-conversion receiver is contemplated.

The modern solutions to the latter consideration are to use either a phase-locked loop local oscillator for continuous coverage, or a digital frequency synthesizer for channelized reception (although if the "channels" are only 100Hz or less apart there is little operational difference). Neither method is particularly simple for home constructors to implement—it should be noted that a free-running local oscillator can prove satisfactory for nbfm reception up to 144MHz providing it is carefully constructed.

The i.f. used in single-conversion receivers is usually 9 or 10·7MHz, and matching sets of crystal filters are available for cw, ssb and fm reception at these frequencies. Sometimes this i.f. is converted down to 455kHz for the fm demodulator in commercial equipment to avoid the necessity of using a crystal in the quadrature detector.

Although a single-conversion receiver potentially gives the best performance, with less spurious responses ("birdies"), a double-conversion arrangement is often to be preferred on the grounds of economy, simplicity and flexibility.

It may merely consist of a crystal-controlled vhf or uhf converter placed ahead of an existing hf receiver (Fig 1). In effect, the latter receiver becomes a tunable i.f. The most popular tuning range used is 28–30MHz. This is because it is the widest continuous coverage available on amateur-band-only receivers, and also because it tends to be a relatively quiet part of the hf spectrum, thus avoiding possible breakthrough problems. If an older hf receiver is in use which has reduced sensitivity or stability at this frequency, it may be necessary to lower this first i.f. into the 2–10MHz region. This may also be necessary if the main receiver uses a low i.f. such as 465kHz and image response is a problem at 28MHz.

A typical 144MHz/28MHz converter consists of an rf stage, mixer and oscillator using a 116MHz overtone crystal. The rf and mixer stages often use dual-gate mosfets, and the lo a bipolar transistor. A Schottky diode double-balanced mixer can be used if better strong-signal handling is required. UHF converters will require frequency multiplication to reach the lo injection frequency, as overtone crystals are not available for use above 200MHz.

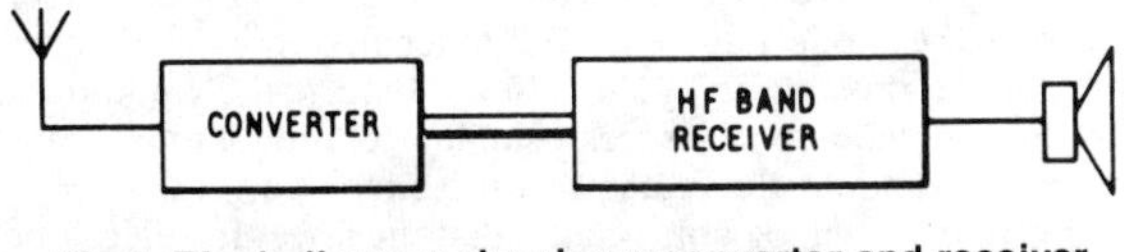

CONVERTER
HF BAND RECEIVER

Fig 1. Block diagram showing a converter and receiver

In selecting the crystal for the local oscillator it is essential to ensure that its fundamental and harmonic frequencies do not occur within the passband of the hf receiver or of the vhf converter.

Care should be taken to match the signal levels of converter output and receiver input so that the receiver's rf stages and mixer are not overloaded. An attenuator may be necessary if a high-gain converter is used, but this is in any case already fitted to most modern hf receivers.

The main receiver should be capable of receiving cw, ssb, a.m. and fm, for all these modes are in use on vhf. If an older receiver does not have an fm demodulator it should be possible to fit one, and this will provide far better performance than slope detection. If a suitable receiver is not available it is worth considering building a special 28–30MHz multimode receiver for use with converters (Fig 2).

One of the attractions of using such a converter-receiver combination is its great flexibility. Several converters for different vhf or uhf bands can be used with the same receiver, either on a switched or plug-in basis. Care should be taken with the screening of these connections to avoid breakthrough from external sources of signals.

Noise

In the vhf and uhf region, the factors which affect the receiver performances are different from those encountered on the hf bands. It is necessary to pay considerable attention to noise reduction within the equipment itself since as the frequency is increased from around 100MHz, noise generated in semiconductors, valves, resistors, inductors and leads becomes of increasing importance.

The lowest of the bands considered in this manual may be regarded as about the transition frequency where the change over from standard methods to more refined techniques becomes necessary. (This of course does not mean that a sudden changeover from the conventional circuit arrangements to

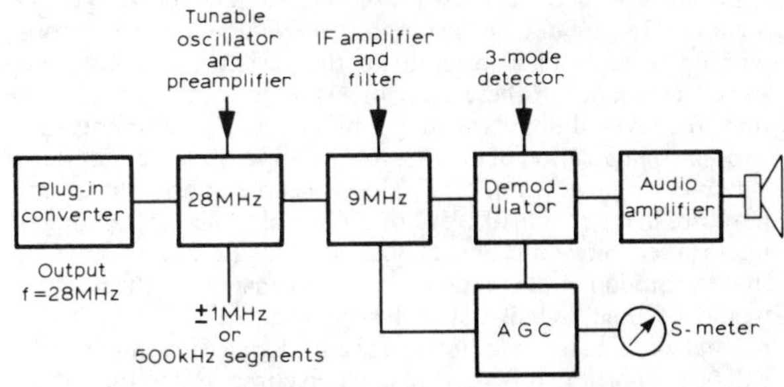

Fig 2. Block diagram of vhf/uhf receiving system using plug-in converters and tunable first i.f. of 28MHz

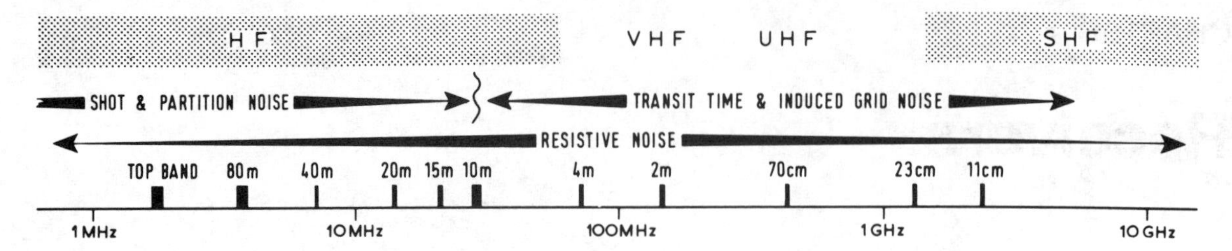

Fig 3. Chart illustrating the relationship between types of noise and frequency

linear or cavities is necessary—this does not really become necessary until frequencies around 400/500MHz are reached.) Attention to small details becomes increasingly important. Lead lengths and self-inductance of leads, apart from contributing noise, may seriously affect the circuit constants.

In order to make use of radio signals it is necessary to amplify them without at the same time introducing any more noise than is absolutely necessary, so it is of prime importance to achieve as high a signal/noise performance as possible. To do this it is important to appreciate the factors which cause noise. Generally the sources of noise can be divided into:

External Noise Atmospherics
Thermal noise from the earth
Solar and cosmic noise
Manmade impulse noise (eg ignition)

Internal Noise Resistive noise
Shot noise
Flicker noise
Partition noise
Transit time and induced grid noise
Thermal effects in transistors

Little can be done in respect of external noise, except in the case of the man-made impulse and other spark noises. Effective noise-cancelling systems can be devised and details of these are given in the RSGB *Radio Communication Handbook.*

On the other hand, considerable influence can be made on the internal noise (noise generated within the equipment) by careful design. It is important to know how this arises, so the various types are briefly described below.

Resistive noise

This type of noise is caused by all resistors, together with the resistive elements of inductance and capacitance. The actual level of resistive noise depends on the type and construction of the resistor.

Even a so-called ideal resistor of the metallic type will generate noise. It is created by the random movement of the electrons within the molecular structure of the resistive element, and since the activity of these electrons is dependent on temperature, the level of noise will vary with changes in temperature.

Some qualification of the foregoing temperature versus noise statement is however needed. Most resistors operate at a temperature in the region of 17°C, or 290K unless special cooling is undertaken. Since it is only at absolute zero (273K below 0°C) that the motion of the random electrons ceases, and the resistor would become "silent", it will be appreciated that over the normal working temperature range any changes in temperature will be proportionately very small when compared to the elevation above absolute zero. For this reason, the inherent noise level within average resistors does not change very appreciably over the range of temperatures encountered under normal working conditions.

Carbon and metal film resistors now almost universally replace the old carbon composition types. The noise characteristics of these resistors are much improved and this fact should be borne in mind when producing items such as high-gain microphone amplifiers.

As a matter of interest, specially designed resistors operated at high and/or low temperatures, are available for use as noise sources for equipment evaluation.

Valve noise

Shot noise

Shot noise arises from the random emission of electrons from a hot cathode within a valve structure.

There are two classifications of emission from the cathode or filament of a valve, one being designated *saturated emission* and the other *non-saturated emission.* In the former, and considering a simple diode with a pure tungsten filament, the anode current will be directly controlled by the temperature of the filament, and when this is at its permitted maximum, the anode will take up all the electrons available from the filament. There are no "spares" drifting around.

Under the non-saturated emission conditions, there is much more emission available from the cathode/filament than that which is being drawn by the anode. This gives rise to a space charge between the filament and the anode, and has the effect of smoothing out some of the fluctuations in anode current caused by the shot effect.

Most valves employed in equipment are operated under space-charge conditions (ie non-saturated emission) so the anode current fluctuations are much less than in the case of the saturated emission diode used in noise generators.

Flicker noise

This takes the form of large-amplitude pulses, and is produced in some types of valves at low frequencies, being generally most troublesome in the frequency range 100Hz to 50kHz.

In high-gain audio amplifiers, the presence of this noise form is most detrimental to satisfactory operation, and led to the development of special low-noise valves for this particular application. The EF86 and its associated types are examples.

Partition noise

In multigrid valves, the division of the total cathode current between the anode and the various other electrodes is subject to the fluctuations caused by shot effects. In turn, these additional electrodes will, by a process similar to modulation, cause increased random fluctuations in the anode current.

From this it will be appreciated that the fewer the electrodes in a valve the better, and moreover, why it is that a triode will always have a much lower noise factor than a pentode or other multi-electrode valve.

Induced grid noise

The random fluctuations in the electron stream emitted from the hot cathode—see *shot noise*—in passing through the grid structure on the way to the anode, will induce a noise voltage on to the grid from the electrostatic charge carried by the electrons themselves.

The magnitude of this will depend on frequency. At low and medium frequencies this noise will be self-neutralized as the voltage induced by the electrons approaching the grid will be cancelled by an equal and opposite voltage induced by those receding from the grid. At higher frequencies, however, 20MHz and upwards, the actual time taken by an electron to pass from the cathode to anode will be an appreciable fraction of the operating cycle, the fraction increasing with frequency. This *transit time*, as it is known, results in a difference in phase between the electrons approaching the grid, and those receding from it. The result is that not all the induced voltage is cancelled.

As the frequency is raised, the magnitude of the current induced in the grid also rises. This approximates to a resistive thermal noise generator operating at a relatively high temperature. This effect is normally termed *transit time conductance*, the value of which is proportional to the square of the operating frequency.

In order to assess the merit of a valve for receiver purposes two parameters are often quoted: *equivalent noise resistance* and *noise factor*.

Equivalent noise resistance

This is defined as an ideal resistance which, when maintained at a normal operating temperature, would, if placed in the grid of a noiseless valve, produce anode current fluctations equal to shot and partition noise of an actual valve of similar characteristics.

This method of assessment has been used for many years on the Continent, but it is only really of value in the frequency range 50kHz to 20MHz. It is of little or no value in equating a valve for suitability in vhf or uhf applications.

The equivalent noise resistance for various types of valves can be calculated as follows:

Triode (shot noise only)

$$R_{eq} = \frac{2 \cdot 5}{g_m} \text{ ohms}$$

Pentode or tetrode (shot and partition noise only)

$$R_{eq} = \frac{I_a}{I_a + I_{g2}} \times \left(\frac{2 \cdot 5}{g_m} + \frac{20 I_{g2}}{g_m^2} \right) \text{ ohms}$$

Triode mixer (shot noise only)

$$R_{eq} = \frac{4 \cdot 0}{g_c} \text{ ohms}$$

Pentode or multigrid (shot and partition noise only)

$$R_{eq} = \frac{I_a}{I_a + I_{g2}} \left(\frac{4 \cdot 0}{g_c} + \frac{20 I_{g2}}{g_c^2} \right) \text{ ohms}$$

In the foregoing formulae, the values of I_a and I_{g2} are expressed in amps, while those for g_m and g_c are in amps/volt.

From these calculations, it will be seen that the lower the equivalent noise resistance, the better the valve. While this is true at frequencies where the induced grid noise is not troublesome, and while valves with a high g_m will produce the lowest equivalent noise resistance, this does not automatically make them the most suitable for every application.

Noise factor

There is more or less a standard method of expressing the performance of a device intended for service as an rf amplifier on frequencies above 20MHz; this is quoted as its *noise factor*. Assuming that the first stage has adequate gain, this can also be used to state the performance of receivers and converters.

The measurement of noise factor is carried out using a diode noise source such as the A2087 whose noise performance can be calculated from:

$$F = \frac{e}{2kT} I_d R_s$$

where e = the electron charge = $1 \cdot 602 \times 10^{-19}$ coulomb
k = Boltzmann's constant = $1 \cdot 381 \times 10^{-23}$ joules/K
T = temperature of source resistance (K)
I_d = noise diode anode current (A)
R_s = source resistance (Ω)

In cases where the normal operating temperature is of the order of 17°C (290K) the formula can be simplified to

$$F = 20\, I_d\, R_s \text{ as a ratio}$$

or

$$F = 10 \log (20\, I_d\, R_s) \text{ decibels}$$

Noise diodes are available for frequencies up to about 500MHz or so but, when measurements are made at or near the maximum frequency of the noise source, some precautions are necessary to avoid producing optimistic results, and corrections are often needed. For most purposes, however, the diode noise generator is an entirely reliable and stable source producing repeatable results, and when used up to about 150MHz little or no correction is needed provided that a suitable diode is employed.

The circuit of a diode valve noise generator is given in Chapter 11. This will perform in the tests required on most amateur equipment for frequencies above 20MHz, and possesses a high degree of repeatability over long periods. It should be noted that if a CV2398 diode is used in place of the A2087, then the filament supply must be increased to 6V.

For comparative tests, and when repeatability over a short period is adequate, then the simpler semiconductor noise generator given in Chapter 11 will be found quite satisfactory.

Full details of the construction and use of noise generators may be found in Chapter 18 of the RSGB *Radio Communication Handbook* and Chapter 6 of *Test Equipment for the Radio Amateur*.

At frequencies of 500MHz and above, it is usual to find that an inert gas discharge tube is employed as the noise source. Some special noise diodes however can be used up to 1,000MHz but corrections for transit time errors must be made and it is for this reason that the gas discharge tube usually takes over.

In a gas discharge tube, the positive column of gas emits electromagnetic radiation, and this can be readily coupled into either a coaxial line or waveguide circuit.

Transit time conductance and induced grid noise

Above 20MHz the induced grid noise effects predominate, imposing a shunt conductance across the input circuit of an amplifier. This shunt conductance, G_e, can be calculated as follows:

$$G_e = \frac{g_m.\ 5.\ (af)^2}{V_1.\ 10^{15}}\left(1 + \frac{3\cdot 3\ b/a}{1 + (V_a/V)^{\frac{1}{2}}}\right)\ (A/V)$$

where $V_1 = 5\cdot 69 \times 10^3 \times a^{4/3} \times J_c^{2/3}$ (V)

g_m = mutual conductance of the valve under the given operating conditions (A/V)
a is the grid cathode spacing (cm)
b is the grid anode spacing (cm)
f is the frequency (Hz)
V_a is the anode voltage (V)
J_e is the cathode current density of the valve under the given operating conditions (A/cm²)

Hence $$G_e \propto f^2$$

This relationship assumes the following:

(a) the valve geometry is planar
(b) the initial velocities of the electrons leaving the cathode surface are zero
(c) the emission is space charge limited
(d) the grid plane can be considered as equipotential
(e) the μ value is large
(f) the signal voltages on grid and anode are small
(g) the transit angles through the cathode-to-grid and grid-to-anode spaces are small

The transit time shunt conductance G_e should not be confused with the shunt conductance placed across the input terminals of an amplifier containing a valve, either in the grounded-cathode or grounded-grid connection.

In the case of the grounded cathode connection, shown in Fig 11, the interaction between the valve and the cathode lead inductance produces a conductance G_c, placed across the amplifier input, of value given by

$$G_c = g_m\ (4\pi^2 f^2)\ L_c\ C_{g\text{-}k}\ (A/V)$$

where
g_m is the mutual conductance of the valve (A/V)
f is the operating frequency (Hz)
L_c is the cathode lead inductance (H)
$C_{g\text{-}k}$ is the grid cathode capacitance (F)

Here again, $$G_c \propto f^2$$

G_c does not contribute any noise to the amplifier but it does serve to apply extra damping to the input of the amplifier, which is not usually desirable.

In the case of the grounded-grid connection, a shunt conductance term G_{in} is applied across the input, taking into account the valve, the transit time conductance G_e and the load applied to the output of the valve circuit.

$$G_{in} = G_e + \frac{g_m}{1 + 1/(r_a\ G_L)}$$

where
g_m is the valve mutual conductance
G_L is the external shunt conductance
r_a^{-1} is the valve anode conductance

To minimize the noise factor of an amplifier, the effects of the equivalent noise resistance and transit time conductance, considered as noise sources, must be made as low as possible at the operating frequency; always bearing in mind the importance of sufficient gain to eliminate the effects of second-stage noise contributions.

Noise in transistors

Noise in transistors can be broadly divided into three classes, which are similar to those affecting valves. These are:

Flicker noise
Thermal noise
Shot noise

Flicker noise occurs at low frequencies and is generally increased as the frequency is decreased. It therefore is only likely to be of concern in audio amplifiers such as microphone and speech amplifiers in transmitters, or the i.f. and audio stages of a receiver.

Thermal noise is caused by the random motion of charges within the device. This motion gives rise to electrical power which is proportional to absolute temperature and the bandwidth. The noise voltage (rms²) which appears across the device terminals is equal to

$$4kTRf_{bw}\ \text{volts}^2$$

k = Boltzmann's constant = $1\cdot 38 \times 10^{-23}$ joule/K
T = absolute temperature (K)
R = resistance (Ω)
f_{bw} = frequency bandwidth (Hz)

Note that this is very similar to the noise factor of a valve.

Shot noise occurs under conditions of current flow. The current flow may be caused by a field, as in the case in a valve, or by diffusion, as in the case of transistors. It is caused by the random nature of the arrival of the charges—if they arrived uniformly, a single frequency would be generated. The shot noise energy associated with a stream of charges (carriers)—the dc current—is proportional to the charge of an electron, the dc current flowing and the bandwidth.

The transistor itself has in effect three self-contained noise generators within the device:

Shot noise in the emitter-base junction
Thermal noise in the base resistance
Shot noise in the collector-base junction

In spite of these problems the modern transistor, and especially the field-effect type, will in general provide a lower-noise rf amplifier or receiver front-end than valves, but care must be taken to prevent accidental overload occurring. So far, no adequately fast protective device has been developed.

Noise in oscillators

Noise is often difficult to characterize due to its random and indeterminate properties. However, the noise spectrum associated with a generated rf carrier signal can be divided into three major components; low-frequency noise (1/f), thermal noise and shot noise. Each of these different types of noise has its own relationship to the main rf carrier and can be identified in the following manner:

Low-frequency noise predominates very close to the carrier, and is amplitude attenuated to very low levels at more than 250Hz away from the carrier frequency. As an example, in a fet, gate current leakage caused by surface contamination will generate lf noise.

In the region from the low-frequency noise decay point to approximately 20kHz from the carrier frequency, thermal noise predominates. It is usually associated with equivalent resistance, becoming the well-known $(4kTBR)^{\frac{1}{2}}$ with the equivalent rms noise value.

Shot noise or white noise, so called because of its typically uniform distribution, predominates beyond 20kHz and is a direct function of noise current.

In a typical oscillator which produces a near-sinusoidal waveform, other fluctations occur, producing results which appear on the carrier as amplitude modulation. However, due to the random nature of the noise, observations cannot be coherent—if the noise contribution consists of discrete sideband frequencies then fairly accurate observations could be made.

Low-frequency noise is the predominant a.m. noise component about an rf carrier, with thermal and shot noise contributing insignificant levels in their respective frequency domains.

An oscillator circuit using an fet in grounded gate as the positive feedback element can give a very good performance in terms of low-noise voltage contribution. A suitable fet for this application must possess a high forward transconductance at the operating frequency, with the gate maintained at ground potential, and its tuned circuit must have a high unloaded Q to serve as an effective filter for sideband noise energy.

Interference

As a result of increasing use of the vhf/uhf bands for transmission and reception of signals, the ability of the tuner in the receiver to pick out weak wanted signals in the presence of strong interfering signals represents a very important performance criterion.

Interference to wanted signals can be caused in the front end by the effects described below.

Spurious responses

The reception of a wanted signal can be degraded by an interfering signal, on a frequency to which the tuner or front-end is simultaneously responsive. Interfering signal frequencies which can promote spurious responses are the intermediate frequency, the image frequency and repeat spot frequency. The repeat spot or half i.f. frequency response leads to what is usually the most serious form of interference, so it is most important to ensure adequate suppression of signals on this frequency.

Intermodulation

When two or more interfering signals combine in a valve or transistor with a non-linear transfer characteristic they can interact to produce a resultant interfering signal on the wanted signal. This intermodulation can occur in either or both the rf amplifier and mixer stages, and determines the maximum tolerable level of interfering signal.

Cross-modulation

Cross-modulation can occur only when an interfering signal has amplitude variation due to transfer function non-linearities. If only pure rf signals are present there can be no transfer of modulation to the wanted signal from an interfering signal.

However, a.m. and ssb signals within and outside the amateur bands will obviously be present and cannot be ignored. FM signals can therefore acquire a.m. components because of their location on the slope of the tuner or front-end rf bandpass response, so that they can be cross-modulated by superimposed interfering amplitude modulation.

Multi-path reception can also cause cross-modulation, on account of signals received directly from a transmitter and also delayed via a reflecting object, introducing phase distortion.

Oscillator pulling

When large signal inputs are present at the input to the mixer, these will cause impedance variations, which in turn may affect the local oscillator frequency. This pulling of the oscillator in turn converts unwanted amplitude modulation to frequency modulation of the wanted signal.

The dynamic range of received signal strengths is extremely large on the amateur bands and signal levels as high as 100mV or more at antenna socket (usually 50 or 75Ω) may be anticipated. It is essential therefore that interference effects due to strong signals are catered for by good large-signal handling ability in the front end.

Repeat spot interference

When harmonics of the oscillator signal mix with harmonics of a strong antenna signal, a signal at intermediate frequency can result. In this example of repeat spot interference to a 144MHz receiver, the oscillator frequency is lf in respect to the signal frequency by an intermediate frequency of 10·7MHz. Suppose an unwanted antenna signal of 139·65MHz is present. The second harmonic of this signal is 279·3MHz. This signal harmonic will mix with the second harmonic of the oscillator signal 268·6MHz (the fundamental frequency being 134·3MHz) to give 10·7MHz. The 134·3MHz oscillator signal corresponds to an antenna signal of 145MHz, thus when the receiver is tuned to 145MHz the signal at 139·65MHz will also be received. It will be realized that the difference frequency is 5·53MHz, or half i.f., from which the more familiar term *half i.f. interference* is derived.

Front-end selectivity

It is important to provide sufficient selectivity in the rf amplifier and mixer stages to ensure freedom from image interference.

When using a high i.f. such as 10·7MHz this is usually no great problem, although it is as well to bear in mind the relative activity on frequencies twice the i.f. below (with the oscillator on the low side) or above (when the oscillator is above the wanted signal frequency).

For example, with a 144MHz receiver near an airport and with the local oscillator on the low side (133·3 to 135·3), air traffic control signals in the range 123·6 to 125·6MHz can be received. If the oscillator is placed on the high side (154·7 to 156·7MHz), however, then it would be free from this particular interference.

A similar problem arises when a simple converter with its oscillator at 120MHz and an output i.f. of 24 to 26MHz is used, because the image interference that can then arise is 50MHz lower—this band is occupied by local broadcast (fm) stations.

As mentioned earlier, the use of single conversion is to be preferred because there is then a much more likely chance of being able to identify the source of image interference, so enabling it to be resolved.

The use of a simple filter can be useful in reinforcing the front-end selectivity of an otherwise-satisfactory receiver. Of course, if a suitable bandpass filter is to be used in the transmitter output as recommended, this can be used in the common feeder to antenna and satisfy both needs.

In a new design three tuned circuits at signal frequency will provide a useful degree of spurious signal suppression. A bandpass-coupled pair correctly matched into the source impedance of the rf amplifier and the load impedance of the mixer, and a single tuned circuit matched into the source impedance preceding the rf stage is recommended. For example, up to 60dB of image suppression can be obtained with loaded Q's of

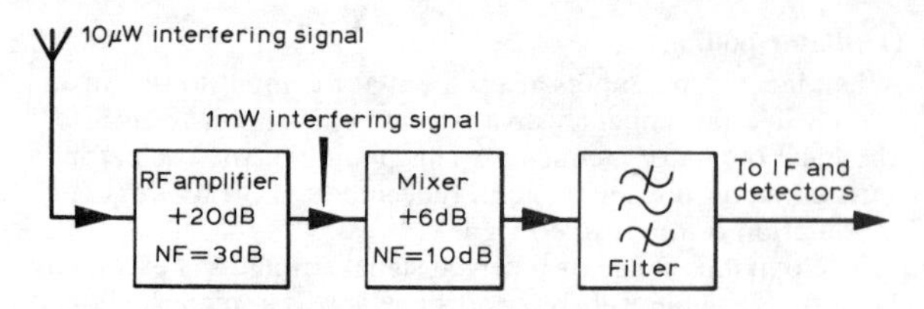

Fig 4. Typical receiver front-end

100 for each inductance and coupling factor of 1 in the bandpass-coupled pair.

Optimizing receiver signal handling

The ability of a receiver to reject unwanted signals is a function of both the selectivity and the linearity of the early stages. The linearity of an amplifier or mixer is always best at low signal levels and so to design a receiver with the highest cross- and intermodulation performance it is important to keep the rf gain to a minimum. This conflicts with the normal requirements of high front-end gain to achieve the best sensitivity.

The answer to the problem is to look at gain distribution in the receiver and optimize it for both high sensitivity and good signal handling. Fig 4 shows the gain and noise figures of the front-end stages of a typical vhf receiver. With an rf gain of 20dB the overall noise figure is 3·2dB and the interfering signal will be at a level of 1mW at the mixer, a very strong signal. If however the rf gain is reduced to 10dB the noise figure is now 4·7dB (1·5dB higher) but the interfering signal at the mixer has dropped by 10dB to 100μW.

This means that for a 1·5dB reduction in sensitivity the receiver can handle signals 10dB (10 times) stronger. The noise figure for two stages such as an rf amplifier and mixer is given by the following formula:

$$\text{Overall noise figure} = F_{rf} + \frac{(F_{mix} - 1)}{G_{rf}}$$

where F_{rf} is rf amplifier noise figure, F_{mix} is the mixer noise figure and G_{rf} is rf amplifier gain. Note that the figures are power ratios not decibels.

If the rf amplifier gain is plotted against the receiver noise figure as shown in Fig 5 it can be seen that there is no advantage in using an rf amplifier gain of greater than about 12dB; above this value little improvement in noise figure is obtained but the signal handling will be degraded.

Preamplifiers are often used in front of commercial equipment to improve their sensitivity, but these will always give rise

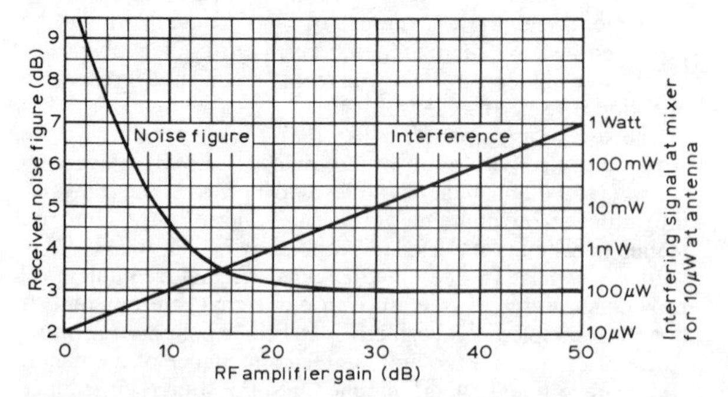

Fig 5. Noise figure and interfering signal levels for various values of rf gain

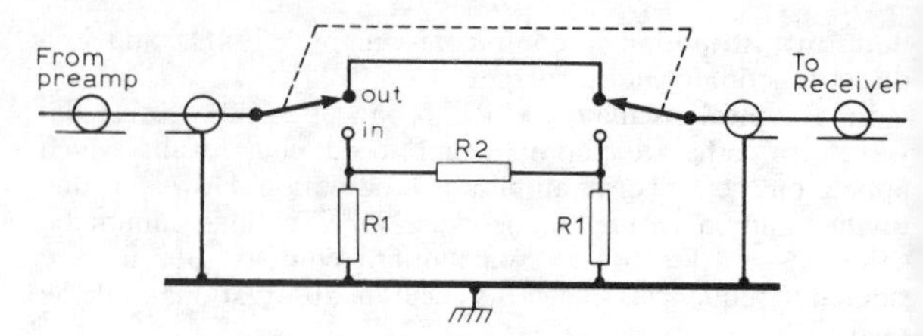

Attenuation dB	50Ω R1 Ω	50Ω R2 Ω	75Ω R1 Ω	75Ω R2 Ω
3	293	17	440	26
6	150	37	225	56
10	96	71	144	106
20	61	247	92	371

Fig 6. Fixed attenuators

to more cross-modulation etc, and it is therefore good practice to arrange for such preamplifiers to be switched in and out of circuit as required.

This is not always easy to achieve, but similar results can be obtained by fitting a switched fixed attenuator between the preamplifier and the receiver. A suitable circuit is shown in Fig 6. The switch should be a double-pole double-throw type and the resistors 0·25W or 0·125W types.

The main considerations in the design of a receiver for best signal handling are listed below:

1. Put main-channel selectivity as close as possible to antenna. This often means using single-conversion receivers with a crystal filter directly after the mixer.
2. Operate rf amplifiers at lowest gain to achieve required sensitivity.
3. Run rf amplifiers and mixer at highest dc power level to achieve best linearity.
4. Ensure that noise sidebands and plateau on the local oscillator are as low as possible to avoid reciprocal mixing effects. See section on frequency synthesizers.
5. Avoid the use of switching diodes, electronic attenuators etc in signal paths as these can cause cross-modulation.

PIN diode attenuators

The pin diode has one important characteristic—its ability to act as a current-controlled resistor at radio frequencies. Although most diodes possess this characteristic, poor linearity and distortion can be introduced into the rf circuit in which the diode is connected by rectification.

The pin diode has an optimized design to achieve not only low distortion with good linearity, but a wide range of resistance. A typical characteristic curve for a pin diode is shown in Fig 7.

For a change of current from 1μA to 100mA the diode resistance will change from over 10,000Ω to about 1Ω. If the diode is connected to an agc drive system then it will act as a resistive attenuator.

The pin diode differs from a standard diode due to an added intrinsic region (i layer) sandwiched between the p+ and n+ layers. The control of minority carriers in this i layer is enhanced and the large width of the layer results in high breakdown voltage and low capacitance.

The conductivity of the i layer is increased by the injection of

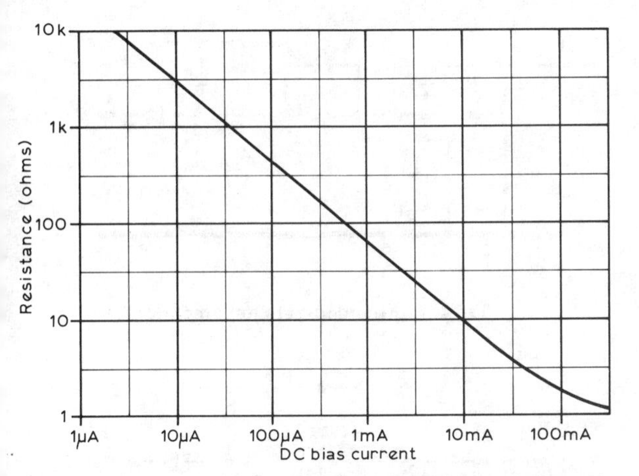

Fig 7. Typical resistance v bias current characteristic for a pin diode

minority carriers when forward bias is applied with the p+ and n+ layers.

The pin diode acts as a pure resistance above a limiting frequency and this resistance at rf is controlled by variation of the forward bias. Below the limiting frequency rectification will occur as in a standard pn junction and in the vicinity of this frequency there is some rectification with resultant distortion.

A number of factors control this distortion, namely bias current, rf power, and the minority carrier lifetime, as well as the limiting frequency. Modern pin diodes designed for low radio frequencies have a lifetime in excess of 1μs, thus finding applications below 10MHz.

A basic three-diode attenuator is shown in Fig 8 with a practical pin diode attenuator driven from an agc source shown in Fig 9.

A graph showing attenuation versus agc drive voltage is shown in Fig 10. With the agc voltage at 0 there is minimum attenuation, but as the agc voltage increases, attenuation

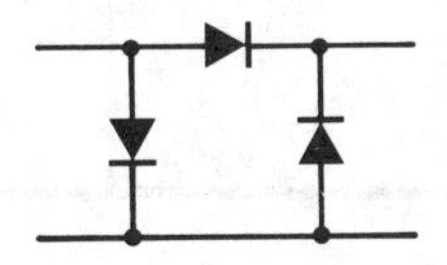

Fig 8. Basic three-diode attenuator

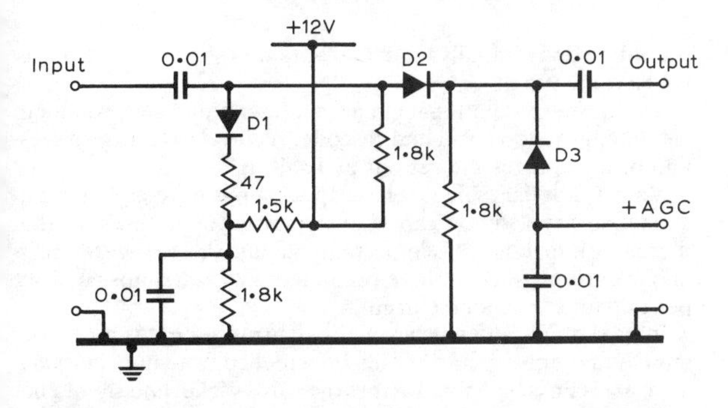

Fig 9. PIN diode attenuator circuit. Suitable diodes are 5082/3080/81 (HP); MPN3411/12 (Motorola); BA379 (Siemens)

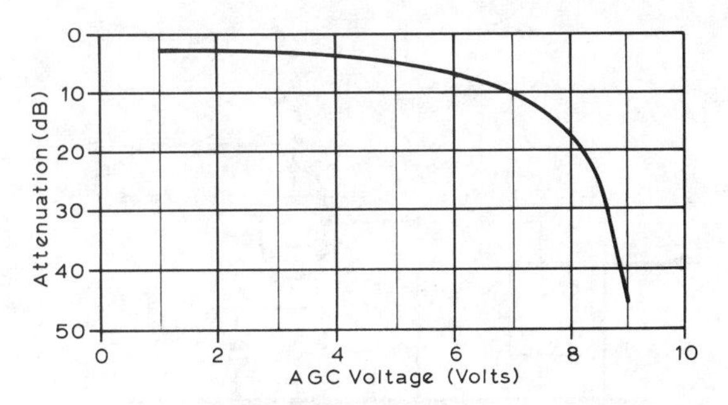

Fig 10. Typical attenuation v agc voltage characteristic for a pin diode

increases to 40dB at 8·75V agc. Power consumption of the pin diode attenuator is 35mW, well within the range of transistorized agc voltage amplifiers. The agc source should preferably have a diode rectifier connected to the i.f. transformer secondary in the front end.

The configuration ensures constant impedance attenuation, so the attenuator can therefore be connected between the antenna socket and the input coil of a front end or converter with minimum degradation of signal-to-noise ratio.

The graph of attenuation versus agc voltage in Fig 10 was taken from results obtained over a range of frequencies from 50 to 200MHz. These results indicate that the attenuator performance is independent of frequencies over a large spectrum. Care is necessary to screen the output from the input at higher frequencies as circuit capacitance and layout can achieve a bypass effect with consequent deterioration of the attenuator performance.

The rf amplifier

Basic forms

Figs 11 to 16 show the connections of valve triode, field effect transistor and bipolar transistor in both grounded (common) grid and grounded (common) cathode configurations and their equivalents. The bias resistor R is bypassed by a capacitor C in order to effectively ground the relevant electrode or to ensure that there is a maximum transfer of rf energy to the appropriate electrode.

In choosing the value of the bypass capacitor it should be borne in mind that most capacitors have an inherent inductance, which together with connecting leads can produce a resonant circuit. A 100pF capacitor with 0·25in leads will be more effective at 144MHz than a 0·01μF one. Reference to Chapter 5 should be made.

Valves suitable for rf amplifiers

As indicated from the discussion on the causes of noise, one of the factors, that due to partition, means the triode is the only suitable type. Pentodes are too noisy for low-noise amplifiers, except possibly on 70MHz where they may be acceptable, but even at this frequency the triode will show some benefit. At 144MHz and above the triode is essential.

The signal-to-noise ratio is the most important factor for any receiving equipment and it is most desirable that the noise factor is measured. Equipment to do this is quite simple, and either a saturated thermionic diode, from which the noise output can be calculated, or a noise source using a semiconductor diode, which can be used for comparative tests, should become

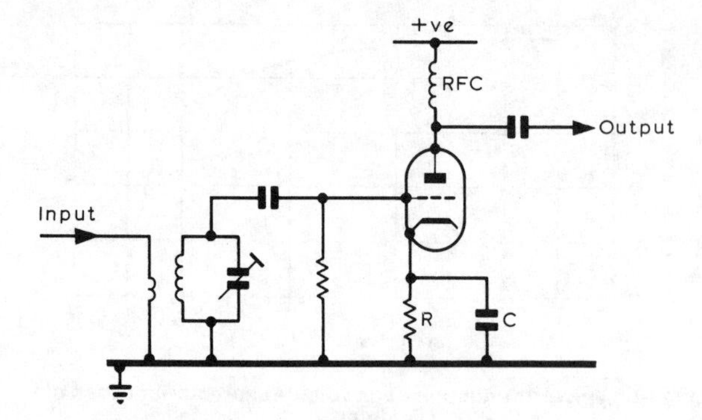

Fig 11. A grounded-cathode valve amplifier

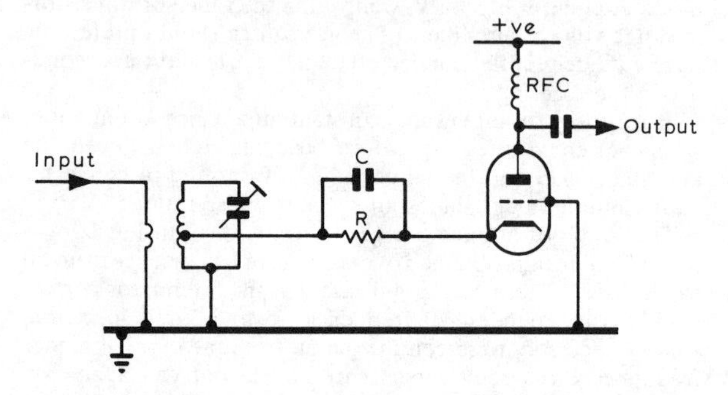

Fig 12. A grounded-grid valve amplifier

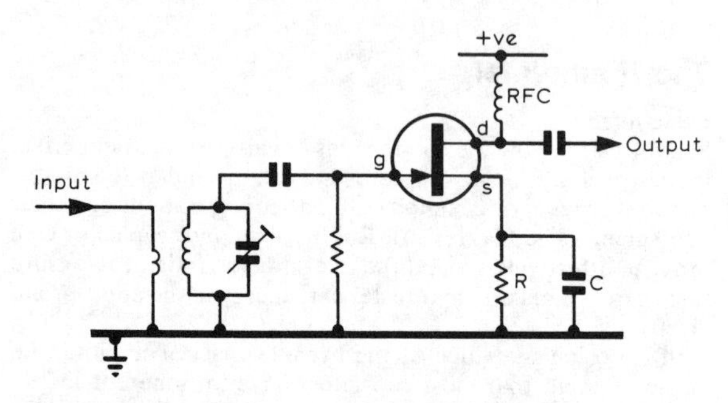

Fig 13. A grounded-source jfet rf amplifier

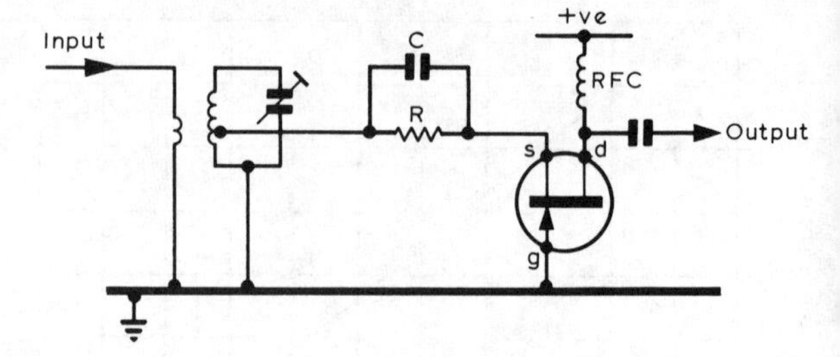

Fig 14. A grounded-gate jfet amplifier

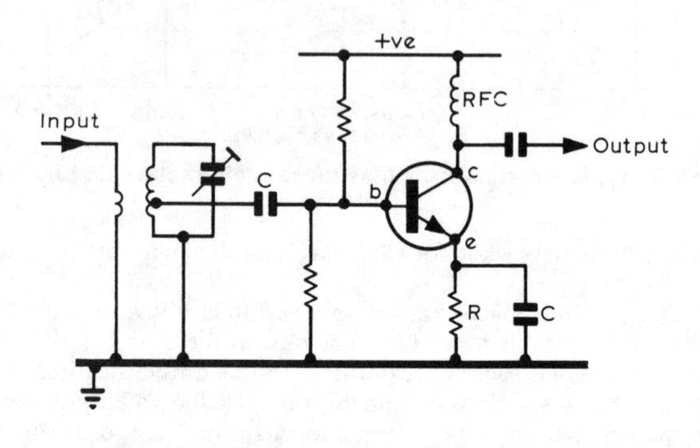

Fig 15. A grounded-emitter rf amplifier

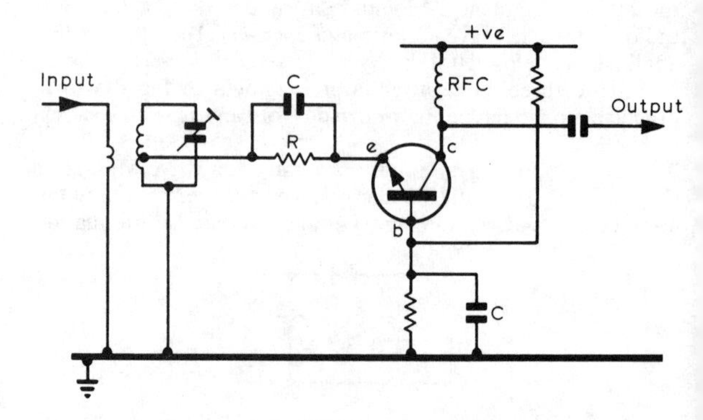

Fig 16. A grounded-base rf amplifier

part of the serious amateur's test equipment. Details of a suitable noise generator are given in Chapter 11. Apart from actual measurements, if an increase in noise can be detected when the antenna is connected the converter has an acceptable noise factor.

Although the noise performance of an rf amplifier is very largely controlled by the valve employed, the circuit itself should be as good as it can be made.

The tuned circuit should have as high *Q* as possible and both the antenna and the amplifier correctly matched, so that as much energy as possible is transferred from the antenna to the amplifier itself.

As will be found from noise generator tests, the best noise factor will not coincide with the maximum signal gain, but preliminary tuning of the circuit for maximum signal output should be done initially, and then varied as shown by the noise measurements.

The three conventional circuit configurations are grounded cathode, grounded grid and cascode; their relative advantages and disadvantages are set out in Table 1.

Valves most suitable for these applications have high mutual conductance and as low capacitance as possible. In assessing the mutual conductance it is important to relate this to the standing anode current and it is therefore in terms of milliamps per volt per milliamp of anode current.

In an rf amplifier, whichever circuit arrangement is used, the input and output circuits should be screened from one another. Such a screen is best fitted across the valve socket and should be a reasonably close fit to the profile of the socket. Careful positioning will provide the maximum isolation between

Table 1. Relative merits of the three principal valve configurations used in rf amplifiers

Circuit	Advantage	Disadvantage	Application
Grounded cathode	High power gain; low input conductance	Requires neutralizing	Narrow-band amplifiers up to 300MHz
Grounded grid	Wideband characteristic; very stable; low input conductance	Low power gain	Wideband amplifiers above 150MHz
Cascode	Stable high power gain; low input and output conductance	Requires two stages, one of which requires neutralizing	Narrow-band amplifiers up to about 300/400MHz

circuits without interfering with the wiring to the socket connections.

As mentioned earlier, triodes operating with grounded cathode need to be neutralized to prevent self-oscillation due to the relatively high anode-to-grid feedback capacitance. There are two normal methods by which this can be achieved.

Inductance neutralizing (Fig 17(a))
Capacitance bridge (Fig 17(b))

The latter is generally rather simpler to arrange and adjust. In the circuit of Fig 17(b) the anode tuning capacitor TC should have an operating value as near as possible to the capacitance between the valve's anode and all other electrodes. In cases where the anode circuit is parallel tuned it may be necessary to introduce a balancing capacitor, in addition to the tuning capacitor.

Valves for grounded-cathode operation at vhf and uhf are normally fitted with a number of cathode leads, in order to lessen the series inductance of the cathode connection. Grounded-grid rf amplifiers have a distinct advantage in obtaining stability without neutralizing, due to the much reduced capacitance between the anode and cathode when the grid is operating as an earthed screen. Input and output circuit isolation is of course necessary as for neutralized amplifiers.

Valves intended primarily for use under these conditions are either fitted with a number of leads to the grid, or are of the disc seal type of construction, thus enabling a very low inductance connection to the grid. There is, however, some difficulty in matching the input to the low impedance of the valve, which is generally in the region of about 100Ω. As indicated in Fig 17(c) the valve may be tapped down the input tuning circuit which will often give a worthwhile improvement in performance. In simple amplifiers the antenna coaxial feeder may be connected directly to the valve as far as rf is concerned, ie through a suitable isolating capacitor to enable cathode current bias to be applied to the valve.

In Fig 19 an example of the amplifier given in Fig 17(a) is shown using a field-effect transistor in place of the valve. The higher input impedance of this type of semiconductor enables it to be substituted for the valve without a great deal of re-designing of the tuned circuit.

In Figs 17(d) and 17(e) are shown typical cascode amplifiers. In this amplifier arrangement the first stage operates as an impedance matching device feeding into a grounded-grid following amplifier. The first stage must be neutralized, usually as shown, by the inductive method, although capacitative arrangements have been used in some designs.

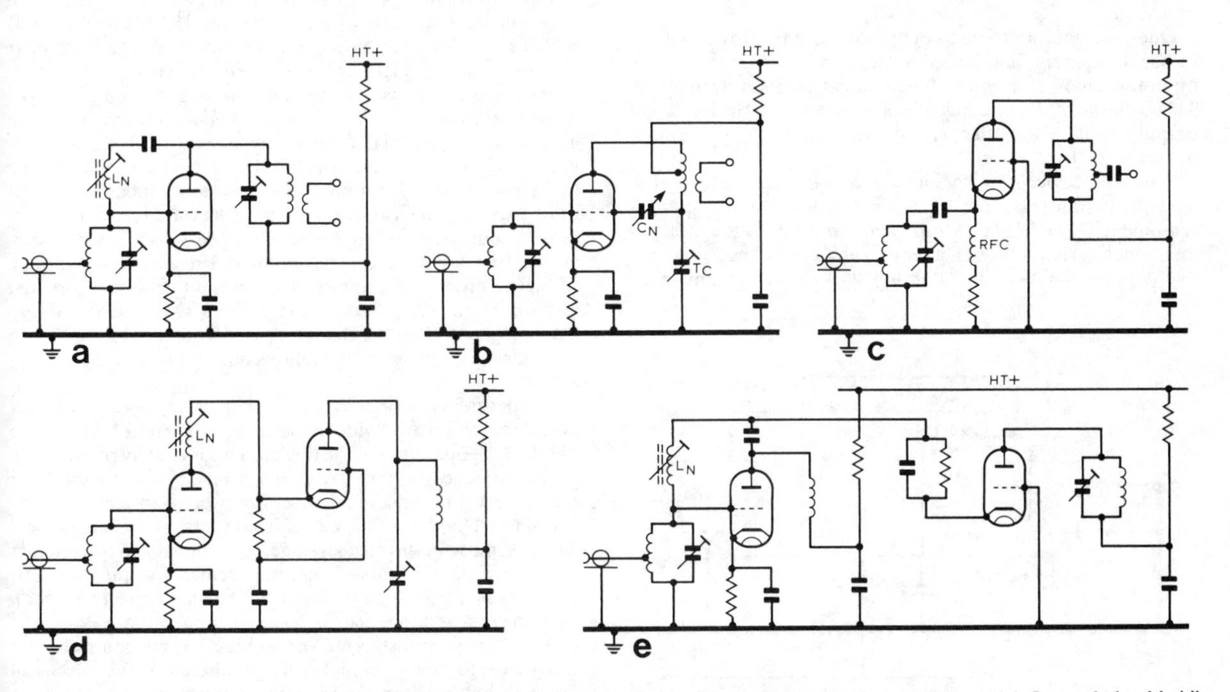

Fig 17. Five types of valve rf amplifiers. (a) Inductively neutralized. (b) Capacitance bridge neutralized. (c) Grounded grid. (d) Simplified or series cascode. (e) Shunt cascode

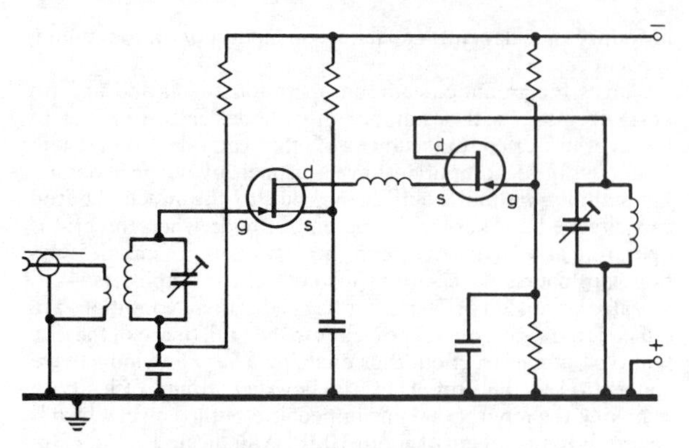

Fig 18. A fet cascode amplifier

Transistors for rf amplifiers

Transistors of high performance and low noise with satisfactory stage gain are freely available and suitable for most receiver preamplifiers or converters. Equally they are suitable for the local oscillator and multiplier use.

Generally, however, unlike valves, few types are entirely interchangeable and the list of available suitable types is very extensive. The typical practical designs given later quote the particular type used but equivalent performance types may, of course, be substituted.

Designs are also given for field-effect transistors. These types have significant advantages over the bipolar types especially in so far as they, like valves, are voltage-operated devices and are of substantially similar input impedance. The bipolar transistor by comparison is essentially a current-operated device of low impedance.

One of the major problems of the bipolar transistor is that it is rather transparent, ie will accept and amplify unwanted signals often far removed from the tuned circuit resonant frequency. This is due largely to the lack of isolation between the input and output circuits. Field-effect types show a marked improvement in this respect.

When the device is of low impedance it is essential to tap the feed points down on the tuned circuit in order to obtain a reasonable Q, and hence a sufficiently narrow bandwidth. As mentioned earlier fets are higher impedance devices and so can be operated in almost the same way as a valve. In many cases typical valve type components are quite suitable for use with these devices.

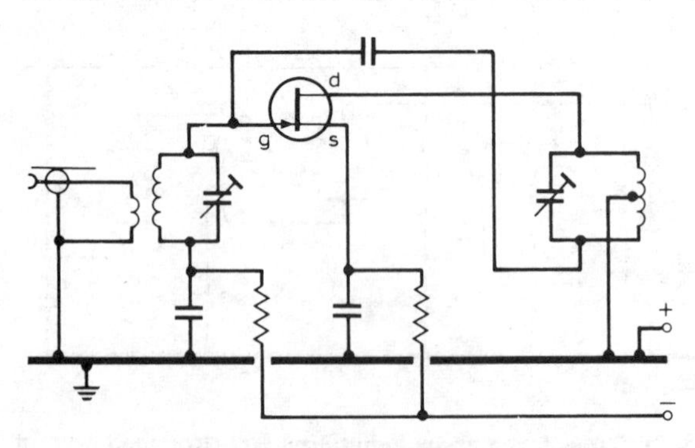

Fig 19. Showing a fet neutralized amplifier

Noise figures for semiconductors are significantly lower than those available from valves, but generally they are easily damaged by the overloads which valves would withstand without trouble. It is important, therefore, to ensure that there is adequate protection against overload, particularly where there is any chance of poor isolation in a transmit-receive relay.

Masthead preamplifiers, provided suitable overload protection is provided, enable superior receiver performance to be obtained and sufficient gain is readily available to more than overcome the noise contributed by the feeder cable. The preamplifier should be powered from a low-voltage dc supply originating in the shack; a built-in battery supply is impractical.

Design principles

Important criteria in the design of an rf amplifier may be listed as follows:

stage gain, more importantly stability limited gain
noise factor and/or signal + noise/noise ratio
large signal handling capability

These criteria hold whether the amplifier is designed around valves or semiconductors.

Nuvistors are an example of an excellent valve type for rf amplifier applications, eg 6CW4 triode (neutralized). Power requirements are very modest and the valve itself is physically small. It can provide 20dB of gain, not including the insertion loss of the tuned circuits.

Bipolar and field effect transistors are readily available for rf amplifiers. The BF324 is a pnp hf device intended for grounded base operation. Excellent large signal handling and optimum noise performance is derived from a high emitter current of 5mA and large value of source resistance. BF479 (SGS, ATES) is also a pnp device for grounded base operation, giving similar performance to the BF324 but at an emitter current of 10mA.

Field effect transistors as rf amplifiers give similar performance to bipolar types in terms of noise performance and stage gain, and are particularly good in respect of large signal handling ability. A very linear transfer-characteristic is inherent due to their square-law function. High-order components above the third order are much less evident in the forward transfer characteristic compared with the bipolar device which has an exponential transfer characteristic and therefore a larger magnitude of higher-order components in the output. Suitable junction fets for rf amplifier service are BF256 (Motorola), BF245 (Mullard) and TIS88 (Texas). Any of these types will give superior performance to the ubiquitous 2N3819 or its equivalents.

It is necessary, however, due to characteristic variations between samples, to provide some form of current feedback to stabilize the operation of the device. This is usually provided by a suitable value of external source resistance giving much closer tolerance values of source current between samples.

Insulated-gate mosfets, oxide silicon fets, and igfets possess the same noise performance, stage gain, transfer characteristics and source current stabilization requirements as junction fets, but possess a very high dc input impedance (gate to source). Gate current is limited to leakage current, usually less than 1nA. Older-type mosfets are very subject to gate-source breakdown due to static or high-voltage discharge (eg electrical storms), but modern types have gate-to-source protection diodes (back-to-back zeners diffused on to the substrate) to prevent breakdown. Experience shows that protected-gate mosfets are more difficult to destroy than bipolar transistors.

Two single-gate fets should be used in cascode configurations to realize high stable gain (grounded source/grounded gate operation). Alternatively, one dual-gate (tetrode) mosfet can be used to realize the same performance. Suitable types are 40673, MPF 121/131, 3N204, 3SK88, BF900 etc. Suitable circuits for this type of transistor are given later.

Local oscillators

The design of the local oscillator is influenced by two major considerations, output level and frequency stability. Both bipolar and field-effect transistors are suitable and have lower noise and greater stability than the valve, due to lower operating temperature.

Class A oscillators are preferred because of the lower levels of generated harmonics. Typical oscillator circuits are shown on p 4.13. While operation of the oscillator on the fundamental required frequency is possible, it is often necessary to use half or third the frequency in the interest of frequency stability and follow it with a frequency doubler or tripler.

Valve mixers (6CW4, ECC88, etc) require a higher oscillator drive voltage, say 2–3V rms. All types of mixer should have a high dynamic load impedance (i.f. transformer primary, high LC ratio). The mixer stage produces the highest noise in the receiver and it is therefore most important that mixer(s) chosen should be those that contribute the minimum noise.

In both receiver (or converter) and transmitter the performance of the local oscillator is of considerable importance. Its stability is of prime importance because it will almost invariably be used with several stages of multiplication to reach the working frequency.

Fixed crystal oscillators are often used for fm operation in the vhf and uhf region, but for cw and ssb there has been a significant change towards some form of variable or tunable oscillator. Band planning has to a large extent been successful and there is not the same need to operate on a common frequency as there is on ssb or hf bands.

SSB operation is normal on these higher-frequency bands and common-frequency working is being practised. Often the equipment is based on hf band apparatus with some form of transverter.

Before deciding the form of oscillator to be used, it is as well to consider the advantages and disadvantages of the fixed oscillator compared with a variable or tunable unit (Table 2).

Crystals

Crystals for frequency control are cut at varying angles from the mother crystal, the actual cut used depending on the frequency at which it is required to operate. For vhf and uhf the normal cuts are AT or BT. For these applications, frequencies in the range of 6 to over 100MHz are usual; above 20MHz the crystals are the overtone type where the frequency is a third, fifth or seventh overtone (harmonic) of the fundamental.

The actual frequency produced by a crystal oscillator is substantially that of the crystal, but it must be remembered that other circuit components can slightly modify the frequency produced. Where a precise frequency is required, provision for some small adjustment must be made. Because temperature changes will affect the frequency, care must also be taken to maintain a stable temperature.

Table 2. Advantages and disadvantages of various types of oscillator

Advantages	Disadvantages
CRYSTAL-CONTROLLED OSCILLATOR	
Absence of controls other than selector switch.	Frequency choice must be such as to avoid spurious signals in the passband.
Clean note and freedom from modulation.	There are likely to be more stages needed to reach the final frequency.
Negligible short term or warm-up drift.	Inability to move frequency when interference from another station is present.
Reliable frequency location in the band.	
VARIABLE CRYSTAL OSCILLATOR (VXO)	
Variable but limited tuning range.	More complex and requires more space and a mechanically good dial for resetting accuracy.
Clean note if tuning range not too great.	Similar number of multiplier stages needed to reach final frequency.
Short term and warm-up drift can be maintained.	
Reliable frequency location in the band.	
VARIABLE FREQUENCY OSCILLATOR (VFO)	
Direct frequency calibration possible.	Stability, often difficult to restrict long term drift to low value.
Free choice of frequency tuning range to suit requirements.	Sensitive to ambient temperature and ventilation conditions.
When high frequency used fewer frequency multiplier stages needed to reach final frequency.	Care needed to ensure clean note free from unwanted modulation.
	Valve or transistor change necessitates recalibration.

Types of crystal oscillator

There are very many suitable circuits for crystal oscillators but those especially suitable for generating harmonics are normally required for the local oscillator in a converter or control of a vhf or uhf transmitter. Crystals in the range 6 to 12MHz are usually used with output frequencies from the multipliers to suit the band in use. In general, all the popular circuits give a substantial output, from a single transistor or valve, of third or fifth harmonic.

The three classic crystal oscillators are the Miller, Colpitts and Pierce, of which the last two are now much more widely used. All these oscillators use the crystal in its parallel mode. A digest of the wide variety of oscillators appears in Chapter 4 of *Amateur Radio Techniques*.

Squier oscillator

This circuit is suitable for use with crystals of the fundamental type, and feedback between the grid and anode by means of direct inductive coupling. The amount of coupling is determined by the position of the ht feed point on the inductor—the feedback increases as the tap is moved away from the grid end.

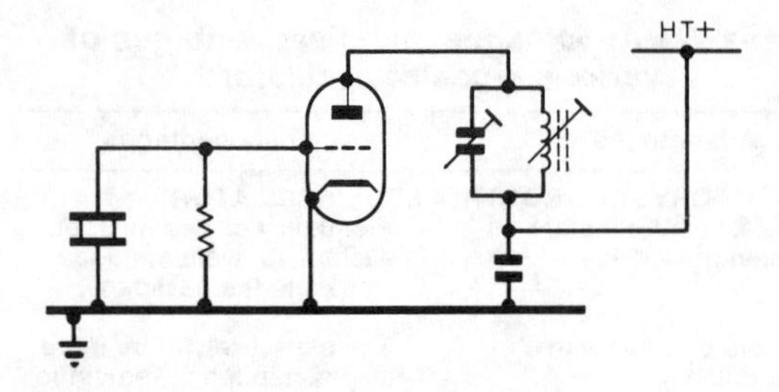

Fig 20. Miller oscillator. Typical frequency stability of about 25ppm can be obtained, with a relatively high output, although the need for a tuned circuit is a disadvantage. Suitable for use with crystals up to 20MHz

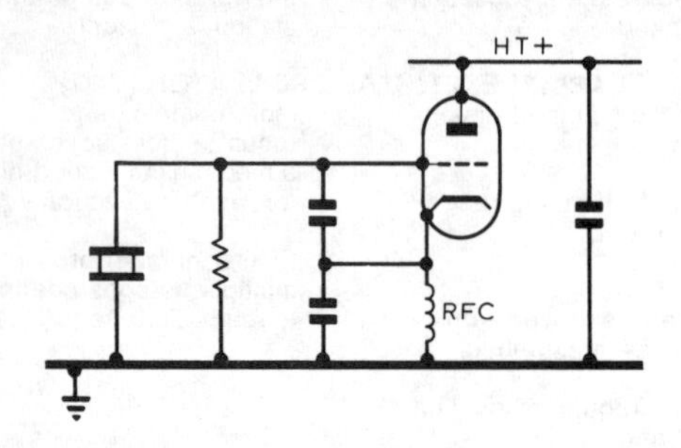

Fig 21. Colpitts oscillator. Although the output of this oscillator is lower than with the Miller circuits, the frequency stability is better, generally about 10ppm

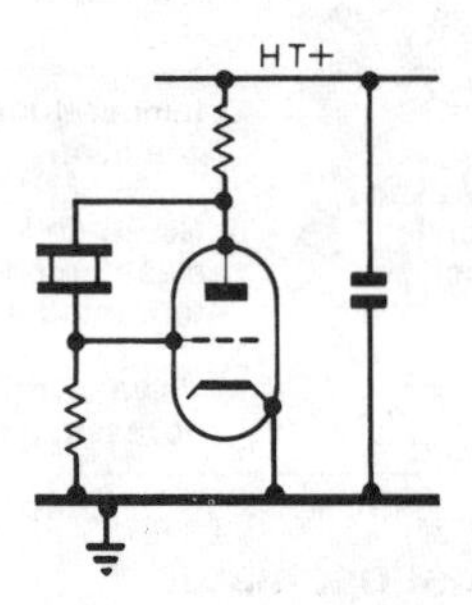

Fig 22. Pierce oscillator. No tuning is needed in the fundamental form, and it is suitable for crystals up to 20MHz. Switching crystals presents no particular problem

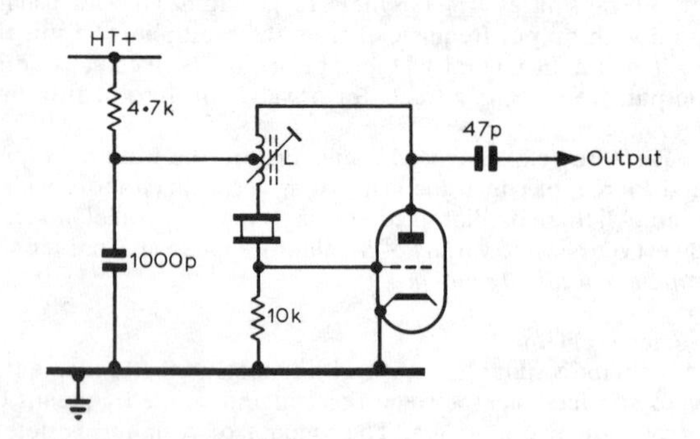

Fig 23. Squier oscillator. Some care is needed in the adjustment of this circuit

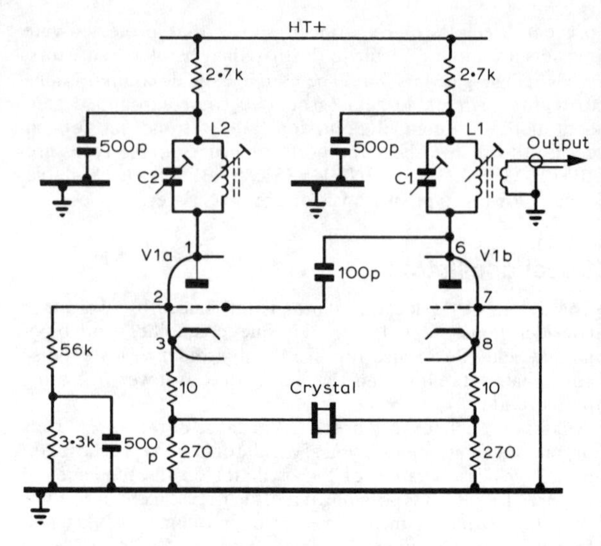

Fig 24. Butler oscillator for use with overtone crystals

When overtone crystals are used the amount of feedback needed is smaller than with fundamental types. The inductor L is tuned to the overtone frequency (harmonic) required. Care must be exercised to ensure that there is not too much feedback, otherwise the crystal will lose control. In addition the output frequency may not be an exact harmonic of the crystal frequency.

Butler oscillator (modified)

This circuit, suitable for use with overtone crystals, consists of a grounded grid amplifier (V1a) and a cathode follower (V1b). The anode circuit of the amplifier is tuned to the required harmonic frequency which is usually second or third, as outputs at higher orders are generally too small for transmitter use. If output only at the overtone frequency is required, this may be obtained by inductive coupling to L1, and the anode of the cathode follower should be earthed to rf and the tuned circuit L2 C2 omitted.

The resistors used in the two cathode circuits should be matched. Increasing the value will increase the output, but the stability will deteriorate, if this is taken too far, while reducing the value will reduce the output until oscillation ceases. A compromise value such as that shown in Fig 24 should be used.

Transistor oscillators

A number of transistor fundamental and overtone circuits are shown in Figs 25 to 33. In all these circuits npn transistors are used but pnp-type devices could be used where a negative supply rail is provided.

To a certain extent the frequency of all these oscillators will be influenced by their supply voltage. It is however a simple matter to regulate the supply voltage by means of an ic regulator or by means of a zener diode. A normal rule-of-thumb for design of a simple shunt zener diode regulator is to ensure that the zener diode passes the same quantity of current as the oscillator itself. A suitable design is shown in Fig 34.

If a 6·8V zener diode is chosen, the supply will have an approximately zero temperature coefficient.

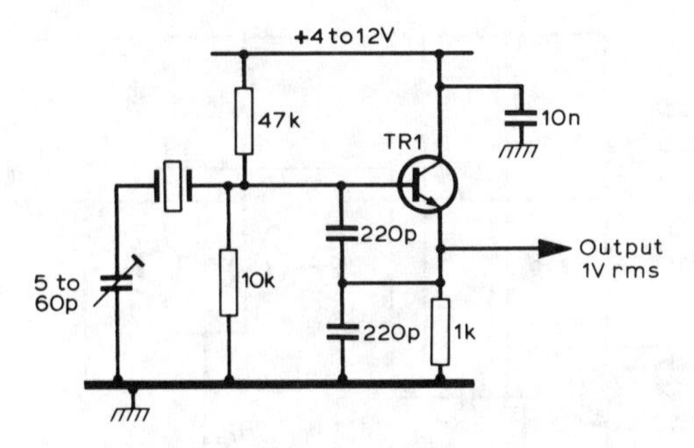

Fig 25. Parallel-mode Colpitts oscillator for 1–15MHz. TR1 is npn planar, eg BC108, 2N2926, BF180, BC547 etc

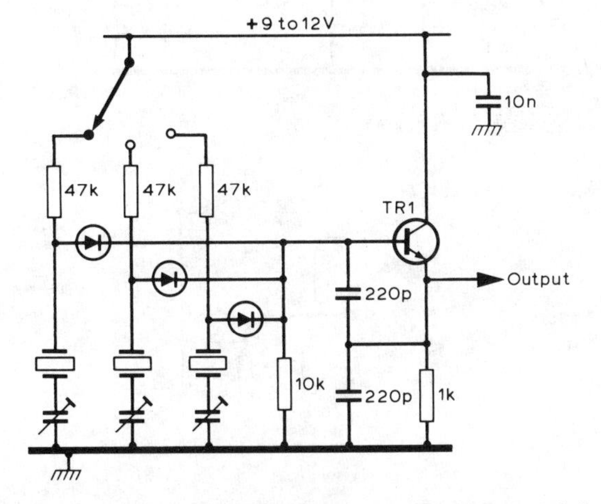

Fig 26. Modification of Fig 25 to give dc switching of crystals by means of diodes

Variable frequency crystal controlled oscillators

In recent years circuits which enable a crystal to be pulled from its fundamental frequency have been actively developed and several reliable circuits are now extensively used, either with a single crystal or with a bank of switched crystals to cover the whole band.

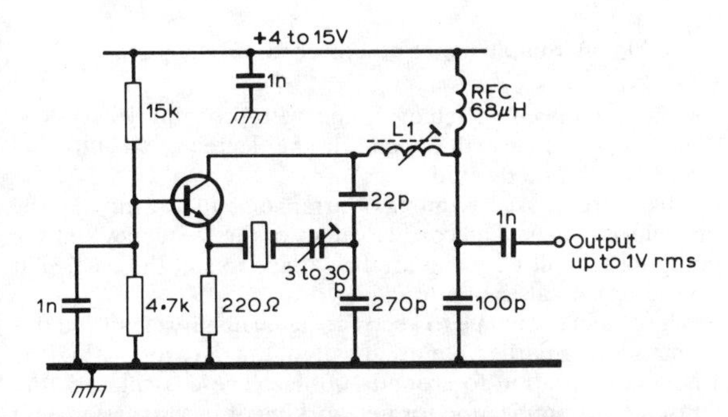

Fig 27. Third-overtone oscillator for 15–65MHz. L1 resonates with 22pF at the crystal frequency (1μH at 15–30MHz, 0·5μH 30–65MHz). Transistor is vhf npn silicon planar, eg BSX20, 2N918, BF180 etc

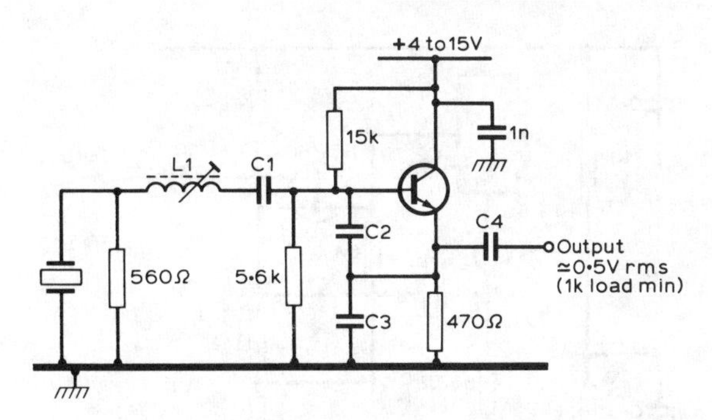

Fig 28. "Impedance inverting" circuit for third-overtone crystals. Transistor as per Fig 27. Component values are given in Table 3

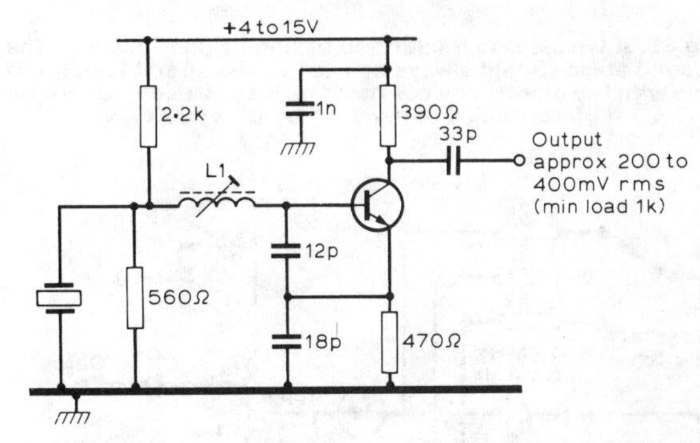

Fig 29. "Impedance inverting" circuit for fifth- and seventh-overtone crystals. Transistor as per Fig 27. L1 is 7t (60–85MHz) or 4t (80–120MHz) spaced 6mm long on 5mm former

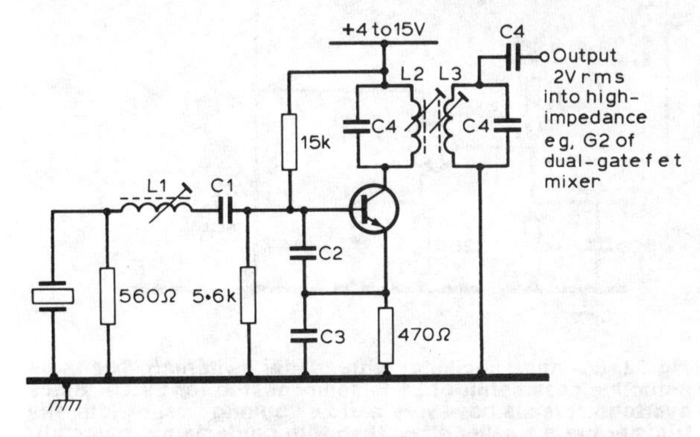

Fig 30. Overtone-multiplier, applicable to vhf converters. For component values see Table 3. L2, L3 are spaced approximately 5mm apart and are 9t (60–90MHz) or 6t (90–130MHz) 0·6mm closewound on 5mm former

Table 3. Component details for Figs 28 and 30

Crystal freq (MHz)	C1 (pF)	C2 (pF)	C3 (pF)	C4 (pF)	L1 (5mm diam former with slug 0·3mm wire close wound)
15–25	100	100	68	33	15t
25–55	100	68	47	33	10t
50–65	68	33	15	22	7t

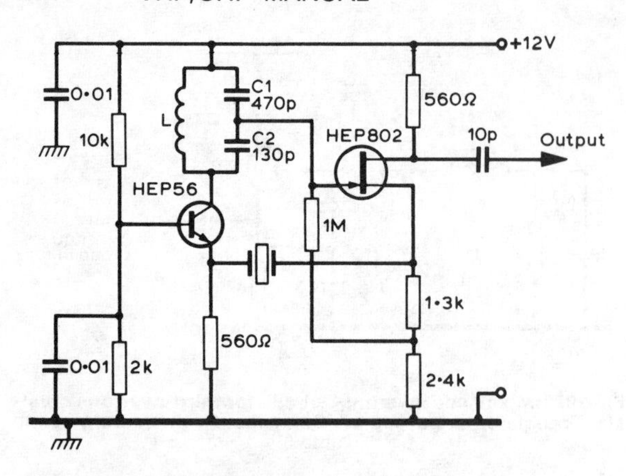

Fig 31. A typical Butler overtone oscillator (20–100MHz). The second stage should always be a fet, as the circuit is not reliable with two bipolar devices (two fets may be used). Overtone frequencies determined by LC values

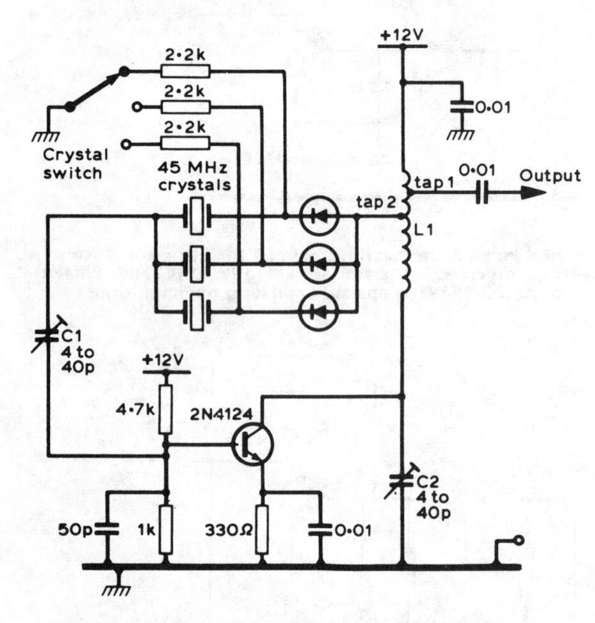

Fig 32. Overtone oscillator with crystal switching. The large inductive phase shift of L1 is compensated for by C1. Since overtone crystals have very narrow "pulling" bandwidth, the trimmer has a smaller effect than with fundamental-mode operation. L1 is 16t 24swg $\frac{3}{16}$in diam $\frac{3}{8}$in long. Tap 1 2t up, tap 2 4t up

In most vhf or uhf bands, the crystal used is usually of relatively low frequency such as 6 to 12MHz, so a fairly high degree of frequency multiplication is needed to reach the operating frequency.

Typical frequency shifts of up to 200–300kHz at 144MHz are common, but better stability will result if the range is limited to about 100kHz. Larger or smaller frequency shifts will become available on higher or lower final frequencies.

If, for example, it is desired to cover the whole of the 144MHz band, 144 to 146MHz, then a simple switched bank of crystals together with a frequency shifting circuit will provide a

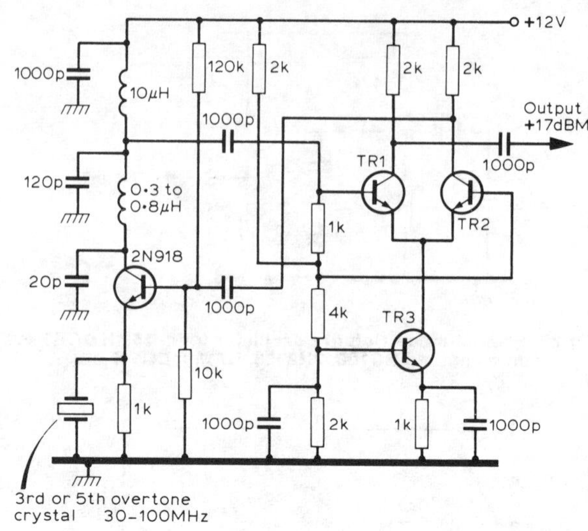

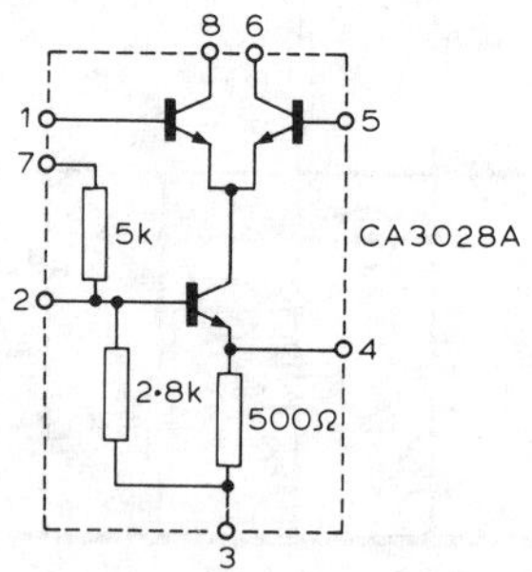

Fig 33. Ultra-low-noise crystal oscillator and buffer for 30–100MHz crystals. TR1–3 may be replaced with a CA3028A ic with suitable component value changes

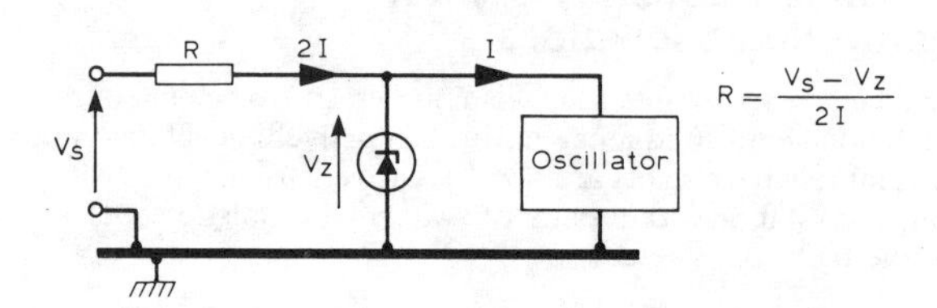

Fig 34. Simple zener stabilizer for an oscillator

satisfactory means of achieving this with probably 10 crystals. The actual number will depend on the degree of stability and clearness of note desired.

There are a large number of arrangements for moving the crystal frequency. The correct values of the frequency shifting components will vary and are best made to suit the particular crystal or crystals being used.

The object should be to keep the signal quality clean and this as mentioned earlier almost inevitably means restricting the frequency variation to around 100kHz. These oscillators find considerable application for net working or in association with ssb transmitters.

Where wider frequency ranges are required a normal variable frequency oscillator should be used.

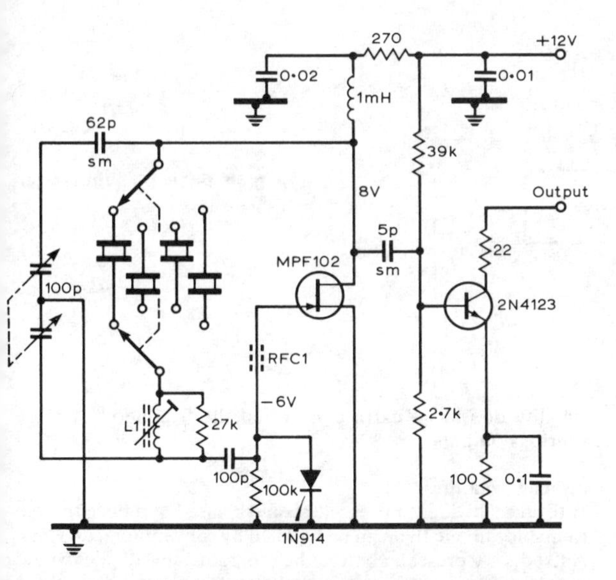

Fig 35. A fet oscillator forming the heart of a vxo for 144MHz operation. L1 is medium-Q construction (38 to 85μH slug tuned). The 1N914 is used as a clamp gate and will typically extend the shift by 1·5kHz at the upper end (representing 36kHz at 146MHz)

Frequency synthesizers

There are two main types of frequency synthesizers: analogue (or mixing) type and the digital phase-locked loop type. The analogue mixing type is rarely found in modern equipment but did find favour for a number of years with a so-called "crystal saving" circuit. This relied on mixing together two banks of crystal frequencies, with A crystals in one bank and B crystals in the other; see Fig 37. A total of A × B channels can be obtained with only A + B crystals.

The disadvantage with this technique is that the mixing process always generates spurious outputs which have to be removed by filtering.

Digital phase-locked synthesizers

This is the most common type of frequency synthesizer found in modern amateur radio equipment. It uses a combination of high-speed digital dividers, a voltage controlled oscillator and a technique analogous to a servo-controlled loop to produce a stable but programmable output frequency. This output frequency cannot be adjusted in a continuous manner as in a vfo but is tuned in a number of discrete steps. In an fm equipment it is convenient to make these steps equal to the channel spacing, ie 25 or 12·5kHz. In the case of an ssb transceiver the step needs to be much smaller in order to ensure that the signal can be recovered correctly. 100Hz should be regarded as the maximum step size on ssb unless some other form of fine tune is available.

The actual programming of the synthesizer can be performed in a number of ways, ranging from simple bcd-coded switches up to microcomputers. It is also possible to use tuning knobs coupled to shaft encoders or mechanical/optical switches to make it appear that the equipment is continuously tuned, the frequency being displayed on a digital display.

A block diagram of a basic pll synthesizer is shown in Fig 38. The output from the synthesizer is provided by a voltage

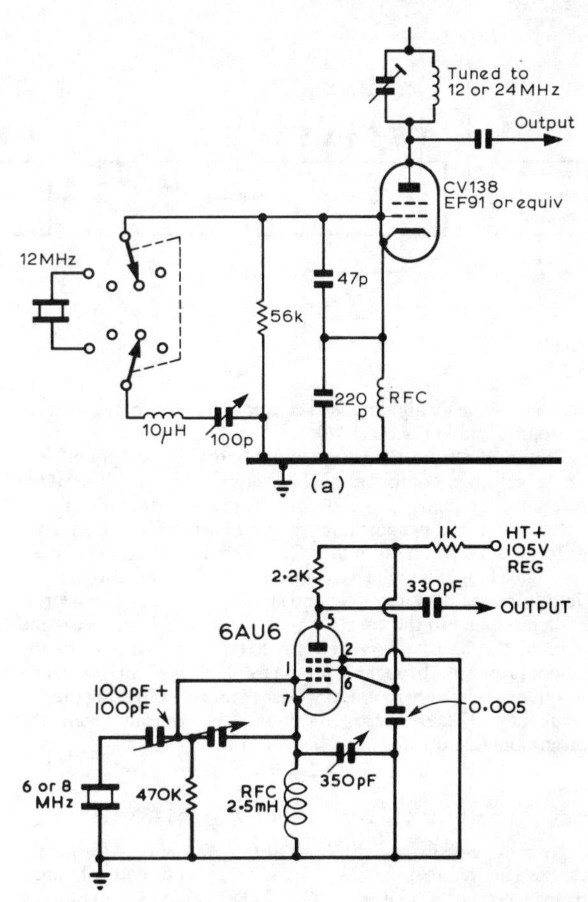

Fig 36. Two valve vxo circuits: (a) gives a wide-range shift

controlled oscillator (vco). This is normally a conventional LC oscillator which has all or part of its tuning capacitance replaced by a varicap diode. This means that its output frequency can be set by the voltage applied to the control input. Under normal circumstances this oscillator would be too unstable to use; the purpose of the synthesizer is to stabilize the frequency of the

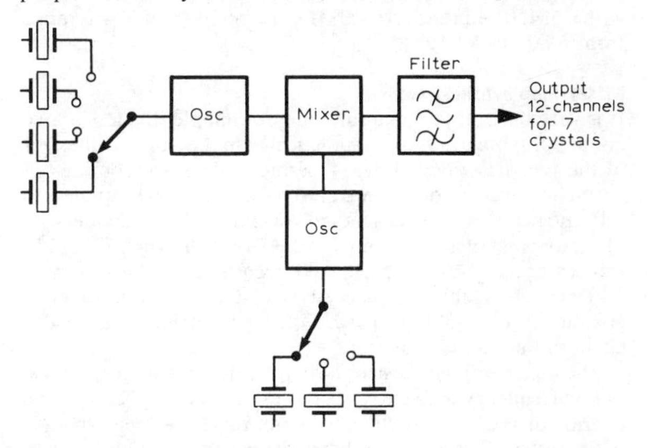

Fig 37. Crystal-saving type of synthesizer

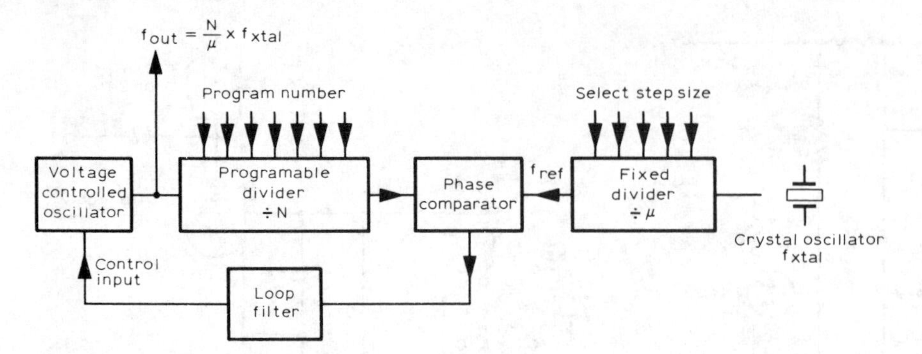

Fig 38. Basic pll synthesizer

vco. This done by dividing the vco frequency down by means of a programmable divider.

The output from the programmable divider is applied to a phase sensitive comparator which is also driven by a stable reference frequency. The output from the comparator is a voltage which is proportional to the phase and or frequency difference between its inputs. This error voltage is passed through a loop filter which cleans up the signal and also helps to determine the response time and stability of the synthesizer. It is then applied to the control input of the vco. The phase and gain of the loop is arranged so that the two inputs to the comparator are brought into phase lock (ie on the same frequency, with zero or a static phase error) by adjusting the vco frequency. Under these conditions the output from the programmable divider must be at frequency F_{ref}.

$$F_{out} = N \times F_{ref}$$

eg if F_{ref} = 1MHz and N= 145 then F_{out} = 145MHz

Now by selecting the division ratio N any output frequency can be achieved in multiples of F_{ref}. As F_{ref} is normally obtained from a crystal oscillator, as far as the long-term stability is concerned, the output is the same as a crystal-controlled source. If the reference divider ratio M is brought into the equation

$$F_{out} = \frac{N}{M} F_{xtal}$$

By selecting N and M any output frequency can be obtained from a given reference crystal. For example, suppose a 145–146MHz fm synthesizer with 25kHz channels is required with a 5MHz reference crystal. M must be 200 and N will range from 5,800 to 5,839.

Mixer loop synthesizers

It is very difficult to make fully programmable dividers above about 30MHz and so it is not practical to make a uhf synthesizer of the type described above. One method of overcoming the speed limitation is to use a mixer to reduce the vco frequency to a frequency that can be handled by conventional dividers. A block diagram of a mixer loop synthesizer is shown in Fig 39. In this case the 145–146MHz vco frequency is mixed with 140MHz obtainable from a crystal oscillator and multiplier to give an i.f. of 4–6MHz. This is then passed into the divider chain in the normal way.

The mixer loop synthesizer has two main advantages: the use of low-frequency dividers saves power, and mixing reduces the overall division ratio which will improve the performance of the system. The main disadvantages are the extra complexity of more rf-type components that are required, possible reduced stability due to an extra crystal and the likelihood of more spurious outputs.

Swallow counting

A fixed ecl divider or prescaler could be used to reduce the vco frequency to one that can be handled by conventional dividers. A fixed ÷ 10 prescaler before the programmable divider would mean that the reference frequency going to the phase comparator would also have to be reduced by a factor of 10. This would slow down the operation of the control loop and give longer locking times together with less protection against vco microphony.

An alternative to using a fixed prescaler is to use a dual modulus device as typified by an ecl ÷10/11 device. It is possible to use this prescaler in conjunction with some low-frequency control logic to make a fully programmable uhf divider. The technique is called *swallow counting*.

The full programmable divider consists of three blocks as shown in Fig 40. Initially the swallow counter is loaded with value 5 and the 10/11 counter is in the ÷ 11 mode. When the swallow counter is empty the modulus of the prescaler is changed to ÷10. At this time there will have been $11 \times S$ pulses at the input. The rest of the cycle, ie until the main divider is empty, is $(N - S)$ counts and as the prescaler is set to 10, corresponds to $10\,(N - S)$ pulses at the input. This gives a total division ratio N' where

$$N' = 11S + 10\,(N - S)$$

$$N' = 10N + S$$

The main divider N will have steps of 10 and single steps are provided by the swallow counter S. This type of divider can be

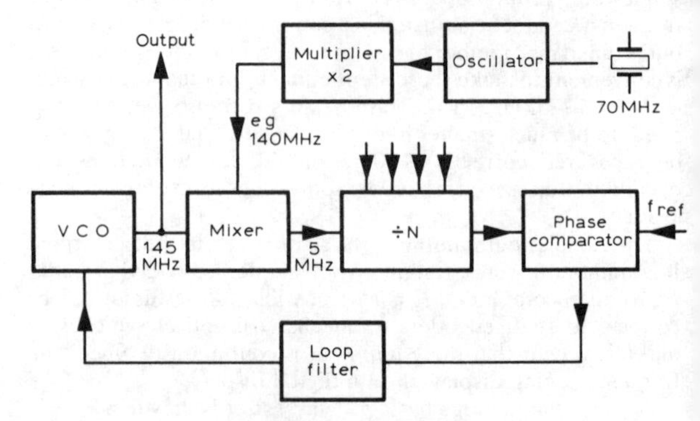

Fig 39. Mixer-loop synthesizer

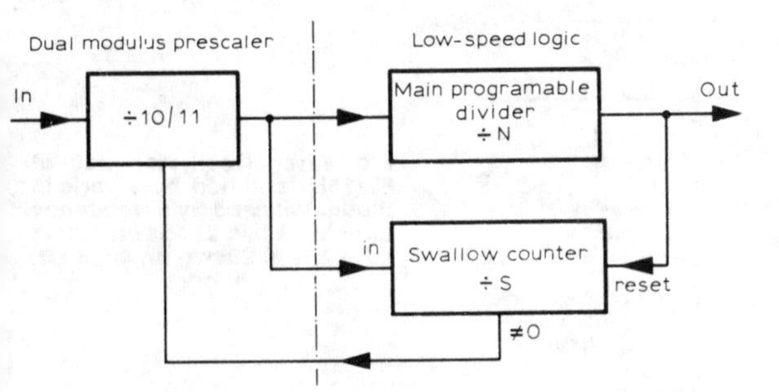

Fig 40. Swallow-counter type of high-speed programmable divider

implemented in ssi/msi packages or in a number of lsi synthesizer systems that are on the market.

Design of frequency syntheiszers

Synthesizers are notoriously difficult to design and to build with a low spurious output level. The design of the phase comparator and loop filter is very critical because any noise or ac components will modulate the vco and produce unwanted sidebands on the output frequency. These can give rise to considerable interference on transmit. Also there is the possiblity of the system going "out of lock"—this will mean that the vco could wander completely out of control up and down the band.

Many of these problems are a function of the phase comparator and fortunately there are lsi circuits available which use very clean type of comparator called a *sample and hold* phase comparator which incorporates foolproof out-of-lock indication. The alignment of a synthesizer requires a spectrum analyser and great care is needed in the construction to prevent unwanted frequencies reaching the vco. It is therefore recommended that synthesizer construction should only be undertaken when suitable experience and test equipment is available.

Variable frequency oscillators

Although crystal control or frequency synthesis is widely used for channelized operation in the fm sections of the bands it is generally inappropriate for ssb and cw operation. Many fm operators also prefer to be able to tune to any frequency rather than a few fixed channels.

A variable frequency oscillator (vfo) is required in these cases and there are four main possibilities:

(a) a free-running vhf oscillator
(b) a free-running hf oscillator multiplied up to vhf
(c) a free-running hf oscillator mixed up to vhf
(d) a vhf oscillator which is phased locked with a free-running hf oscillator.

The high stability needed for ssb makes the use of on-frequency free-running oscillators or multiplied oscillators impractical and options (c) and (d) are therefore preferred.

The problem of making a vhf vfo can be bypassed by using a crystal-controlled converter or transverter ahead of an hf band unit. However, for both the simplest and highest-performance equipments, some form of vfo on or close to the final frequency is required. Normally the vfo will be offset from the amateur band by the amount of a fixed intermediate frequency (i.f.), eg for 144MHz ssb with a 10·7MHz i.f., a vfo covering 133·3–134·3MHz will give 144–145MHz coverage.

Free-running vhf vfo

This is generally only suitable for fm reception purposes. Its stability, unless very carefully constructed, is usually very poor, but it may nevertheless be appropriate in, for example, a low-cost monitor receiver.

The quality of construction is much more important than the circuit chosen. Microphony may be a particular problem, and, though frequency-determing components should be firmly mounted, it may be advantageous to incorporate rubber washers into the pcb mounting. Varicap diode tuning is preferred to variable capacitors—although the intrinsic electrical stability is lower, the mechanical stability is superior in this case. An example of a typical circuit is shown in Fig 41, and two similar designs using frequency multiplication in Figs 42 and 43.

Multiplier vfo

This was at one time the most popular form of vfo control on both the hf and vhf bands, but has now been superseded by the mixer-vfo and phase-locked loop systems described later. It is suitable for both fm receivers and transmitters, but its stability is generally inadequate for ssb or cw systems unless carefully built.

Its basis is a very stable hf oscillator multiplied up to the working frequency. Generally a frequency of around 8 to 18MHz is used for 144MHz work. A typical design is given below.

12MHz multiplier vfo

If a satisfactory variable frequency oscillator is to be stable enough for reliable calibration, it will generally operate below about 20MHz and will need adequate temperature compensation and followed by an appropriate isolating amplifier.

The oscillator described here fulfils these requirements, and is of necessity somewhat elaborate. It was originally designed for a transmitter but will be suitable for a receiver, providing the final frequency is changed to allow for the i.f. offset.

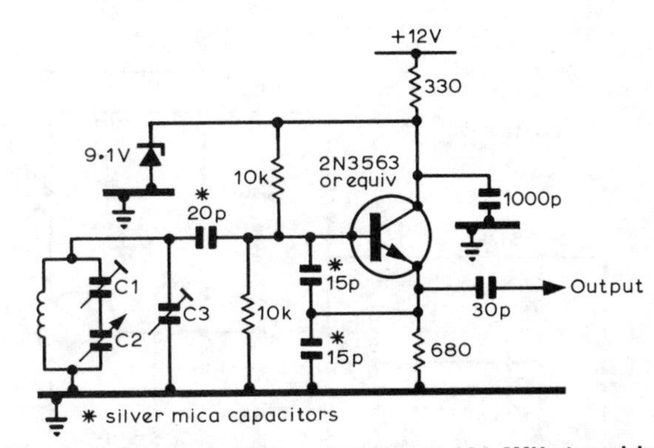

Fig 41. A simple oscillator operating at 134·3MHz tuned by means of a variable capacitor. C1 is a 5–15pF trimmer; C2 a 15pF variable; C3 a 3–8pF trimmer; and the inductor is 3t 16swg ⅜in od ½in long

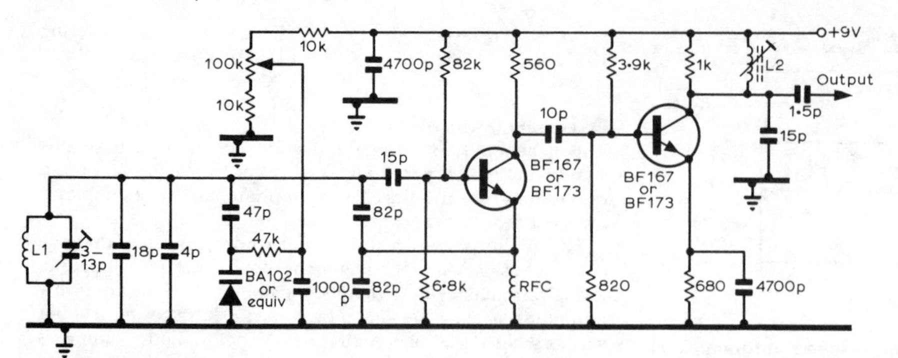

Fig 42(a) Oscillator set at 67·15MHz, tuned by a varicap diode, followed by a frequency doubler. L1 is 2t 16swg 10mm i.d. L2 is 4t 20swg on 4mm i.d. vhf core

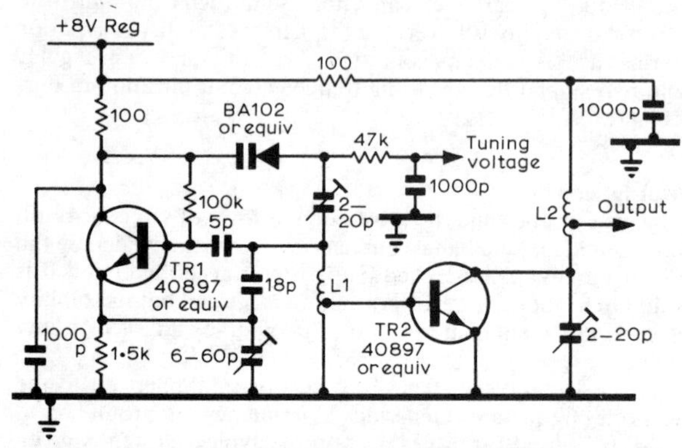

Fig 42(b). Alternative arrangement to that shown in Fig 42(a). L1 is 5t 20swg ¼in diam, tapped 1t up. L2 is 4½t 20swg ⅜in diam, tapped at centre

The oscillator

The oscillator operates at 12MHz and the circuit is shown in Fig 44. The trimmers VC2, VC3 and VC4 are all air dielectric variable types giving control of tuning range, feedback and frequency respectively, although all are interdependent. VC5 is a Tempatrimmer of 6·5pF capacitance, and provides an adjustable temperature coefficient from +2,000 to −2,000 ppm/°C. Frequency modulation is produced by a varactor but its effect is reduced by a small series capacitor and a large shunt capacitor, the overall effect being to produce 3kHz deviation at 144MHz for an audio signal of 1V peak.

The varactor is biased to one-half of the stabilized oscillator supply voltage by a potential divider of 33kΩ + 33kΩ. Much higher values were originally used but it was found that small changes of varactor leakage current with temperature led to a change of frequency. The deviation for a 1V audio signal can conveniently be checked by shunting the lower 33kΩ resistor with another of equal value. This changes the bias from 3V to 2V approximately; if required frequency shift does not occur, either the series or shunt capacitors may be modified. Care is needed to prevent rf being fed into the audio amplifier; until the choke-capacitor-resistor (RFC1, C3, R7) network was fitted there was a small frequency shift when the gain control of the speech amplifier was varied.

The setting of the feedback capacitor VC3 is most important in achieving good frequency stability; no more feedback should be applied than is necessary to provide certain oscillation over the band. This was achieved with the variable trimmer rather less than half meshed, representing about 12pF. With the feedback set and VC2 and VC4 adjusted so that the required tuning range is just covered by the full range of VC1, the frequency drift should be examined with the Tempatrimmer in its mid position. A likely result is an increase of frequency of some 9kHz at 144MHz during the first 2min, due mainly to

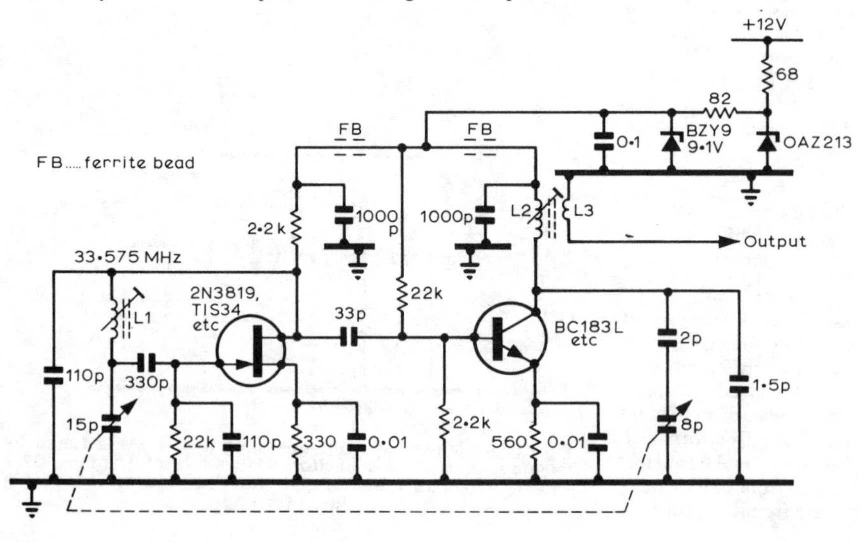

Fig 43. Oscillator working at 33·575MHz followed by a frequency quadrupler. The oscillator and multiplier tuning capacitors are ganged to ensure adequate output at the band edges. L1 is 6t 24swg ¼in ⅛in long with half-length slug. L2 is 4t 16swg ¼in long with half-length slug. L3 is 2t 24swg on the earthy end of L2. The tuning capacitor is two-gang with one section reduced to 8pF max by the removal of plates

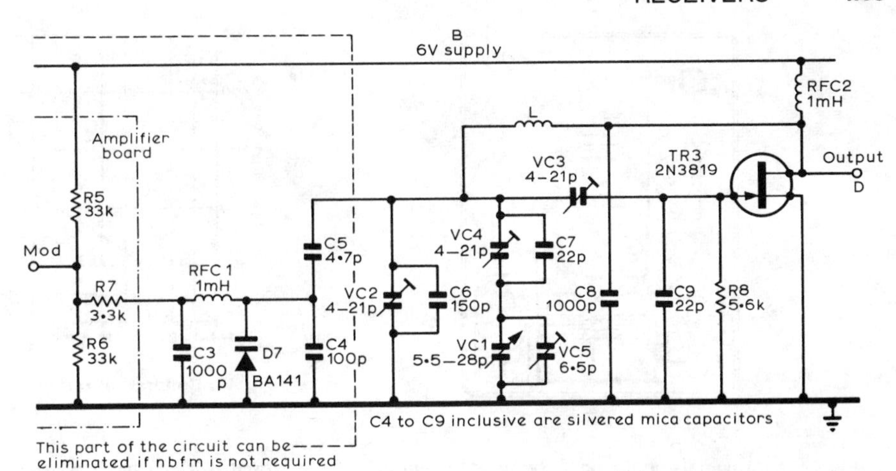

Fig 44. Oscillator circuit

heating in the transistor, followed by a similar drift over the following 20min as the whole unit reaches a stable operating temperature. This second drift can be almost entirely eliminated by careful adjustment of the Tempatrimmer, and frequency stability from hour to hour of ± 100Hz is achievable.

During construction it is worth taking care that no connecting leads are in a state of mechanical stress: such leads tend to move with time and during heating cycles which leads to small changes of calibration. The coil was wound on a polystyrene rod and heavily doped with polystyrene cement. The fixed capacitors were anchored to solid objects with Araldite, which was also used to anchor the output lead as it passed through a hole in the cast box.

The amplifier

The oscillator output is only a few tens of millivolts and this must be raised to about 1V. Existing amplifier designs did not seem to give sufficient isolation, and two additional stages were added. The first of these, TR4, is a fet as a source follower feeding a bipolar transistor, TR5, with rf grounded base. The collector output from TR5 drives a conventional feedback amplifier, the resistor R14 controlling the current drive to the base of TR6; this may be any value from zero upwards and in the original design was 2·2kΩ.

The power supply

The vfo is mains driven using OA202 diodes in a bridge rectifier followed by a capacitor-resistor-capacitor filter. An earlier version used a single diode half-wave rectifier but produced an unacceptably rough note. The source resistance of the supply plus the smoothing resistor adequately limits the current through the 12V zener diode to about 10mA, the current drain of the amplifier and oscillator being 24mA. The highly stable supply for the oscillator and first buffer amplifier uses a AC128 as a controlled series transistor, the output voltage being that of the zener diode plus the forward drop across one OA202 diode. Should it be desired to operate the oscillator from a battery supply, this stabilizer circuit will give substantially constant output until the battery has fallen to 6V. If a 9V battery is used to supply the entire vfo, the total battery drain is 22mA.

Construction

The oscillator is constructed in a cast box 4½in by 3½in by 2in, while the amplifier and power supply components were in a similar box. In the prototype, the two boxes were bolted together, but a small gap between them might be an advantage to reduce heat conduction to the oscillator components. However, the Tempatrimmer will compensate for heating from the components or changes of ambient temperature. The layout in the oscillator box is sketched in Fig 47 but is not important provided that every component is rigidly mounted or "Aralditеd" to one that is.

The tuning capacitor is bolted directly to the base of the box and all the air-spaced trimmers are mounted off the base by 2BA bolts. TR3, R8, C8 and C9 are mounted on a piece of 0·15in matrix Veroboard about 1in square, also mounted on a 2BA bolt. The 6V supply, audio and rf output leads pass

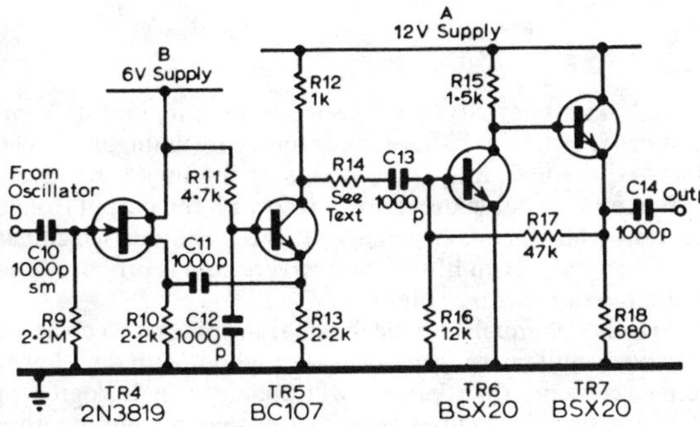

Fig 45. Amplifier circuit

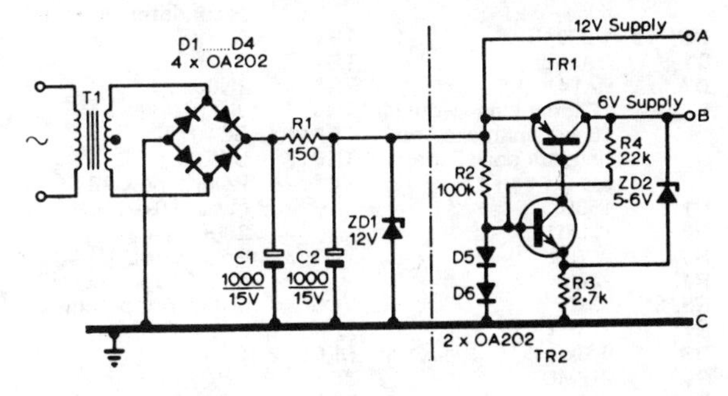

Fig 46. Power supply unit (for battery operation omit all to left of dotted line). TR1: AC128, TR2: BC107.

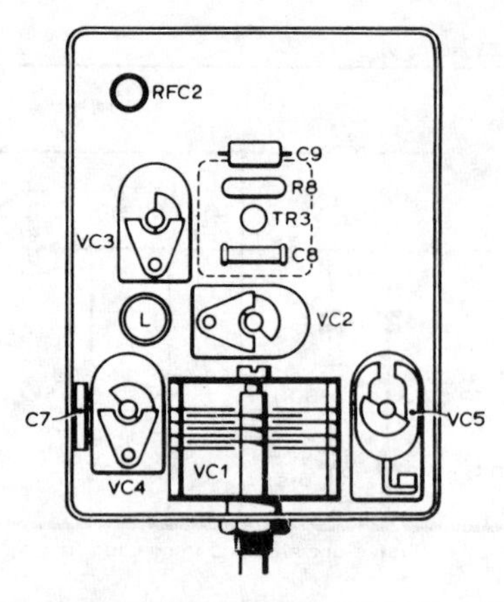

Fig 47. Approximate component layout of oscillator

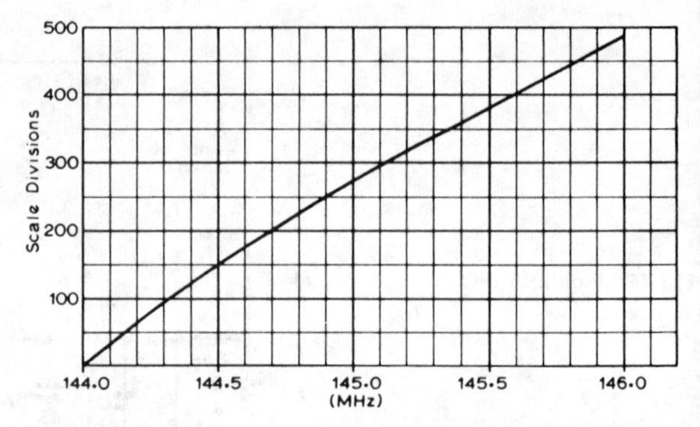

Fig 48. Calibration curve for 12MHz vfo in terms of 144MHz frequencies

through clearance holes in the walls of the two boxes and are "Araldited" to prevent movement. The amplifier and the stabilizer are mounted on a strip of Veroboard 3¾in by 1½in; the only important connection is the rf ground to the base of TR5 which should be short and direct. The mains transformer, rectifiers, smoothing components and zener diode occupy the rest of the box and could, of course, be replaced by a battery for mobile operation.

Calibration

Calibration should not be attempted until the vfo can be vigorously tapped with little transient change of frequency and no permanent change at all. It should also be heat cycled a number of times, preferably to a higher temperature than it will ever reach in practice (say 50°C) as this helps to relieve mechanical strains in the wiring and components. Screwing the lid on to the oscillator box has a considerable effect on frequency and the final adjustment of the trimmers for frequency and bandspread will have to be done by cut and try. In the final stages, the lid should be firmly screwed at each corner. The calibration of the prototype was reasonably close to linear, as can be seen from Fig 48.

Table 4. Component details for 12MHz multiplier vfo

C1, 2	1,000μF 15V	**R11**	4·7kΩ
C3	1,000pF	**R12**	1kΩ
C4	100pF silvered mica	**R13**	2·2kΩ
C5	4·7pF silvered mica	**R14**	see text
C6	150pF silvered mica	**R15**	1·5kΩ
C7	22pF silvered mica	**R16**	12kΩ
C8	1,000pF silvered mica	**R17**	47kΩ
		R18	680Ω
C9	22pF silvered mica	**T1**	Radiospares miniature mains—2, 6V secondaries in series
C10	1,000pF silvered mica		
C11-14	1,000pF	**TR1**	AC128
D1-6	OA202	**TR2**	BC107
D7	BA141	**TR3**	2N3819
L	17 turns close wound 18swg enamelled on ⅜in diam polystyrene rod (1·1 μH)	**TR4**	2N3819
		TR5	BC107
		TR6, 7	BSX20
		VC1	Polar type C28, 6 gaps of 0·015in (5·5–28pF)
R1	150Ω		
R2	100kΩ		
R3	2·7kΩ	**VC2, 3, 4**	Polar type C31, 9 gaps of 0·015in (4-21pF)
R4	22kΩ		
R5, 6*	33kΩ	**VC5**	Oxley Tempatrimmer 6·5pF
R7*	3·3kΩ		
R8	5·6kΩ	**RFC1, 2**	1μH
R9	2·2MΩ	**ZD1**	12V
R10	2·2kΩ	**ZD2**	5·6V

* These resistors are mounted on the amplifier board.

Franklin oscillator

One of the most stable variable oscillators is the Franklin, originally designed for use with two triode valves or later with two pentodes. This may be substituted for the Vackar oscillator in the previous design.

In this oscillator a pair of active devices are connected to the frequency-determining circuit through small capacitors, the value of which should be as low as possible consistent with adequate operation.

For some time this form of oscillator was neglected because normal bipolar transistors are of too low impedance for satisfactory operation, however with field effect transistors (where the input impedance is very much higher) satisfactory performance can be obtained.

In this circuit (Fig 49), dual-gate devices are used and can give very stable output; of course, as with any free-running oscillator, it is necessary to have an adequately stabilized voltage supply.

For the best stability the inductance should be small with a large tuning capacitance. Usually, for limited frequency range, this is best arranged using a large preset capacitor with the actual tuning accomplished by a suitable size variable capacitor in parallel. The preset capacitor may be a silver mica or air-spaced trimmer.

Mixer vfos

Although multiplier vfos can be successful, temperature compensation is often a tedious and time-consuming job. The mixer-type variable frequency oscillator features a relatively low-frequency variable oscillator mixed with the output from a significantly high crystal oscillator. It is a technique which has proved its reliability in hf ssb transceivers, and is probably one of the most satisfactory solutions.

The method is equally applicable to transmitters, receivers or transceivers, and, using transistors throughout with their lower thermal problems than valves, will enable a high degree of calibration stability. This is not to say that no temperature compensation will be needed—it will, to take care of ambient

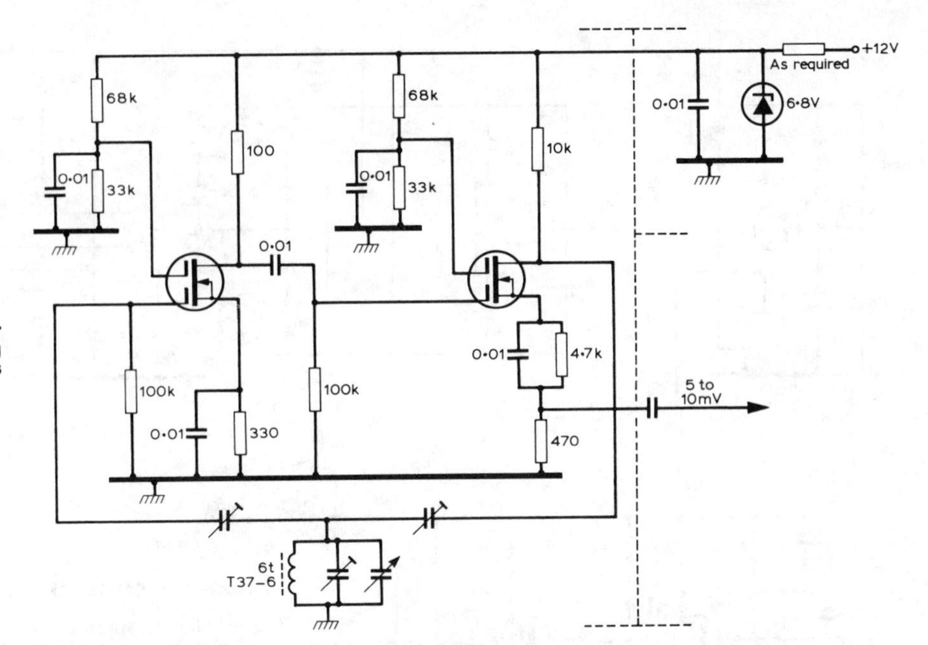

Fig 49. A Franlkin oscillator using dual-gate mosfets, eg 3N204, suitable for frequencies in the region of 30MHz

temperature variations, especially for portable mobile equipment which may meet very wide variations of temperature.

If a vfo covers the range 5–6MHz this can be mixed with a signal on 128·3MHz to give a coverage of 133·3–134·3MHz. This arrangement is shown in block form in Fig 50. The stable 128·3MHz signal is obtained by tripling the output frequency of a 42·766MHz crystal oscillator.

It is important that the output of the tripler does not contain any second or fourth harmonics of the crystal frequency. These can be removed by means of a suitable filter.

The outputs of the crystal oscillator and the vfo are mixed and the resulting output will contain both the input frequencies and the sum and difference frequencies, all of which have been filtered out (except the wanted sum frequency) to provide a clean signal for use.

Two examples of mixer vfos are shown in Figs 51 and 52. That in Fig 52 has an output of 72 to 73MHz for use with a doubler for 144 to 146MHz. They illustrate the use of bipolar transistors and field-effect transistors in the mixer stage. A more modern and satisfactory approach would be to use a balanced modulator ic such as the Plessey SL640 or a hot-carrier diode package such as the MD108. For further information on mixers see the "Mixers" section.

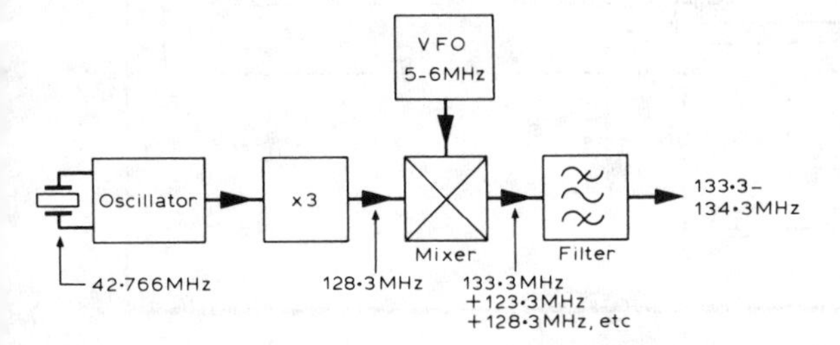

Fig 50. Mixer-type vfo for 144MHz

Table 5. Component details for mixer vfo (70MHz)

(1) All decoupling capacitors are low-voltage disc ceramics.
(2) Low-value capacitors are low-voltage polystyrene except where labelled "sm" (silvered mica).
(3) Transistors shown are low-cost plastic encapsulated types made by Microelectronics Ltd. Suitable equivalents for the ME3011 are 2N918, ZTX320. Almost any silicon planar device would replace the HK301. A suitable replacement for the MEFET would be the ubiquitous 2N3819.
(4) The vfo tuning capacitors were one section of a Jackson Bros Ltd Type C21 2-gang vhf variable capacitor. A very similar type is the 3/CG80–03 made by Wingrove and Rogers Ltd. Both types have a three-to-one reduction drive built-in.
(5) Coil data is as follows:
L1, 5t tapped 1t from earthy end.
L2, 13¾in of 32swg close-wound, link winding 10in of 32swg close-wound.
L3, 5t with 2½t link winding.
L4, 7t with 3½t link winding.
L5, 10½in of 32swg close-wound (14½t).
All coils except L5 and L6 were wound on 3/16in o/d Aladdin formers and use appropriate ferrite slugs. L5 and L6 were wound on Cambion ceramic formers with lockable ferrite cores and of ¼in o/d.

Table 6. Component details for 144 to 146MHz vfo

L1 15t 22swg enam on 0·31in former with slug.
L2 2t wound over centre of L3.
L3 12t 22swg ⅜in diam, ⅞in long, centre tapped.
L4 5t 18swg ½in diam, ½in long, centre tapped.
L5 2t wound over the centre of L4.
L6 7t 22swg ¾in diam ¾in long.
L7 3t wound over cold end of L6.
L8 2t wound over cold end of L9.
L9 7t 22swg ½in diam ¾in long.
RFC1, 3 single pie—inductance unknown. Value not critical.
RFC2 2·5mH.
RFC4 1·5mH.
R1 may be varied for minimum harmonic output from oscillator
R2 replaced by fixed resistor when correct value ascertained.

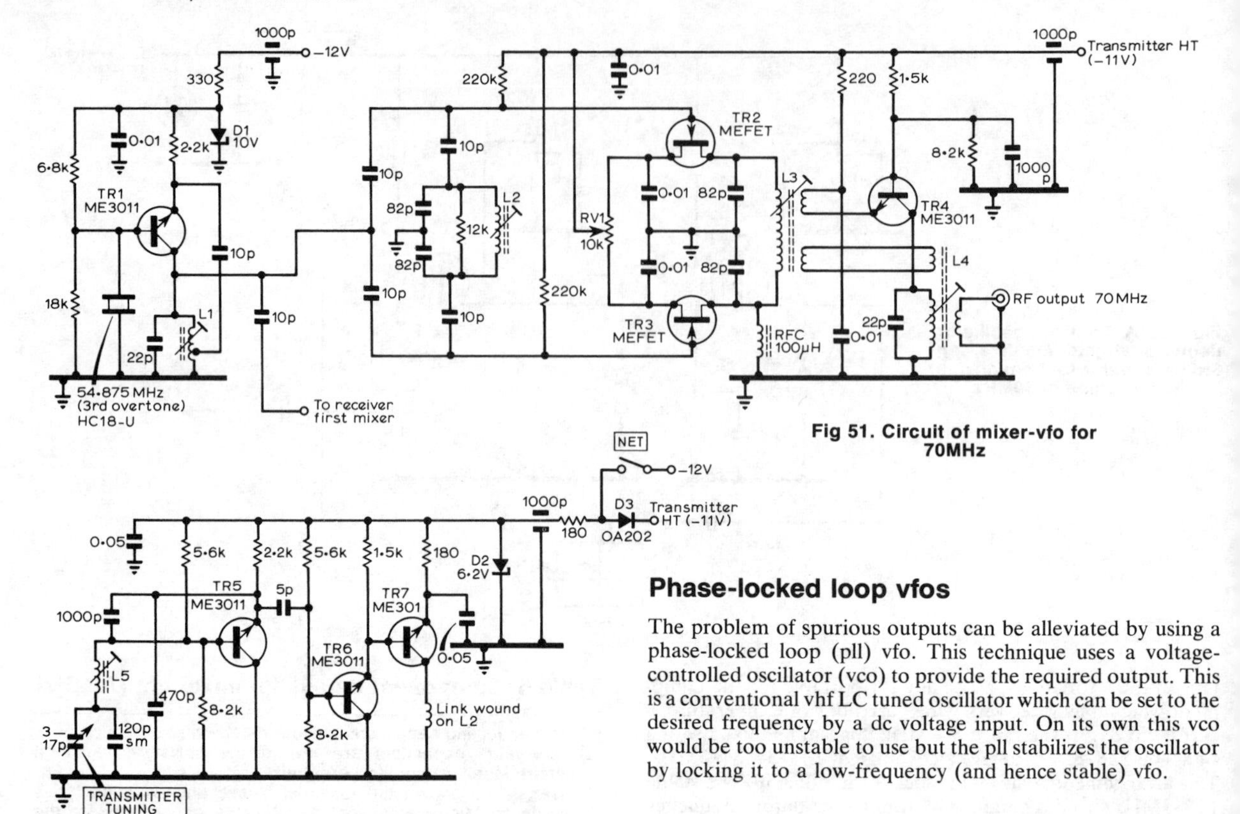

Fig 51. Circuit of mixer-vfo for 70MHz

Phase-locked loop vfos

The problem of spurious outputs can be alleviated by using a phase-locked loop (pll) vfo. This technique uses a voltage-controlled oscillator (vco) to provide the required output. This is a conventional vhf LC tuned oscillator which can be set to the desired frequency by a dc voltage input. On its own this vco would be too unstable to use but the pll stabilizes the oscillator by locking it to a low-frequency (and hence stable) vfo.

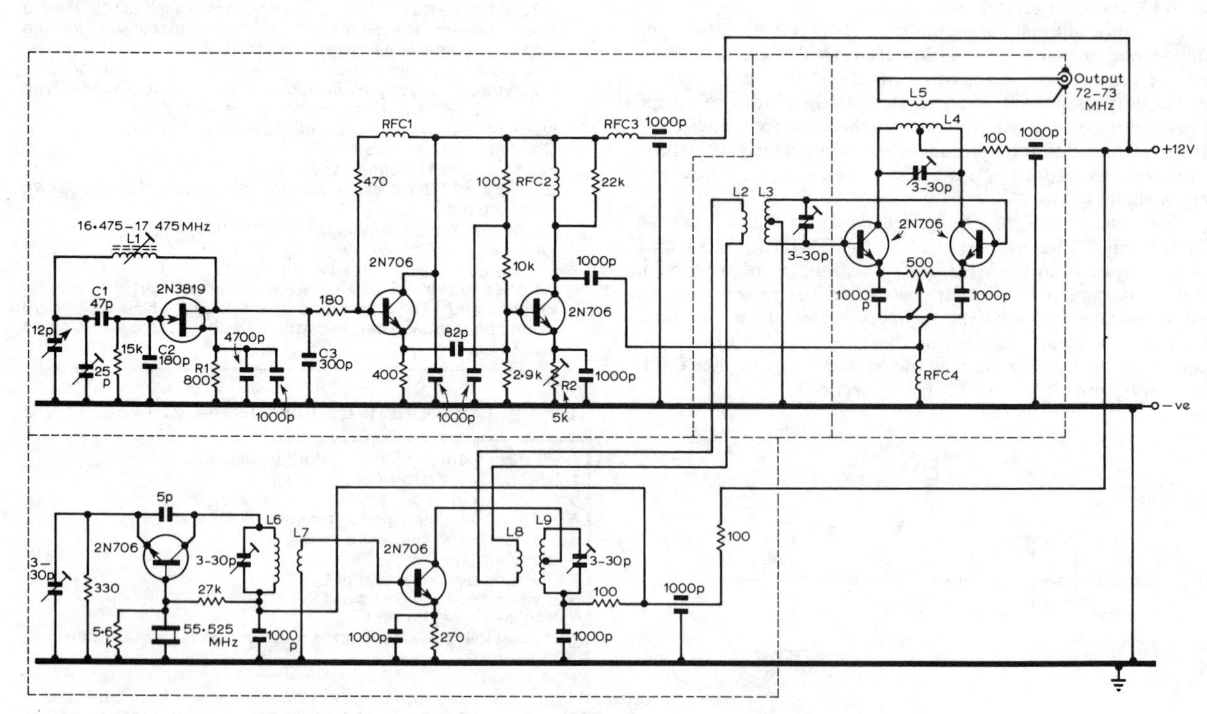

Fig 52. Circuit of mixer-vfo for 144–146MHz

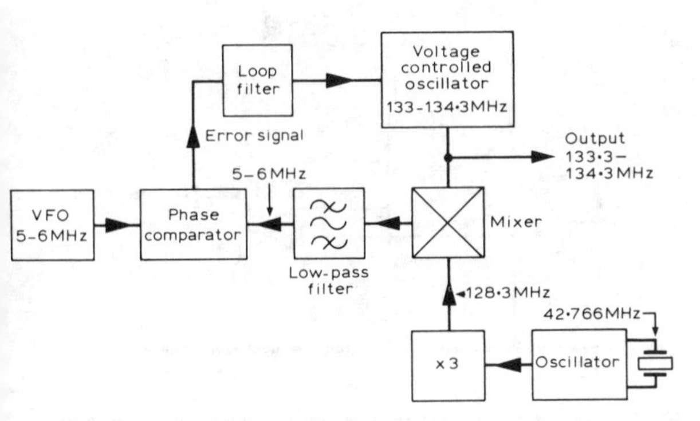

Fig 53. PLL-type vfo for 144MHz

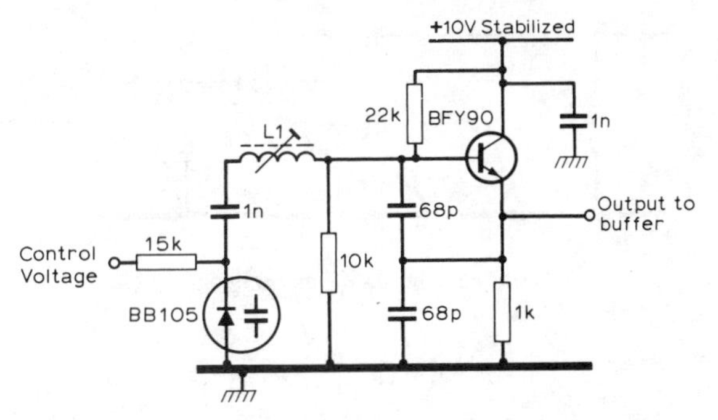

Fig 54. Clapp voltage-controlled oscillator. L1 is 5t (144MHz) or 6t (100MHz) 0·3mm on 5mm ferrite slug-tuned former

An example of how this may be done is shown diagramatically in Fig 53. The vco is mixed with 128·3MHz from a crystal oscillator/multiplier chain and then the signal is low-pass filtered to give a signal between 5 and 6MHz. This unstable signal is compared with a vfo covering the same frequency range in a phase comparator. The phase comparator produces an error voltage which is proportional to the phase/frequency difference between its two inputs.

This voltage is then filtered in the loop filter and applied to the control input of the vco in such a way that it brings the two inputs of the comparator on to the same frequency and then into phase lock. When the system is locked, the output frequency must be equal to the vfo plus 128·3MHz. If the vco were to drift, the mixer output would change by the same amount, the comparator would produce a change in output voltage and hence correct the drift. Conversely if the vfo frequency is altered, the vco control voltage will change in such a way as to maintain the phase lock.

This is a very simplified explanation of the operation of such a vfo, but it does show the advantage over the conventional mixer type. In the pll vfo the output is obtained from an oscillator on the final frequency and so has no spurious mixing components present. Design of such a vfo is fairly complicated because considerations such as ensuring that on switch-on-phase lock is obtained and that there is no possibility of the system going out of lock. If the loop was to unlock the vco would be uncontrolled and could wander up and down the band.

The design of the loop characteristics is also complicated in order to ensure that the vco will track rapid changes in the vfo frequency and similarly any microphony is removed by the loop.

The components used in such a vfo are conventional, for instance, the vco is a normal tuned oscillator with the variable capacitor replaced by a varicap diode. An example of a vco is shown in Fig 54. The phase comparator is simply a mixer and can be made using diodes, transistors or digital circuits. A complete pll vco forms part of a 144MHz multi-mode receiver described later in this chapter.

Mixers

The performance of the mixer stage is of prime importance. Fundamentally it is a frequency converter and it is important that this function is carried out with the greatest effectiveness. The various devices used for this purpose may be judged on their conversion gain/forward transfer characteristic and noise. Conversion gain is a junction of the amplitude of the local oscillator injection voltage.

In a simple unbalanced mixer using a diode, transistor or triode, the possible outputs are $\pm m\,f_s \pm mf_o$ where f_s and f_o are the signal and oscillator frequencies respectively and m and n are numbers which may vary from 1 to infinity. There are obviously many values of m and n which give output frequencies close to that desired, which is normally either $f_s + f_o$ or $f_s - f_o$. Table 7 shows these combinations.

In order to reduce the number of products of mixing to reasonably manageable proportions it is obvious from the table that some form of balanced, or better still double-balanced, mixer is desirable. The actual levels of the various mixing products will to a significant extent depend on the suitability of the active device(s) used for the purpose.

Bipolar mixer devices such as the BF324 require fairly low oscillator injection voltage, in an unbalanced case, in parallel with the signal to the base. For this type of elementary mixer an oscillator voltage of 50–70mV is usually adequate for appropriate conversion gain.

The intrinsic exponential forward transfer characteristic of this type of device limits the signal handling capacity and therefore restricts the amount of rf gain that can be used before the mixer.

Table 7. Frequencies present in the output for unbalanced, balanced and double balanced mixers

	f_o	$2f_o$	$3f_o$	$4f_o$	$5f_o$	
Unbalanced mixer						
f_s	$f_s \pm f_o$	$f_s \pm 2f_o$	$f_s \pm 3f_o$	$f_s \pm 4f_o$	$f_s \pm 5f_o$	
$2f_s$	$2f_s \pm f_o$	$2f_s \pm 2f_o$	$2f_s \pm 3f_o$	$2f_s \pm 4f_o$	$2f_s \pm 5f_o$	
$3f_s$	$3f_s \pm f_o$	$3f_s \pm 2f_o$	$3f_s \pm 3f_o$	$3f_s \pm 4f_o$	$3f_s \pm 5f_o$	
$4f_s$	$4f_s \pm f_o$	$4f_s \pm 2f_o$	$4f_s \pm 3f_o$	$4f_s \pm 4f_o$	$4f_s \pm 5f_o$	
$5f_s$	$5f_s \pm f_o$	$5f_s \pm 2f_o$	$5f_s \pm 3f_o$	$5f_s \pm 4f_o$	$5f_s \pm 5f_o$	etc
Balanced mixer						
f_s	$f_s \pm f_o$	$f_s \pm 2f_o$	$f_s \pm 3f_o$	$f_s \pm 4f_o$	$f_s \pm 5f_o$	
$2f_s$	—	—	—	—	—	
$3f_s$	$3f_s \pm f_o$	$3f_s \pm 2f_o$	$3f_s \pm 3f_o$	$3f_s \pm 4f_o$	$3f_s \pm 5f_o$	
$4f_s$	—	—	—	—	—	
$5f_s$	$5f_s \pm f_o$	$5f_s \pm 2f_o$	$5f_s \pm 3f_o$	$5f_s \pm 4f_o$	$5f_s \pm 5f_o$	etc
Double-balanced mixer						
f_s	$f_s \pm f_o$	—	$f_s \pm 3f_o$	—	$f_s \pm 5f_o$	
$2f_s$	—	—	—	—	—	
$3f_s$	$3f_s \pm f_o$	—	$3f_s \pm 3f_o$	—	$3f_s \pm 5f_o$	
$4f_s$	—	—	—	—	—	
$5f_s$	$5f_s \pm f_o$	—	$5f_s \pm 3f_o$	—	$5f_s \pm 5f_o$	

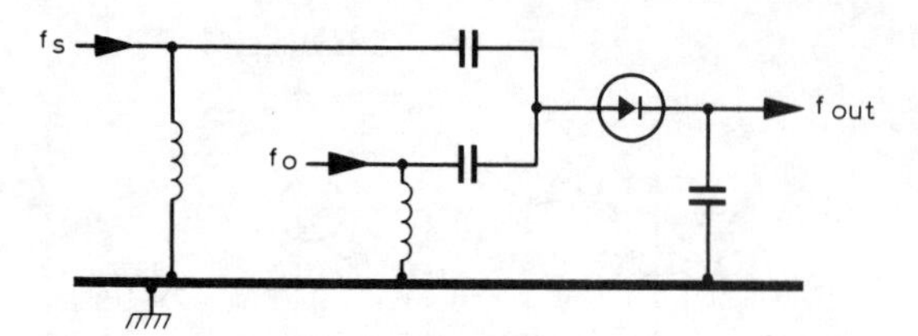

Fig 55. Simple diode mixer

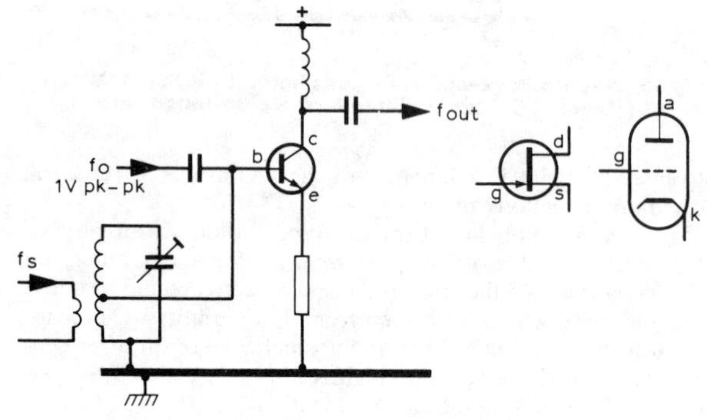

Fig 56. Simple mixer using three-electrode device

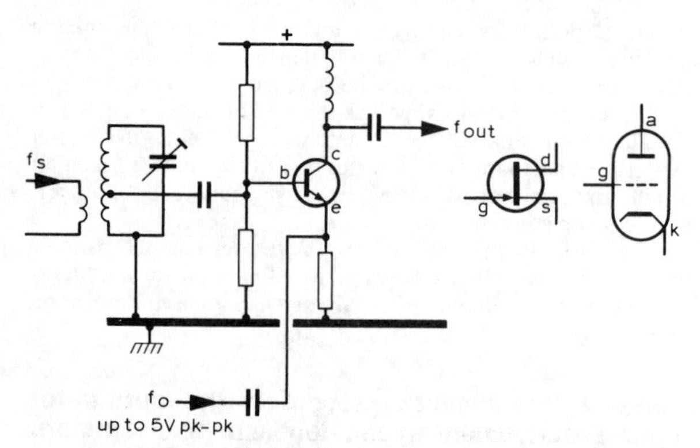

Fig 57. Simple mixer using three-electrode device but with the two inputs injected on different electrodes to provide increased isolation

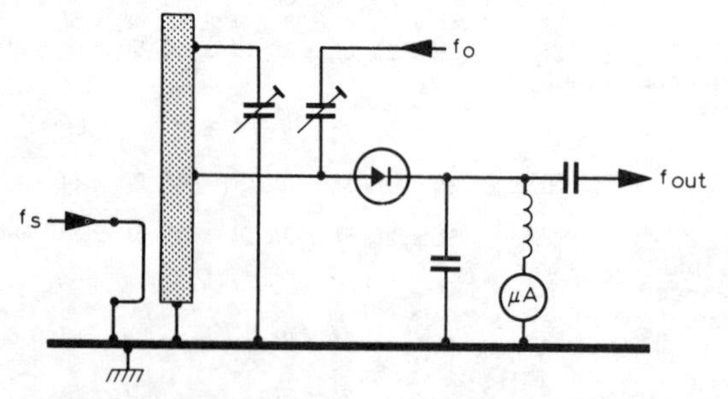

Fig 58. A uhf version of Fig 55, using a low-noise diode designed for this type of service. The oscillator power at f_o should be sufficient to give a diode current of 300μA

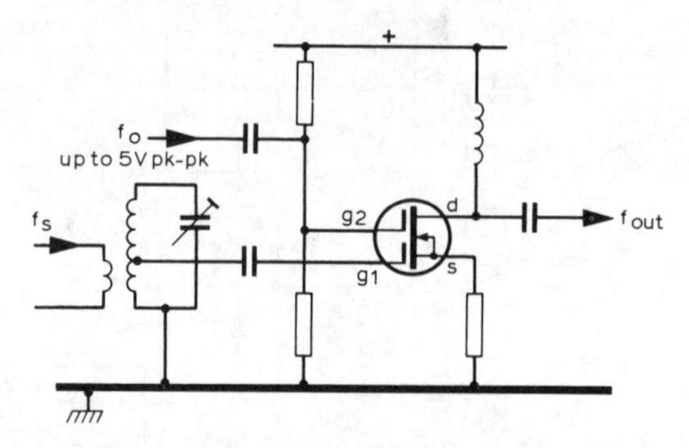

Fig 59. Similar mixer to that shown in Fig 57 but using a dual-gate fet with the oscillator injection applied to gate 2, providing increased isolation

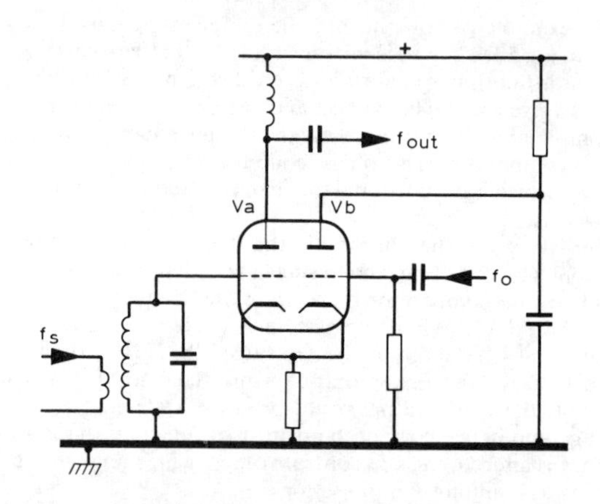

Fig 60. A double-triode valve used as a low-noise mixer. The second section V_b operates as a cathode-follower, providing increased isolation of the oscillator

FETs of either type have more satisfactory forward characteristics for mixer service. Types such as 40673, 3N201, 3N205, SD600 and MPF122/131 are suitable replacements for bipolar devices.

The dual-gate mosfet usually has the signal applied to gate 1 and the oscillator injection applied to gate 2. This arrangement provides considerable isolation between the signal and oscillator inputs.

FETs do however require higher oscillator injection voltage, about 0·7V rms for a junction fet and 1·0V rms for a mosfet, to produce the correct conversion gain.

Figs 61 and 62 show practical front-end circuits using the unbalanced types of mixer shown respectively in Figs 56 and 59.

A balanced mixer offers the advantage of even harmonic cancellation to one of the input signals. This is normally applied to the local oscillator.

In a double-balanced mixer, even harmonic cancellation can be applied to both input signals. In Table 7 this is clearly illustrated. There are several forms of double-balanced mixer: the two most likely to be of interest to the equipment designer are

(a) Cross-connected pair of fets
(b) Diode-ring mixer (modulator)

The cross-connected pair of fets offers several advantages, apart from the fundamental reduction of harmonics in the

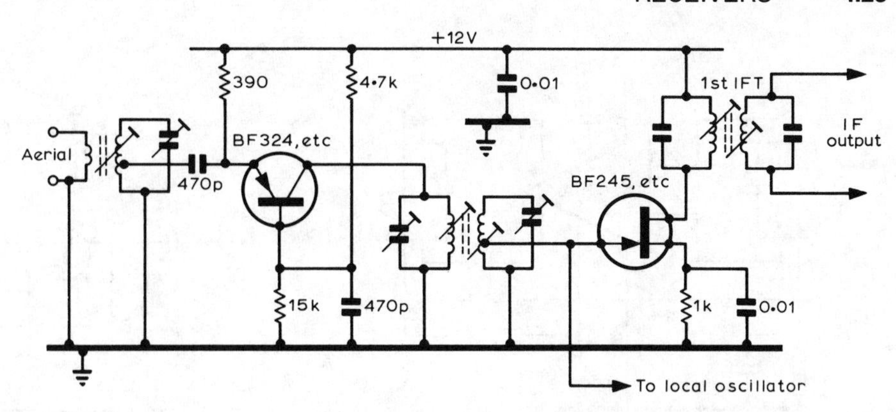

Fig 61. An example of a front-end circuit using a bipolar rf amplifier and a jfet mixer of the type shown in Fig 56

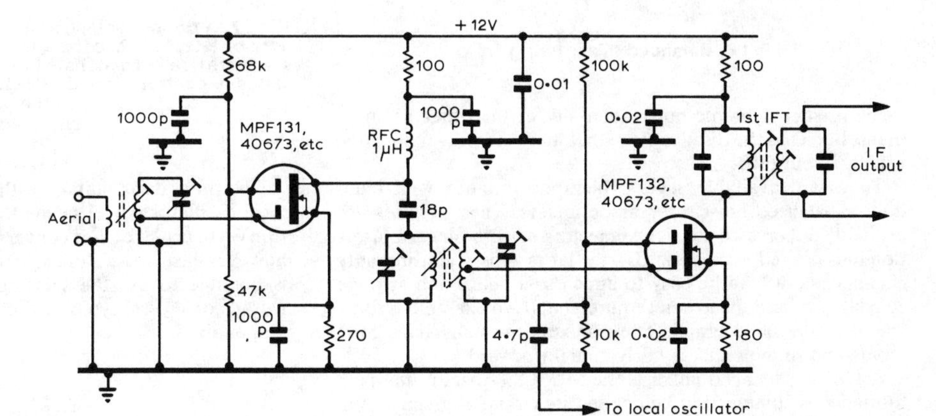

Fig 62. An example of a front-end circuit using a dual-gate mosfet rf amplifier and mixer of the type shown in Fig 59

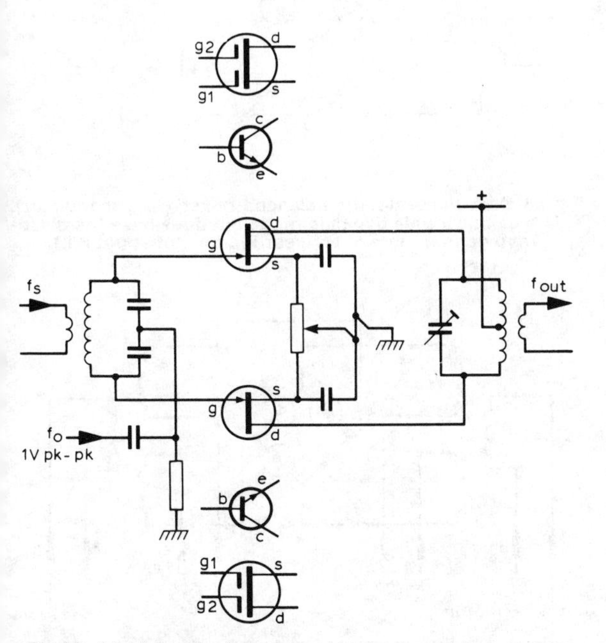

Fig 63. A balanced mixer using bipolar transistors or fets

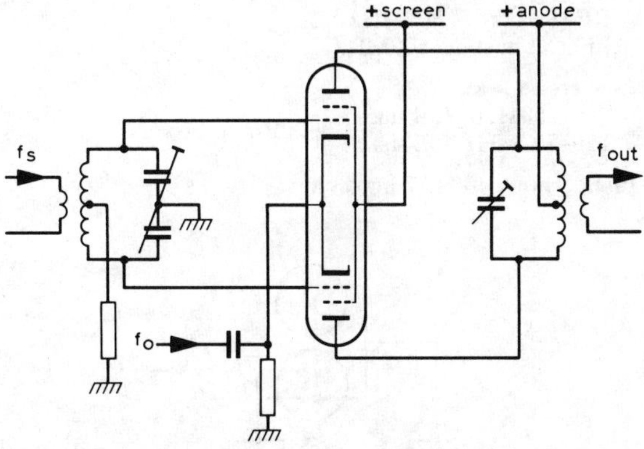

Fig 64. Balanced mixer using double-tetrode valve

output. There are no difficult transformers needed unless wide-band couplings are required. A simple balance adjustment can be arranged and the dynamic range is significantly greater than in the case of a balanced mixer, allowing much larger signal inputs. However, the conversion gain is reduced as would be expected.

The diode ring mixer (modulator) shown in Fig 68(a) has a

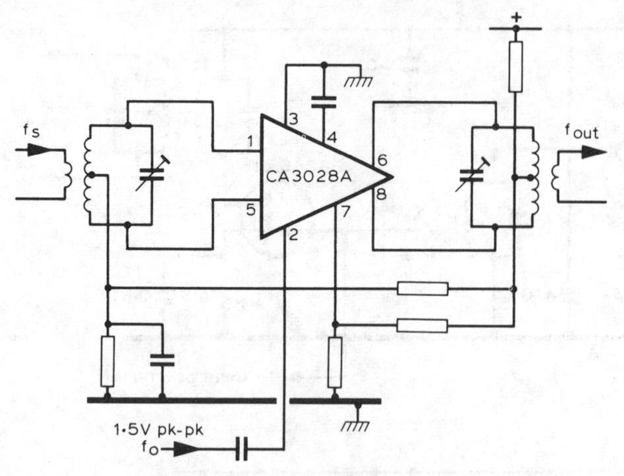

Fig 65. Balanced mixer using an ic

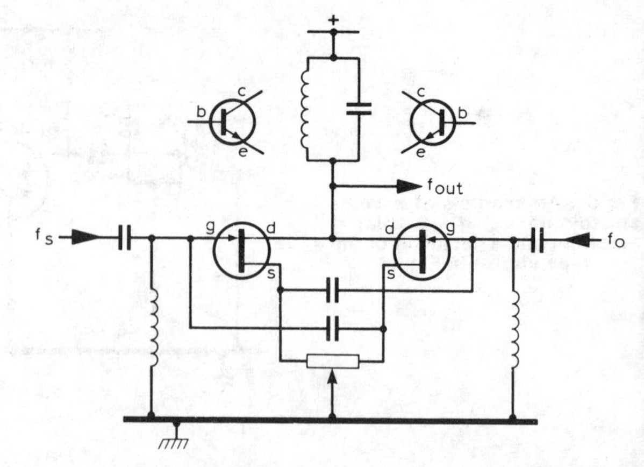

Fig 67. A double-balanced mixer using either bipolar transistors or fets. This has the advantages that no special transformers are needed and there is a small conversion gain. A simple balance control is used to reduce oscillator frequency (f_o) in the output

much greater dynamic range than any of the other arrangements but it has the disadvantage that there is a conversion loss, usually about 6dB.

There are available several high-performance wide-band double-balanced hot-carrier diode mixers. These devices are available either with coaxial connectors or with pins for insertion into printed circuit boards—the latter type is considerably cheaper and it is quite easy to attach to a board and arrange coaxial terminations to suit requirements. An example is illustrated in the photograph. These mixers normally have 50Ω inputs and so matching is fairly straightforward.

A typical packaged mixer is the MD108 (Anzac)—the performance is summarized below and its circuit is given in Fig 68(b).

Frequency range:
LO (L) port 5–50MHz
RF (R) port 5–500MHz
I.F. (X) port dc–500MHz

Conversion loss:
5–500MHz 7dB max
150–500MHz 9dB max
+7dBm lo power

Input power: 400mW maximum

The main disadvantage with this type of mixer is the high local oscillator power needed, normally greater than +5dBm (3mW) to achieve a low conversion loss. This combination does however ensure excellent signal handling, and in transceivers it is possible to use the same mixer on transmit and receive. Details of several types of this form of mixer are given in the Appendix.

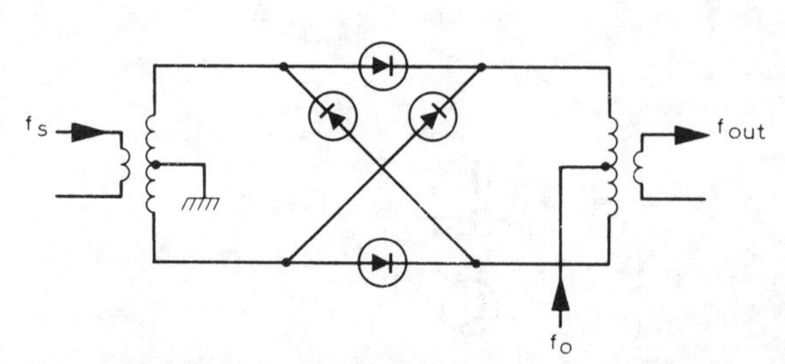

Fig 68(a). A diode double-balanced mixer (ring modulator). This type has a wide dynamic range but does have the disadvantage that there is an insertion loss of about 6dB

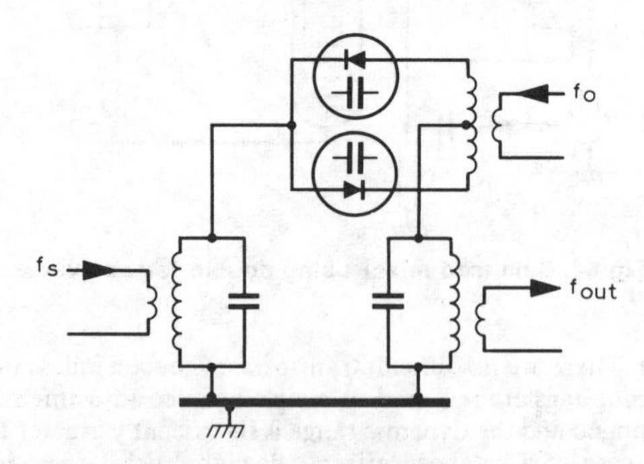

Fig 66. A special type of balanced mixer using varactor diodes which is suitable for use in up-converters. The oscillator frequency should be three to five times that of the highest signal frequency

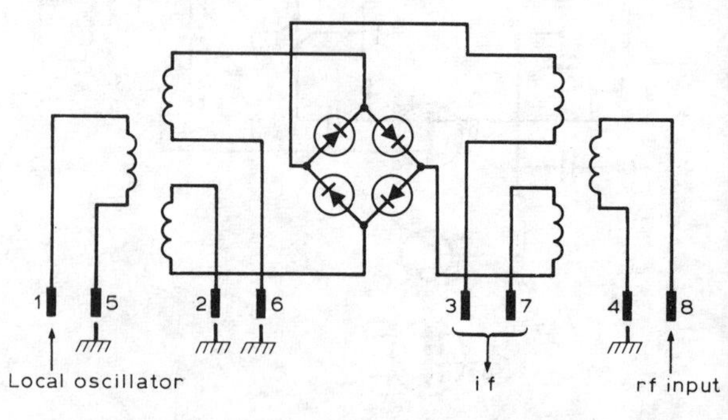

Fig 68(b). Circuit of the MD108 double-balanced mixer

A mixer board using the MD108 and miniature coaxial connectors

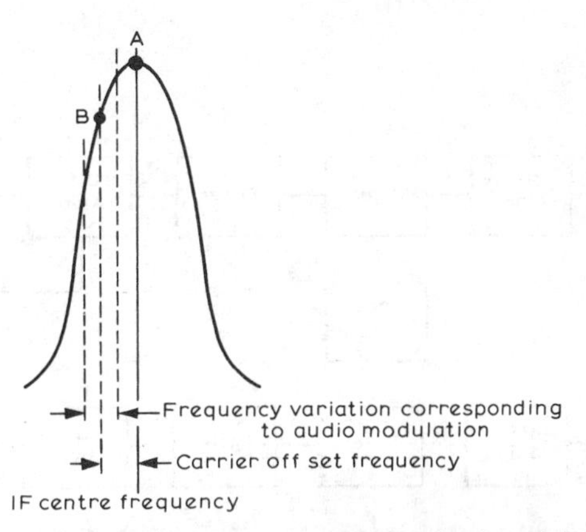

Fig 69. How slope detection can be used for the demodulation of fm signals in an a.m. receiver. By tuning the receiver so that the carrier of an nbfm signal is offset (either side) from the maximum (centre) of the i.f. amplifier response (A) to a position (B), the audio causing the frequency variation up and down the selectivity curve will cause corresponding currents to flow through the detector, thus providing an audio output

High-level (power) mixers

Although for most purposes one or other of the mixer circuit arrangements shown will be found suitable for many applications, there are nevertheless a few cases where high-level (power) mixing is required.

Some higher-level diode ring mixers are available but these are usually expensive. Valves, either triodes (2C39A) or double tetrodes (QQV02–6/3–10), offer a ready solution.

Frequency modulated signals

The receiver for the proper reception of fm signals is significantly different from an ordinary a.m. signal receiver. The difference lies primarily in the use of a discriminator preceded by one or more limiter i.f. amplifier stages, instead of the usual envelope demodulator.

Fortunately, however, this does not prevent the a.m. receiver from being used to demodulate fm signals which can be done by use of slope detection. It should be remembered that although reception by this method is quite effective for signals of good carrier strength, it *is* only a compromise and loses a considerable amount of the benefit that can be achieved when a proper limiter-discriminator is used.

It is apparent from Fig 69 that by using slope detection the receiver is not tuned to the peak signal; and an additional problem is that without adequate limiting noise is just as big a problem as with a.m. signals so that it may be an advantage to switch off the agc where this is possible.

The most satisfactory approach to the problem of reception of fm signals, using an existing a.m. receiver is, of course, to add the additional circuits, as a correctly designed adaptor. This may either be added internally or externally depending on the actual receiver concerned, but the addition will be well worth the effort.

An important point which should be borne in mind, however, is that most amateur communications use only narrow band frequency modulation (nbfm), which makes necessary a somewhat different approach to discriminator design than that used for fm broadcast programmes. The i.f. amplifier bandwidth should be compatible with the signal bandwidth, similar to that normally used in the general purpose communications receiver, eg 3dB bandwidth of 7·5kHz. Undoubtedly, as with any form of signal, the most satisfactory type of receiver is one specially designed for receiving nbfm signals.

Single-conversion superheterodyne receivers are used now that high-frequency i.f. block filters designed to give the bandwidth/bandshape characteristic necessary for adequate adjacent channel selectivity for nbfm signals are available. An immediate advantage of this type of receiver is in the absence of spurious signals, which in a double conversion (or tunable i.f. plus converter) receiver can be caused by the two local oscillators beating to produce signals at the intermediate frequency.

Apart from the requirements of correct choice of intermediate frequency characteristics, which will be discussed in more detail later, there are several important features to be considered before building a special receiver (see Fig 70). Taken from the front end to the reproducer (loudspeaker or phones), these are as follows:

- RF stage gain and pre-mixer selectivity;
- Mixer conversion gain and choice of local oscillator;
- Choice of intermediate frequency, bandwidth/bandshape characteristics;
- I.F. amplifier gain and limiting characteristics;
- FM detector characteristics, including a.m. rejection, capture ratio and noise;
- Audio frequency amplifier, gain, frequency response and power output.

Intermediate frequency

Most readers will be familiar with the effects of multiple response in the presence of strong signals, frequently found when receivers with an i.f. of 455kHz or lower are used.

It is an advantage to use a reasonably high frequency such as 9 or 10·7MHz or even higher, remembering that at these frequencies the amplifier selectivity will require an appropriate filter. The actual choice will depend upon the filter that is available, or assembled from separate crystals or ceramic elements.

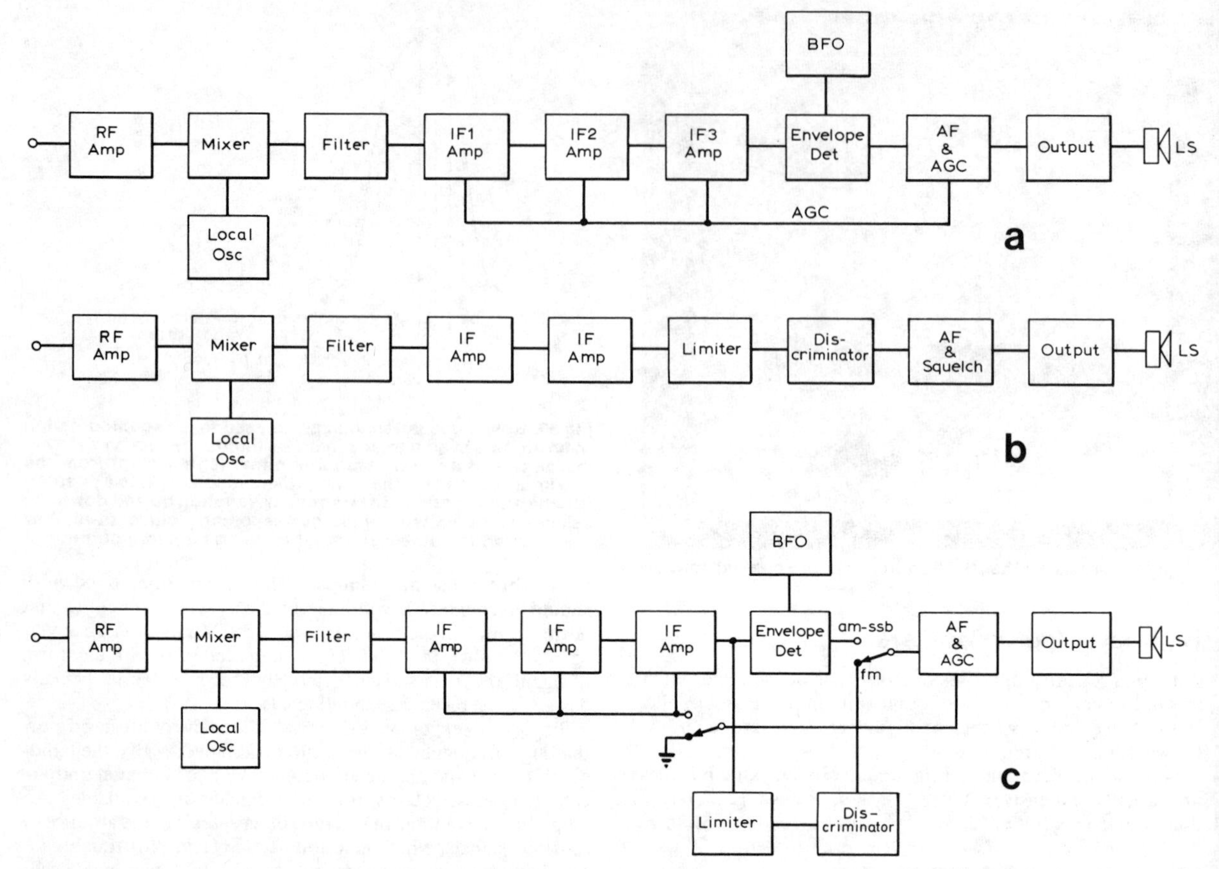

Fig 70. Comparison of the essential stages of receivers for a.m., ssb and fm reception. (a) shows an a.m./ssb receiver, (b) an fm receiver and (c) a combined receiver

There are many commercial filters available for both 9 and 10·7MHz, and for the latter coupling transformers are available for use with either valves or semiconductors.

While the price of the filter will be very high compared to the cheaply and readily available wideband ceramic filters, it must be realized that the narrow-band filter is at the heart of the receiver in terms of the all-important selectivity characteristics. The performance of the receiver in terms of overall selectivity is determined by correct choice of i.f. filter employed.

Bandwidth

The use of a suitable crystal or ceramic filter will both set the i.f. bandwidth and bandshape and also simplify the alignment of the whole i.f. amplifier. It should be placed in the circuit as early as possible, preferably between the mixer and the first i.f. amplifier stage, but this may not always be possible. Where, for example, a noise blanker is used for the reception of a.m./ssb, the noise blanker requires wide bandwidth (>50kHz) to reduce noise pulse distortion to a minimum. So for correct operation the blanker must be fitted before the narrow-bandwidth filter.

Commercial crystal filters usually have low input and output impedances (eg 470Ω at 20pF) and require to be fed and matched to low source and load impedances.

A multi-element filter is essential in an fm receiver design incorporating an integrated circuit i.f. amplifier. The i.f. stages within the ic are dc coupled internally and therefore no extra filter elements can be added to these stages. That means that all selectivity/bandwidth requirements must be satisfied before the i.f. amplifier.

The actual bandwidth should be, for preference, narrow and compatible with the amateurs' definition of narrow band. That is, with a maximum deviation of 2·5kHz from centre frequency (compared with the 75kHz deviation of broadcast signals on Band II).

Block filter characteristics

While i.f. block filters for use with a.m. and ssb receivers introduce negligible audio modulation distortion before the detector, care should be taken in choosing a filter which will introduce negligible audio modulation distortion in a narrow-band fm receiving system.

SSB filters in particular possess (depending on the number of poles), a near ideal rectangular characteristic, that is, a substantially flat passband with sharply defined cut-off frequencies and rapid cut-off in the attenuation band, necessary to obtain the required selectivity characteristics. However, this type of characteristic can introduce severe phase distortion and hence audio modulation distortion into a narrow-band fm system even

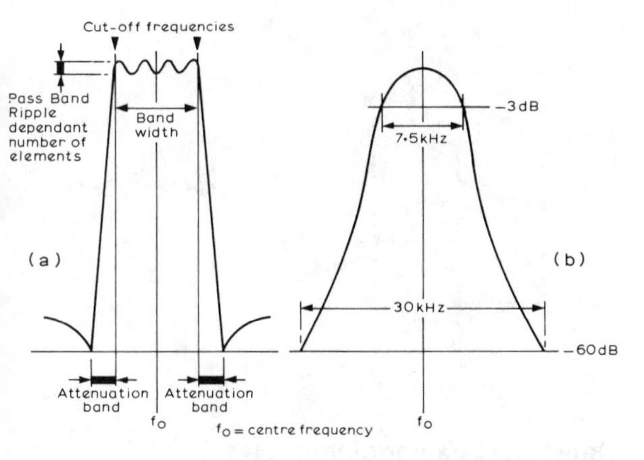

Fig 71. Block filter characteristics: (a) ssb, (b) nbfm

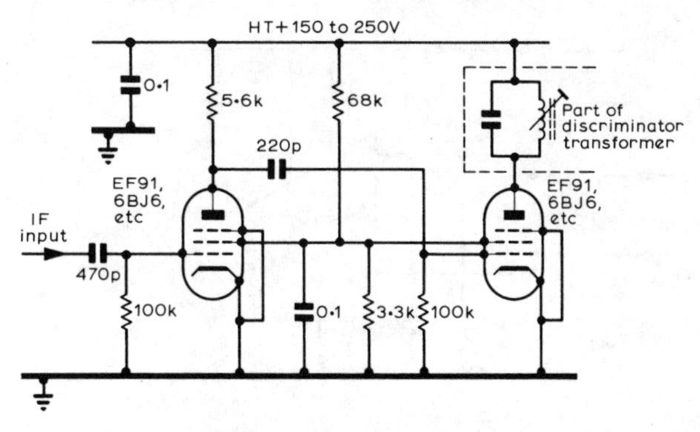

Fig 72. A two-stage valve limiter

Table 8. Performance of typical crystal filters for 10·7MHz

	OC1121A	OC1062G	
Pass band −3dB	±7·5	±3·75	kHz
Pass band ripple pk to pk	2	2	dB
Stop band loss*	55	90	dB
for frequencies beyond	±55	±12·5	kHz
maintained to	±300	±300	kHz
Terminating impedance	910	560	Ω
across	25	25	pF
Insertion loss*	3	3	dB

* Relative to maximum transmission level.

though peak deviation is limited to ±3kHz from the centre frequency.

A correctly designed filter for nbfm should have a −3dB bandwidth of not less than 7·5kHz and a −60dB bandwidth of approximately 30kHz. The passband and attenuation band shape should possess a rounded characteristic with non-defined cut-off frequencies approximating to a linear phase type filter. Fig 71 illustrates the differences of characteristic.

Note that any amplitude component introduced by the filter on a carrier will be eliminated by the limiting i.f. amplifier in the receiver.

I.F. amplifier and limiter

In a typical fm receiver, using valves or transistors with three stages of amplification, the first two stages are operated linearly and the final stage as a limiter amplifier. The limiter ensures that any fm signals containing amplitude variations are clipped, so maintaining the fm carrier level at constant amplitude. Therefore, the limiter provides a high degree of a.m. rejection before the fm detector stage.

The linear i.f. amplifiers should provide high gain to ensure that the limiter amplifier is operating as a limiter even with the large changes of signal level. The limiting sensitivity of an fm receiver is usually expressed as the signal level reduction at the antenna terminal necessary to cause the output at the detector to fall by 3dB (termed *−3dB limiting sensitivity*).

Where valves are used as in Fig 72 they are normal straight μ or sharp cut-off types (such as EF91, 6BH6 etc) operating with low screen voltage to ensure limiting (overloading). The same types of valve operated at normal screen voltage can be used in the linear i.f. amplifier stages.

In i.f. amplifiers designed to use discrete transistors (Fig 73) standard npn or pnp hf silicon types can be used without unilateralization (neutralized) for maximum stability and limited gain. Suitable types for this application are:

npn types BF194/195 (Mullard) BF394/395 (Motorola)
pnp type BF450/451 (ITT/Siemens)

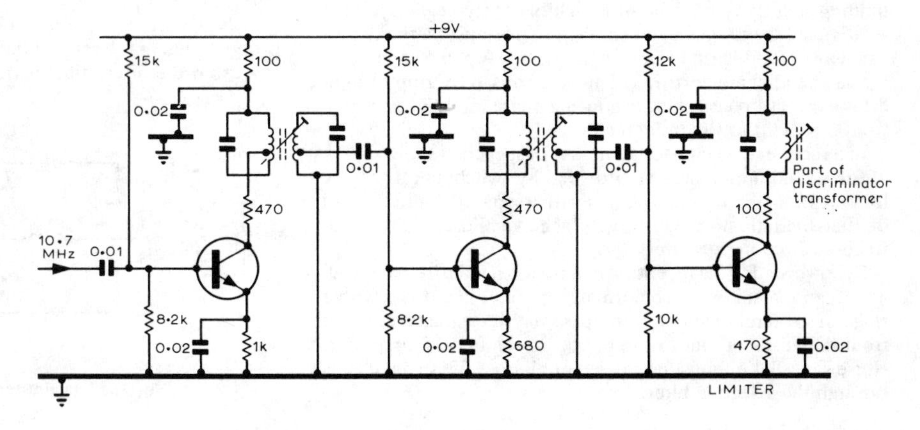

Fig 73. A three-stage i.f. amplifier and limiter. Transistors are BF194 etc

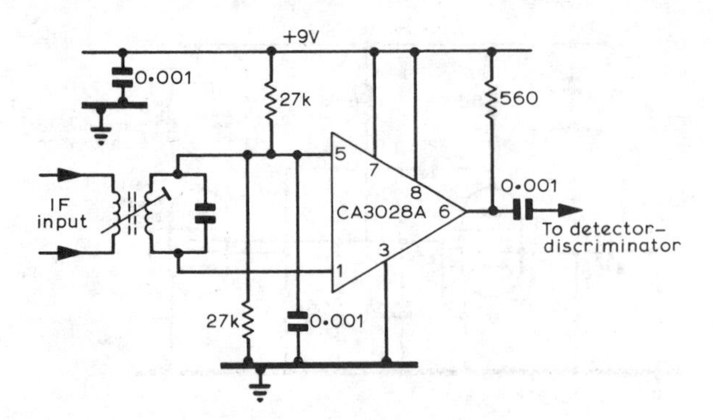

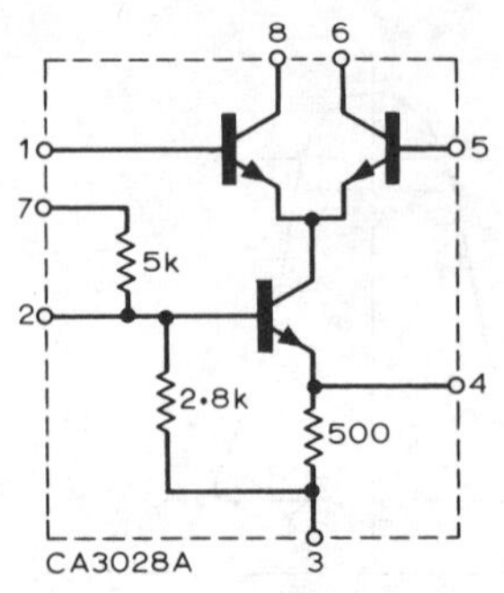

Fig 74. An ic limiter

In this design standard 10·7MHz i.f. transformer couplings are used and as will be seen from Fig 73 the base and collector of each transistor feed into a low source and load impedance. The impedances are low compared to the transistor input and output impedances at 10·7MHz. This arrangement is most suitable for a very high stability i.f. amplifier with an overall i.f. gain of about 86dB.

Capture effect and capture ratio

Capture effect occurs when two carrier-frequency signals each of varying signal strength at the antenna sockets of an fm receiver are co-channel—that is, the two carrier frequencies are identical (to the order of a few hertz). Assuming each carrier is deviated with a different modulation content, and the signal strength of either carrier is varying above and below the other, the recovered signal at the fm detector will alternate between one modulation content and the other. Note that the transmitters will not normally be co-sited.

Capture ratio is that between the relative strengths of the received signal (carriers) to cause the modulation content to change between one and the other source. Theoretically, for zero capture effect there should be zero capture ratio, but this would indicate an a.m. rejection capability at the limiter and fm detector approaching infinity. In practice the ratio is always finite although the better the design of limiter and detector in relation to a.m. rejection the lower the ratio.

A well-designed system can give a capture ratio of 2 to 3dB. Capture effect is a very important aspect to be considered for fm mobile operation, particularly on 144MHz where co-channel working is the rule rather than the exception. Apart from very careful design of the limiter and fm detector, overall limiting sensitivity must be of a high order (typically 1μV for −3dB) and the i.f. passband characteristics must be ripple free to at least ±2·5kHz of i.f. centre frequency. A poor shape in the i.f. passband characteristic (such as is caused by ripple) indicates excessive phase shift, producing phase modulation which will be present at the fm detector.

In a receiver designed for all modes of speech as shown in Fig 70(c) initial limiting may be provided by switching off the agc for reception of fm. This, together with a separate limiter ahead of the discriminator, will largely achieve the advantages of freedom from impulse noise.

If, however, for the reception of a.m./ssb it is desired to install an i.f. noise blanker which normally operates in parallel with a stage of i.f. amplification, in this case the filter must be moved from the mixer output to the output of the first i.f. amplifier. Noise cancellation must be carried out before the signal passes through the selective filter.

Detectors, demodulators and discriminators

The means by which fm signals are converted into audio are significantly different from those used for a.m. signals. There are a number of classic types, but to some extent the choice will depend on the intermediate frequency and bandwidth used.

The Foster-Seeley discriminator

This is sometimes called *phase difference* type because it depends for its operation on the phase difference of 90° between the two tuned circuits of the coupling transformer (Fig 75). The voltage across the primary is injected into the centre tap of the secondary. The voltage developed across each diode load resistor is (or should be) equal and of opposite polarity for an unmodulated carrier. When the frequency is deviated by modulation the signal across one load resistor will increase while the other will be decreased, so that an output proportional to the frequency deviation is produced.

This type has very good linearity when preceded by adequate limiter(s), but is, however, of relatively poor sensitivity.

Ratio detector

The ratio detector is probably the most common type used in fm receivers, it is a self limiting device but should preferably be preceded by a limiter stage to obtain best results. The linearity is somewhat poorer than the Foster-Seeley but its sensitivity is appreciably greater (Figs 76 to 78).

Compared to the Foster-Seeley discriminator the ratio detector type has inherently a higher amplitude rejection capability. The problem of making the detectors insensitive to amplitude variations is accomplished by dividing the rectified i.f. voltages into two parts so that the ratio of the rectified voltages is proportional to the ratio of the i.f. voltage applied to the detectors from the discriminator transformer.

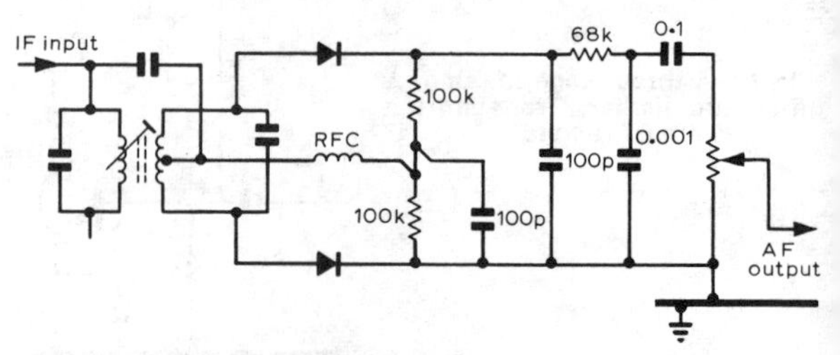

Fig 75. The Foster-Seeley discriminator

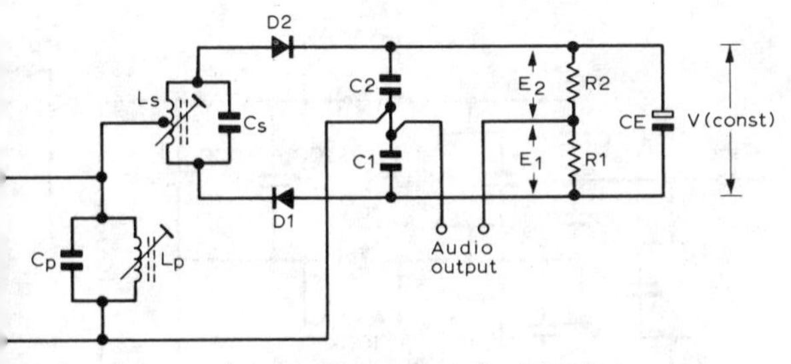

Fig 76. The basic ratio detector

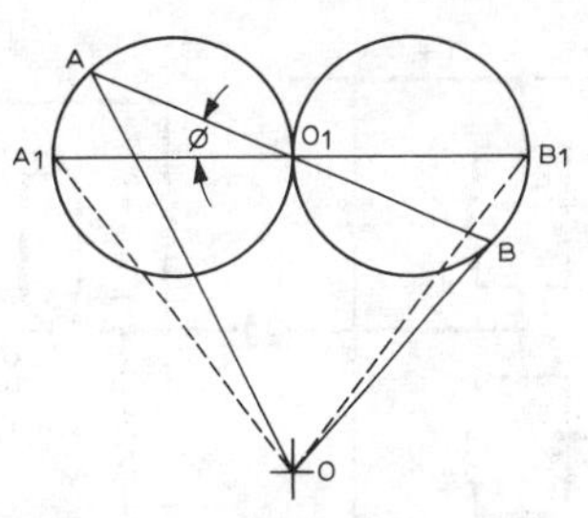

Fig 77. Representation of a voltage applied to each diode with variation of frequency. The rectified voltages E_1 and E_2 are approximately equal to OA and OB, the phase angle is zero at the centre frequency

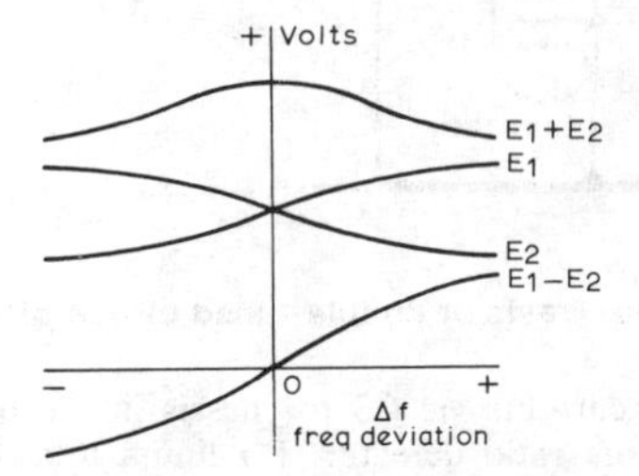

Fig 78. Alternative method of illustrating voltages present in Fig 76

Providing the sum of the rectified voltages is held constant by a suitable method, and if their ratio remains constant, then the individual rectified voltages will also remain constant. Short- and/or long-term variations in the amplitude of the input signal will therefore have negligible effect on the rectified output signal. This sum voltage is normally held constant by a capacitor of several microfarads, large enough to prevent the rectified output voltage varying at speech modulation frequencies: a time constant of the order of 200ms (0·2s) is required. The voltage across this capacitor will vary in proportion to the average signal amplitude and therefore adjust itself automatically to an optimum operating level. Providing that the input signal to the detector does not fall below such a level determined by deteriorating diode characteristic at low levels, a wide range of input signals will not affect amplitude rejection.

In the circuit of the basic ratio detector, Fig 76, it will be evident that the detector diodes are series connected so they each carry the same current.

The rectified voltages add to produce the constant sum voltage $E_1 + E_2$. The ratio detector is sensitive only to frequency deviation, in the case of amateur receivers deviation at an audio rate by speech frequencies. At centre frequency there is zero deviation. Therefore the phase angle (ϕ) is zero (Fig 77). The phase angle value is changed with deviation and increases as the deviation increases. The resultant recovered audio signal amplitude at the audio output point will vary as the deviation varies. However, as the diodes are connected in reverse polarity there will be a 6dB loss in audio recovery, so when $E_1 - E_2$ changes by a given amount, the audio recovery will be $E_1 - E_2$. When the rectified voltage is stabilized by the capacitor as in Fig 76, the output characteristic changes. For small deviations from centre frequency where $E_1 + E_2$ is constant, the circuit will have the same output as a conventional discriminator (with one diode reversed). With large deviations $E_1 + E_2$ falls and the constant stabilized voltage will improve linearity and therefore increase the maximum deviation for a given amount of distortion.

A practical ratio detector is illustrated in Fig 79. The circuit includes the final limiting i.f. amplifier. The ratio detector transformer can be a standard broadcast fm receiver type, centred on 10·7MHz, which will eliminate any transformer design problems. If a valve limiter is used the primary dynamic resistance will need to be of such a value as to obtain the necessary power match to the anode impedance. The diodes should be germanium all-glass construction types (D07) such as AA119 or the gold-bonded AA143—matched pairs are to be preferred. Resistors R1 and R2 assist in dynamic balance and maximize a.m. rejection at centre frequency. Capacitors C1 and C2

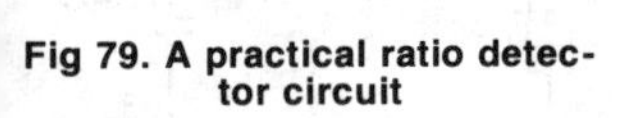
Fig 79. A practical ratio detector circuit

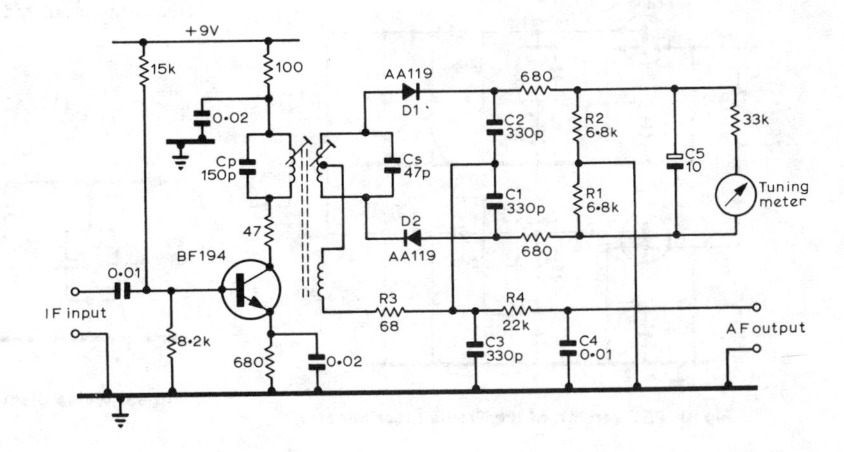

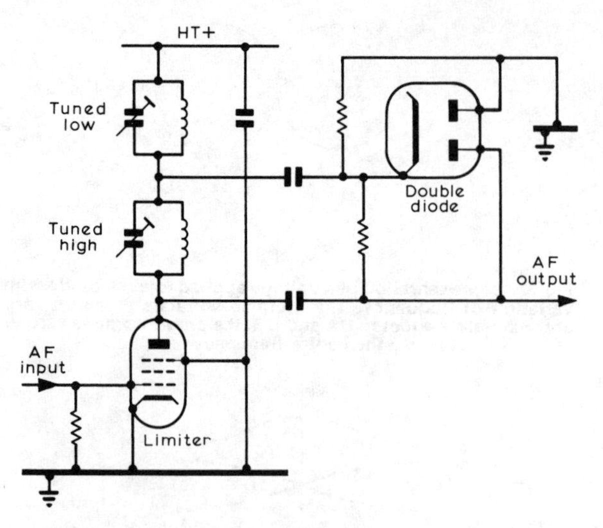

Fig 80. Travis or double-tuned circuit discriminator

bypass i.f. currents via C3 to chassis in the balanced phase bridge of the ratio detector. R3 limits total diode current, improving bridge balance and further improving a.m. rejection characteristic. R4 and C4 form a low-pass filter to limit the high af response.

The input impedance of the following audio amplifier should be high, not less than 50kΩ, to prevent undue attenuation of the recovered audio. A tuning meter can be driven by the detector as shown. Alignment of the ratio detector is simple, although best carried out at a low carrier level. The tuning meter itself provides indication of maximum output at centre frequency, and primary resonance is achieved by adjusting inductance Lp. A centre zero meter is necessary for setting up Ls. The meter is connected to the junction R3/C3 and chassis and Ls is adjusted for zero output at centre frequency.

Travis or double-tuned circuit discriminator

In the arrangement shown in Figs 80 and 81, two tuned circuits are used. One is tuned above and the other below the i.f. centre frequency by an amount comparable with the maximum deviation to be used. It is important to prevent coupling between two

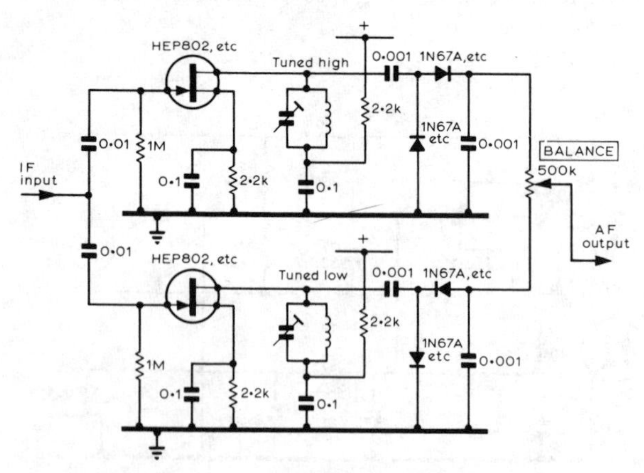

Fig 81. FET version of the Travis discriminator

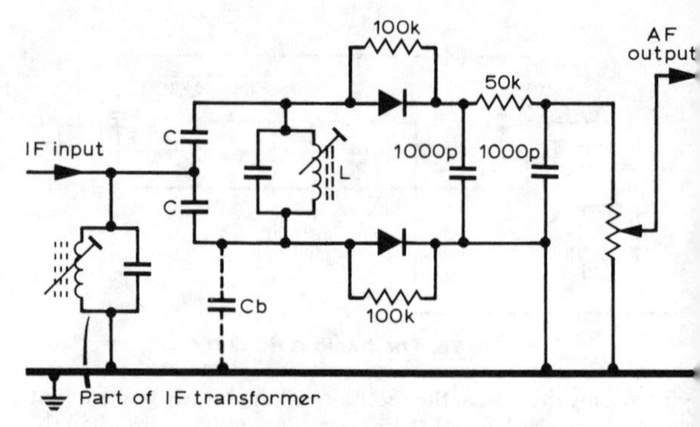

Fig 82. Weiss discriminator

circuits and as shown in the fet version (Fig 81) there are virtually two complete units, with their outputs combined.

For nbfm purposes the circuits should be resonated at + and −5kHz from the centre frequency.

Weiss discriminator

The considerable advantage of this type of discriminator, shown in Fig 82, is that no special transformer is required. The input is taken from the limiter to the discriminator via two equal capacitors C, and the tuned circuit C/L is resonated at the intermediate frequency.

The *Q* of the tuned circuit will to a large extent determine the performance of the unit. For higher frequencies such as 9 or 10·7MHz use is made of a crystal (x) to provide a suitably highly selective element (Fig 83) to give a good output level at a very small bandwidth relative to the i.f. frequency. This may be shunted by a suitable inductor or resistor to obtain an appropriate bandwidth.

Locked oscillator limiter discriminator

This type has enjoyed a considerable popularity as a simple means of converting valve receivers, and is notable for its considerable sensitivity. It does, however, have the disadvantage of requiring a special valve, the 6DT6A or 6BN6, the latter having been used quite extensively for adaptations.

The quadrature circuit (Fig 84) L1/C1 is tuned to the i.f. frequency. This can be checked by adjusting for the maximum negative voltage at testpoint TP when the receiver is tuned to a steady unmodulated signal.

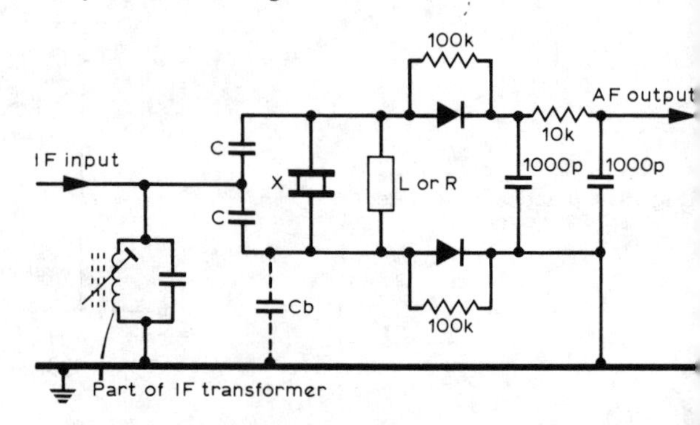

Fig 83. Weiss discriminator with additional crystal for better selectivity

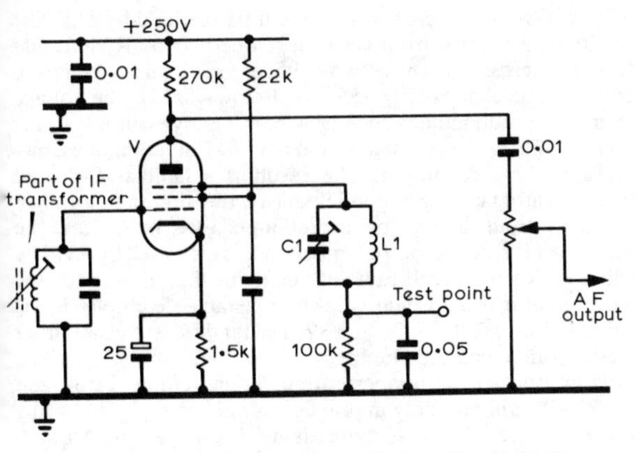

Fig 84. The locked oscillator limiter-discriminator

Pulse count discriminator

An advantage of this type of discriminator (Fig 85) is that no special coils or transformers are needed.

The i.f. signal at 450 to 470kHz is applied to the long-tailed pair limiter TR1 and TR2, and the variable resistor adjusts the limiting threshold and is set for best a.m. rejection. The limited output is used to switch TR3 on and off, giving a square wave of nearly 12V amplitude, which provides a constant quantity of charge via C into the emitter of TR4. Hence the emitter current of TR4 is directly proportional to frequency, and so variations in frequency produce a corresponding voltage variation across R.

As shown, the circuit is set up for about 500kHz = 10V, ie 20mV/kHz, so ± 2·5kHz deviation produces ± 50mV peak. This is amplified about 50 times by TR5 and TR6 to give an output suitable for feeding into the receiver af stages.

The circuit can be used at any i.f. up to 500kHz without adjustment, but for a much lower i.f. (eg 100kHz), C can with advantage be raised to increase the af output. Conversely, if C is reduced for a higher i.f. then the af output will fall, and a mixer converting to a lower i.f. may be preferable. The voltage produced across R is given by

$$V = v.C.R.f$$

where v = output pulse amplitude of TR4 = 12V−0·2V and f = the instantaneous i.f. frequency

Hence a frequency deviation of $\pm\ \Delta f$ produces a peak-to-peak voltage of $2.v.C.R.\Delta f$.

As all these quantities are either easily measured or can be defined with accurate components, an ac peak millivoltmeter can be used to measure the deviation at TR4 output.

In practice it may be convenient to find the dc output across R when a crystal controlled bfo is fed in and derive its millivolts per kilohertz this way, and measure the ac gain of the amplifier TR5, TR6 so that a less sensitive ac voltmeter can be used at the output of TR1. The meter will then not be upset by the residual i.f. voltages.

In use, the prototype device has rendered a weak fm signal quite readable when skirt detection gave barely detectable af output.

Note that TR5 and TR6, as well as amplifying the signal, also serve as an af limiter since, although the discriminator output is only 50mV peak of audio, noise voltages can produce outputs of 9·5V when a signal is near the i.f. limiter threshold. Although the circuit may work without TR5 and TR6, their omission will show the need for some form of limiter.

NBFM adaptors

With the circuit of Fig 86 full limiting is achieved with an input of about 200μV and output is about 100mV for a deviation of 5kHz, or 300mV for 15kHz. Maximum audio output occurs with the volume control at maximum resistance. For zero output pin 4 can be shunted to earth, a feature which would be useful in a switched a.m./fm receiver.

Input to the unit shown in Fig 87 is taken from the receiver i.f. via a 50pF capacitor and a length of screened cable as shown in the small inset diagram, and applied across the base of the first transistor, a BC107. This is followed by an integrated circuit device, an RCA CA3013 or CA3014. The transformer T1 must be suitable for the intermediate frequency chosen, which can be anywhere in the frequency range 100kHz to 50MHz. With the link in position 1, a de-emphasis of −6dB per octave will be applied for phase modulation. In position 2, attenuation is introduced but with a flat frequency response so that output levels are similar for fm or pm.

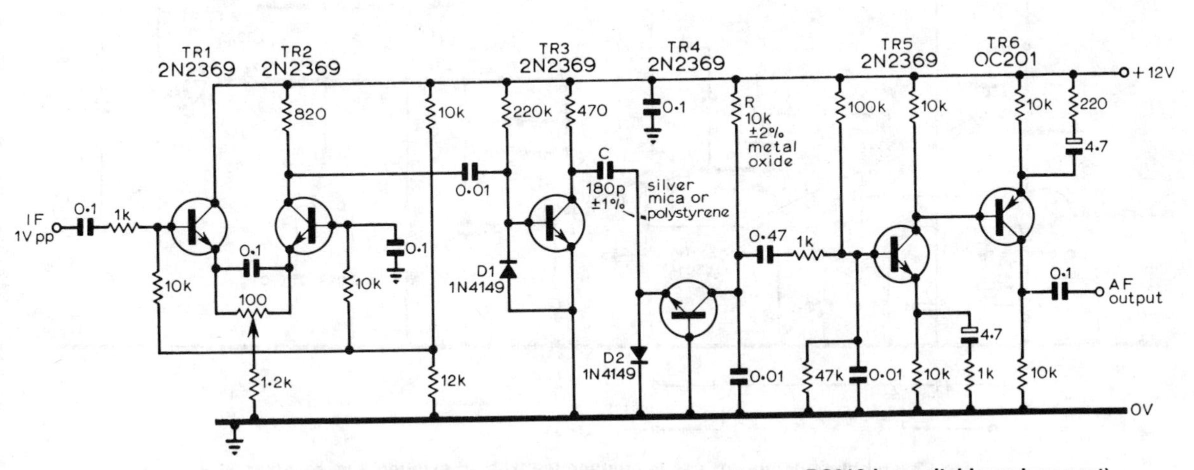

Fig 85. A pulse-count discriminator (note that OC201 is now obsolete—a BC212 is a suitable replacement)

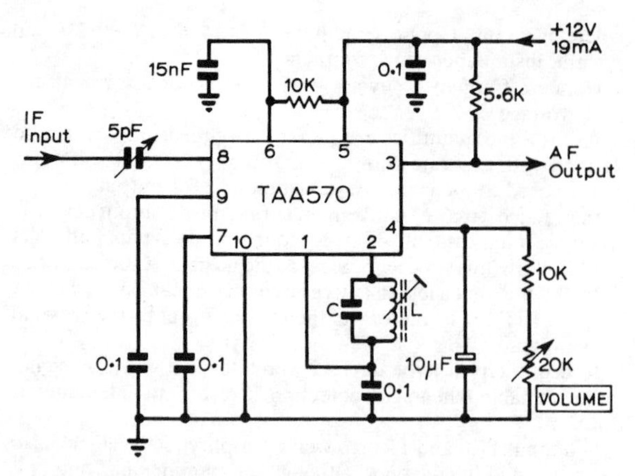

Fig 86. NBFM adaptor suitable for receivers having an i.f. of up to 6MHz. The values of L and C should provide resonance at the i.f. of the receiver in use

Specification: Input 30µV rms to commence limiting, 100µV—7dB, 300µV—1½dB, 1mV and over is 0dB. Output is in excess of 100mV rms for 5kHz deviation.

The principle of the receiver adaptor (Fig 88) is that a 455kHz signal from the receiver's first i.f. stage or mixer is amplified by TR4 and delivered to the limiter TR5. For simplicity and broad bandwidth both these stages are R–C coupled. The R–C values are chosen for a flat frequency response in the neighbourhood of 455kHz and a roll-off in gain above and below this frequency. The fm signal from TR5 is demodulated by the diodes D1 and D2. The parallel tuned circuit, C3–L5, is adjusted to resonate at a frequency slightly above 455kHz. At resonance, C3–L5 is essentially an open circuit and the signal is rectified almost entirely by D1. Slightly below 455kHz C3–L5 becomes inductively reactive, and at some frequency will be series resonant with C4. At such a frequency a large i.f. voltage will be developed across C4 and will be rectified by D2. The rectified i.f. voltage from D1 is developed across R2 and that from D2 across R3. These two voltages are equal and opposite and will cancel at exactly 455kHz. Below 455kHz the voltage from D2 predominates, giving a net negative output at S1; above 455kHz the rectified signal from D1 predominates, giving a positive dc output. The result is a familiar S-shaped discriminator curve. For good linearity, the discriminator must be driven from a source of correct impedance. In this case the source is TR5, and its output impedance is increased by R1. The value of R1 has significant influence on the linearity of the discriminator response curve. An adjustable de-emphasis circuit consists of R4, C5, C6 and S2. The fet differential amplifier feeds a microammeter tuning indicator. The af amplifier is a little unusual, being temperature compensated by TR8—and the 2N498 will probably in practice usually be replaced by any silicon npn transistor of more than ½W dissipation. An a.m. detector is included, and it is necessary to keep the gain below the limiting level when receiving a.m.

NBFM discriminator for 455kHz

In this design (Fig 89) the limiter is fed from the same point as the a.m. detector, the final i.f. transformer being re-trimmed if necessary. The discriminator uses the standard Foster-Seeley arrangement with a centre-tapped secondary winding. A small amount of pre-emphasis is applied (100Ω and 47pF). If pre-emphasis were a standard feature of nbfm transmissions, values nearer to broadcast practice (100Ω and 1,000pF) would be more appropriate.

The performance of the discriminator is shown in Fig 90 and is substantially linear up to ± 4kHz deviation. At 2·5kHz deviation, audio output up to 5V peak may be expected. The limiter performance is given in the table.

The noise limiter is in no way an essential part of the fm discriminator. It just happened to be developed at the same time and was built into the discriminator chassis. The diodes are biased into conduction by the negative voltage derived from the

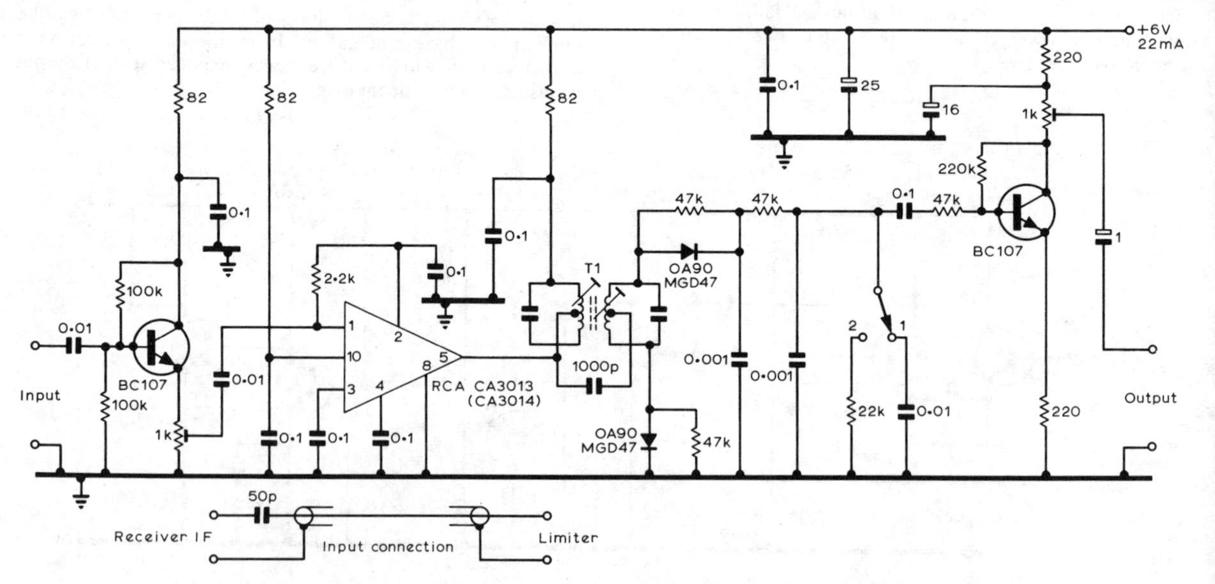

Fig 87. An nbfm adaptor for use in conjunction with an existing a.m. receiver

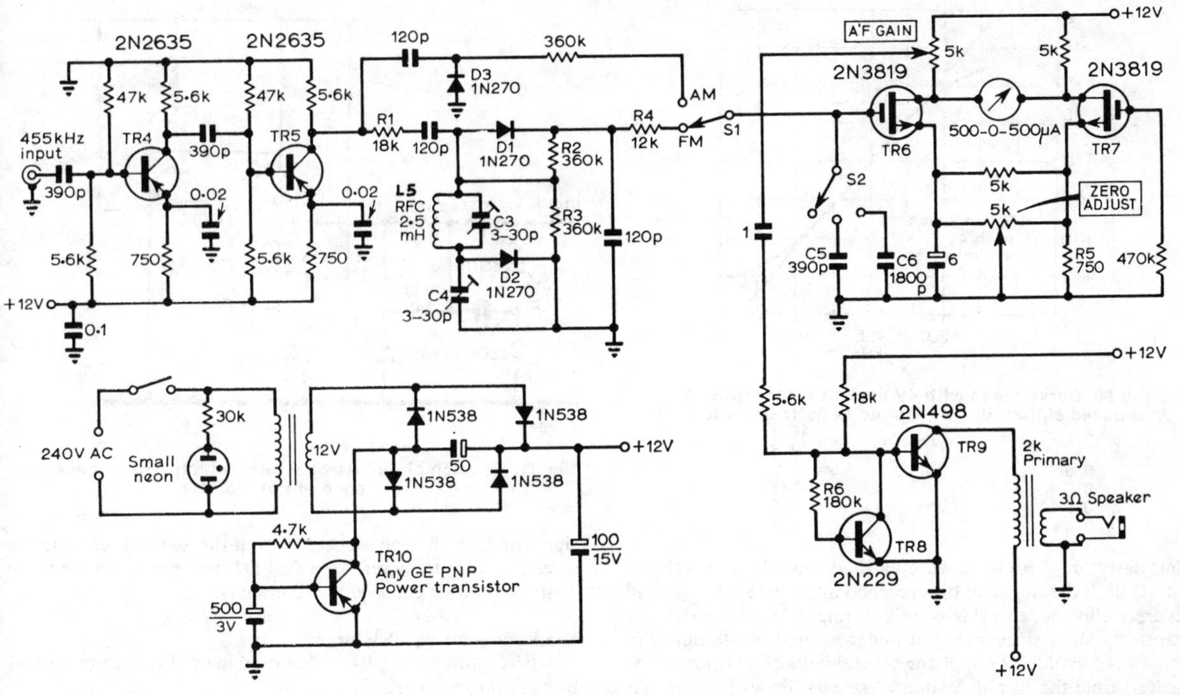

Fig 88. 455kHz fm receiving adaptor which does not require special discriminator transformer and offering simple alignment

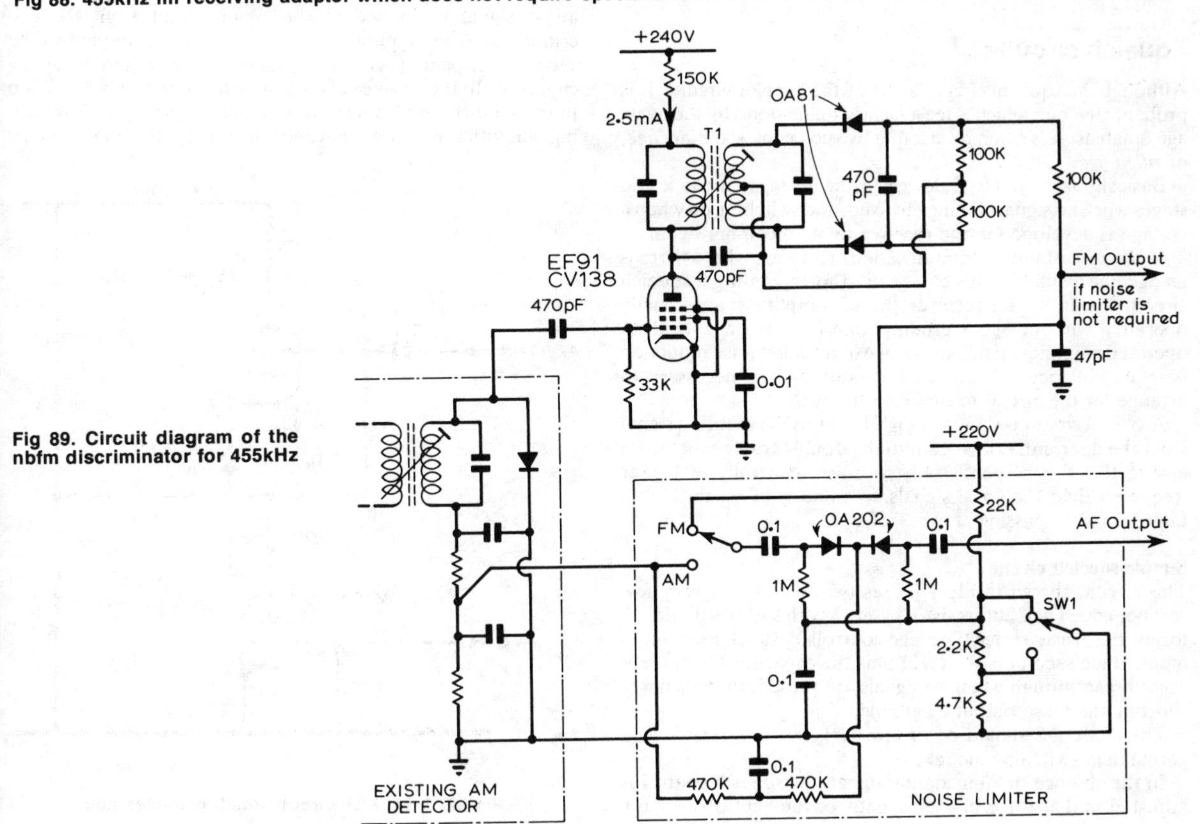

Fig 89. Circuit diagram of the nbfm discriminator for 455kHz

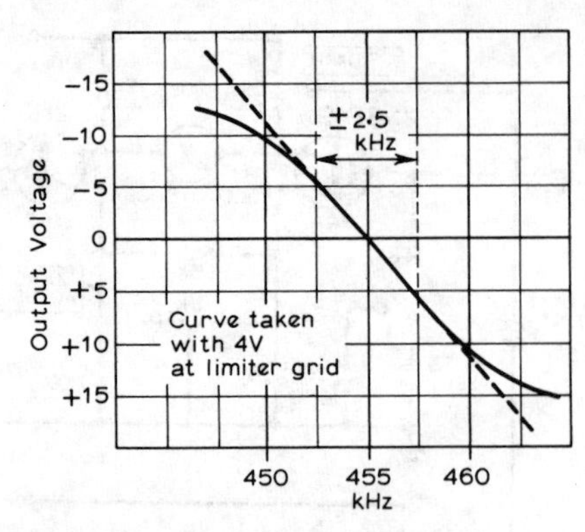

Fig 90. Curve taken with 4V peak at limiter grid

At reduced signal (V)	Output at 5kHz deviation (V)
4	10·1
1	9·8
0·5	8·9
0·2	5·7
0·1	3·0
0·05	1·5

a.m. detector. If point A were earthed, the diodes would be cut-off until the negative bias reached about 0·5V and would severely clip speech. This condition might be acceptable for extremely noisy situations, but under normal conditions clipping can be avoided by applying several volts of additional bias derived from the ht rail. Switch S1 selects the amount of bias from this source.

Squelch circuits

Although the squelch circuit is one of the simpler circuits, it is probably the one which is least clearly understood by the average amateur. It is often referred to by such names as *quiet agc*, or *silent agc*.

Basically it is simply a device for switching out the audio stages when no signal is being received, and switching on when a voltage is developed in the receiver by an incoming signal.

In the case of most communications receivers where there is an agc line available, this can be used for operating a squelch circuit, but in an fm receiver the i.f. amplifiers are usually operating without agc. Certainly, one or two stages will be operated as limiters if full advantage of impulse noise reduction is to be obtained. Under these conditions it is necessary to arrange for the circuit to operate on noise.

A typical circuit is shown in Fig 91. In this the rectified signal from the discriminator is fed into the double triode switch. To ensure that this responds only to noise, generally of higher frequency than the voice signals, its input is taken through a high-pass filter passing above 3kHz.

Simple squelch circuit

This circuit, shown in Fig 93, uses two diodes and very few components. The 220Ω resistor in series with a silicon diode D1 forms the usual series-type agc-controlled squelch arrangement. But a second diode (D2) plus the capacitor C1 prevent noise breakthrough when no signals are present by effectively shorting the noise output to ground.

The diode D2 should be of low back resistance, such as a germanium switching diode.

In the absence of an incoming signal, the squelch control is adjusted so that D1 is biassed slightly beyond cut-off; when a

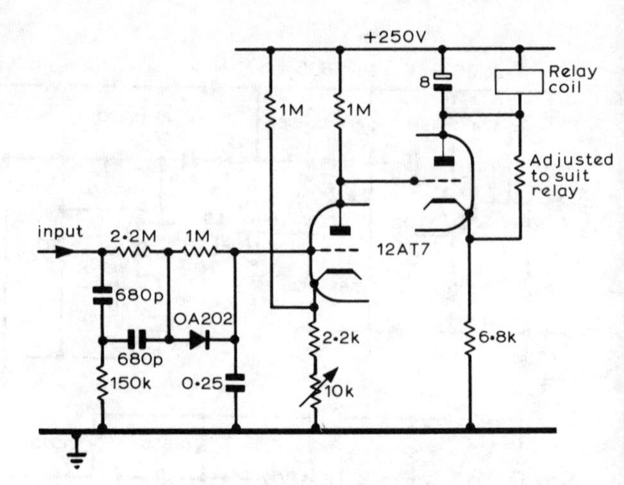

Fig 91. Squelch circuit using a relay which should have a resistance of around 8kΩ

signal arrives, the agc reduces current through V1, causing the screen voltage to increase, so that D1 now has its anode more positive than its cathode and conducts.

Semiconductor squelch circuits

The first, shown in Fig 94, is that used in the Pye Cambridge fm transmitter receiver.

The audio switching amplifier TR4 conducts only when an audio signal is applied to the squelch unit from the discriminator. The amplified audio signal is then coupled to the receiver af stages via the volume control and coupling capacitor. In the absence of a signal, when noise only is applied to the squelch unit from the discriminator, the squelch switching amplifier is biased beyond cut-off by the bias voltage

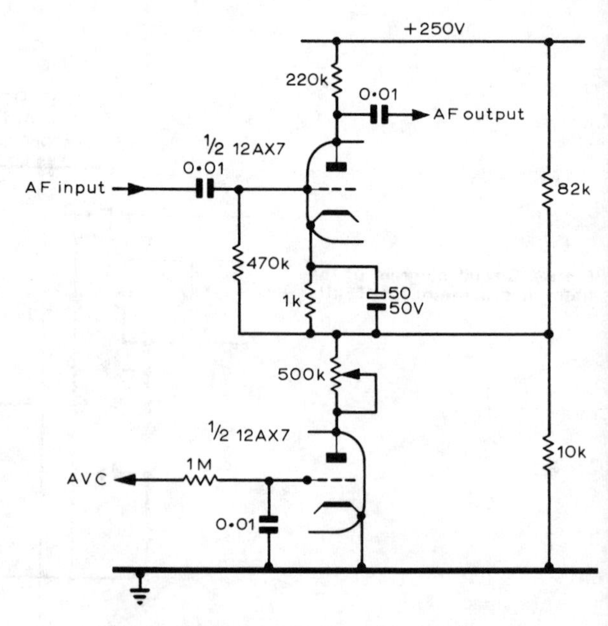

Fig 92. A squelch circuit which provides agc

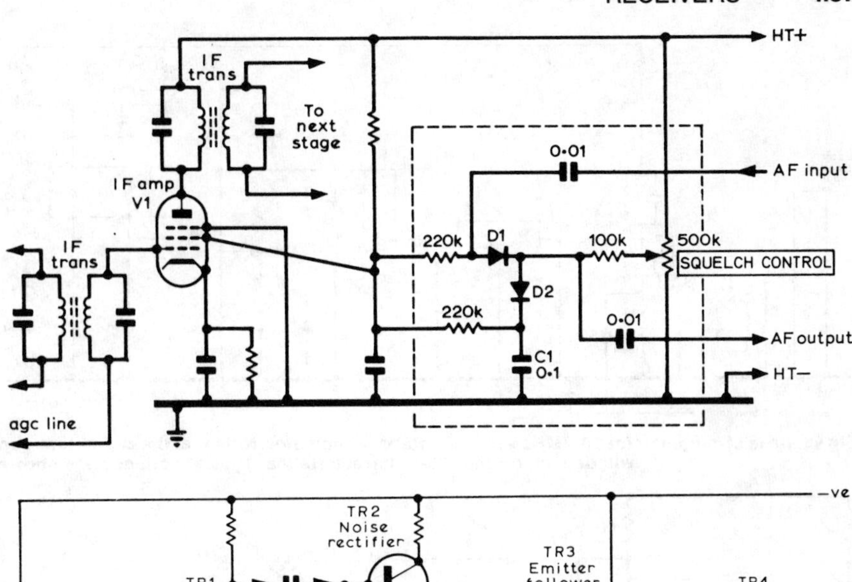

Fig 93. Simple squelch circuit suitable for adding to an existing valve receiver

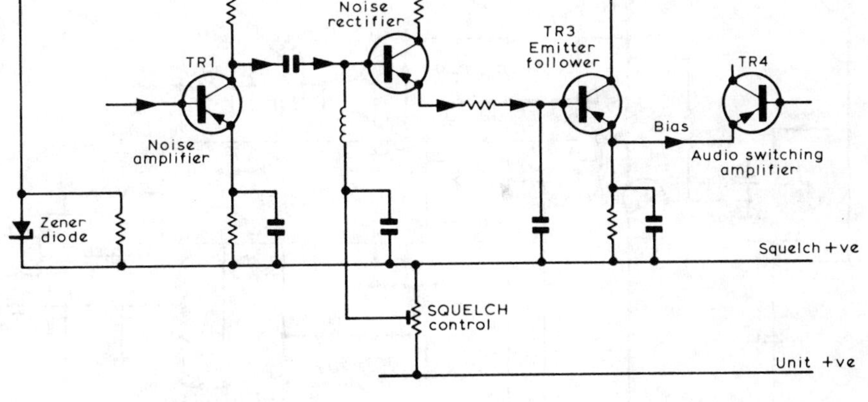

Fig 94. The squelch circuit used in the Pye Cambridge fm transmitter/receiver

applied to its emitter. The bias applied to the emitter when the output from the discriminator is noise only, is obtained from the preceding stages as shown below. The zener diode stabilizes the supply voltage to the complete squelch circuit and compensates the squelch sensitivity for changes in the supply voltage. The setting of the squelch control determines the bias reference level.

The circuit of Fig 95 illustrates the use of a Darlington amplifier which, when blocked by a high noise-level signal, will remove voltage from the relay coil. As soon as a signal of sufficient strength is received, the noise component will be decreased so that the amplifier is able to energize the relay. The time constant of the squelch switching can be matched to the required value by altering the capacitance of CT.

IC i.f. amplifier/detectors for fm

Two typical designs are shown in Figs 96 and 97, but for many applications the Plessey SL664 and SL665 (Fig 98) offer a simple solution to the i.f. amplifier, detector and audio amplifier requirement of small receivers. Although these units are essentially narrow band, the bandwidth is suitable for vehicle, hand-held or other receivers.

The tuned circuit connected between pins 4 and 5 may consist of a single tuned i.f. transformer, but a small toroid of about 15 turns tuned by a trimmer will give improved performance, having a higher Q. Supply voltage is normally 6V but this may be varied between 5 and 12V; consumption at 6V is 3mA (squelched) rising to 10mA (unsquelched) for SL664. The SL665 draws 6mA in either case. The audio power output from the SL664 is 250mW.

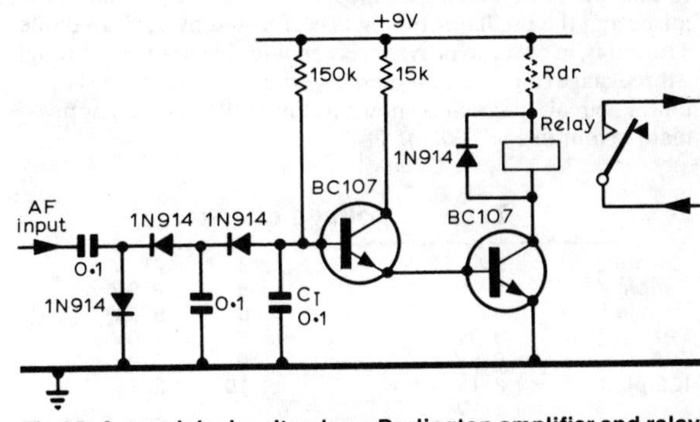

Fig 95. A squelch circuit using a Darlington amplifier and relay

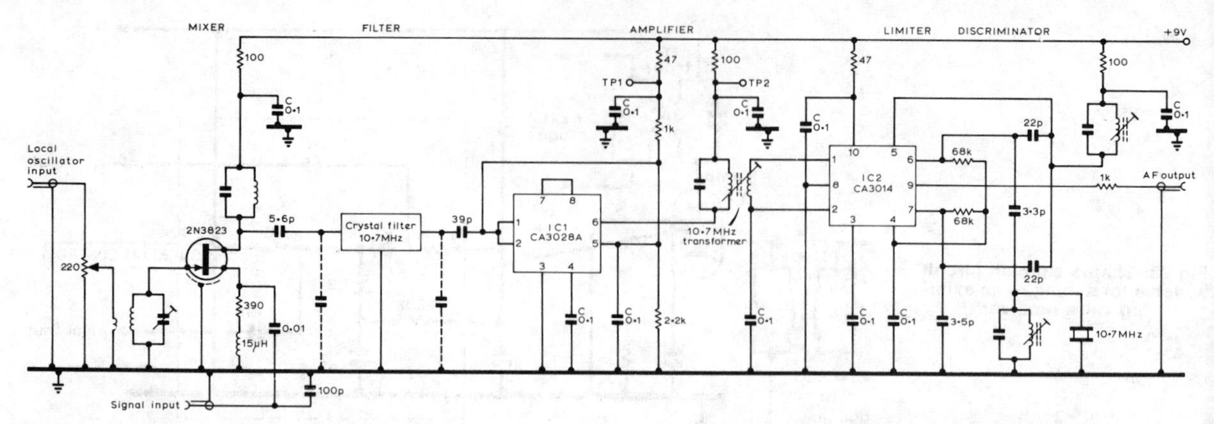

Fig 96. An ic i.f. amplifier for 10·7MHz with a crystal discriminator. Note that the capacitor coupling and those shown in dotted lines will depend on the filter characteristics. Typical voltages are shown in Table 9

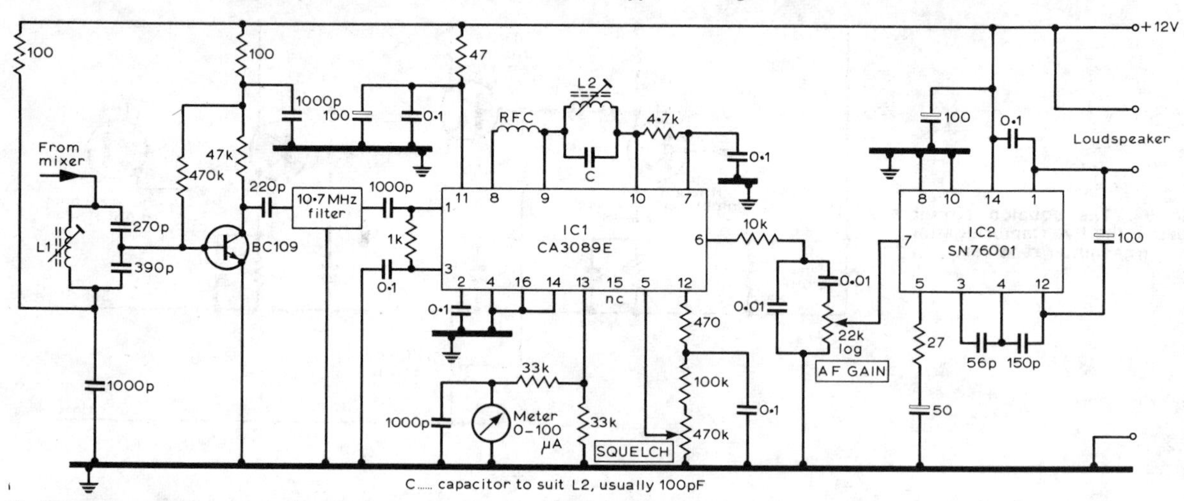

Fig 97. An i.f. amplifier with quadrature detector. L1 and L2 are both 20t 30swg $\frac{3}{16}$ in diam with dust core in screening can. RFC is 80t 30swg on $\frac{1}{4}$W resistor. Typical voltages are shown in Table 10

PRACTICAL DESIGNS

Single mosfet 144MHz converter

In this converter a dual-gate mosfet is used as a self-oscillating mixer and the oscillator tuning is performed by varicap diode. The input, in order to provide reasonable selectivity, is through a three-stage filter which should be screened from the rest of the unit. A circuit diagram is shown in Fig 100(a) and an approximate layout in Fig 100(b).

Table 9. Voltage check

IC1 pin 2	3V	**IC2 pin 4**	2·1V
pin 4	2·1V	**5**	8·9V
pin 5	6V	**6**	5·5V
TP1	8·9V	**7**	1·0V
TP2	8·5V	**9**	0·9V
IC2 pin 1	2·1V	**10**	8·1V
3	2·1V		

A converter of this type, with an appropriate i.f. output frequency, is likely to be useful for use with general-purpose shortwave receivers.

Table 10. Test voltages

Pin	IC1	IC2
1	1·6	12·0
2	1·6	—
3	1·6	7·2
4	—	0·8
5	—	0·5
6	5·2	—
7	5·2	—
8	5·3	—
9	5·3	—
10	5·3	—
11	11·3	—
12	4·7	6·0
14	—	12·0
15	1·6	—

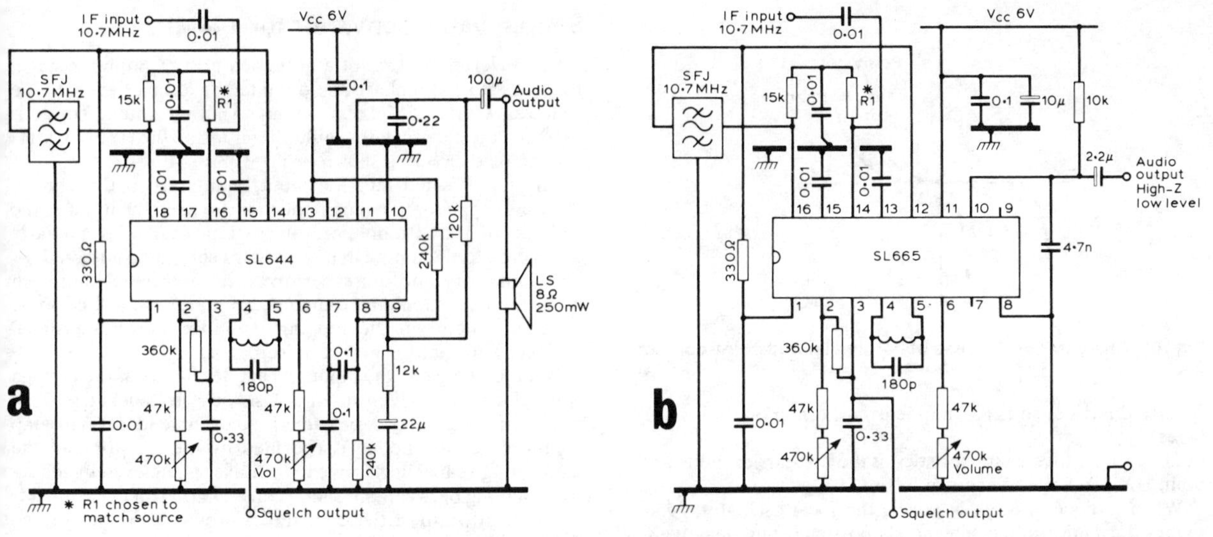

Fig 98. SL664 and SL665 circuits

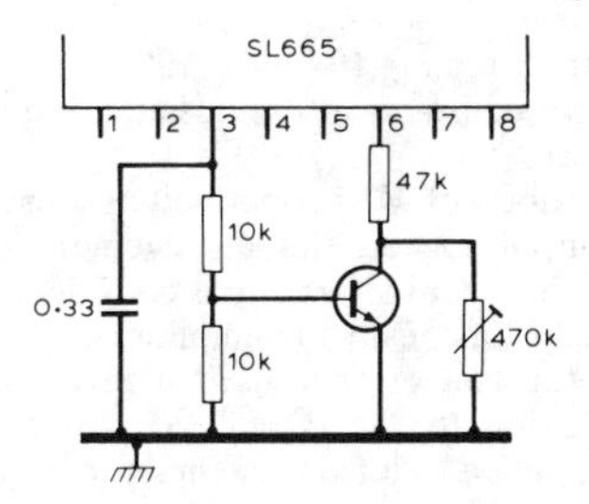

Fig 99. External circuit to provide muting for addition to SL665

Converter for 144MHz using hot-carrier diodes

In the conventional converters using either transistors or valves, it is usual to use an rf amplifier ahead of the mixer to achieve a satisfactory low noise factor, it being necessary to obtain sufficient gain at low noise to overcome the mixer noise.

The availability of hot carrier (or Schottky) diodes at a reasonable cost offers an alternative approach to a high-performance converter.

The important difference between the hot-carrier diodes and normal types of diode is that the reverse breakdown voltage of the former is much greater and it conducts less easily in the

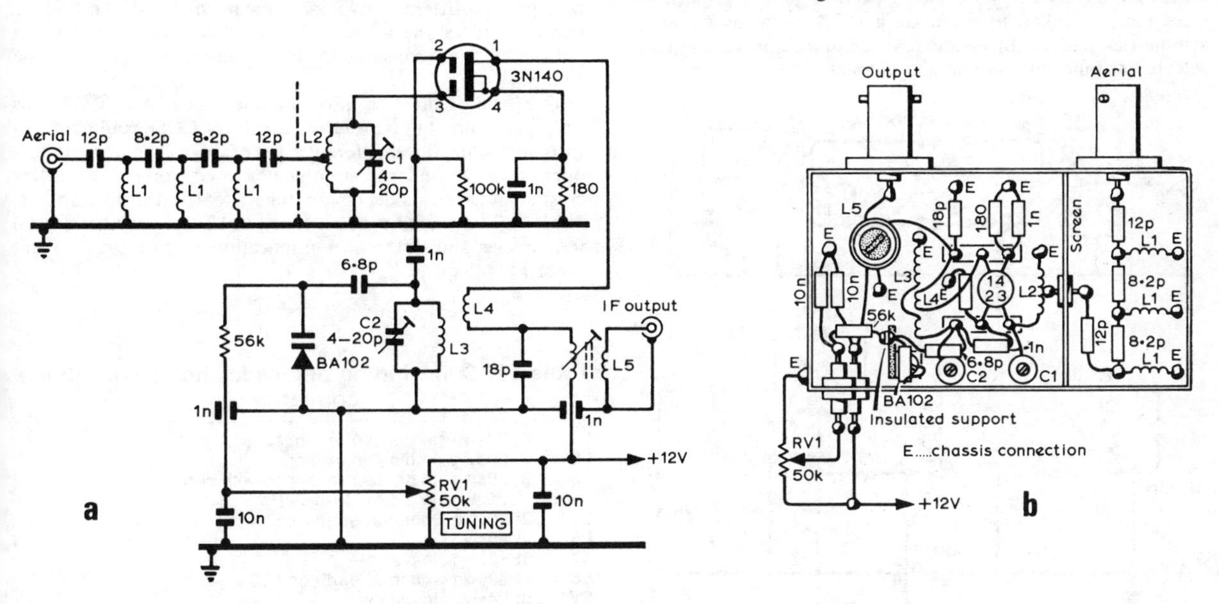

Fig 100. Single dual-gate mosfet 144MHz tunable converter. L1 is 5t spaced 1mm with 2mm diam. L2 is 8t 6mm core. L3 is 5t as L2. L4 is 3t 6mm. L5 is 15t 0·32mm spaced on 6mm core with 1t coupling link. A 40673 mosfet would be preferred to the 3N140 as it has built-in protective diodes

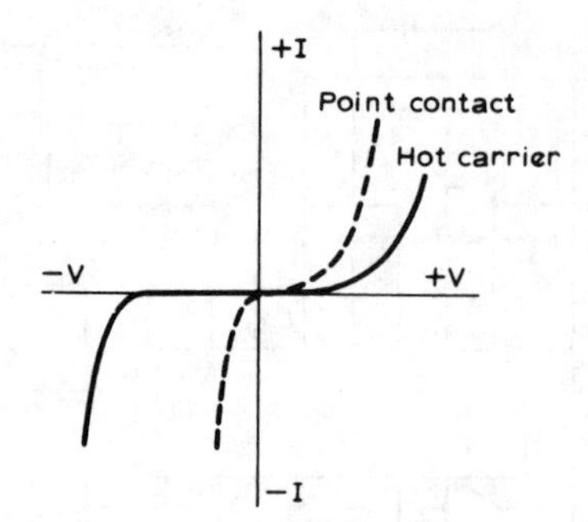

Fig 101. Characteristic curves of hot-carrier and point-contact diodes

reverse direction, so is much quieter at normal operating voltages.

The comparative characteristics of the hot-carrier diode and point-contact diode are shown in Fig 101.

When a diode is used as mixer, the local oscillator signal swings the diode voltage alternately positively and negatively. In the negative direction, within the breakdown voltage, virtually no current flows and therefore shot noise is not generated to any significant extent.

Another characteristic of these diodes is a large dynamic square law range which reduces cross-modulation problems.

There can of course be no gain in a hot-carrier diode circuit—there is in fact an insertion loss of −2 to −3dB. In some cases this will require more i.f. gain, though this rarely happens when using a communications receiver as an i.f. amplifier.

An rf preamplifier will almost certainly be needed to provide adequate selectivity; this should obviously be of as low a noise factor as possible.

In the diagram a diode frequency multiplier is shown which may alternatively be a standard type transistor if preferred. Care must be taken to make L2 and L4 as far as possible symmetrical and ideally the diodes used in the mixer should be selected as four diodes of similar characteristic.

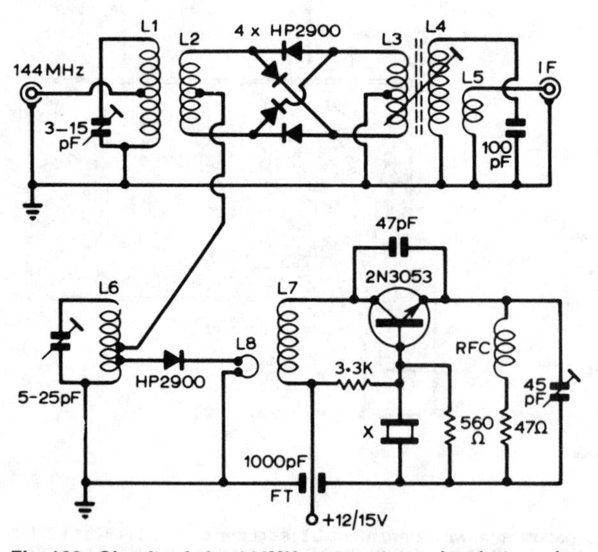

Fig 102. Circuit of the 144MHz converter using hot-carrier diodes

Simple valve converter for 144MHz

This converter consists of a grounded-grid rf amplifier stage, feeding into a double triode operated as a mixer-i.f. cathode follower with a 25MHz i.f. output. Another double triode is used as a crystal oscillator-multiplier using a 10MHz or 30MHz crystal. The circuit is shown in Fig 103.

The input is fed into the input tuning circuit through an isolating capacitor to a tap on the inductor, and the input to the cathode of the rf amplifier valve V1, a 6CW4, is similarly connected to the input circuit. The taps should be adjusted for best sensitivity and noise performance, and in making such adjustments it should be remembered that there will be some difference between the tapping point for maximum signal strength and that for lowest noise factor.

Isolation between the input and anode circuits of the rf stage is provided by a screen fitted across the valve socket.

The anode circuit is series tuned and the ht feed taken to a tap on the coil. Decoupling is provided by the resistor and the feedthrough capacitor. Drive to the mixer is achieved by inductive coupling between the anode coil and grid coil of the mixer.

The bandwidth of these circuits is provided by the spacing between the two coils. The anode circuit should be tuned to the centre of the band.

As can be seen from Fig 104 the oscillator coil is mounted in line with the two coils and so provides the required inductive injection.

The second triode of V2 is operated as a cathode follower feeding the output socket; this arrangement has previously been used in earlier converters and is considered to be preferable to the inclusion of an i.f. amplifier stage which is not needed when the converter is used with a communications receiver. In addition, for the extra i.f. amplifier to be effective, agc should be applied to it from the main receiver, which is an additional complication.

When the tuned circuits are properly adjusted the gain of the rf stage is sufficient to overcome the mixer noise. An ECC88 was chosen for the mixer-cathode follower because it has a reasonably good noise factor and is easier to drive than the ECC85.

The local oscillator is also a double triode. An ECC85 has been used here, but if preferred another ECC88 could be used to avoid having three different types of valve. The first triode is operated as a standard harmonic type oscillator with a 10MHz crystal and the anode circuit tuned to the third harmonic, 30MHz. The second triode is tuned to 120MHz. Other crystal frequencies and different multiplication may be used to suit other i.f. values.

Table 11. Coil winding details for hot carrier diode converter

L1	5t 20swg $\frac{3}{8}$in dia centre tapped
L2	3t 20swg $\frac{3}{8}$in dia centre tapped
L3	3t 20swg $\frac{3}{8}$in dia centre tapped with core
L4	11t 20swg $\frac{3}{8}$in dia for 14–16MHz
L5	2t 20swg wound at earth end L4
L6	4t 20swg $\frac{1}{2}$in dia
L7	6t 20swg $\frac{1}{2}$in dia
L8	1t 20swg wound at earth end L6
RFC	20t 24swg $\frac{1}{4}$in dia cw
Diodes	HP2900 (matched)
X	43·33MHz for 14 to 16MHz i.f.
Transistor	2N3053

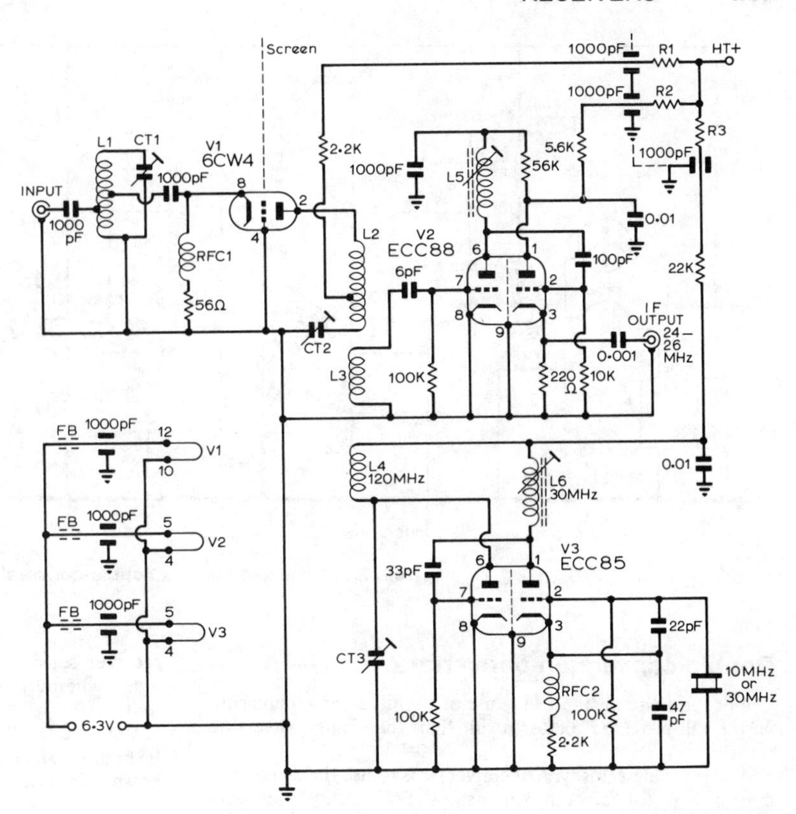

Fig 103. The 144MHz grounded-grid converter circuit. CT1, 2, 3, 12pF swing trimmers (Mullard C004EA/12E). FB: ferrite beads. R1, 2, 3 values depend on ht—with 150V, R2 and R3 are 1kΩ and R1 is selected to provide 100V on the anode of V1. RFC1 is 23in of 26swg on ⅛in former. RFC2 1mH. V1 6CW4, V2 ECC88, V3 ECC85

Construction

As shown in Fig 104, the whole converter is built into a medium-size Eddystone die-cast box. With this size of box some care is needed to fit the various components into their proper positions.

Under the lid of the box on which components are fixed is mounted a screen to provide isolation for the power input. Attached to this is the screen mounted across the rf stage valve socket. These screens provide a suitable mounting for the feed-through capacitors used in the heater and anode leads to each valve. RF chokes often used in heater circuits have been replaced by ferrite beads slipped directly on the feedthrough capacitor leads. An HC-6/U crystal socket is shown in the layout diagram which is more commonly used than the B7G type used in the prototype.

Power supply

Any small power supply that will give 150V (or more) at 30mA and 6·3V at 1A is suitable.

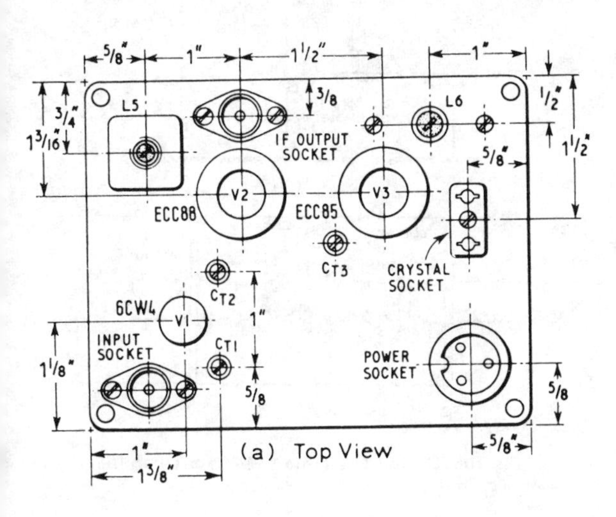

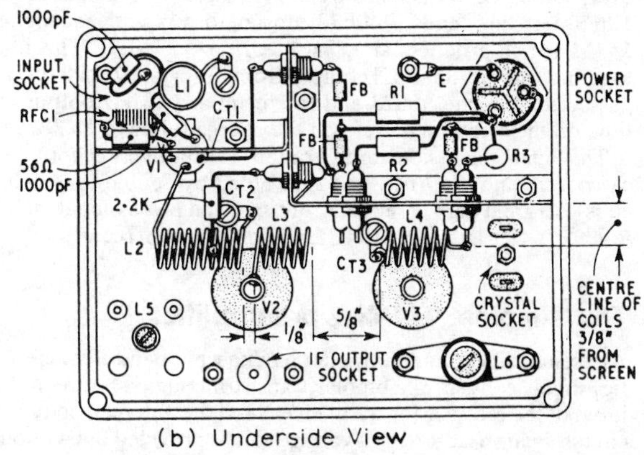

Fig 104. Layout of components above and below the lid of the die-cast box

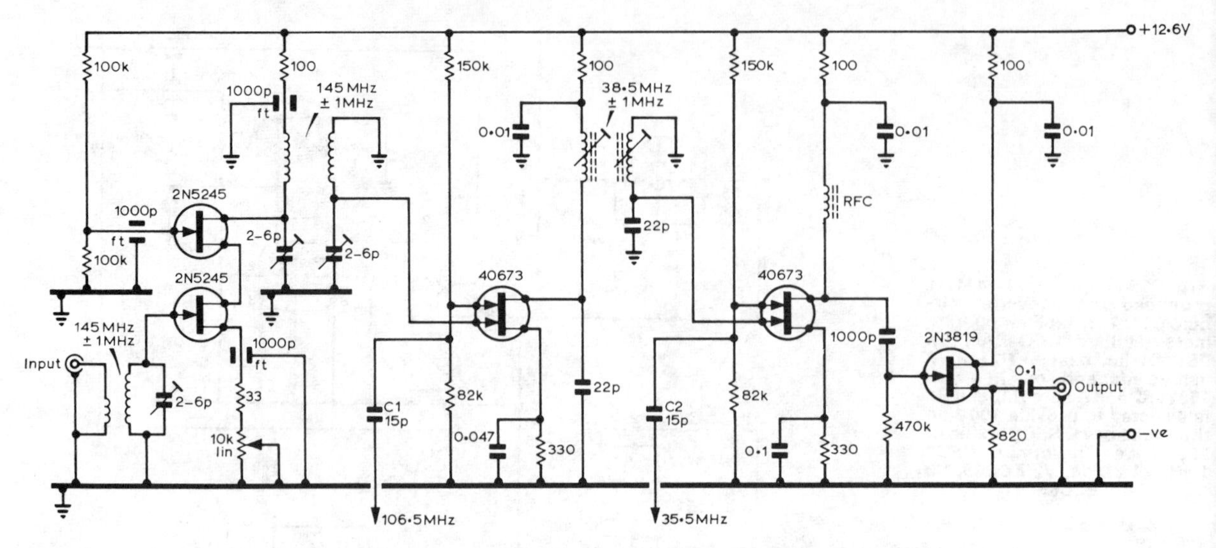

Fig 105. Front-end section of a double-conversion converter

Double-conversion converters

Under some circumstances the use of a double-conversion converter will provide a better result than the single-conversion type.

An essential of this type of converter is to use the same local crystal oscillator for both conversions. For example, an oscillator operating at, say, between 35 and 35·5MHz followed by a tripler tuned to between 105 and 106·5MHz provides a first i.f. of between 40 and 38·5MHz and a second i.f. of between 3 and 5MHz.

The use of a relatively high first i.f. frequency reduces the likely out-of-band signals from introducing image frequency interference which is often the case when using a relatively low i.f. frequency.

Only the front end of the converter is shown in Fig 105. The crystal oscillator section is perfectly straightforward and so not shown; it consists of a crystal oscillator (2N706) at 35·5MHz followed by a tripler (a further 2N706) to 106·5MHz. However, both these frequencies are used in the mixing process. The 106·5MHz line feeds a 40673 mosfet to mix with incoming 144MHz and produces an i.f. at 38·5MHz ± 1MHz. This i.f., together with the 35·5MHz output from the crystal oscillator, is passed to a second 40673 and the result is a 3MHz output to tune on the station receiver, via the source follower 2N3819.

This dual-conversion configuration, in conjunction with the cascode rf amplifier (two 2N5245s aided by double-tuned circuits) is a great help in reducing out-of-band professional interference, which is an increasing problem on the vhf scene today.

The simplest 144MHz preamplifier

An elementary voltage amplifier having wide-band characteristics simply consists of a bipolar transistor coupled between the input of the receiver (or transceiver) and the antenna, no tuned circuits being used so that a voltage gain is provided but without additional selectivity. A suitable circuit is shown in Fig 106. Such a device is useful to provide a worthwhile increase in receiver sensitivity to correspond with increased range provided when a power amplifier is attached to small hand-held units.

With the small number of components involved the unit can be built into a very small space, or incorporated into the add-on power amplifier.

144MHz preamplifier

Fig 107 shows a tuned preamplifier using a dual-gate mosfet. The original version of this amplifier used an enhancement-mode fet type SD301 (Signetics).

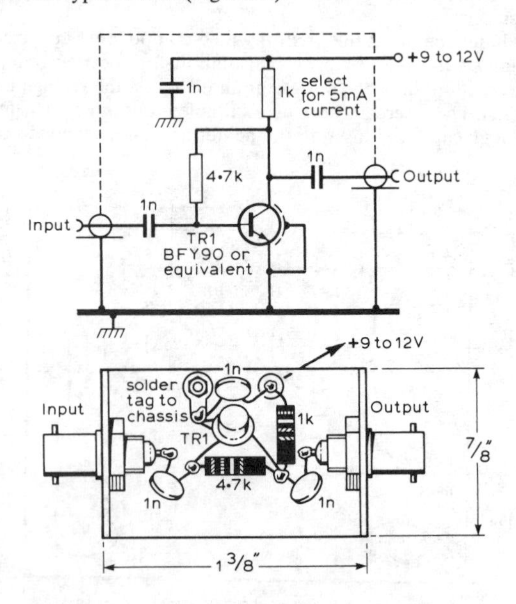

Fig 106. Circuit of simple 144MHz preamplifier

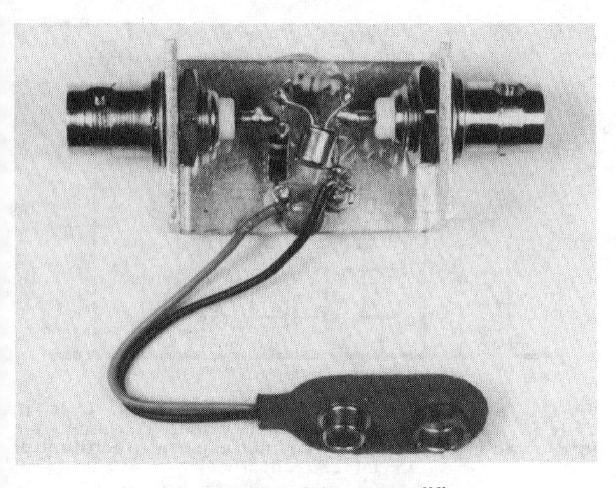

Interior view of the preamplifier

The advantage of this type at 144MHz is that its best noise figure coincides with its maximum gain. This means that it is only necessary to adjust the three circuits for maximum gain. In this condition it was found to have a power gain of 20dB and a noise figure of 1·8dB.

Other types of device can be used but it may then be necessary to adjust the input tuning and perhaps the tap for best noise figure. This can either be done with a noise generator or a weak signal. If a depletion-mode fet such as the 40673 is used, the 150kΩ resistor (bias) can be omitted.

In construction a screen should be fitted between the input and output tuned circuits and L1 should be mounted at right-angles to L2/L3.

Alternative preamplifier for 144MHz

In this unit a 2N204 dual-gate mosfet is used with single-tuned circuits (Fig 108). The input and output, together with the transistor connection, will need to be adjusted for the best performance. The details of these as given will provide a gain of between 12 and 14dB at a noise factor which is more than adequate for the average urban location.

The mechanical details have been elaborated to assist the newcomer in building such units (Figs 109 and 110).

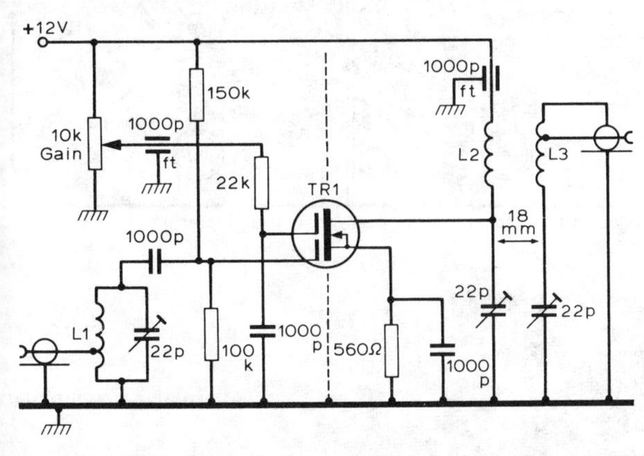

Fig 107. 144MHz low-noise preamplifier using enhancement-mode dual-gate mosfet. TR1 in the prototype was an SD301. Depletion-type mosfets such as the 40673 may be used and the 150kΩ resistor can then be eliminated. L1: 5t 0·3mm tinned copper, 10mm long, tap 1t, 6mm. L2: 6t 1·0mm tinned copper, 18mm long, 8mm. L3: 6t 1·0mm tinned copper, 18mm long, tap 1t, 8mm. L2 and L3 are mounted parallel with 18mm between centres

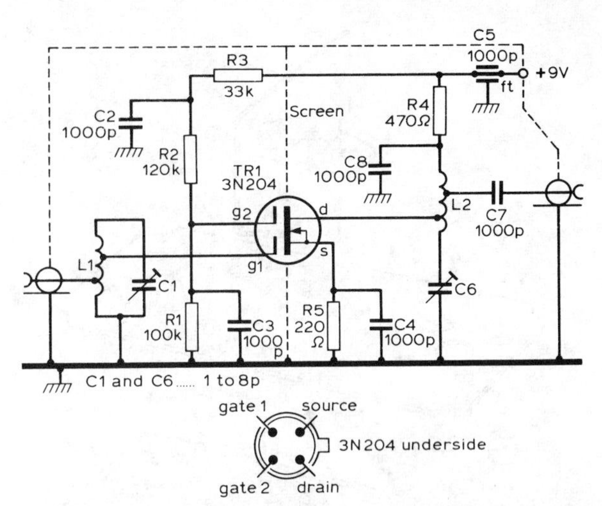

Fig 108. Alternative preamplifier circuit. For component details see Table 12

Grounded-gate fet preamplifier for 144MHz

An alternative to the dual-gate mosfet amplifier is a grounded-gate fet which is suitable for many purposes, particularly for fm applications where the low noise factor is not generally needed.

As shown in Fig 111 this unit, designed by G2AIH, simply consists of two tuned circuits with inductive input and output coupling, the tuned circuits being resonated by dust cores in place of small trimmer capacitors, though these may of course be used if preferred.

The advantage of the dust core tuned circuits is that it enables the unit to be made into a smaller space when necessary.

Construction is straightforward; the pc board as shown in Fig 112 is 2·5 by 1·1in double-sided glassfibre. Connections for input, output and power are made using 18swg wires forced in

Table 12. Component details for alternative preamplifier

L1	6½t ¼in diam. Antenna tap 1½t from ground, gate 1 tap 4½t from ground
L2	6½t ¼in diam. Output tap 2½t from ground, drain tap 4¾t from capacitor
R1	100kΩ ¼W or less
R2	120kΩ ¼W or less
R3	33kΩ ¼W or less
R4	470Ω ⅛W
R5	220Ω ⅛W
C	1,000pF 30V disc ceramic
C_T	15pF trimmer
C_{FT}	1,000pF feedthrough capacitor which forms supply terminal
TR1	3N204
Cast box	Eddystone 7969P

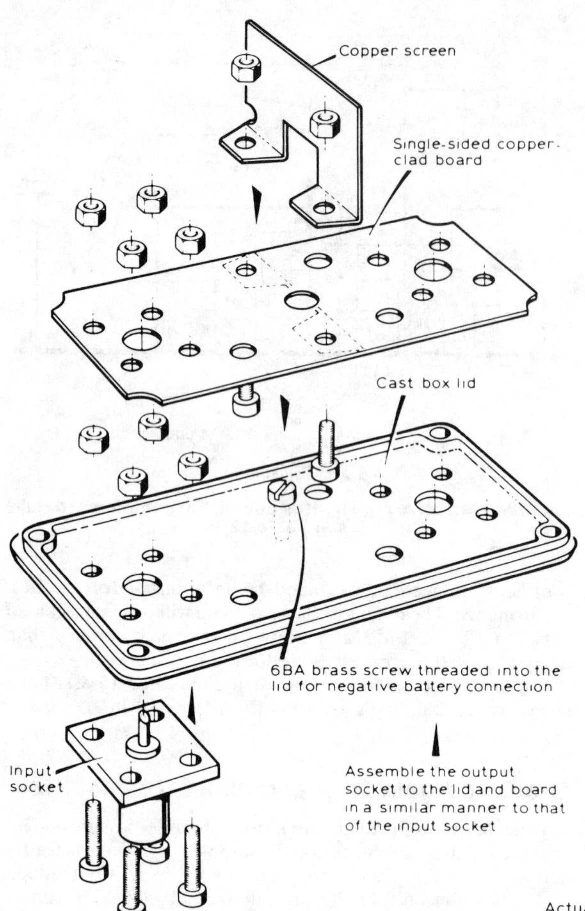

Fig 109. Assembly of copper-clad board and cast box lid

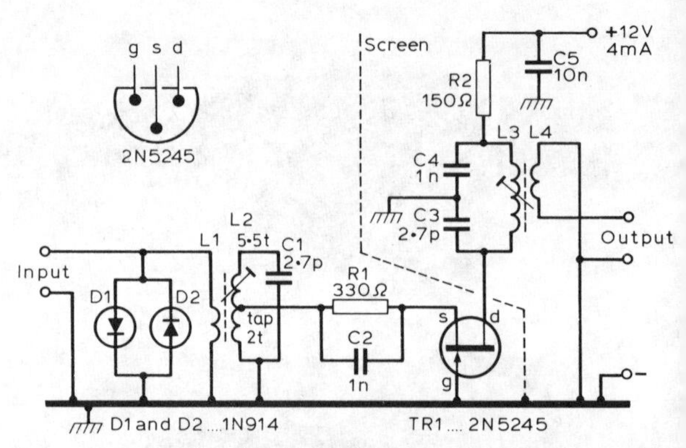

Fig 111. Grounded-gate fet preamplifier for 144MHz. L1 is 1½t, L2 is 5½t, L3 is 5t, L4 is 1½t, all close wound 22swg on 4mm formers with vhf cores. L1 and L4 fitted adjacent to earth end of L2 and L3 respectively

holes (No 56 drill). Insulated pins such as Oxley 093/20P are very suitable for this purpose.

Isolation between the input and output circuits can be made of either thin copper sheet or a piece of board soldered to the main board. This should be 1·1 by 0·75in and all earth connections should be soldered to both sides of the board.

A neutralized 6CW4 preamplifier for 144MHz

In this preamplifier the valve is used in the standard grounded cathode mode with bridge neutralizing. Apart from its intrinsic value as a useful device, it also serves to illustrate the principle of the method of neutralization of a triode rf amplifier.

The equivalent circuit of Fig 113 shows clearly the bridge

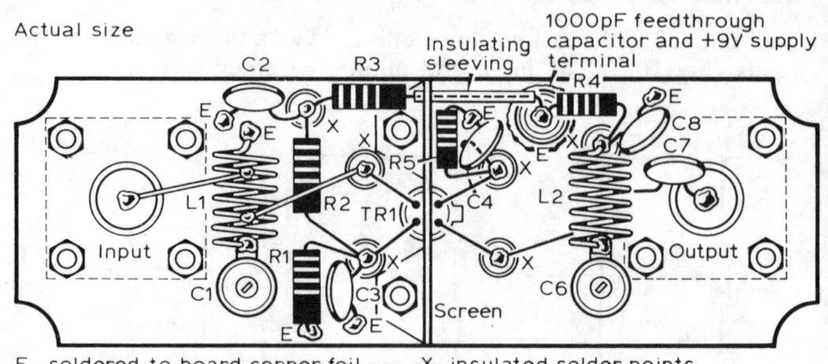

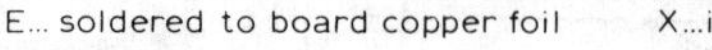

Fig 110. Component layout

Alternative preamplifier

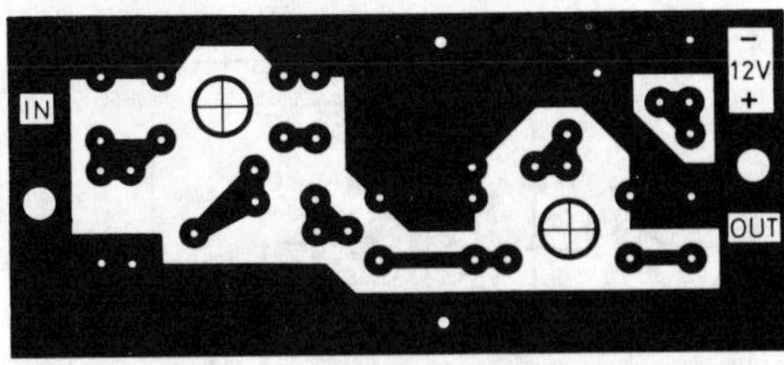

Underside view..... Track layout

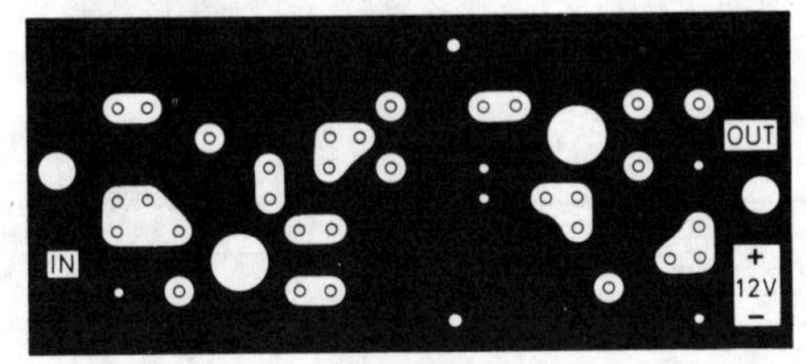

Topside view..... Etching pattern

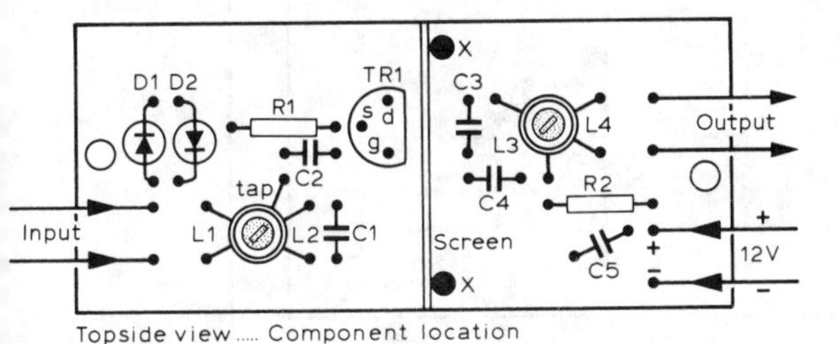

Topside view..... Component location

Fig 112. PCB constructional details

configuration of the amplifier, the bridge being formed by Cn, Cga, VC2 and Cgk, and it will be balanced when CN/Cga = VC2/Cgk. Under this connection feedback from anode to grid will theoretically be zero.

The practical amplifier is constructed in a die-cast box and the component positions together with the inter-circuit screening are shown in the layout diagram (Fig 115). A noise factor of approximately 3dB is obtainable with this amplifier at 145MHz; optimum adjustment of noise can only be achieved by use of a noise generator.

Simple converter for 432MHz

This converter (Fig 116) is based on the use of uhf silicon transistors type BF180 (which were produced for uhf tv tuners),

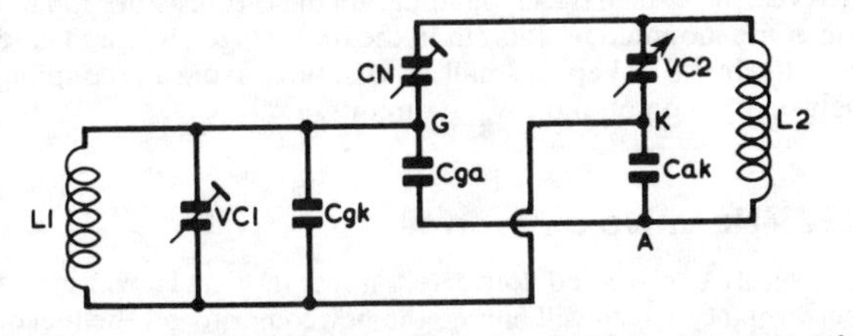

Fig 113. Equivalent circuit. Cgk = capacitance between grid and cathode. Cak = capacitance between anode and cathode. Cga = capacitance between grid and anode. Other components marked as in Fig 114

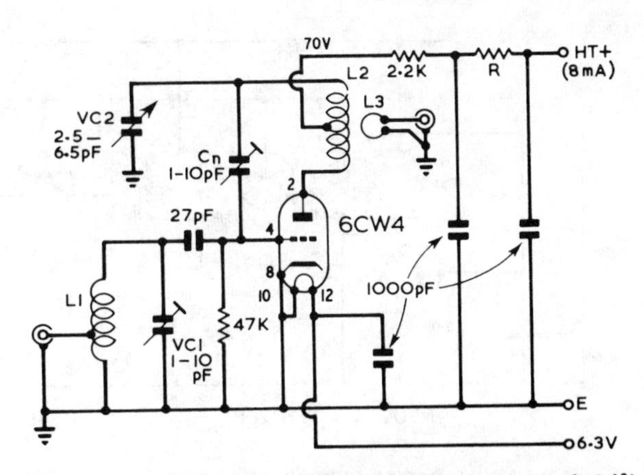

Fig 114. A practical preamplifier. L1 is 5t 20swg, tapped at 1¾t ¼in diam, ¾in long. L2 is 8t 16swg, tapped 4½t from anode end, ⅜in diam, 1in long. L3 is 1t link coil of insulated wire fitted around centre of L2. R is adjusted to suit ht for an anode current of 8mA

in the two rf amplifiers. These transistors have a suitably low noise figure of 5·7dB at 800MHz with a gain of 12–14dB when operated with grounded base.

The tuned circuits consist of shortened tuned lines, the input and output of the transistors being suitably tapped down the lines and using inductive coupling between the two rf amplifiers and into the mixer.

The mixer TR3 is a TIS88A fet which is followed by a transistor isolation amplifier to the i.f. output. The i.f. output coil L7 is tuned to the required frequency such as 13MHz, or any other convenient frequency.

The local oscillator chain comprises four stages, tuned to 35, 70, 140 and 420MHz respectively, using a 35MHz crystal. The three frequency multipliers are operated in the grounded-base configuration.

The output at 420MHz is taken from a tap on the final multiplier tuned circuit and inductively coupled into the mixer by L5, L6 being coupled to the rf amplifier and connected in the gate of the mixer.

Small feedthrough capacitors of the discoidal type are used

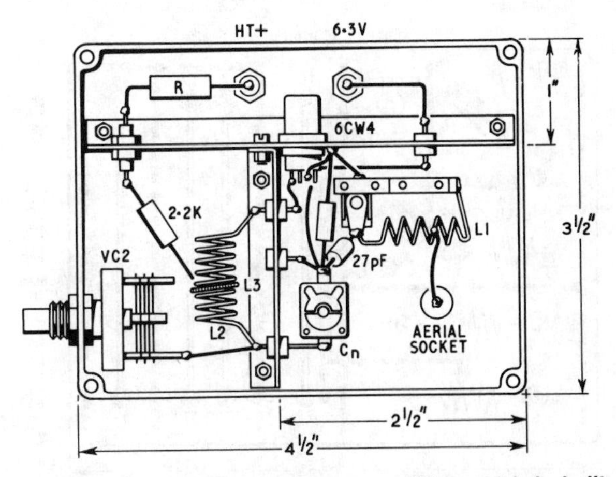

Fig 115. Layout of the 144MHz preamplifier, which is built inside an Eddystone box, 3½in by 4½in. The output socket is mounted immediately below L3

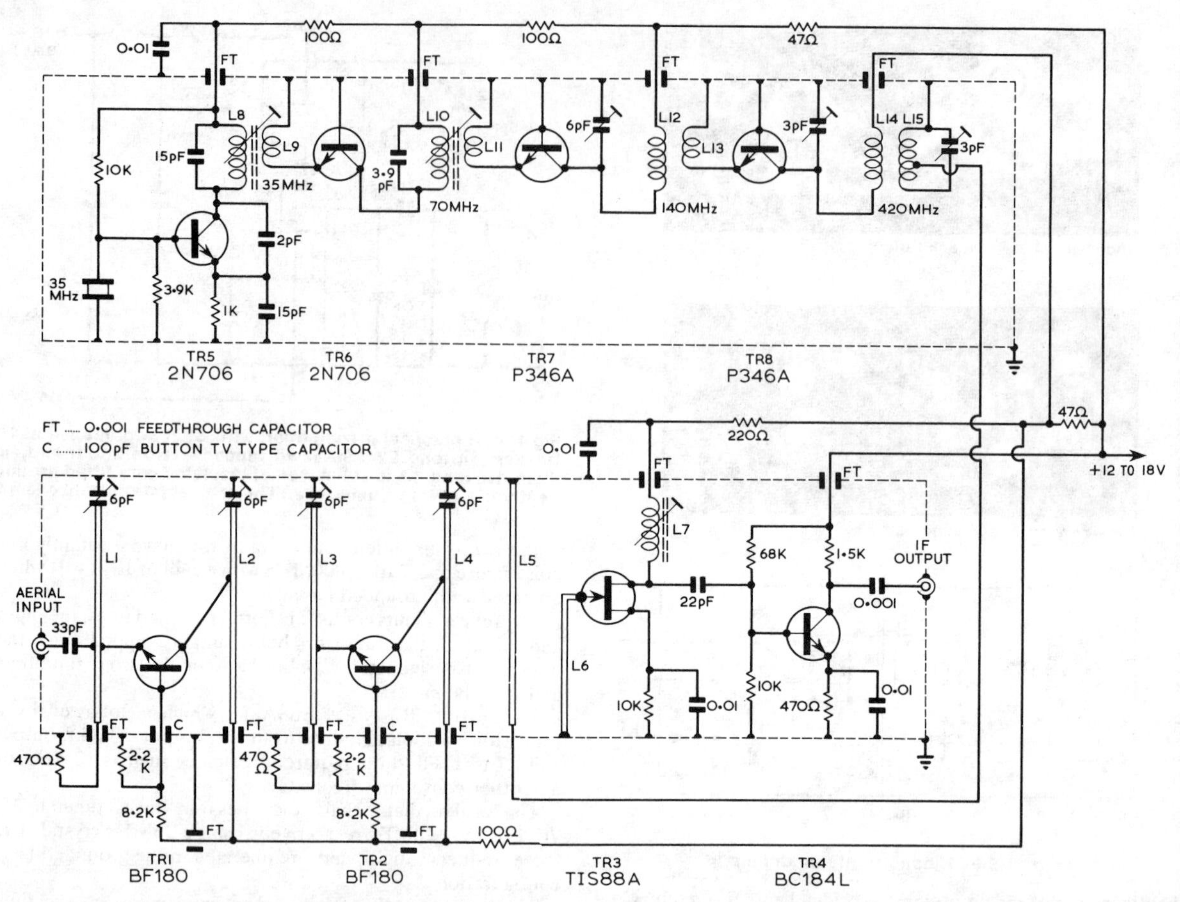

Fig 116. The simple transistor converter for 432MHz. L1, 2, 3 and 4 are all 3in lengths of 1/8in diam silver plated, with L1 tapped at 3/4in, L2 at 2in, L3 at 3/4in and L4 at 2in. L5 and L6 are insulated coupling loops (see Fig 117). L7 is a 13MHz i.f. coil with 35t 30swg on 0·3in diam dust core. L8 is 10t 22swg on 0·3in diam dust core, with L9 (1t insulated) wound. L10 is 5t 22swg on 0·3in diam dust core, with L11 (1t insulated) wound round. L12 is 2t 18swg, 1/4in diam, 3/8in long, with L13 (1t insulated) wound round. L14 is 2t 18swg, 1/4in diam, 1/2in long. L15 is 3t 18swg tapped at 1t, 1/4in diam, 3/8in long (note that P346A is now obsolete—BSX20 is a suitable replacement)

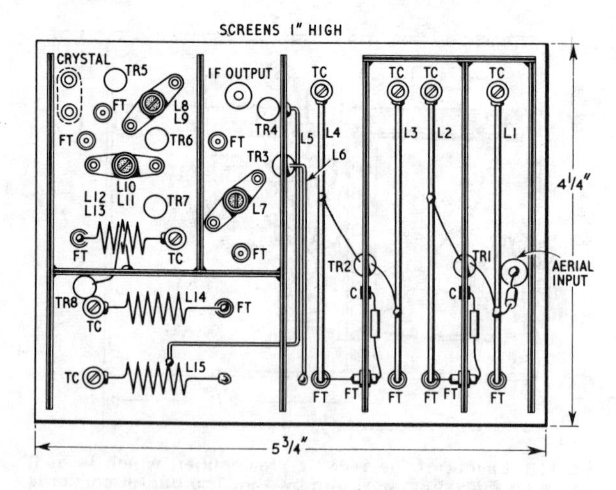

Fig 117. Component layout of 432MHz converter

extensively. They provide low inductance coupled with small size and are suitable for direct soldering to the chassis, which may either be copper, brass or copper-clad board.

The layout of the main components is shown in Fig 117—this drawing is approximately to scale so that the detailed arrangement and sizes can be readily determined. The interstage screening should be 1in high and the whole unit mounted in a suitable screening box.

As can be seen in the layout diagram the rf transistors and the mixer are mounted in slots cut in the inter-stage screens. These cutouts should be kept as small as possible to avoid any coupling between the input and output circuits.

432MHz valve converter

The easily constructed converter shown in Fig 118 will give a performance which will enable the newcomer to get the feel of the band. It is constructed largely of the type of components usually available for the hf bands.

The only uhf components are the slab type inductors used for

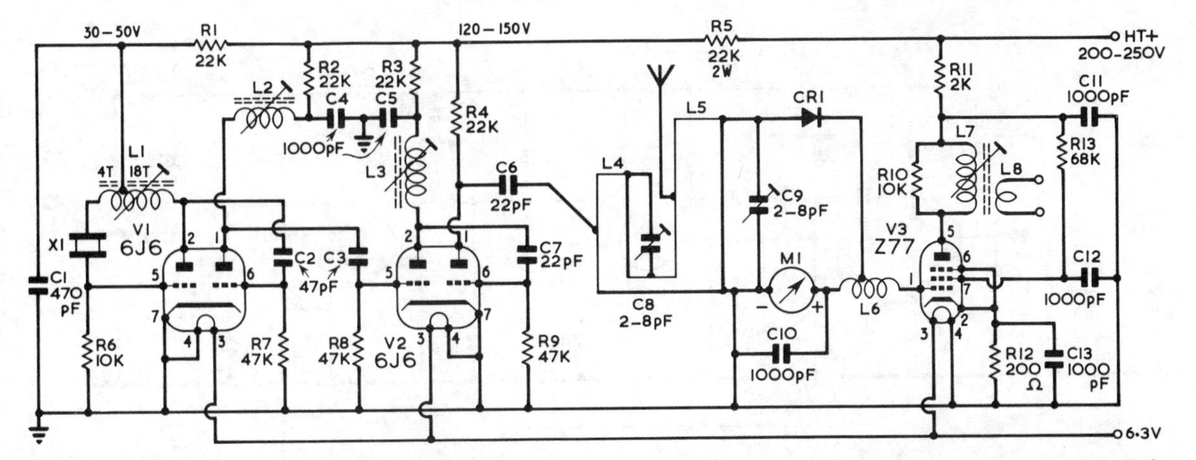

Fig 118. Circuit of 432MHz converter using valves. C1, 4, 5, 6, 10, 11, 12, 13 are midget mica. C2, 3, 7 are ceramicons. C8, 9 are Philips trimmers 3–8pF. CR1, silicon diode. L1 is 22t 22swg close wound, tapped at 4t. L2 is 6t 20swg, close wound. L3 is 2t 20swg, close wound. L4, L5, see Fig 119. L6 is 22t 32swg, close wound, centre tapped. L7 is 37t 32swg close wound. L8 is 4t 32swg wound at earthy end of L7. All formers are ⅜in diam Aladdin with hf cores. Crystal is 35MHz overtone

L4 and L5, and illustrated in Fig 119. The diode (CR1) should be a low-noise silicon type such as the CV102, CV103 or equivalent. Although the crystal oscillator and multiplier stages are given as 6J6 valves, any of the double triodes such as the 12AT7 and ECC85 may be substituted, but note that in this case some minor adjustment to the various inductors may be necessary, notably L3 and tapping point on L4. The crystal oscillator chain for an i.f. of 12–14MHz (L7) may be based on a crystal frequency of either 7·777 or 35MHz.

Alternative crystal oscillator circuits may be used by those who prefer the Colpitts or Butler oscillators, to that of the Squier shown in the diagram of Fig 118.

In the case of the Colpitts circuit (Fig 120) using a 7·777MHz crystal, two 12AT7 valves would be needed. The anode circuit of the first triode would be tuned to 23MHz (actually 23·331MHz), and that of the second to three times this frequency which would be almost 70MHz. The two following anode circuits would then be tuned to 140MHz and 420MHz respectively.

A Butler oscillator circuit using a 35MHz crystal has a considerable advantage over the others because it is easier to avoid

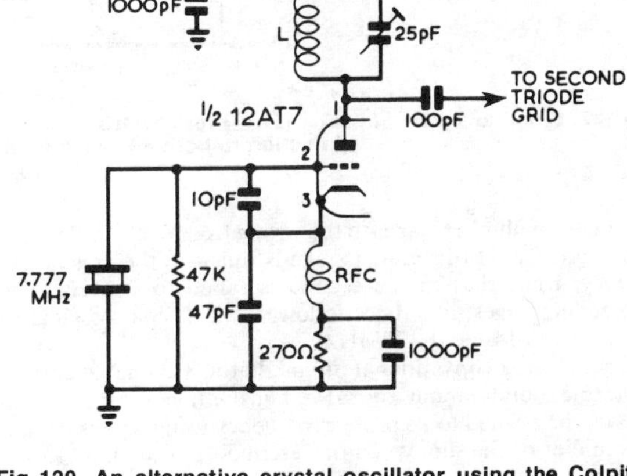

Fig 120. An alternative crystal oscillator using the Colpitts circuit

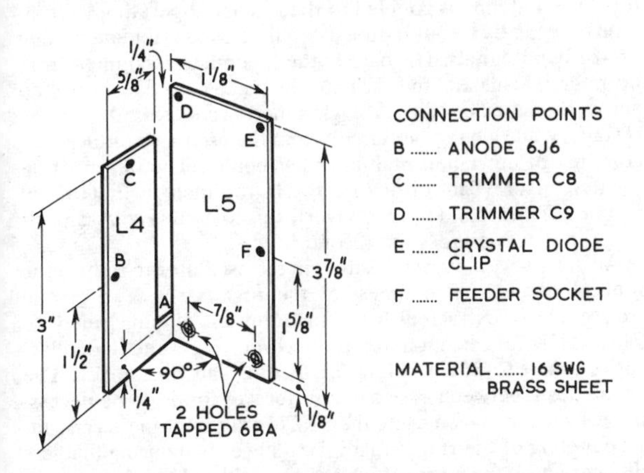

Fig 119. Dimensions of strip line. L4 and L5 are mounted $\frac{3}{16}$in from chassis

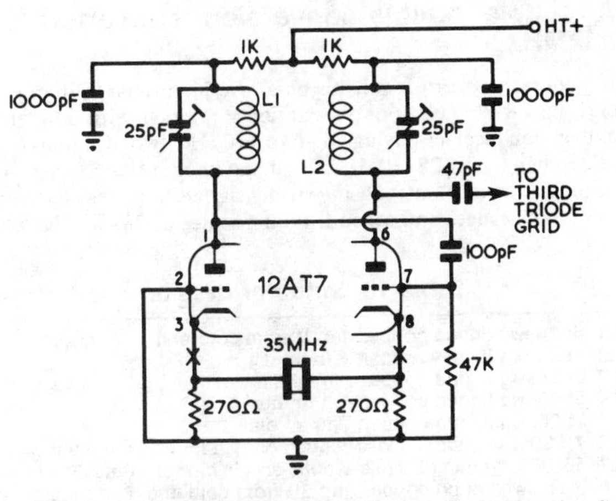

Fig 121. A further alternative oscillator using the Butler circuit and a 35MHz crystal

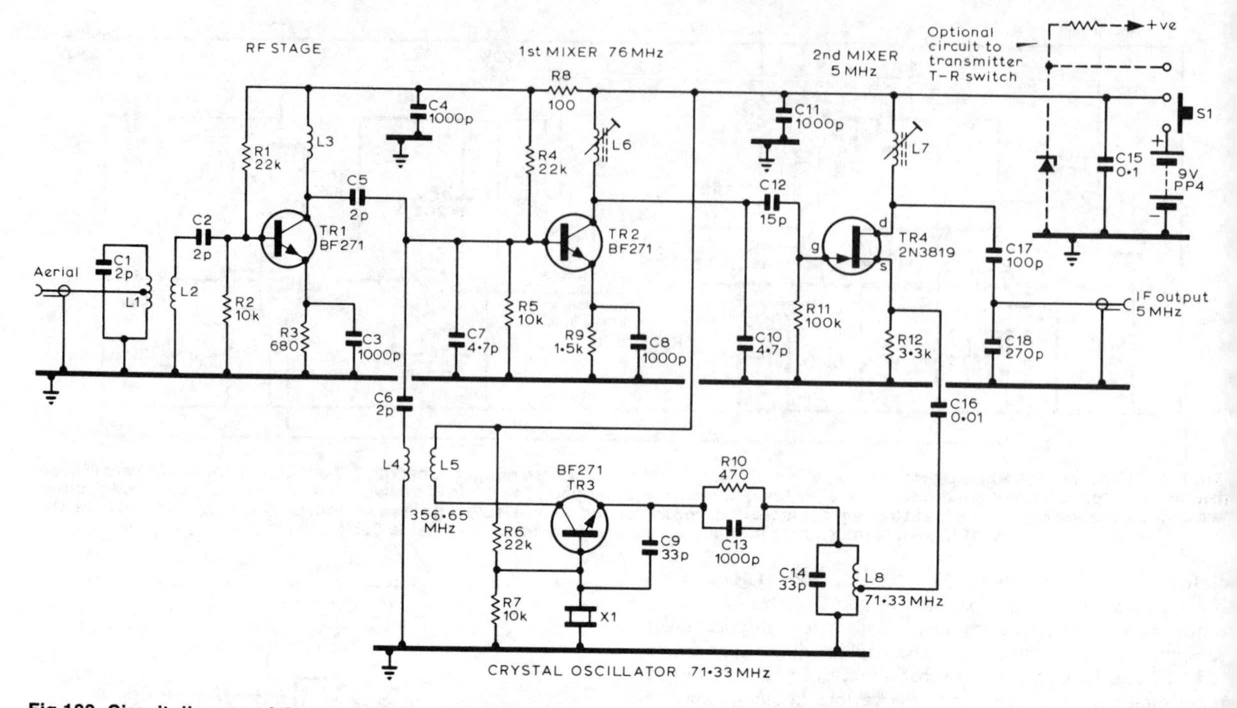

Fig 122. Circuit diagram of the converter for 432MHz in which a double-conversion process is used to reach an i.f. of 5MHz with injection to both mixers from a single crystal oscillator at 71·33MHz

tuning the multiplier stages to the wrong frequency. In this case the anode circuit of the first stage is tuned to the crystal frequency, while that of the second is tuned to 70MHz. The succeeding stages, like those following the Colpitts oscillator, are tuned to 140 and 420MHz.

The use of a conventional dip oscillator will enable correct adjustment up to about 200MHz, but the final multiplier will need to be aligned to its proper frequency using an absorption wavemeter or the dip oscillator described in Chapter 11.

A simple double-conversion converter for 432MHz

In general, converters for this band use high tunable frequencies, eg 28–30MHz. For the station equipped with a single-conversion receiver having an i.f. of 470kHz, two problems can arise when tuning 28–30MHz. First, the image rejection may be virtually non-existent, causing strong signals to appear twice in the tuning range, and second, tuning scales at 28–30MHz are often cramped. If a low tunable frequency of, say, 4–6MHz is employed, then even the poorest receivers attain a useful degree of image rejection and the calibration becomes much less cramped.

To achieve this double conversion offers a satisfactory method provided this is based on the use of a single crystal oscillator. The design described below was featured in *Radio Communication* December 1974.

Table 13. Inductor details

L1	4t 20swg tinned copper, tap ½t from cold end, 3/16in int dia
L2	4t 20swg tinned copper, 3/16in int dia
L3	2t 20swg tinned copper, ¼in int dia
L4	5t 20swg tinned copper 3/16in int dia
L5	7t 20swg tinned copper, 3/16in int dia
L6	7½t 30swg enamel, close-wound on 3/16in former, 6mm vhf core
L7	35t 36swg enamel, close-wound on 3/16in former, 10mm F14 core
L8	9t 20swg tinned copper, tap 3¼t from cold end, 3/16in int dia

Slight variation in gauge of wire is permissible for L6 and L7

Circuit (Fig 122)

The rf stage, crystal oscillator and first mixer use BF271 transistors. The antenna is coupled to the rf stage, operating in common emitter, by a double-tuned circuit so as to attenuate strong out-of-band signals. The base of the first mixer is coupled from both the rf stage and the oscillator by means of a capacitive tap across the tuned circuits. A single tuned circuit is used from the rf stage, while a bandpass circuit from the oscillator reduces the coupling of unwanted multiplier harmonics. The output from the first mixer is centred at 76·33MHz, to which the first i.f. coil is tuned. The second mixer converts this to 4–6MHz. A capacitive tap is used across the second i.f. coil.

A fifth-overtone crystal is used in the oscillator to reduce the multiplication to five times for the first mixer. The crystal frequency is extracted from the emitter circuit tuned to 71·33MHz for injection into the second mixer, and the collector is tuned to 356·65MHz for feeding the first mixer. The capacitance between base and emitter was found to be necessary for stability when using the BF271 transistor in this circuit. Decoupling of the rf and first mixer stages is by using leadless disc ceramic capacitors, which are carefully soldered in slots in the board, thus significantly reducing series inductance.

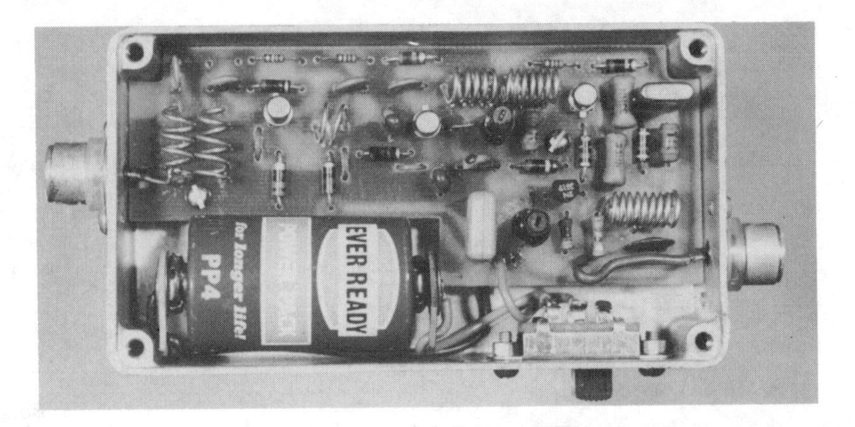

Double-conversion 432MHz converter

Construction

The pcb (Fig 123) is supported by $\frac{1}{4}$in pillars from the box. As shown in the photograph, the board is cut out to allow space for the self-contained battery. The inner connectors of the input and output sockets are cut down to $\frac{1}{8}$in to allow the pcb to be fitted into the box. At the right-hand end of the board a slot is also cut to assist in the insertion into the box. Slots are cut into the board to allow the capacitors C3, C4 and C8 to be soldered in position.

The transistors are soldered in position with the minimum lead length and pressed down so they are 1mm above the board, and the coils are fitted so that the turns rest on the board. They are all wound in the same direction.

Alignment

Connect the converter to the receiver by a length of coaxial cable and tune to 5MHz. Turn up the receiver gain until noise is heard and then adjust the second i.f. core L7 for maximum noise output.

Next check the oscillator coil L8—short two turns together with the insulated metal blade; a reduction in noise will show that the oscillator is functioning. If no change is detected squeeze the turns together until the test shows it is functioning. Leave it functioning and move to the first i.f. coil L6, which can now be peaked, screwing the core down from the top of the former. Stop at the first peak in noise; the second is incorrect.

To adjust L4, the first mixer oscillator coil, short two turns at the earthy end adjacent to L5. Squeeze or expand the turns a little at a time until a change in noise is heard on shorting the same two turns. The noise should increase when the short is removed, showing coupling of oscillator power. A change of 0·05V should be seen in the first mixer emitter voltage when the short is applied. The primary coil L5 is best left at this stage unless insufficient power is available. The rf stage collector coil L3 can be adjusted, using the same procedure. A change in noise should now occur when the base coil L2 is shorted. It must be emphasized that the noise changes at each stage are quite small but should not go unnoticed by the keen ear.

If the antenna is now connected, 432MHz signals should be heard, allowing a final touch to be made to each coil to obtain maximum S-meter reading. Finally, re-peak the second i.f. coil L7 to 4·5MHz; this should give the most even distribution of gain across the band. Little change in performance should be noticed when the lid is screwed down. A signal source will be found a useful device in the initial tune-up.

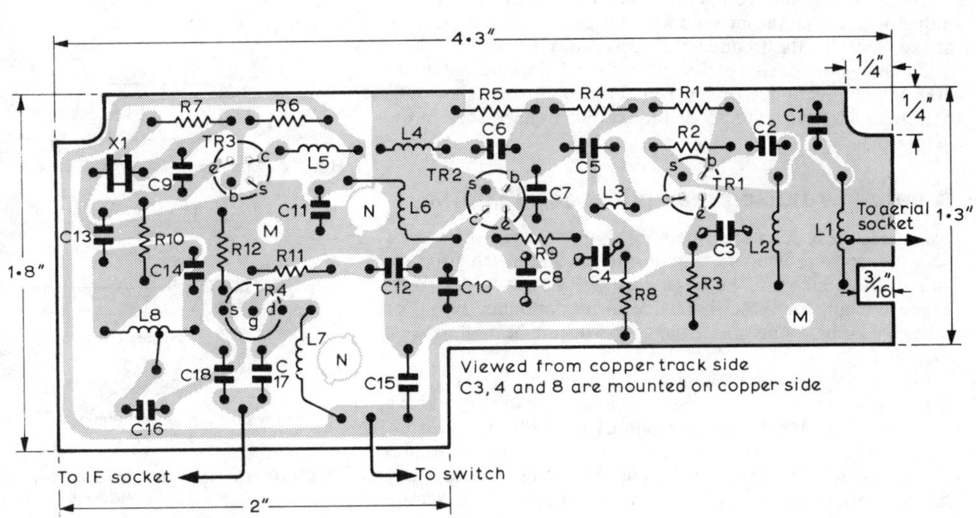

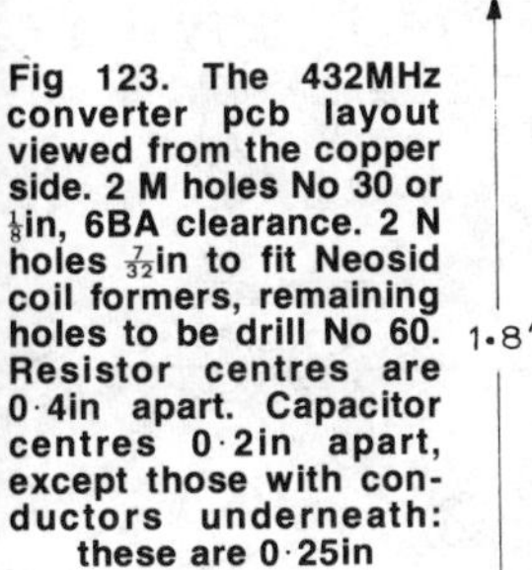

Fig 123. The 432MHz converter pcb layout viewed from the copper side. 2 M holes No 30 or $\frac{1}{8}$in, 6BA clearance. 2 N holes $\frac{7}{32}$in to fit Neosid coil formers, remaining holes to be drill No 60. Resistor centres are 0·4in apart. Capacitor centres 0·2in apart, except those with conductors underneath: these are 0·25in

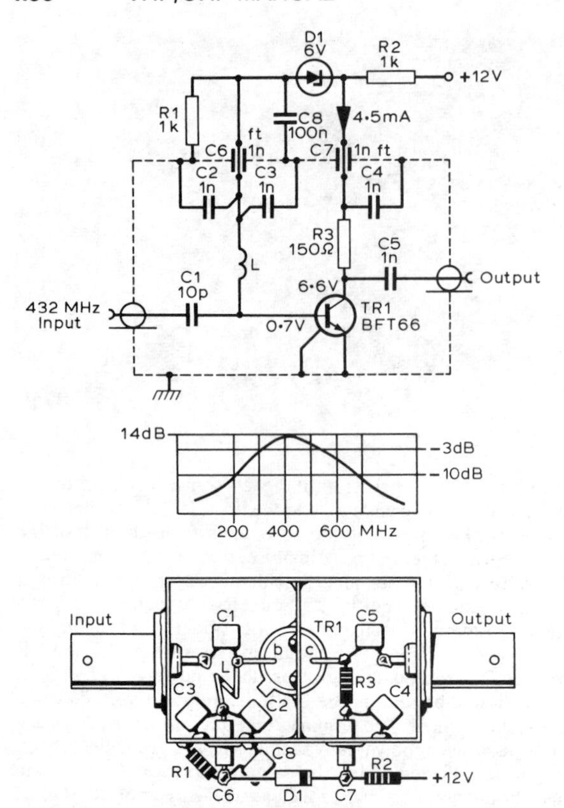

Fig 124. Circuit of simple 432MHz preamplifier by YU1PKW

Simple 432MHz preamplifier

A simple but effective low-noise preamplifier for 432MHz operation can be made as indicated in Fig 124. It is based on the BFT66 transistor which is relatively inexpensive, and will provide a gain of 14dB at a noise figure of 1·5dB.

There is only one component that needs adjustment, the inductor L, so that the maximum gain occurs as near as possible at the centre of the frequency range required.

The inductor consists of a single turn of 5mm internal diameter of 0·8mm copper, or silver-plated copper wire, short tails of a millimetre or so are needed for connections as seen in the layout diagram.

A very-low-noise preamplifier for 432MHz

Advances made in recent years in bipolar transistors enable very-low-noise preamplifiers to be constructed which also provide substantial gain. Such devices are however relatively expensive but, for those interested in moonbounce (eme) or other long-range operation, the cost will not be regarded as excessive.

Fig 125 shows a circuit described by A. Ward, WB5LUA, in *Ham Radio* October 1978, which with the NE64535 can give a noise figure of 0·8–1·0dB and gain of 14–15dB at 432MHz. The input circuit is a parallel-tuned strip line; the output is simply resistive—any attempt to tune this circuit will normally result in instability. Tuning the input circuit for optimum noise

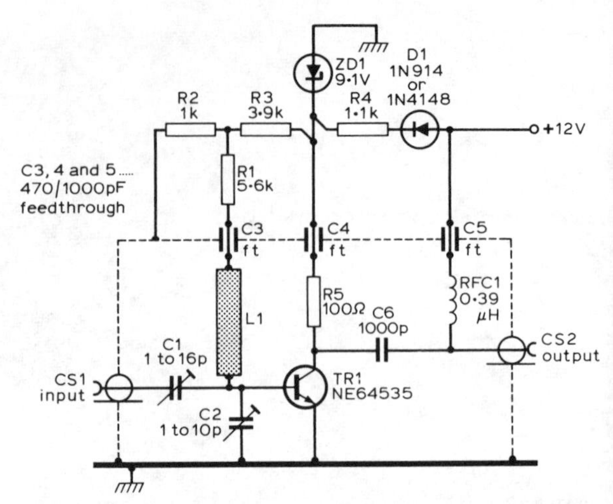

Fig 125. Very-low-noise preamplifier for 432MHz. C, 470/1,000pF feedthrough. C1, 1–16pF. C2, 1–10pF. ZD, 9·1V. D, 1N914 or 1N4148. L1, 15 by 53mm. TR1, NE64535. RFC, 0·39μH

figure is done by setting the series capacitor C1 to the minimum value consistent with the lowest noise figure, C2 being used to resonate the circuit. The actual value of C1 will be around 10pF under normal conditions. Tuning of this circuit is best done using a noise-figure meter but it can however also be set up using a weak-signal source or noise generator.

As mentioned above the value of C1 should be kept as low as possible; excessive coupling will reduce the selectivity of the circuit without improving the noise figure.

Included in the circuit is an rf choke to allow for power to be supplied to the amplifier through its connecting coaxial cable for masthead use. If this is not required it should not be used. In amplifier of such low noise figure it is important that any components in the circuit, particularly the tuning capacitors, are themselves of low loss and have low noise contribution.

As shown in the component layout diagrams (Fig 126) only the rf components are mounted on the side enclosed in the screening box; the supply components are mounted externally.

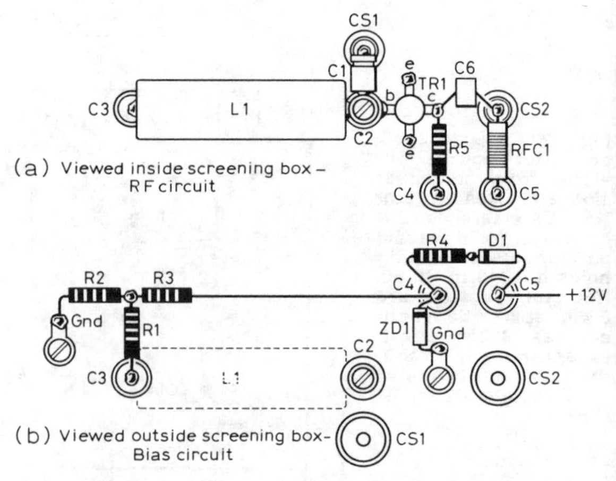

Fig 126. Component layout. (a) Inside—rf circuit. (b) Outside—bias circuit

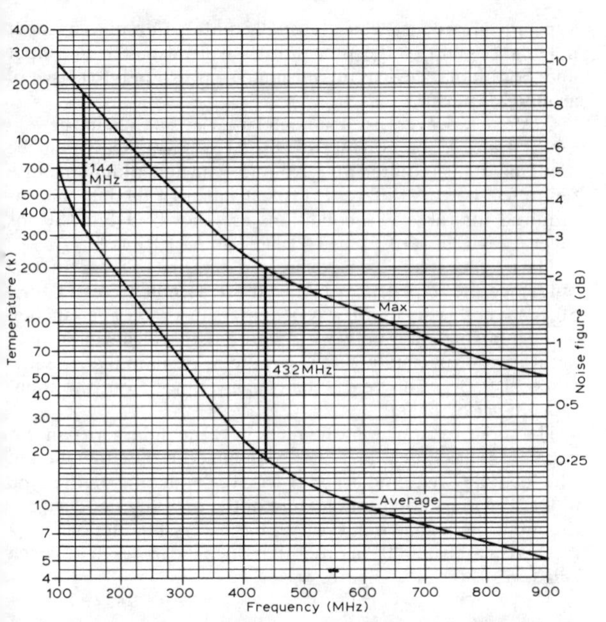

Fig 127. Plot of sky temperature against frequency. (Errata: in Figs 127, 128, 129, 135 and 136. "k" should read "K", signifying degrees Kelvin)

The stripline inductance plate (copper or brass) should be mounted 5mm above the chassis and fixed by soldering to the feedthrough capacitor at one end and the trimmer C2 at the other.

To set up the unit, connect to the main receiver with a short length of 50Ω cable and terminate the input with a 50Ω resistor. With 12V applied to the amplifier, the total current drain should be 5–6mA for the lowest noise. The collector current will be about 1mA less than the total current due to the bias chain. The resistor R may need to be adjusted slightly to achieve the 4–5mA collector current.

The preamplifier should be built into a close-fitting box, with a good connection between the lid and the body of the box. Probably one of the most satisfactory boxes is a cast box with a brass plate lid, with the addition of thin copper foil to improve the sealing.

GaAsFET preamplifier for 432MHz

This section describes the construction of a state-of-the-art preamplifier with a noise figure of 0·5dB, and is based on an article by J. N. Gannaway, G3YGF, and C. W. Suckling, G3WDG, which appeared in *Radio Communication* December 1980.

The benefits obtained from a low receiver noise figure will depend on the ambient noise level, which is the sum of contributions from several sources. Thermal noise will be picked up by the antenna from both the sky and the earth—man-made noise sources being ignored, as they are not a fundamental limitation, and are usually only of short duration.

Typical values of the noise level from the sky are given in Fig 127; at some time during the day the most noisy parts of the sky can be near the horizon, and so may be in the antenna beam. The sky's noise level may be expressed both as a noise figure in decibels and as an absolute temperature; this is the value of system noise figure or temperature for which the noise from the sky will be equal to the noise generated in the receiving system. The noise contribution from the earth will be at a temperature of around 290K (3dB nf), although this decreases at lower frequencies where the ground reflects, rather than absorbs, the signals. Feeder losses also introduce noise as well as attenuating the wanted signal. Finally there is the noise generated in the receiver front-end. The noise from the receiver preamplifier is only a part of the noise present at the receiver output.

On the lower vhf bands the thermal noise from the sky does not make it worthwhile to use a receiver with a noise figure of less than about 2dB. Even if an ideal, noiseless receiver were used, the s:n would only be improved by a decibel or so. At higher frequencies, however, particularly when the antenna is beaming upwards, less noise is picked up from the ground and the noise level from the sky is also much lower, so it is worthwhile building receivers with a much lower noise figure. On 432MHz, with the antenna pointing skywards for satellite or moonbounce work, the improvement in s:n obtained by going from a 3dB to a 0·5dB nf could be up to 6dB, so the effort involved in developing very-low noise-figure preamplifiers is well rewarded.

This improvement, much greater than the difference between the two noise figures, may seem illogical, but it is a consequence of noise figures being expressed relative to room temperature (290K), so they cannot be used directly to calculate the s:n when the noise source is at a different temperature. The concept of noise temperature is a better way of expressing both receiver and external noise levels, and is very useful in these cases. It is a means of specifying noise powers, eg the equivalent noise power at the input of the amplifier, and the actual noise power from the sky.

The available noise power P is directly proportional to absolute temperature T, $P = k \times T \times B$, where k is Boltzman's constant, $1{\cdot}38 \times 10^{-23}$ J/K, and B the bandwidth (Hz), so it is very simple to calculate s:n ratios using temperatures to represent the noise powers. The relation between noise figure and noise temperature is shown in Fig 128, which is a curve of the following relation:

$$NF_{dB} = 10 \log\left(1 + \frac{T}{290}\right)$$

Noise figures of 2–3dB are readily obtainable on 432MHz using inexpensive bipolar devices. The lower limit is about 1dB, but this figure is not easily achieved.

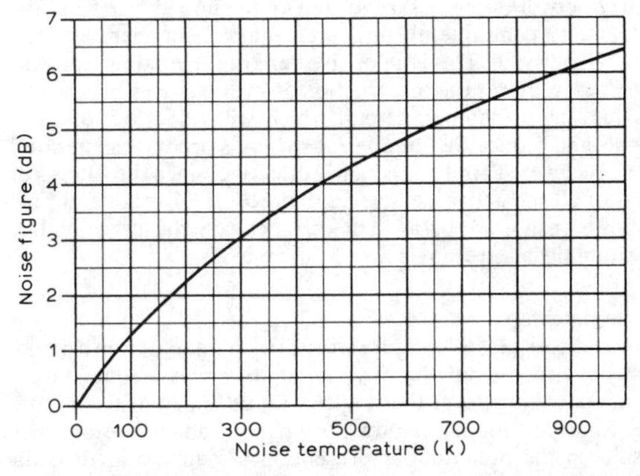

Fig 128. Graph for converting noise figure to noise temperature

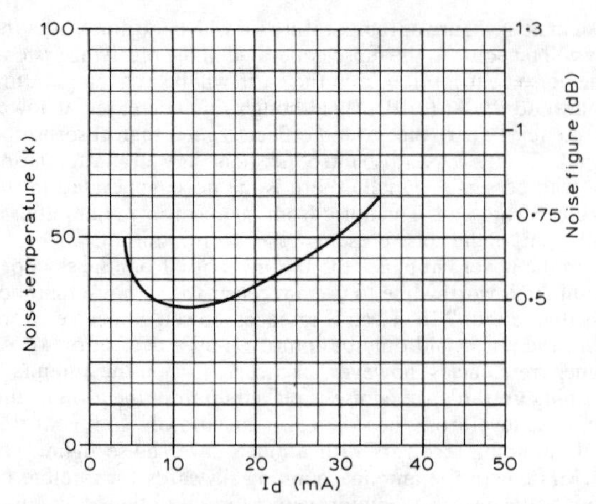

Fig 129. Variation of noise temperature of the gasfet preamplifier with drain current

Previously, the way to improve on these noise figures was to use techniques such as masers and parametric amplifiers, but GaAs fets ("gasfets") are now available and they offer a very simple solution to the problem. They are really intended for use in the 2–20GHz region where they can give noise figures of 1–3dB with associated gains of 15–8dB. Their performance is even better at lower frequencies (uhf). The devices themselves have noise figures of around 0·3dB (21K) in the 300–600MHz region, with gains of 18dB achievable with an untuned output circuit. The noise figure begins to rise again below 300MHz due to flicker noise. Their strong-signal performance is superior to bipolar devices because they produce the best noise figure at a higher device current, typically 10–15mA, whereas bipolars optimize at around 4mA. They will also hold a very low noise figure up to much higher drain currents, 20–30mA, see Fig 129. For many terrestrial applications, this high dynamic range will be more important, so the device would be run at 30–40mA drain current, giving an nf of around 1dB.

The one major problem in their use is that they have a very high input impedance. Bipolars have input impedances which are relatively close to 50Ω, typically a few hundred ohms, so they are quite easy to match in either narrow or broadband systems, leaving open the option of fitting a narrow, low-loss, bandpass filter in front of the preamplifier. On the other hand, gasfet input impedances are many tens of kilohms, so a very high *Q* network is necessary to step up the impedance with low loss, and it is consequently difficult to make them operate over a broad bandwidth. This is a positive benefit for amateur applications, as it requires the construction of a very narrow bandwidth low-loss input matching circuit which will reject out-of-band signals and reduce the number of spurious products generated in the receiver. This is particularly effective, since the filter is in front of all the active devices in the receiver. Broadband preamplifiers can suffer badly in this respect from the large number of strong signals present in the vhf/uhf bands.

Noise matching

The best possible noise figure will not be obtained from a device just by stepping up the 50Ω input to a value equal to the complex conjugate of the device's input impedance, which is the condition for maximum power gain, and therefore also results in the preamplifier presenting a matched load to the input line. For the best noise figure the device must be fed from a specific impedance which is usually quite different to its input impedance, and so the preamplifier will mismatch the input line. For bipolar devices this mismatch corresponds to a vswr of around 2:1 at vhf.

Gasfets, however, need a much larger mismatch, in the region of 15:1. A consequence of this large mismatch is that the input matching required for maximum gain and minimum noise figure will be very different. Typical values of the impedances required for these two conditions are shown in Fig 130 for several devices, a GAT5, a GAT4 and an ALF1000.

These values can also be expressed in terms of S parameters but, since the impedances involved are so much greater than 50Ω, it is not a very useful way of expressing them. The function of the input matching network is therefore to transform the 50Ω input to approximately 2kΩ in parallel with an inductive reactance of 900Ω. This reactance roughly cancels out the input capacitance of the fet.

The input resistance of the fet is very much larger than this value, so it has little effect on the loaded *Q* of the input circuit. The loaded *Q* required is about 15–30, depending on the type of fet. The most important feature of the preamplifier design is the input matching circuit, which has a very high unloaded *Q* (approximately 1,000) in order to reduce the losses in it, which will degrade the noise figure.

The circuit

The circuit of the gasfet preamplifier is given in Fig 131. It is built on double-sided pcb which is used as a ground plane, and the whole amplifier fits in a 4·4 by 2·4 by 1·25in die-cast box, with the ground plane replacing the lid. The screens are also made from double-sided pcb for rigidity and ease of soldering, and the covers for the input inductor L1 are made from thin brass or copper foil. The layout is shown in Fig 132 and the photograph.

First, mark and cut out the pcb to fit over the top of the box, and drill holes for the mounting screws in each corner. Mark the position of the posts in the corners of the box on the pcb, so as to avoid mounting anything on the board which will foul them; this is likely to occur if the input socket is too near the corner of the box. Solder the three pieces of pcb screen (0·8in high) in place, soldering both sides of the board all along their length. Mount the feedthrough capacitors in the screens and lid. The one into the drain compartment should be about halfway up the screen, and the one into the gate line about 0·2in from the top of the screen. Cut out two small pieces of pcb about 0·125in square for use as mounting pads for the fet leads, and glue them down flat to the ground plane on each side of the gap in the screen. Mount the input and output sockets and C2, making sure that the sockets do not foul the sides of the box. If four-hole mounting sockets are used they can be pushed through the pcb and

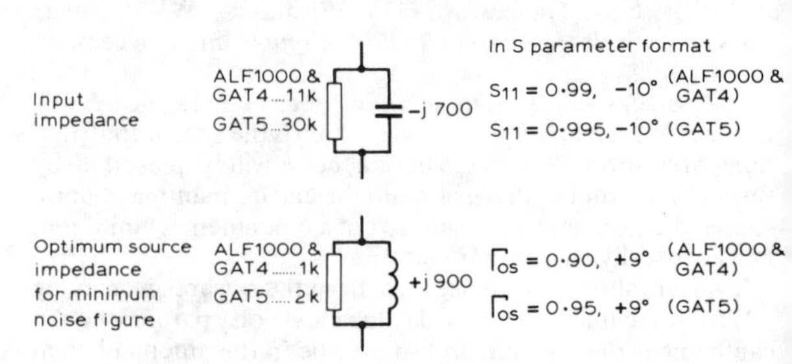

Fig 130. Input and optimum source impedances for several gasfets

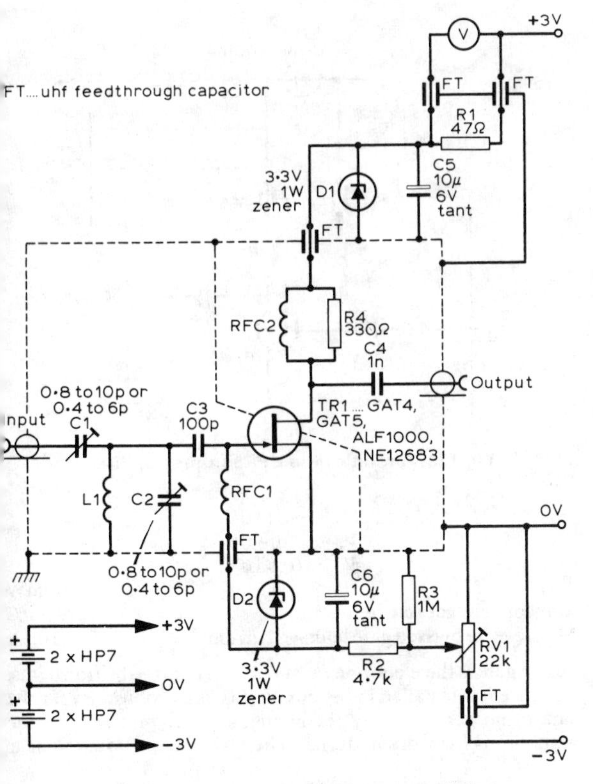

Fig 131. Circuit of the gasfet preamplifier

soldered to the ground plane inside the box. Single-hole fixing sockets can either be used in this way or bolted in. SMA, TNC or BNC sockets are particularly suitable on grounds of size, but BNC are rather less reliable electrically as they can become intermittent after a lot of use. N type sockets are too large.

Adjust the distance by which the input socket protrudes above the pcb so that C1 can easily be soldered to both C2 and the input socket. Next, bend up the input inductor L1 from some copper sheet about 0·040in thick, and solder it in place—at the grounded end first and then the end resting on C2. All the other components can then be installed. Take care when

The gasfet preamplifier before installing the final screen across the fet and input line

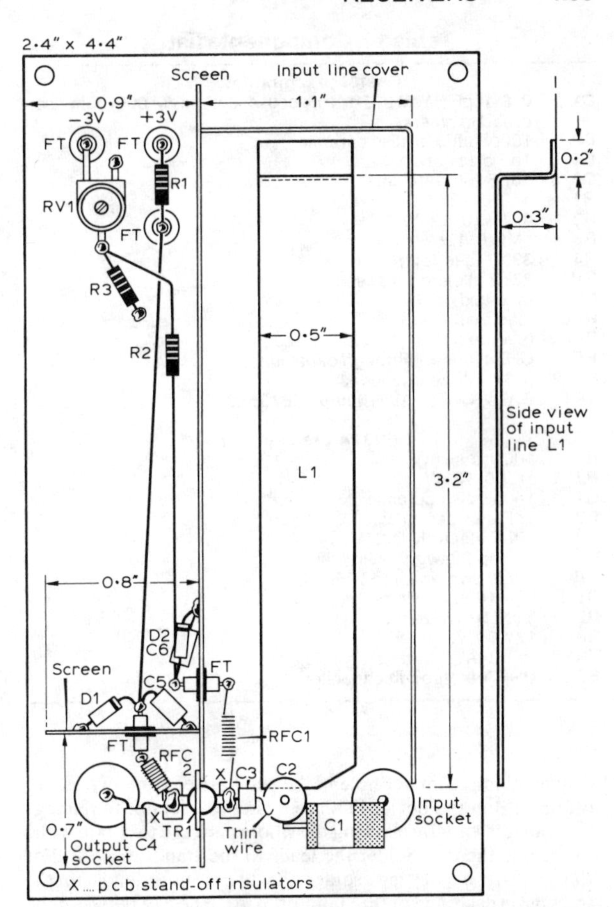

Fig 132. Layout of the gasfet preamplifier

soldering to the Johanson trimmers, as the top connections can become unsoldered from the body if they get too hot. A piece of flexible wire, rather than copper strip, should be used to connect C2 to C3 to prevent any stress being applied to C3. Next bend the screen to cover L1, and solder it in place all along the joins. It should stop just at the end of L1, leaving access to both the variable capacitors and the fet, and be about 0·3in above the inductor L1.

Check that the line can be made to resonate at 432MHz with C1 set approximately midway and with a 50Ω load on the input socket. Apply power and check that the correct voltages appear at the fet connection pads.

Install the gasfet, observing the following precautions:

1. Do not handle the device in a room where one can draw sparks from objects after walking across the floor.
2. Touch earthed objects frequently.
3. Touch the source first when picking up the gasfet.
4. When installing the device in the amplifier, hold the amplifier at the same time, thus keeping them both at the same potential.
5. When soldering the gasfet into the circuit, unplug the iron from the mains and ensure that the iron is earthed to the pcb during soldering.

For devices in the P103 package (threaded stud mounting),

Table 14. Components list

	Gasfet preamplifier
C1, 2	0·8–10pF (MVM 010 or 106, or 0·4–6pF (MVM 006) Johanson or JFD trimmers
C3	100pF chip or disc ceramic
C4	1nF disc ceramic
C5, 6	10μF 6V tantalum
R1	47Ω 0·125W
R2	4·7kΩ 0·125W
R3	1MΩ 0·125W
R4	330Ω (see text)
RV1	22kΩ skeleton preset
L1	(see text)
RFC1	(see text)
RFC2	(see text)
FT	UHF type feedthrough capacitors
D1, 2	3·3V 1W zener diodes
TR1	GAT4, GAT5, ALF1000 or NE12683
	BFR34A preamplifier
R1	100Ω 0·125W
R2, 3	1kΩ 0·125W
C1	100pF disc ceramic
C2	1nF disc ceramic
C3	10μF electrolytic 25V
L1	1t loop 22swg 0·25in diam
RFC1	10t 26swg enam 0·125in diam
D1	50V 100mA silicon
D2	6·8V 0·5W zener
D3	12V 0·5W zener
TR1	BFR34A
FT	UHF feedthrough capacitor

drill a 1·2mm diameter hole in the pcb between the two stand-off pads. Bolt the device in place, being careful not to damage the thin foil leads by allowing the whole package to rotate while tightening the nut. Solder the leads to the stand-off pads. For the cross-type package, solder the two source leads to the screens on each side of the stand-off pads. The gap between the two screens can now be closed by soldering some thin metal foil across it, and another foil screen can be soldered over the end and top of the input circuit, leaving access to adjust C1.

C1 will need to be about 1–2pF and C2 about 3pF. These components must be very low loss, and Johanson or JFD types are recommended. Miniature ptfe dielectric gold-plated trimmers have also been used successfully for C1. C3 is ideally a 100pF chip capacitor, but ordinary disc ceramic types may be suitable. RFC1 must also be of low-loss construction; it is about 15 turns of 26swg enamelled wire, self-supporting, 0·125in diameter with the turns slightly pulled apart. RFC2 is 10 turns of similar wire wound on the body of a resistor of a few hundred ohms (R4). The resistor R3 is used as a stand-off insulator to support the preset, RV1.

Second-stage preamplifier

The BFR34A preamplifier having a 2dB noise figure, shown in Fig 133, is built in a very similar manner in a smaller die-cast box, but screens will probably not be needed, other than the one shown in the layout in Fig 134.

Power supplies

Gasfets are very sensitive to transients because of the very small capacitances and dimensions of the chip. The width of the gate is about 1 micron, so even relatively low voltages can produce very high electric fields in the chip. The manufacturer's maximum ratings are typically as follows:

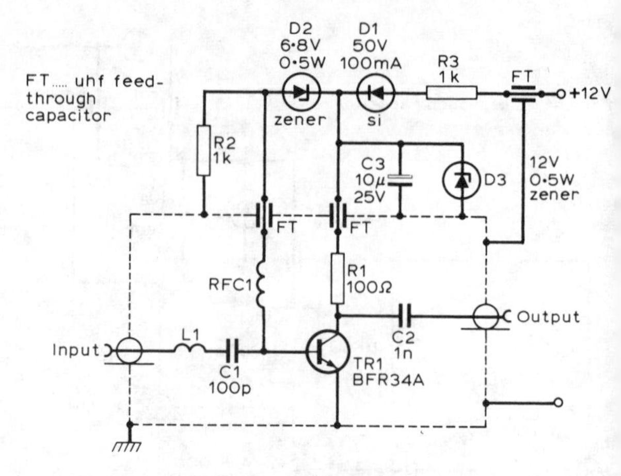

Fig 133. Circuit of the BFR34A preamplifier

V_{gs} −6 to 0V.
V_{ds} 0 to +6V.
V_{dg} 0 to 10V.

P_{max}	500mW
Max forward gate current	2mA
Max reverse biassed gate leakage current	10μA

The gate is the electrode most liable to damage by transients, but once it is installed in the circuit it is fairly robust. By far the safest and very strongly recommended way of powering the amplifier is from dry batteries. These should be mounted near

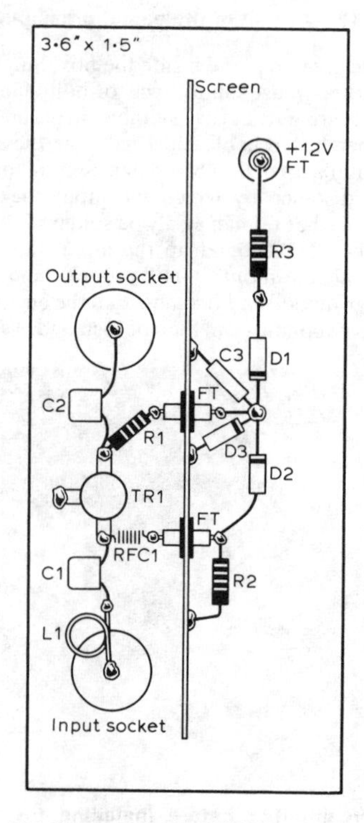

Fig 134. Layout of the BFR34A preamplifier

the preamplifier, as excessively long leads will increase the chance of picking up transients from other circuits, such as relays, which will also be at the masthead. The circuit given provides some protection, but zener diodes are fairly slow-acting devices and can still allow transients through.

Testing

Set RV1 to about half-way, then apply first the gate and then the drain supply. This order avoids the device taking I_{dss} (50–100mA), which occurs if the gate bias is applied later. Reverse the order when switching off. The drain current should be set to 10mA initially, and can be monitored by measuring the voltage across the 47Ω resistor. The preamplifier may oscillate if it is run without a 50Ω load on the input.

Once the gasfet and a suitable second stage amplifier have been built, the matching of the gasfet will have to be carefully optimized to achieve the 0·5dB noise figure. The two preamplifiers should be connected by a fairly short piece of cable to avoid introducing further losses; it should be the same piece of cable which will be used when they are installed in the system.

There are two approaches to the optimization. If facilities are available to measure and adjust the antenna accurately to 50Ω, then the preamplifiers can be optimized on the bench when fed from a noise source with a 50Ω source impedance. The impedances should be kept to a vswr of less than 1·1:1 if the best noise figure is to be maintained. This method is the best, in that the preamplifiers will be set up for 50Ω sources and can be measured on standard laboratory test gear.

Alternatively the preamplifiers can be installed on the antenna, and noise injected by running the noise source into a small antenna near the main one, taking care that neither it, nor the presence of the operator, will upset the matching of the main antenna. Once it has been optimized in this way, the cables, relays etc between the antenna and the gasfet should not be changed, as they may alter the matching. With care, both methods can produce equally good results, since the actual antenna impedance is not important, provided that it is transformed to the correct impedance at the fet gate.

C1 should be set initially to 1–2pF, and C2 adjusted for best noise figure. Then C1 can be altered and C2 re-optimized. This procedure is necessary because both ends of C1 are floating, and the presence of the trimming tool alters the impedances. Both V_d and I_d will affect the noise figure. The effect of I_d is shown in Fig 129, while V_d has been found to produce a broad optimum in nf around 1·5 to 3V; typical values being 2·5V and 10mA. Whichever method is used, some form of noise-figure indicating meter is necessary. A suitable instrument is described in Chapter 11. This turns a noise source on and off at about 10Hz and, by measuring the ratio between the two noise levels at the audio output of the receiver when the noise source is on and off, it can display the s:n ratio, which will be related to the noise figure. It is a very simple and extremely useful piece of test equipment, and can be used to optimize almost any receiver. In the absence of any test equipment it may be possible to set up the preamplifier by listening to a weak carrier, and adjusting for best s:n, but the nf meter is far more accurate, and quicker and easier to use. One word of warning: be careful not to tune up the gasfet preamplifier on the image frequency of the converter. These two preamplifiers have enough gain to give quite a good noise figure even when tuned up on the image frequency, as some converters have very poor rejection of the image frequency; one using a 28MHz i.f. only had 10dB image rejection!

After optimization, the gain should be about 18dB and the overall noise figure 0·5dB. The BFR34A should give a noise figure of about 2dB (173K) and a gain of 13dB. The effect of the source impedance differing from 50Ω is shown in Fig 135. The worse the vswr, the greater the worst case noise figure, although—depending on the phase of the mismatch—it can also still be quite close to the best value.

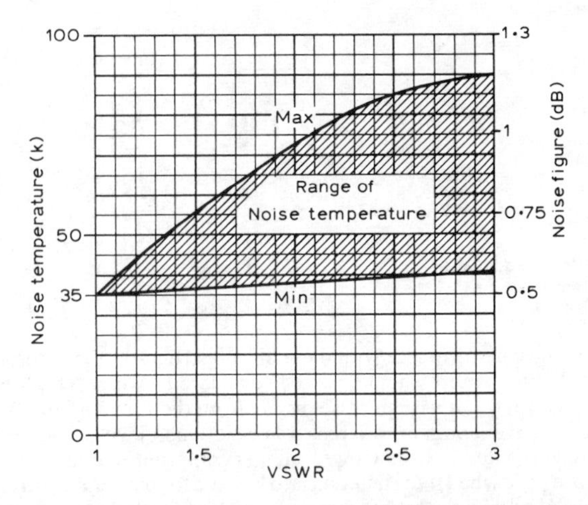

Fig 135. Variation of noise temperature of the gasfet preamplifier with source vswr

Measurement of the final noise figure is not easy. Few commercial nf meters are accurate to better than ±0·2dB in this region, and there are many other sources of error that can creep in. The best method is the hot/cold load technique, where the preamplifier is fed from 50Ω resistors held at two different temperatures. The ratio of the receiver noise outputs is measured, and compared with the ratio of the two temperatures and, hence, the ratio of the two noise powers. This technique is usually done using liquid nitrogen (77K) or dry ice for the lower temperature, and room temperature for the higher one. Kitchen table type measurements can be done using the temperature difference between ice and boiling water, but great care must be taken to ensure that the load impedance does not change between these two temperatures as this may also alter the noise output from the preamplifier. The liquid nitrogen/room temperature method was used to obtain the noise figures quoted here. They should be accurate to ±0·15dB.

Various gasfets have been tried in this circuit, including the Plessey GAT4, GAT5 and GAT6, the NEC NE1283, and the Alpha ALF1000, having gate widths from 1 to 0·5 micron; all of them giving very similar performance. The GAT2, having a 2 micron gate, is considerably worse at over 1dB. Although the first five devices all gave similar noise figures in the circuit, their inherent noise figures are actually somewhat lower than 0·5dB. The extra noise comes from the losses in the input circuit, and it is here that there is much scope for improvement.

Other devices, having gate widths of 1 micron or less, such as the Mitsubishi MGF1400 series, or NEC V244 or V388 may be suitable.

Installation

The preamplifier should be mounted as close to the antenna as possible, as any feeder loss will degrade the noise figure; 0·1dB loss will add 7K (0·1dB) to the system noise temperature. If the feeder from the masthead has a loss exceeding 1dB, then the second-stage preamplifier should be at the masthead as well.

	Feeder loss 0·1dB	Input matching circuit losses 0·12dB	Gasfet device NF 0·34dB (Gain 50x)	Contribution from 2nd stage amplifier (NF=3dB) $= \frac{T}{G} = \frac{290}{50} = 6k$	Overall
NF added (dB)	0·1	+ 0·12	+ 0·34	+ 0·09	= 0·65dB
Temperature added (k)	7	+ 10	+ 24	+ 6	= 47k

Fig 136. Diagram showing the sources of noise in a typical receiving system

For best performance with these low noise figures, the antenna radiation pattern should also be considered. A high side-lobe level will result in high noise pickup from the surroundings but give maximum gain, whereas a low side-lobe level will give a quieter antenna with a lower gain. A compromise must therefore be reached if the antenna is to be used for both transmitting and receiving, as the requirements for the two conflict.

The noise coming out of the second stage can be split into contributions from several places in the preceding circuits. The losses in a typical system are shown in Fig 136, giving an overall receiver noise figure of 0·65dB. Noise introduced by the antenna has to be added to this figure to get the overall system temperature, so it will be seen that a great deal of effort must be put into the rest of the system, as well as the first preamplifier, if it is to be used to its best advantage. The actual noise temperature of the fet chip is 15–30K (nf 0·2–0·4dB), depending on the device, so much of the noise is still coming from the passive components in the circuit, hence the strong emphasis on low loss in the design.

The two preamplifiers may be considered to have a rather large gain (30dB) to put in front of the converter, as it will degrade the strong-signal performance of the system. If this is an important consideration, then the whole receiver front-end must be designed with it in mind.

Super-regenerative receivers for vhf-uhf operation

Although this type of receiver has been little used by amateurs for very many years, there is possibly a case for their use where simple equipment is desired.

Basically these receivers are highly sensitive and noisy in the absence of a signal. They also cause radiation problems unless an isolating stage is used but the radiation likely from transistors is very much lower than was the case with valves. Without special arrangements they are only suitable for the reception of amplitude or tone-modulated signals.

It is possible that such a receiver used with a gate-modulated vmos power fet transmitter could provide a useful short-range system. In Fig 137(a) is shown a basic super-regenerative detector which originally appeared in *Break-In* November 1978. In this the quench frequency is controlled by the values of C and R, a suitable value for C being 1,000–1,500pF, while the value of R could be fixed once the suitable value has been found for a given frequency. Fig 137(b) illustrates an isolating rf amplifier.

Fig 138 shows a typical separately quenched detector which can provide significantly improved results; it is basically similar to that most favoured for use on 56 and 112MHz many years ago.

A more refined arrangement by ZL3VN is illustrated in Fig 139 (*Break-In* May 1979). In this the detection function has been removed from the super-regenerative stage to improve the audio quality and also included is an elaborated quench oscillator and wave-shaping circuit.

In the interests of other users of the bands it is recommended that an rf isolating stage is always used.

Simple direct-conversion receiver for 144MHz ssb

Direct conversion for 144MHz reception, as an alternative to the usual superheterodyne, offers a very simple unit of significant performance without the need for complex alignment of an intermediate amplifier. Naturally the basic selectivity will be of a lower standard, but for many purposes it is quite adequate, particularly if a selective preamplifier is used before the mixer.

The basic sensitivity of the unit described is 5μV. By the

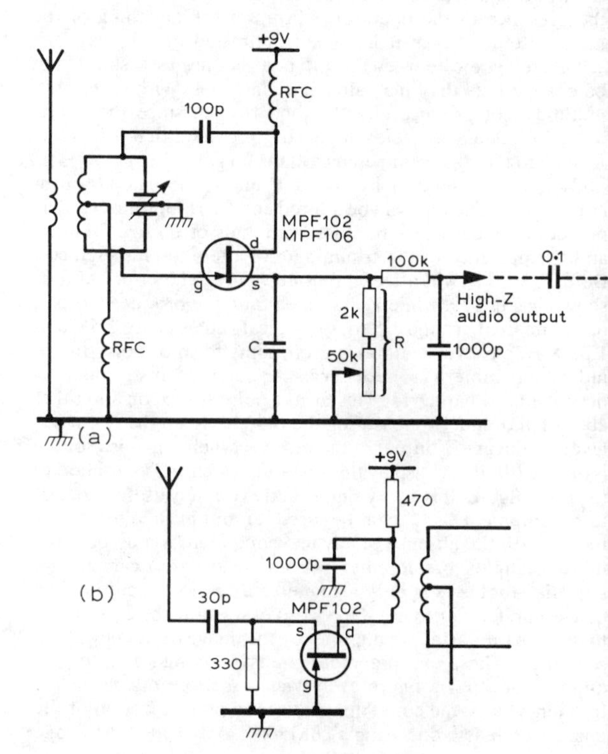

Fig 137. (a) Basic self-quenched fet super-regenerative detector. (b) Untuned fet rf stage

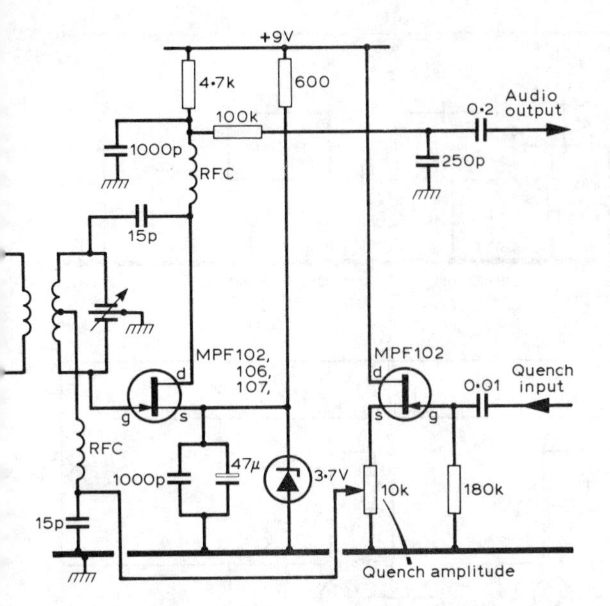

Fig 138. Separately quenched detector which can provide significantly improved results

addition of the simplest of preamplifiers this can be increased to better than 1μV.

The circuit, Fig 140, is based on the use of a wideband double-balanced hot-carrier ring diode mixer, MD108 or equivalent. This unit, which includes the coupling transformer, has good isolation between each of the ports, and if adequate oscillator injection is provided has a suitably high s:n ratio. Although the local oscillator power needed for satisfactory operation is higher than some other mixers, this can be readily supplied from an ordinary crystal oscillator-frequency multiplier chain.

One local oscillator in this receiver comprises a variable crystal oscillator (vxo) at 18MHz followed by three frequency doublers to produce an output frequency of 144·3MHz. The tuning range of the oscillator is ±100kHz (144·2 to 144·4). The output power of 5mW is sufficient for efficient mixer operation.

Following the mixer, a fet (2N3819 or equivalent) is used as an impedance-matching amplifier, which is more satisfactory than using a high-ratio transformer. This stage is followed by a low-pass audio filter into an audio preamplifier (BC108) feeding an ic audio amplifier (LM380).

Although a vxo has been detailed for the local oscillator any other equally stable oscillator may be used if preferred.

Construction of this type of receiver needs little detailing, other than to point out that the tuning capacitor should have a reliable backlash-free slow-motion control that can be readily reset to any given frequency. It should be rigidly fixed to the rest of the oscillator circuit.

An fm receiver for 144MHz

This receiver (*Radio Communication* September 1979) is suitable as a standby receiver, particularly for local working, although with an adequate antenna it has sufficient sensitivity for other purposes.

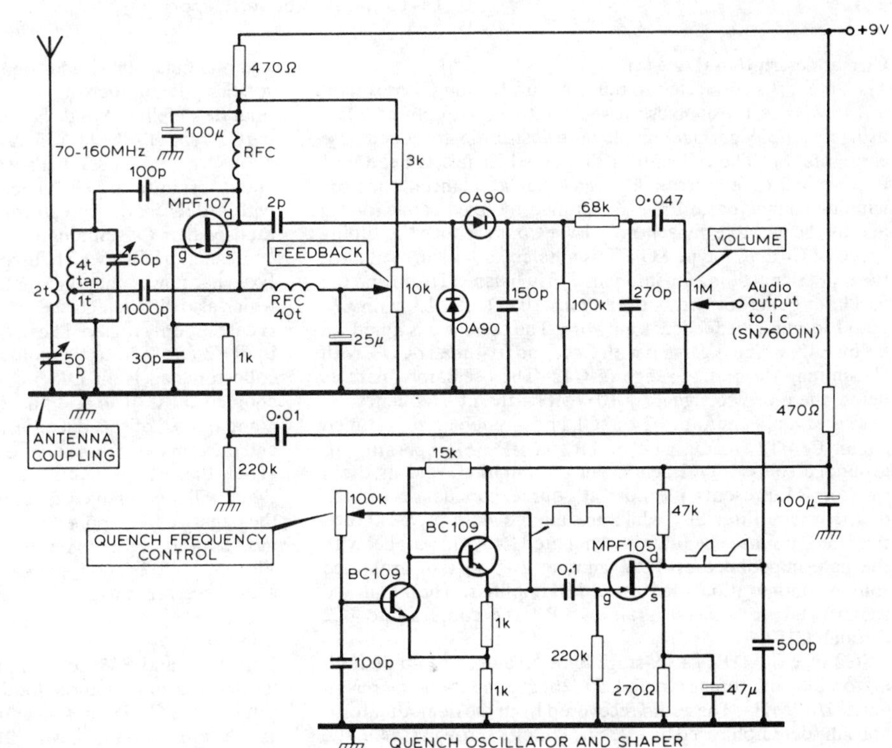

Fig 139. Super-regenerative rf stage with separate detector, quench oscillator and shaper

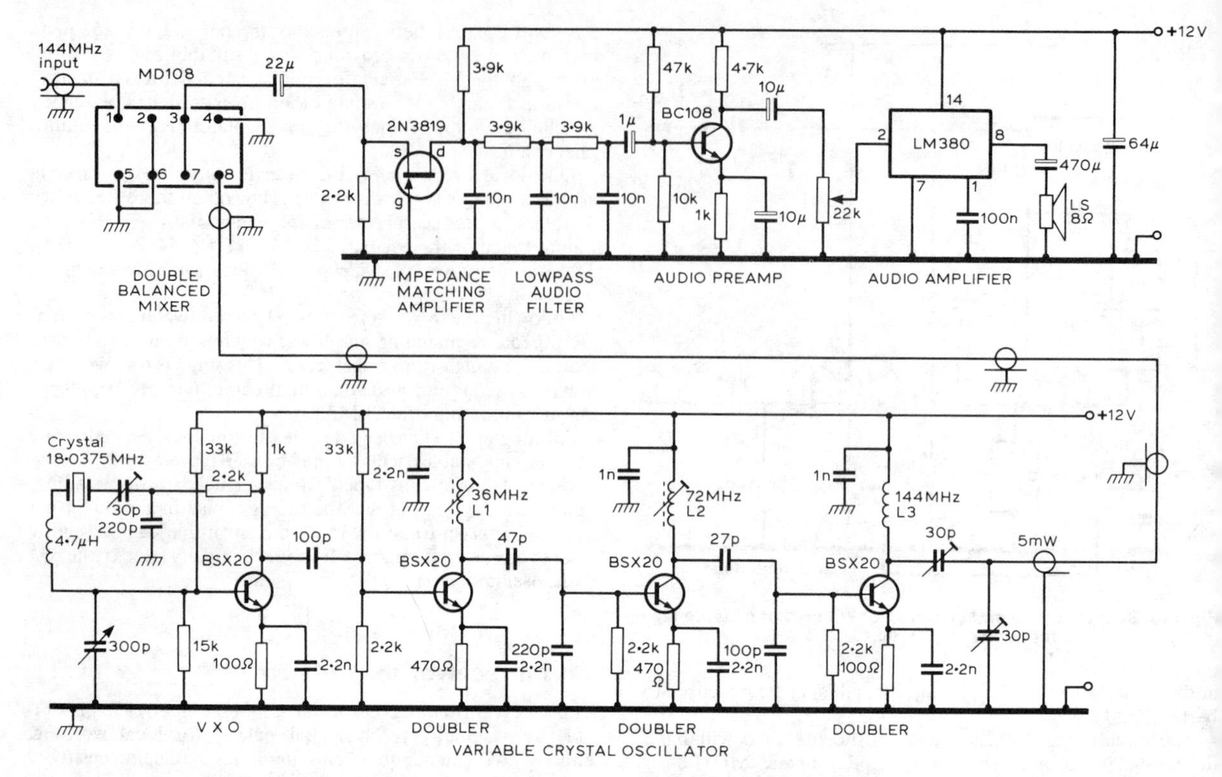

Fig 140. Simple direct-conversion 144MHz ssb receiver with vxo tuning. L1 13t 26swg cw; L2 6t 22swg cw; L3 3t 22swg ¼in long. L1–L3 ¼in diam on ferrite core

Circuit description (Fig 141)

The antenna is connected to tuned circuit L1 and C1, resonant at 145MHz. A tap couples the signal into an rf amplifier, TR1, using an AF239 germanium planar transistor in grounded base configuration. The collector of TR1 is fed via ferrite bead FB1 to a second tuned circuit L2 which has a balanced coupling winding connected to IC1. L2 is tuned by fixed capacitor C5 and by the variable capacitor C41 via C6, to reduce the tuning range of C41. IC1 type SO42P is a balanced/mixer/oscillator, the input signal being fed into pins 7, 8 in balanced form and the oscillator being formed between pins 10, 11, 12, 13, with C9, 10, 11 forming the feedback network. The oscillator is tuned via L3 by C42, which is ganged with C41, and fix-tuned by C8, with C7 limiting the tuning range of C42. The oscillator operates below the received signal by 10·7MHz, the i.f. frequency.

The i.f. appears at pin 2 of IC1 and is coupled by a tuned circuit C14/T1, to the gate of TR2, a BF256A operating in grounded source. TR2 acts as an i.f. amplifier, and its drain resistor R4 presents the correct source impedance for the quartz crystal filter FL1 which has a bandwidth of 7·5kHz at the −3dB points. The filter is terminated by R6 in parallel with the gate impedance of TR3, another BF256A in grounded source configuration used as an i.f. amplifier. The amplified signal is taken from the drain of TR3 and couples into IC2 through C19.

IC2 type SO41P is a six-stage limiting amplifier/fm demodulator, the tank tuning circuit C25, 26, 27, and L4 being resonant at 10·7MHz. The audio recovered from the demodulator is partially de-emphasized by C23 and couples through C24 to the audio circuits. The audio signal passes to TR5, BF256A, as a squelch gate, to the volume control RV1 and R14, C32 (giving final de-emphasis) and then to the audio amplifier IC3.

IC3 type TAA611A55 raises the level to a maximum of about 1W into an 8Ω loudspeaker. R15, C36, 37, 38 tailor the audio response to be 120Hz to 4kHz −3dB relative to 1kHz with a 22Ω load. An external load such as a low-impedance loudspeaker (4Ω minimum) or a pair of headphones may be connected by JK1 which disconnects the internal loudspeaker. External power may be applied to the receiver through JK2 which also disconnects the internal battery. In the absence of an rf carrier, only noise will exist at point "E". This will be passed by RV2 and C28 to the noise amplifier TR4, a BC172B. The collector load is an LC circuit tuned to about 10kHz and is coupled by C30 to a diode detector/doubler. The negative-going output of this detector turns off TR5 (the squelch gate) and prevents the noise from being passed to the audio amplifier. When the receiver is tuned to a carrier, stronger levels of rf signal will progressively quieten the limiting rf amplifier, reduce the negative bias applied to the squelch gate, and allow any fm modulation on the carrier to be passed to the audio amplifier. The links B to D and C to G are provided to allow for switching if the receiver is to be interconnected with a transmitter.

Alignment

Turn RV1 and RV2 to a minimum and switch off the squelch (switch shorting) and the loudspeaker load to M and L. Make connections C–G and B–D and ensure that the power lines to P and N are decoupled with 220μF if testing with a battery,

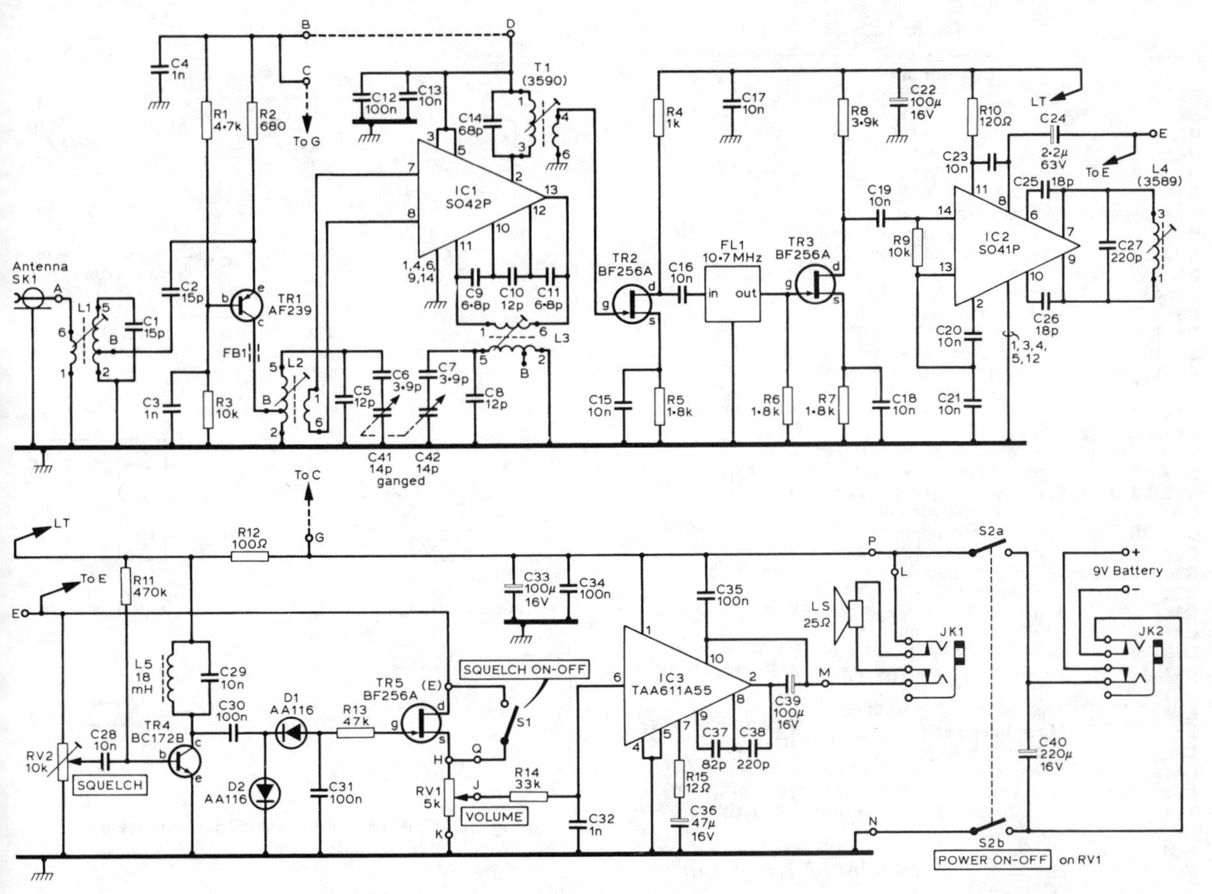

Fig 141. Circuit of 144MHz receiver

otherwise af instability may result due to high dynamic source impedance.

Inject to pin 14 of IC2, via a 10nF capacitor, a signal at 10·7MHz with a deviation of 3kHz peak at about 1mV amplitude and 1kHz modulation. Adjust L4 for maximum recovered audio at H or M.

Inject at point H a sine wave of 1kHz and 10mV p–p, and check for undistorted output at M with an oscilloscope. Output will be approximately 1W (8Ω) or 250mW (25Ω) for about 20mV p–p at H with maximum volume.

Adjust C41/42 to mid-travel and inject a sweep generator into the antenna socket, taking the output from IC2 pin 14 to the equipment demodulator via a 10nF capacitor. Locate the 145MHz marker on the sweep generator and align L3 to produce a response on this marker. Then adjust L1, L2 and T1 to produce maximum amplitude, being careful not to overload the receiver as this will mask the alignment. Check that adjusting C41/42 that the whole of 144–146MHz is tunable with about 0·5MHz extra at either end.

Remove all input signals, switch on the squelch (S1 open) and check that the noise at the audio output is killed when RV2 is adjusted anticlockwise between 40 and 75 per cent of travel. The receiver is now ready to use.

144MHz multimode receiver incorporating a phase-lock loop local oscillator, receiver incremental tuning and digital frequency display

The design of this receiver (Fig 145) is based on a single-conversion superhet using 10·7MHz as the i.f. It will demodulate a.m., nbfm and ssb signals, additionally resolving cw signals via an audio-peaking filter. The receiver incorporates dual-gate fets, linear and logic ics, as well as junction fets and bipolar transistors in the design. Varicap diodes are employed for rit and control of the vco which in turn drives the receiver mixer. Employing a pll local oscillator gives very high frequency stability, minimizes generation of spurious responses and enables a digital-frequency readout to be used in place of a calibrated scale system. This section is described later. The receiver operates from a 13V station or mobile supply.

Receiver section (Figs 146 and 147)

Signals within the 144MHz band are routed to the antenna tuned circuit L2 via the antenna socket and coupling winding L1. L2 is resonated by C3 to 145MHz.

Table 15

Components list

R1	4·7kΩ	**R10**	120Ω
R2	680Ω	**R11**	470Ω
R3, 9	10kΩ	**R12**	100Ω
R4	1kΩ	**R13**	47kΩ
R5, 6, 7	1·8kΩ	**R14**	33kΩ
R8	3·9kΩ	**R15**	12kΩ

All resistors 0·25W 5% carbon film

RV1	5kΩ carbon pot log with switch
RV2	10kΩ carbon pot linear
C1, 2	15pF ceramic plate ±2%
C3, 4	1nF ceramic plate ±10%
C5	12pF ceramic plate ±2%
C6, 7	3·9pF ceramic plate ±2%
C8, 10	12pF ceramic plate ±2%
C9, 11	6·8pF ceramic plate ±2%
C12	100nF polyester ±20%
C13, 15, 16, 17, 18, 19, 20, 22, 23, 28, 29	10nF ceramic plate −20 +80%
C14	68pF ceramic plate ±2%
C22, 33, 39	100μF electrolytic pluggable 16V
C24	2·2μF electrolytic 63V
C25, 26	18pF ceramic plate ±2%
C27, 38	220pF ceramic plate ±2%
C30, 31, 34, 35	100nF polyester ±20%
C32	1nF ceramic plate ±10%
C36	47μF electrolytic pluggable 16V
C37	82pF ceramic plate ±2%
C40	220μF electrolytic (with mechanical sets only)
C41, 42	15pF swing tuner (Wingrove & Rogers 3/CG80-03/1)
L1	Antenna coupling winding } Toko type E515HNS – 210170 RIE9
L2	Mixer tuning coil } Toko type E515HNS – 210170 RIE9
L3	Local oscillator coil } Toko type E515HNS – 210170 RIE9
L4	Demodulator tank coil Toko type KAN–K3589ABD
L5	Squelch inductor 18mH Toko type 187LY–183
T1	I.F. coupling transformer Toko type KAN–K3590ABD
FB1	Ferrite bead
FL1	Crystal filter 10·7MHz bw ±7·5kHz, ITT type 024BG/923B
D1, D2	Germanium diode type AA116 noise demodulator
TR1	AF239 germanium pnp rf amplifier
TR2, 3	BF256A jfet i.f. amp/filter matching
TR4	BC172B silicon npn squelch amplifier
TR5	BF256A jfet squelch switch/gate (identified with white spot)
IC1	SO42P balanced mixer/oscillator (Siemens)
IC2	SO41P limiting amplifier/demodulator (Siemens)
IC3	TAA611A55 af output amplifier
LS1	Internal loudspeaker 25Ω/1W Mullard type AD2071/Z25
SK1	Belling-Lee antenna socket
JK1	0·25in headphone jack
JK2	3·5mm power jack
S1	SPST squelch on-off
S2a, b	Power on-off dpst (on RV1)

Variations

It is recommended that a 6:1 reduction drive is used with the tuning gang. Also, some experiments with the removal of rotor vanes would produce a more expanded scale if less coverage was required.

Coil winding details

Coil	Toko part No	Function	Winding (0·7mm wire) 1	2	3
			Pins 2–5	Pins 2–8	Pins 1–6
L1	E515HNS-210170 RIE9	Antenna coupling	2½ turns	¾ turn	2⅙ turns
L2	E515HNS-201070 RIE9	Mixer tuning	2½ turns	¾ turn	2⅙ turns
L3	E515HNS-210170 RIE9	Local oscillator	2½ turns	¾ turn	2⅙ turns
T1	KAN K3590 ABD	1st i.f.	Pins 1–3 15 turns	Pins 4–6 8 turns	—
L4	KAN K3589 ABD	Demodulator tank coil	Pins 1–3 7 turns	—	—

All wound on ferrite cores. (Original coils custom-made by Toko.)

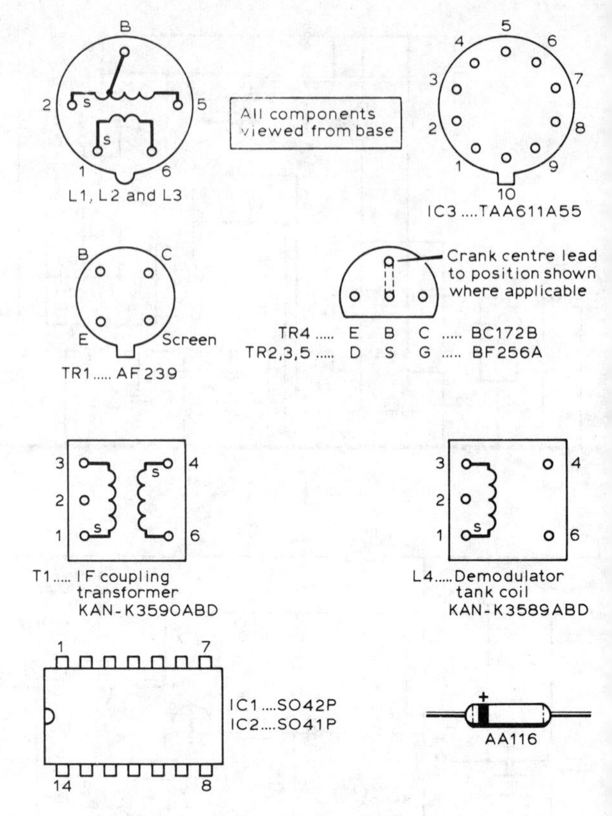

Fig 142. Connection diagrams, bottom views

RF amplifier

The amplifier stage gain is limited to about 12dB by tapping down L2 to feed gate 1 of TR1 (40673), a dual-gate mosfet. Amplified signals appearing at the drain of TR1 are routed to L3 via RFC1 and C8. L3 is tuned by C9. L5 and L6 form a link coupling between L3 and L6 to form a bandpass circuit. L6 is resonated by C13.

Mixer

Signals present at the low-impedance tap on L6 are routed to gate 1 of a second dual-gate mosfet TR3 (40673), operated as a mixer. The impedance between this tap and ground is very low at 10·7MHz, thus giving high rejection of signals present at or near the i.f. The local oscillator voltage from the vco buffer amplifier is applied to g2 of TR3. This lo input mixes (multiplicatively) with the rf signal in TR3, the resultant difference signal (10·7MHz) being present across IFT1 primary, resonated by C14. The i.f. signal is coupled to IFT2 secondary, resonated by C18, to the diode switch via C22 and C23.

SSB filter (10·7MHz)

With the receiver switched to ssb or cw mode, D2 (1N4148) routes the i.f. to FL1, a six-pole crystal filter (−6dB bandwidth 2·4kHz) via C24. R17 and R22 provide correct termination for FL1. Additionally a.m. signals pass through FL1. Although theoretically the bandwidth is too narrow for a.m. signals, they can be resolved satisfactorily by the receiver envelope detector.

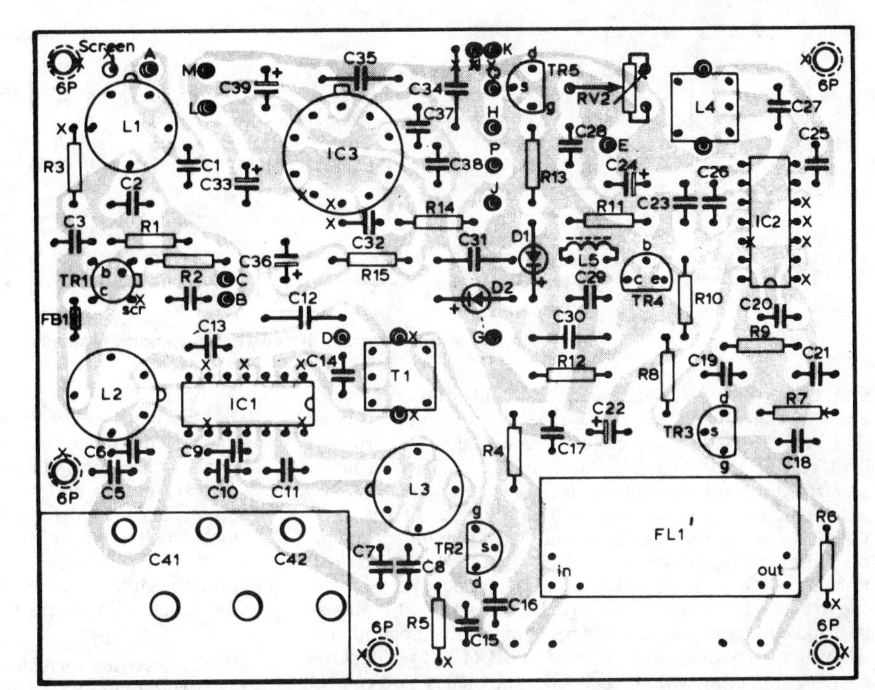

Fig 143. Component layout, pcb, top view

6P indicates 6BA tapped × 0·5in long pillars

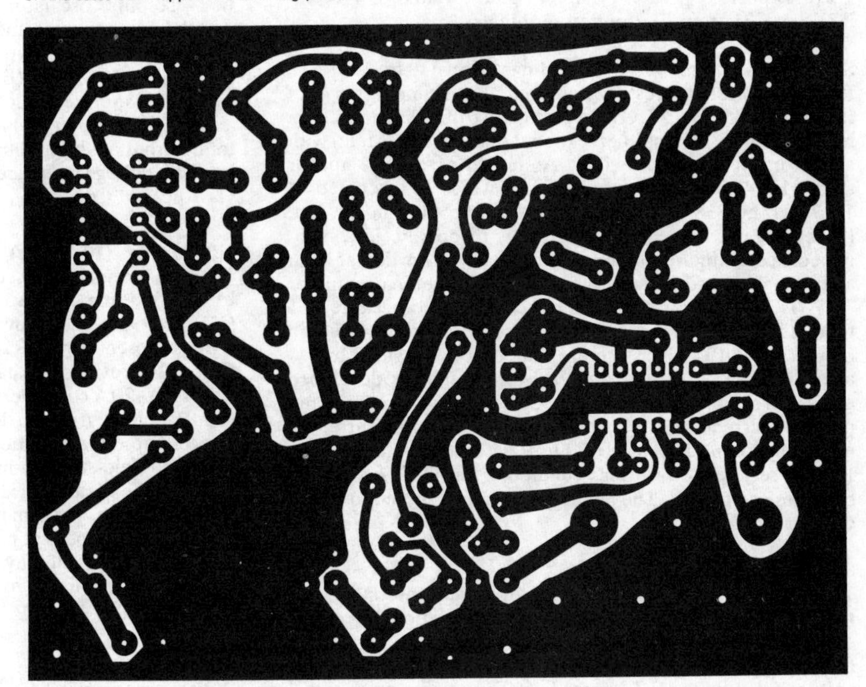

Fig 144. PCB etching, underside view

Delayed agc i.f. amplifier

I.F. signals present across R22 are routed via R20 and C21 to the base of TR4 (BF241), the delayed agc i.f. amplifier. The stage gain is designed to overcome the insertion loss of the filter and to provide sufficient signal level to drive the delayed diode D1 (AA119) and dc amplifier TR2 (BC149). TR2 is non-conductive with signal levels less than 500μV at the antenna socket.

Delayed agc system

When the signal level is equal to or greater than 500μV, amplified i.f. signals appearing across IFT3 are routed to D1 via

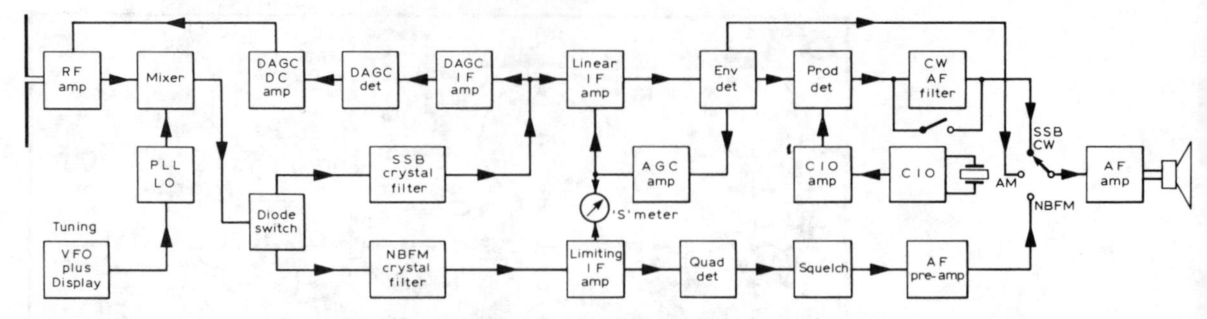

Fig 145. Block diagram of 144MHz multimode receiver

C11. D1 rectifies the signal and the resultant dc is filtered by R7 and C10 and applied to TR2 base. TR2 is driven into conduction. As R3 (68kΩ) provides an extremely high value collector load, g2 voltage on TR1 (V_{g2s} normally + 4V) is driven almost to zero with respect to chassis, ie V_{g2s} is approximately −2V with increasing input signal level. The rf gain of TR1 is simultaneously reduced to a factor of one. This form of delayed agc prevents blocking of the mixer TR3—there is little deterioration in cross- and intermodulation characteristics of the receiver due to high signal levels. Single-signal levels of up to 1V rms can be handled before the receiver performance is impaired. The delayed agc provides an additional 40dB (100×) of receiver control, dispensing with the need for a manual rf gain control. The system also operates on nbfm signals, routed to TR4 via R21 and C21 from FL2 output terminals.

SSB/cw/a.m. i.f. amplifier and primary agc system

I.F. signals present across R22 are routed to the input (pin 4) of IC1 (MC1349) via C28. C30 bypasses pin 6 of IC1 at i.f. IC1 is a high-gain linear i.f. amplifier ic (about 66dB at 10·7MHz) with a built-in forward agc facility. Amplified i.f. signals appear across IFT4 primary (centre-tapped) which is resonated at 10·7MHz by C38. IFT4 has a 1:1 turns ratio allowing the a.m. (envelope) agc detector D4 (AA119) to operate in a high-impedance configuration for extracting low-distortion af from a.m. signals and for driving the emitter-follower agc amplifier TR7 (BC149). An external amplifier is needed because IC1 requires 100–200μA of agc drive current for maximum gain reduction (66dB) which is more than can be provided by D4 alone. The amplified agc and recovered audio is developed across R41. R35, C42, R27 and C34 filter the agc loop and provide the required time constant. TR7 collector current is nominally 500μA, rising to 700μA with large signal inputs. R38/36 set the forward bias conditions for TR7. R37 is the detector load for D4. The audio signal is then routed to S1 via C53 and R42.

SSB/cw detector

This detector is provided by a four-quadrant multiplier IC3 (MC1496) used in a product-detector configuration. It requires only 10μV of input signal for a 10dB s/n ratio. I.F. signals are routed to IC3 via R44 and C57 providing a 27:1 stepdown of voltage appearing at IFT4 secondary. Even under weak-signal conditions sufficient level will appear at IC3 input for correct operation while its low input impedance will not be reflected back across IFT4. SSB/cw signals at pin 1 and carrier insertion at pin 10 are mixed in IC3, the resultant product appears at pin 6. Carrier and signal filtering is provided by C65, R66 and C69. The audio signal is then routed to S1 via C70.

CW filter

The frequency-selective audio amplifier TR10 (40822) is switched into circuit by S1 to improve reception of weak cw signals under crowded band conditions. The circuit employs a dual-gate mosfet and has a twin "T" RC filter circuit in its output. The network provides regenerative feedback to its input circuit at an audio frequency determined by C74, 75, 76 and RV5. The amplifier is selective at 1kHz with a rapid fall off in output either side off this frequency. RV2 allows − 10 per cent variation in the peak frequency.

Carrier insertion oscillator

The oscillator employs a hf transistor TR11 (BF241) in a modified Colpitts oscillator circuit. X3 (10,698·5kHz) is a parallel-mode crystal and is set exactly to this frequency by C82. The oscillator output from TR11 emitter is routed to buffer amplifier TR12 (BF451) via C88 and R80. The resistor prevents overdrive of TR12 base. The amplified output appears across IFT5 primary which is tuned to 10·7MHz by C92. A total output of about 500mV rms appears across IFT5 secondary. This voltage is applied to pin 10 of the product detector IC3 via R86 and C60.

NBFM filter (10·7MHz), i.f. amplifier/detector

With the receiver switched to nbfm, D3 (1N4148) routes the i.f. to FL2 six-pole crystal filter (−3dB bandwidth 7·5kHz) via C25. R19 and R23 provide correct termination for FL2. I.F. signals present across R23 are routed to IC2 (TCA420A) via C29. R24 provides a dc path for the input transistor within IC2. The TCA420A combines the following functions: high i.f. gain (66dB), symmetrical fm detection with very low distortion (0·2 per cent at 3kHz deviation), automatic side-response suppression, and field-strength indicator current. In this receiver IC2 provides the i.f. amplification with amplitude limiting, a quadrature detector, and S-meter drive for nbfm signals. Recovered audio signals appear at pin 6, and partial de-emphasis is given by C44. L7 resonated by C41 to 10·7MHz forms the quadrature detector, coupled to the final i.f. amplifier within IC2 by C37 and C39.

S-meter

With the mode switch S1/2/3 set to nbfm the meter is connected to pins 8 and 10 of IC2 via RLA contacts 3 and 4 and RV1/2. RV1 sets the fsd current of the meter at high-level receiver input signals to 200μA. RV2 sets "zero" for the meter under no-signal conditions. With mode switch set to ssb, cw or a.m. contacts 1 and 2 on RLA connect the meter to the agc amplifier TR7. R40 provides voltage drive and RV4 sets "zero". C56

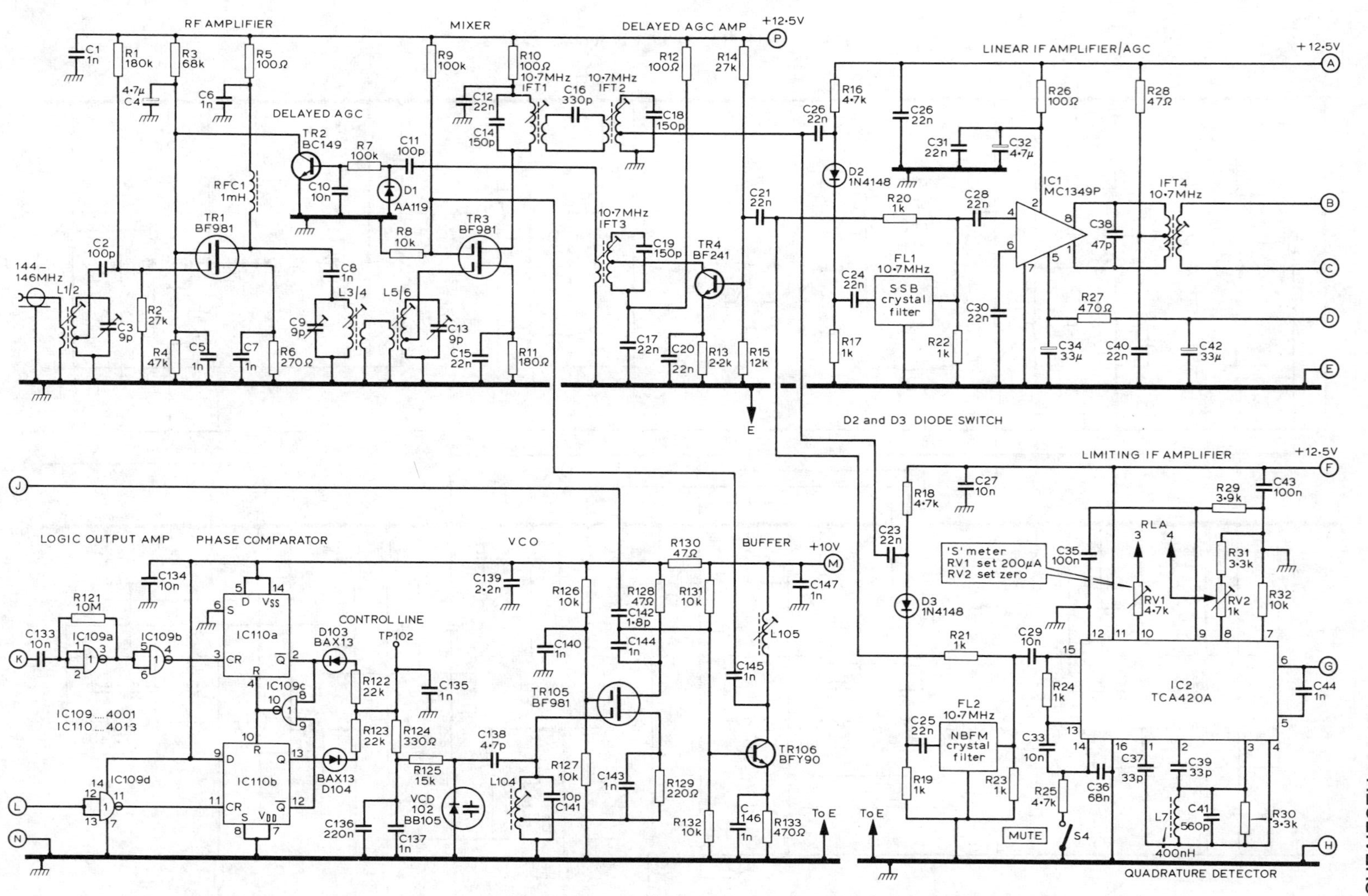

Fig 146. Circuit of multimode receiver. Note that L1-L6 are airspaced, not with dust cores as shown on the diagram

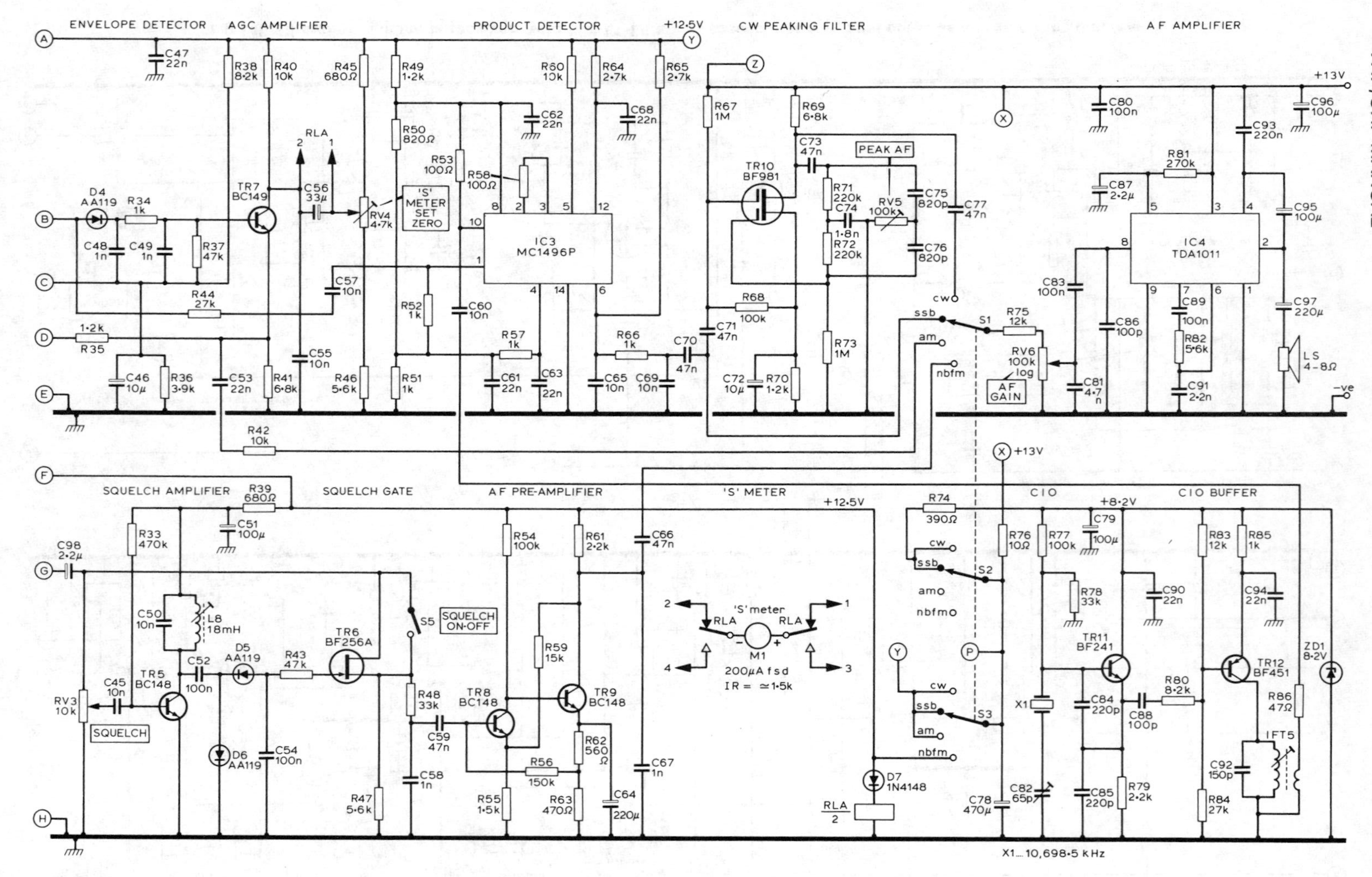

Fig 147. Circuit of multimode receiver (continued)

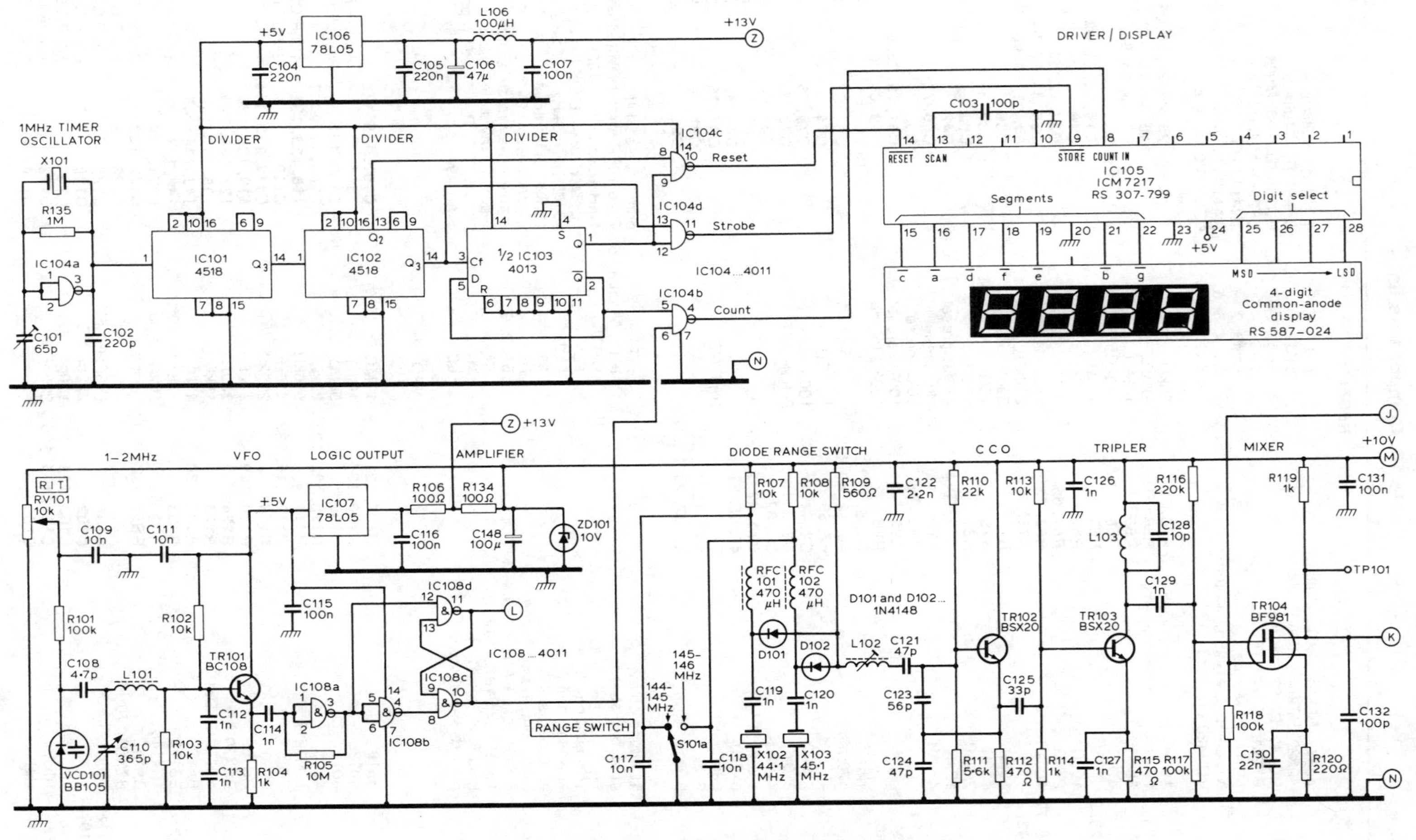

Fig 148. Circuit of multimode receiver (continued)

Table 16. Components list

RECEIVER

TR1, 3	40673 (BF961), RCA (Mullard)
TR10	40822 (BF961), RCA (Mullard)
TR2, 7	BC149 (BC109), Mullard
TR4, 11,	BF241 (BF194), ITT (Mullard)
IC1	MC1439p Motorola
IC3	MC1496p (LM1496p), Motorola (NS)
IC2	TCA420A Mullard
IC4	TDA1011 Mullard
TR12	BF451 ITT, Mullard
TR5, 8, 9	BC148 (BC108) Mullard
TR6	BF256A Mullard
D2, 3, 7	1N4148 ITT
D1, 4, 5, 6	AA119 Mullard
ZD1	BZCC8V2 Mullard

R1	180kΩ
R2, 14, 44, 84	27kΩ
R3	68kΩ
R4, 37, 43	47kΩ
R5, 10, 12, 26, 53, 58	100Ω
R6	270Ω
R7, 9, 54, 68, 77	100kΩ
R8, 32, 40, 42, 60	10kΩ
R11	180Ω
R13, 61, 79	2·2kΩ
R15, 75, 83	12kΩ
R16, 18, 25	4·7kΩ
R17, 19, 20, 21, 22, 23, 24, 34, 51, 52, 57, 66, 85	1kΩ
R27, 63	470Ω
R28, 86	47Ω
R29, 36	3·9kΩ
R30, 31	3·3kΩ
R33	470kΩ
R35, 49, 70	1·2kΩ
R38, 80	8·2kΩ
R39, 45	680Ω
R41, 69	6·8kΩ
R46, 47, 82	5·6kΩ
R48, 78	33kΩ
R50	820Ω
R55	1·5kΩ
R56	150kΩ
R59	15kΩ
R62	560Ω
R64, 65	2·7kΩ
R67, 73	1MΩ
R71, 72	220kΩ
R74	390Ω
R76	10Ω
R81	270kΩ
RV1, RV4	4·7kΩ preset
RV2	1kΩ preset
RV3	10kΩ preset
RV5	100kΩ preset
RV6	100kΩ log pot
C1, 5, 6, 7, 8, 44, 48, 49, 58, 67, 69	1nF CD
C2, 11, 86, 88	100pF CD
C3, 9, 13	2–9pF SFT
C4, 32	4·7μF E
C10, 27, 29, 33, 45, 55, 57, 60, 65	10nF CD
C12, 15, 17, 20, 21, 22, 23, 24, 25, 26, 28, 30, 31, 40, 47, 53, 61, 62, 63, 68, 90, 94	2nF
C14, 18, 19, 92	150pF Part of ifts
C16	330pF CD
C34, 42, 56	33μF E
C35, 43, 52, 54, 80, 83, 89, 96	100nF P
C36	68nF P
C37, 39	33pF CD
C38	47pF Part of IFT4
C41	560pF PF
C46, 72	10μF E
C50	10nF PF
C51, 79, 95, 96	100μF E
C59, 66, 70, 71, 73, 77	17nF CD
C64, 97	220μF E
C74	1·8nF PF
C75, 76	820pF PF
C78	470μF
C81	4·7nF
C82	5–65pF SFT
C84, 85	220pF PF
C87, 98	2·2μF E
C91	2·2nF CD
C93	220nF P

L1	1t wound on L2
L2	4t tapped at 1t
L3	4t
L4	1t wound on L3
L5	1t wound on L6
L6	4t tapped at 1t
L2, 3, 6 8mm od, 12mm long 22swg tinned	
L7	400nH Toko KANS K1893HM
L8	18mH Toko 187LY–183
IFT1, 3, 5	prim 8t ct, sec 1t
IFT2	prim 1t, sec 8t tapped at 1t
IFT4	prim 14t, sec 14t
IFT1, 5 wound on Toko 10EZ formers with 36swg enam	
RFC1	1mH Toko 187LY–102k
FL1	10·7MHz 2·4kHz cf (−6dB)
FL2	10·7MHz 7·5kHz cf (−3dB)
X1	10,698·5kHz crystal
RL1	2-pole 2-way 12V relay
S1, 2, 3	3-pole 4-way rotary switch
S4, 5	1-pole 2-way slide switch
M1	200μA FSD, R = 1·5kΩ (approx)
LS	4–8Ω 4W

PLL VFO

IC101, 102	4518
IC103, 110	4013
IC104, 108	4011
IC109	4001
IC105	ICM7217
IC106	7805
IC107	78L05
TR101	BC108
TR102, 103	BSX20
TR104, 105	40673 (BF981)
TR106	BFY90
VCD101, 102	BB105
D101, 102	1N4148
D103, 104	BAX13
ZD101	BZXC10V0
R101, 117, 118	100kΩ
R102, 103, 107, 108, 113, 126, 127, 131, 132	10kΩ
R104, 114, 119	1kΩ
R105, 121	10MΩ (± 10%)
R106, 134	100Ω
R109	560Ω
R110, 122, 123	22kΩ
R111	5·6kΩ
R112, 115, 133	470Ω
R116	220kΩ
R120, 129	220Ω
R124	330Ω
R125	15kΩ
R128, 130	47Ω
R135	1MΩ (± 10%)
RV101	10kΩ lin pot
RS587-024 4-digit display	
C101	5–65pF SFT
C102	220pF CD
C103, 132	100pF CD
C104, 105, 136	220nF P
C106	47μF E
C107, 115, 116, 131	100nF P
C108, 138	4·7pF CD
C109, 111, 117, 118, 133, 134	10nF CD
C110	365pF variable airspaced
C112, 113, 114, 119, 120, 126, 127, 128, 129, 135, 137, 140, 143, 144, 145, 146, 147	1nF CD
C121, 124	47pF CD
C122, 139	2·2nF CD
C123	56pF CD
C125	33pF CD
C130	22nF CD
C141	10pF CD
C142	1·8pF CD
C148	100μF E

L101	Toko 10 by 10mm mw osc coil	**L106**	100μH Toko 187LY-101k
L102	10t 0·3mm enam 5mm diam	**RFC1/2**	470μH Toko 7BA-144HY-471k
L103	5t 0·6mm tinned 5mm diam	**X101**	1MHz crystal
L104	5t 0·6mm tinned 5mm diam tap 1t from ground end	**X102**	44·1MHz crystal
		X103	45·1MHz crystal
L105	3t on ferrite bead (FX1115)	**S101**	2-pole 2-way rotary

Key: CD = ceramic disc or plate 50V dc, SFT = solid film trimmer, E = electrolytic, 16V dc, P = polyester, 100V dc, PF = polystyrene foil, 160V dc. Resistors ⅓W 5 per cent carbon-film (eg Mullard CR25).

provides sufficient damping of the meter movement, preventing needle "bounce" on ssb and cw signals.

NBFM squelch amplifier and gate

The audio recovered from the detector is coupled to the amplifier and gate via C98. In the absence of a carrier only noise will be present at "G". This will be passed via RV3 and C45 to noise amplifier TR5 (BC148). The collector load is a LC circuit tuned to about 10kHz. This is coupled to a diode detector/doubler D5/D6 (AA119). The negative-going output of this detector turns off TR6, the squelch gate (BF256A), and prevents this noise reaching the audio amplifier circuits. When a carrier is received, stronger levels of signal will progressively quieten the i.f. limiting amplifier IC2, reduce the negative bias applied to the squelch gate and therefore allow fm on the carrier to be passed to the audio amplifiers. By varying the setting of RV3, the squelch circuit sensitivity may be set to an appropriate carrier level, eg adjusted so that levels below, say, 1μV may be effectively cut off. R48 and C58 provide further de-emphasis for the recovered audio.

AF preamplifier

With 3kHz deviation of the carrier the audio recovery level from the nbfm detector is not sufficient to drive the audio amplifier to full output power. Lower levels of deviation will in turn further limit audio output. The preamplifier provides 20dB of voltage gain (10×). TR8 and 9 (BC148) are employed in a high-input/low-output impedance amplifier. DC and ac voltage negative feedback stabilizes the dc operating conditions (R56) and reduces distortion to a very low level (R59). Audio output appears across R61 with further de-emphasis provided by C67. The amplified audio is routed to S1 via C66.

AF power amplifier

Mode switch S1 selects the required signal. This signal is routed to IC4 (TDA1011) via R75, RV6 (af gain control) and C83. The TDA1011 can provide up to 4W into 4Ω with a 12V dc supply (10 per cent total distortion). This ic is packaged in a nine-lead single inline plastic package to give a compact peripheral component layout and easy mounting of the heat sink to its metal tab. The pcb however requires adequate copper foil connections around the output circuit (pins 1, 2 and 3) as the peak output current can reach 2A. A higher-impedance loudspeaker (eg 8Ω) will reduce the output power. C81, 86 and 91 limit the upper-frequency response. C97 couples IC4 to the speaker, limiting low-frequency output.

Phase-lock loop local oscillator and display section (Fig 148)

The local oscillator drive to the receiver mixer is obtained from a voltage controlled oscillator (vco) which is controlled by a low-frequency master oscillator operating within a phase locked loop (pll). The main vfo covers the range of 1–2MHz, therefore its stability is very good. TR101 (BC108) is used in a Clapp oscillator configuration. L101 and C110 are medium-wave oscillator coil and tuning capacitor (365pF) respectively. Receiver incremental tuning is provided by VCD101 (BB105). RV1 is the rit control. The vfo output at TR101 emitter is routed via C114 to cmos IC108 (4001), employed as a buffer giving two square-wave outputs: one for the pll, the other for the display counter.

The 1–2MHz vfo range corresponds to 144–145 and 145–146MHz coverage of the receiver. A simple frequency counter driven by the vfo and buffer will then give a direct indication of frequency without the need for a high-frequency prescaler and a counter with i.f. offset facility. This counter is based on the ICM7217 lsi device and drives a four-digit display with a resolution of ±100Hz. The necessary timing signals for the counter are provided by a 1MHz crystal and dividers IC101, 102 and 103. The simplest type of display is used in this receiver, ie a common-anode multiplex seven-segment type. However four individual common-anode seven-segment devices can be used with each segment of the four digits connected together. Care must be taken to ensure that the switching signals in the counter do not radiate into the receiver rf mixer and i.f. stages. It is recommended that the counter is built into a separate screened box with a feedthrough capacitor on the power input terminal. Coaxial sockets should be used for input and output connections.

Supply for the vfo is regulated by an ic regulator IC106 (78L05) and the counter by regulator IC107 (7805). Each supplies +5V. The local oscillator drive for the receiver is derived from the vco TR105 (40823). The modified oscillator circuit of L104, C141 is coupled by C138 to, and is tuned by, VCD102 (BB105), a variable capacitance diode. The coil L104 is tuned to the receiver mid-range (133·8MHz), when there is +5V on the pll control line to the vco. The vco output is coupled to g1 of the mixer TR104 (40823) via C142.

A carrier is generated by a crystal-controlled oscillator at 44·1MHz employing a modified Colpitts circuit L102, C121, C123, C124 and TR102 (BSX20). This carrier is tripled by TR103 (BSX20), C103 and C128 to 132·3MHz and coupled to g2 of TR104 by C129. These two signals are mixed in TR104 to produce a difference frequency of 1·5MHz, ie the mid-range frequency of the vfo. An oscilloscope connected to TR104 drain at TP1 will display a signal at 1·5MHz of about 500mV peak-to-peak. L103 is tuned to maximize this signal. Three parts of IC109 (4001) provide amplification to give a logic-level signal to drive the phase comparator IC110 (4103) and the remaining part of IC109. The other input to the comparator comes from the vfo (L).

The output from the comparator is integrated in the loop filter R124 and C136 and forms the control voltage for the vco. This voltage will tune the vco, such that the difference frequency from TR104 will be phase locked and hence the same frequency as the reference frequency input from the vfo. As the vfo frequency is varied the vco will track it. This can be monitored at TP2 where tuning the vfo from 1 to 2MHz will cause the control voltage to rise and vice versa. A simple indication of receiver frequency can be obtained by connecting a high input impedance voltmeter to TP2.

The loop characteristics indicate a 3dB bandwidth of about 20kHz and a damping factor of approximately 1. Variation of loop damping factor is obtained by adjusting the value of R124. The phase comparator is also frequency sensitive; this ensures rapid lock in on receiver switch-on and vco frequency changes.

CHAPTER 5

Transmitters

This chapter divides conveniently into two parts. The first covers the basic theory of equipment necessary for transmitting those signals that fall within the terms of the amateur licence. In many instances complete circuits are given, showing practical ways of realizing the theory, using ics, transistors or valves, and the information will be of interest to the more advanced constructor.

The second part of this chapter is devoted to constructional details for a wide range of transmission equipment, accompanied in many cases by working drawings, photographs, and full instructions for construction.

Exciter stages

The stages of a transmitter—those circuits up to the power amplifier—are often referred to as *exciter* stages. In these sections it is necessary to arrange for an rf signal to be generated and then multiplied or mixed up to a power level suitable to drive the power amplifier.

Suitable oscillators were described in Chapter 4, to which the reader is referred. Some details of mixing and pll frequency conversion systems are also given there; these would be appropriate for an ssb or multimode transmitter or transceiver. NBFM transmitters still usually employ the classic frequency multiplication system but this runs at higher power than those in receivers and more careful attenuation of unwanted signals is necessary. The design considerations for a transmitter frequency multiplication system are therefore discussed in detail below.

Frequency multipliers

The actual number of stages will, of course, depend on the starting frequency (oscillator) and the final frequency required, together with the multiplication factor used in each stage. Generally this is confined to doubling and trebling, although sometimes quadrupling is used at lower frequencies.

In addition to the actual multiplier further amplifier stages may sometimes be required, for example as an isolation amplifier (buffer) between a variable frequency oscillator and the following stage to prevent frequency pulling, or as an amplifier after the final frequency multiplication to drive the power amplifier.

Decision on the oscillator and other exciter stages will be governed by the crystals or suitable variable frequency oscillator available. These two sources of frequency control may require a different starting frequency since the required stability of a variable frequency oscillator becomes more difficult to attain as the frequency is raised, whereas with crystals this is generally not a problem provided they are operated within their rating.

Some thought should also be given to the actual frequencies that are to be used, to ensure that if there is any radiation from these they do not cause interference. In this connection it is always advisable to operate exciter stages at low power level even if this makes necessary the addition of a driver/amplifier. Such an amplifier will not only provide an increase in power but also assist in attenuating in its tuned circuits unwanted harmonics generated earlier.

To assist in the selection of a starting frequency (crystal or vfo) Table 1 shows the various frequencies and the multiplication needed to reach the individual bands.

From the table it will be seen that the use of a 72MHz oscillator needs only a doubler to reach 144MHz, a doubler and a trebler to reach 432MHz and a doubler and two treblers to reach 1,296MHz. At this starting frequency separation of harmonics at the high frequencies is an easy matter.

Table 1 assumes that the transmitted frequency is generated from a basic oscillator followed by straightforward frequency multiplication.

For ssb, where mixing of two or more frequencies are used, the required frequency will depend on various factors. Usually for uhf bands this is obtained using either an hf or vhf transceiver, in which case the input frequency is either 28 or 144MHz.

In any local oscillator used, care must be exercised to ensure that harmonics of the oscillator do not fall within the tuning of the particular band required. Also for such use it is always an advantage for the crystal to be used in the oscillator to be of the highest frequency.

Valve multipliers

All frequency multipliers operate under Class C conditions, that is they are cut off in the absence of drive. The angle of conduction is much less than 180°; the higher the multiplication required the smaller the conduction angle.

Typical conduction angles are:

Harmonic	Conduction angle
2nd	90–120°
3rd	90–120°
4th	70–90°
5th	60–70°

In the classic designs, although single-ended frequency doubler and tripler can be used to good effect, the push-pull and push-push connections are to be preferred.

The push-pull arrangement is suitable for odd-harmonic (3, 5 or 7) mode. For even-harmonic use the output circuit must be common to both outputs, providing a push-push arrangement.

The tuned circuits normally used with valves have relatively high Q and therefore have good frequency discrimination without recourse to additional auxiliary filters or traps to remove the fundamental (input) frequency or the second harmonic (in the case of a tripler) from the output. Although in the outline

Table 1. How oscillators at various frequencies can be used on different bands, by suitable multiplication

Multiplication factor	70·025–70·5	144–146	432–434*	1,296–1,298*
× 2	35·013–35·250	72–73		
× 3	23·342–23·5	48–48·6		
×4 (×2×2)	17·507–17·625	36–36·5	108–108·5	
×5	14·005–14·1	28·8–29·2	86·4– 86·8	
×6 (×2×3)	11·671–11·75	24–24·3	72– 72·3	
×8 (×2×2×2)	8·753– 8·813	18–18·25	54– 54·25	
×9 (×3×3)	7·781– 7·833	14·4–14·6	48– 48·2	144 –144·2
×10 (×5×2)	7·025– 7·050	16–16·2	43·2– 43·4	129·6 –129·8
×12 (×3×2×2)	5·836– 5·875	12–12·16	36– 36·165	108 –108·16
×16 (×2×2×2×2)		9– 9·125	27– 27·125	81 – 81·125
×18 (×3×3×2)		8– 8·11	24– 24·1	72 – 72·1
×20 (×5×2×2)		7·2– 7·3	21·6– 21·7	64·8 – 64·9
×24 (×3×2×2×2)		6–6·083	18– 18·0825	54 – 54·08
×32 (×2×2×2×2×2)			13·5– 13·653	40·5 – 40·563
×36(×3×3×2×2)			12– 12·05	36 – 36·05
×40 (×5×2×2×2)			10·8–10·85	32·4 – 32·45
×48 (×3×4×4)			9– 9·04125	27 – 27·04
×64 (×4×2×2×2×2)			6·75– 6·7813	20·25– 20·2813

* Communication section

circuits shown in Fig 1 a negative bias is indicated, grid leak bias may be used as an alternative if preferred, remembering that loss of drive would leave no protective bias.

The valves most suitable for multipliers are generally those of high mutual conductance (high sensitivity). Since the grid and anode circuits are tuned to a different frequency, instability is not usually a problem provided there are no circuit conditions which could provide a tuned anode tuned grid oscillator. In some types there may be some chance of parasitic oscillation which can usually be prevented by suitable isolation of input and output circuit components and adequate bypassing.

Pentodes are suitable for frequencies up to about 200MHz but triodes are much more satisfactory at higher frequencies. The types generally are of the receiving valve class, such as pentodes CV138, EF80, 6AK5, E180F, 5763 or triodes 6J6, 6C4, EC8010, ECC85, 12AT7. In Table 2 typical results are given for three examples and these show that quite worthwhile power outputs are attainable under fairly low power input conditions.

Expensive valves, such as E280F, E282F, E810F and D3A, are pentodes specially designed for wide-band applications and are not really suitable because their input and output capacitance is relatively high.

Of course, for the early stages triode-pentodes such as ECF80 are suitable and can be a convenient means of reducing the equipment size. The tuned circuits for the exciter stages, although handling relatively low power, should be designed for as high Q as possible so as to give the maximum attenuation of all unwanted frequencies, and similar methods to those proposed for power amplifiers may be used. They can however be relatively small for the lower-frequency stages, and up to about 100MHz core tuned inductors are quite suitable. Above this frequency, self-supporting coils up to the frequency limit where these are permissible should be used. At the highest frequencies parallel lines, trough lines and cavities will have to be employed.

The use of link coupling is often a suitable means of coupling circuits together to make a compact layout which may otherwise be difficult mechanically.

In building circuits, the series resonance of such components as capacitors should be borne in mind and their connecting lead lengths should be as short as possible. Sometimes the self-resonance is intentionally used.

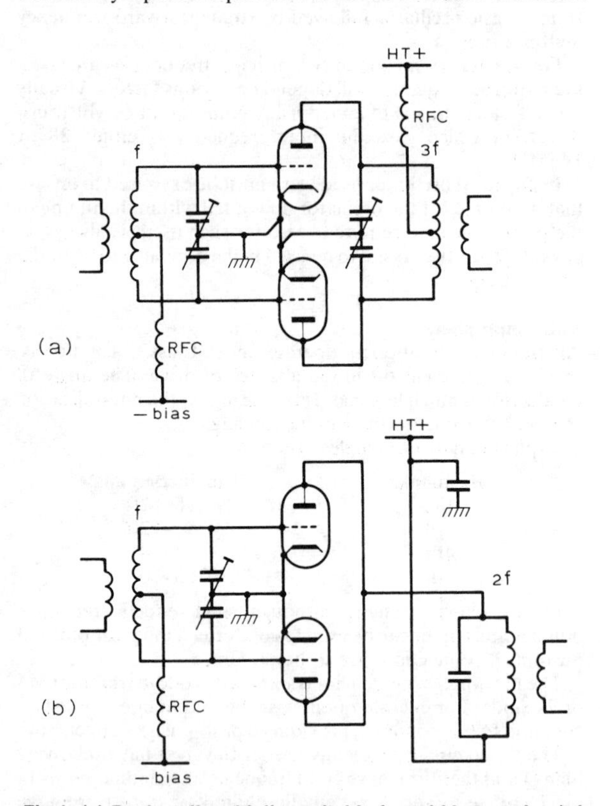

Fig 1. (a) Push-pull multiplier suitable for odd harmonics (tripler). (b) Push-push multiplier suitable for even harmonics (doubler)

Bipolar transistor multipliers

Bipolar transistors, as frequency multipliers, make use of the non-linear characteristics of the base-emitter diode. Fig 2(a) shows a transistor frequency doubler and the input and output matching circuits are of the pi-coupling type. This type of circuit, having a low-pass characteristic, makes necessary the

Table 2. Some suitable valves for multipliers

EF91/6AM6 with anode voltage of 300V, screen voltage of 250, and grid bias of −20V

Class of operation	Frequency input (MHz)	Frequency output (MHz)	Anode current (mA)	Screen current (mA)	Grid current (mA)	Power output (W)
	60	60	11·5	3·2	1·5	1·9
Amplifier	120	120	11·5	3·2	1·7	1·7
	200	200	9·7	3·2	1·9	0·4
Frequency doubler	30	60	10·0	3·2	1·5	1·5
	65	130	10·0	3·2	1·6	1·1
	90	180	9·0	3·2	1·8	0·25
Frequency tripler	20	60	10·5	3·2	1·6	1·1
	30	90	10·0	3·2	1·7	0·9
	50	150	9·0	3·2	1·8	0·2

EC91/6J6 with anode voltage of 200

Class of operation	Frequency (MHz)	Cathode current (mA)	Anode current I_a(tot) (mA)	Grid current I_g(tot) (mA)	Grid resistor common (kΩ)	Power output (W)
Amplifier (Grid bias −14V Cathode resistor 330Ω)	50	22	17·2	4·8	1·5	2·1
	100	22	17·8	4·2	1·5	1·9
	150	22	18·2	3·8	1·5	1·7
	200	22	18·8	3·2	2·2	1·4
	250	22	19·3	2·7	2·7	1·1
Frequency tripler (Grid bias −100V Cathode resistor 120Ω)	50	22	16	6	15	0·95
	100	22	16·7	5·3	18	0·9
	150	22	17·2	4·8	22	0·8
	200	22	17·7	4·3	22	0·7
	250	22	18·2	3·8	27	0·6

EC8010 with anode voltage of 200

Class of operation	Frequency (MHz)	Cathode current (mA)	Anode current (mA)	Grid current (mA)	Power output (W)
Amplifier (grounded grid)	432	39	29	5	3·7
Frequency tripler from 144MHz	432	34	30	4	2·8
Frequency doubler from 432MHz	864	31	30	1	1·4

inclusion of an additional tuned circuit, tuned to the fundamental (input) frequency.

In Fig 2(b) a modified form of the circuit is shown; in this the output circuit is a double-tuned coupling with appropriate tapping points to match the transistor into the circuit. Fig 3(a) and (b) show a transistor equivalent circuit of the classical push-push tripler and push-push doubler. As can be seen, the transistors are tapped down both in the input and output tuned circuits.

In operation the transistor does not conduct current until the base-emitter junction is forward biased and it is necessary for a small fraction of a volt to appear across this junction for appreciable multiplier action. For this reason, if the drive voltage is low, it is advisable to use a little forward dc bias to cause the transistor to conduct. However, forward bias and low drive voltage minimize the non-linearity of the base-emitter junction and decrease the effectiveness as a multiplier.

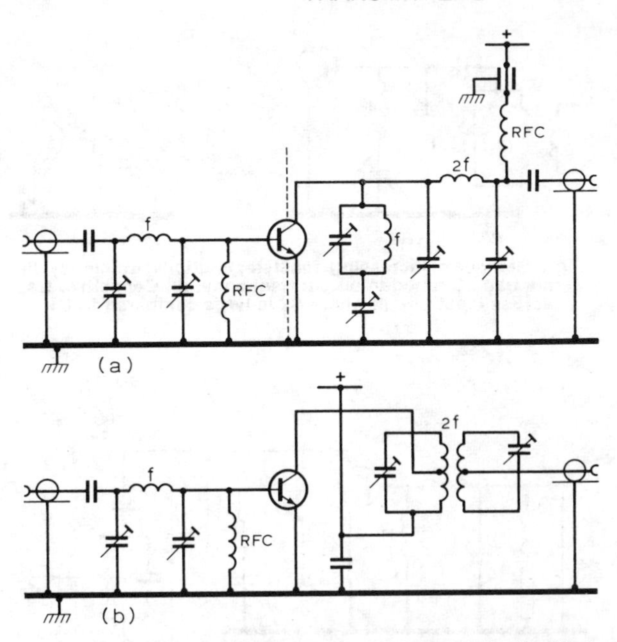

Fig 2. (a) Bipolar transistor frequency doubler. (b) Modified bipolar translator frequency doubler

The forward bias voltage required for a silicon transistor is somewhat higher than that needed by germanium types.

In Fig 4 are circuits which are intended to reduce the effect of base-to-collector capacitance, so improving the operating efficiency.

A second manner in which a transistor may be used as a multiplier is by use of the base-collector depletion capacitance, this being called *parametric* multiplication. To take full advantage of the mode of operation the collector circuit must include appropriate idler circuits to reflect unwanted harmonics back to the collector-base capacitance.

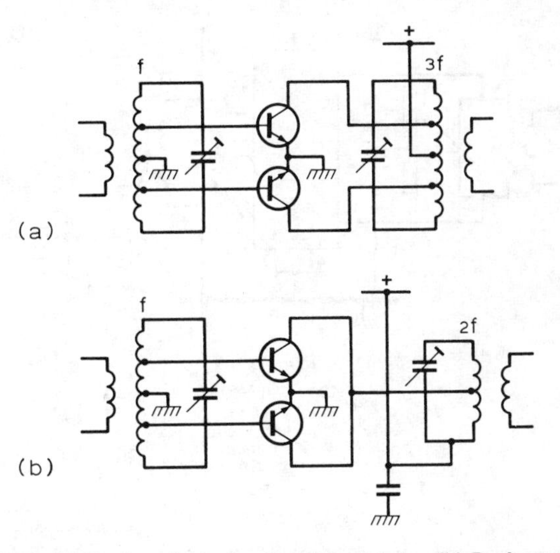

Fig 3. (a) Push-pull bipolar transistor tripler. (b) Push-push bipolar transistor doubler

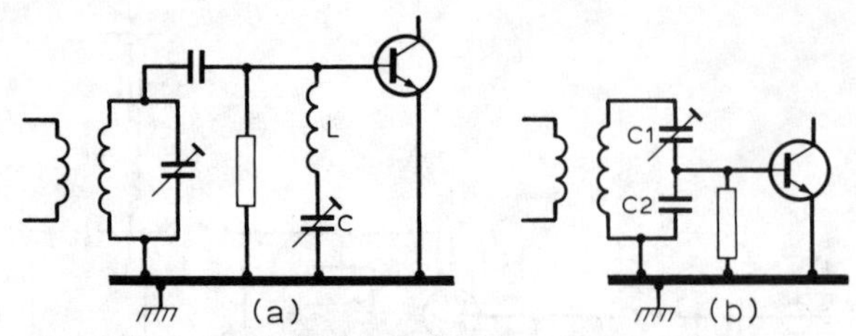

Fig 4. Methods of increasing transistor multiplier efficiency. (a) Series trap LC tuned to output frequency. (b) Capacitive trap across input circuit where C2 is large compared to C1

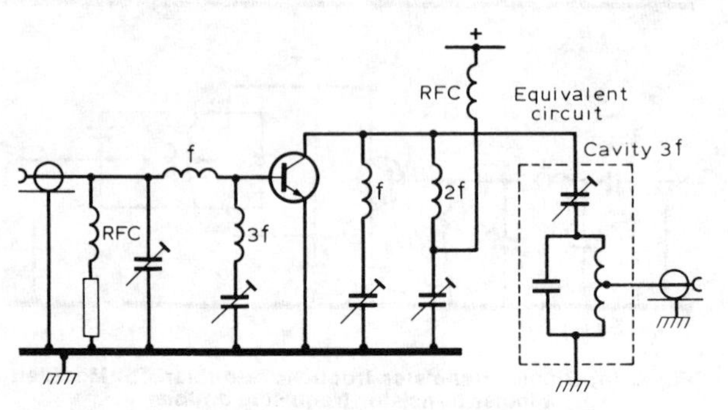

Fig 5. UHF transistor "parametric" multiplier

Fig 5 shows a typical circuit arrangement for a uhf tripler.

The chief merit of using push-push doublers is in the "clean" signal passed on to the next stage. This is of significant importance in many applications such as a source of power for checking antennas, filters and of course as a driver to a power amplifier or converters/transverters.

The method may be used with separate transistors (Fig 3(b))

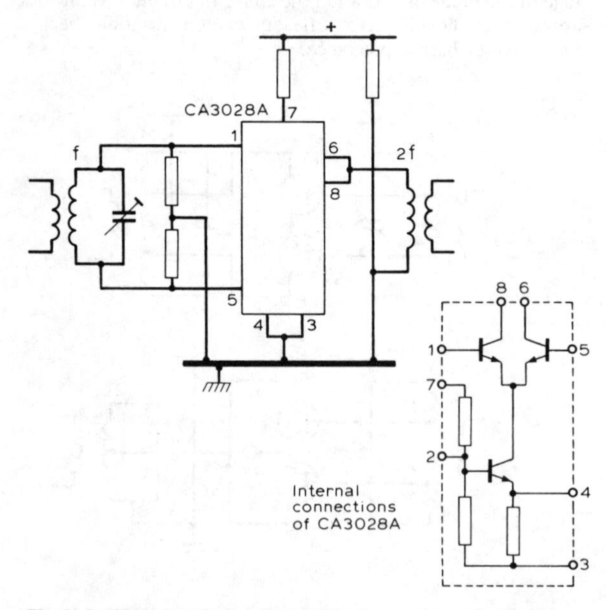

Fig 6. An integrated circuit suitable for push-push doubler up to 120MHz. Other units are available for use up to 500MHz

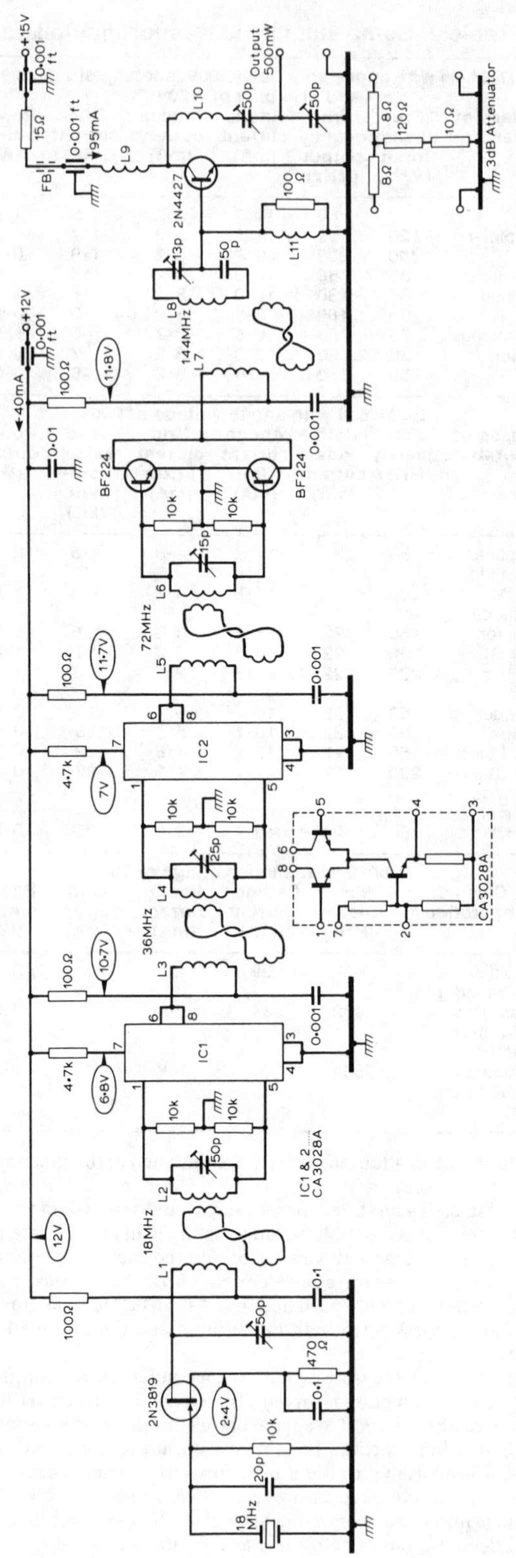

Fig 7. A 144MHz transmitter using ics for early frequency-doubler stages

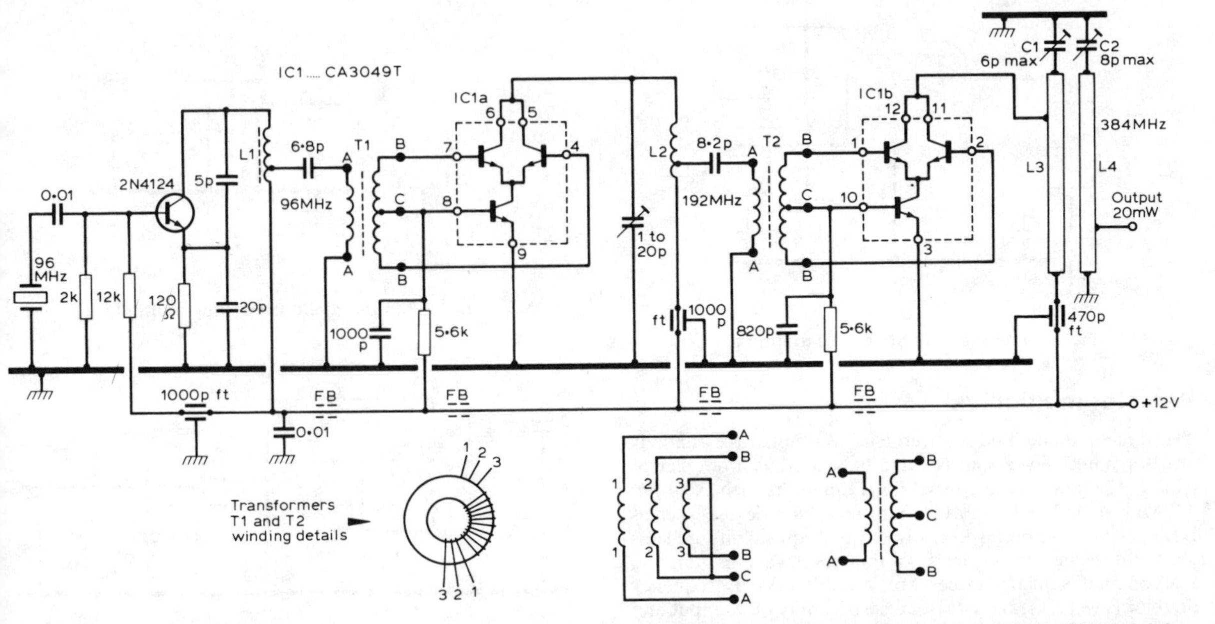

Fig 8. Push-push doublers used to change frequency from 96MHz to 384MHz. Suitable as an exciter for a 384/1,152MHz tripler

but it is an advantage to use the simple integrated circuits such as the CA3028A hf differential amplifier for up to 120MHz or CA3049T dual hf differential amplifier for up to 500MHz (Fig 6). The latter item contains two units in one package—this may also be obtained as the CA3102E which is in a 14-pin dual-in-line package and has a separate substrate connection for great circuit flexibility. Fig 7 shows a typical exciter/source for 144MHz. In this a 2N3819 is used as a crystal oscillator followed by two stages of CA3028A to reach 72MHz; the final push-push stage in this case uses a pair of BF224 transistors in push-push connection driving an 2N4427 amplifier to give an output of 0·5W.

Fig 8 shows an exciter to multiply the crystal frequency of 96MHz to 384MHz, which was described in *Ham Radio* October 1978. A 2N4124 is used as a crystal oscillator coupled through a toroidal transformer to the first stage of a CA3049T or 3102E; this is followed by a second stage of the device to reach the final frequency which is tuned by a stripline circuit, and an output of about 20mW is produced. In this it should be noted that the toroidal transformers T1 and T2 are only used to provide a balanced input to differential amplifiers.

The inductors L3 and L 4 could alternatively be formed from rod or wire. See the table in the Appendix.

FET multiplier

Field-effect transistors operate satisfactorily as frequency multipliers. They may be treated in much the same manner as a valve, with appropriate cut-off bias applied to the gate.

Fig 9 shows a simple single-ended multiplier. Note that the collector is tapped down the output tuned circuit. Fig 10 shows the push-pull tripler and push-push doubler circuits.

Diode multipliers

Although point-contact (signal) diodes and silicon junction types have been used as frequency multipliers, hot-carrier or Schottky-barrier diodes are superior to the other types. Fig 11 shows a simple circuit arrangement but this is of low efficiency. An improvement may be achieved by using a pair of diodes arranged as a "full-wave" rectifier as shown in Fig 12 and a reasonably efficient doubler can be made. In Fig 13 is shown an arrangement for the enhancement of harmonic output from an oscillator or earlier multiplier.

Table 3. Inductors for Fig 7

L1	18t $\frac{7}{16}$in diam 22swg
L2	14t $\frac{7}{16}$in diam 24swg
L3	10t $\frac{7}{16}$in diam 18swg
L4	8t $\frac{7}{16}$in diam 22swg
L5	7t 0·3in diam 20swg
L6	4 + 4t 0·3in diam 24swg
L7	5t 0·3in diam 18swg
L8	6t 0·3in diam 16swg
L9	2t $\frac{1}{2}$in diam 18swg
L10	5t $\frac{7}{16}$in diam 22swg
L11	6t on 100Ω resistor

Link couplings 1t each end with twisted leads.

Table 4. Components list for Fig 8

L1	6t 24swg closewound 5mm diam, tap $1\frac{1}{2}$t, on powdered iron core
L2	4t 18swg 5mm diam, 16mm long, tap $1\frac{3}{4}$t
L3	40nH stripline or rod/wire
L4	43nH stripline or rod/wire
T1, T2	4t 30swg trifilar winding (Amidon FT25 mix 43 former)
FB	ferrite bead
C1	miniature air-spaced trimmer 6pF max
C2	miniature air-spaced trimmer 8pF max

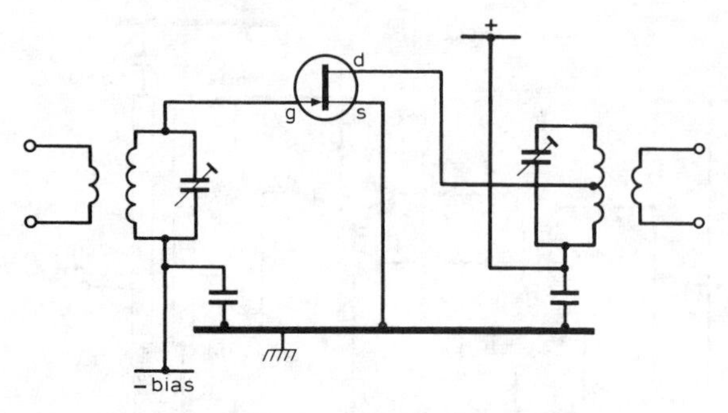

Fig 9. Simple single-ended fet multiplier

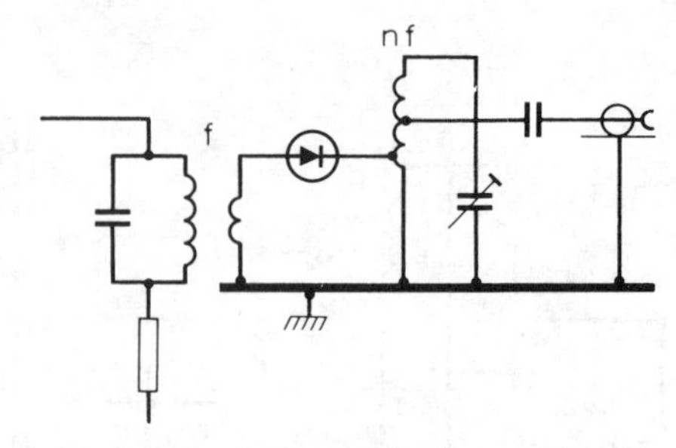

Fig 11. Simple diode frequency multiplier

Varactor multipliers

The varactor diode used as a frequency multiplier is essentially an rf-operated device and is commonly used as a doubler or tripler. The latter is more usual for frequencies such as 144 to 432MHz or 432 to 1,296MHz. For this service devices such as BAY96 and BAY66 respectively or their equivalents are suitable; for higher frequencies in the microwave region the BXY36 and similar devices are suitable. As a frequency doubler (Fig 14(a)) the circuit consists simply of an input and ouput tuned circuit, but for the tripler (Fig 14(b)) it is necessary to include an additional circuit tuned to the second harmonic to remove this frequency from the wanted third-harmonic output.

Although the varactor multiplier is a wholly rf-operated device its efficiency is quite high and should be more than 50 per cent. Another application for the varactor diode is in a parametric up-converter, where a signal is mixed with an rf pump (local oscillator) frequency to produce a higher wanted

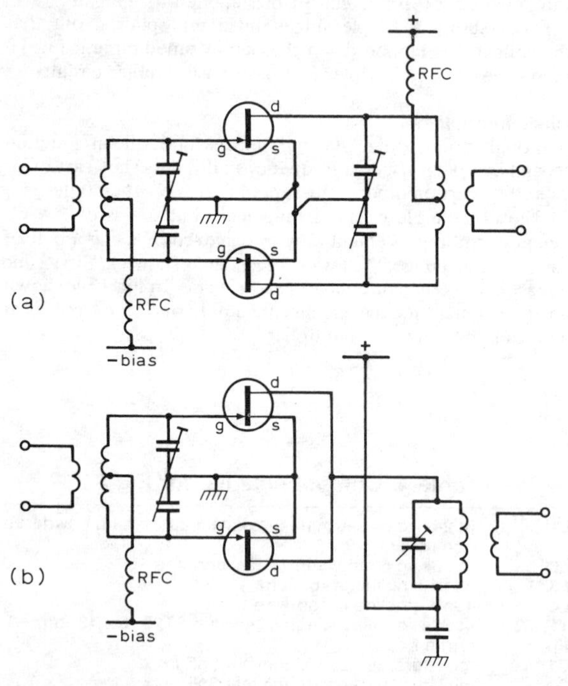

Fig 10. (a) FET push-pull tripler. (b) FET push-push doubler

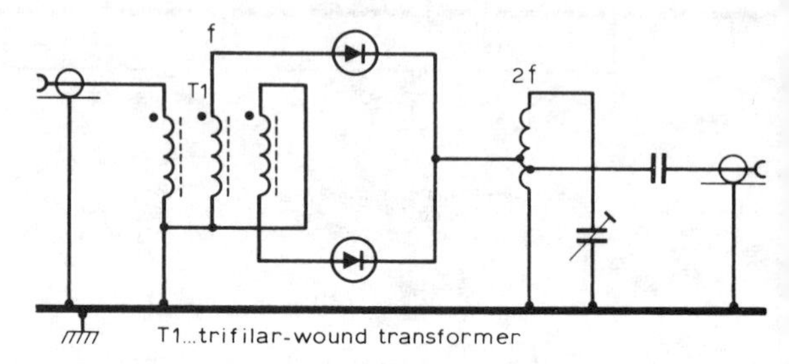

Fig 12. Balanced diode frequency doubler

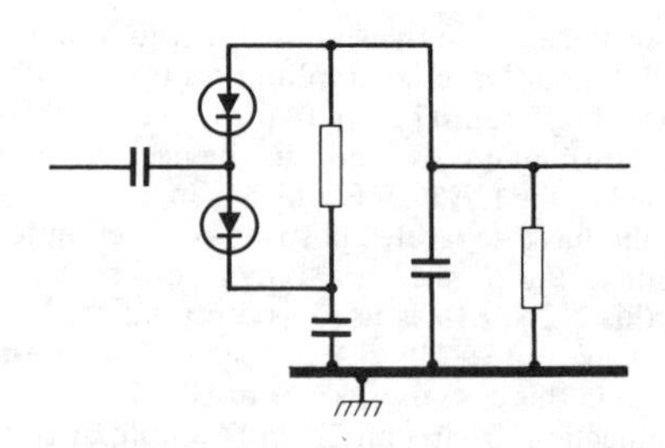

Fig 13. Diode arrangement to enhance harmonic output from an oscillator. Point-contact germanium diode should be used

frequency. In this case the varactor functions both as a multiplier and mixer.

The pump frequency (f_p) should always be considerably higher than the signal frequency (f_s), although its actual frequency may be doubled by the varactor if this is needed. It is however preferable for the pump input to be at the full required frequency. The power input from the pump is normally considerably higher than that of the signal (at least twice the signal frequency). The power output at the wanted frequency is largely dependent on the pump power input.

With this circuit arrangement it is necessary to include idler circuits for the pump frequency (or its harmonic if multiplication is being used) and also the difference frequency if the sum frequency is being taken for the output. Fig 14(c) shows a typical circuit—in this the pump frequency (f_p) is also being doubled by the varactor so that the idler circuits need to be tuned to $2f_p$ and also $2f_p - f_s$, the output being $2f_p + f_s$.

In use all forms of varactor multiplier need to be followed by some form of selective circuit or filter to exclude from the output the unwanted signals.

The bias resistor (R) across the diode may be 50 to 250kΩ, 100kΩ being a typical value.

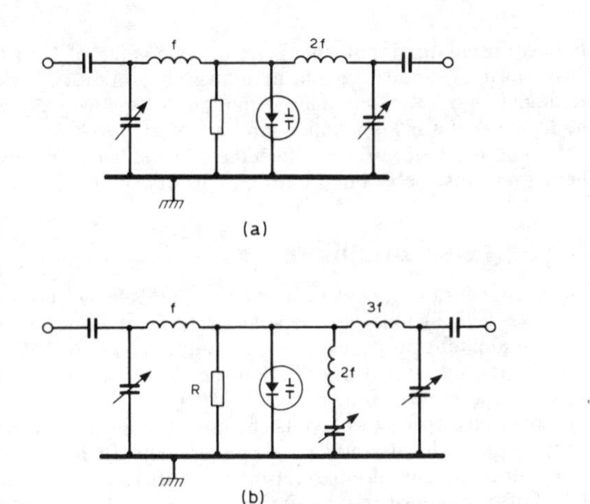

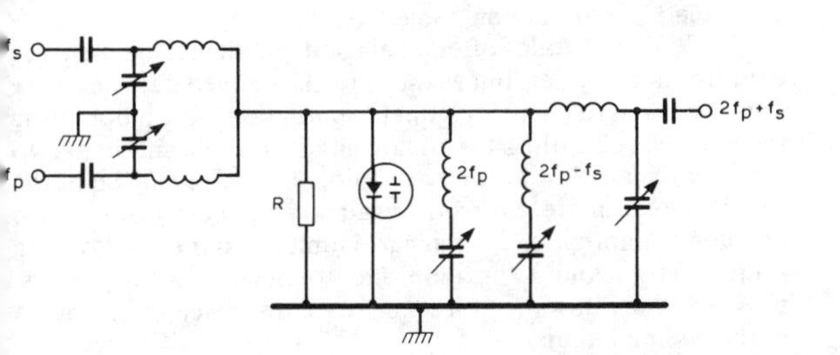

Fig 14. (a) Varactor frequency doubler. (b) Varactor frequency tripler. (c) Parametric converter: f_s = signal frequency, f_p = pump frequency (high compared with f_s)

In Fig 15 a balanced parametric diode tripler is shown—an efficiency of up to 70 per cent is often possible with this arrangement.

Step-recovery diode multipliers

The step-recovery diode multiplier has a considerable advantage over the normal varactor diode, insofar that it is capable of multiplication of 10 times and over with reasonable efficiency. There is also no need to add the usual idler circuits used in varactor multipliers.

In a step-recovery diode frequency multiplier, the harmonic power is proportional to $1/n$ where n is the harmonic number. The curve given in Fig 16 illustrates the percentage efficiency against the harmonic number—this is better than can be

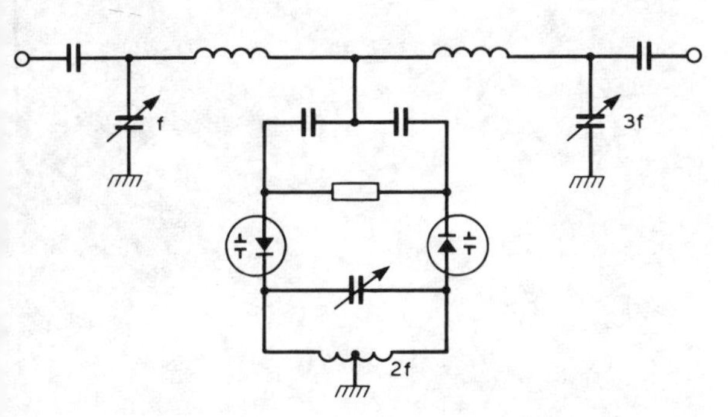

Fig 15. Balanced parametric diode tripler

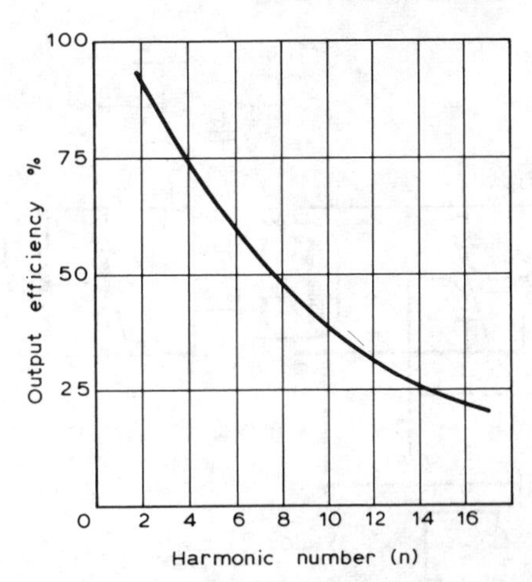

Fig 16. Typical output efficiency of a step-recovery diode multiplier versus harmonic number

obtained from a varactor where the harmonic power is proportional to $1/n^2$. Since significant output can be obtained at the higher harmonics, multipliers of nine times such as from 144 to 1,296MHz become practical. However, to achieve the full output it is necessary to keep circuit losses to the minimum, and cavities are recommended where this type of circuit is suitable.

As with all types of diode multiplier the output should be fed through a selective filter to remove any of the unwanted signals from the output; Fig 17 shows the general circuit form.

High-level mixers

Although double-balanced diode, cross-coupled bipolar mixers or a pair of fets (see Chapter 4) may be used for low-level mixing in transmitter applications, they do really need a considerable increase in the number of linear amplifier stages to raise the output to an appropriate output level, and this may be difficult at uhf.

Another approach to the problem is to use some form of high-level mixer. For vhf and uhf up to the 432MHz band the double tetrode offers a convenient circuit, using such valve types as QQV02–6 or 3–20. In these the local oscillator input is normally injected into the two control grids (in push-push) and the other signal input into the cathode circuit (in parallel). Care is necessary of course to preserve a good balance as possible in the push-push tuned circuits to ensure maximum attenuation of the unwanted signals. See Fig 18.

For uhf (particularly for the 1·3GHz band) there is often little choice but to use one or other of the grounded-grid triodes

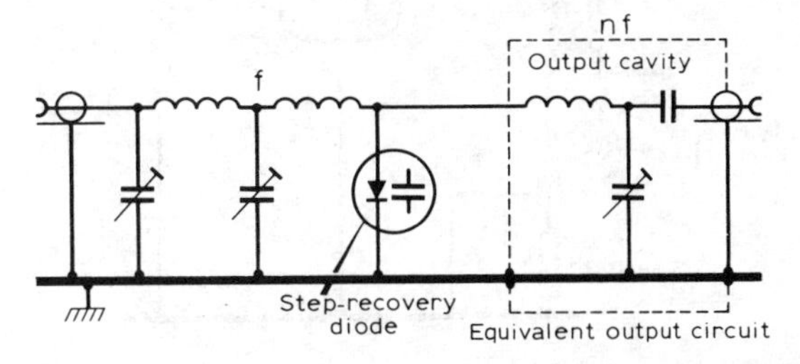

Fig 17. General form of a step-recovery diode frequency multiplier

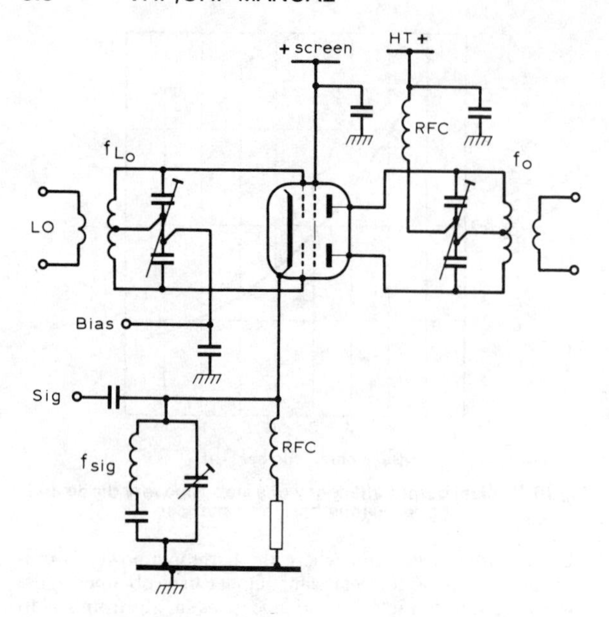

Fig 18. High-level valve mixer

such as the 8255 or EC88 for relatively low power, or 2C39A for higher power. In this case the two input signals to be mixed are either injected into the grid and cathode or, more commonly, the grid is grounded and both are injected into the cathode. See Fig 19. In the latter case some care is needed to isolate the two signals at their input and at the same time to adequately ground the local oscillator input tuned circuit. The value of C in Fig 19(b) must be small to avoid excessive absorption of lower-frequency signal and yet be large enough to effectively ground the local oscillator input tuned circuit.

With all types of mixer in which the cathode has an rf input, the heater must be isolated by rf chokes in each lead.

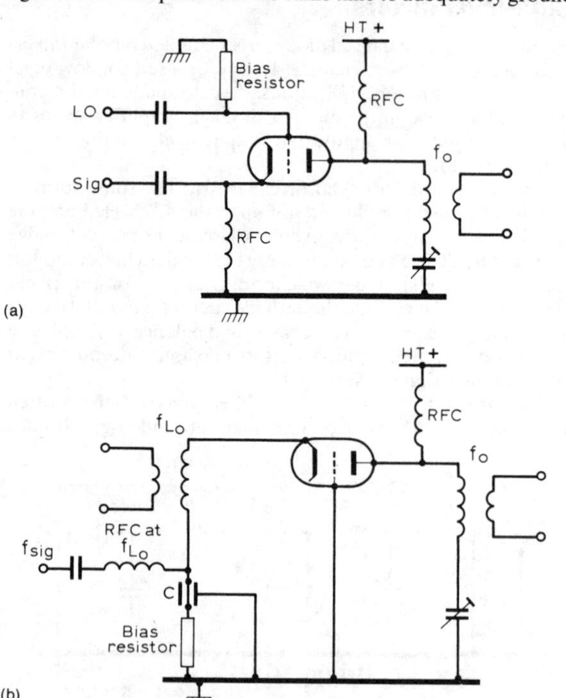

Fig 19. Grounded grid valve mixers. (a) Grid and cathode injection (b) Cathode injection

Valve power amplifiers

For the higher output powers at 144 and 432MHz the choice of amplifier device will largely depend on the level required, and for most amateur purposes, where an output power of 50W or more is desired, valves are likely to be the most satisfactory device at the present time.

Power transistors may of course be used if these are available but their power levels and gain are generally less suitable than such valves as the double tetrodes, 6–40A, 7–50 or the 4CX250B, or one of the many similar types, either as forced air-cooled or conduction-cooled versions.

The double tetrodes offer an elegant circuit arrangement for a push-pull amplifier, but as they are glass envelope types, care must be taken to ensure adequate ventilation. When operating them at the full rating it is an advantage to use a simple fan to increase the air flow around the bulb. Such a fan may be of the simplest form, merely stirring the air around the valve. It is also possible to improve the cooling to a limited extent by providing a metal clip around the bulb and connected to the chassis, provided due allowance for its increase in capacitance is made in the tuning circuit.

In the case of the 4CX250B and similar types of forced

The 4CX250B air-cooled tetrode

CCS1 conduction-cooled tetrode, equivalent to 4CX250B

air-cooled valves, it is essential to ensure that there is an adequate pressure for the air to pass through the coooler. The air should be applied (for preference) from the base end, thereby cooling the grid and other base connections, then on through the anode cooler. In the standard sockets a ceramic ring is normally provided to direct the air into a finned radiator. If this is not used the amount of air passing through the cooler will fall very considerably.

Several types of conduction-cooled tetrodes are available, some with the conducting element forming part of the valve envelope while others require a separate heat-conducting block. The latter has the advantage that the heat conductor is (or can be) part of the amplifier assembly and is therefore a permanent fixture, whereas if the heat conductor is built into the valve, it is wasted when the valve fails.

The use of linear amplifiers instead of the Class C type is recommended for amateur applications. While it is true that the efficiency is lower with Class AB1 than Class C, a theoretical efficiency of 66 per cent is possible and 50 to 55 per cent is readily realizable in a practical design, whereas under Class C an efficiency of 60 to 70 per cent is usual. The difference in output is unlikely to be significant except in a limited number of cases.

There are advantages which a linear amplifier has over Class C operation, which should be seriously considered. These may be summarized as:

- suitable for all modes of operation: a.m., ssb, nbfm and cw;
- harmonic generation will be very much lower than in a Class C amplifier; and
- drive power required will be much lower.

From this it can be appreciated that:

- there will be a significant saving in cost and weight, when compared with a high-level modulator needed for a Class C amplifier;
- lower harmonic power will be generated by the amplifier, since by definition it is a linear device. Usually harmonics will be 25dB or more below the fundamental. It will however amplify any harmonics present in the input waveform. However a Class C amplifier will generate harmonics with a pure input signal. The reduction of harmonic output will be an advantage, reducing interference to vhf television;
- the lower drive can readily be provided by a transistor exciter, since as far as the amplifier is concerned only voltage and not power is needed to drive it. However, some power will be absorbed in the input circuit and valve capacitance. To provide a reasonably constant input load, some power will also be dissipated in an appropriate loading resistor.

CCS1 with HC1 heat conduction block

The type of power amplifier used will to a degree depend on the frequency of operation, and the efficiency will vary considerably over the range of 70 to 1,296MHz.

At the low-frequency end of this range the power amplifier stage may well be very similar to that used on the hf bands and substantially similar valves or transistors can usually be used, although recourse to series-tuned circuits is often necessary because of the relatively high output capacitance.

Table 5. Choice of tuned circuits

Frequency	Valve/semiconductor	Tuned circuit
70MHz	Tetrode	Standard parallel or series tuned
	Transistor	Lumped constants circuit
144MHz	Tetrode	Series tuned / Parallel tuned } Lumped constant circuits
	Double tetrode	Linear circuit
	Transistor	Linear circuit
432MHz	Double tetrode	Slab line
	Grounded grid triode	Cavity or trough
	Varactor diode	Lumped constants series tuned
1,296MHz	Grounded grid triode	Cavity
	Varactor diode	Linear circuits series tuned

As the frequency of operation is increased a change from the tetrode, to double tetrode (push-pull), and on to grounded-grid triodes is usually employed. Just where these changes occur depend on a number of factors and to some extent on personal choice.

In Table 5 a rough guide to the choice of tuned circuit is given and as can be seen there is not a clear-cut change from one type of circuit for any particular frequency, the final decision usually depending on the actual valve or semiconductor used.

Probably the variety is greatest at 432MHz, not only in the circuit form but also in the choice of amplifying device. There are two popular valve amplifier arrangements which at the power levels usually encountered in amateur equipment compete strongly for favour. These are the push-pull double tetrode (QQV03/20A) or the grounded-grid triode (DET24). Similar power levels and efficiencies can usually be obtained with either arrangement.

In higher-power stages the most popular is the forced-air-cooled single tetrode such as the 4X150A or 4CX250B. Two valves of this type may be used in a push-pull arrangement.

Tetrodes

The design of single tetrodes for use at frequencies of 70MHz and above requires, among other features, low anode-to-control-grid capacitance in order to avoid instability. Most types will require neutralization by some means or other, either by the capacitance bridge method or screen tuning system.

Typical circuit arrangements for neutralization are shown in Fig 20. In (a) the anode circuit is of a balanced type so that the neutralizing capacitor NC is connected to the opposite side of the tuned circuit to the anode, and thus forms with the valve capacitance a bridge. The NC may be either an adjustable capacitor or a suitable length of wire from the grid so placed to form a capacitor.

In (b) the out-of-phase voltage required is obtained from the grid circuit and is the method usually used when a pi-anode circuit is used. It is also applicable for series-tuned anode circuits.

In (c) stabilization is obtained by tuning the screen circuit in which there is a series inductance NL and tuning capacitor NC. In many cases NL is provided by the capacitor leads themselves and additional inductance is not needed.

In some specially designed types for operation in the frequency range 150 to 500MHz, such as the 4X150A or 4CX250B, there is complete mechanical isolation between the grid and anode, the screen being brought out to an annular ring which, when fitted into an appropriate socket with built-in bypass capacitor, can be thoroughly earthed with respect to rf.

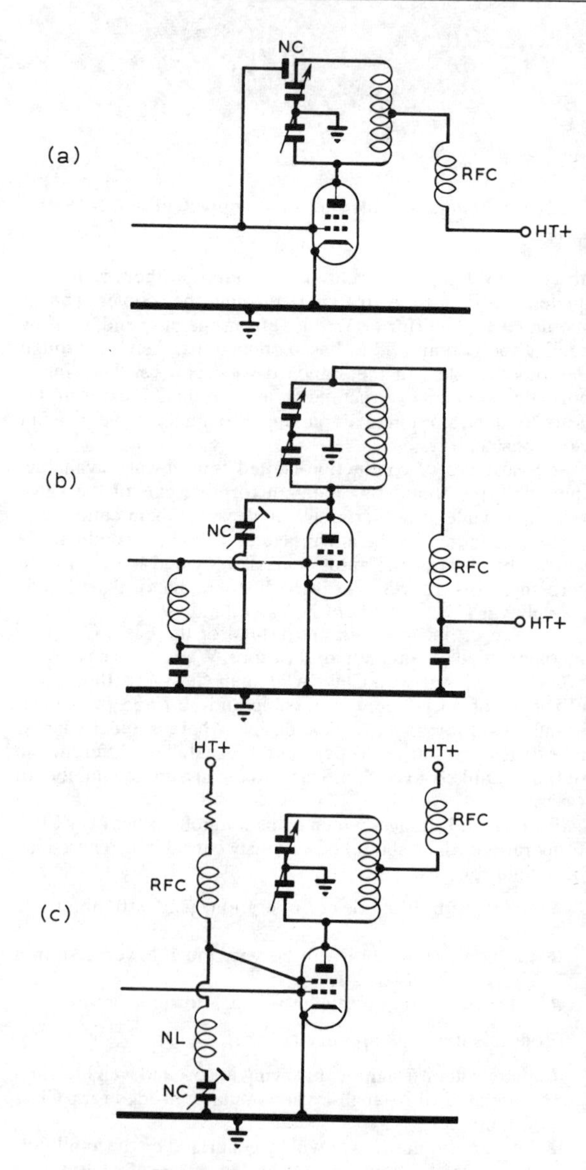

Fig 20. Methods of neutralizing

Table 6. Typical operating conditions of 4CX250B (one valve)

Parameter	Units	Class AB1 linear amp (ssb)			Class C cw and fm		
V_a	kV	1	1·5	2	1	1·5	2
V_{g2}	V	350	350	350	250	250	250
V_{g1}	−V	55*	55*	55*	90	90	90
I_a (zero signal)	mA	100	100	100	—	—	—
V_{g1} (peak)	V	50	50	50	114	112	112
I_a (max signal)	mA	250	250	250	250	250	250
I_{g2}	mA	10	8	5	38	21	19
I_{g1}	mA	—	—	—	31	28	26
P_{drive}	W	—	—	—	3·5	3·2	2·9
P_{out} mean	W	60	107	150	70	190	280
P_{out} p.e.p.	W	120	214	300	—	—	—
I_a two tone	mA	190	190	190	—	—	—
I_{g2} two-tone	mA	2	−1	−2	—	—	—

* V_{g1} adjusted to set I_a (zero signal). Cooling: 6·4 ft³/min. Pressure drop across valve 0·8in water gauge. Maximum anode (core) temperature 200°C.

The feedthrough capacitance between grid and anode is then usually too small to cause self-oscillation in a properly designed circuit layout.

In this class of valve the screen should be supplied from a fixed-voltage source interlocked with the anode supply, because the screen current varies fairly widely, due to secondary emission, and is often negative. In addition, as the frequency is increased it may be necessary to reduce the input power to the heater to prevent excessive internal heating.

Double tetrodes

There are two distinct varieties of these valves, which may be classified as *American*, such as the 832A and 829B, and *European*, such as the QQV03-20A and 6-40A.

In the American type the electrode system consists of two separate tetrodes in one envelope with or without a common screen bypass capacitor mounted inside, and neutralization is required externally. These are now an old design of valve.

A QQV03–20A and QQV06–40A

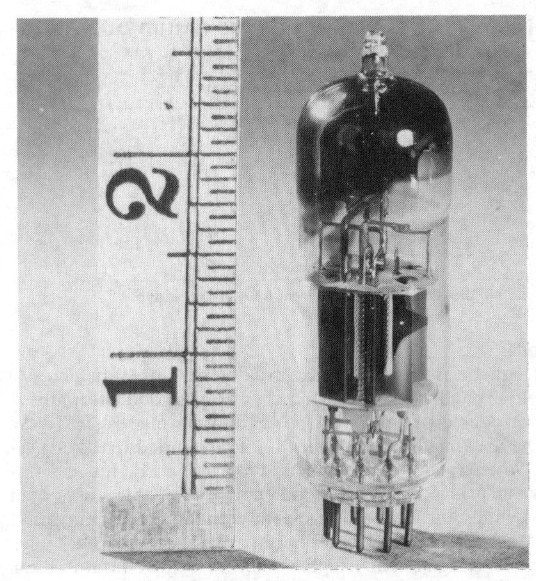

A QQV02–6 double tetrode

A typical method of crossover neutralizing arrangement is shown in Fig 21. It usually consists of a wire connected to the grid circuit of one triode being placed near to the anode of the other tetrode, with the capacitance between the wire and the anode adjusted by bending to give stability.

The European types such as the QQV03-20A or QQV06-40A are designed on the basis of a common cathode and a common screen grid (Fig 22). The separate systems are achieved by the use of single-sided control grids and anodes. The design also includes the neutralizing capacitors.

A table in the Appendix lists some of the more popular valves at present in use. Their power output ranges from 1W upwards.

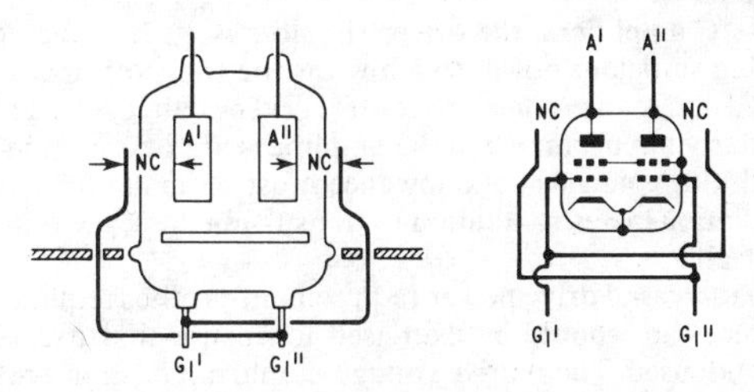

Fig 21. A cross-section of an 829B showing method of neutralizing

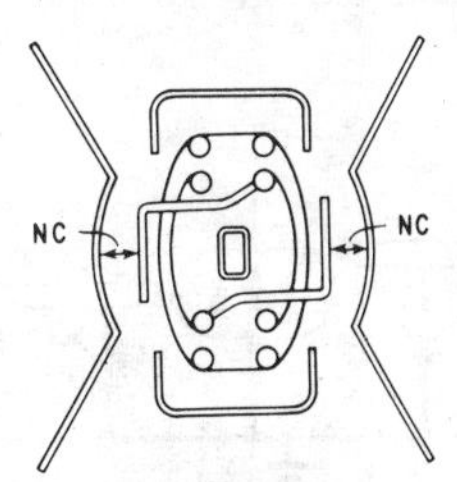

Fig 22. A cross-section of a European vhf double tetrode such as QQV03–20A

Table 7. Double-tetrode maximum operating conditions for 175MHz Class C cw or fm

	QQV03-20A		QQV06-40A		QQV07-50		YL1060*	
Anode *V*	400	600	400	600	400	600	900	1,000
Screen *V*	250	250	250	250	250	250	250	250
Grid *V*	−50	−60	−60	−80	−60	−80	−90	−85
Anode *I*	2 × 50		2 × 100		2 × 115		2 × 110	2 × 100
Screen *I*	2 × 4		2 × 8	2 × 9	2 × 7	2 × 8	2 × 6·3	2 × 5·6
Grid *I*	2 × 0·7		2 × 3	2×3·5	2 × 3	2 × 4	2 × 3	2 × 2·9
Power *W*o	30	48	55	90	64	103	150	146
Power *W*I	25	38	47	78	54	87	132	125
Efficiency (%)	75	80	70	75	70	75	75	73

* Anode pin diam and centres different from the other types.

Triodes

At frequencies above 432MHz, triodes are more satisfactory as amplifiers and even at 432MHz they offer a good alternative to the tetrodes, especially in the power output range of 10 to 20W.

The usual method of connection is grounded (earthed) grid and when valves of the planar type are used, the isolation between grid and anode is good enough to enable stable operation without trouble as long as the cathode (input) and anode (output) circuits are suitably separated. The drive power required is significantly higher than for a tetrode, but a considerable proportion of this is fed through into the output circuit and adds to the amplifier's total output power.

Since the drive power forms part of the output, it is necessary for a.m. service to modulate the driver stage as well as the amplifier, but because of this they cannot be driven from a frequency multiplier.

The best-known valve for this type of use is 2C39A (100W dissipation).

In addition to the 2C39A, there are a number of smaller types which are suitable either as drivers or lower-power amplifiers. Such types are DET29, A2521, EC157, EC8010 and Nuvistor 8058, and of these both the EC157 and DET29 may be used at higher frequencies than 1·3GHz and with reasonable output up to about 4 or 5GHz.

Driving power

In Class C amplifiers, the driver should always be capable of providing sufficient power to allow for the range of operation required and to overcome the control grid circuit losses. This is particularly important when the amplifiers are operated in the vhf and uhf region where allowance must be made for circuit and radiation losses in addition to transit-time losses within the valve itself.

With increased drive power requirements as the frequency is increased, care should be exercised to ensure that excessive drive is not used. The rf drive voltage should not be greater than that required to give the maximum output and this can readily be seen if a power control is available in the driver stage and an rf output monitor connected into the output circuit. This may take the form of a simple rf voltmeter connected across the output coupling of a reflectometer set to read forward power.

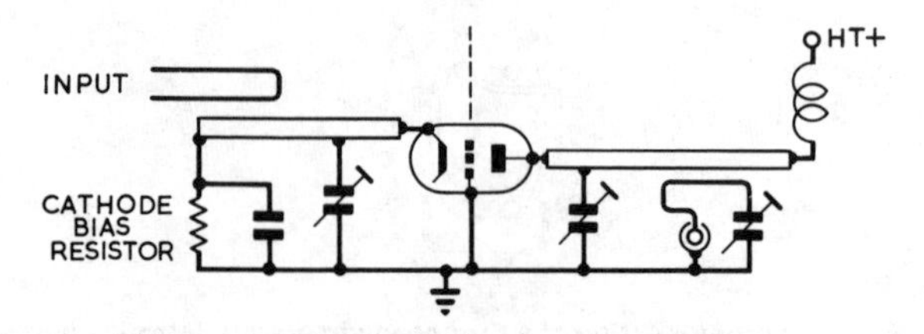

Fig 23. A typical grounded-grid amplifier

Overloading valves

All oxide-coated cathodes can fairly easily be damaged if the anode and grid are allowed to become excessively hot. The anode, for example, should never be allowed to become hot enough for it to be visibly red when viewed in normal room lighting.

In amplifiers operating within their rated conditions overheating is most likely to occur if there is a failure of rf drive when the grid bias is wholly obtained by the grid resistance method. It is wise to include a suitable cathode bias resistor to provide some part of the bias and its value should be chosen such that in the absence of rf drive the anode and screen currents are kept down to safe levels. Such a cathode bias resistor must be bypassed effectively to maintain the cathode at substantially earth potential. Alternatively a clamp valve system may be used.

Cooling valves

Cooling of valves is important and the makers' recommendation should be observed if satisfactory performance is to be obtained.

Operation of any radiation-cooled power valve at its maximum rating of input power, especially at or near its upper frequency limits, invariably requires an increase in air cooling to prevent overheating of the envelope. Simple fans which will provide the necessary additional air flow over the static convection air flow should be switched on by being interconnected with the power supply switch.

The extra cooling is particularly necessary in amplifiers which are fully screened, as they should be to avoid any appreciable losses introduced by free rf radiation. Adequate air inlet and outlet holes should be provided to ensure a free flow of air into and out from the enclosure.

Transistor power amplifiers

Transistors capable of delivering useful amounts of power at vhf have been available since the mid-'sixties. Transistor technology has advanced rapidly since then and present-day devices are available giving over 100W output for frequencies up to 250MHz, 80W at 500MHz and 50W at 1GHz. The availability of 12V devices at a reasonable cost has resulted in widespread adoption of fully solid-state equipment for mobile and portable use. Typical output stage gains of 10dB are achieved at 70MHz or 5dB at 432MHz. The low circuit impedances require a totally different design approach compared with valve equipment.

Modern devices employ a silicon planar epitaxial construction, using many parallel-connected devices in an interdigitated structure on one chip. This enables a large area device to be produced but minimizes stray capacitances and inductances, essential for high-frequency operation. Emitter ballast resistors are diffused into the crystal to improve current sharing and hence ruggedness. Aluminium or gold metallization is used to interconnect the appropriate emitter and base areas. The chip is mounted on a suitable header or encapsulation and wire bonded.

The encapsulation of an rf power transistor is often the limiting factor in the performance of the device. The input impedance of a power transistor may be as low as 1Ω and it only requires 1nH of lead inductance (approximately 1·5mm of transistor lead) to give a reactance of 1Ω at 144MHz. Lead

Typical rf power transistors showing low-inductance electrical connections and heat sink mountings

inductance in the grounded terminal, normally the emitter, should in particular be kept to the absolute minimum. Hence rf power envelopes normally have multiple-emitter leads comprising wide copper or nickel strips. Typical examples are shown in the photo. A beryllium oxide (beryllia) disc is used between the stud or flange and the crystal, as this material has excellent thermal conductivity together with being an electrical insulator. Beryllium oxide is a fired ceramic and, during normal handling and usage, it is entirely safe. However, the dust is hazardous and no attempt should be made to tamper with the component parts of such an envelope.

Initial considerations

The first stage in designing an amplifier is to select a suitable device. Manufacturers' published data will enable such factors as frequency, gain, dc and rf safe ratings, impedances, allowable dissipation and other parameters to be obtained. To ensure reliable operation and long life, the device should be operated well within the maximum ratings under all possible conditions. There is no margin for abuse with transistors as is generally the case for valves. Devices intended for 12V battery operation are generally safe for voltages up to 15 or 16V providing other ratings are not exceeded.

If higher voltages or transient surges are expected, some form of voltage limiter should be used such as that shown in Fig 24. Similarly, accidents do happen and output stages should be operated within the ratings that allow short-term operation into high load mismatch. Extra protection is advisable, particularly

Inside view of rf power transistor showing interdigitated structure

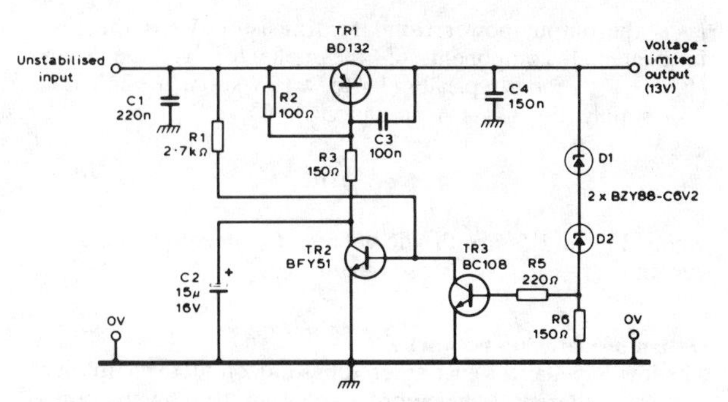

Fig 24. Voltage limiter for 12V battery equipment with 3A rating

for high-power amplifiers, and can comprise a directional coupler power sensor to reduce the rf drive in the event of a mismatch. Device dissipation can often approach four times normal dissipation under mismatch conditions. Supply current limiting can be employed to reduce dissipation under such conditions. It is essential to provide adequate heat sinking to keep the device well within the maximum temperature limit under the highest expected ambient temperatures. Forced air cooling may offer advantages in high-power equipment.

In common with valves, the class of operation is determined by the modulation mode. SSB equipment requires linear operation in Class AB or, for low-power driver stages, Class A. FM or cw equipment uses zero-added-bias Class C stages. Multimode add-on amplifiers use Class AB biasing. The reverse emitter-base breakdown voltage of most rf power transistors is small, typically 4V. Any attempt to add additional reverse bias in Class C operation, usually by including a small resistor in series with the base choke, may cause this voltage to be exceeded. This is often not immediately catastrophic, but will considerably reduce the life of the transistor. It is recommended that for Class C biasing, at power levels greater than 5W, a low dc resistance choke is connected directly from base to emitter. For Class A or AB biasing reference to the published data is necessary to determine the maximum allowable dc biasing conditions.

The dc safe operating area (s.o.a.r.) is a graph of V_{CE} against maximum allowable dc I_C. The device must be biased inside this area. The maximum allowable dc current will be considerably less than the peak rf current.

Many rf power transistors are suitable for use as Class AB linear amplifiers for ssb. However, very little information is published by manufacturers regarding this class of use. As a rule of thumb, a low-voltage transistor (12V) used as a linear amplifier will give a p.e.p. output of about 0·7 times the fm cw rating with acceptable distortion. A high-voltage transistor (28V) will give a p.e.p. output of about 0·9 to 1·0 times the fm cw rating, again with acceptable distortion products. For low-distortion amplification, the F_T variation with collector current should be relatively small.

The input and output impedances are usually quoted in published data. The input impedance of a vhf or uhf power device is typically 1 to 5Ω resistive in series with a reactance. At low frequencies (70MHz), the device appears capacitive but at higher frequencies, due to the internal bond wires, the device appears inductive. The required collector load impedance may be calculated from

$$R_L = \frac{V_o^2}{2P_o}$$

P_o is the output power from the transistor. V_o is the peak fundamental component of the collector voltage swing ($V_{CC} - V_{sat}$) and is typically 11V for a 12V supply or 26V for a 28V supply. For Class A operation

$$R_L = \frac{V_{CE}}{I_C}$$

where V_{CE} and I_C are the dc values of collector voltage and current.

Design of matching networks

The low impedances encountered in semiconductor amplifiers require a different design approach compared with valve counterparts, pi networks, parallel-tuned circuits and high-Q lines, popular with valve designs, give rise to impractical component values when scaled for transistor impedances. Suitable networks for use with transistors are given in Fig 25 together with appropriate formulae. These networks give rise to practical components at vhf and uhf up to about 800MHz.

Above 400MHz an alternative approach to matching is to use sections of microstrip transmission lines fabricated on printed circuit board. These networks are most conveniently designed using transmission-line impedance plots such as the Smith chart. Networks of this form may be used well into the microwave region. To provide for variations in tuning and matching of the networks shown in Fig 25, two components should be made variable. This is most easily accomplished with trimmer capacitors.

Double pi and L-pi networks can also yield practical values if the intermediate impedance level is suitably selected (around 1,000Ω). These networks can give rise to excellent harmonic rejection. Output networks which have an inductive element connected to the transistor such as those in Fig 25, give rise to higher efficiencies than those which have a capacitive shunt feed. This is due to the nature of the impedance presented to the device at harmonic frequencies.

The loaded Q of the network should be typically in the range 3 to 12. High-Q networks give better harmonic rejection but result in higher circulating currents, higher voltages, greater losses and are more critical on tuning. For high-power stages or where large impedance transformation is involved, it is often preferable to use two cascaded low-Q networks rather than one high-Q network. A suitable combination from Fig 25 is A nearest the transistor followed by B or C. The intermediate impedance level should lie between the source and load impedances and can be conveniently the geometric mean

$$R = \sqrt{R_1 . R_2}$$

Impedance is usually quoted in published data as either a series combination of resistance and reactance $Z = R + jX$ or a parallel combination of conductance and susceptance $Y = G + jB$. It is often necessary to convert from series to parallel and vice versa. The following relationships may be used (Fig 26).

$$Z = R_s + jX_s \qquad Y = G + jB$$

$$Y = \frac{1}{Z} \qquad R_p = \frac{1}{G} \qquad X_p = -\frac{1}{B}$$

$$R_s = \frac{R_p . X_p^2}{R_p^2 + X_p^2} \qquad X_s = \frac{R_p^2 . X_p}{R_p^2 + X_p^2}$$

$$R_p = \frac{R_s^2 + X_s^2}{R_s} \qquad X_p = \frac{R_s^2 + X_s^2}{X_s}$$

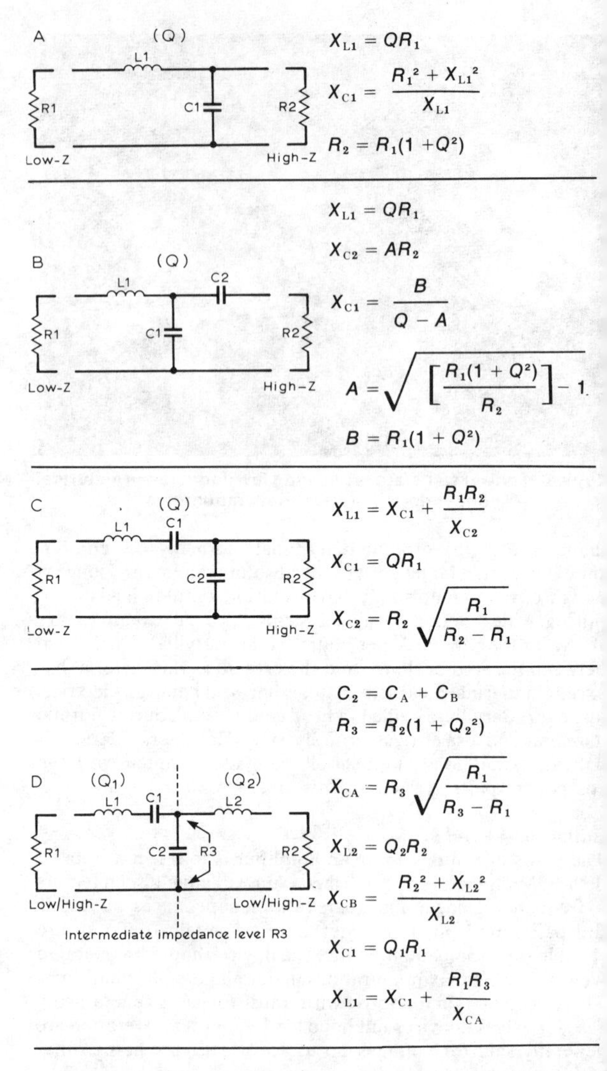

Fig 25. Tuning networks for transistor rf power amplifiers. (a) Simple L-network which often lacks flexibility, and will only match unequal impedances. (b) and (c) are ideal for transistor input/output tuning networks but will only match between unequal impedances. In (d) Q_1 and Q_2 need not be the same. The intermediate impedance level is higher than R_1 or R_2. This network is ideal for matching near-equal impedances

For a capacitor jX will be negative and jB will be positive. For an inductor jX will be positive and jB will be negative. If X_s is a capacitive reactance, X_p will also be a capacitive reactance and similarly for inductive reactances.

Fig 27 shows a typical design for a vhf power amplifier. The input network is required to match from typically 50Ω, or from the load impedance of the previous stage, to the input impedance of the device $R_i + jX_i$. The value of R_i is used in the design formulae B. The value calculated for L1 should be reduced by an amount X_i if the input impedance is inductive (jX_i positive) or increased by an amount X_i if the input impedance is capacitive (jX_i negative). It is often the case with

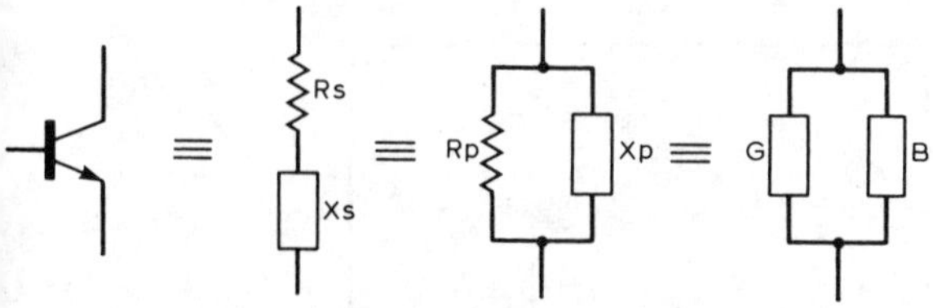

Fig 26. Series-to-parallel conversions

high-power devices and low input impedances that a single network solution will not be possible at moderate Q values. By placing capacitors directly from base to emitter an L network is formed with the transistor bond wires, raising the input impedance to a manageable level. At uhf, where X_i can be large compared with R_i, $X_{L1} - X_i$ can result in impracticably small values for L1 and again the solution is to place capacitors directly from base to emitter to form an L-network with the transistor bond wires. Some fixed capacitance from base to emitter is often desirable on grounds of stability in any case.

The output network is required to match from the calculated value of R_L to the load impedance which is typically 50Ω. L3 should resonate with the parallel output capacitance of the transistor obtained from the data.

$$2\pi f.L_3 = \frac{1}{2\pi f.C_{out}}$$

The value of L3 is non-critical as the loaded Q of this parallel circuit is very low. Keeping the value of L3 to a minimum will enhance the overall stability. Component values for L4, C3 and C4 can be obtained from Fig 25.

Example

Mullard BLY89A operating as a 25W fm amplifier at 144MHz used in the circuit described and operating between 50Ω source and loads. Supply voltage 12·5V.

From published data $Z_i = 1{\cdot}7 + j1{\cdot}4\Omega$; $C_L = 65\text{pF}$; $V_{cc} = 12{\cdot}5\text{V}$; V_o typically 11V;

$$R_L = \frac{V_o^2}{2P_o} \qquad R_L = 2{\cdot}4\Omega.$$

Select $Q = 10$ for both input and output networks. Output network must match 2·4Ω to 50Ω.

From Fig 25(c),
$X_{C3} = 24\Omega$; $X_{L4} = 34{\cdot}7\Omega$; $X_{C4} = 11{\cdot}2\Omega$
L3 must resonate with $C_L = 65\text{pF}$ at 144MHz.
$X_{L3} = 17\Omega$.

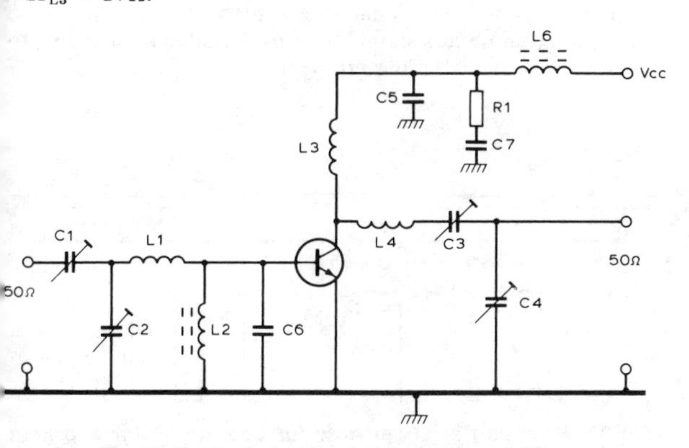

Fig 27. Typical circuit of vhf power amplifier

The input network must match 50Ω to $1{\cdot}7 + j1{\cdot}4\Omega$. This corresponds to a resistor of 1·7Ω in series with an inductive reactance of 1·4Ω.

From Fig 25(b), to match 1·7Ω to 50Ω,
$X_{C1} = 78\Omega$; $X_{C2} = 20{\cdot}3\Omega$; $X_{L1}' = 17\Omega$
To account for the 1·4Ω series inductance seen at the transistor base terminal, this value must be subtracted from $X_{L1}' = 17\Omega$ to give $X_{L1} = 15{\cdot}6\Omega$.
Inductance and capacitance values can be found from

$$L = \frac{X}{\omega} \text{ and } C = \frac{1}{\omega X} \qquad (\omega = 2\pi f)$$

Components list: C1 14pF; C2 54pF; C3 46pF; C4 98pF; L1 17nH; L3 19nH; L4 38nH.

Practical amplifier construction

The simplest and most reliable method of constructing a vhf power amplifier is to use a printed circuit board. $\frac{1}{16}$in double-sided glassfibre board is suitable for use up to 432MHz. PTFE loaded board is desirable at higher frequencies. Fig 28 shows a typical layout adopted for the amplifier shown in Fig 27. It is most important to keep stray inductances to a minimum, particularly the emitter lead inductance.

The underside of the board should be plain copper used as the earth plane and grounding points taken through the board using copper tabs or rivets at every point where a component connects to ground. The most satisfactory method of grounding the emitters is to wrap copper foil through the transistor locating hole to connect the emitter leads directly to the earth plane at a point where the leads emerge from the body of the transistor (Fig 29). The printed board should be supported to avoid strain or flexing of the transistor leads (Fig 30).

Components for the matching networks should be selected for high current capability, low loss and low lead inductance. For fixed capacitors, npo ceramic tubular or plate capacitors are suitable but miniature types should be avoided. At high power levels it will be necessary to use porcelain chip or mica capacitors. Decoupling capacitors should be low-inductance types such as feedthrough capacitors. For trimmer capacitors, professional-grade film dielectric trimmers are suitable for use up to 432MHz, and for higher capacitance values mica compression trimmers are suitable at lower vhf. Inductors can conveniently be wound self-supporting using bare copper wire. The wire diameter should be as large as possible. On 432MHz, the small inductance values often required may be easier to fabricate using copper strips on the circuit board. These may be designed with the aid of the charts in the Appendix. Base chokes should be of low Q to improve stability. For 144MHz, a suitable choke can comprise 1·5 turns of enamelled copper wire wound through a ferrite bead such as FX1115.

Several precautions may be taken to ensure stability. The layout should ensure that input and output networks are adequately isolated and low grounding impedances are achieved. A low-Q base choke should be used, possibly with extra damping in the form of a resistor of 5 to 22Ω connected base to ground. Referring to Fig 27, C5 should have a low impedance at the operating frequency but not at low frequencies. R1 and C7 ensure low-frequency stability. R1 should be a few ohms and C7 should have a reactance of a few ohms at a frequency of several hundred kilohertz. Typically R1 can be 4·7Ω and C7 100nF. L6 may be a ferrite choke with adequate dc current handling for the power levels involved. For high-gain devices operated well below F_T, it may be necessary to add some capacitance from collector to ground. Some fixed capacitance

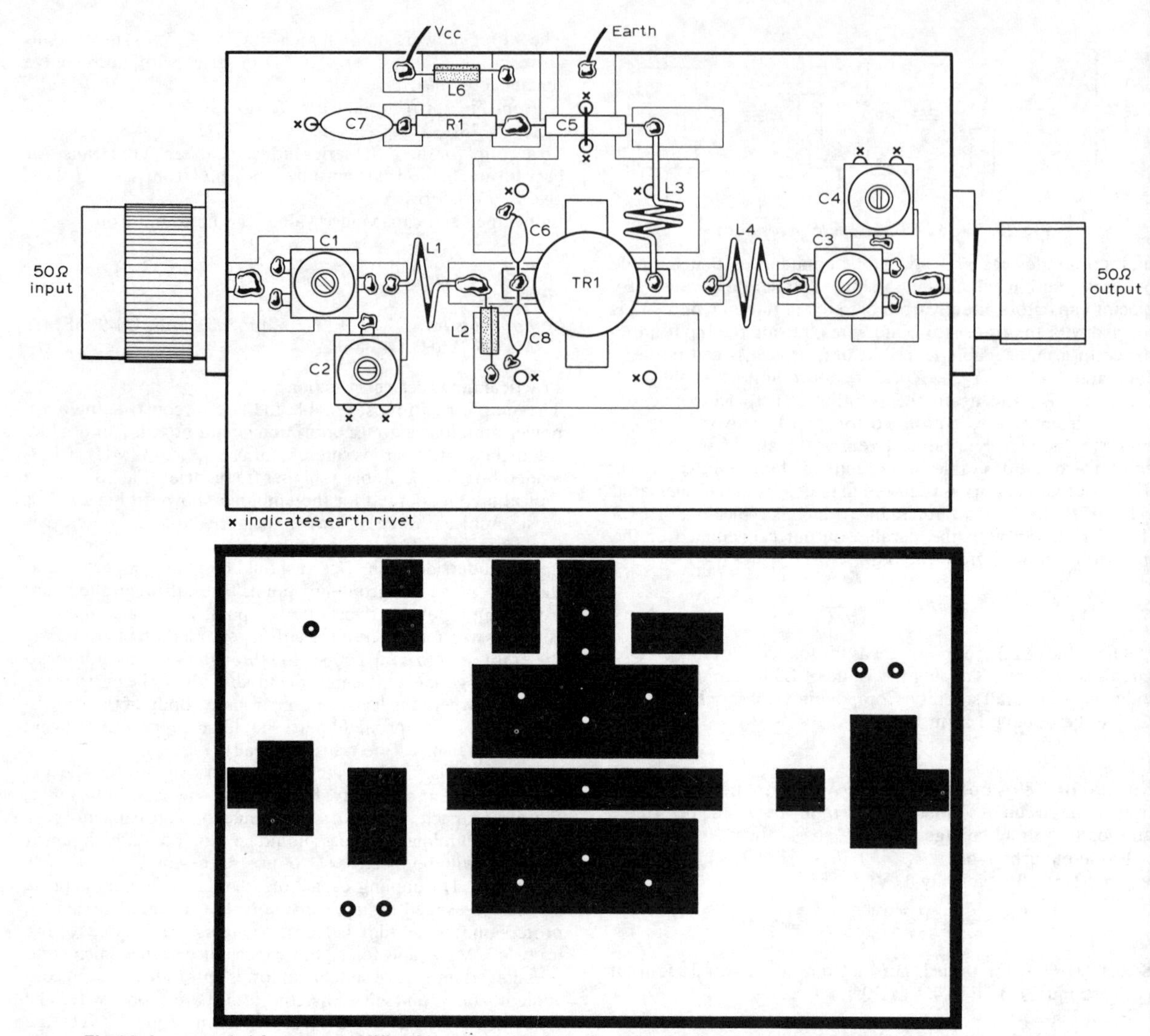

Fig 28. Layout of vhf power amplifier (the mounting hole for TR1 breaks the central conductor into two sections)

added base to emitter will often improve stability. Two capacitors should be used, one to each emitter lead, keeping lead lengths to an absolute minimum.

Multi-stage amplifiers should not present any particular problems. Interstage matching should be designed to match from the collector impedance of one stage to the base impedance of the following stage. It is often convenient to use two matching networks with a 50Ω intermediate impedance level. This enables the individual stages to be tested separately. Multi-stage amplifiers should be constructed in a single line to eliminate mutual coupling problems.

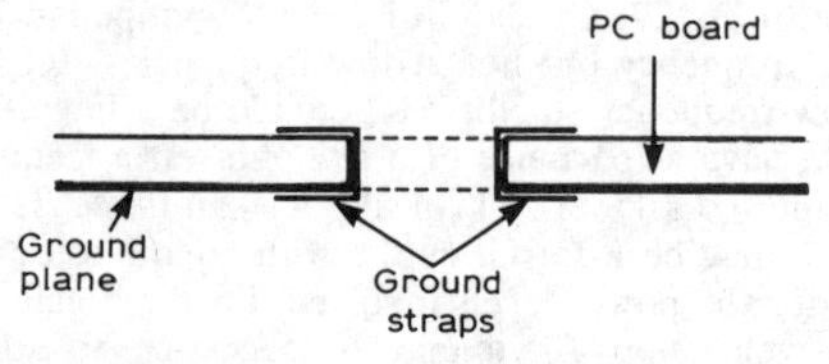

Fig 29. Earthing straps for the emitters

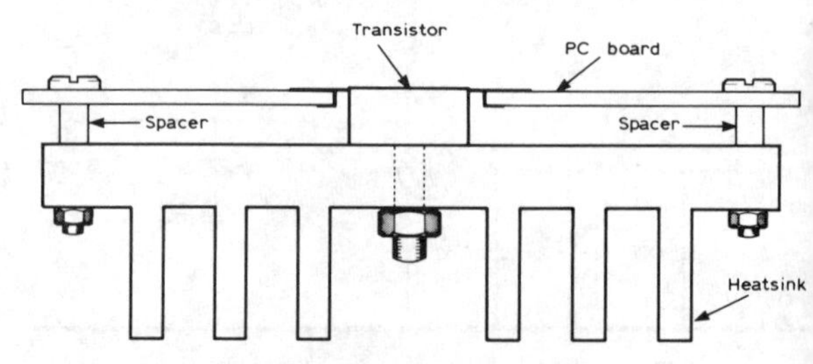

Fig 30. Mounting arrangements for pcb, transistor and heat sink

Alignment of the amplifier should be done initially at reduced drive and supply voltage while monitoring the supply current. The input network trimmers C1 and C2 should be adjusted for best input match (zero reflected power on a reflectometer) and the output network trimmers C3 and C4 should be adjusted for maximum output power. Once the networks have been initially aligned and the amplifier appears to be stable, the drive and supply voltage may be increased and the alignment procedure repeated in steps to the required operating levels. Stability may be checked by listening on a loosely coupled receiver for any unwanted spurious signals, noise or modulations. In addition, alteration of the trimmers or varying the drive or supply voltage should result in smooth variations of supply current and output power with no steps or jumps. Cascaded Class C stages will tend to have a switch on/switch off characteristic as the drive is reduced to zero. This should not be confused with instability.

Higher powers

Higher power levels may be achieved in a number of ways. The most obvious method is to use the largest available device. The limit from a single device is about 100W at vhf.

Transistors may be operated in parallel provided certain precautions are taken to achieve correct power sharing. The devices should be matched and a symmetrical layout adopted. The devices should be close together and tightly coupled thermally on the same heat sink.

Paralleling should not be attempted directly at the base or collector but should occur at a higher-impedance point. This implies using separate L-networks on the base and collectors for the individual transistors and then paralleling through a common matching network which may contain adjustable elements. Common-mode resistors may be added base-to-base and collector-to-collector (10–47Ω is typical). The number of devices paralleled should be limited to two.

Push-pull operation may be used, although network design becomes complicated. Impedances are four times higher than the equivalent parallel case. Push-pull operation is convenient to use with wideband ferrite-cored transformers. This mode of operation is popular at hf but may also be used at low vhf, particularly 70MHz.

Hybrid couplers may be used to couple two or more complete amplifier stages in parallel. It is important that the amplifiers are identical in terms of power output and phase characteristics. Hybrid couplers have the advantage that each amplifier is isolated from its counterparts and failure of one amplifier will still result in continued operation although at a lower power level. Solid-state vhf broadcast transmitters are constructed along these lines. There are various types of hybrid coupler that are suitable—hybrid ring coupler, Wilkinson multi-port combiner and the 3dB quadrature coupler. Hybrid ring and Wilkinson couplers may be constructed from $\lambda/4$ and $3\lambda/4$ lengths of coaxial cable.

Bias units for linear operation

For ssb operation, forward biasing of amplifier stages into Class AB is required. A suitable quiescent current is often 50–100mA. Low-distortion amplification requires that a low-impedance bias unit is used and two such circuits are shown in Figs 31 and 32. The diode biasing system is suitable for low power levels only. The bleed current through the series resistor must be greater than the peak bias current demand of the amplifier stage.

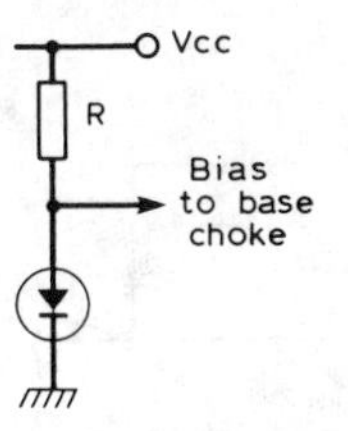

Fig 31. Diode biasing for Class AB amplifiers

$$R < \frac{(V_{cc} - 0 \cdot 8)\, h_{FE}}{I_C}$$

where I_C is the dc collector current drawn by the amplifier under sustained p.e.p. conditions and h_{FE} is the current gain of the transistor at this current level. It is important that the diode is mounted in tight thermal contact with the amplifier transistor to prevent possible thermal runaway and maintain a constant quiscent collector current with variations in temperature.

The circuit shown in Fig 32 is capable of superior results and lower internal impedance. With the component values shown, it will provide 0·5A bias current. TR1 should be mounted in thermal contact with the amplifier transistor to prevent thermal runaway as before. TR2 will require heat sinking and can conveniently share the same heat sink as TR1 and the amplifier transistor.

Heat sinks

Adequate cooling should be provided to keep power devices well within their rated specification. Maximum junction temperature is normally quoted in published data as typically 200°C. This should not be exceeded under any condition. Knowing the total power dissipation and thermal resistances of the device and heat sink it is possible to calculate the maximum junction temperature.

Referring to Fig 33, $\theta_{j\text{-}mb}$ is the thermal resistance of the crystal and header. This is quoted in published data and varies from typically 25°C/W for small metal-cased TO5 devices down to 0·8°C/W for large flange- or stud-mounted devices. $\theta_{mb\text{-}h}$ is the thermal resistance of the interface between the mounting base of the device and the heat sink. This figure can be reduced considerably by the application of a thin smear of heat sink

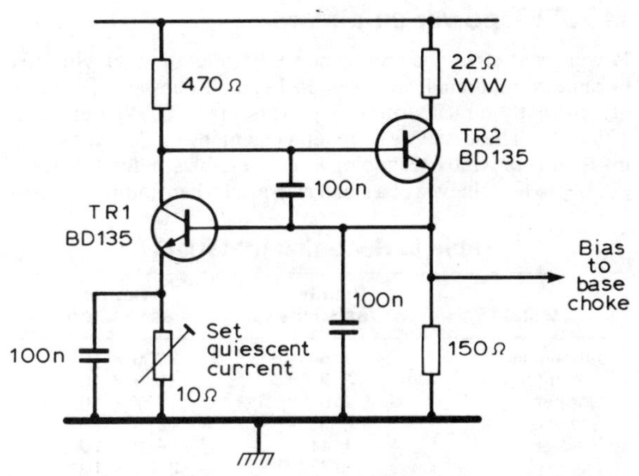

Fig 32. Low-impedance transistor bias unit for Class AB amplifiers

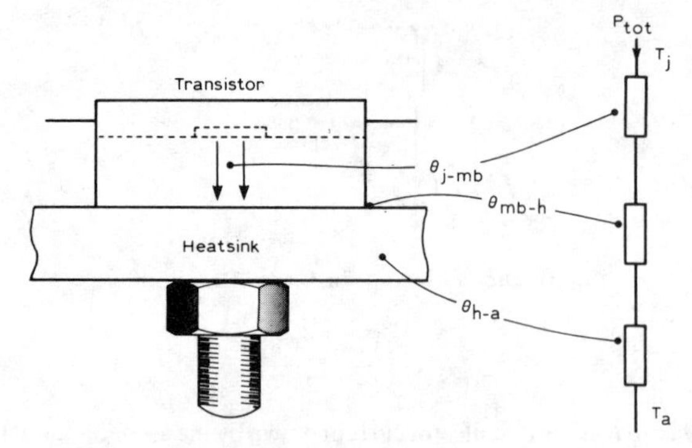

Fig 33. Factors controlling the heat dissipation from the transistor crystal

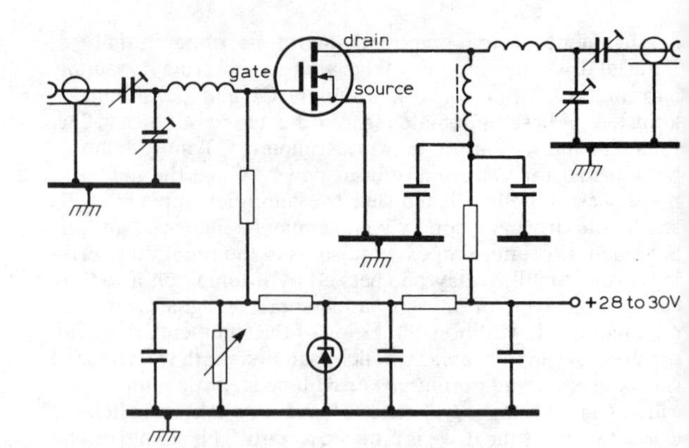

Fig 34. Typical vmos amplifier and bias circuit

compound. A typical figure is less than 0·5°C/W. θ_{h-a} is the thermal resistance of the heat sink and where a standard extruded heat sink is used, it is quoted by the manufacturer.

$$T_j = T_a + P_{tot}\ (\theta_{j-mb} + \theta_{mb-h} + \theta_{h-a}).$$

where T_j is the junction temperature, T_a is the ambient temperature and P_{tot} is the total device dissipation.

Studded devices should be tightened to the specified torque. Undertightening will impair heat sinking whereas overtightening will stretch the copper stud. Mounting holes in the heat sink should be free from burrs and its face should be flat. A little heat-sink grease should be used. Above all, an adequately sized heat sink must be employed.

Materials with higher thermal conductivity are the most suitable for heat sinks. It is however important to ensure that there is no significant contact potential between the device and the heat-sink material, otherwise electrolytic corrosion will occur. Coolers made of metal other than copper or aluminium will need to be of greater thickness to give the same performance.

The thermal efficiency of a heat sink may be improved when the surface is roughened and covered with matt black paint, such as lamp black, or anodizing.

The characteristics of suitable materials are shown in Table 8.

MOSFET power amplifiers

Power field-effect devices capable of operating at vhf first became commercially available in 1976. A number of devices are currently on sale, offering powers up to 100W output at 175MHz. These devices are enhancement-mode types and make use of vmos technology. This enables a high current density to be achieved in a small chip area when compared with small-signal fets. Most current power fets are intended for 28 or 35V operation and give much lower output powers and gain if used on a 12V rail. Devices for use up to 400MHz are available.

Compared with bipolar devices (transistors), power fets have the following characteristics.

- No thermal runaway
- Ease of biasing and switching
- Lower harmonic output
- Higher but reactive input impedances
- Simplified parallel operation
- Low noise at small and large signal levels
- Improved stability

Many of the comments made regarding transistor power amplifier design apply equally to power fets.

In the vhf range, the input impedance is sufficiently close in magnitude to that of a bipolar transistor to enable similar input tuning networks incorporating trimmer capacitors to be used.

The output load impedance may be calculated in the same way as for a bipolar transistor and a similar network used.

As the devices are enhancement-mode types, some positive forward bias must be applied for Class B or AB operation. Zero-bias Class C operation tends to give low power output and gain. MOS devices draw no gate dc current and biasing can simply be achieved with two resistors as a potential divider. Low-impedance, stabilized and temperature-compensated bias units as used with bipolars are not required.

Fig 35 depicts a typical transfer characteristic curve which shows the drain current is largely a linear function of the gate-to-source voltage. Fig 36 shows the power output against frequency—it is likely that these devices would equally be suitable for power triplers, for example from 144 to 432MHz.

Table 8. Heat-sink materials

Metal	Relative resistivity	Thermal expansion
Aluminium	1·64	25·5 × 10⁻⁴
Brass (typical)	3·9	18·9 × 10⁻⁴
Copper	1·0	16·7 × 10⁻⁴
Silver	0·95	19·5 × 10⁻⁴
Gold	1·416	14·3 × 10⁻⁴
Tin	8·72	26·9 × 10⁻⁴
Nickel	7·8	12·8 × 10⁻⁴

Modulation

There are many methods of impressing speech or other audio frequencies on an rf carrier. Those normally used are:

Amplitude modulation—in which the audio frequency varies the amplitude of the rf output.

Frequency modulation—in this case the actual frequency of the carrier is varied at the audio frequency.

Single sideband—this is a special type of amplitude modulation where the rf carrier is not radiated, nor is the unwanted sideband, but the carrier has to be re-inserted at the receiver.

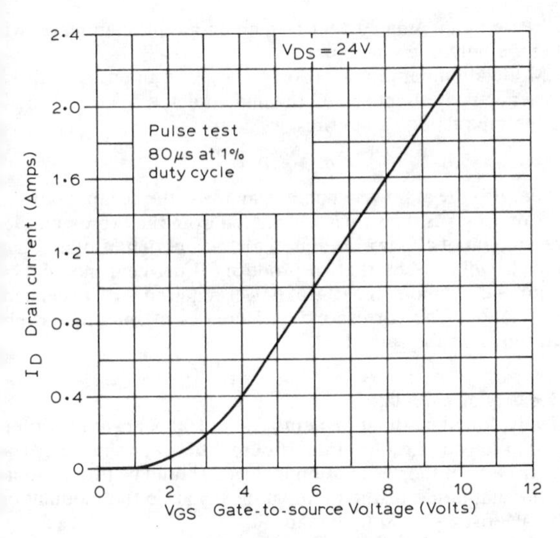

Fig 35. Transfer characteristic of a typical power mosfet

Amplitude modulation

Amplitude modulation is little used at present in amateur communication on the vhf and uhf bands. Details of the methods of application are given here for completeness. It is probably the easiest system to operate and understand but it does have a strong disadvantage that it is relatively expensive both in terms of power consumed, as well as size and weight of the equipment.

In addition, valves and semiconductors have to be derated to allow for the peak voltage swings that must occur, and this is particularly important in semiconductors because of their sensitivity to over-voltage which can permanently damage them.

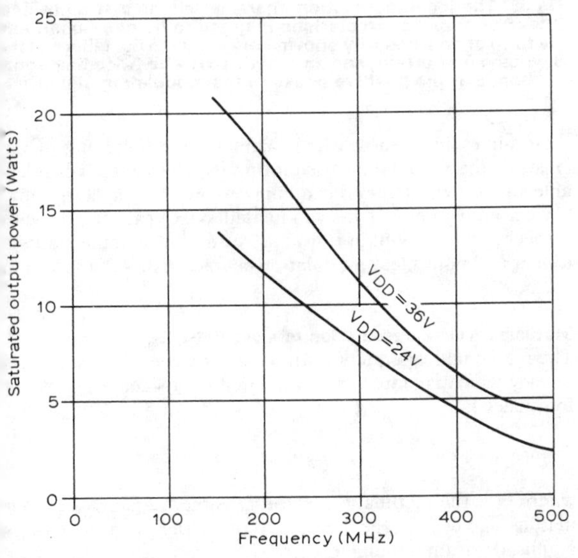

Fig 36. Output (saturated) versus frequency of Siliconix VMP4, assuming that the input and output impedances are matched. Drive power is 1W, drain current is 0·8A

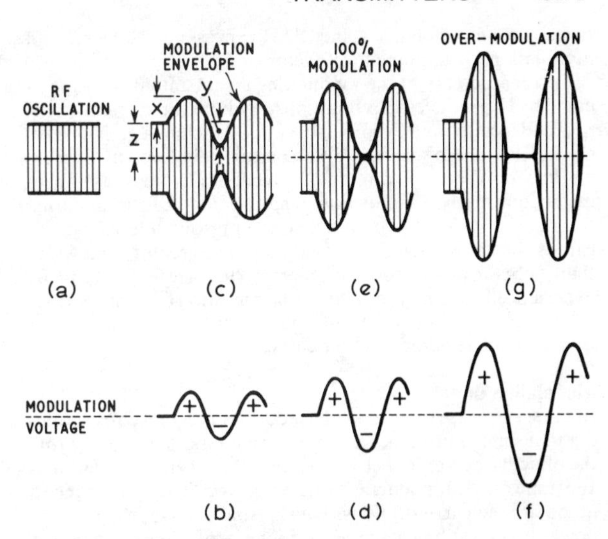

Fig 37. Graphical representation of an amplitude-modulated wave

The valve can sustain substantial over-voltage temporarily without being permanently damaged.

No matter what system is employed, the process of modulation produces additional frequencies above and below that of the carrier wave. Thus, the modulated carrier wave consists of a band of frequencies as distinct from the single frequency of the carrier. The bandwidth depends upon the modulation system and the frequency of the modulating signals.

The bands of frequencies provided above and below the carrier wave frequency by complex modulating signals (ie composed of many different frequencies as in speech or music) are known as the upper and lower sidebands respectively). In the case of amplitude modulation the highest sideband frequency is equal to the sum of the carrier frequency and the highest modulation frequency, similarly the lowest sideband frquency is the difference between the carrier frequency and the highest modulation frequency. Thus the total bandwidth occupied is equal to twice the highest frequency in the modulating signal. For example, if the highest frequency in the modulating signal is 15kHz and the carrier frequency is 1,000kHz, the sideband will extend from 1,015kHz to 985kHz. The total bandwidth occupied is therefore 30kHz.

Modulation depth

The amplitude-modulated wave is shown graphically in Fig 37. Here (a) represents the unmodulated carrier wave of constant amplitude and frequency which when modulated by the audio-frequency wave (b) acquires a varying amplitude as shown at (c). This is the modulated carrier wave, and the two curved lines touching the crests of the modulated carrier wave constitute the modulation envelope. The modulation amplitude is represented by either x or y (which in most cases can be assumed to be equal) and the ratio of this to the amplitude of the unmodulated carrier wave is known as the *modulation depth* or *modulation factor*. This ratio may also be expressed as a percentage. When the amplitude of the modulating signal is increased as at (d), the condition (E) is reached where the negative peak of the modulating signal has reduced the amplitude of the carrier to zero, while the positive peak increases the carrier amplitude to twice the unmodulated value. This represents 100 per cent modulation, or a modulation factor of 1.

Further increase of the modulating signal amplitude as indicated by (f) produces the condition (g) where the carrier wave is reduced to zero for an appreciable period by the negative peaks of the modulating signal. This condition is known as *over-modulation*. The breaking up of the carrier in this way causes distortion and the introduction of harmonics of the modulating frequencies which will be radiated as spurious sidebands; this causes the transmission to occupy a much greater bandwidth than necessary, and considerable interference is likely to be experienced in nearby receivers. The radiation of such spurious sidebands by over-modulation (sometimes known as *splatter* or *spitch*) must be avoided at all costs.

Modulation power

In the special case of a sinusoidal modulating signal corresponding to a single pure tone, it can be proved mathematically that the effective power in such a wave at 100 per cent modulation is 1·5 times the unmodulated carrier power. Thus, in order to modulate the carrier fully with a sinusoidal wave, the average power in it must be increased by 50 per cent. This extra power must be supplied from the modulator. For example, to modulate fully a radio frequency stage operating with a dc power input of 150W, the amount of af power would be 75W.

It must not be assumed, however, that the antenna current of a fully modulated transmission will increase by 50 per cent. The relationship between the modulated and unmodulated antenna current for sine wave modulation is given by

$$I_m = I_0\sqrt{1 + \frac{m^2}{2}}$$

where I_m is the rms value of modulated antenna current, I_0 is the rms value of unmodulated antenna current and m is the modulation factor. Thus, for 100 per cent modulation by a sinusoidal signal

$$I_m = I_0\sqrt{1 + \tfrac{1}{2}}$$

$$= 1{\cdot}226I_0$$

In other words, the antenna current will increase by 22·6 per cent.

The position is somewhat different when the modulating signal consists of the "peaky" waveform of speech. Assuming that the peaks drive the transmitter into full modulation, the 22·6 per cent increase will occur at these peaks, but for most of the remainder of the time the modulation depth is much lower; the increase in antenna current will also be much lower.

The average modulation depth when the peaks fully modulate will be of the order of 30 per cent, and the average

Table 9. Effect of amplitude modulation on antenna current

Depth of modulation (per cent)	Ratio of af power: dc power	Increase in antenna current (per cent)
100	0·5	22·6
90	0·405	18·5
80	0·32	15·1
70	0·245	11·5
60	0·18	8·6
50	0·125	6·0

increase in antenna current as seen on a typical ammeter will then be only a few per cent.

Modulation depth may also be expressed in terms of the af power actually supplied and the unmodulated dc power supplied to the modulated stage; thus

$$m = \sqrt{2A/W}$$

where A is the af power supplied, and W is the dc input power.

Table 9 gives the values, calculated from the expression, for the amount of af power required for various depths of modulation. It will be seen that to produce 70 per cent modulation requires only one-half of the af power required for 100 per cent modulation. The corresponding increases in antenna current are shown in the same table.

Linearity of modulation

Ideally, for all modulation depths up to 100 per cent the difference in the amplitudes of the rf output between the crests and the troughs of the modulation involved should be proportional to the amplitude of the modulating signal, ie the modulation characteristic should be linear.

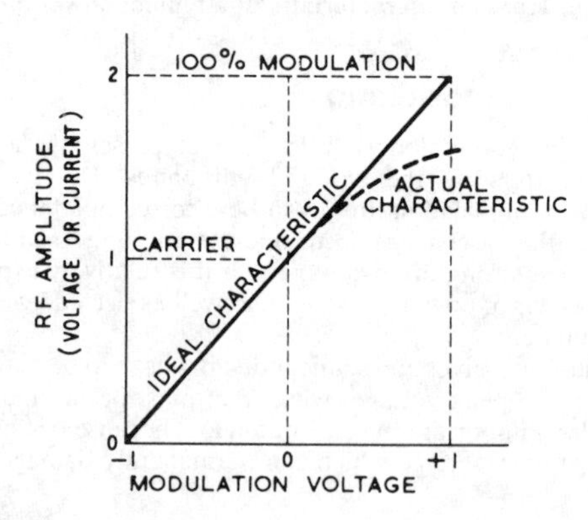

Fig 38. The ideal modulation characteristic is a straight line. Often the actual characteristic is found to be non-linear, and the form of non-linearity shown here is due to the failure of the rf voltage (or current) and amplitude to rise to twice its normal value at the positive peaks of the modulating signal

Non-linearity is most often manifest as a flattening of the crests of the modulation waveform, and this causes considerable distortion. It may be minimized by careful design and correct adjustment of the modulated stage, particularly with respect to the amount of rf grid drive and the antenna loading. Linear and non-linear modulation characteristics are shown in Fig 38.

Mathematical representation of sidebands

The mathematical equation for a carrier wave of constant frequency which is amplitude-modulated by a signal of constant frequency is

$$e = E_0\,(1 + m \sin 2\pi f_m t) \sin 2\pi f_c t$$

where m is the modulation factor, f_m is the frequency of modulating signal, f_c is the frequency of carrier wave and E_0 is amplitude of unmodulated carrier.

This equation may be expanded, giving

$$e = E_0 \sin 2\pi f_c t + m \frac{E_0}{2} \cos 2\pi (f_c - f_m)t$$

$$- m \frac{E_0}{2} \cos 2\pi (f_c + f_m)t$$

Inspection of this expanded form shows that it is made up of three separate terms. The first, $E_0 \sin 2\pi f_c t$, represents original carrier, while $m \frac{E_0}{2} \cos 2\pi (f_c - f_m)t$ and $m \frac{E_0}{2} \cos 2\pi (f_c + f_m)t$ correspond to the lower and upper sideband frequencies respectively which are the result of applying a modulating signal of frequency f_m. The total bandwidth of this amplitude-modulated wave is $(f_c + f_m) - (f_c - f_m)$ or $2f_m$; ie the bandwidth is equal to twice the modulation frequency.

It should be noted from the last equation that the carrier wave is not fundamentally essential to communication since all the intelligence is contained in the sidebands. The carrier wave can therefore be suppressed and need not be transmitted; indeed it is sufficient to transmit only one of the sidebands. This method is often used and is known as single sideband (see later).

Bandwidth of a modulated wave

For the faithful reproduction of sound and video it is necessary to transmit frequencies in the whole range of the audio spectrum (ie approximately 40 to 15,000Hz). The total bandwidth for this purpose would therefore be 30kHz. For a communication system, however, it is the intelligibility and not the fidelity which is of prime importance, and experience has shown that for the intelligible transmission of speech it is sufficient to transmit frequencies up to about 2·5 or 3kHz. Thus, the transmitted bandwidth need not exceed approximately 5kHz. In the overcrowded conditions of the present-day amateur bands it is obviously important to ensure that no transmission occupies a greater bandwidth than is necessary for intelligible communication.

Anode and screen modulation

The screen supply with its dropper resistor R may be connected to anode at point A or to an appropriate tap on the modulation transformer or choke at point B (Fig 39).

In (b) the use of a simple choke is shown, as a means of impressing the modulation on the rf amplifier. In this arrangement to obtain 100 per cent modulation it is necessary to reduce the voltage applied to the modulated amplifier with respect to the modulator. This is done by inserting Rx in the feed line and Cx is provided to bypass the audio round the resistor.

The screen of the amplifier may be connected to the point A or a tapping point B on the choke. This method is generally only used for low-power transmitters.

The modulation transformer has to match the impedance of the amplifier to the specified modulator load impedance, and that of the amplifier may be found by:

$$\text{Amplifier impedance } Z_a = \frac{V_a}{I_a} \times 1{,}000\Omega$$

where V_a is the dc anode voltage and I_a is the dc anode current in milliamps.

Screen modulation

The efficiency of screen modulation is lower than anode or anode-screen methods, the main drawback being that the steady voltage must be reduced so that under maximum excursions it does not exceed the maximum rating for the valve. The modulation depth cannot reach 100 per cent and generally 75 to 80 per cent is the maximum that can be achieved.

The modulation power however is very low and only a few watts are required for maximum modulation.

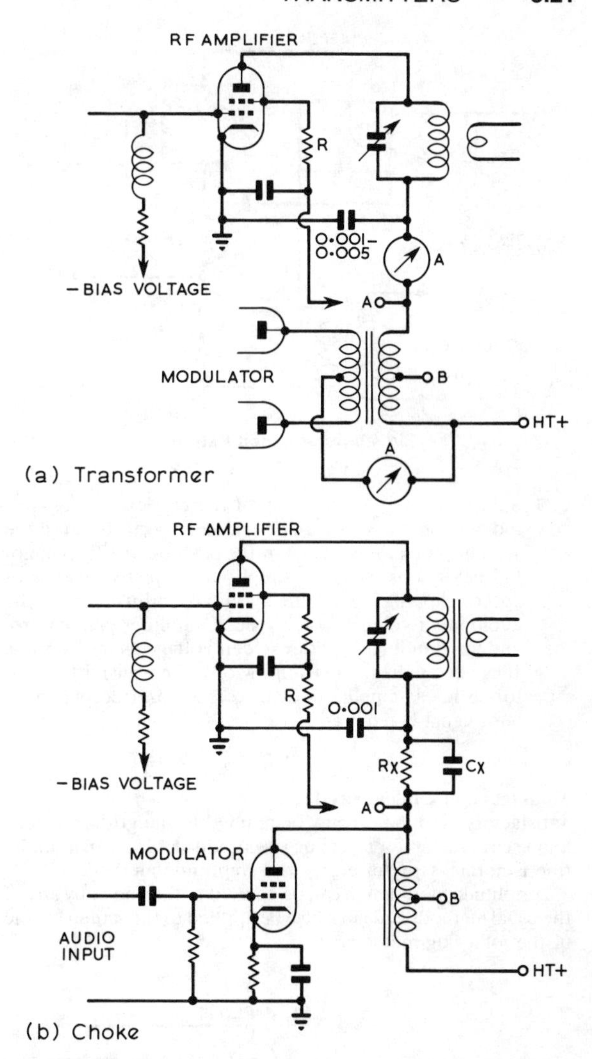

Fig 39. Anode and screen modulation. (a) Transformer method. (b) Choke method

Screen (series gate) modulation

Probably the most satisfactory method of screen modulation—that known as series gate modulation—is both simple and effective. The advantages of this method (Fig 41) are:

- The standing power amplifier anode current can be set to any desired level by the variable resistor VR1 in the cathode of the first section of the double triode series gate valve.
- Over-modulation on positive peaks cannot occur because the audio input voltage applied to the first section of the double triode will cause limiting and thus the voltage applied to the amplifier screen cannot rise too high.

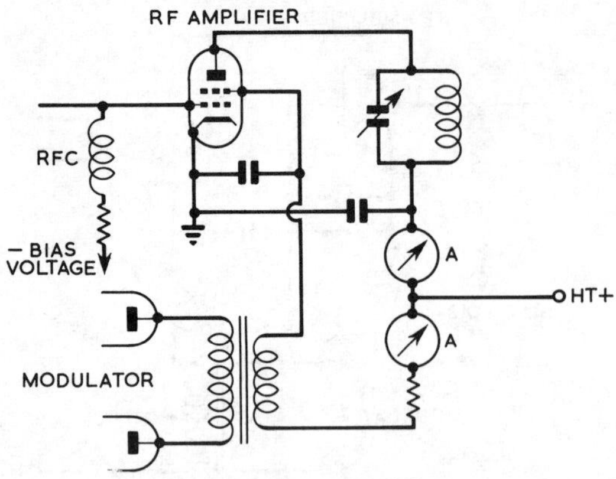

Fig 40. Screen modulation

- Splatter caused by break-up of the carrier due to over-modulation on negative peaks cannot occur because the screen voltage, which is set by the position of VR1, cannot fall below this value. A simple and effective means of speech clipping is available by suitable adjustment of the audio input voltage by the speech amplifier gain control and the standing amplifier screen voltage as set by VR1.
- It can be applied to existing cw or nbfm transmitters and to ssb linear amplifiers, with carrier inserted, when an a.m. signal is required.

Modulation of double tetrodes

Satisfactory modulation may be applied to the grid, screen or anode circuits, but for most purposes anode and screen modulation is normally preferred for the amplitude method.

Amplitude modulation can be applied to the anode by any of the usual methods and must also be applied to the screen by one of the following methods:

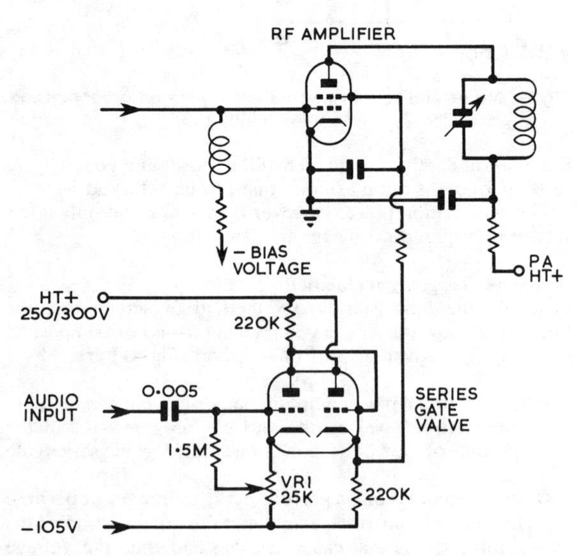

Fig 41. Series-gate modulation

1. Series resistor from the modulated anode voltage.
2. Separate winding on the modulation transformer, with series resistor to the anode ht voltage as shown in Fig 42(a). The screen voltage dropping resistor must be bypassed to audio frequencies on the supply.
3. A tapped modulation transformer may be used, in which case the screen dropper which must be connected in series with the tap must be bypassed to audio frequencies as shown in Fig 42(b).
4. In Fig 42(c) a resistive potential divider is placed across a standard modulation transformer, and the values of the upper and lower resistor must be chosen to provide the proper screen voltage.

It should be remembered that for optimum operation the screen voltage is critical, and can never remain reasonably constant when supplied from a series resistor, since any change in anode current results in a change in screen current.

Practical series gate modulator for a QQV06-40A power amplifier

This series gate modulator for a QQV06-40A double tetrode power amplifier is comprised of two valves only and is shown in Fig 43. V1a is a straightforward af voltage amplifier feeding V1b; this stage operating as a dc control valve and af voltage amplifier directly coupled to V2 which acts as a cathode follower feeding the screen of the power amplifier.

The only critical components in the modulator are C4 and R5 (1·5MΩ) which determine the period that the increased screen voltage is retained once the af signal has disappeared and this is important with speech signals. The optimum values are those given in Fig 43. R9 must be located immediately adjacent to pin 3 of the holder for the QQV06-40A.

The switch in the cathode return of V1b permits the screen voltage of the power amplifier to rise to the maximum and is used for setting up or for cw operation. The method of operation is to set S1 to cw and tune the amplifier in the normal way. Set S1 to phone and adjust VR2 to give approximately a fifth of the maximum rf output obtained in the cw position. Apply the af signal and set the gain control VR1 so that the amplifier anode current indicates 0·7 of the full cw anode current and this will ensure that the amplifier is fully modulated.

Transistor amplitude modulation

There are two common methods of applying amplitude modulation to rf power transistors—transformer coupled modulation and series modulation.

Using transformer coupled modulation, the peak supply voltage applied to the power amplifier stage will reach twice the nominal voltage at 100 per cent modulation. Hence for a typical 12V supply rail, devices rated for use at 24 to 28V should be used. The peak envelope power will be four times the carrier power and devices must be selected capable of delivering the full peak power level. For a 10W carrier power a.m. transmitter operating from a 12V rail, a 28V 40W output device will be required. Modulation should be applied over at least two stages and preferably three. 28V devices will be required for all modulated stages. Reduced modulation may be applied to the earlier stages. There is also an advantage in providing a wave-shaping circuit across the secondary of the modulation transformer so that negative half-cycles are reduced in level (Fig 44).

Series modulation uses a series transistor in the supply to the power amplifier stages. For a 12V 10W carrier power a.m. transmitter, the pa transistor should be rated for 40W output at

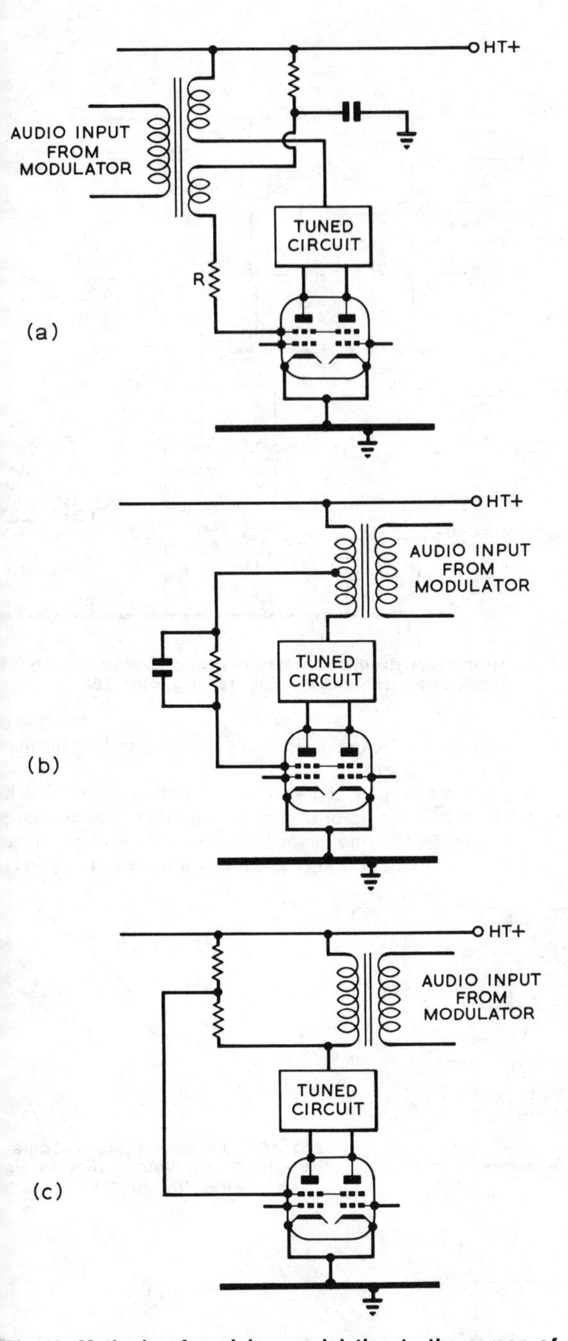

Fig 42. Methods of applying modulation to the screen of a double tetrode

12V, and under carrier only conditions would operate with approximately 6V on the collector.

An alternative method of applying a.m. is to use low-level modulation and linear amplifiers. The linearity requirement is not as severe as for ssb operation and forward biasing can often be dispensed with. Careful attention to stability is important whichever method is used.

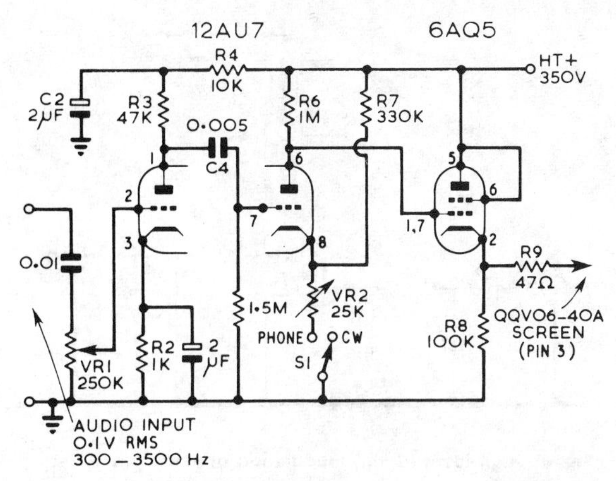

Fig 43. Circuit of a series-gate modulator for a QQV06–40A valve

Power fet modulation

These devices, with their higher input impedances, function rather more like valves than the bipolar types. They may be modulated by either high-level (drain, equivalent to the anode method) or low-level (gate, equivalent to the grid method) modulation.

Modulation may be applied to the drain circuit by a conventional transformer or by a transistor circuit which produces the same result. A typical circuit is shown in Fig 45. An alternative arrangement is shown in Fig 46 in which the modulation is impressed on the drain by use of a simple integrated circuit and semiconductors in place of the transformer and audio power stages. Substantially better linearity can be obtained with these devices than can be achieved by bipolar transistors.

This method does however require considerable audio power and a relatively large transformer so that the overall efficiency of the rf amplifier and modulator is relatively low in respect of modulated output compared with total dc input power.

In Fig 47 is shown a low-level (gate) modulation system which, when feedback is applied, will provide good linearity. Its spectral output is comparable with that produced by high-level (drain) modulation.

As a method of modulation it may well rival frequency modulation for simplicity; it does not require a chain of frequency multipliers.

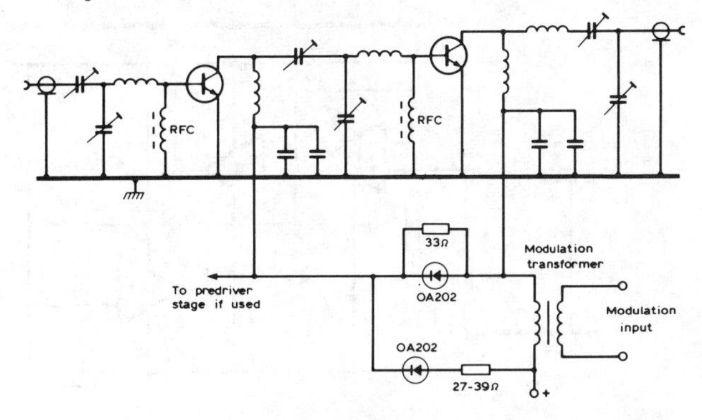

Fig 44. Typical amplitude modulation applied to both driver and output stages of bipolar transistors

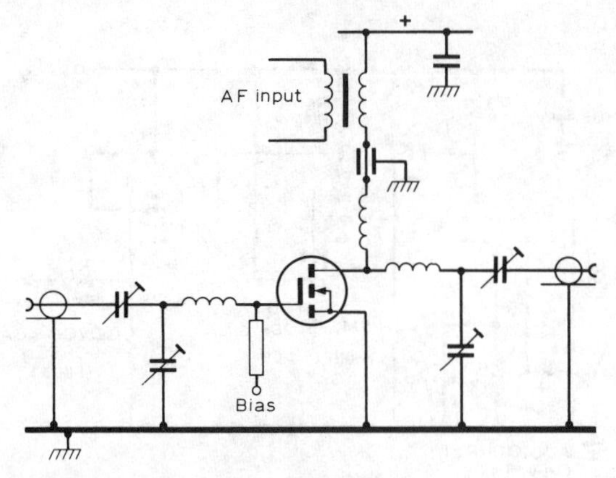

Fig 45. High-level (drain) modulation of vmos power fet

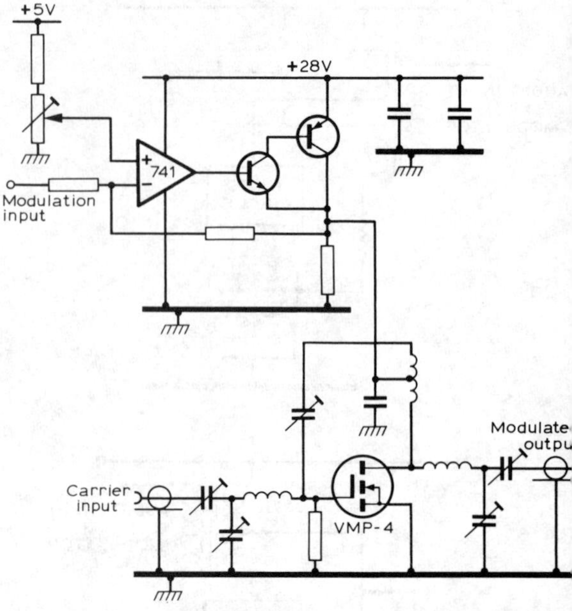

Fig 46. High-level (drain) modulation of vmos power fet without transformer (*Electronic Enginerring* June 1978)

Frequency and phase modulation

Although there are an increasing number of operators using one form or other of frequency modulation or, more properly, narrow-band fm, it is apparent that many have little knowledge of the processes involved.

For most amateur purposes there is little doubt that the indirect or phase method is to be preferred because, when properly adjusted, it is much less likely to produce wide deviation.

The advantages of this method of modulation compared with a.m. may be summarized:

(a) Elimination of the high-power modulator and the consequent cost saving in equipment and running cost, together with smaller size and reduced weight. These latter points are of considerable importance for portable or mobile operation.

(b) The modulating system can be used at any power level.

(c) The driver power for the power amplifier does not have to cater for the varying load presented to the driver stage by the amplifier during the modulation cycle. The power

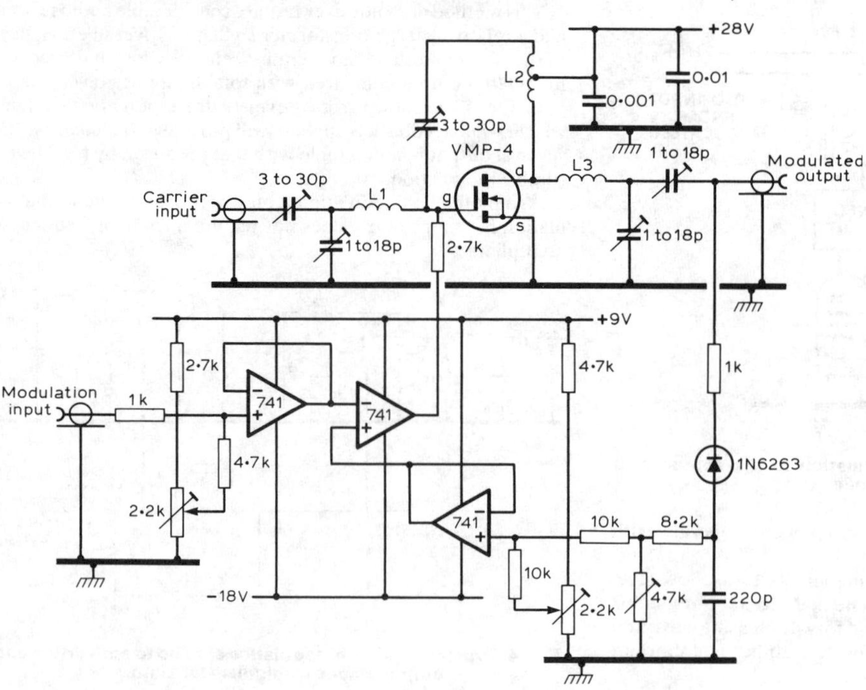

Fig 47. Low-level (gate) modulation of vmos power fet (*Electronic Engineering* June 1978)

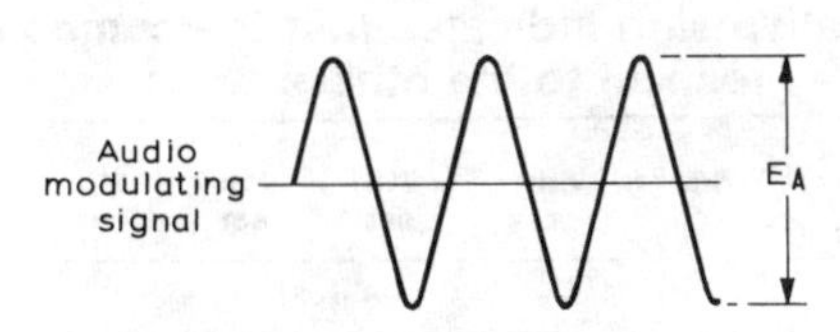

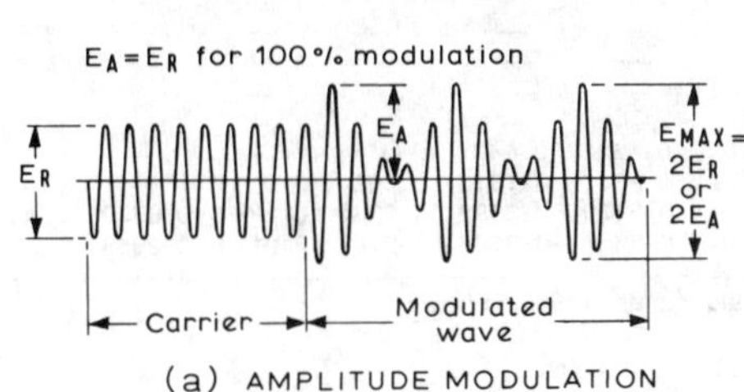

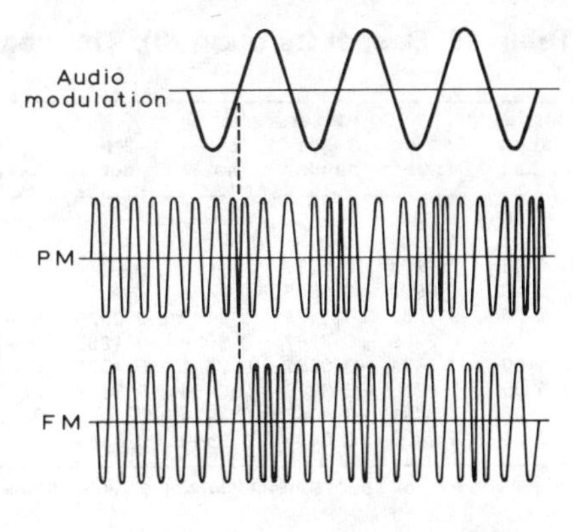

Fig 48. Amplitude modulation (a) and angular modulation (b) of an rf carrier by the same audio signal

amplifier may be operated in AB1 or AB2 with only a small reduction in efficiency, under which conditions the power output requirements of the driver can be still further reduced and lower harmonic powers produced.

(d) The peak voltage in the pa output circuit does not vary with modulation, thus allowing the use of smaller and lower-rated components, especially transistors.
(e) The output power level may be changed without any corresponding changes to the modulating system.
(f) The addition of frequency modulators for higher-frequency bands can be made without difficulty, it is only necessary to reduce the deviation.
(g) Television and broad interference is markedly reduced since frequency modulation is not demodulated by the usual rectification method. Consequently interference to a.m. receivers, both sound and television, tape recorders, record players and deaf aids is very much reduced and, in many cases, eliminated.

Deviation

Most of us understand the process involved when an a.m. signal is produced, but frequency modulation and more particularly phase modulation are quite different. These may be shown graphically as in Fig 48.

If the modulating signal is, say, 1kHz, two sidebands, one at carrier frequency minus 1kHz (lower sideband, lsb) and the other at a carrier frequency plus 1kHz (upper sideband, usb) are produced. The total power in the sidebands is half the carrier power for 100 per cent modulation, as shown in Fig 49.

When a frequency modulated signal is produced with 1kHz modulating frequency, sidebands are produced at 1kHz intervals to infinity (Fig 50).

However, beyond a certain point the amount of power contained in higher-order sidebands is insignificant. The number of significant sidebands and the amount of power transmitted in them can be determined using Bessel functions. A Bessel function chart is given in Table 10 and illustrated in Fig 51.

There are several points to note with reference to Fig 50:

(a) The carrier power diminishes during modulation.
(b) The energy taken from the carrier goes into the sidebands—greater amplitude of modulating signal produces more energy in the sidebands.
(c) One or more sidebands can contain more power than the carrier.

A small-amplitude audio modulating signal of frequency 1kHz may produce sidebands as shown in Fig 52(a). If the amplitude is increased, the frequency spectrum of the signal may change to that shown in Fig 52(b) which has greater deviation than that in Fig 52(a).

A signal modulated with a 1kHz tone with 10 significant sidebands requires a total bandwidth of 20kHz, while a 100Hz tone giving rise to 10 significant sidebands requires a total bandwidth of 2kHz.

The bandwidth required for a signal therefore depends on:

(i) The amplitude of the modulating signal.
(ii) The frequency of this signal.

The modulation index of a frequency modulated signal is defined as:

$$\text{Modulation index} = \frac{\text{Deviation of fm carrier}}{\text{Audio frequency producing this deviation}}$$

For a maximum carrier shift of (±) 15kHz and a highest modulating frequency of 3kHz, the modulation index = 15 ÷ 3 = 5.

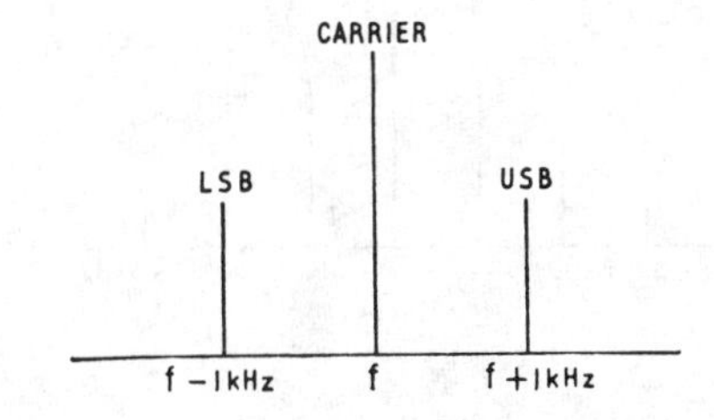

Fig 49. A.M. signal with 1kHz modulation

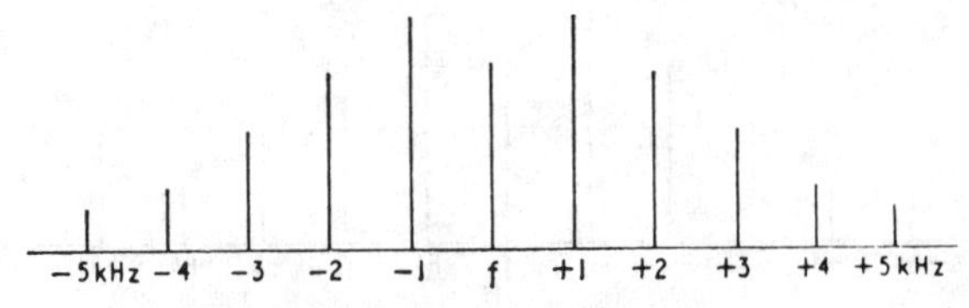

Fig 50. FM signal with 1kHz modulation

Table 10. Bessel function (2). The negative sign indicates that the component is 180° out of phase with respect to the others

Modulation Index	Carrier value	1st set of sidebands	2nd set	3rd set	4th set	5th set	6th set	7th set	8th set	9th set	10th set	11th set	12th set	13th set	14th set
0·00	1·000	—	—	—	—	—	—	—	—	—	—	—	—	—	—
0·01	1·000	0·005	—	—	—	—	—	—	—	—	—	—	—	—	—
0·05	0·9994	0·025	—	—	—	—	—	—	—	—	—	—	—	—	—
0·20	0·9900	0·0995	—	—	—	—	—	—	—	—	—	—	—	—	—
1·00	0·7652	0·4401	0·1149	0·0020	—	—	—	—	—	—	—	—	—	—	—
2·00	0·2239	0·5767	0·3528	0·1289	0·0341	—	—	—	—	—	—	—	—	—	—
4·00	−0·3971	−0·0661	0·3641	0·4302	0·2811	0·1321	0·0491	0·0152	—	—	—	—	—	—	—
5·00	−0·1776	−0·3276	0·0466	0·3648	0·3912	0·2611	0·1310	0·0534	0·0184	—	—	—	—	—	—
7·00	0·3001	−0·0047	−0·3014	−0·1676	0·1578	0·3479	0·3392	0·2336	0·1280	0·0589	0·2035	—	—	—	—
10·00	−0·2459	0·0435	0·2546	0·0584	−0·2196	−0·2341	−0·0145	0·2167	0·3179	0·2919	0·2075	0·1231	0·0634	0·0290	0·0120

Note: Where blank spaces are indicated the values of the sidebands are insignificant.

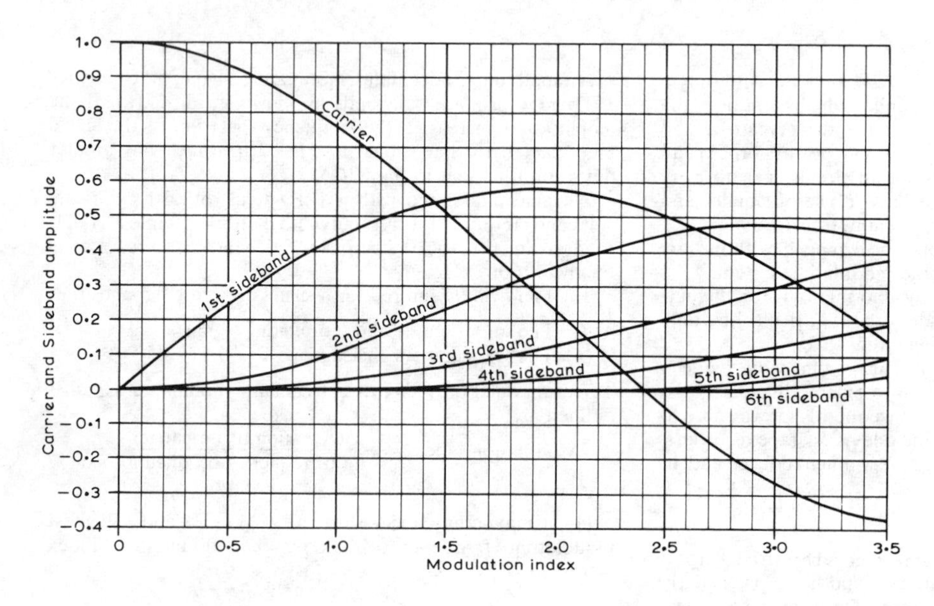

Fig 51. Bessel curves showing variation in carrier and sideband amplitude with modulation index

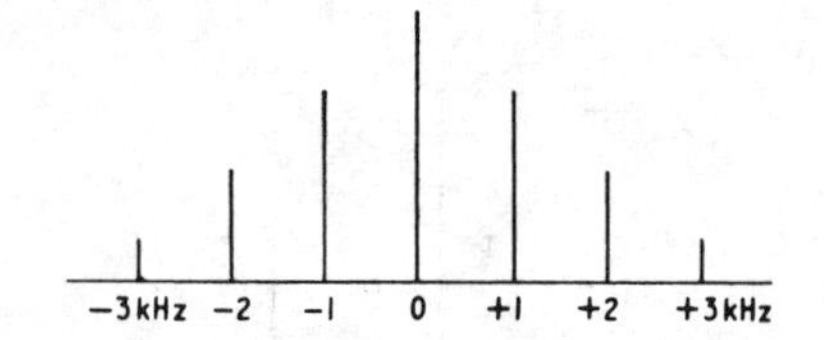

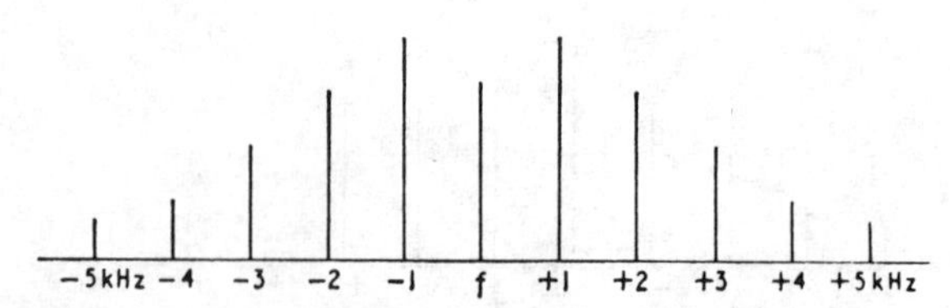

Fig 52. (a) Small deviation. (b) Large deviation

The relative amplitudes of the sideband sets are obtained from the Bessel functions.

Note that although the carrier is never shifted beyond (±) 15kHz, significant sidebands are produced beyond this limit Hence the seemingly wide spacing between fm channels.

Note also that for a modulation index less than 0·4, only two significant sidebands are produced. A modulation index of 0·4 with an upper audio limit of 3kHz corresponds to a carrier deviation of (±) 1·2kHz (Fig 51).

Phase modulation

Consider an audio signal modulating a carrier such that the phase of the carrier is changed corresponding to change in the amplitude of the modulating signal. This is shown in Fig 55 relative to a reference carrier whose phase is constant. An alternative representative in terms of rotating phasors is shown in Fig 56, where OB is the reference carrier and OA is the phase-modulated signal.

Actually, OA is rotating at angular frequency ω, while the phase varies, relatively, very slowly. Consider now the change

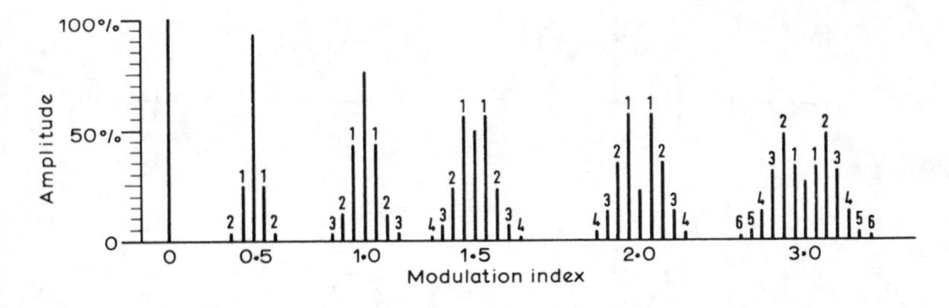

ig 53. Relative carrier and sideband evels for various modulation indices. his diagram clearly illustrates the ideband increase for increasing values f modulation index. It is for this reason hat the following should be observed: (a) laximum deviation 2·5kHz (3kHz generally acceptable). (b) Maximum effective nodulating frequency should be limited o 4kHz and the audio frequency input to he frequency modulator at frequencies bove 4kHz should be attenuated by 26dB 20 times down) below the maximum input t the lower frequencies (400–1,000Hz). c) Carrier frequency should be not less than 10kHz within the band edges

n vector OA in going from (i) to (ii) and (iv) to (v). In the first ase OA must speed up to go from position (1) to position (2), hile in the second case OA must slow down to go from osition (1) to position (3). This speeding up corresponds to an ncrease in frequency of the carrier represented by OA and the lowing down corresponds to a decrease in carrier frequency.

Each time the carrier phasor wobbles back and forth to reach he new phase positions dictated by the audio modulation, the requency also changes in order to have the phasors reach the ew positions. Note, however, that over the whole audio cycle he average frequency of the carrier represented by OA is onstant.

In producing phase modulation of the carrier we have in fact roduced indirect fm. What we are doing is adding sufficient hange, either positive or negative, to a fixed frequency to ermit the carrier to reach the desired phase position. In pure m the carrier frequency itself is directly affected and shifted in esponse to the modulating voltage.

Factors affecting indirect fm

The amount of indirect fm produced depends on the extent of phase shift and the frequency of the modulating audio signal. The extent of indirect fm produced varies directly with both the frequency and maximum phase shift of the carrier.

In direct fm the value of the carrier itself swings between its maximum limits. The carrier is shifted directly by the modulation. In indirect fm (from pm) the carrier is not actually shifted by the modulation. Rather, the effect of the phase shifts is to either add to or subtract frequency variations from a fixed carrier.

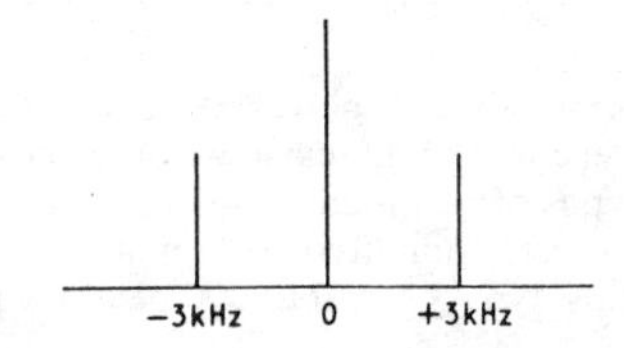

Fig 54. Small modulation index

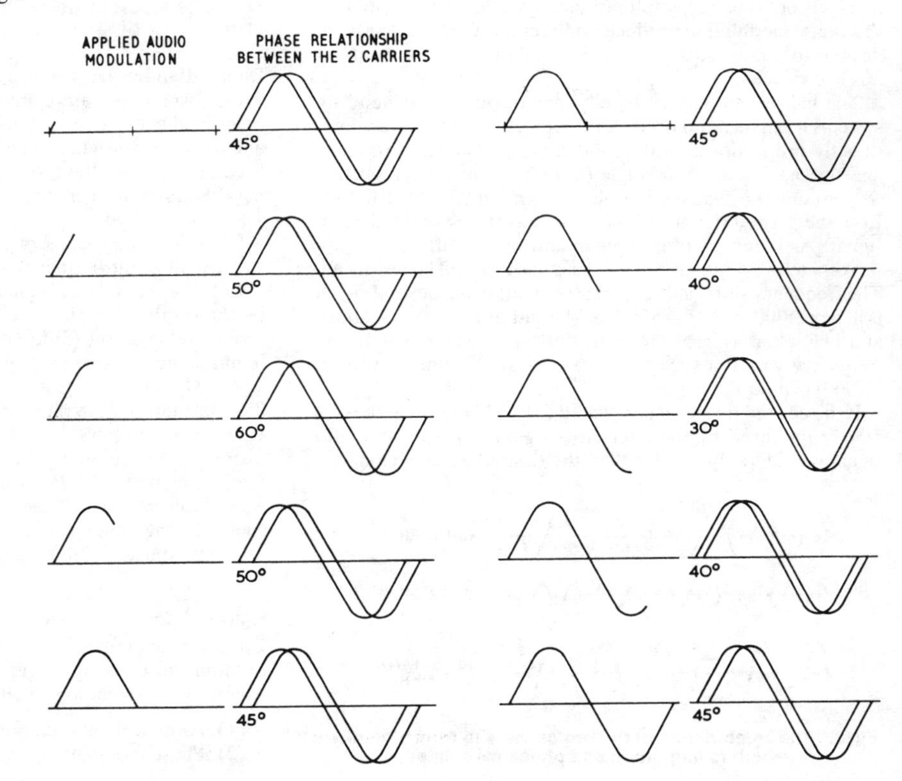

Fig 55. A simplified illustration of phase modulation

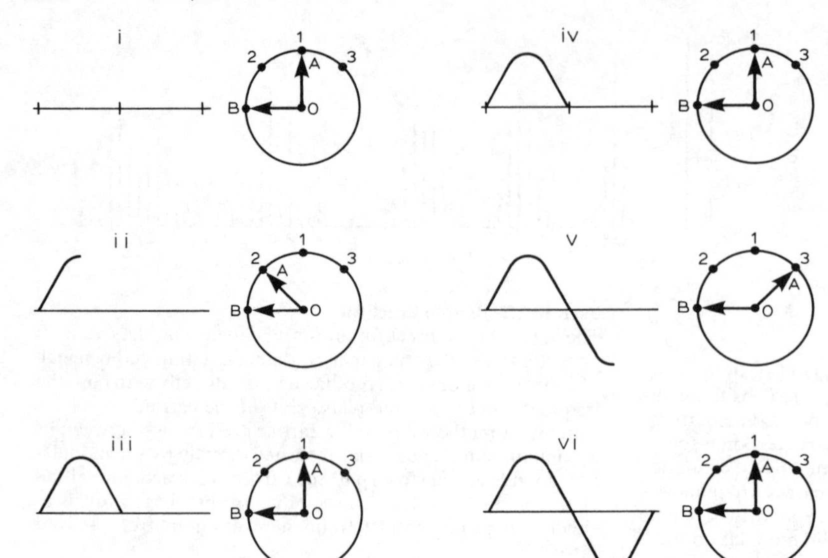

Fig 56. An alternative representation of Fig 55

Interference

Consider two carrier waves slightly different in amplitude and frequency. The resultant of these two waves is shown in Fig 57. There are two types of variation in this signal as compared to carrier 1. They are: (1) amplitude, (2) phase.

In a.m. systems type (1) produces beat frequencies (eg 10kHz whistle).

In fm systems type (1) is eliminated by limiters in the receiver, but type (2) is still present at the detector. Note that this phase modulation produces indirect fm. With a 2:1 ratio of desired to unwanted signals, a maximum phase shift of about 30° is produced.

The indirect fm cannot be eliminated, but in wideband fm systems it can be minimized. As noted before, the indirect fm is directly proportional to the modulation frequency (in hertz) and the maximum phase angle (in radians) of carrier shift.

Now suppose that the interfering signal differs by 1,000Hz from the desired signal and is only half as strong as the desired signal. As noted before, a maximum phase shift of 30° (approximately 0·5 radians) in the desired signal will be produced. The frequency shift (indirect fm produced) in the desired signal is in fact 1,000 × 0·5 or 500 Hz. The shift is periodically above and below the average frequency of the stronger signal. The frequency variations shift at a rate of 1,000 times a second (1,000Hz mod signal).

If the desired fm signal is deviated to (±) 15kHz then the (±) 500Hz produced by the interfering signal produces an audio signal considerably smaller than the desired audio signal.

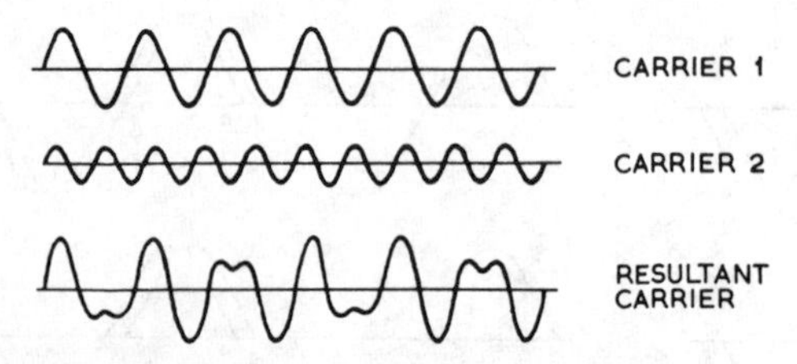

Fig 57. The combination of the two carriers to form a resultant which is amplitude and phase modulated

For a desired to undesired signal ratio of 10:1 this effect is even more marked. Thus the wideband fm completely swamps the small indirect fm developed from the interference. Herein lies the interference reduction power of fm.

Note that if the two signals are of the same frequency no interfering indirect fm is produced, and the greater the frequency separation of the two signals the greater the amount of interference produced. However, the amplitude will be reduced by the bandpass characteristics of the receiver.

Domination by the stronger signal

When two signals are comparable in amplitude, the moment one signal becomes even a trifle stronger the response changes and the stronger signal assumes noticeable control. The process is complete when the ratio reaches the 2-1 point. (For a comparable amount of interference in an a.m. system, a ratio of 100:1 is required.)

Consider two signals of nearly equal amplitude and only slightly different frequency (Fig 58).

Let 1 be the stronger signal, 2 be the interfering signal and R be the resultant carrier due to these two signals. As 2 rotates around relative to 1 (different in frequency), R changes greatly in phase but its average frequency is still that of 1, the stronger signal. Hence by bringing the two signals close in amplitude we have produced more phase modulation in the resultant phasor R, but R still follows signal 1, so we hear signal 1 but with some distortion produced by the indirect fm caused by signal 2 interacting with 1. If 2 was stronger than 1, then the phasor R would follow signal 2, hence the sharp transition from one signal to the other and this is why the predominant signal assumes control in fm systems.

Noise

Consider random noise in the receiver. Interactions between random noise voltages and the carrier, and interactions between the random noise voltages, produce:

(1) Amplitude modulation of the carrier.
(2) Phase modulation (and thus indirect fm) of the carrier.

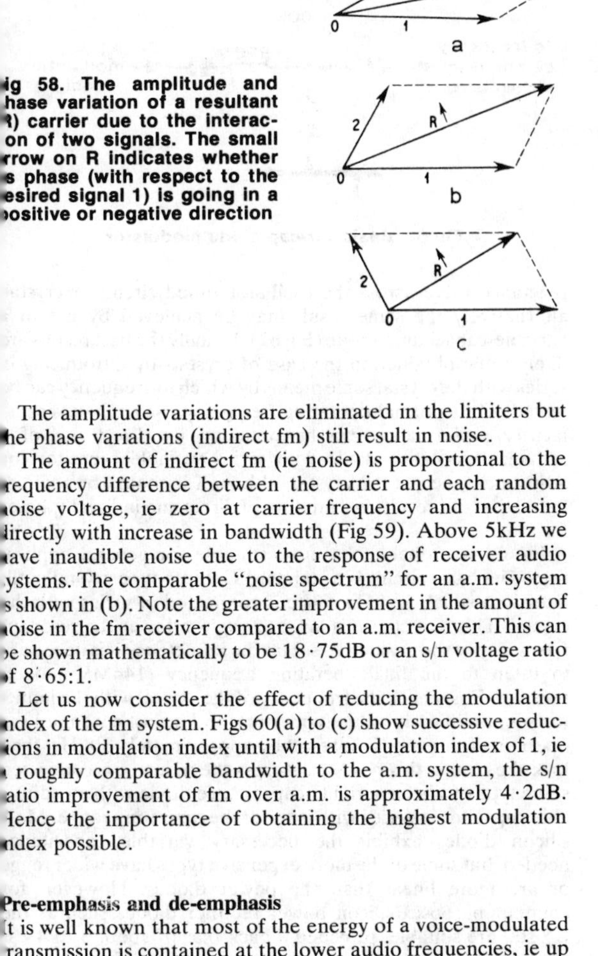

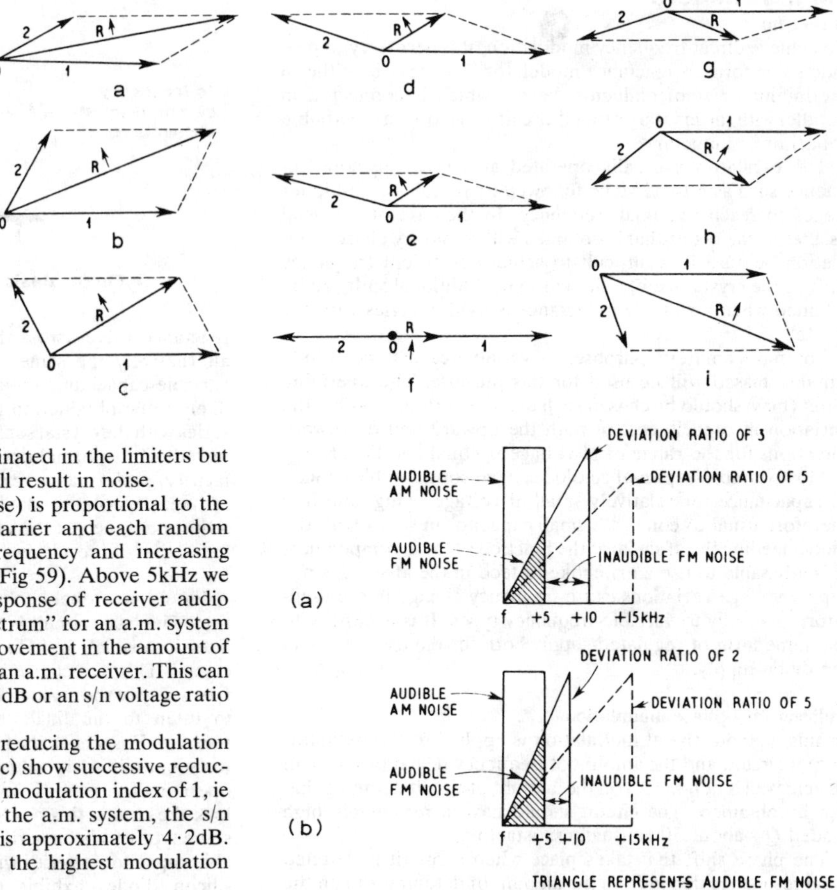

ig 58. The amplitude and hase variation of a resultant R) carrier due to the interac- on of two signals. The small rrow on R indicates whether s phase (with respect to the esired signal 1) is going in a ositive or negative direction

Fig 60. Further comparisons between the noise in a.m. and fm systems with various fm deviation ratios

The amplitude variations are eliminated in the limiters but he phase variations (indirect fm) still result in noise.

The amount of indirect fm (ie noise) is proportional to the requency difference between the carrier and each random oise voltage, ie zero at carrier frequency and increasing irectly with increase in bandwidth (Fig 59). Above 5kHz we ave inaudible noise due to the response of receiver audio ystems. The comparable "noise spectrum" for an a.m. system s shown in (b). Note the greater improvement in the amount of oise in the fm receiver compared to an a.m. receiver. This can e shown mathematically to be 18·75dB or an s/n voltage ratio f 8·65:1.

Let us now consider the effect of reducing the modulation ndex of the fm system. Figs 60(a) to (c) show successive reduc- ions in modulation index until with a modulation index of 1, ie roughly comparable bandwidth to the a.m. system, the s/n atio improvement of fm over a.m. is approximately 4·2dB. Hence the importance of obtaining the highest modulation ndex possible.

Pre-emphasis and de-emphasis

It is well known that most of the energy of a voice-modulated ransmission is contained at the lower audio frequencies, ie up o 3kHz. In addition, it has further been brought to light that the greatest irritating noise generated is located from 3kHz up. To reduce the effect of this noise, a pre-emphasis network is nserted in the audio section of the transmitter. Its purpose is to boost the frequencies above 1kHz.

At the receiver there is a de-emphasis network to reduce frequencies above 1kHz to their original values. The overall effect is a return of the signal to its proper relative proportions, but with a considerable reduction in noise.

Another beneficial effect of de-emphasis is concerned with the noise produced by another signal or the ever-present ran- dom noise.

As previously noted, the greater the difference between the carrier frequency and the interference, the greater the indirect fm produced. By the use of the de-emphasis network the trian- gular response of Fig 60 is modified to the trapezium of Fig 61. The de-emphasis action, by reducing the level of all frequencies above 1kHz, slices off a considerable portion of the noise.

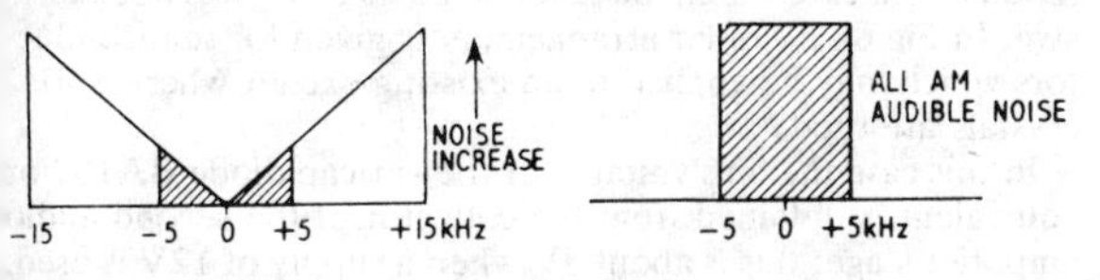

Fig 59. (a) Noise in fm system. (b) Noise in a.m. system

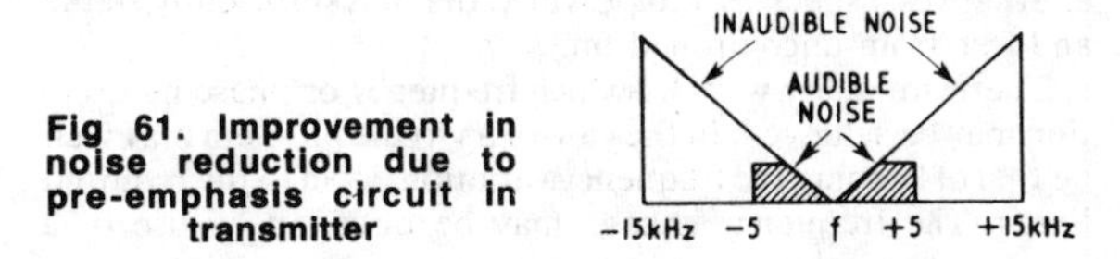

Fig 61. Improvement in noise reduction due to pre-emphasis circuit in transmitter

FM transmitters

Direct fm

To achieve direct frequency modulation, it is necessary to provide some form of reactance modulator. This may be either a thermionic or semiconductor device, which is connected in parallel with the crystal or tuned circuit so as to act as a variable capacitor or inductance.

The oscillator is usually operated at a relatively low frequency such as 6 to 12MHz, followed by frequency multiplier stages to reach the final frequency. In the case of a crystal oscillator, the result that is obtained will be mostly phase modulation because it is difficult to achieve sufficient frequency shift of the crystal itself, although some additional shift can be attained when a suitable inductance is used in series with the crystal.

For most amateur purposes, a variable-capacitance diode suitably biased will be used for this purpose. The operating point (bias) should be chosen such that as nearly as possible the variation in capacitance, in both the upward and downward directions for the range of af voltage is equal and linear.

Most variable-capacitance diodes have considerable change of capacitance for relatively small af voltage swing, and it is therefore usual to connect a small capacitor in series with the diode, feeding the af signal at the junction of these components. It is advisable to use an rf choke to feed in the af signal since supply voltage variations cause frequency change in the oscillator, especially to variable-frequency types. It is necessary to use some form of regulated supply both for the oscillator and the diode supply.

Indirect fm—phase modulation

In this method, the af modulation is applied to the oscillator output circuit, and the amount of frequency deviation that can be achieved is dependent on the amount of circuit detuning that can be obtained. The circuit should have a reasonably high loaded *Q*—about 50 is usually satisfactory.

The phase shift that takes place when a circuit is detuned from resonance depends on the amount of detuning and on the *Q* of the circuit. The higher the *Q*, the smaller the amount of detuning needed to obtain a given number of degrees of phase shift. In this type of modulation, since the actual frequency deviation increases with the af modulation, it is necessary to cut off frequencies above 3,000Hz before modulation, otherwise unnecessary sidebands will be generated.

Methods of obtaining modulation

In both direct and indirect (phase) frequency modulation it is necessary for the modulated stage to be followed by a suitable frequency multiplication. Crystals of 6, 8 or 12MHz for use on a final frequency of 144 and 432MHz will need frequency multiplication of 24, 18, 12, and 72, 54, 36 times respectively. A usually accepted frequency deviation of 3kHz will require a relatively small frequency change at the control oscillator frequency. For operation at 70MHz the control oscillator frequency must be in the region of 5·85MHz, to fulfil the minimum of 12 times frequency multiplication. Although this assumes that crystal control is to be used there is of course no reason why vxo or vfo should not be used as more flexible alternatives, especially vxo provided that it is sufficiently stable and free from uncontrolled fm.

There are many ways by which frequency or phase modulation may be achieved. In the case of a vfo the problem may well be that of keeping the frequency variation down to the required limits. The frequency change may be obtained by use of a

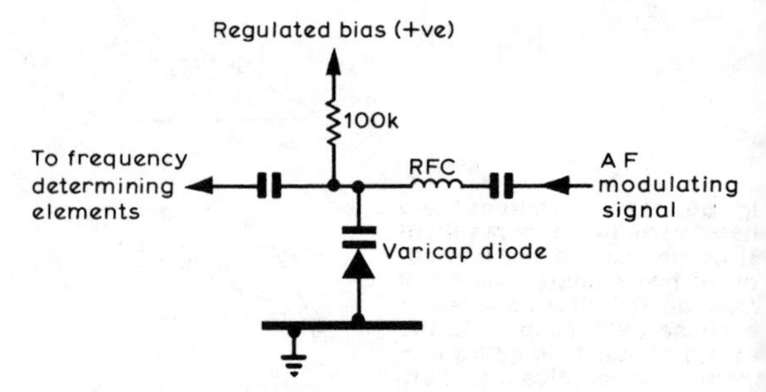

Fig 62. Basic varicap diode modulator

reactance valve across the oscillator tuned circuit or crystal alternatively the same result may be achieved by use of a variable-capacitance diode (Fig 62). Usually the best results are likely to be obtained in the case of crystals by introducing in series with the crystal some means by which its frequency can be pulled off its normal operating frequency. Nevertheless satisfactory performance can be obtained by direct use of a variable-capacitance diode with series variable capacitor for adjustment, across the crystal, although it should be remembered that this results in a mixture of direct and indirect (phase) fm.

Fig 63 is probably the most suitable for general application. The basic circuit is a standard Colpitts-type crystal oscillator into which an inductance is connected in series with the crystal. This inductance is large enough to lower the resonant frequency of the crystal. To set up the inductance it is necessary to listen to the final operating frequency (144MHz) on a receiver. First check the frequency of the crystal with the inductor set at minimum value (core out), and adjust core until the operating frequency is lowered by approximately 30kHz, then lock the core in this position. Across the inductor is connected some type of silicon variable-capacitance diode with an adjustable capacitor in series with it to set the operating range. Most silicon diodes exhibit the necessary variable capacitance needed, but some of the more expensive types have wider range or are more linear than the power diodes. However, for amateur purposes silicon power rectifier diodes such as the BY100 are suitable, provided a back bias of about 3 to 4V is applied. With this bias a signal of around 2V peak to peak will produce a suitable capacitance change which is sufficiently linear for the application. A more satisfactory result can be obtained using tuning diodes such as BA110 etc.

An audio amplifier to provide a signal of only 2V peak to peak can be quite simple (in Fig 63 a single stage with a crystal microphone is sufficient). A dc test should be made in order to check that the frequency change of $2\frac{1}{2}$kHz is obtained for (±) 1V around the set diode bias. It may be preferable to cover a wider range, say, from +2V to −2V in steps of 0·5V, the results being plotted. If the required linearity over the (±) 1V range is not achieved it may be necessary to select a different bias point for the diode. The series capacitor should be adjusted to give the (±)2·5kHz change for about (±) 1V. As with all types of modulation, care should be taken to ensure that it is not excessive. In Fig 64 a similar arrangement is given for semiconductors which may be applied to an existing exciter where 8MHz crystals are used.

In this case the bias voltage for the varicap diode BA102 or equivalent is obtained from the collector of the second audio amplifier stage; this is about 8V when a supply of 12V is used. The resistor R (10kΩ) and capacitor (0·1μF) provide a suitable

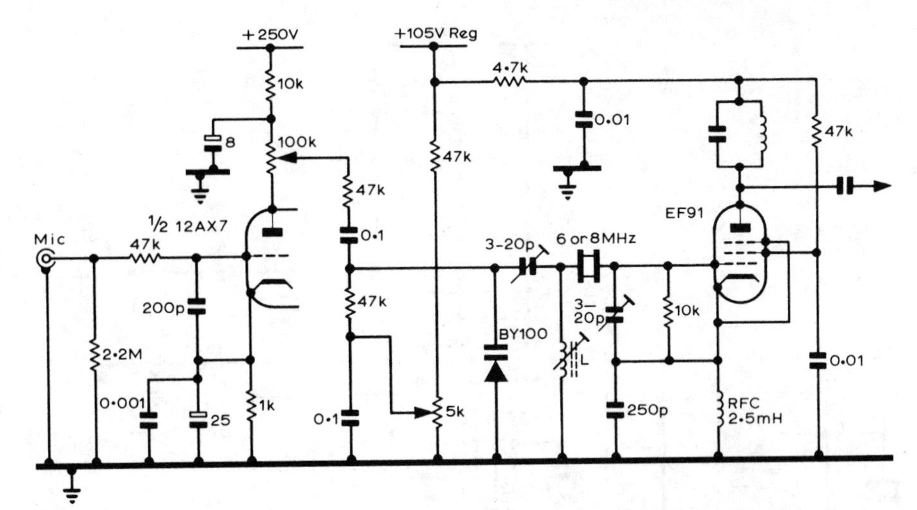

Fig 63. Modified Colpitts-type oscillator with an inductance in series with the crystal

reduction of the higher audio frequencies. The oscillator drive level can be adjusted by the trimmer in series with the oscillator input. A simple audio level indicator is included at the output of the audio amplifier. This, once set, can be used to monitor the audio input to the varicap diode modulator.

Phase modulators

The most common method of producing narrow-band frequency modulation (nbfm) is by phase shift of a tuned circuit after the frequency-determining components. It is important that the frequency response of the audio amplifier should be adjusted to provide suitable attenuation of the higher audio frequencies; this should be carried out as described in a later section describing speech amplifiers for fm. The amount of phase shift that can be obtained will be dependent on the Q of the circuit concerned and for most purposes a sufficiently good circuit can be provided using normally available components. Generally it is necessary to have at least eight times multiplication following the modulator to obtain suitable deviation. In Fig 65 is given what may be described as the standard form of valve phase modulator and in this a double triode such as a 12AT7 is used. The first section operates as the crystal oscillator which is RC coupled to the second section operating as the modulator. The tuned circuit is normally tuned to the same frequency as the oscillator and the output is relatively low, but sufficient to drive a pentode frequency multiplier.

A higher output is obtainable from the circuit of Fig 66. In this case two pentodes are used in place of the triodes. Any high mutual conductance types are suitable for this application, such as EF91, 6BH6, EF183, E180F, or 6AK5.

In Fig 67 two typical phase modulators are shown, together with the crystal oscillator and buffer amplifier or frequency multiplier stages. In these circuits two varicap diodes are used to provide the modulation, each acting on a separate inductor. The bias potential of these diodes is fixed by a potential divider with the actual voltage stabilized by a zener diode. Note that the two inductors are separately screened. In Figs 68 and 69 are shown simple circuits for the introduction of modulation between an rf input (crystal or vfo) and the succeeding stage. Either of these may be applied to an existing exciter.

Fig 70 illustrates a complete phase modulator unit including the speech amplifier and Pierce crystal oscillator. The use of this particular oscillator allows the use of a 12MHz vfo and details of such a unit are given later. Extensive tests and adjustments have shown that this unit will give a symmetrical output, with virtually no amplitude modulation of the carrier and full modulation within ($\pm$) 3kHz. The speech frequency range is restricted by the two stage RC filter. The rf output to the first multiplier through the coupling transformer, T, is adequate, being about 250μA through a 47Ω bias grid leak (approximately 12V). The modulation is likely to be mistaken for a.m. unless the signal is tuned precisely to the carrier. Care is needed to correctly bias the phase modulator to avoid asymmetrical modulation, although with the values shown this is unlikely to arise.

Direct nbfm with a crystal oscillator

The difficulty of obtaining satisfactory direct nbfm from a crystal-controlled oscillator is the main reason for the popularity of phase rather than frequency modulation.

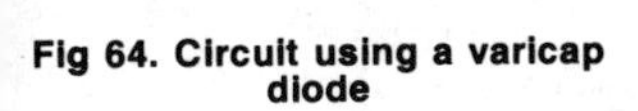
Fig 64. Circuit using a varicap diode

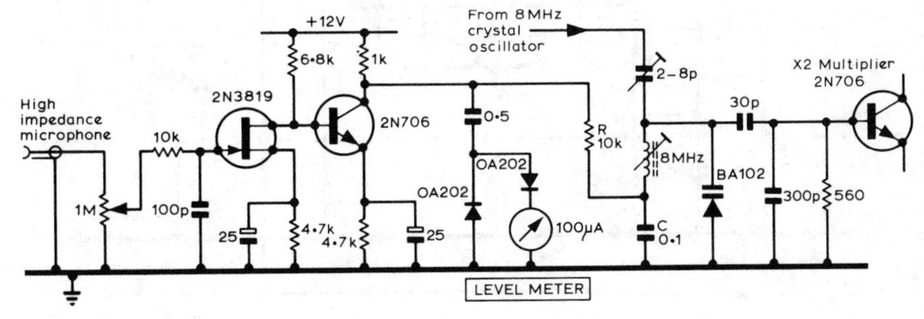

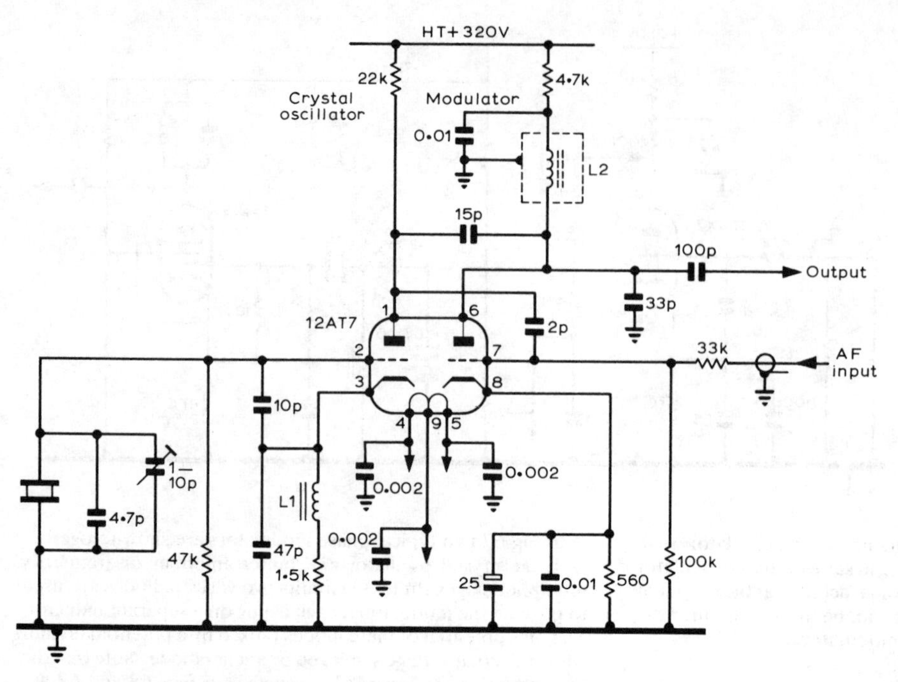

Fig 65. Standard phase modulator circuit

A narrow-deviation voltage-controlled crystal oscillator that exhibits a near-linear tuning characteristic is shown in Fig 74. This was originally described in *IEEE Transactions on Vehicular Technology* May 1978.

As well as providing true nbfm, the circuit also permits temperature compensation to be applied to an AT-cut crystal, an important consideration for amateurs who wish to come up dead in the centre of the 144MHz channels regardless of ambient temperature. A single temperature-compensation control circuit can be used with a number of crystals.

The varactor is an abrupt junction diode with a capacitance of 100pF at −4V. Sensitivity is 250Hz/V, with a maximum tuning range of ±500Hz. The inductance L2 forms, in effect, a vxo-type arrangement and requires care: it consists of a moulded 4·7μH choke. It is possible to achieve added flexibility by including a second inductor to provide wider tuning range, with operation nominally at crystal series resonance. However, the single-inductor arrangement, if used at about 12MHz and multiplied up, should provide ample deviation at 144MHz (and possibly also at 70MHz). With the suggested temperature-compensated arrangement it is claimed that ±3 parts per million can be "readily achieved".

Speech amplifiers for fm

In any frequency- or phase-modulated system the speech amplifier should provide:

- audio gain
- clipping
- low-pass filter
- frequency correction network.

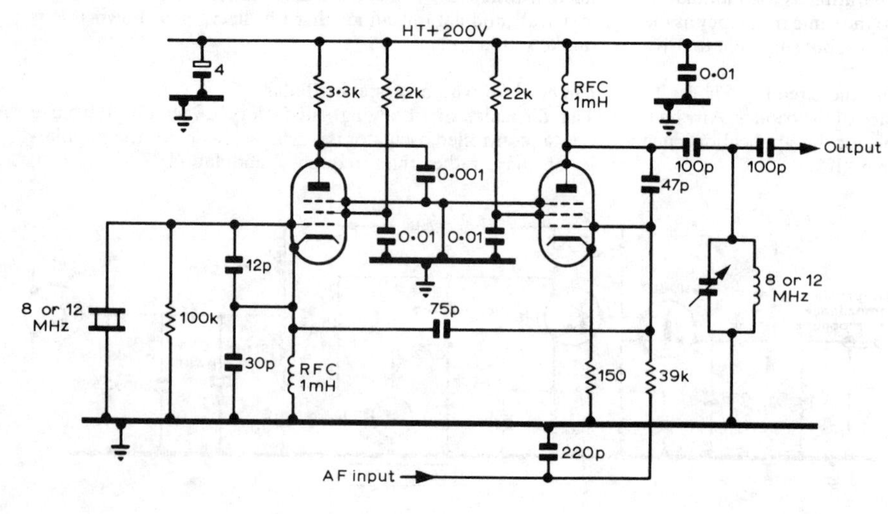

Fig 66. Phase modulator circuit using pentodes and providing greater output than the circuit shown in Fig 65

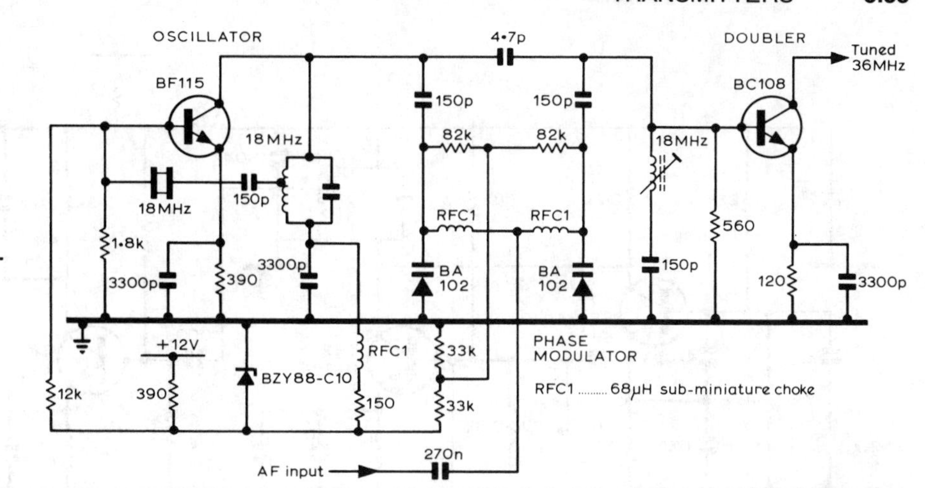

Fig 67. Varicap phase modulator

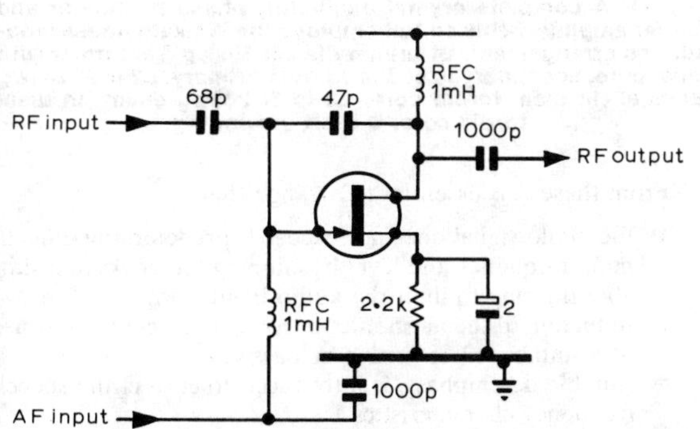

Fig 68. Introduction of modulation between a vfo and the following stage

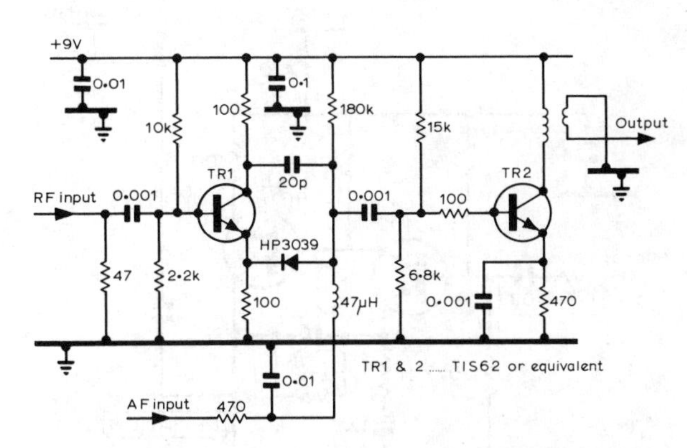

Fig 69. Introduction of modulation into an existing exciter

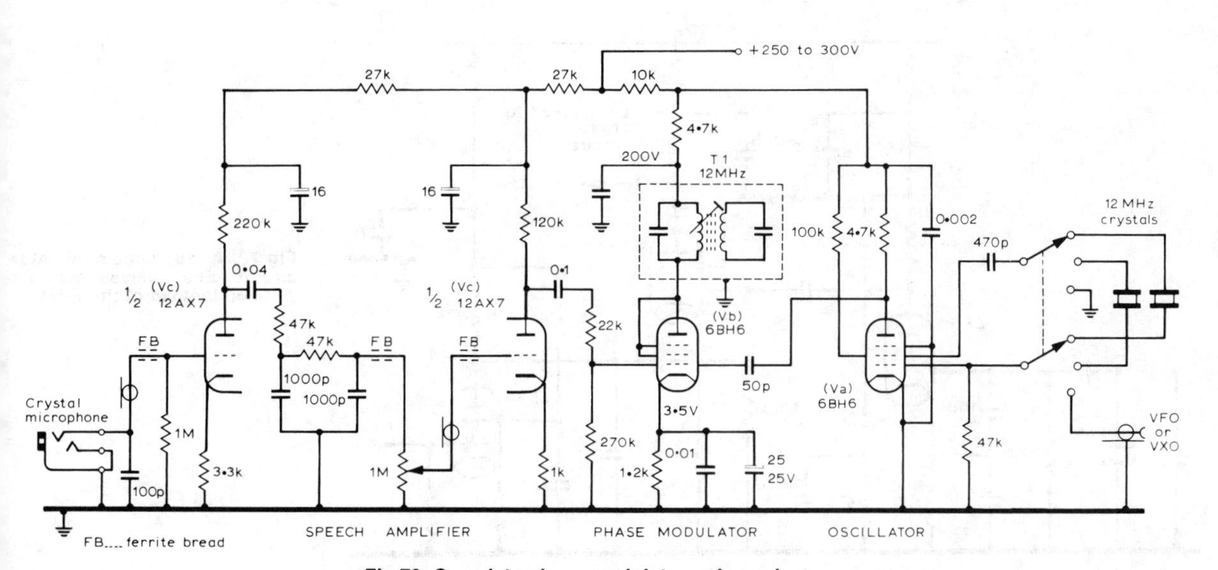

Fig 70. Complete phase modulator using valves

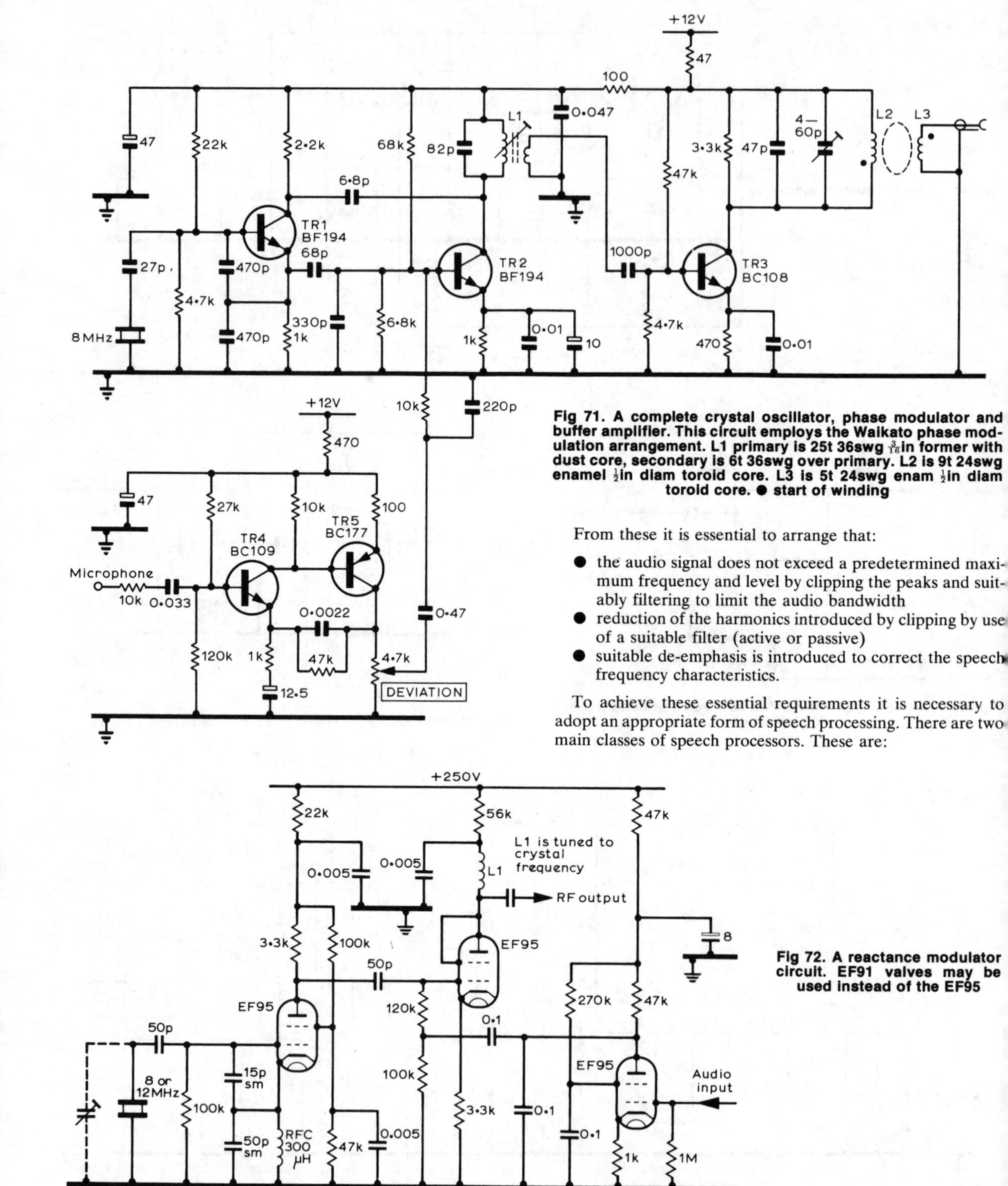

Fig 71. A complete crystal oscillator, phase modulator and buffer amplifier. This circuit employs the Waikato phase modulation arrangement. L1 primary is 25t 36swg $\frac{3}{16}$in former with dust core, secondary is 6t 36swg over primary. L2 is 9t 24swg enamel $\frac{1}{2}$in diam toroid core. L3 is 5t 24swg enam $\frac{1}{2}$in diam toroid core. ● start of winding

From these it is essential to arrange that:

- the audio signal does not exceed a predetermined maximum frequency and level by clipping the peaks and suitably filtering to limit the audio bandwidth
- reduction of the harmonics introduced by clipping by use of a suitable filter (active or passive)
- suitable de-emphasis is introduced to correct the speech frequency characteristics.

To achieve these essential requirements it is necessary to adopt an appropriate form of speech processing. There are two main classes of speech processors. These are:

Fig 72. A reactance modulator circuit. EF91 valves may be used instead of the EF95

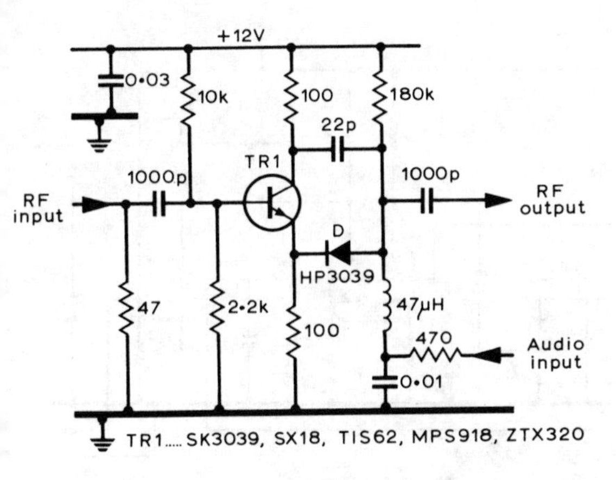

Fig 73. A transistorized version of the modulator shown in Fig 72

(a) compressors in which the dynamic range is compressed
(b) amplitude limiters (clippers).

Both of these have their individual merits. Their object, of course, is to increase the modulation depth by improving the intelligibility without over-modulation (excessive deviation). The bandwidth required should be kept down to 6kHz by use of a frequency range such as 300 to 3,000Hz.

Dynamic compression

In this type of circuit, feedback is arranged so as to keep the ouput to the required level by use of an automatic gain control. In these circuits distortion need not be introduced. However, it is difficult to attain the rise and fall time constants needed and because of these difficulties it is probably easier to adopt the amplitude limiter method.

Amplitude limiting (clipper)

There are two main methods of amplitude limiting of speech frequency signals; these are rf and af limiters (clippers) and either are capable of producing good performance. The rf method is however considerably more complex and therefore more expensive than the af method. This latter method is probably the more suitable for use with nbfm.

AF limiting, providing clipping of the peaks, both positive and negative, and employing either diodes or triodes, will provide a very satisfactory performance when a moderate degree of limiting is used. Some distortion is unavoidable, but by careful design this can be kept down to an acceptable level. The bandwidth of the speech frequencies should however be kept to within the range 300 to 3,000Hz before the amplitude limiter (clipper), with a considerable fall-off of the bass response below 300Hz of about −6dB per octave. The reduction of these lower frequencies is important, because their harmonics would fall in the passband of the filter, which for preference should take the form of a bandpass filter, such as a combination of a low-pass plus high-pass stages. However, provided proper attention is given to the reduction of low-frequency response, a low-pass filter is usually adequate.

A block diagram of the component units of a straightforward amplifier is shown in Fig 75 and Fig 76 indicates the addition of compression (audio agc).

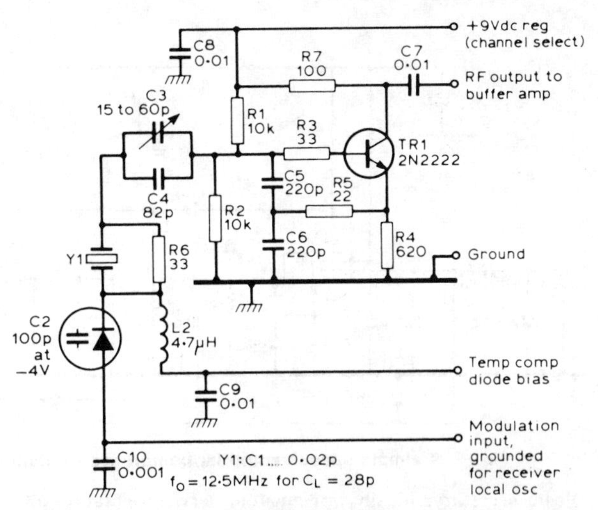

Fig 74. Linear direct-fm crystal oscillator. A similar arrangement can be used for the receiver local oscillator by grounding af modulation line

Indirect (phase) modulation

In an indirect (phase) modulator, there is an automatic pre-emphasis, which gives a rising af characteristic, and it is necessary to introduce compensation for this at approximately 6dB/octave. However, since we are concerned with narrow-band fm a further attenuation of the higher audio frequencies

Fig 75. Block diagram of speech amplifier, clipper and filter

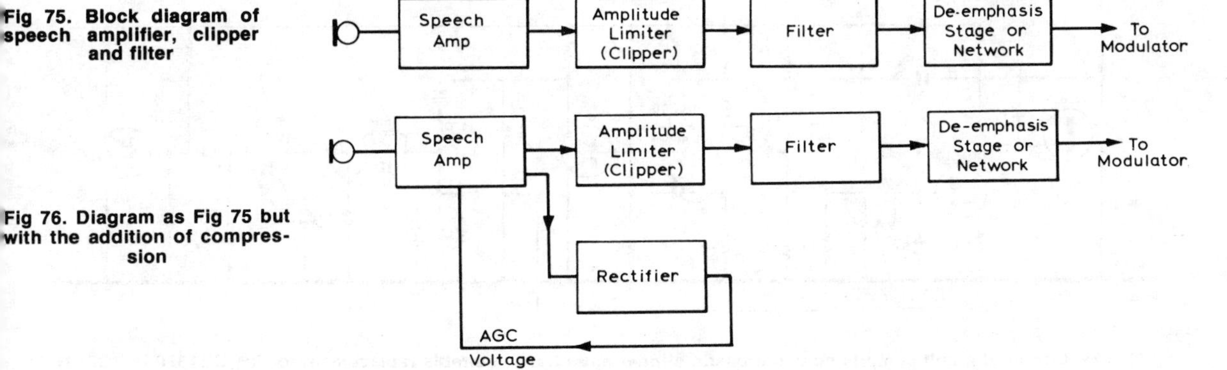

Fig 76. Diagram as Fig 75 but with the addition of compression

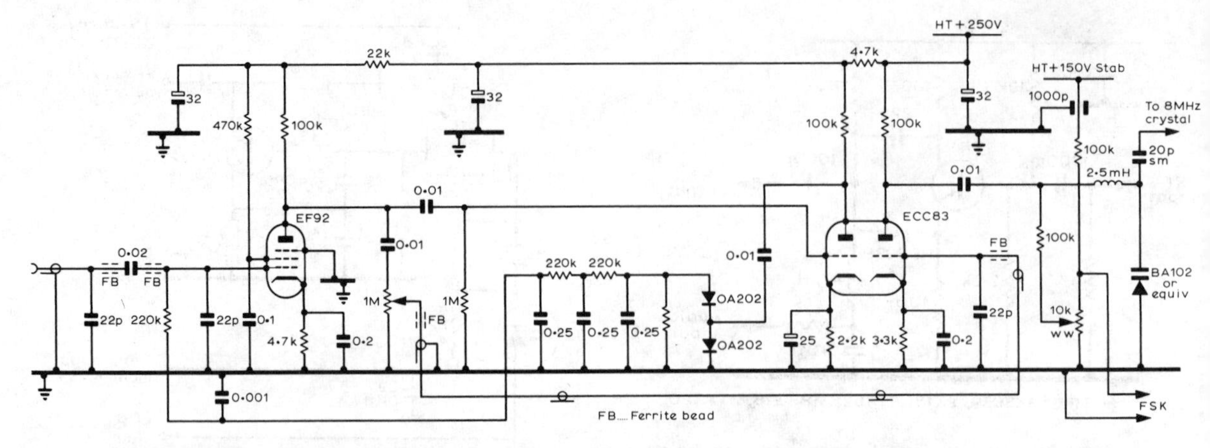

Fig 77. A simple speech amplifier/compressor suitable for use with existing 8 or 12MHz crystal oscillators

will be necessary. Ideally, for amateur service operation all audio frequencies above 3kHz should be removed by means of a band-stop filter. In practice this can be substantially achieved by use of an additional 6dB/octave filter effective at or around 3kHz.

Simple speech amplifier compressors

A valve design is shown in Fig 77 and it will be seen that the first stage is a standard variable (remote cut-off) pentode (EF92 or equivalent) and is only different from a normal speech amplifier in that provision is made for agc. Output from the preamplifier is fed into the second stage, one triode section of an ECC83 or equivalent, and thence on to the varicap diode to provide the modulation. The second triode of this stage is fed with the full output from the preamplifier, the output of this feeding a diode voltage doubler. After filtering by an RC network, the voltage produced is applied to the grid of the first stage.

The actual modulator consists of a varicap diode with a 20pF fixed capacitor in series; these are connected directly across the crystal(s), the audio being fed into the junction of the varicap diode and the fixed capacitor. Provision is made for the correct bias to be applied to the varicap diode. As shown in the diagram a key may be placed across the 10kΩ potentiometer to provide frequency-shift keying. In this unit it is important to provide well-smoothed ht. The amount of compression provided is sufficient to cater for all normal ranges of voice levels without unduly increasing room background noise or street traffic noises.

A more comprehensive arrangement is shown in Fig 78 an in this unit there is no overall gain, giving an output of 0·5V rm for the same input. The filter cutoff frequency is 4kHz. Th speech amplifier consists of a stage using a fet coupled to a amplifier which provides the variable gain obtained from th rectifier output of the overall amplifier. Clipping is provided b two diodes D2 and D3. The output is then passed through th filter on to an amplifier stage to bring the output level back u to the same as the input to the unit. It may usefully be impose in an existing audio amplifier to provide the constant outpu characteristics desirable.

In Figs 79 and 80 are shown two simple speech amp lifier/clipper/filter circuits with de-emphasis being obtained b the 22kΩ resistor and 0·01μF capacitor used between outpu and the input to the phase modulator. In each of these, th speech amplifier consists of two amplifier stages, followed by double-diode clipper, the output being passed through a suit able filter.

A more comprehensive amplifier is shown in Fig 81. In thi the speech amplifier consists of two stages with feed-back t improve the frequency response, and these are followed by double diode clipper. The third and fourth stages are activ filters having a passband of 500 to 3,000Hz. This is followed b a de-emphasis stage. This unit has a significant gain, giving a output of 100mV for an input of 2mV at 300Ω, and input an output controls are provided.

Fig 82 shows a speech amplifier similar to that shown in Fi 81 but in this case an integrated circuit (CA3046) is employe to perform most of the functions. The first two transisto

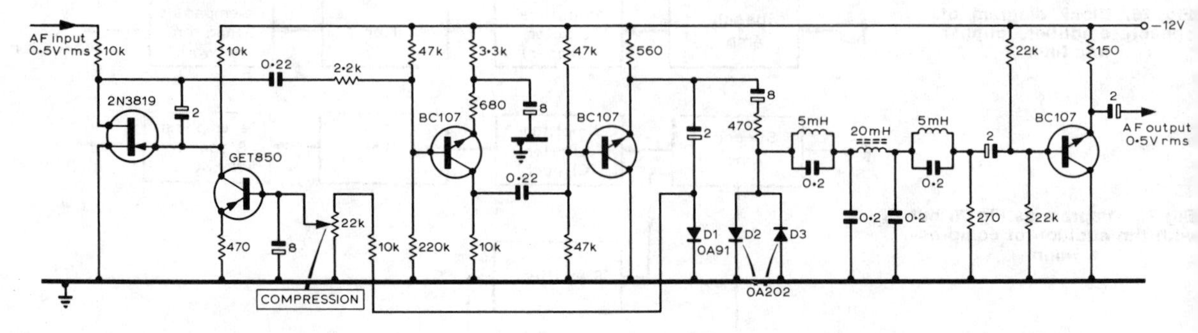

Fig 78. Circuit of a unit comprising compressor, clipper and filter (a suitable replacement for the GET850 is BC214)

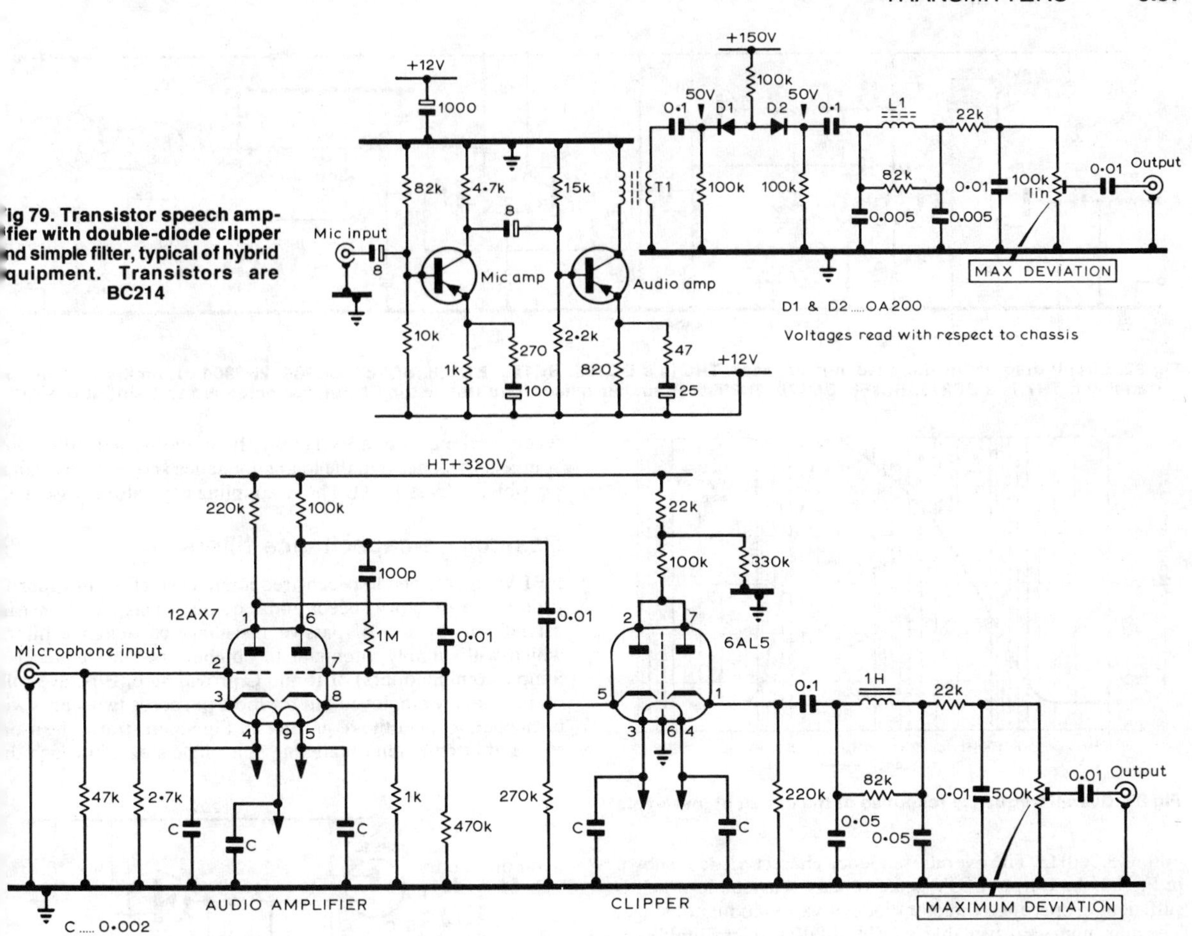

ig 79. Transistor speech amplifier with double-diode clipper nd simple filter, typical of hybrid quipment. Transistors are BC214

Fig 80. The valve equivalent of Fig 79

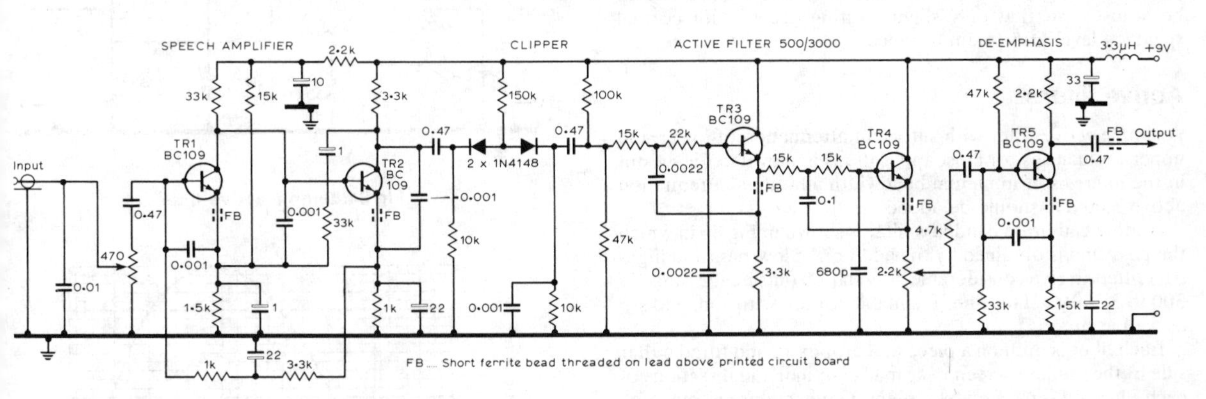

Fig 81. A complete speech amplifier, clipper, active filter and de-emphasis stage. For an input of 2mV at 300Ω the output will be 100mV. Transistor voltages are as follows:

	e	b	c
TR1	**1·1**	**1·7**	**2·2**
TR2	**1·7**	**2·2**	**5·5/6·0**
TR3	**2·0**	**2·0**	**9·0**
TR4	**1·5**	**1·7**	**9·0**
TR5	**3·0**	**3·3**	**4·7**

elements TR1 and TR2 function as simple speech amplifiers, followed by an active filter with TR3 which attenuates the frequencies below 300Hz. Feedback is provided for good stabilization. This is followed by transistor units TR4 and TR5 which form a differential amplifier operating as a balanced limiter. The output is next passed through the second active filter, which has a sharp cutoff above 3kHz. This filter, together with that associated with TR3, forms an effective bandpass filter for

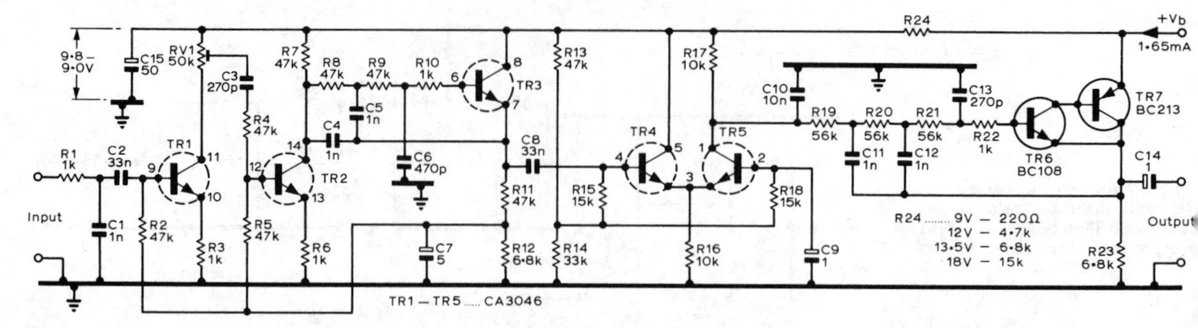

Fig 82. Circuit diagram of the speech processor. TR6 is a BC108, BC148, BC168, BC183, BC238, 2N3904 or similar silicon np transistor. TR7 is a BC213, BC158, BC178, 2N3906 or similar silicon pnp transistor. C3 can be increased to 1–2nF if desired

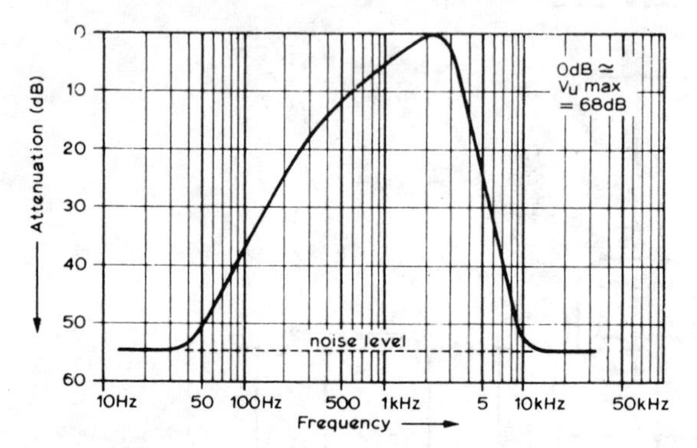

Fig 83. Overall frequency response of the circuit at low levels

300 to 3,000Hz. The overall frequency characteristic is shown in Fig 83. An output of 3V peak to peak is available which is sufficient to operate a varactor diode or valve modulator stage. The maximum gain available is 2,500 (68dB) and is suitable for use with dynamic microphones. The gain control RV1 should be adjusted so that only slight limiting occurs with normal speaking level at 5 to 8in distance.

Active filters

A simple active filter with sufficient attenuation of lower and upper frequencies for most applications is shown in Fig 84 but in the interests of minimum bandwidth additional attenuation above 3,000Hz should be added.

A more elaborate bandpass filter is shown in Fig 86 in which the passband is obtained by the addition of low-pass and high-pass filters to give considerable attenuation outside the range of 300 to 3,200Hz. This filter is suitable for use with a.m. and ssb as well as nbfm.

Each filter is built on a piece of Veroboard, and fitted either side of the tinplate screen in a small can; individual sections of each filter are separated by screens. Connections are made by feedthrough connectors mounted in the lid. All filter resistors should be 2 per cent, and capacitors in the low-pass sections 2·5 per cent polystyrene types. Resistor values in the high-pass sections were calculated after choosing the capacitors, which can vary in value by as much as 20 per cent, but the effect on the filter is not too great, being only to move the "corner" and vary the overshoot ripple by a few tenths of a decibel.

The filter can handle a maximum input of 5V peak to peak when working from a 9V supply. It should be fed from a lo source impedance and the load impedance should be as high a possible, at least 10kΩ. The decoupling capacitor is essentia

Resistance-capacitance filters

NBFM signals need speech frequency correction in order produce satisfactory speech tonal quality. This is most easi carried out by use of passive resistance-capacitance filter which will suitably attenuate the higher speech frequencie Simple combination(s) of R and C providing 6dB/octave rol off are usually employed but for most purposes two stages wi be needed to meet the requirement. Fig 88 illustrates the usu shape of attenuation obtainable in a single stage, in which th

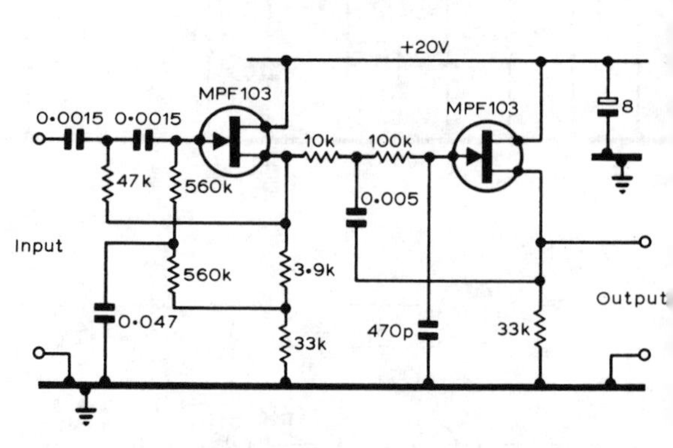

Fig 84. Simple active filter

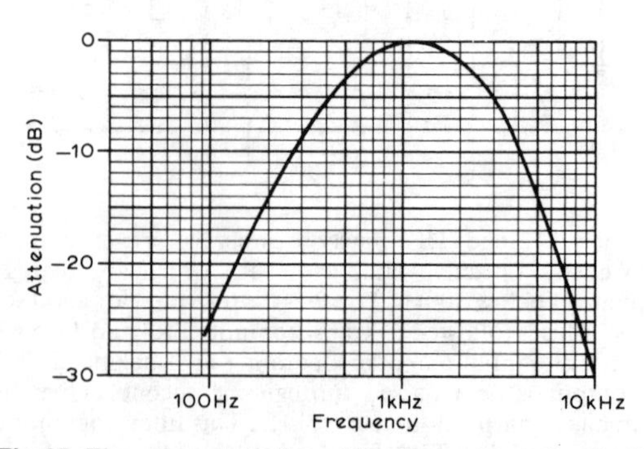

Fig 85. The characteristics of the filter shown in Fig 84

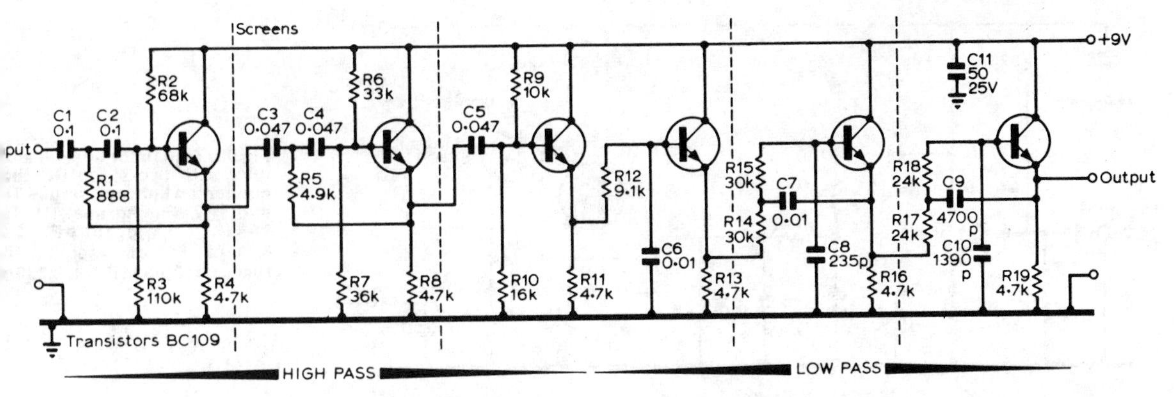

Fig 86. Circuit diagram of the bandpass filter

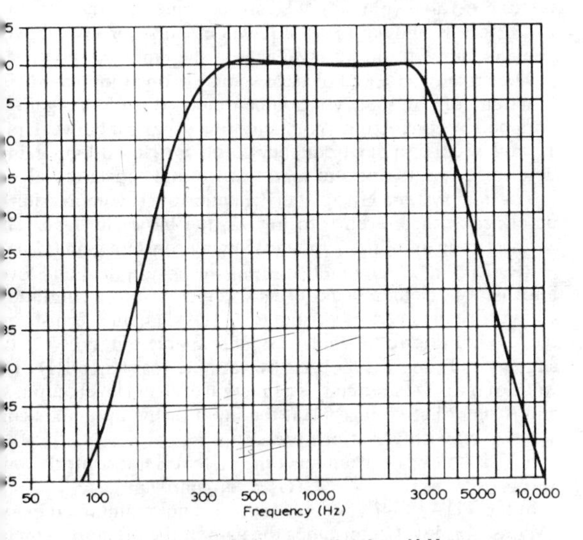

Fig 87. Response normalized to 1kHz

ate of attenuation becomes 6dB/octave. The choice of the alues of R and C determine the "knee" of the curve and its osition on the frequency scale.

To simplify this, two typical circuits (Figs 89 and 90) are iven for valve and transistor amplifers incorporating the filter etwork as an interstage coupling. Values are given for both requency modulation and phase modulation to take care of the ifferent requirements for these two methods of modulation. 'he cathode bypass capacitors may be reduced in value or liminated where a reduction of voltage gain is needed.

RC filters are also useful for the attenuation of rf at the nicrophone input—suitable arrangements are illustrated in Fig 1 and they should, of course, be included in the amplifier nput.

A single ic microphone amplifier with dynamic range compression (drc)

The integrated circuit TDA1054M (SGS/ATES) is primarily esigned for use as the record/playback equalization amplifier n cassette recorders with drc for high average level recordings; ee Fig 92.

The ic comprises four sections; a low-noise preamplifier IC1a, an operational amplifier with high open-loop gain (≈60dB), IC1b, a linear drc (alc) generator IC1c, and a supply ripple rejection circuit IC1d, which makes it a good choice for the purpose in which it is used here.

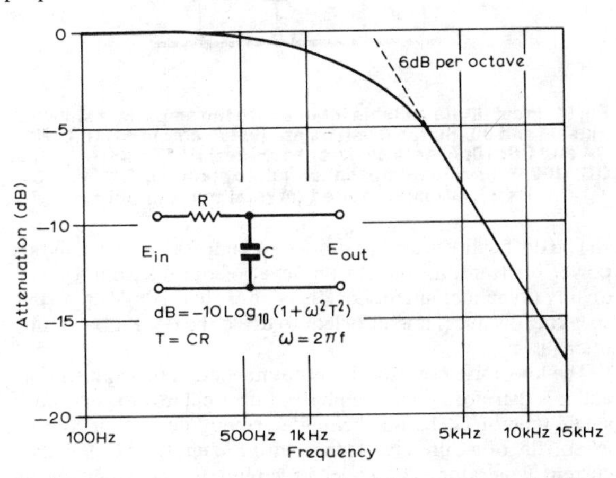

Fig 88. Typical attenuation curve of a single RC combination

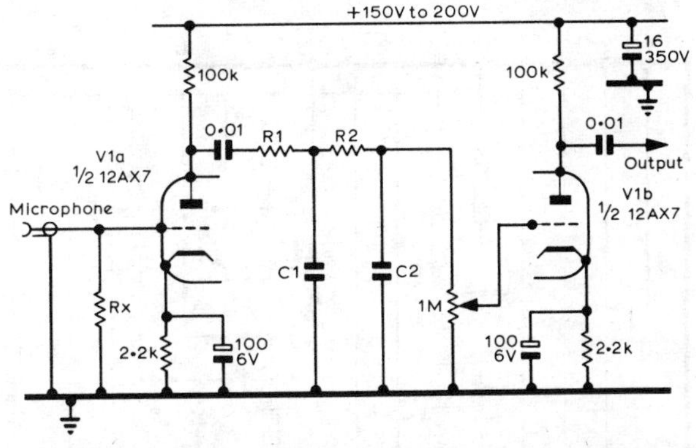

Fig 89. Typical valve speech amplifier incorporating a two-stage RC filter between V1A and V1B. For fm use: R1, R2: 47kΩ. C1: 1,000pF. C2: 470pF. For pm use: R1, R2: 47kΩ. C1: 6,800pF. C2: 470pF. The value of Rx depends on the type of microphone to be used

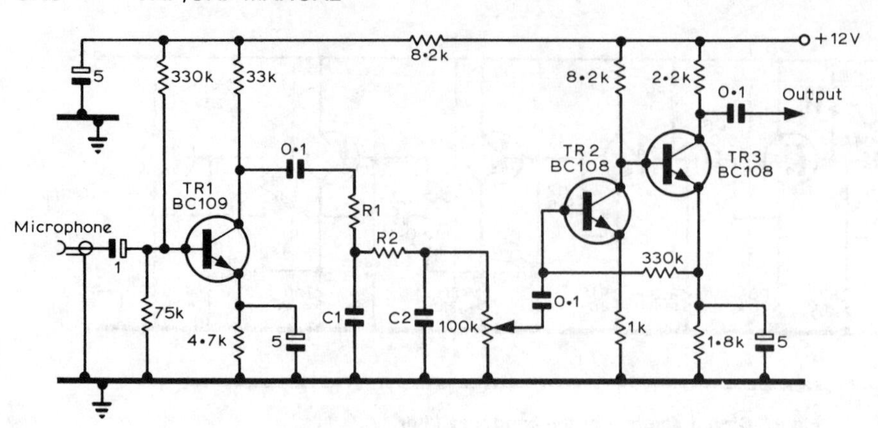

Fig 90. Transistor speech amp lifier with two-stage RC filt connected between stages TR and TR2. For fm use: R1, R2 10kΩ. C1: 4,700pF. C2 2,200pF. For pm use: R1, R2 10kΩ. C1: 0·033μF. C2: 2,200p

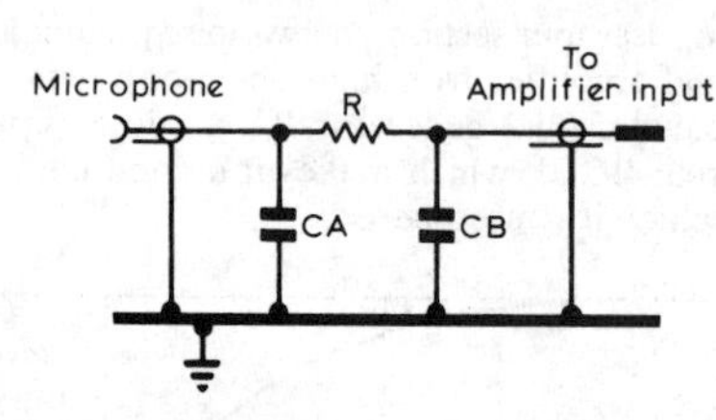

Fig 91. Input filters suitable for use with the amplifiers shown in Figs 89 and 90. Suitable values are (valve amplifier) R: 4·7kΩ, CA and CB: 10pF, or (transistor amplifier) R: 47kΩ, CA: 470pF, CB: 100pF (medium-impedance microphones), R: 1MΩ, CA: 100pF, CB not required (crystal microphones)

The drc facility is used to produce a high average level of talk power for transmission. As the level of output from a good-quality (dynamic) microphone is greater than 10mV at normal speaking distance, it is sufficient to drive the operational amplifier directly.

The low-noise preamplifier is not needed in this application, and it is therefore used as a phase-shift oscillator to generate a single tone of 1kHz, this being described later. IC1b consists essentially of a differential stage with the emitters driven by a current generator. The collector circuit is decoupled by an emitter follower from the output transistors, and this ensures the differential stage gain depends entirely upon the collector resistance value (pin 12). The stage formed by the two fin transistors is similar to an equivalent pnp transistor havi voltage gain with output available at the emitter.

The op-amp gain and phase response in open-loop mode is function of frequency. Compensated open-loop gain obtained by connecting a compensating capacitor between pi 12 and 13; the upper frequency cutoff for closed-loop gain determined by the output load resistor and capacitor values

The agc system giving the dynamic range compression described with reference to Fig 93, the basic alc stage. Th consists of an amplifier (op-amp) having constant gain (G_v = + (R_4/R_3)) in which feedback transforms output signal leve information, using a peak-to-peak detector, into a continuo voltage driving networks T and RD. The element T transform the level of this voltage into a signal capable of modifying th circuit conditions symbolized by variable resistance RD. Th value of the RD (assumed) is a function of signal level output V and is such that voltage V_c at the input of the op-amp is co stant, even with variations present at V_i.

If V_o is below a certain level the system is not controlled. I this case $V_i \approx V_c = V_o/G_v$ (G_v = op-amp gain).

In the TDA1054M system, control is not maintained belo 1V rms; this level determines the gain of the op-amp to mai tain system control with a certain V_{in}. A suitable threshold lev is V_i = 10mV, above which, distortion increases from a lo level to about 0·4 per cent under full system control (G_v greate than 40dB).

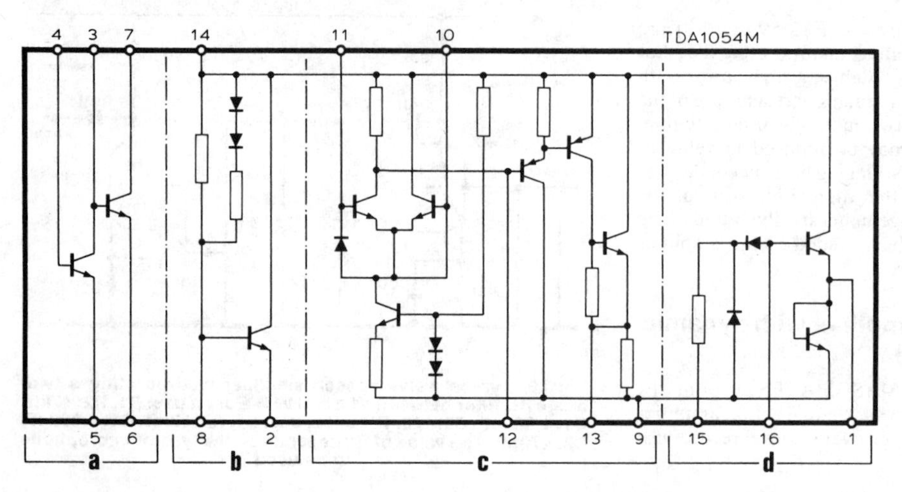

Fig 92. TDA1054M circuit. (Low-noise preamplifier. (Supply voltage ripple filter. (Amplifier. (d) DRC (alc)

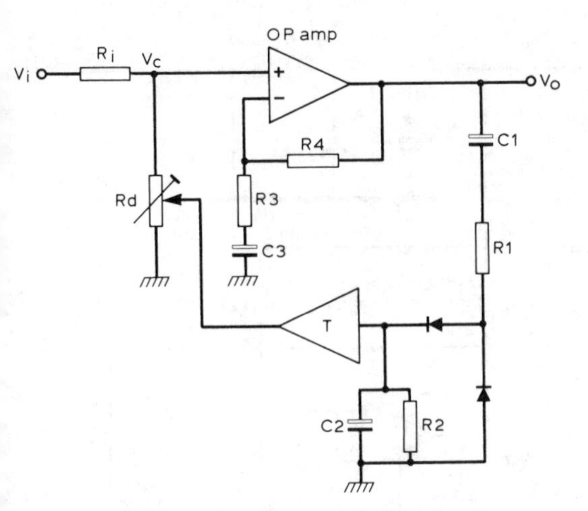

Fig 93. Basic diagram of alc stage

With such a system the speed of response to the instantane-us signal and the no-signal input is important, ie limiting and eturn to normal level times. The limiting time (op-amp driven nto saturation) depends upon relationships between external apacitances, the approximate time constant $T = R_1C_1$, supply oltage and signal variation.

If the limiting time is too long, there will be significant distor-on, as during this time the output will be a square wave. If it is o short, the drc effect of increased level will be lost and stability may occur.

The time of return to normal level is roughly five times miting time. From tests made on the drc for speech input, the me of return should be about 50ms. Recovery time is also an nportant factor and is dependent on the time constant of R2, 2. For normal speech input with normal "gaps" between ords or sentences, the recovery time is about 5s.

The supply voltage ripple filter (svrf) stage IC1d (Fig 94) lows high rejection of supply interference with very short harging times for the filter capacitor and low voltage drop etween supply and filter output.

At the moment of switch-on the capacitor C is charged by the iodes and R2 (about 100Ω), giving a very short time constant. When the voltage across C = $V_s - 2V_{BE}$, D1 and D2 are cut off. 1 and C form the filter section. A well-filtered output appears cross Z_L which is V_s −1V. Load current must not exceed 0mA to prevent cut-off of the filter action; V_s is normally bout 8V. A suitable value of resistor must be introduced etween V_s and svrf input (pin 14) for higher values of V_s.

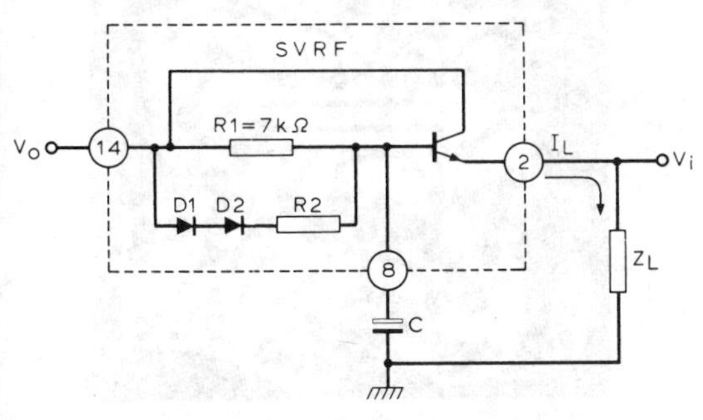

Fig 94. Equivalent circuit of svrf stage

A practical circuit of a microphone amplifier with drc and a lf phase-shift oscillator is shown in Fig 95. Input changes to the amplifier for 0dB output change exceed 40dB (100×), the constant output reference level being 1V rms. This indicates that the amplifier will accommodate many types of microphone (medium to high impedance); at the same time it will not overdrive the following modulator, given correct interface design.

The output load resistor (R8) may take the form of a poten-tiometer with output taken from the slider when a continuously variable output level is required. Alternatively a switch level control consisting of a one-pole 12-way switch and 10 ⅛W 27Ω resistors mounted on the switch can be used. The spare pos-itions can be utilized for an on/off facility.

The usual input filtering is included to prevent any rf on the microphone lead modulating the amplifier (R1, C3).

The phase-shift oscillator output can be connected to the amplifier input via RV1 for checking drc range, ie variations in settings of RV1 should not change the output level across R8. The oscillator can therefore be used for setting up the transmit-ter (single-tone modulation).

R16 needs to be grounded to cause the oscillator to function. For cw operation the phase-shift oscillator can be keyed by connecting R16 to the key line (assuming a "grounded" key circuit). With the key up the oscillator is inoperative.

The oscillator can also provide side tone to the receiver af amplifier for cw monitoring. The drc stage must be dis-connected by S1 at pin 1 of IC1d, to prevent unwanted limiting and recovery time adversely affecting the cw output wave form. Under these conditions the amplifier is not controlled by drc and the 1kHz input level must be controlled by RV1 to prevent overload of IC1b and the following modulator.

Figs 96 and 97 show the component layout (top view) and foil layout of the pcb which may be made from single-sided srbp laminate. The whole unit is only 50mm square and of low power consumption so that it can be installed in an existing equipment or used as an add-on unit.

Fig 98 shows the internal connections of the TDA1054M.

Toneburst circuits

UK fm repeaters operating to IARU Region 1 specifications require a short audio tone (toneburst) at the start of the trans-missions. This tells the repeater to switch on its transmitter. Once this has been done other stations may carrier access the repeater indefinitely until it is no longer required. It will then automatically switch its transmitter off, and another audio tone will be required if further use is to be made of it.

Fundamentally, there are only three requirements for a toneburst unit able to access all UK repeaters—it has to pro-duce a tone of 1,750Hz ±5Hz lasting for about 500ms and deviating the carrier by about 2·5kHz. The tone frequency of 1,750Hz is standard in Europe, but the duration of the tone required varies from repeater to repeater, some requiring as little as 200ms, others (including some in Continental Europe) requiring much longer. However 500ms will be sufficient in the UK.

These three requirements may be quite easy to achieve indoors at a fairly steady temperature of around 20°C, but the interior temperature of a car can range from −10°C on a cold winter morning to 40°C when it has been standing out in the sun on a summer's day. Even some commercial units are incapable of meeting the requirements over this temperature range. Add to this the fluctuations in battery voltage and the constant

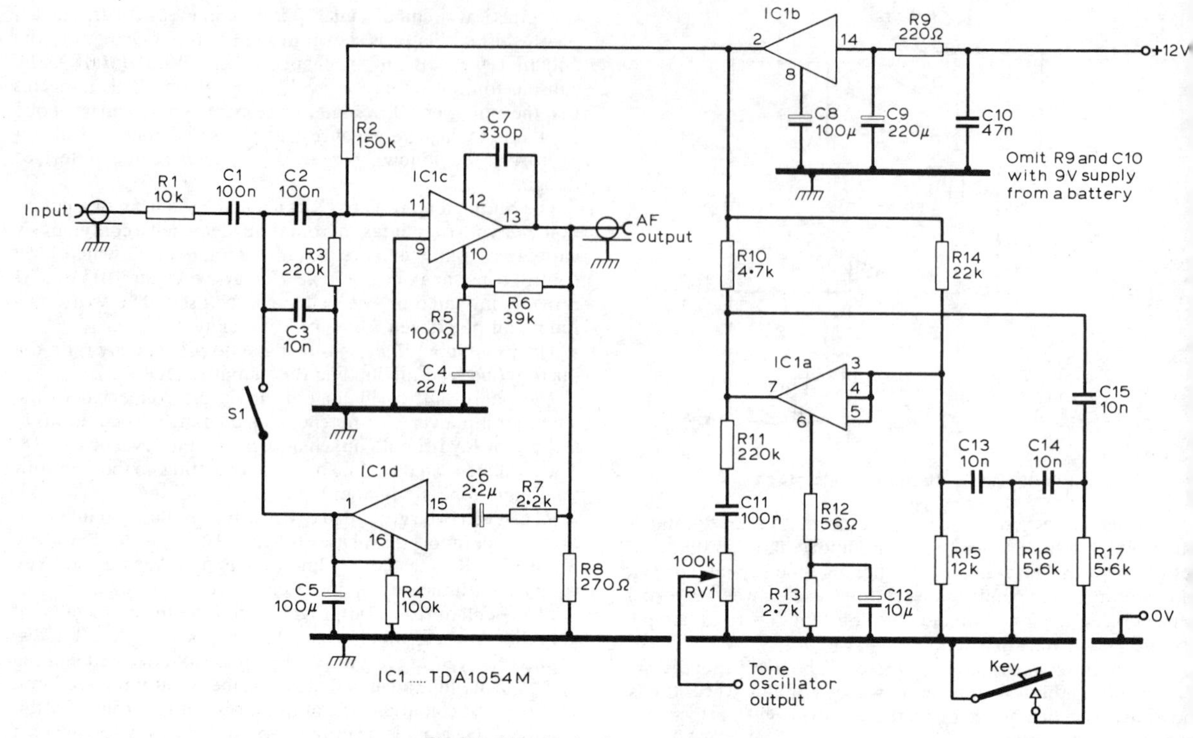

Fig 95. Circuit of microphone amplifier

vibration encountered in mobile service and it can be seen that problems can readily occur.

There are two approaches widely used to solve this difficulty. One is to use an RC oscillator but with high-quality components, the other to use a crystal-controlled oscillator and divide its frequency down to the toneburst frequency. An example c each type of circuit is described later.

If the toneburst unit is of the RC type it will require setting o to the correct frequency of 1,750Hz. This can easily be don with, for example, a digital frequency meter, but this type of tes equipment may not be to hand. In this case one possible metho is to ask a station with a correctly set toneburst to transmit th tone on a simplex channel and beat this against the tone fron the circuit being adjusted, which for this purpose should have it output connected to an audio amplifier and loudspeaker.

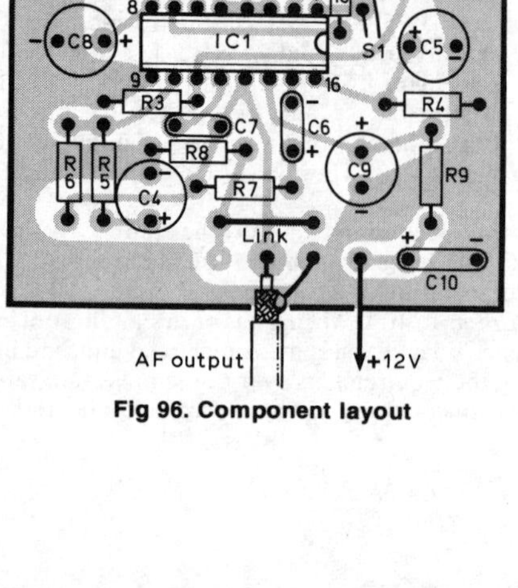

Fig 96. Component layout

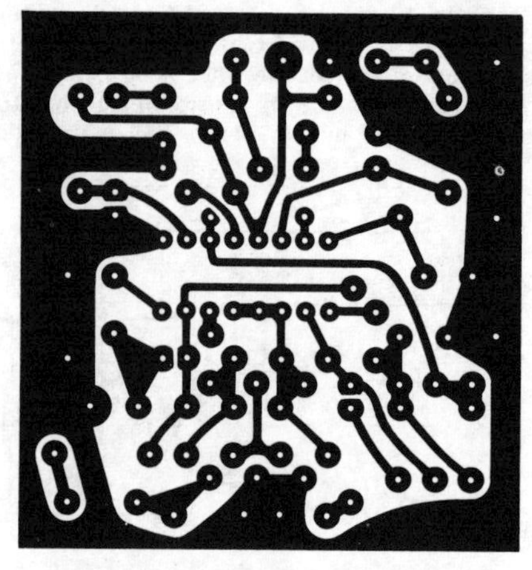

Fig 97. Foil pattern (actual size)

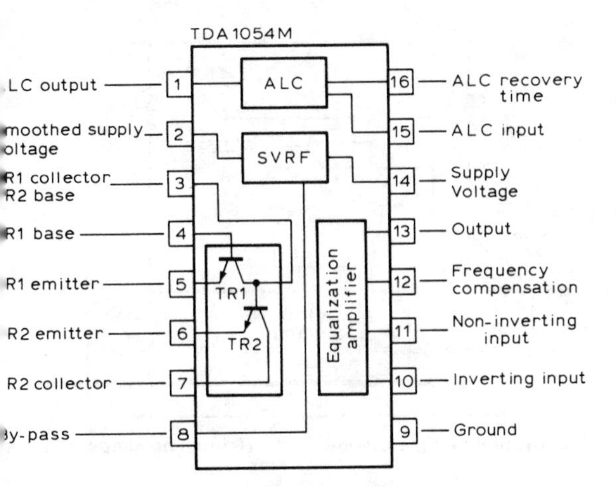

Fig 98. TDA1054M connection diagram

possible both toneburst units should be set to run continuously as it is more difficult to adjust a half-second bleep accurately.

If another station's co-operation cannot be enlisted then the next best method is to listen on the input frequency of the local repeater and compare the toneburst frequency with those of the stations using the repeater.

Only when it is considered that the toneburst is on the right frequency should a test call be made into the repeater, eg "G4XYZ testing access through GB3ZZ". If access is achieved the repeater will respond with a "K" or some other indication. If it does not the toneburst should be re-adjusted *off-the-air*. Under no circumstances should a continuous transmission be made to the repeater while adjustment of the tone frequency is being carried out.

G3VEH "Super-bleep"

This circuit, shown in Fig 99, uses two μL741 operational amplifiers. IC1 is connected as an oscillator using a T-network to derive the frequency, while IC2 is arranged as a timing device.

The frequency of the oscillator is set by RV1 and the output level by RV2. Keying is achieved by either switching the 12V positive line or by grounding the negative line on transmit. When this occurs the oscillator will start sending a tone, C7 will commence to charge up and the voltage at pin 2 will rise. When it passes the voltage at pin 3, set to half the supply voltage by potential divider R7 and R8, IC2 will switch off the oscillator.

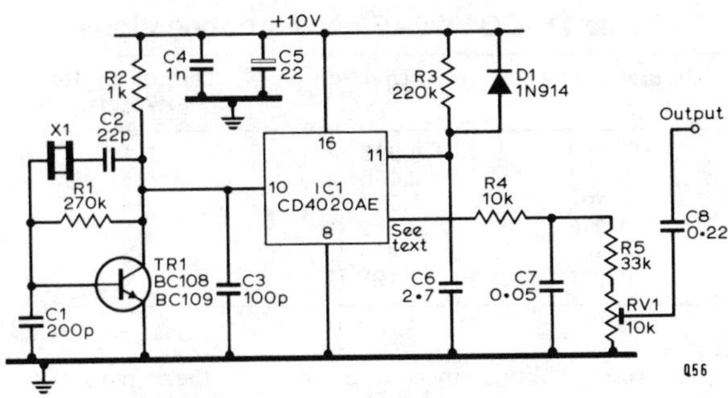

Fig 100. Crystal-controlled toneburst unit

Thus the values of R6, C7 determine the duration of the tone —increasing the value of C7 will give a longer burst and vice versa. When at the end of the transmission the 10V supply is switched off, C7 will discharge through D1, thus resetting the timer ready for the next transmission.

There is no need to stabilize the power supply as the oscillator does not vary in frequency by more than a few hertz over a supply range of 5–15V. However, it is essential that C1, C2 and C3 are polystyrene capacitors and R1, R2, R3, R4 and R5 are metal film resistors.

When initial adjustments are being made to RV1 and RV2, it will be found convenient to temporarily ground pin 2 of IC2, thus ensuring a continuous tone.

Crystal-controlled toneburst

Crystal-controlled tonebursts have two great advantages over those using RC oscillators: they are not so temperature-sensitive and they usually require no initial frequency adjustment before use.

This toneburst design (Fig 100) uses a simple crystal-controlled oscillator, the output of which is divided down to 1,750Hz in a cmos divider, type CD4020AE. This particular device is capable of dividing by 2^n, where $n = 7$ to 12, according to which output pin is selected. Consequently there is a choice of crystal frequencies possible; Table 11 gives details. It will be seen that it is possible to use 450kHz FT241 crystals from the junk box and Table 12 shows those channel numbers which will give the required 1,750Hz when divided by 2^8. If these older crystals or other low-frequency crystals are used the oscillator may need to be modified by increasing its capacitances. A change of C1 to 470pF, C2 to 100pF and C3 to 1,000pF has been found to work well with FT241 crystals.

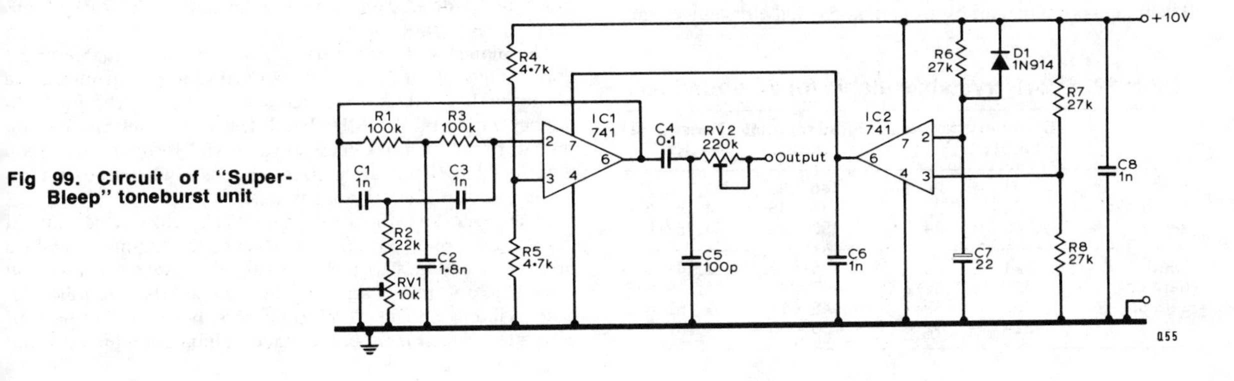

Fig 99. Circuit of "Super-Bleep" toneburst unit

Table 11. CD4020AE divider connections

Crystal frequency (MHz)	Division	Output pin for 1,750Hz
7·168	4,096 (2^{12})	1
3·584	2,048 (2^{11})	15
1·792	1,024 (2^{10})	14
0·896	512 (2^9)	12
0·448	256 (2^8)	13
0·224	128 (2^7)	6

The reset facility connected to pin 11 on the ic permits an extremely simple timing circuit to be used. When C5 has charged up to above half the supply voltage (this takes about 400ms) the ic resets and mutes the tone automatically, although the oscillator continues to function. D1 provides a fast discharge path for C5.

The output from the divider is a square wave which is changed to triangular waveform by R4, C6. The output-voltage level is adjusted by RV1 to give about 2·5kHz deviation.

Power for the unit may be taken from any 10V+ regulated source in the transmitter, such as that which often feeds the rf oscillator. Power consumption is minimal. If no such regulated source is available a simple zener diode and series resistor regulator will be sufficient—good regulation is not required but the unit should be protected against voltage spikes or overvoltage.

Time-out indicator

The circuit is a standard monostable or pulse generator (Fig 101). The only components which affect the time delay are C2 and R3, and since the time involved is fairly long, the capacitor should have low leakage and thus preferably be a tantalum type. Various combinations of R and C are usable, provided a limit of 3·3MΩ for R3 is not exceeded. The formula for on-time is $T = 1 \cdot 1\, RC$, R in megohms, C in microfarads, provided the leakage of C is negligible. The values given provide a time of 54s, but if a slightly shorter time is required reduce the value of R3 slightly.

Output voltage at pin 3 is high while timing is in progress, falling to zero at the end of the timing process, and is able to source up to 200mA. A suitable lamp would in many transceivers be the TRANSMIT lamp, and if this were used, no drilling of the front panel would be necessary.

The timer is switched on by a short negative pulse at pin 2, which is normally held at V_{cc}. This can usually be conveniently obtained from the receiver supply voltage, which will drop from 10–12V to zero on transmit. The pulse is formed by C1 and R2. The timer is switched off by grounding pin 4, the reset line, and this is accomplished by TR1, which may be almost any npn transistor, inverting the positive transition of the receiver supply.

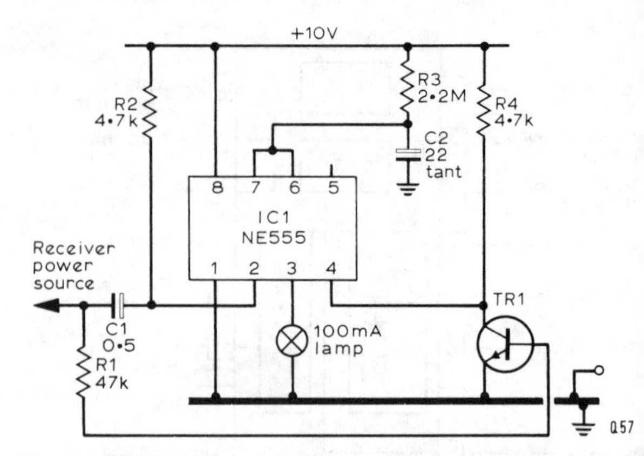

Fig 101. Simple time-out indicator. TR1 can be almost any npn transistor

The timer should be permanently connected to a filtered source of +10V to avoid transients that occur in the power supply.

The only problem that may be encountered with this circuit is that of capacitor leakage. Even if C2 is a tantalum type, it will need several cycles of charge and discharge before its leakage settles down to its normally very low value of under 1mA, and until this happens the timing period will vary. This will show up in the period being too long when the timer is first activated each day, but it will settle down to the correct value after two or three operations. There is nothing much that can be done about this without greatly complicating the circuit, and in practice the effect does not seem to matter very much.

Table 12. FT241 crystals suitable for toneburst use

	Channel number	Marked	Fundamental (kHz)	Toneburst (Hz)
54th harmonic series:	41	24·1	446·296	1,743·3
	42	24·2	448·148	1,750·6
	43	24·3	450·000	1,757·8
72nd harmonic series:	321	32·1	445·833	1,741·5
	322	32·2	447·222	1,746·9
	323	32·3	448·611	1,752·4
	324	32·4	450·000	1,757·8

Single sideband

General requirements

There are basically two methods of achieving ssb output in the vhf range: (i) by the construction of a purpose-built transmitter, and (ii) the use of existing hf band ssb equipment together with a transverter which will provide the appropriate frequency translation. A number of operators desiring to retain their hf band capabilities, while also wishing to operate in the vhf or uhf bands, have adopted the latter method. The basic principle of a transverter is not new, but the blending of the principles involved with the practical application has, in some cases, left much to be desired in so far as the generation of spurious frequencies is concerned.

The pioneers of vhf ssb used whatever was available to get going. They often used an hf ssb transmitter and mixed the output with a crystal-controlled source to bring the final frequency within the 144MHz band. It was perhaps unfortunate that this approach has been so successful for communication that there have been few queries raised as to whether or not this is the most satisfactory approach.

Some operators who are geographically close to certain vhf ssb stations report signals from these ssb stations which are present in addition to the main signal. This is obviously an unsatisfactory state of affairs and it is hoped that the following notes will encourage vhf ssb operators, both old and new, to generate a signal from home-made equipment which is clean

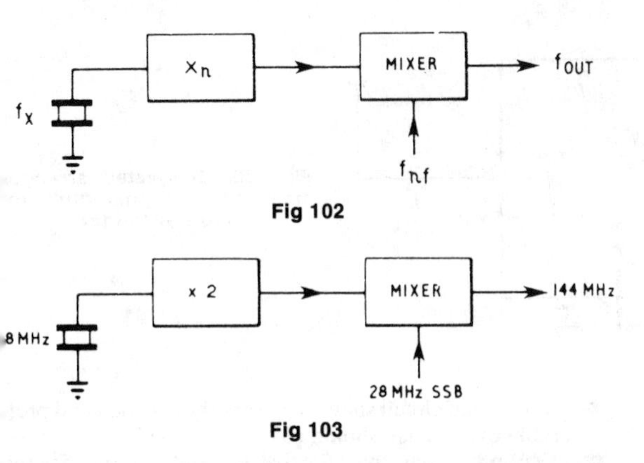

Fig 102

Fig 103

and not a nuisance to the other users of this portion of the frequency spectrum.

Choice of mixing frequencies

Any transmission will contain not only harmonics of the main output frequency, but harmonics of any oscillator involved in the final frequency generation, and mixing products of any frequency present. It is essential to take steps to attenuate these outputs to a minimum, but they will always be present even if at very low level.

The wanted result is $nf_x + f_{nf} = f_{out}$, but in addition the output will contain:

(1) f_x, $2f_x$, $3f_x$, $4f_x$, $5f_x$, . . . etc.
(2) f_{nf}, $2f_{nf}$, $3f_{nf}$, $4f_{nf}$, f_{nf}, . . . etc.
(3) $nf_x \pm mf_{nf}$ where n and m are any integers.

All of these are important and it is often not appreciated how large n and m can be. They can (but admittedly rarely) reach three digits.

To take an actual case, as in Fig 103,
Not only does (2 by 58) + 28 = 144MHz but
(3 by 58) − 28 = 146MHz.

In this case, since post-mixer selectivity is invariably of low Q, the unwanted 146MHz transmission could be expected to be at a high level.

However, both Figs 102 and 103 are simplified. The actual generation of the hf ssb injection involves yet more frequencies in the hf transceiver shown in Fig 104.

The total arrangement thus involves up to three crystal oscillators and one vfo. The calculation of potential spurious emissions from this is a task for a computer. It should not be forgotten that the crystal-controlled injection frequency can be higher than the output frequency. Some problems concerning spurious frequencies can be solved in this manner, but the approach does result in inverted tuning direction and sideband transposition.

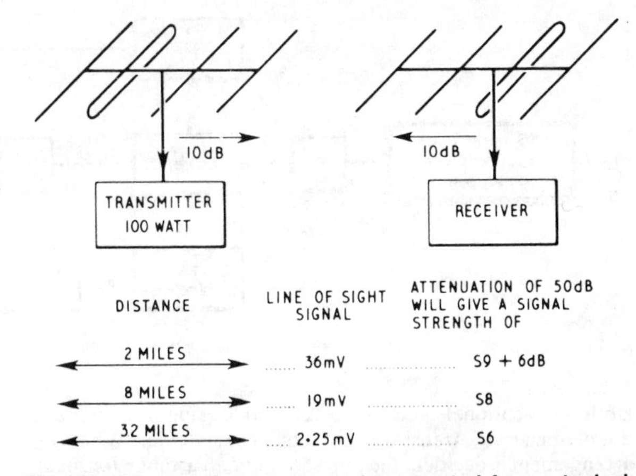

Fig 105. The signal strengths to be expected from a typical situation at various distances. A spurious transmission attenuated by 50dB from the desired signal will produce the strength given in the third column

The levels involved

Measurements on transmitters where no deliberate attempt has been made to reduce spurious emissions show that 40dB spurious attenuation is typical. Thus if a local receiver receives an S9 + 40dB wanted signal from a vhf ssb transmitter, a spurious signal of S9 could also be received. Assuming 3dB per S-point and an acceptable interference level of S2, the extra attenuation required is (7 × 3)dB, ie 21dB. We are looking for approximately 60dB spurious attenuation in this case. However, local signals can well be in excess of S9 + 40dB and a case can be made for a target of 100dB spurious emission attenuation.

Only the professional engineer with access to specialized test gear and who has had experience of attempting to design to this target can truly appreciate the enormity of the task. It is possible however to indicate lines of approach which will at least show a major improvement on the 40dB figure.

The design approach with an hf ssb transmitter

Both hf and crystal frequencies should be chosen so that no spurious emissions produced by low-order harmonics fall in the band or close to it. The crystal frequency should be as high as possible, eg 116MHz with a 28 MHz transmitter. 28MHz ssb is preferable to the lower frequency in that the greater spacing between the carrier and injection frequency the better the attenuation of the 144MHz circuits to the injection frequency and image.

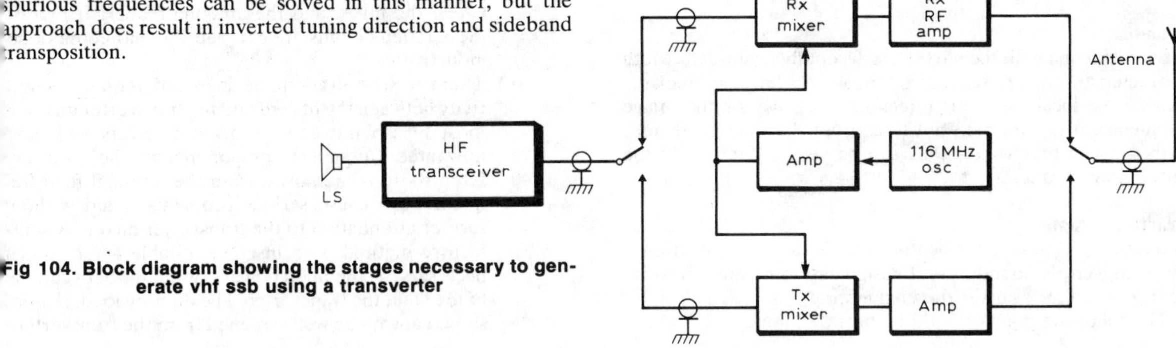

Fig 104. Block diagram showing the stages necessary to generate vhf ssb using a transverter

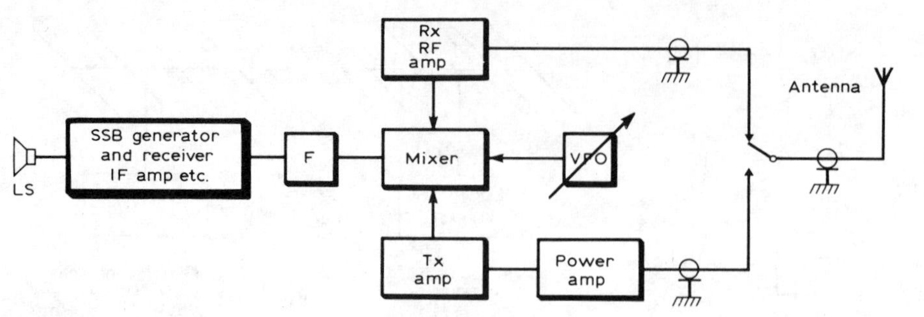

Fig 106. Suggested arrangement for a purpose-built vhf ssb transmitter

Final mixer
Both conventional and Schottky diode ring mixers, and double-balanced transistor circuits are suitable. Whatever arrangement is decided, the aim should be to arrange for maximum rejection of the vhf injection frequency. Provision for balance adjustment should always be provided.

With a high-level ssb input in which high power is dissipated in a resistive load, "hop over" effects can occur, in which appreciable ssb energy (with doubtful spectral purity) gets into both pre- and post-mixer circuits, thus bypassing any selectivity in the ssb input. If this energy mixes with a second frequency to produce a third frequency within the bandwidth of either the oscillator or 144MHz circuits a spurious emission close to the wanted output frequency will result.

Crystal oscillator and multiplier
In order to provide the mixer with injection of excellent spectral purity, coupled tuned circuits should be used throughout, with low-impedance link coupling.

HF ssb input
The input level should be kept to a minimum. It is bad practice to use many watts of hf only to dissipate them in a resistor located on the converter chassis. On the other hand bad carrier rejection will result in the hf ssb transmitter if the level is turned down by reducing the audio drive. The best approach is to feed the input to the hf pa direct to the converter and it is often possible to obtain sufficient level by switching off the pa screen voltage and using the feed through voltage. Bandpass filtering should be used in the converter hf feed in order to filter unwanted emissions.

Post mixer filtering
Band pass filtering should be provided immediately after the mixer. A series of low-working *Q* tuned circuits in successive amplifiers is not considered sufficient.

Antenna
Use an antenna with the narrowest acceptable gain-bandwidth characteristic. A broadband antenna may have appreciable gain at the local oscillator injection frequency or the image frequency. It is important not to confuse the vswr bandwidth with the gain bandwidth; they can be very different and the latter is rarely quoted.

Practical design
A near-perfect design can be unsuccessful if the engineering is poor, conversely an indifferent design can sometimes produce near-acceptable results if the engineering is excellent.

The following points should be borne in mind:

- Every tuned circuit should be properly screened and preferably every stage should also be screened.
- Decoupling must be effective not only at the desired frequency but also on high-order harmonics.
- Power supply feeds to individual stages must be thoroughly decoupled.
- In-line layout should be employed with the oscillator at one end and the output at the other.

Recommendations for ssb out-of-band radiations
Great care must be taken to ensure that no out-of-band spurious radiations occur. All rf circuits should be adequately screened and a bandpass filter with sufficient out-of-band attenuation should be included in the antenna feeder.

In-band radiations
To avoid interference with other operators:

1. Every effort should be made to keep the spurious radiations down to 90dB below the wanted signal.
2. The following precautions should be taken when a transverter is used in association with an hf bands transmitter/transceiver as an ssb source:
   (a) The transverter crystal oscillator should be on as high a frequency as possible (although certain high frequencies must be avoided, eg 58MHz). The use of fundamental crystal oscillators below 30MHz must be avoided unless very special design precautions are taken. Any frequency that gives in-band signals of less than tenth order should be avoided.
   (b) Precautions must be taken to minimize radiation of the crystal oscillator chain output frequency. This can be done by using a balanced mixer—which can attenuate this component by 20dB or more—and by subsequent tuned circuit selectivity. In the latter case a minimum of *four* tuned circuits are required between the mixer and the antenna feeder. If two of these tuned circuits are coupled this should be done inductively.
   (c) There must be an adequate degree of frequency selectivity between the hf feed and the transverter mixer as most hf ssb transmitters or transceivers will have unwanted frequency components in their output. Even those far removed from the nominal feed frequency can cause serious problems if fed without further attenuation to the transverter mixer. A satisfactory method is to insert a suitable filter and, if necessary, a combined power attenuator between the hf feed and the transverter. The dummy load, if used, should always be well screened from the transverter.

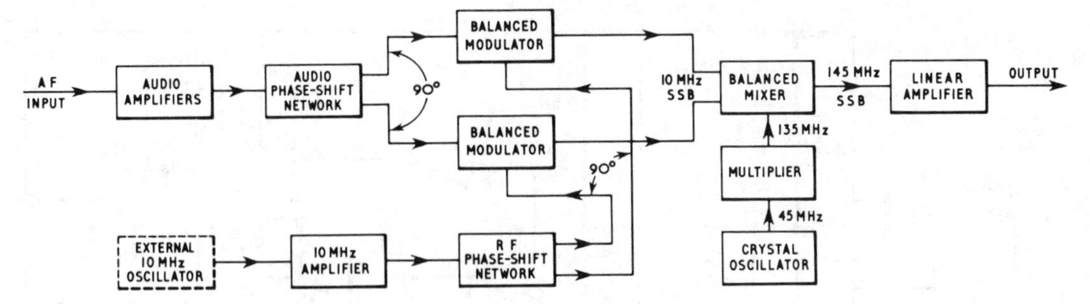

Fig 107. Block diagram of the 144MHz phasing exciter

3. Preference should be given to the use of equipment specifically designed for operation on 144MHz using a high-frequency ssb generator. Recommended are 9, 10·7 or 28MHz as suitable for this purpose.
4. Care must be taken in all amplifier stages following the final mixer to ensure that the operating conditions are such that intermodulation does not produce spurious frequency signals in the region of the unwanted sideband of level worse than −40dB relative to the wanted signal.

Having dealt with the requirements for vhf ssb, descriptions are given of equipment specifically designed for the purpose and also transverters for use with hf band generators.

The use of the phasing method offers a greater degree of flexibility. Although more care will be needed to obtain the required results it offers the chance to use wider audio frequency range than is usually available from the narrower-bandwidth hf band filters.

The rf phasing may be carried out at generator frequency and mixed to reach the final frequency; alternatively this may be done at final frequency—sometimes called direct rf phasing. To some extent the method or generator frequency will be determined by whether the equipment is required for one or more vhf bands.

Phasing exciters for 144MHz

The first exciter described uses transistors throughout; field effect transistors are used in the balanced modulator and mixer stages.

An external 10 ± 1MHz vfo provides the variable generator frequency, this and the audio output after passing through their respective phase shift networks are combined in the double balanced modulator. The output is then mixed with 135MHz in a balanced mixer to produce the final frequency in the 144MHz band. The individual sections are indicated in the block diagram, Fig 107.

AF amplifier

The frequency passband of the audio stages has to be shaped so that it matches the phase-shift network, which for simplicity is designed to operate over a restricted range; in this case 300Hz to 3kHz. This means that the phase shift produced by the network is within 2 per cent of 90° only over this range and that any frequency outside will produce a phase shift greater than the above limits; this results in the sideband suppression suffering. Therefore frequencies below 300Hz and above 3kHz are attenuated by suitable choice of components, but it is important that this is done before the phase-shift network, and that the circuits after that have a reasonably flat response. This is because circuits which change the amplitude of signals relative to their frequency nearly always change the phase of the signals as well, and after taking reasonable care to make the psn accurate it is not desirable deliberately to impair this by introducing further phase changes.

In Fig 108 are shown the af stages of the exciter. TR1 and TR2 are a dc coupled pair in a bootstrap circuit designed to produce a high input impedance and a low output impedance.

The 100kΩ resistor in TR1 gate can be changed if desired and the input impedance will be changed by the same ratio without affecting any other parameter.

The output from TR2 is coupled to the af gain control via a relatively small coupling capacitor which provides attenuation to signals below 500Hz in order to meet the above requirements. TR3 is a straight amplifier, the high frequency response of which is attenuated by the 0·001μF capacitor between collector and base.

The audio psn requires an asymmetrical low source impedance with an amplitude difference of 2:7; this is provided by a 3:1 step-down transformer T1, the output of which is loaded by 390 and 110Ω resistors in order to produce the amplitude difference. The psn itself is taken from the RSGB *Handbook* and is exactly as specified for valve use (see Fig 109). It must be terminated in a very high impedance and this is provided by the fets TR4 and TR6. These are self-biased by source resistors and the 100Ω af balance potentiometer provides the means of making the output signals equal during setting up. TR5 and TR7 are dc coupled to the fets and are there for two reasons: (a) to provide a low-impedance drive for the transformers T2 and T3 to ensure low distortion at the lower frequencies; (b) to provide a high-impedance load for the fets so that the gain can be as high as possible.

The transformers T2 and T3 are 2·8:1 with centre-tapped secondaries to produce anti-phase outputs for the balanced modulators, connected via 22kΩ resistors. Some circuits use rf chokes in this position but these are not necessary here as the audio sees the balanced modulator inputs as a few picofarads, hence the time constant is too short to affect the audio in any way. The rf sees a relatively high impedance so very little is lost.

The rf circuits

The 10MHz vfo is external to the exciter unit and is not shown here. It produces about 1·5V rms and is coupled to the exciter via a short length of coaxial cable. TR8 (Fig 110) is an emitter follower since some isolation was found to be necessary to reduce oscillator pulling.

TR9 is an amplifier tuned to 10MHz in its collector circuit by

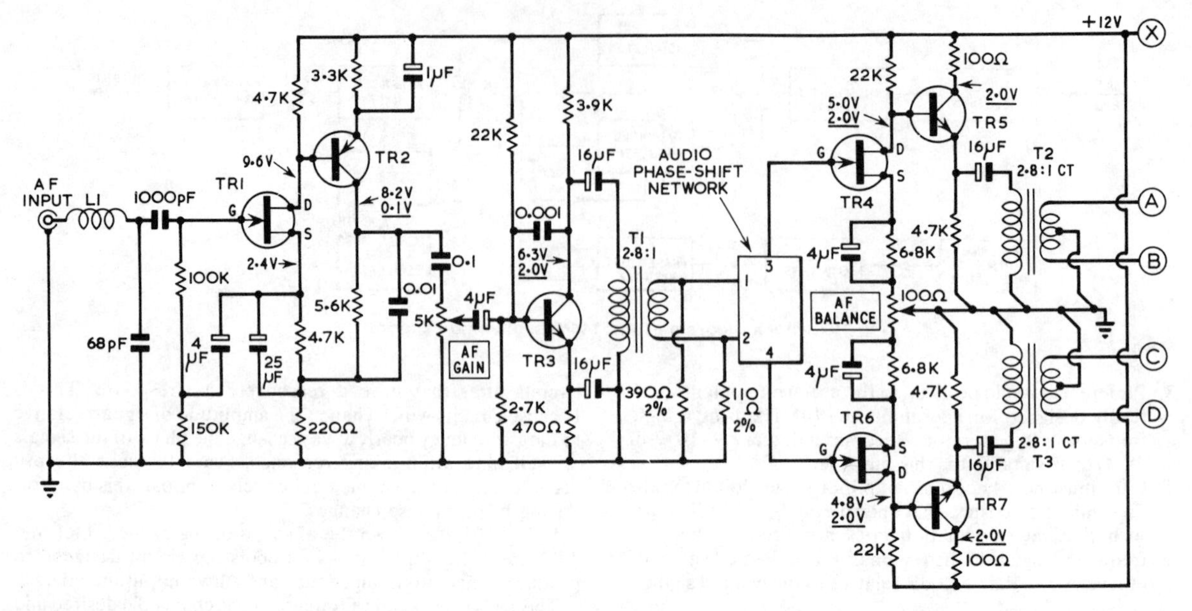

Fig 108. The audio stages of the phasing exciter. L1 is 50t 38swg enam close wound on a 1in diam former. T1, 2 and 3 can be Radiospares type TT6 or any 3:1 interstage transformers. Signal voltages are underlined.

L2 and its low-impedance coupling coil connects it to the rf phase-shift network. This uses capacitors and resistors only, adjustment being provided by two Philips trimmers. The phase-shifted rf is then applied to the balanced modulators which consist of four fets TR10–TR13 and along with the audio is fed into the gates. Balancing of the modulators is carried out by means of 1kΩ potentiometers in the source circuits of each pair. The 10MHz ssb suppressed carrier signal is taken from the drain circuits which are tuned to 10MHz by a bifilar wound coil, L3. This must now be converted to the required operating frequency by a mixer.

Mixer for 144MHz

The circuit of this section is shown in Fig 111. As will be seen, a pair of fets are used in the balanced mixer, operating in push-pull as far as the 10MHz signal is concerned and as a push-pull device for the 135MHz heterodyning signal; hence the 135MHz is cancelled in the output circuit.

TR14 is a crystal oscillator using a 45MHz crystal and TR15 operates as a frequency tripler with its collector series tuned to 135MHz.

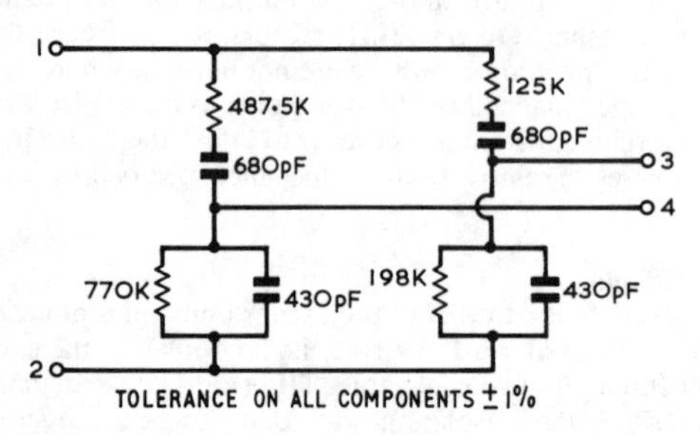

Fig 109. The audio phase-shift network circuit and component values

This is link coupled to the common connection of a bifilar-wound coil tuned to 10MHz which matches the incoming 10MHz signal to the gates of the fets TR16 and TR17. These are self-biased by source resistors, and the output is resonated to 144MHz by L4, the output being link coupled to a grounded base amplifier, TR18.

Construction

No specialized form of construction is necessary but care should be taken to prevent hum pick-up in the gate circuits of TR1, TR4 and TR5. The filter components at the audio input should have short direct leads as they are intended to reduce rf pick-up at 144MHz.

Care should also be taken that 10MHz rf cannot leak from input to output which could impair the carrier suppression.

The prototype was constructed on three pieces of Veroboard some 8in long and 3in wide. The audio section was built on one as far as the outputs of TR2 and TR3, while the rf section and balanced modulators were built on the second and the mixer on the third. The three were then stacked one on top of the other with short interconnecting leads to take audio, rf and supply lines between them, and the whole placed in a metal box for screening.

For convenience, the *af gain*, *af balance*, *carrier balance* controls and the cores of L7 and L8 should be made adjustable from outside the box as they are affected by stray capacitances.

Alignment—af section

After a check of wiring the dc can be connected and a current check will show if all is well, that of the rf and af sections being 18–20mA at 12V and the mixer unit being 10mA.

Transistors being what they are, some check of voltages may be worthwhile and these are shown on the circuits. In particular, TR3 collector and the drains of TR4 and TR5 should be about 6V to obtain the full swing at these points. If these are not so,

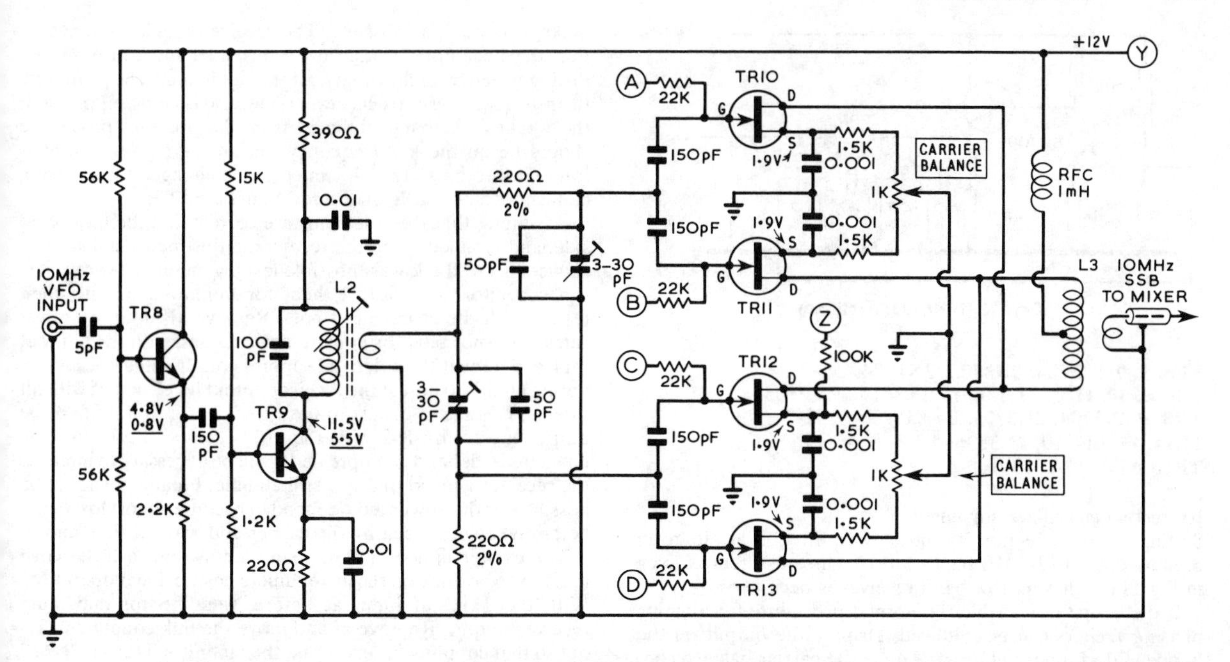

Fig 110. The low-frequency rf stages. The 10MHz drive is obtained from an external vfo capable of delivering 1·5V. L2 is 18t 28swg enam, close wound Radiospares former, plus 2t coupling at earthy end. L3 is 20t + 20t 36swg enam, close wound on Radiospares former, plus 1t coupling at centre of main coil

then the bias on TR3 should be altered until the correct collector voltage is obtained, and the source resistors of TR4 and TR5 should be changed in pairs for the correct result. The drains of TR4 and TR5 should be within about 0·5V of each other if they are sufficiently well matched.

Next a signal check can be carried out by applying a 1kHz tone to the af input, a suitable circuit for producing this being shown in Fig 112.

Turn all potentiometers to mid-travel, and examine the waveform at TR3 collector with a 'scope and adjust the af gain to give a 2V pk-pk signal. Check through the circuit for the correct signal voltage levels as shown underlined on the circuits.

Apply 10MHz from a vfo or signal generator to the rf input and ensure that there is some 0·4V rms at the output of L2 when it is tuned for maximum. The coupling capacitor on TR8 base should be adjusted in value to obtain this voltage.

Transistors used

TR1 2N3819.

TR2 2N1305, 2N3702, 2N3703.

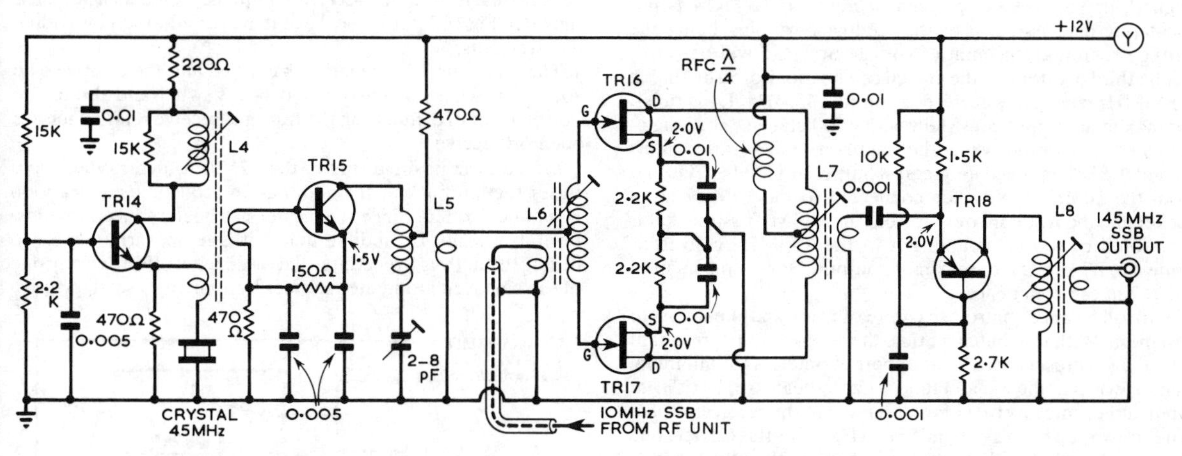

Fig 111. The mixer section which provides the output at 144MHz. L4 is 12t 28swg enam, close wound on Radiospares former (feedback winding 1t, output winding 2t, both over earthy end of L4). L5 is 8t ½in diam, 1in long, 18swg tinned copper plus 1t coupling in centre. L6 is 20t + 20t bifilar wound on Radiospares former with 2t coupling around centre. L7 is 8t close wound, 22swg enam, on Radiospares former, with 2t coupling around centre. L8 is 6t ½in long, 22swg on Radiospares former, with 2t coupling around centre. L8 is 6t ½in long, 22swg, on Radiospares former, with 2t coupling at earthy end

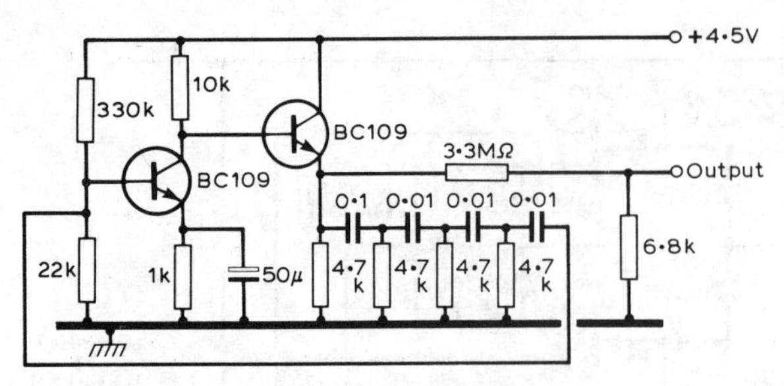

Fig 112. 1kHz test oscillator

TR3, 5, 7 2N3704, 2N3705, 2N1304.
TR4, 6, 10, 11, 12, 13, 16, 17 2N3819, MFP105.
TR8, 9 2N3704, 2N3705, BFY19.
TR14, 15, BFY19, 2N3826.
TR18 AFZ12, AF139.

RF section and mixer alignment

Setting up the rf section is a little more difficult as either an oscilloscope with 10MHz bandwidth or a mixer system as given in Fig 111 with a narrow-band receiver is necessary.

If the 'scope is available the normal procedure for aligning phasing exciters can be followed. Display the output on the 'scope with rf input but no af. Adjust the carrier balance controls for minimum deflection. Apply af at the same level when the trace should be deflected at rf while showing considerable af ripple.

Tune L2 for maximum output, then the rf psn capacitors and the af balance control for minimum ripple. Repeat carrier balance and rf psn adjustments.

However, most amateurs will not have such a 'scope available and the alternative procedure will have to be adopted.

It is not possible to monitor the output of the exciter directly on the receiver as it will pick up a very strong signal from the 10MHz oscillator, but the mixer enables the ssb signal to be heard on the frequency on which it will be used.

At this point the mixer circuit should be checked and roughly aligned, dc voltages being given in Fig 111. If TR14 is not oscillating due, perhaps, to the feedback winding being the wrong way round, the emitter voltage of TR15 will be zero.

The third overtone of the crystal can be monitored by tuning a 144MHz converter/receiver set-up to 135MHz. L4 is tuned for maximum output consistent with good starting and single-frequency operation when the supply is temporarily interrupted. L5 is then tuned for greatest output at 135MHz. Output from the 10MHz vfo is then connected to the 10MHz input socket and the resultant output from the 144MHz ssb socket is monitored by loosely coupling it to the 144MHz converter. Tune L6, L7 and L8 for maximum output. Now adjustment of the rf psn can commence.

Turn all balance controls to centre of track and capacitors to half mesh. With rf in but no af tune the receiver to the resultant signal, and adjust carrier balance potentiometers for minimum signal. Switch in the bfo and tune for zero beat. Apply 1kHz at input at the same level as before, noting that the receiver should tune in two separate sidebands at 1kHz from the carrier, one above and one below, but one much stronger than the other. It should in fact be possible to get three separate zero beats as the receiver is tuned across the signal; one very strong, the next one weak (being the remaining carrier) and the other, at this time, fairly strong. This last one is the one to tune to as it is desired to make it as weak as possible. The receiver should be tuned so that the beat note produced by this sideband can easily be distinguished from the others. At this point, it may be profitable to ensure that the correct (lower) sideband is being suppressed; the weakest sideband obtained from the previous procedure should be on the low frequency side of the carrier. If this is found not to be so then it can easily be changed by reversing connections A and B or C and D on T2 or T3.

Assuming that the sidebands are correct and the unwanted sideband is tuned in on the receiver, adjustments can start to reduce this to the lowest possible level. Commence with the rf psn capacitors and adjust them for minimum output, then repeat with the af balanced pots. Remove af input, re-adjust carrier balance pots for minimum carrier and with the af input replaced, repeat the sideband suppression. It will be necessary during all this to adjust the receiver output level, and as with all sideband signals it is best to have the af gain well up and the output level adjusted with the rf/i.f. gain controls. As the unwanted sideband is suppressed it will be necessary to increase the receiver gain so that it is still audible. Finally, it should be possible for the unwanted sideband to become almost lost in the heterodynes produced by the carrier and wanted sideband.

The exciter is now almost ready for use but a little work remains to be done on the mixer unit to ensure linear operation. With the 1kHz af input as before, tune L6 for maximum receiver output. Remove af and move the link coupling to L5 out so that coupling is very weak, then monitor TR16 or TR17 source voltage and note reading. Replace af and increase coupling to L5 until the source voltage just starts to rise and then reduce it a fraction.

All that remains to be done is to replace the af oscillator with the microphone and adjust the audio gain so that the af voltage at TR3 collector is around 2V, pk-pk. A few milliwatts of ssb at 144MHz are now available and can be amplified to any desired power level using Class A single ended or Class AB push-pull stages.

Supply switching

To make the unit operational the supplies have to be switched on and off at the right times and some provision made for netting the vfo on to the received frequency. One such system is shown in Fig 113 but it may have to be varied to suit individual requirements.

The incoming 12V negative is earthed and the positive side goes to the wipers of a two-pole two-way switch and also to one side of a pair of contacts on the transmit/receive relay which are open on receive.

On net, the positive side of the 12V is routed to the rf and mixer section but not the audio as an acoustic feedback loop would be formed. Since the carrier has been reduced to a low level it may not be audible unless it is temporarily increased during the netting procedure. This is done by offsetting any one of the balanced modulator sources by applying a small positive

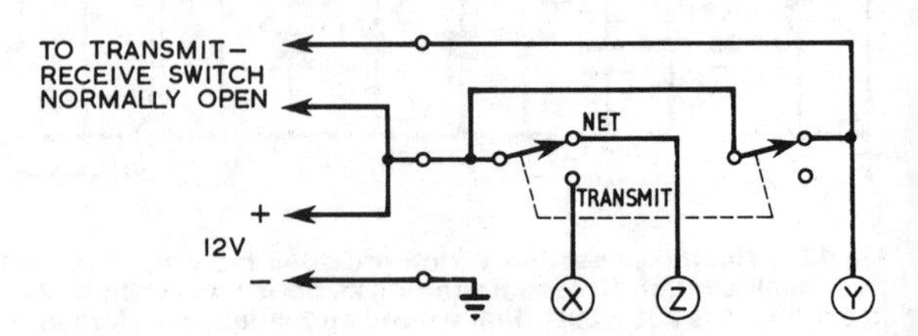

Fig 113. Power supply switching

potential to it via a 100kΩ resistor, which could be made adjustable if desired but should not be made less than 10kΩ. On receive, the audio section only is energized by the switch, and use can be made of this during setting-up as a jumper lead can be taken to other sections as required. The output from the exciter is now controlled by the transmit-receive switch, which puts voltage on the rf and mixer sections when transmit is selected. It is safe to interrupt the supply to the crystal oscillator TR14 as the power dissipated is very low and there is little oscillator drift due to thermal effects on the crystal.

Alternative phasing exciter

Another example of a phasing type which illustrates a number of different methods of achieving the same results as that just described.

In this case the ssb signal is generated at 108MHz, the balanced modulator is basically a diode ring type; the final frequency is obtained by mixing the generated ssb signal with a relatively lower frequency crystal oscillator of 37·5MHz in a balanced mixer and the output is amplified to a level suitable for driving a linear amplifier.

Output on both 70 and 144MHz may be obtained by retuning the final frequency stages—this is conveniently accomplished by use of a miniature four-gang capacitor.

VXO, doubler and amplifier

The vxo circuit enables the frequency to be varied by ±5kHz around the centre frequency of 54·35MHz. A BSX20 is used in the oscillator position, and the doubler stage uses a pair of BCY70 in cascode. The output from this stage is effectively pi-coupled into the amplifier stage, and the input capacitance completes the pi network. In the amplifier stage another BSX20 is used, the output lead to the diode balanced modulator being well tapped down the tuned circuit.

Diode ring balanced modulator

To provide an ssb suppressed carrier by the phasing method, two things are needed:

(a) two af signals of equal amplitude and with a 90° phase difference,

(b) four signals at carrier frequency of substantially equal amplitude and 90° apart in phase.

The first of the above is provided by the audio amplifier which includes the phase-shift network and transformerless outputs. The second is satisfied by use of the four-diode ring modulator utilizing a low-Q phase shifter together with two phase-inverting ferrite-cored bifilar-wound transformers to produce the four rf signals needed.

The low-Q phase shifter consists of a centre-fed $\lambda/4$ LC circuit in which each half provides 45° phase shift, so that there is a 90° difference at the terminals. The requirements for this are satisfied when the reactances of L and C are numerically equal and equal also to the terminating impedance R_0. In this case R_0 is chosen as 100Ω, making the input impedance of the network 50Ω. (The loading resistors used are 220Ω and the effect of transformer loss reduces this to 100Ω.) For 108MHz the values are approximately C = 15pF and L = 0·17μH.

The two phase-inverting transformers are each two plus two turns of 36swg wire bifilar wound on ferrite beads. Details of these transformers are illustrated in Fig 116.

It is important in this type of circuit that mechanical and electrical symmetry is preserved in detail in the construction of the unit if good balance is to be achieved.

A suitable component layout is shown diagrammatically in Fig 115, the whole unit being fitted into a screened box, with a coaxial input for the rf input and the two output leads brought out using miniature feedthrough terminals.

The rf balancing capacitors are best fabricated for the purpose using ¼in diameter discs fitted appropriately to the circuit component or pin if these are used. The earthed plate is a similar disc fixed to a 6BA bolt to allow adequate adjustment.

The modulator may be set up by disconnecting each potentiometer slider output in turn from the following amplifier input and then adjusting the balancing capacitors and potentiometer in turn on the other side, for minimum output. Then with both outputs connected to the following amplifier, L8 should be adjusted for minimum output of the unwanted sideband.

It should be possible to maintain 40dB carrier and unwanted sideband rejection, but 50dB may be attained by careful adjustment.

CW operation can be obtained by keying dc to unbalance the bridge. A 3·3kΩ resistor on one side of the switch connected to either of the af input points to the modulator (af1 or af2) and the other side via the key to the 12V (negative line) will produce the required result.

Audio amplifier, phase-shift network and output stage

This is conventional but differs from that used in the previous design in the component details of the phase-shift network. In this the values chosen are more readily available and this and the elimination of the transformers provides a simpler and smaller unit.

The first three stages are straight RC coupled using BC107 transistors, and the output feeds into the audio phase-shift network which in turn feeds a pair of fets (2N3819). The output from the sources are each fed into the base of two BC107 operated as emitter followers.

Sideband switching is provided at the output of one of the fets. The output from the modulator is fed into an fet source follower and then to a cascode output amplifier using BSX20 transistors.

Crystal oscillator, mixer, amplifiers

The crystal oscillator which operates at 37·5MHz with a miniature third-overtone crystal uses a BSX20 in a standard circuit. This is followed by another BSX20 amplifier with the output taken from the collector. The mixer uses a pair of BSX20 connected as a balanced pair with a balance control in the emitters. The 108MHz ssb signal is fed into the centre of the mixer input coil and the 37·5MHz crystal oscillator output is fed into one side of the input circuit. The output of the mixer is a double-tuned (split-capacitor) circuit with the output link coupled to the driver stage. The 108MHz ssb signal is introduced into the centre tap of L10.

The amplifier following the mixer uses a BSX20 and the output stage a 2N3553. Their tuned circuits are tuned by a miniature four-gang capacitor to allow them to be resonated at either 70 or 144MHz.

The bypass and damping components used in these stages are needed for the suppression of parametric oscillation. In the case of the output stage, two capacitors in parallel are necessary to obtain a sufficiently low emitter-to-ground impedance.

The necessary terminal bias for the driver and amplifier stages is produced by a potentiometer across a line at −9V to ground and the −12V line.

All the bias is obtained in this manner from a single supply line to facilitate transmit-receive switching. When on stand-by

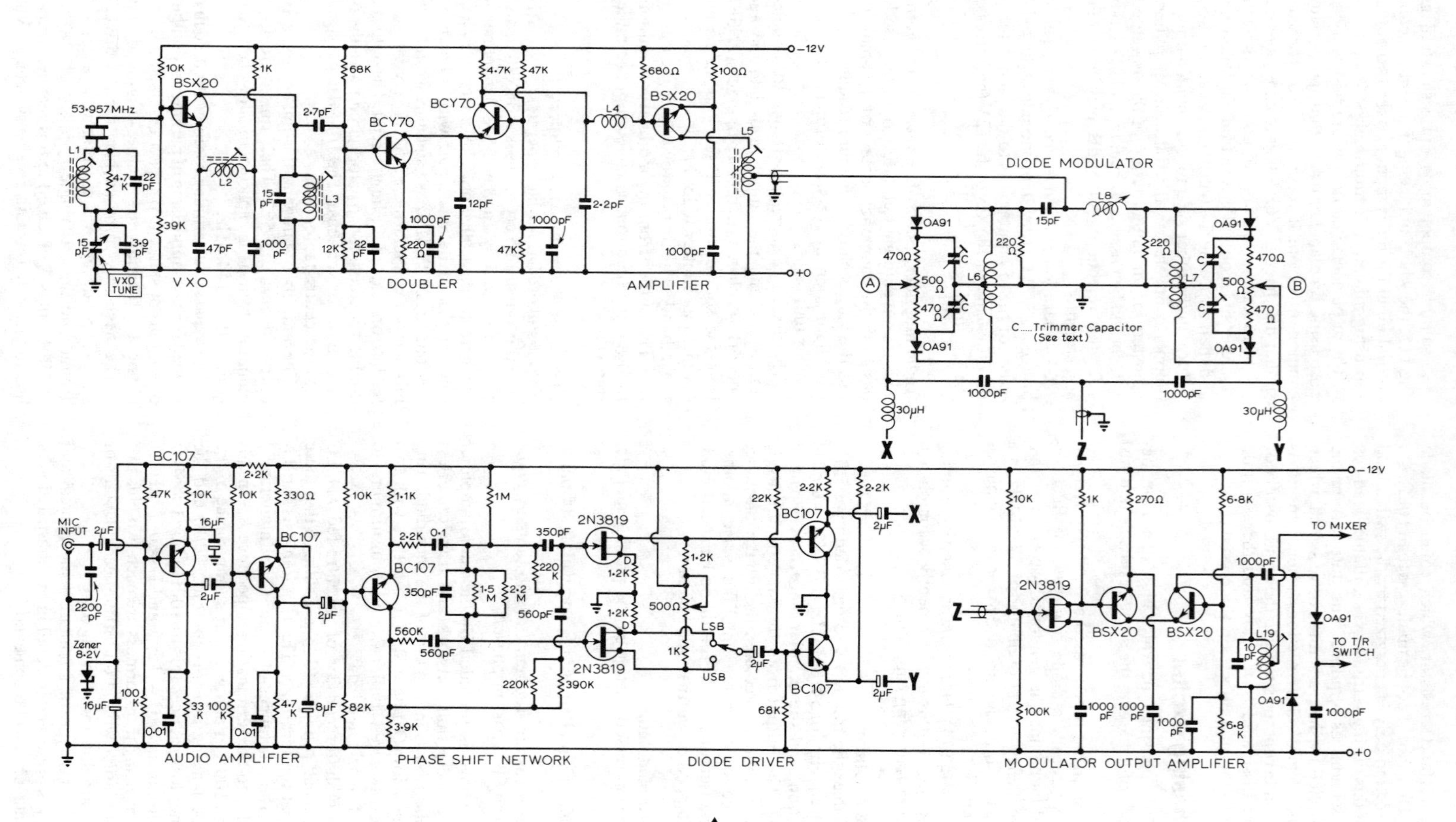

Fig 114. Circuit diagram of the phasing exciter

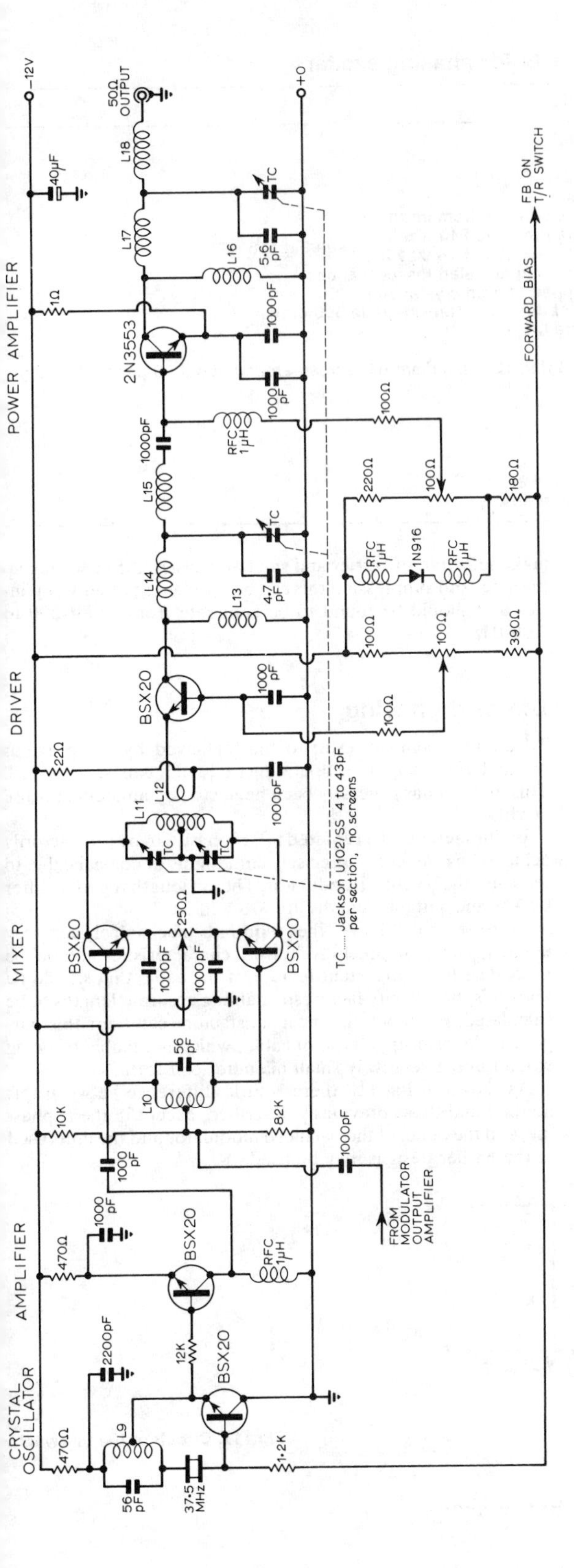

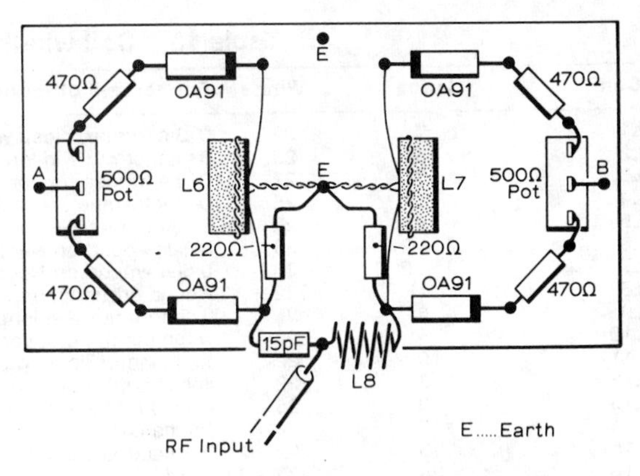

Fig 115. Layout of the diode modulator

or receive, the forward bias line voltage is allowed to fall to −12V by a suitable arrangement of the t/r switch.

To complete the t/r switching system, the crystal oscillator is also forward biased from the same line, to prevent spurious signals being received.

Tune-up procedure

1. Tune the vxo, doubler and amplifier to give at least 2V rms rf output into the junction of L8 and the 15pF capacitor, which is the input to the diode modulator.
2. Tune L19 for maximum output, this may be observed at the point marked *TR switch* shown in Fig 114.
3. Disconnect the slider connection of one of the 500Ω balance potentiometers in the diode modulator.
4. With the balance trimmer capacitors approaching minimum capacitance, adjust the remaining 500Ω potentiometer for minimum rf output from L19. This may be done initially as in (2) but for final adjustments monitoring of the 144MHz ssb output will have to be carried out with a receiver as a monitor. Now increase the capacitance settings of the two balance trimmers on the connected side of the diode modulator. One of these will probably be found to reduce the output as its capacitance is increased, disregarding the other, adjust the first trimmer and the 500Ω potentiometer alternately to minimize the output.
5. Disconnect the slider connection from the potentiometer of the side that has been adjusted, reconnect the other side and make similar adjustments for minimum output.
6. With connections to both the sliders, little or no increase in signal should result. If this is not so give a final check to all the adjustments.

The carrier balance is now complete and the final stage of balancing out the unwanted sideband should not result in any appreciable increase in the carrier output.

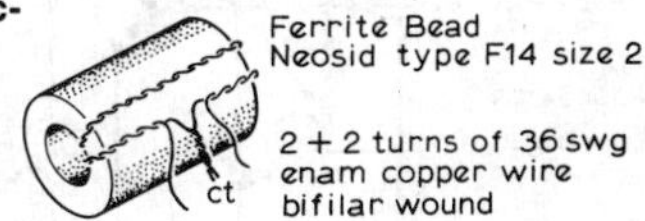

Fig 116. Detail of the inductors L6 and L7

Table 13. Coil winding data for phasing exciter

Coil	Turns	Wire	Former and other details
L1	7	22	0·3in former, close wound
L2	5	22	0·3in former $\frac{5}{16}$in long
L3	3	22	0·3in former $\frac{3}{16}$in long
L4	11	26	on high value $\frac{1}{4}$W resistor
L5	5	22	0·3in former $\frac{5}{16}$in long tapped 2t up from earth
L6	2 + 2	36	bifilar wound on Neosid ferrite head F14 size 2 } see Fig 116
L7	2 + 2	36	bifilar wound on Neosid ferrite head F14 size 2 } see Fig 116
L8	7	22	wound on $\frac{1}{4}$in mandrel $\frac{7}{16}$in long adjusted for resonance
L9	5	26	0·3in former $\frac{7}{16}$in long tapped 2t from crystal end
L10	6	26	wound in the grooves of hf dust core Neosid grade 500 grey
L11	10	22	$\frac{1}{4}$in mandrel $\frac{3}{4}$in long centre tapped
L12	3	22	link in centre of L11
L13	20	26	wound on Mullard FX1593 ring 12·7mm diam A4 (spread around about 75 per cent of ring)
L14	12	22	$\frac{1}{4}$in mandrel
L15	6	22	$\frac{1}{4}$in mandrel $\frac{7}{16}$in long
L16	20	26	as L13
L17	8	22	$\frac{1}{4}$in mandrel $\frac{1}{2}$in long
L18	7	22	$\frac{1}{4}$in mandrel $\frac{3}{8}$in long
L19	5	22	0·3in former $\frac{5}{16}$in long tapped 2t up

Main tuning capacitor Jackson U 102/SS 4-43pF per section (4), no screens.

Sideband suppression procedure

1. Unbalance the diode modulator by applying −12V through a 1kΩ resistor as for cw operation to the connection between one of the audio amplifier output capacitors and the rf choke feeding into the diode modulator. Peak up the output stages of the transmitter—this should result in an output of 0·6 to 0·8W at 144MHz and rather more at 70MHz.
2. Feed into the microphone input a few tens of millivolts of 2kHz tone, preferably a pure sinewave.
3. Switch off the modulator dc unbalance and switch to usb. Then increase audio drive until the indicated rf output is about half that obtained under carrier driven conditions (as found in 1).
4. Tune in the unwanted (lower) sideband on a selective receiver and then adjust L8 by opening or closing the turns until the lower sideband is reduced in strength. It should be possible to adjust this so that it is at least 40dB below the wanted sideband. It is usually possible to attain 50dB suppression without difficulty.

The carrier suppression should not be degraded by more than 60dB at the most, in the driven condition as compared with the undriven condition. The undriven carrier suppression should not appreciably change after the sideband balancing has been carried out. If it alters, or if thermal drift unbalance is noticed, the modulator is probably not being driven hard enough. The choice of a relatively high audio tone (2kHz) is to make selection of carrier and sideband easier. After setting up the sideband suppression this can be checked at other frequencies and should be found to be adequate from about 200 to 4,000Hz.

Direct rf phasing

To obtain a similar result to that achieved by the previous method, rf phasing at the operating frequency can be employed. This method has generally been neglected by amateurs for use at vhf.

In this method, the required 90° rf phase can be satisfactorily achieved by the use of precisely cut lengths of coaxial cable to feed into the balanced modulator. The cut lengths need to differ by $\lambda/4$ and suitable lengths are $\lambda/8$ and $3\lambda/8$.

In order to achieve the required mechanical accuracy needed, cable of precisely known characteristics should be used. The most important feature of the cable that should be known is the velocity factor, so enabling accurate lengths to be calculated. Probably, the most satisfactory cable for this purpose is the semi-rigid type of cable, which is capable of being wound into a relatively small diameter coil form.

As shown in Fig 118 there is little difference between this method and those previously described, except in the rf phasing, and the detail of the balanced modulator and the units used in the earlier designs may be used.

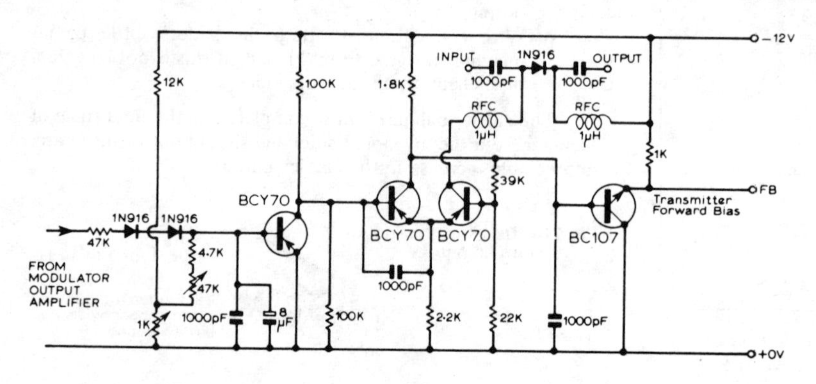

Fig 117. Circuit of the t/r switch

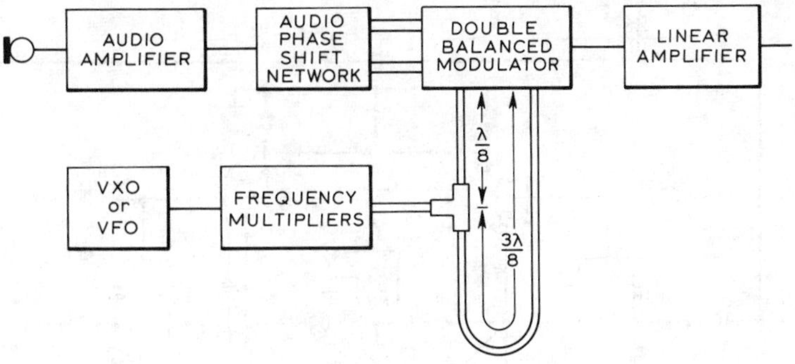

ig 118. Direct rf phasing with coaxial cable

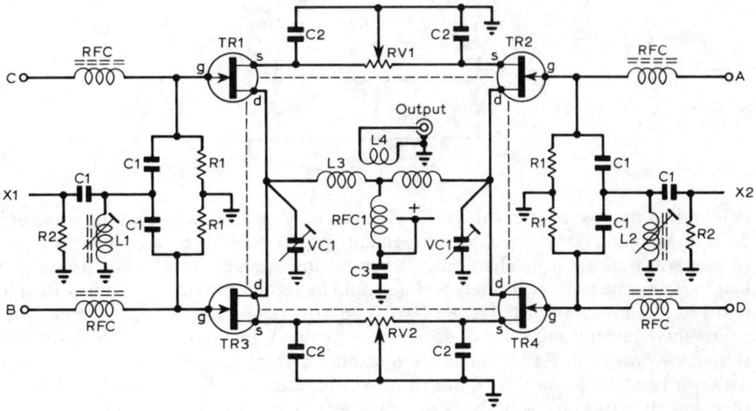

ig 119. FET double-balanced mixer

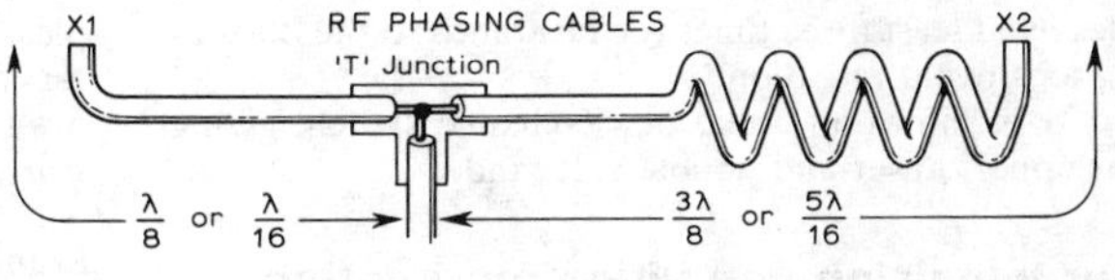

Detail is therefore confined to the double-balanced modulator, and the rf phasing arrangement. Also given are details of the audio phase change switch for selection of sideband.

Double-balanced modulator

This unit consists of a ring of four fets (Fig 119). For the preservation of mechanical symmetry it is necessary to use a fet device which is constructed symmetrically, so that the source and drain connections can be interchanged.

As an alternative to the field effect transistors, triode valves such as 6C4 or 6CW4 may be used. The circuit of a valve double-balanced mixer is given in Fig 120.

The rf signal is fed into the gates of TR1 and TR3 in parallel and the 90° delayed signal is fed into TR2 and TR4. Also the four connections from the two phases are into the gates of the four fets.

The input balance of the rf signal is achieved by adjusting the inductors L1 and L2 and balancing of transistors is by adjustment of RV1 and RV2. RF balance in output is by careful adjustment of VC1 at each end of the output coil.

It is important that the carrier signal does not feed round the circuit and it is therefore necessary to screen the whole of the output circuit, as indicated in Fig 119. This should preferably take the form of a small square box with a close-fitting lid, with the output being taken out above the chassis.

The input from the rf phasing cables to the two input connections, which should be mechanically and electrically as similar as possible, is connected directly to the points X1 and X2.

Production of the required 90° delay needs a difference of $\lambda/4$

Table 14. Component list for both valve and fet circuits

RFC	17t 28swg $\frac{1}{4}$in ferrite former
RFC1	50-100Ω ww
R1	15kΩ
R2	82-100Ω
RV	1,000Ω
VC1	disc or ceramic trimmers, 2 to 6pF
C1	100pF miniature
C2	1,000pF
C3	500pF feedthrough
L1 and L2	3t 26swg $\frac{1}{4}$in diam vhf slug
L3	3 + 3t 20swg $\frac{3}{8}$in diam each $\frac{1}{2}$in long $\frac{3}{8}$in gap
L4	2t 20swg $\frac{3}{8}$in diam in centre of L3

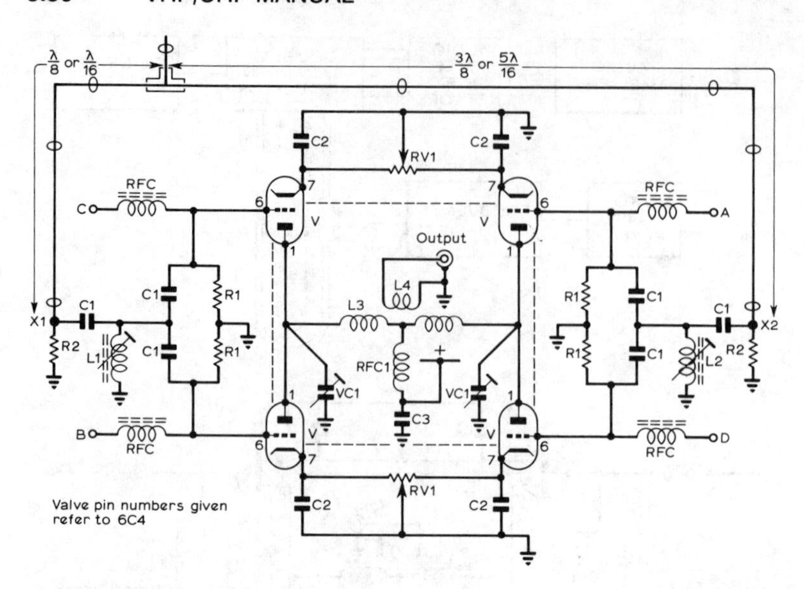

Fig 120. Valve-type double balanced mixer

in length of the two coaxial cables. The lengths may be $\lambda/8$ and $3\lambda/8$ or $\lambda/16$ and $5\lambda/16$ or other convenient size, possibly the former is most suitable mechanically. When cutting the cable to length it must be done accurately and it should be remembered that 1° for a cable of velocity factor of 0·6 is approximately ⅛in.

For this reason some form of adjustment of the T junction should be provided. Rather than use a standard T connector with the associated connectors, this can easily be achieved by a short length of trough line of the same characteristic impedance as the coaxial cable. The centre conductor should be below the top of sides by at least three times the clearance to the bottom and sides, to prevent radiation.

In Fig 121 is shown an audio phase-change switch, giving output for upper, lower and double sideband.

Amateur television and video modulation

There are several methods of picture transmission: television (high and low definition), slow-scan and facsimile (fax). RTTY operators will also know how to send pictures. Television is of particular interest, and the following outline of the principles and equipment involved is very brief but should indicate some of the areas of interest necessary to get a station on the air. Th British Amateur Television Club publishes an excellent man ual, *Amateur Television*, which covers the basic theory an much valuable practical information. BATC also publis *Slow-scan Television*. Membership of the Club ensures receip of the journal *CQ-TV*, which provides the latest information o slow-scan and television. A Low-Definition Television Associ ation has been formed in which the members use Baird's orig inal 30-line system (ldtv) with modern techniques.

Television, slow-scan and fax all use the same basic princi ples. Unlike the human eye, which has about 150 million simul taneous channels of visual communication, only one channel i available on a radio system. As a result, a process terme *scanning* has to be used.

Scanning

Scanning requires, first, that the picture to be transmitted i *framed* in a field of view with an *aspect ratio*. The standard rati for television is 4 by 3 units, as shown in Fig 122(a). Fo slow-scan, the ratio is 1 by 1. It is seen that picture size is of n importance so long as the ratio is correct.

Fig 122(a) shows a scanning spot that traverses the field lin

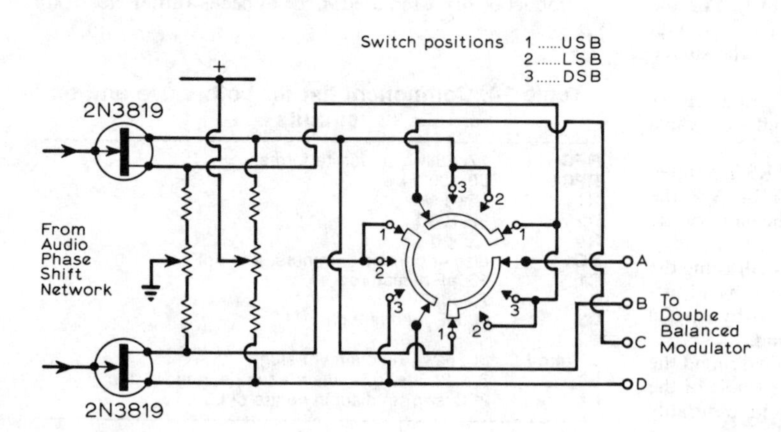

Fig 121. Audio phase-change switch

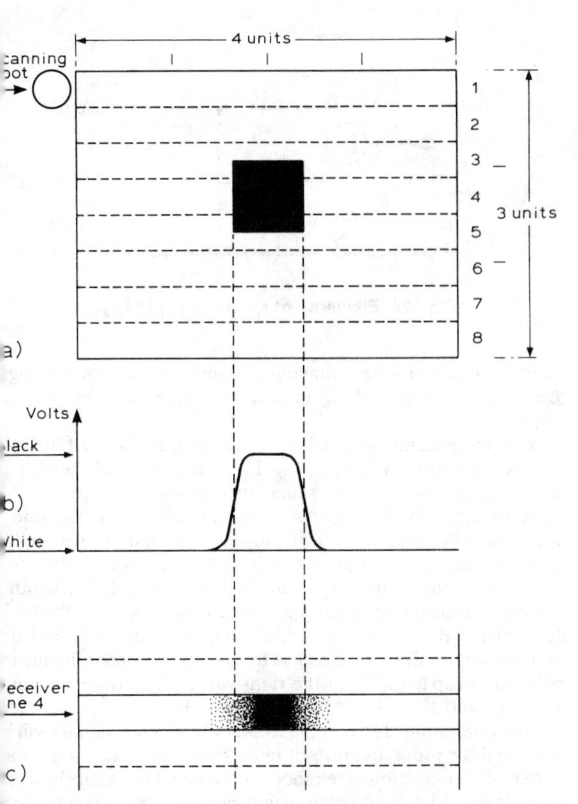

ig 122. (a) Complete scan of a white background. (b) Voltage utput from scan of line 4. (c) Reproduction of line 4 in a perfect receiver

y line (similar to the way a book is read), translating the ariations of light and shade (and possibly colour) that it ncounters, into voltage variations which are used to amplitude odulate the transmitter. The camera, with its optics and elec-onics, carries out this operation for television, but slow-scan nd fax can use simpler systems to scan the field. At the ceiver, a crt beam is swept across the face of the tube in nchronism with the camera scan, and the demodulated signal used to modulate the beam current, thus "writing" a repro-uction of the picture. Fig 122(a) shows a complete scan of a hite background with a black square in the middle, being rovided by eight lines. In Fig 122(b) the voltage output from e scan of line 4 shows that the edges of the black square will be urred and ill-defined. It will be noted that the top and bottom dges scanned by lines 3 and 5 will be similarly ill-defined. A erfect receiver will reproduce the edges of the line 4 scan as own in Fig 122(c). In order to improve resolution of the dges, the spot must be smaller and more lines will be needed. elevision, dealing with moving pictures, requires a complete an to be so fast that, compared with any movement taking ace in the scene, each complete scan is of a virtually still icture. Standard broadcast UK tv scans 25 pictures each sec-nd. Slow-scan and fax, dealing with still pictures, can use as any lines as may be required for high definition, and can take comparatively long time to complete a picture scan.

The scanning process generates modulation-frequency com-onents that can be very high for television, where a complete icture scan must be completed in a very short time. For still pictures, the scanning time can be slowed to the point where the highest modulation frequencies that are generated come within a 3kHz channel width (slow-scan), or even a 1kHz channel (fax). LDTV can be accommodated in a 5kHz channel.

All broadcast systems use a modified system of scanning, termed *interlaced scanning*. Referring to Fig 122(a), interlaced scanning would require that the complete field would be scanned by lines 1, 3, 5 and 7, and then the gaps would be filled by re-scanning the field with lines 2, 4, 6 and 8.

Television standards

Picture quality is determined by spot size and, therefore, the number of lines required to fully scan the field. There are many reasons why amateur television should follow existing broadcast practice, not least of which is the availability of receivers. There are two UK standards. One, the original 405-line black-and-white system, and the later 625-line system which includes colour and Teletext. Both use an aspect ratio of 4 by 3, and both transmit 25 complete pictures per second. The highest modulation frequency generated in the 405-line system is about 3MHz, while 5–5·5MHz is generated in the 625-line standard.

The video bandwidth of the 625-line system includes a sub-carrier on about 4·43MHz for carrying the colour information to a colour receiver but, for amateur use, there is no reason why a 405-line system should not handle colour by means of a similar sub-carrier method within the 3MHz video channel.

The modulating waveform

A single communication channel can only handle one bit of information at any one instant of time, but a television channel requires a minimum of three types of information to be transmitted for a black-and-white system. An additional type of information would be required for colour. The scanner output will amplitude modulate the transmitter, and it is necessary for the receiver tube beam to be in exactly the same two-dimensional position as the scanning beam in the transmitter camera. This requires synchronizing information to be transmitted that will tell the receiver the precise position of the scanning spot in both the horizontal and vertical planes.

Fig 123(a) shows the modulating waveform of a 405-line system during a one-line scan. The video modulation varies the transmitter output from 30 per cent to maximum, and not from zero to maximum as would be the case for a voice transmission. The video is "blanked" for a fraction of the total line period, and a *line sync* pulse inserted from the 30 per cent black level to zero. This pulse tells the receiver when to start its sweep across the tube. When the line scanning reaches the bottom of the field another, longer, blanking pulse blanks several lines, and the inserted pulses are changed to a train of broad pulses (Fig 123(b)) which the receiver can use to return the crt beam to the top, to restart its vertical sweep downwards. The receiver separates the pulses from the video information by amplitude discrimination. The broad and narrow pulses can be separated by passive circuitry.

The 405-line waveform shows what is termed *positive* modulation, in that peak white corresponds to maximum transmitter output. The 625-line system uses an inverted waveform (*negative* modulation), in which sync tips are at peak rf output, and peak white is near zero.

Video signal processing

Good-quality picture transmission requires that bandwidth considerations are fully observed, not only for picture quality, but to ensure that all the pulses on which the timing depends are

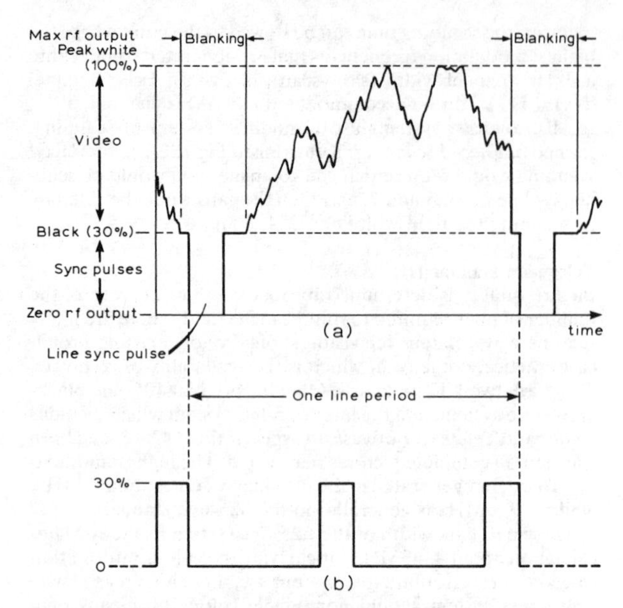

Fig 123. (a) Modulating waveform of 405-line system during one-line scan. (b) Train of broad pulses which the receiver can use to return to crt beam to the top of screen

as near rectangular in waveform as possible. Amplifying and processing the signal output from the camera or scanner up to final modulation requires uniform treatment over a video-frequency range from dc to 5·5MHz, and this requires greater care than is required for audio processing.

Fig 124 shows the elements of any amplifying stage, in which the output load R_c is in shunt with a capacitance C_t. This capacitance, made up of the output capacitance of the stage, plus the input capacitance of the next stage, is seldom shown in circuit diagrams. C_t may not be very significant for audio stages but, for video amplification, its presence is very real, as shown in Fig 125. Assuming that the stage gain is proportional to R_c of Fig 124 and that the upper useful frequency limit is reached when the gain falls by 3dB, curve (1) shows how the gain varies with frequency, the highest useful frequency being f_1. If R_c is halved in value, the gain will fall by 6dB, and the resulting response curve (2) shows how the highest useful frequency (ie −6 to −9dB) has moved up to f_2. Thus, for wide-band video amplification we can trade off gain against bandwidth, but a

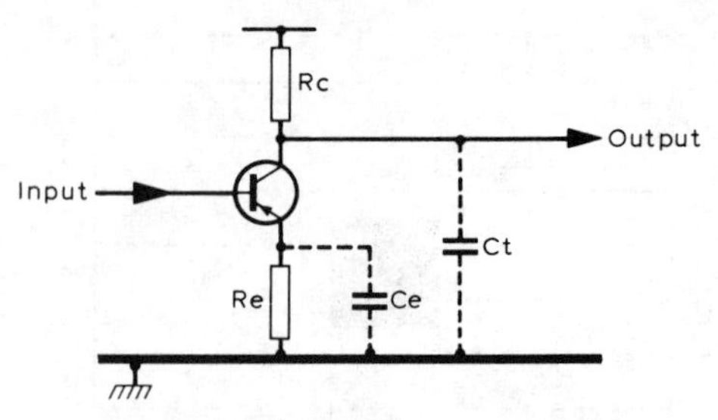

Fig 124. Elements of an amplifying stage

limit is reached when, having obtained an adequate high frequency response, the gain may be too small to be of much value.

Various systems are used to compensate for the fall in video gain shown in curve (1) in Fig 125. One method consists of including in series with R_c a reactance of opposite sign to C_t, ie an inductance. With the correct value of inductance, the gain at f_1 can be fully restored to 0dB and the −dB limit moved higher up in frequency. A variation consists of including an inductor in series with the output lead marked X in Fig 124. Another compensation system takes advantage of the fact that the emitter resistor R_e introduces overall negative feedback, and this can be progressively reduced as frequency increases, by means of a shunt capacitor C_e of the right value. (The time constants $R_e - C_e$ and $R_c - C_t$ need to be equal.)

Any interconnected equipment handling video signals will be designed for input and output impedances of 75Ω (sometimes 50Ω) and connections are made with coaxial cable of the same impedance. Matching is important because any mismatch can produce reflections of the video signals with, of course, drastic effects on picture quality. 75Ω circuits would require very large shunt reactances to produce the effects shown in Fig 125. Therefore relatively simple passive circuitry, designed for 75Ω impedances throughout, can be used for switching and mixing video sources.

Bandwidth and channel space

Television is characterized by the need to handle very high video frequencies right through the system from the camera to the display tube (and this includes the antenna systems!). Amplitude modulation of the transmitter would produce the normal double sidebands which, for 405 lines, would require a channel

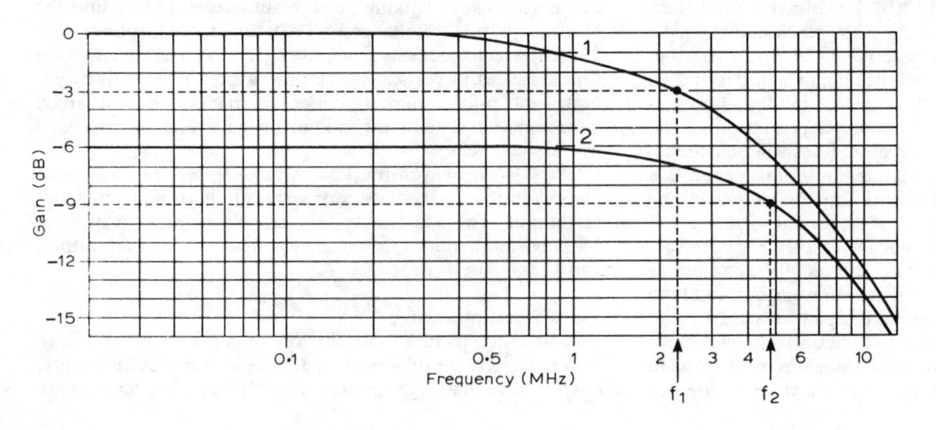

Fig 125. Variation of gain with frequency in Fig 124

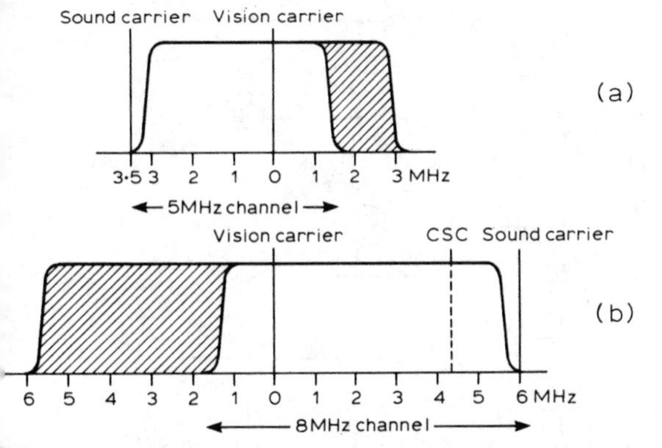

Fig 126. (a) Sound and vision spacings for (a) standard 405-line system, (b) standard 625-line system

space of 6MHz, and up to 11MHz for a 625-line system. Including a sound channel to either system would increase the channel width by about another 1MHz.

It was realized very early in the history of broadcast television that the heavy demands for channel space would limit the available number of channels, and a new system for saving channel space was evolved, termed *vestigial sideband* (vsb), or *asymmetric sideband* (asb). Fig 126(a) shows the sound and vision carrier spacings for a standard 405-line system. VSB involves filtering off a large part of the upper vision sideband (shown cross-hatched), leaving only 1MHz or so, and an overall channel width of only 5MHz. With suitable trimming of the receiver i.f. circuits, distortion of the vision signal by the loss of part of a sideband can be reduced to negligible proportions. The saving in bandwidth is even more pronounced for a 625-line channel, as shown in Fig 126(b), which also shows the position of a colour sub-carrier (csc) for transmission of colour information.

Modulation

When the transmitter is amplitude modulated with a video signal, it is essential that, from the modulated stage onwards, the rf circuits have a bandwidth adequate to ensure that all the video-frequency sideband information is radiated—preferably in the vsb form shown in Fig 126. Problems of transmitter rf bandwidth are easier to solve for high carrier frequencies, such as 10·5GHz, than for lower-frequency bands such as 430MHz, where the required sideband width is a large percentage of the carrier frequency.

Consider output-circuit tuning first. A fully-loaded tank circuit will have a low Q, and the consequent wide bandwidth will be adequate for all likely television bands. Tuning of the final output stage should not be centred on the video carrier, but should be offset towards the full-width sideband. This assists in filtering off the undesired part of the other sideband.

Assuming that the final stage is a valve, grid modulation with a dc coupling is favoured because, unlike sound modulation, the rf output has to be "turned on" to a degree required by the random video modulation, as examination of Fig 123 will show. If the stage is fully-driven, grid current will generally ensure a low-Q grid circuit but, if grid current does not flow during the whole of the drive cycle, it may be necessary to load the grid circuit with a resistor to ensure an adequate "flat" response. This puts extra demands on both the power from the modulator and the rf drive.

If the final stage transfer characteristic is not linear, it may introduce "stretching" or "crushing" of the modulation envelope, and this can distort the proportions of video and sync pulse amplitudes shown in Fig 123. In this case, it is preferable to modulate the stage previous to the final, where some "pre-distortion" can be introduced to compensate for the non-linearity of the output stage.

Equipment

Fig 127 shows a block diagram for a television system. The heart of the system is the pulse generator (spg). This unit provides all the timing and generates all the necessary pulses. All timing is derived from a master oscillator and, using transistors and ics, construction of designs published by BATC can be relatively simple. Fig 128 shows the details of an spg using discrete transistors, and Fig 129 shows a later design using a "one chip" ic.

A start can be made without a camera. It is possible to scan a photo or caption with a *flying spot* scanner, as shown in Fig 130.

A crt is driven from the spg to display a bright, well-focussed 4 by 3 scan on the tube face. This scan is optically focussed onto the picture transparency, and the light passing through is collected by a light-sensitive tube to provide the video signal output. The camera can be added later and, again, can be readily built from BATC published designs.

Linearity is essential in the processing of video signals, and the correct proportions of pulse to video amplitude in the modulating waveform must be closely observed. For these reasons, valves often provide easier solutions to some problems, and hybrid transistor/valve designs are often used, as shown in the modulator of Fig 131.

The principles of equipment interconnection are shown in Fig 127. The spg drives the scanning generator for the camera

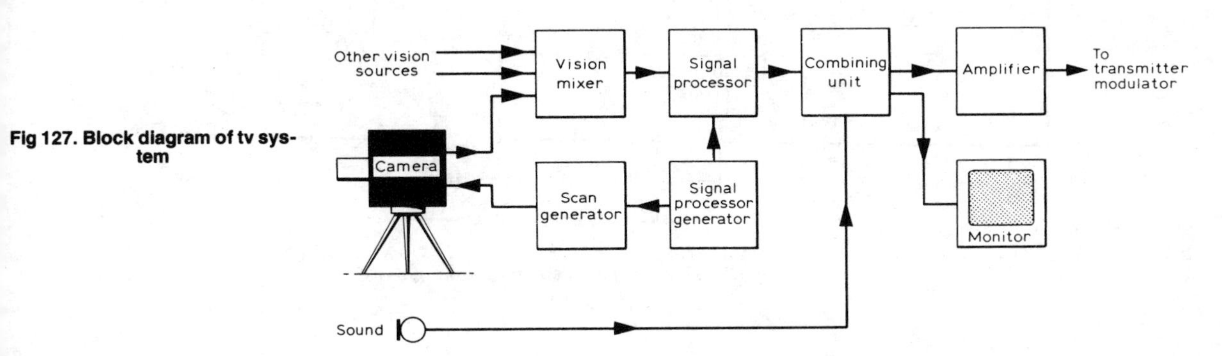

Fig 127. Block diagram of tv system

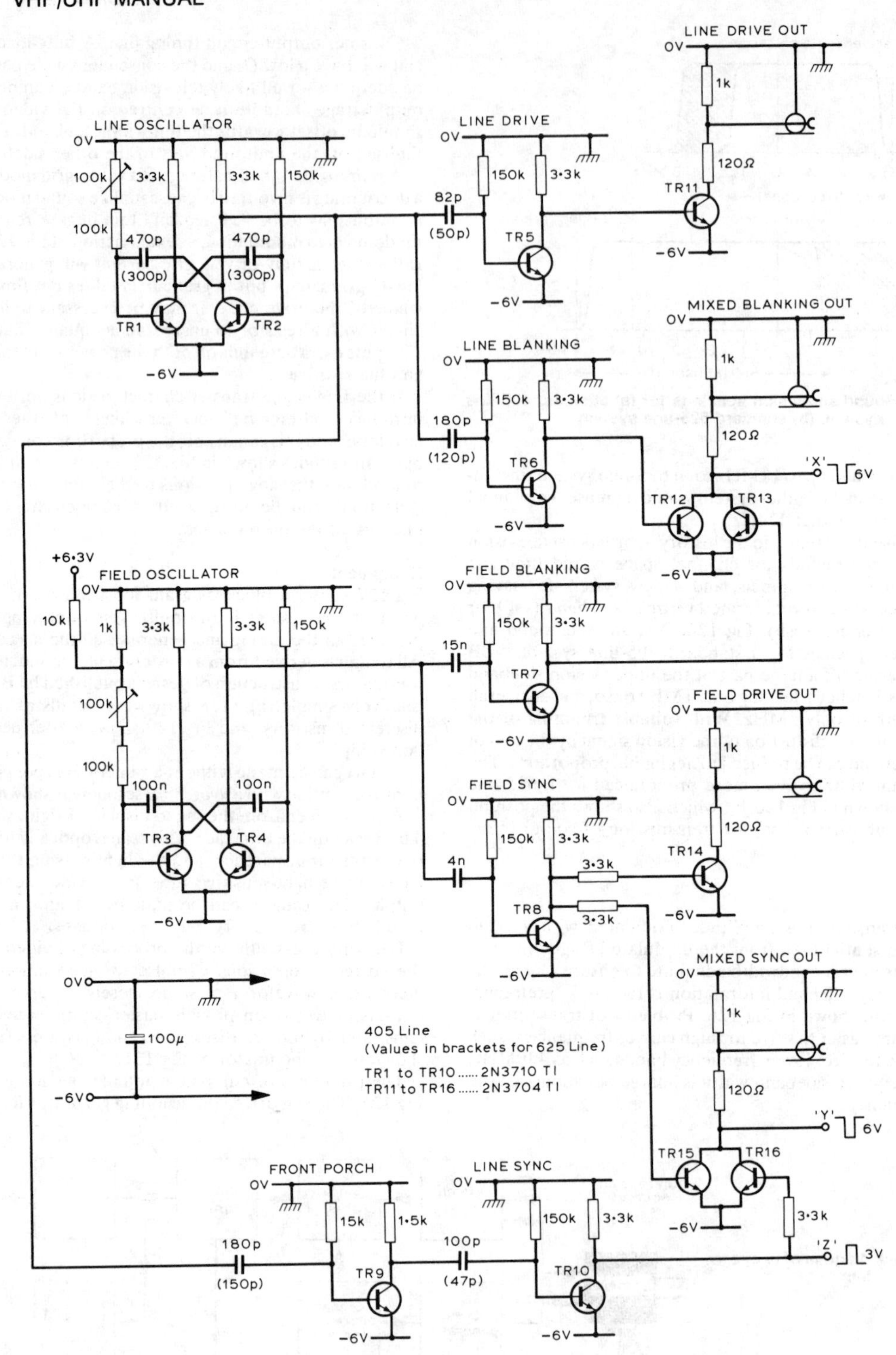

Fig 128. SPG using discrete transistors (*CQ-TV*)

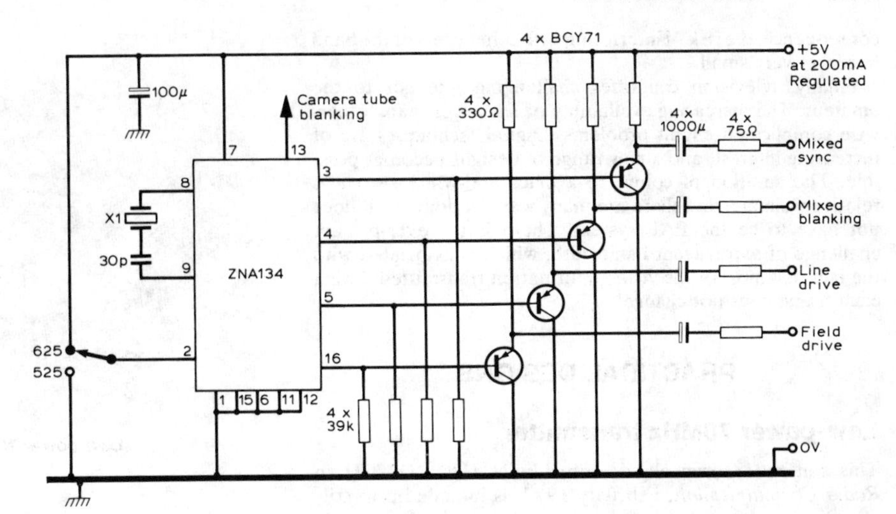

Fig 129. SPG using "one-chip" ic (CQ-TV)

Caption or photo-transparency
CRT
Electron multiplier
Video output

Fig 130. Flying-spot scanner

tube, and the video output from the camera is passed to the signal processor, where the blanking and sync pulses from the spg are inserted to provide the composite waveform shown in Fig 123. A vision mixer can provide for mixing with signals from other sources, such as a caption scanner or tape recordings.

A difficult choice for anyone setting up a television station is which standard to use. 405-line systems have the present advantage that receivers are relatively easy to come by, but the trend is to use 625 lines from the start. A switchable spg that will change from 405 to 625 would clearly ease a later change from a 405 start.

Another consideration is which band to use. 144MHz is clearly out of the question because the whole band is not wide enough for one 405-line channel. 430MHz is wide enough for a 405-line channel, but barely for one 625-line channel. Questions of interference with other users of the bands are important, and the higher-frequency bands are much more suitable for television. The 10GHz band is particularly suitable for several reasons, the most important of which are (a) the band is 500MHz wide and very many television channels can be accommodated, (b) a look at the microwave chapter in this book will show how simple the rf circuitry can be, and (c) on this band, it is necessary to use an antenna system that will generate narrow beams at both the transmitter and receiver and, as a

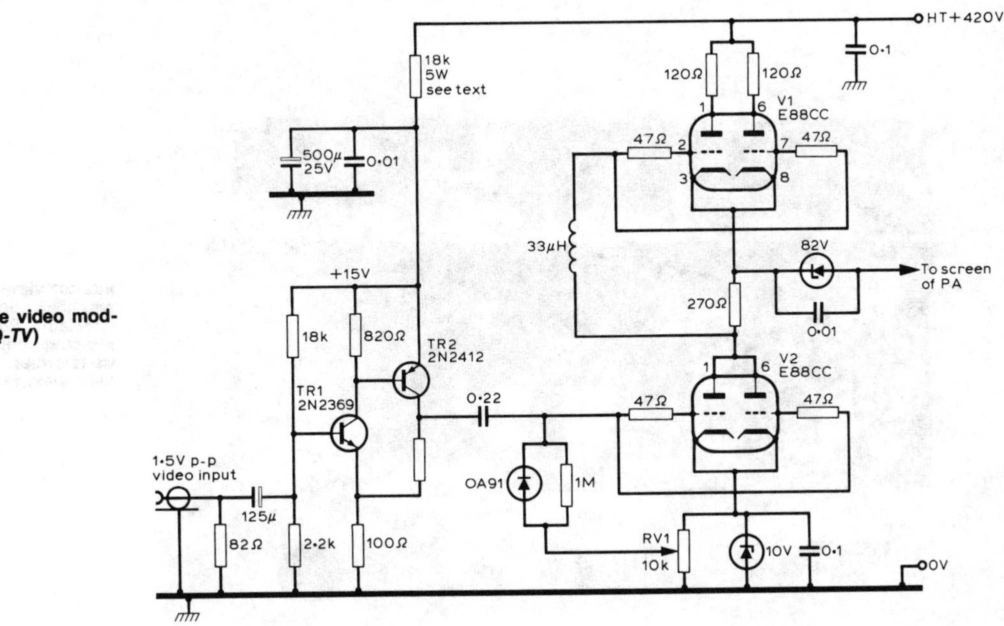

Fig 131. A negative video modulator (CQ-TV)

consequence, the risk of interfering with other users of the band becomes very small.

Finally, television can offer challenging interests to the amateur. The increasing availability of ics solves many otherwise complicated circuit problems. Digital techniques are of increasing interest, and a new range of designs becomes possible. The addition of colour to a black-and-white system is relatively simple, and there are many ways of doing it; it does not have to be the PAL system! There is the ever-present challenge of extravagant bandwidth, which is associated with the fact that most of the visual information transmitted during each frame does not change!

PRACTICAL DESIGNS

Low-power 70MHz transmitter

This transmitter, originally described by N. Hyde, G2AIH, in *Radio Communication*, February 1977, is intended primarily for portable operation and is powered from a 12V vehicle battery. Four transistors are employed in the rf section, with two ics in the modulator. The dc power input to the pa transistor is approximately 6W, and the total current consumption on peaks of speech is about 1A.

Low-power 70MHz transmitter

Circuit description

The circuit diagram of the rf section is shown in Fig 132. TR1, the crystal oscillator, is a BFX89 vhf amplifier transistor, feedback from collector to emitter being obtained via a tap on L1. An HC25U third-overtone crystal in the 35MHz range is used, and the value of the series capacitance C2 permits variation of the crystal frequency to a certain extent. Power supply to TR1 is regulated at 10V by the zener diode ZD1.

L1 is tuned by C4 and C5 in series; these two capacitors form a divider to match the oscillator to the following stage, TR2, BSX20, which functions as a frequency doubler. A small amount of forward bias is applied to TR2 via R5 and R6.

TR2 is coupled to a 70MHz amplifier stage TR3 via a capacitive tap on the doubler tuned circuit, which consists of L2, C8 and C9 in parallel, and C10. TR3 is a BSX61.

Output from the driver transistor is coupled to the power amplifier TR4 through a matching network consisting of the parallel-tuned circuit L3, C13, C14 and C15 in parallel, and the series inductor L4. The collector tuned circuit of the pa is an inverted-L circuit formed by L5, L6, and C19, with C20 and C21 in parallel; this arrangement matches the collector impedance to the 75Ω impedance of the antenna feeder.

TR4 is a TRW PT4176B capstan-type rf transistor or BLY85, or the BLY83 if it is desired to operate at a higher power. If either of these types is used it will be necessary to increase slightly the hole spacing on the rf pcb to accommodate the collector, base and emitter terminations. It may also be necessary to adjust the values of inductance and capacitance associated with the pa stage tuning, and to this effect provision has been made in the design of the pcb to permit additional

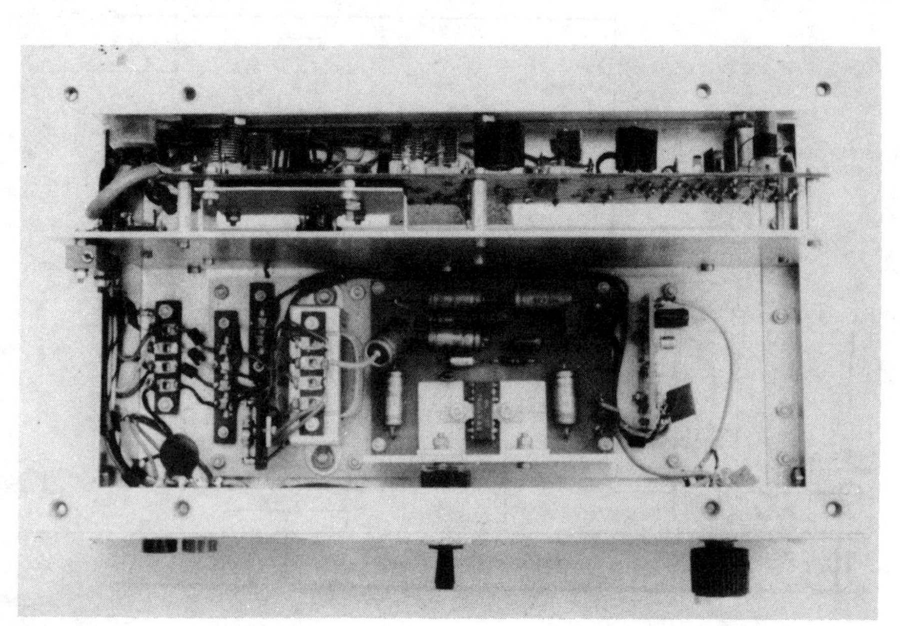

Interior view. Top, l to r: power amplifier, doubler and crystal oscillator. Bottom, l to r: wave-shaping network, modulation transformer, modulator ic and heat sink, microphone preamplifer

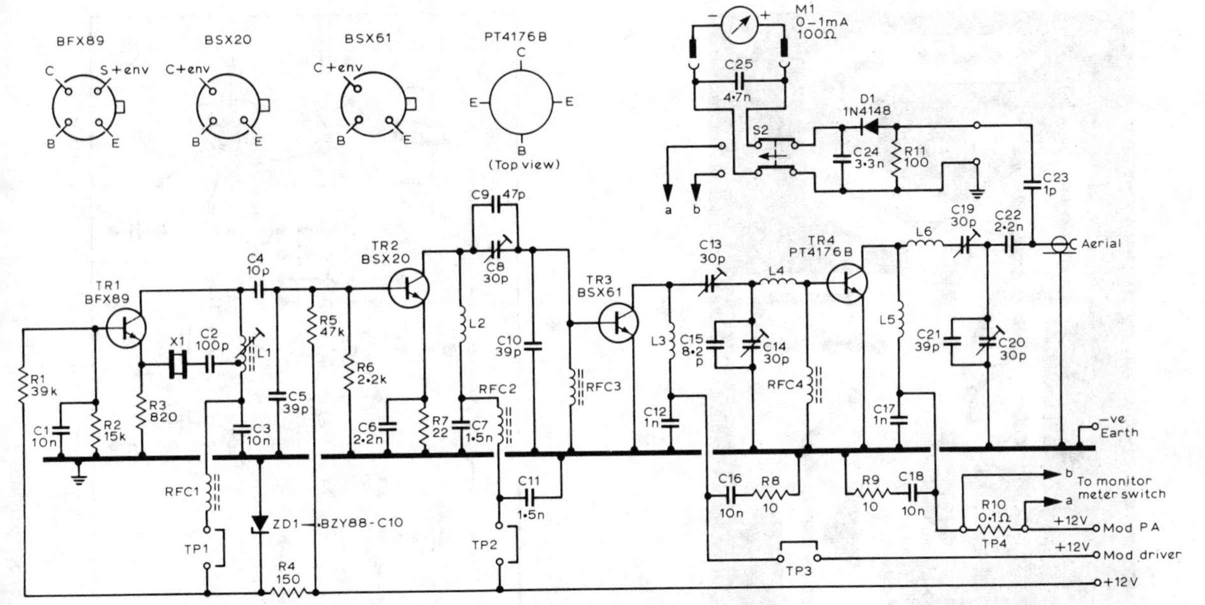

Fig 132. 70MHz transmitter circuit diagram

fixed capacitors to be included in the transistor base and collector circuits.

To eliminate any parametric oscillation in TR3 and TR4 circuits, parametric traps (C16, R8 and C18, R9) are associated with both transistors. Inductors L3 and L5 are used instead of rf chokes in the collector circuits and, while presenting negligible damping at the operating frequency, they act as short-circuits at the much lower parametric frequency.

A small proportion of the rf output is applied via a 1pF capacitance C23 to an rf monitor consisting of a diode rectifier circuit (D1, R11, C24) and an external 0–1 milliammeter M1. Test points (TP1 to TP4) are included in the collector circuits of all four transistors to permit current measurement during initial alignment, and any subsequent checking. In operation TP1, TP2 and TP3 are short-circuited by links and an external 0·1Ω resistor is connected across TP4, the value of this resistor being such that a 100Ω milliammeter at M1 will have a full-scale deflection of 1A.

The modulator (Fig 133) consists of two ics, a TAA263 preamplifier (IC1) and a TBA810AS power amplifier (IC2). The TAA263, which is a three-stage amplifier, is suitable for a dynamic microphone.

As the recommended operating voltage for the TAA263 is 7–8V the 12V supply is reduced to an acceptable level of 6·8V by R14 and the zener diode ZD2. R12 is the collector load resistor of the final transistor in the ic, with R13 applying negative feedback between output and input of the device. C26 is an rf bypass capacitor.

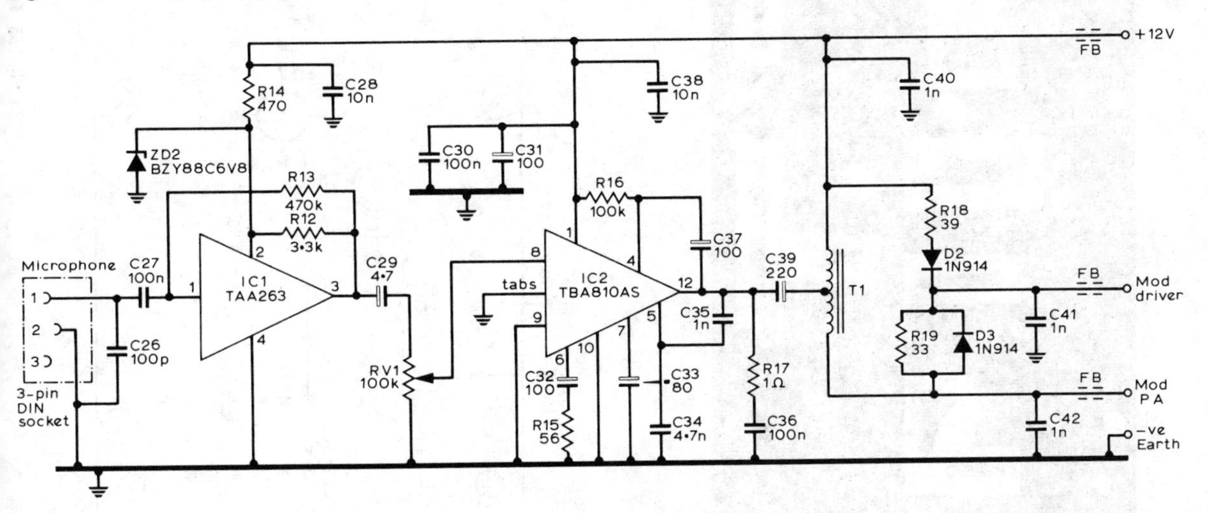

Fig 133. Modulator circuit diagram

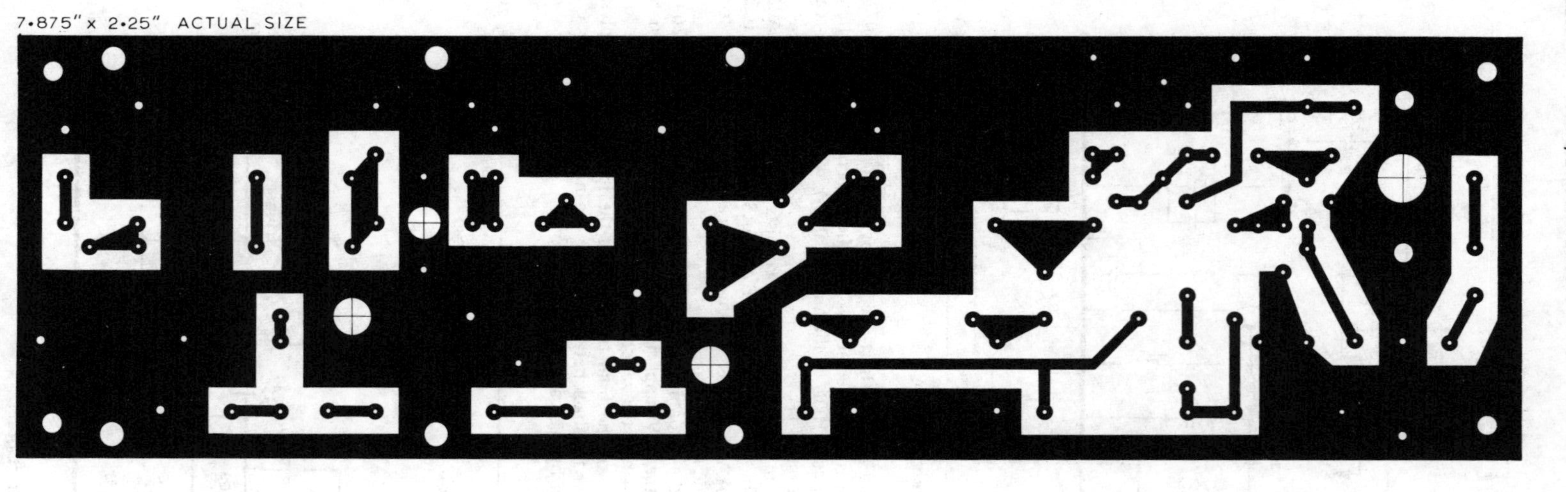

Fig 134. Transmitter pcb track layout

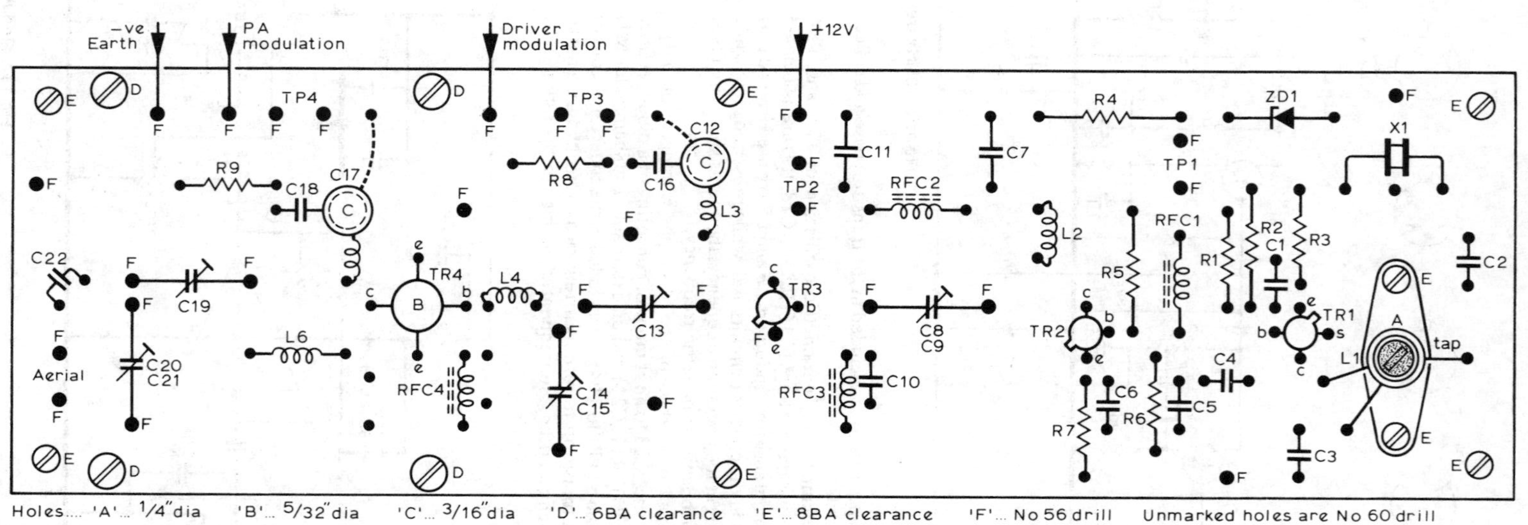

Fig 135. Top view of transmitter pcb showing location of components

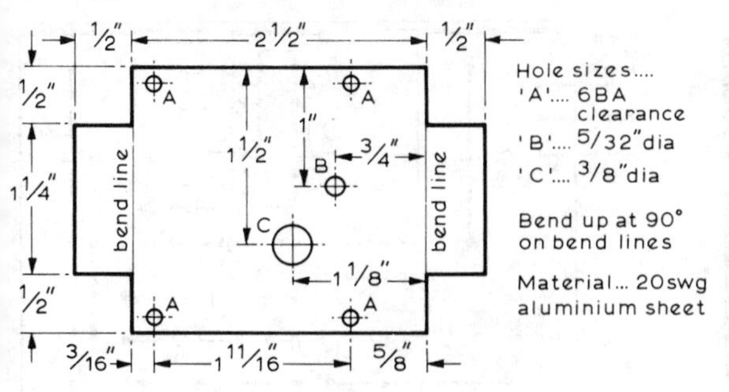

Fig 136. PA transistor heat sink

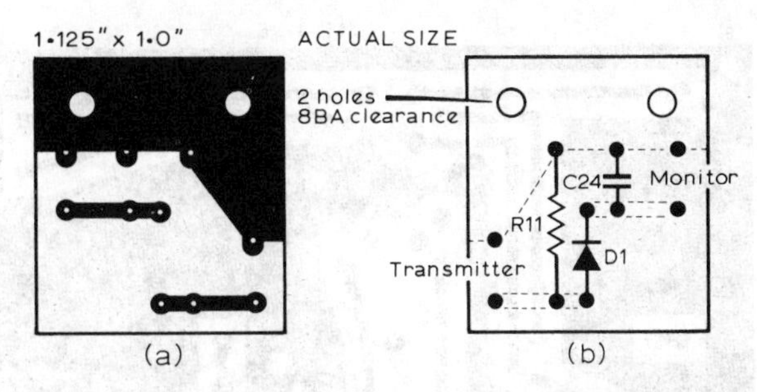

Fig 137. (a) RF monitor pcb track layout and (b) location of components

Output from a preamplifier is coupled to the main amplifier through a modulation depth control RV1. Audio output from the modulator is applied to the pa through an autotransformer T1, which has a step-up ratio of 1:2, but a transformer having a slightly higher ratio of 1:2·5 would give a better match between the 4Ω output impedance of the modulator and the pa collector impedance.

Modulation is also applied to the driver transistor through a wave-shaping circuit R18, D2 and R19, D3 connected across the modulation transformer; the function of this circuit is to clip the negative-going half-cycle of the modulation waveform applied to the driver, thus increasing the drive level to the pa on positive-going half-cycles, which results in an improved modulation waveform from the pa stage. Ferrite beads with bypass capacitors are included in the positive supply lead, and in the output leads to prevent rf feedback into the modulator.

It should be noted that, if the modulator is tested as an af amplifier driving a loudspeaker with one terminal earthed, then the polarity of C39 must be reversed for this test.

Constructional details

With one small exception, construction is on glassfibre-based pcbs. Double-sided board is used for the transmitter rf section, and single-sided board for the rf monitor, the preamplifier and the modulator proper. The exception is the modulation wave-shaping circuit which is constructed on a miniature four-way group board. No attempt has been made to miniaturize the equipment.

The rf board measures 7·765 by 2·25in and the circuit is constructed on a 0·125in grid. The track layout on the underside of the board, and the position of clearance holes in the copper on the topside of the board, are shown in Figs 134 and 135 respectively. Connections to the power supply, modulator output and test points are to pins made of short lengths of 18swg copper wire, soldered to the relevant land on the pcb and subsequently tinned; connections to the 30pF tuning capacitors are made to similar pins. At various points on the board 18swg wire is also used to connect the upper and lower surfaces; after soldering, these are cut off close to the copper foil. All pins at earth potential are soldered to both sides of the board. Holes for the pins are made with a No 56 drill, and adequate clearance around these must be allowed before etching the topside of the board. Holes for component leads are made with a No 60 drill.

The two feedthrough capacitors C12 and C17 are wired on the underside of the pcb to the lands adjacent to TP3 and TP4 respectively. The two emitter connections on TR4 are soldered to both upper and lower surfaces of the board. This transistor is fitted with a heat sink located on the underside. The heat sink (Fig 136) is fabricated from 20swg aluminium (the length of the threaded stud on the transistor determines the maximum gauge of metal that can be used) and is fitted with a spacing washer to clear the underside of the board, to which it is secured with four 6BA bolts and nuts. Clip-on heat sinks are fitted to TR2 and TR3.

Details of the rf monitor pcb are shown in Fig 137. This circuit is also constructed on a 0·125in grid and the board measures 1·125 by 1·0in. Coupling capacitor C23 is connected externally between the rf board and the adjacent monitor board.

Alignment

It is recommended that for initial alignment the modulator is not connected, and that a lower voltage, eg 9–10V, is applied to the rf board. Correct frequency of operation should be checked as each stage is adjusted. Alignment procedure is as follows:

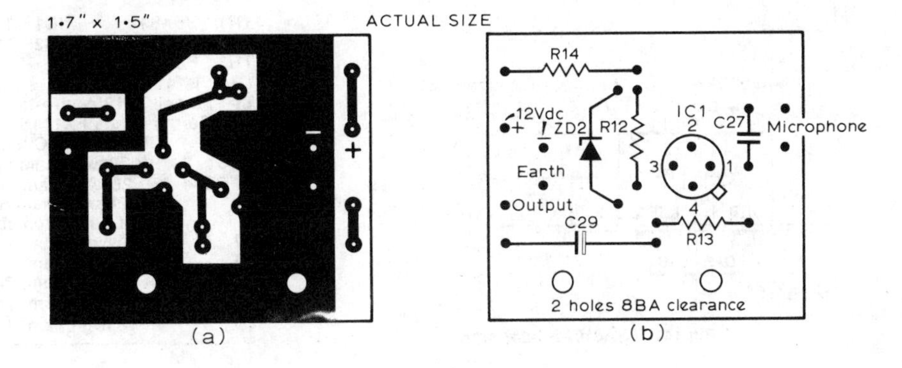

Fig 138. (a) Microphone preamplifier pcb track layout and (b) location of components

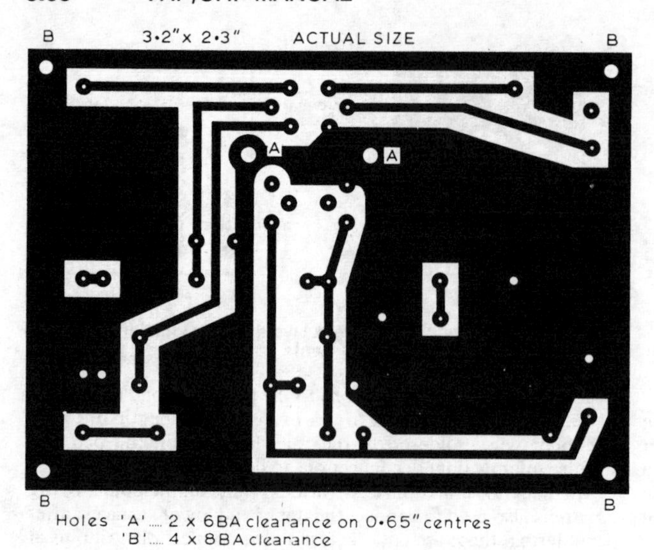

Fig 139. Modulator pcb track layout

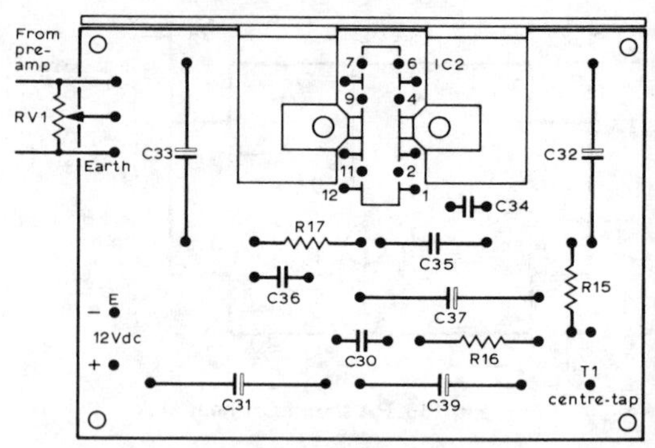

Fig 140. Modulator—location of components

1. With TP2, TP3 and TP4 open-circuited, connect a milliammeter (5mA maximum) across TP1. Adjust the dust-iron core of L1 for minimum current and then detune slightly to one side of resonance. (Tuning about the resonance point will not be symmetrical and the core should be set to the side at which the current rise is more gradual.)
2. Connect a milliammeter (25mA maximum) across TP2 and check that the resonance position of L1 corresponds to maximum collector current to TR2. Connect a milliammeter (100mA maximum) across TP3 and adjust C8 for maximum drive to TR3.
3. Connect a suitable load to the transmitter output pins. Connect a milliammeter (500mA maximum for initial

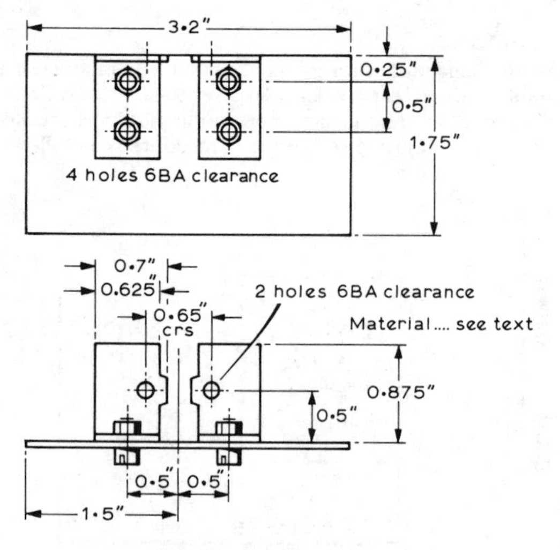

Fig 141. TBA810AS heat sink

Table 15. Components list

R1	39kΩ	**R7**	22Ω	**R14**	470Ω
R2	15kΩ	**R8, 9**	10Ω	**R15**	56Ω
R3	820Ω	**R10**	0·1Ω	**R17**	1Ω
R4	150Ω	**R11, 16**	100Ω	**R18**	39Ω
R5	47kΩ	**R12**	3·3kΩ	**R19**	33Ω
R6	2·2kΩ	**R13**	470kΩ		

All resistors except R6, R10–$\frac{1}{8}$ W carbon film. R6–$\frac{1}{3}$ W carbon film; R10 wire-wound.

RV1 100kΩ potentiometer

C1, 3, 16, 18	10nF		
C2	100pF	**C25**	4·7nF
C4	10pF	**C26**	100pF
C5, 10, 21	39pF	**C27, 30, 36**	100nF 100V mini mylar
C6, 22	2·2nF		
C7, 11	1·5nF	**C28, 38**	10nF
C8, 13, 14	30pF miniature air-spaced trimmers	**C29**	4·7μF 15V electrolytic
C19, 20	(30pF miniature air-spaced trimmers)	**C31, 37**	100μF 25V electrolytic
		C32	100μF 10V electrolytic
C9	47pF	**C33**	80μF 16V electrolytic
C12, 17	1nF feedthrough type	**C34**	4·7nF
		C35	1nF polystyrene (or miniature ceramic)
C15	8·2pF		
C23	1pF	**C39**	220μF 16V electrolytic
C24	3·3nF	**C40, 41, 42**	1nf

All fixed capacitors are miniature 50V ceramics except those described.

TR1	BFX89	**IC1**	TAA263	**ZD1**	BZY88C10
TR2	BSX20	**IC2**	TBA810AS	**ZD2**	BZY88C6V8
TR3	BSX61			**D1**	1N4148
TR4	PT4176B (TRW)			**D2, 3**	1N914

T1 Farnell T213 centre-tapped autotransformer
FB Ferrite beads FX1115
X1 35·13MHz HC25U 3rd overtone (for 70·26MHz)
RFC1, 2 2½t 28swg enam on FX1898 ferrite bead
RFC3, 4 2½t 26swg enam on FX1115 ferrite bead
L1 14t 28swg enam, tapped 2t, on Aladdin 7mm former, with dust-iron core
L2 4t 18swg enam, 7mm diameter 7mm long
L3 5t 18swg enam, 7mm diameter closewound
L4 4t 18swg enam, 7mm diameter 7mm long
L5 3t 18swg enam, 7mm diameter 8mm long
L6 5t 18swg enam, 10mm diameter 13mm long

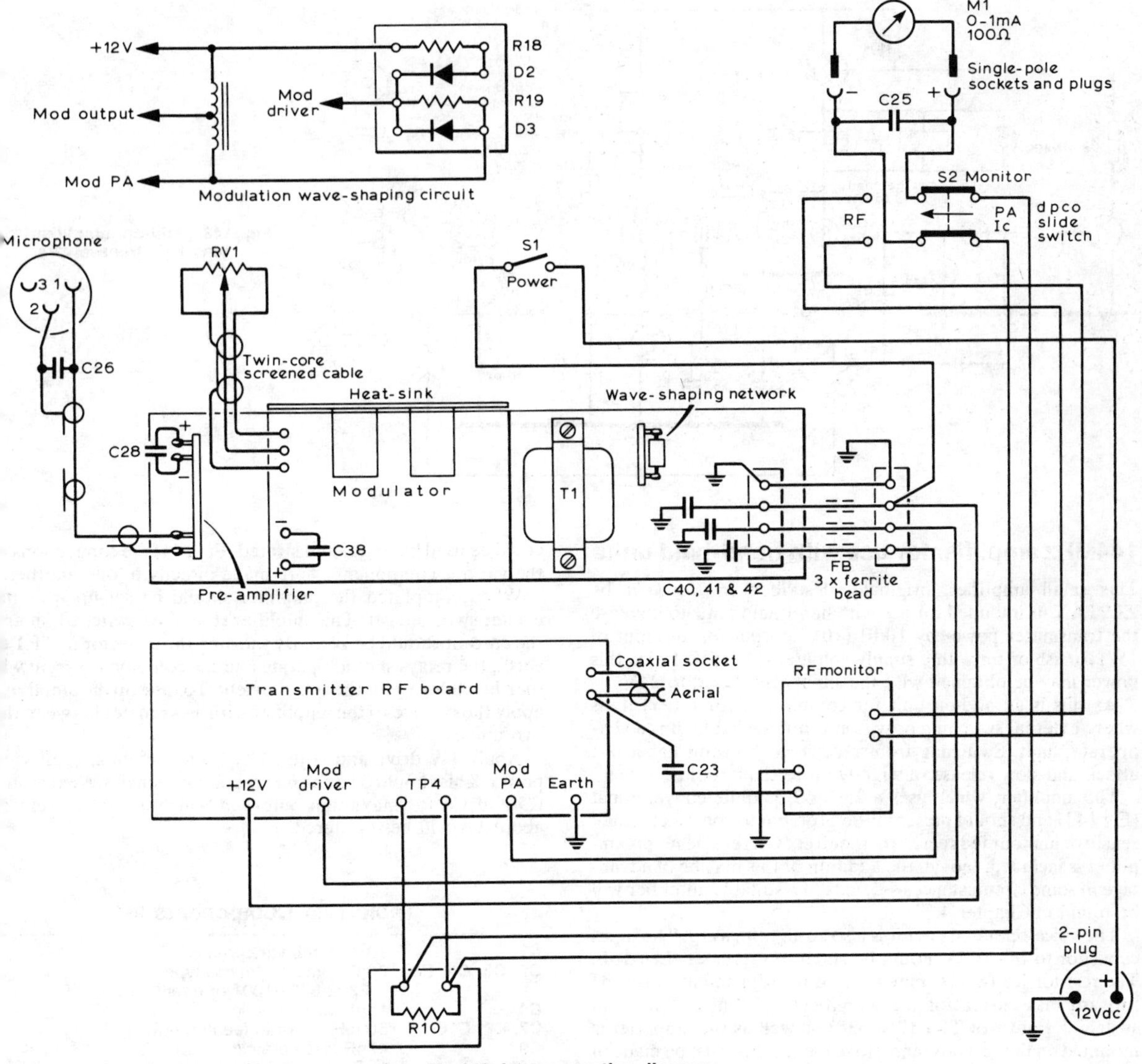

Fig 142. Interconnection diagram

alignment) across TP4 and quickly adjust C13 and C14 for maximum collector current to TR4. Should this be excessive (eg more than 250mA at this stage) reduce the value of C14 until an acceptable level is obtained.

4. Adjust C19 and C20 for maximum rf output.
5. Apply 12V to all stages and repeat the alignment procedure several times until maximum rf into the load is obtained. This is necessary as due to varactor effect the transistors are voltage-conscious. After alignment, TP1, TP2 and TP3 should be short-circuited, and R10 connected externally across TP4. Modulation may now be applied.

If required, C14 can be used as a drive level control to the pa stage; a decrease in the value of this capacitance results in reduced drive to TR4.

Table 16. Typical current readings with 12V power supply

Stage	Current	(mA)
TR1	(oscillator)	1·8
TR2	(doubler)	13·5
TR3	(driver	20 to 40
TR4	(pa)	approx 500
IC1	(preamplifier)	11
IC2	(modulator) quiescent	12
	speech peaks	approx 400

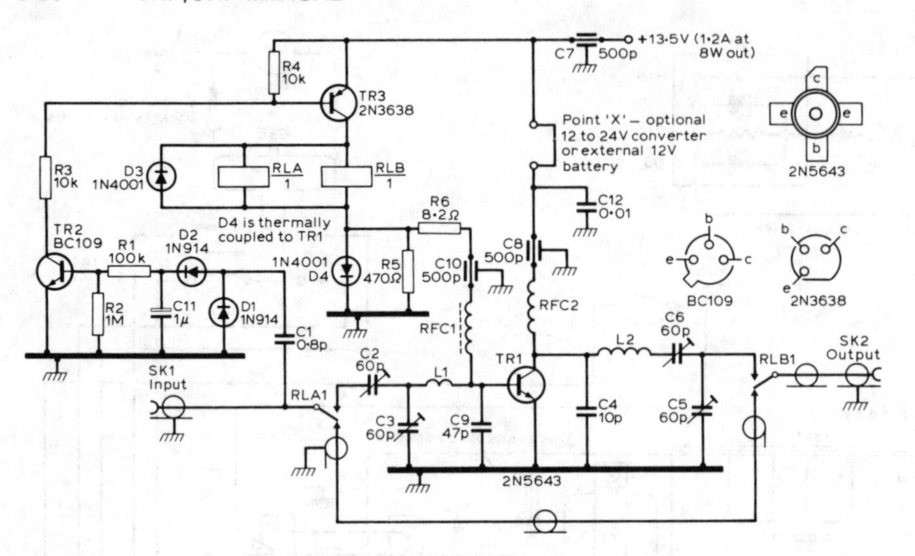

Fig 143. Add-on amplifier for hand-held transceivers

144MHz amplifier for use with hand-held units

This small amplifier, originally described in *Break-In* by ZL2TAX, is intended for use with hand-held units to increase the transmitter power by 10dB (10W output for an input of 1W) for ssb or fm with a supply voltage of 13·5V. Twice this power may be obtained with the supply increased to 24V.

As this is an add-on unit for commercial (or other) units where external switching provision is not available, it is a vox-operated unit. Switching from receive to transmit has a fast attack and slow release of slightly more than 600ms.

The amplifier, which uses a 2N5643, is quite conventional (Fig 143) and should present little problem to construct. Small sensitive unmounted relays are required. On receive no preamplifier is included, though the addition of this may be of advantage in some circumstances—details of a suitable amplifier will be found in Chapter 4.

The voice-operated circuit is also straightforward. The input capacitor to this (C1) should be small, not greater than 1pF. The resistor R5 (8·2Ω) may need some adjustment to set the forward bias current of the amplifier to 100mA. The main switching transistor TR1 (2N3638) as well as the amplifier is mounted on the cast box, and provision for this must be made in the copper-coated glassfibre ground plane. Of course a pcb could be used but in that illustrated (Fig 144) the connections t the various components were made directly to one another.

When completed the amplifier should be set up with th exciter switched off. The amplifier should be switched on an the current should be zero. By shorting the collector of TR1 t earth, the relays should operate and the combined current wi then be 100mA plus the relay current. To tune up the amplifie apply the rf drive to the amplifier with a swr meter between th two units.

Apply 1W drive and adjust C2, C3 for minimum reflecte power. This should be done on several frequencies. Next adjus C5 and C6 for maximum output at which a total current o about 1A will be registered.

Fig 144. Layout of add-on amplifier

Table 17. Components list

C1	10·8pF tubular ceramic
C2, C3, C5, C6	60pF trimmer, Philips type 2222 808 01001 or equiv
C4	10pF disc ceramic
C7, C8, C10	500pF solder in feedthrough
C9	47pF disc ceramic
C11	1μF 12V electrolytic
C12	0·01μF disc ceramic
R1	100kΩ ¼W
R2	1MΩ ¼W
R3, R4	10kΩ ¼W
R5	470Ω ¼W
R6	¼W (adjust on test)
TR1	2N5643
TR2	BC109
TR3	2N3638
D1, D2	1N914 or 1N4148
D3, D4	1N4001 or similar
RFC1	3t on ferrite bead 4312 020 31500 (Philips 6-hole)
RFC2	4½t ¼in i.d., 22 gauge
L1	1in 22 gauge wire
L2	3 turns 0·25in i.d. 22 gauge

Die-cast box, Eddystone part No 7134P
Heat sink (optional for 12V operation)
Connectors SO239
Relays spdt, 12V 45mA

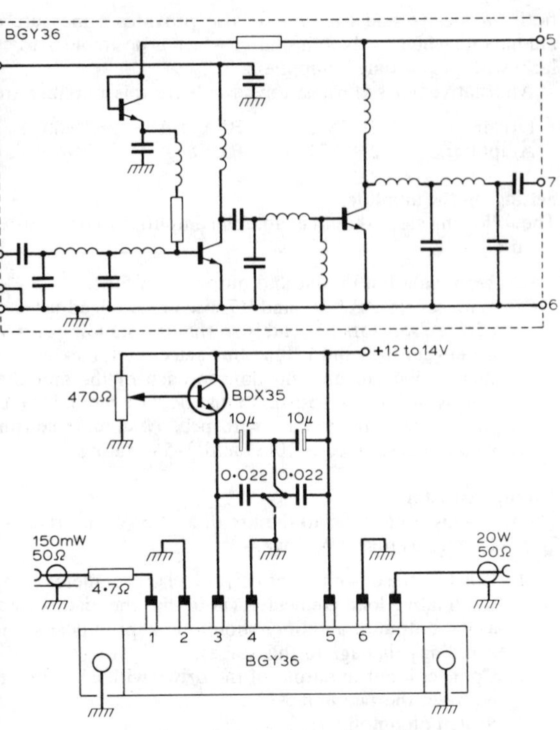

Fig 145. 144MHz broadband amplifier

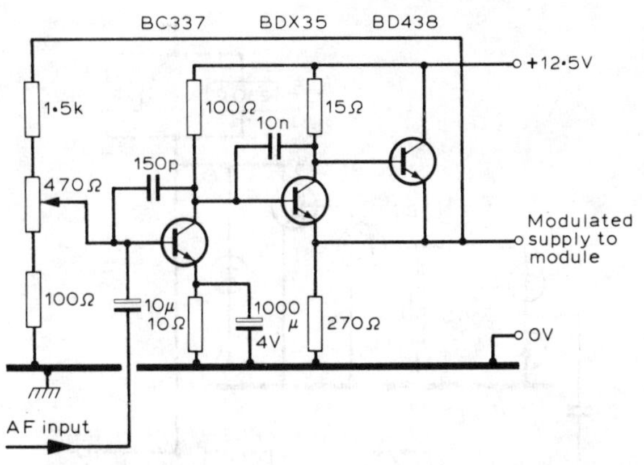

Fig 146. Amplitude modulator for broadband amplifier

Broadband amplifier module for nbfm

An alternative approach to the power amplifier problem is the use of a broadband amplifier module (Fig 145). Suitable devices are available for use on the 70 and 144MHz bands but they are naturally significantly more expensive than the discrete components because of their increased complexity.

The modules usually consist of a two-stage cascade amplifier, in which the driver stage operates in Class AB and the output amplifier in Class B. Included in the module is a bias stabilizer for the driver stage to maintain a constant bias point over the operating temperature range.

The circuit includes at the input a two-stage low-pass impedance-transforming network and a similar network incorporating a second harmonic trap to improve the harmonic rejection at the output. The interstage coupling is by means of a combination low-pass/high-pass network.

Separate supply terminals are available for the driver and output stages to enable a power output control by control of the driver supply voltage.

With this type of device the power gain is quite considerable and some 20W output is available for an input of 100mW on 70MHz (or 150mW on 144MHz) with a supply voltage of 12·5V. The input and output impedance is 50Ω and the harmonic output is more than −25dB down; an output filter is needed to reduce the harmonics to an acceptable level and ideally a bandpass filter is preferred for this purpose.

Amplitude modulation may be applied to these modules, a suitable series modulator being given in Fig 146. Under this condition a carrier output of 5W is available.

An rf switched 17W fm amplifier, which is suitable as an add-on for hand-held equipment, is shown in Fig 147.

A suitable heat sink for the BGY36 is of course required in both these amplifiers.

A typical broadband amplifier module, the BGY32 for 70MHz or BGY36 for 144MHz (Mullard)

144MHz linear amplifier

This amplifier, first described in *Amateur Radio* October 1978, with subsequent modification, is a generic design which offers several alternatives to the constructor, consisting of two stages—a driver stage followed by a push-pull amplifier (Fig 148). The following options are available:

(a) Driver stage alone with a 2N5590 or BLY88A. 1·5W input will give 10W output (using a 2N5591 or BLY89A with 4W input will deliver 20W output).

(b) A two-stage amplifier with 2N5591 as driver and amplifiers. This will produce 40–45W for an input of 2W (with 2N5590 as driver and 2N5591 as amplifier an input of 1W will produce 40W output).

(c) A single-stage amplifier using only the output stage—a 2N5591 and input of 10–12W will produce up 50W output.

The choice of the above options will decide the actual board needed. Details of the complete amplifier board is given in Fig 150 but if only the second stage is to be built to follow one or other of the transceivers with 10W or more output then the board can be rearranged as shown in Fig 151. In this case space has been allowed for the addition of a preamplifier on receive which will in most cases be needed when the output power is increased to avoid having a "deaf" receiver with a longer-range transmission.

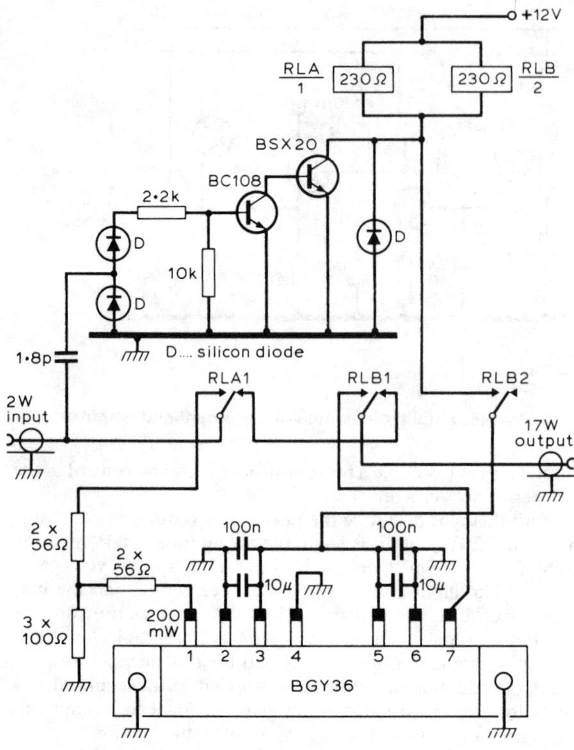

Fig 147. RF-switched 17W add-on amplifier for fm

The amplifier should be followed by a suitable filter to reduce the second and third harmonic radiation. This may be a simple pi coupling as shown in Fig 152 or a band-pass filter such as that detailed in Chapter 7 which the author has found very effective.

both on receive and transmit. It also provides a measure o antenna matching to the transmitter which is desirable, particu larly with preset tuned amplifiers.

Alternative types of transistor suitable for this amplifier are

Driver	2N5590	BLY88A	2N6081
Amplifier	2N5591	BLY89A	2N6083

Setting up the amplifier

The following steps should enable the amplifier to be adjuste for use.

(a) Terminate both input and output with 50Ω.
(b) With resistors R3, R6 and R7 disconnected, adjust each of these resistors separately so that the standing curren is between 100 and 120mA in each circuit, making sure that similar current will flow to each of the amplifie transistors. These resistors must be wire wound. Make sure there is no contact with pcb. A suitable starting value of resistance is 100Ω and 3–5W rating.

Tuning procedure

The following notes refer to the use of a 2N5591 as driver—a 2N5590 requires only 1W drive.

1. Connect the output of the driver to a power meter with a terminating load connected (note that the load resisto at the output of amplifier should be kept in position to avoid any damage to this stage).
2. Connect input to output of the drive, with a swr bridge between the two units.
3. Switch on amplifier.
4. Switch on drive with an output of 0·5–1·0W.
5. With C2 set at about half value, adjust C10 and C11 for maximum output, adjust C2 for minimum swr. An swr of less 1·1:1 should be attainable.
6. Increase drive to 2W and re-adjust C10, C11 and C2 for maximum output. 10–12W should be attained.
7. Connect output to power meter and a suitable load and connect driver to input of pa stage.

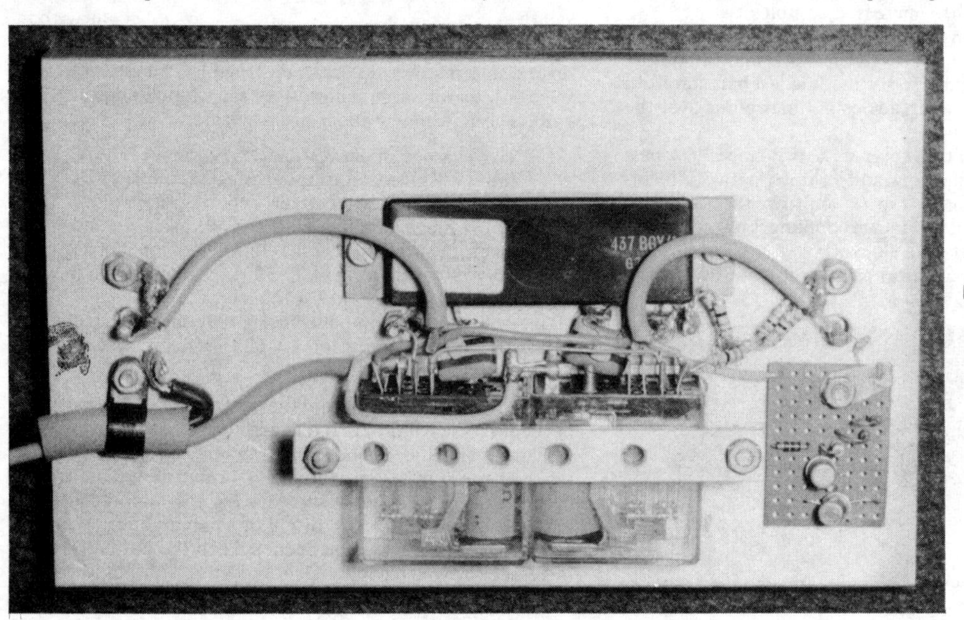
RF-switched 17W amplifie

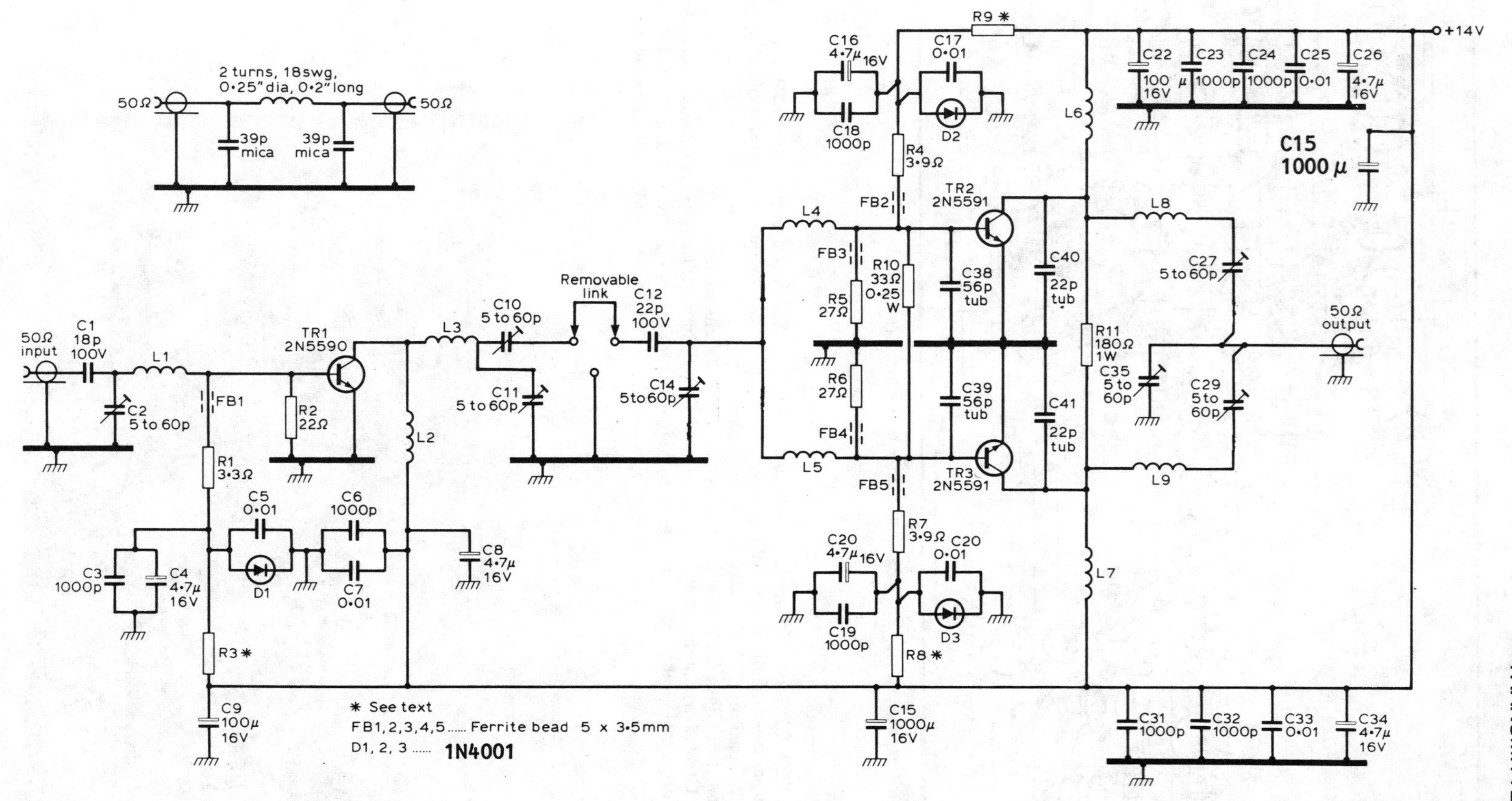

Fig 148. Two-stage linear amplifier

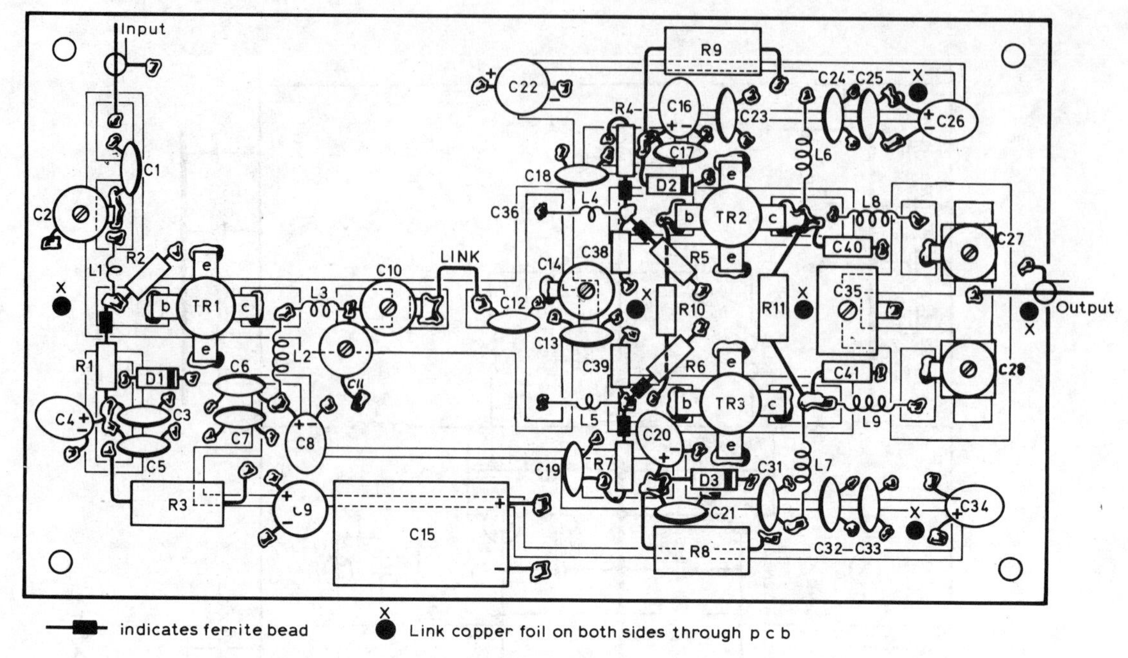

Fig 149. Component layout

8. Set C14, C27, C28 and C35 at about half value and adjust output from the drive to 0·5W.
9. Adjust the capacitors C27, C28 and C35 for maximum output and then adjust C14, re-adjust C27, C28, C35 and then C14 for maximum output.
10. Increase drive to 1W and repeat tuning for maximum output.
11. Increase drive to full 2W and again repeat adjustmen An output of more than 40W should be attainable.

Construction

The amplifier is built on double-sided glassfibre board etched a shown in Fig 150 or 151. Connections between the upper an lower surfaces of the foil should be made with substantial wir

144MHz linear amplifie

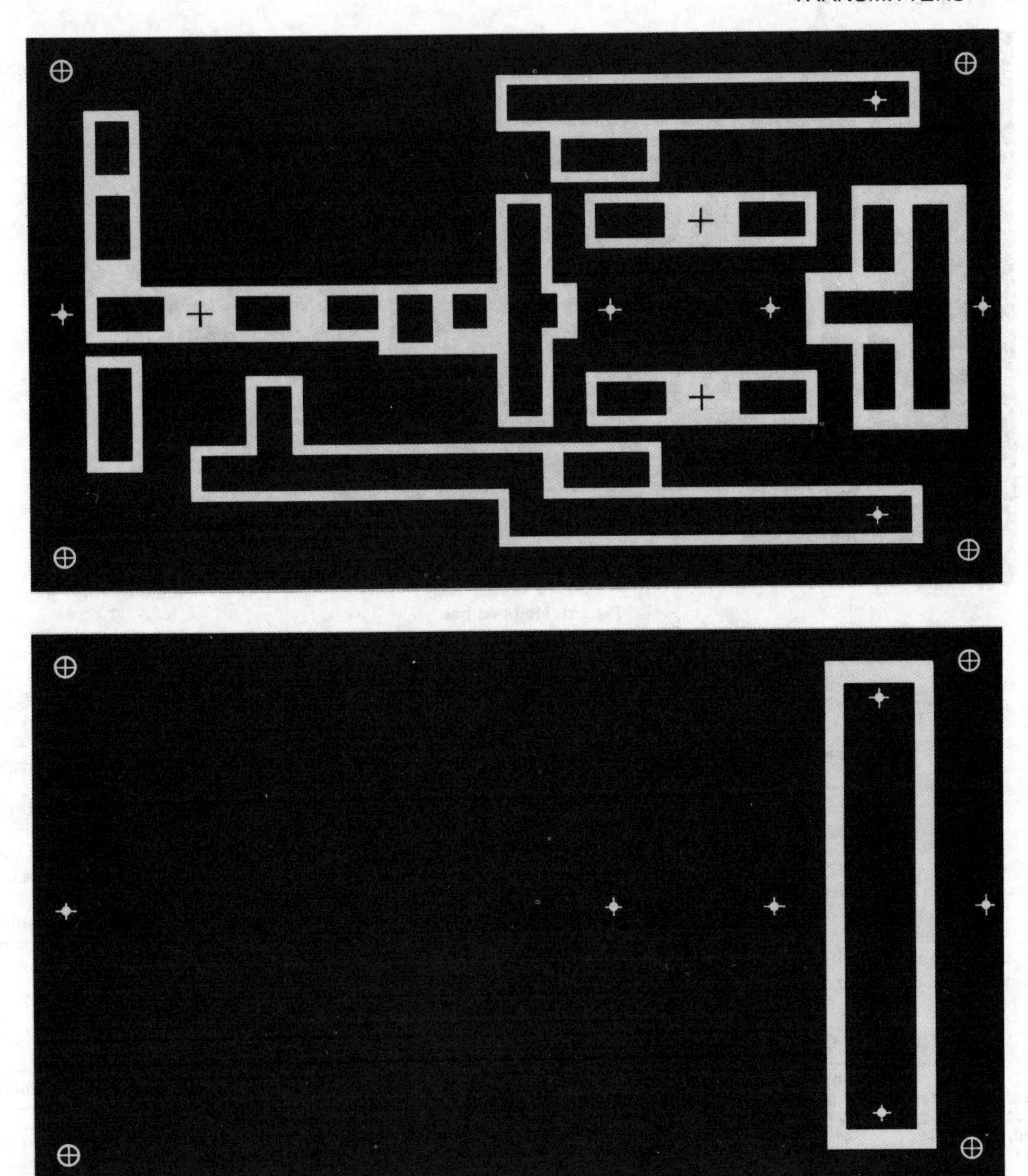

Fig 150. Double-sided pcb layout (actual size)

such as 16swg or rivets. The board must be drilled to allow the body of each transistor through the board so that the connections sit down on to the surface of the foil. This means that the heat sink is approximately 2mm away from the board.

Before soldering the transistors into position their leads should be reduced to ⅜in long, the outer ⅛in being bent at right-angles (vertically upward). This allows easier installation and removal if needed.

As can be seen in the component layout, the bias diodes D1, D1 and D3 are arranged so that there is good thermal coupling with their respective transistors by use of heat-conducting cement.

Power fet amplifier for 144MHz

The recent advances made in the development of power fets has given rise to some considerable interest as possible replacements for the usual bipolar devices. Details of their properties are described earlier in this chapter.

The amplifier described here makes use of a medium-power

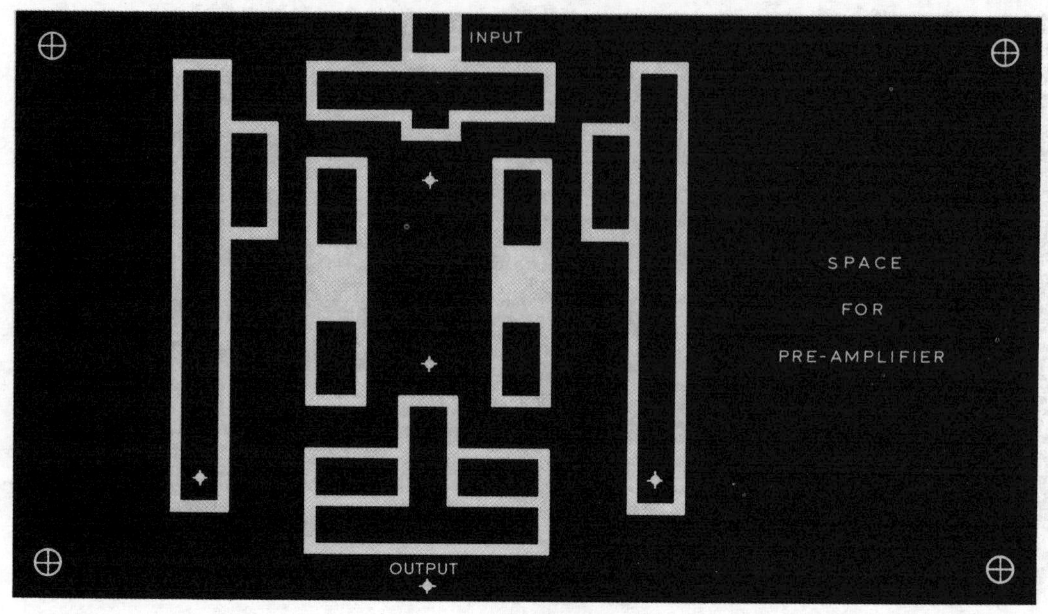

Fig 151. Modified pcb

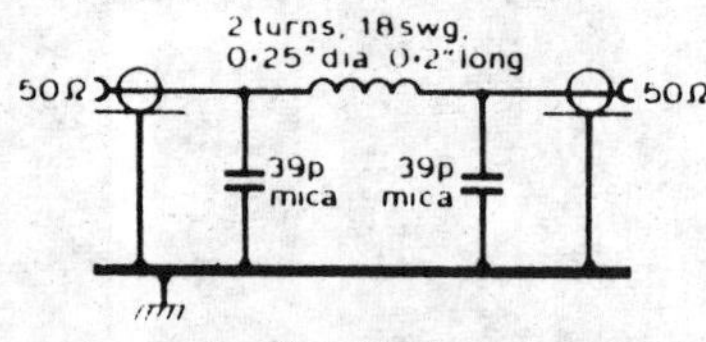

Fig 152. Pi-filter

device, the DV1007 (DV2840S). As shown, the complete amplifier also includes a simple preamplifier for reception, having a gain of 15dB, together with relay switching from transmit to receive. A preamplifier with rf selectivity would be desirable in a low-noise environment or if strong signals are encountered, and other designs in Chapter 4 can be substituted.

The complete circuit is shown in Fig 153 and, as can be seen, a 5dB attenuator is included in the input to the amplifier so that it is suitable for taking the output from a transceiver in the region of 10W. For lower powers this attenuator can be omitted and the full 10dB gain of the amplifier can be realized. The psu is shown in Fig 154 and interconnections in Fig 155.

Fig 156 shows the component layout of the whole unit which is built on to a heat sink of approximately 6in by 4½in. It is intended to be mounted vertically and attached to its power supply unit, in order to give adequate air flow over the heat sink surface.

Switching of the amplifier is accomplished by switching the bias supply rather than the much higher-current main supply, which can be more readily accomplished from within the driver transceiver.

Table 18. Components

C1	19pF disc ceramic 100V	
C3, 6, 18, 19, 23, 24, 31, 32	1,000pF disc ceramic	
C2, 10, 11, 14, 27, 29	5–65pF	
C4, 8, 20, 16, 26, 34	4·7μF tantalum 16V	
C5, 7, 21, 17, 25, 33	0·01μF disc ceramic	
C12	22pF disc ceramic	
C13	56pF mica	
C15	1,000μF 16V	
C9, 22	100μF 16V	
C36, 37	1,000pF	
C38, 39	56pF tubular	
C40, 41	22pF tubular	
R1	3·3Ω	¼ or ½W
R2	22Ω	¼ or ½W
R3, 8, 9	see text	¼ or ½W
R4, 7	3·9Ω	¼ or ½W
R5, 6	27Ω	¼ or ½W
R10	33Ω ¼W	
R11	180Ω 1W	
X1, 2, 3, 4, 5	Ferrite bead 5mm long 3·5mm diam	

Table 19. Inductor detail

Inductor	Turns	SWG	I.D. (in)	Other details
L1	1	20	0·25 (6mm)	
L2	3	20	0·125 (3mm)	0·25in (6mm) long
L3	2	18	0·375 (4·5mm)	0·25in (6mm) long
L4, L5	1	18	0·375 (4·5mm)	lead length about $\frac{3}{16}$in
L6, L7	2	20	$\frac{3}{16}$	
L8, L9	3	18	0·375 (4·5mm)	lead length about ¼in

Table 20. Performance

Power input (W)	Power output (W)	I_c (A)	2nd harmonic (dB)	3rd harmonic (dB)
0·2	12 rms	3·2	—	−34
0·3	18 rms	3·8	—	−26
0·4	20 rms	4·0	—	−23
0·8	38 p.e.p.	—	−45	−55

Test frequency 144·2MHz, supply voltage 13·5V dc

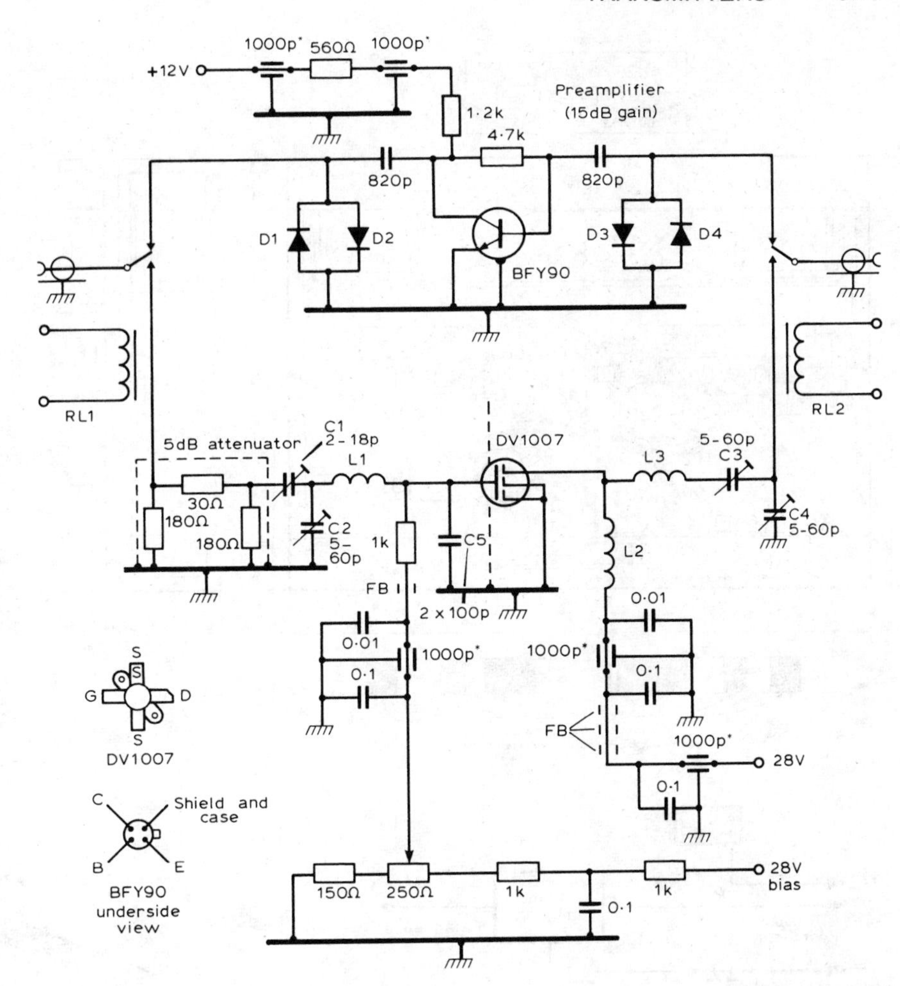

Fig 153. Circuit of 144MHz power fet amplifier. L1 2t 16swg 6·3mm (¼in). L2 5t 18swg 6·3mm (¼in). L3 2t 16swg 9·6mm (⅜in). C1 2–18pF 809 09003. C2, C3 5–60pF 809 08003. C5 two 100pF. Note that DV1007 is now known as the DV2840S. D1 and D2 were included in the original design but are probably unnecessary and can be omitted if desired

Construction

Details of the construction are given in Figs 157 and 158 from which it is shown that the heat sink forms the basic component. To this are bolted U-sections fixed along its length, and these provide the sides if the unit is to be used with a remote power unit, or alternatively allow a means of fixing the unit to an integral power supply.

The general arrangement of the copper-clad boards is in the form of a "railway station"; the two "main platforms" are of double-sided glassfibre material, while the input and output circuit boards are single-sided material with the various gaps in the foil removed.

All the boards are stood off from the heat sink by spacers so that the connections from the amplifier fet lay flat on the copper

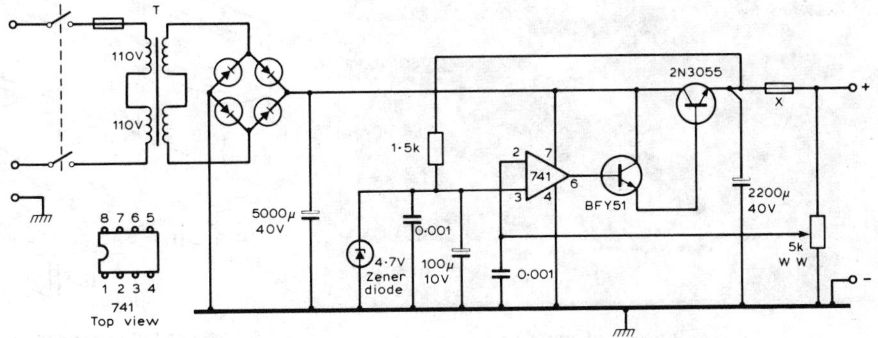

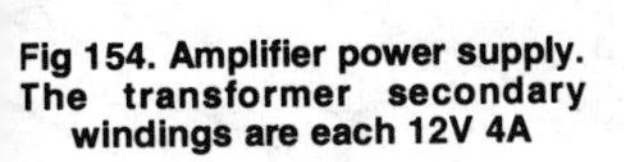
Fig 154. Amplifier power supply. The transformer secondary windings are each 12V 4A

Fig 156. Component layout

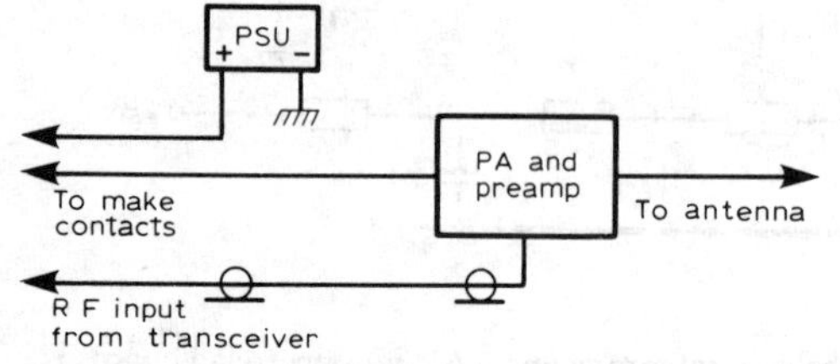

Fig 155. Interconnections

Top view of amplifier

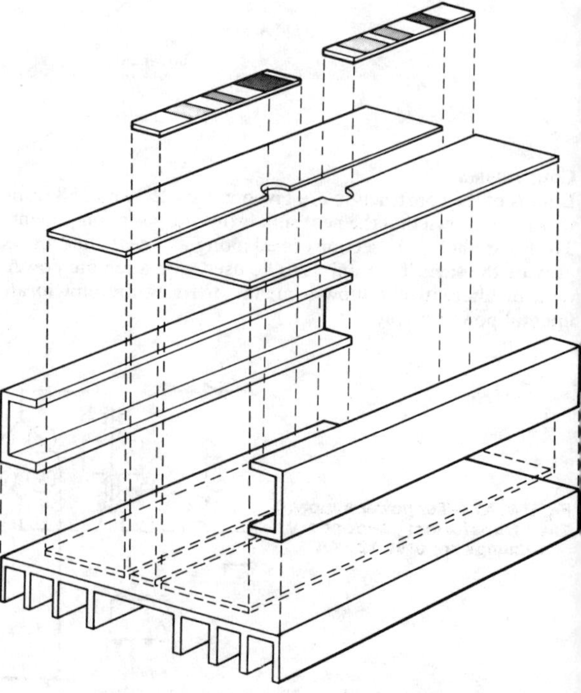

Fig 157. Exploded view of major component assembly

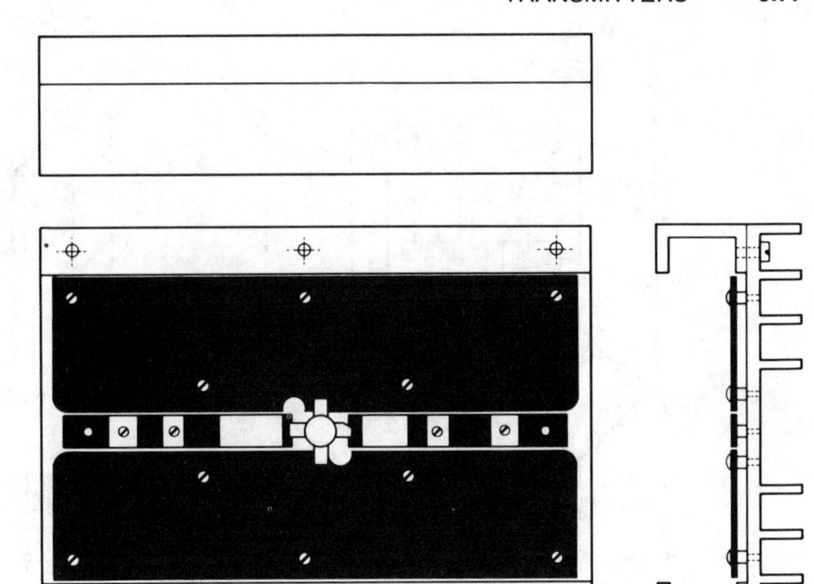

Fig 158. Board and heat sink assembly

urfaces. The main boards of the unit have the two sides connected together by either rivets or short pieces of thick copper vire in addition to the connections made by the fixing screws nd spacers.

The input and output connectors used BNC flange fixing with BA screws (¼in long) and half-nuts which allow free space between them and the boards.

A screen is fitted across the fet to separate the input and output circuits; this is of thin brass suitably bent but copper or aluminium could be used. The input and output relays are bolted directly to the relevant board by long 6BA screws with half-nuts at the top (free end).

Table 21. Performance of the fet amplifier

M (Class C) V_{dd} 28V, I_{dq} 200mA

Drive (W)	Power (load) (W)
[illegible]	22
[illegible]	32
[illegible]	40
[illegible]	44

ET efficiency 55 per cent

SSB (Class AB) (linear)
Drive is two tones 10kHz spacing, ip products measured with respect to the amplitude of one tone (with respect to p.e.p. a 6dB improvement).
Power drive 2·5W p.e.p., power load 25W p.e.p.
3rd order intermodulation distortion −26dB.
With 5dB attenuation in circuit:
Power drive 9W p.e.p., power load 25W p.e.p.
FET efficiency 33 per cent.

Harmonics
Under either 40W fm or 25W p.e.p. conditions.
2nd harmonic output: −54dB
3rd harmonic output: −48dB

Bypassing of the gate and drain circuits is arranged in the conventional manner, comprising several different values: 1,000pF feedthroughs are used as stand off, with disc ceramics of 0·01μF and 0·1μF in parallel. The only other bypass capacitors are two 100pF connected directly from gate to earth: these were found to improve the amplifier's stability and linearity.

The bias circuit is a simple potential divider with a 250Ω adjustable component near the earth end. As mentioned elsewhere the amplifier is controlled by switching the bias supply, leaving the main supply connected permanently.

The relay supply can conveniently be taken from the 28V supply with a suitable resistor to drop the excess voltage to 24V to suit the relays connected in series, and a diode is connected across the 24V terminals. Also the 12V supply to the preamplifier may be taken from the 28V supply if a series resistor and a 12V zener diode is added.

Although plugs and sockets have been used in the prototype any alternative arrangement may of course be used, especially if the amplifier is to be completed as a unit with a separate power source.

A general-purpose double-tetrode power amplifier for 144MHz

Although many of the modern transistor transceivers give a substantial power output on fm, cw and ssb, the need for higher power is felt sooner or later, particularly for longer-range contacts. Generally a power level of the order of 100W is adequate in most cases and an amplifier to give this output can readily be built using twin tetrodes such as QQV06-40A (QQE06-40) or QQV07-50. Amplifiers using this class of valve have considerable power gain, are normally easy to build and do not require either expensive valve sockets or a cooling blower.

The amplifier described here is simple to build and may be

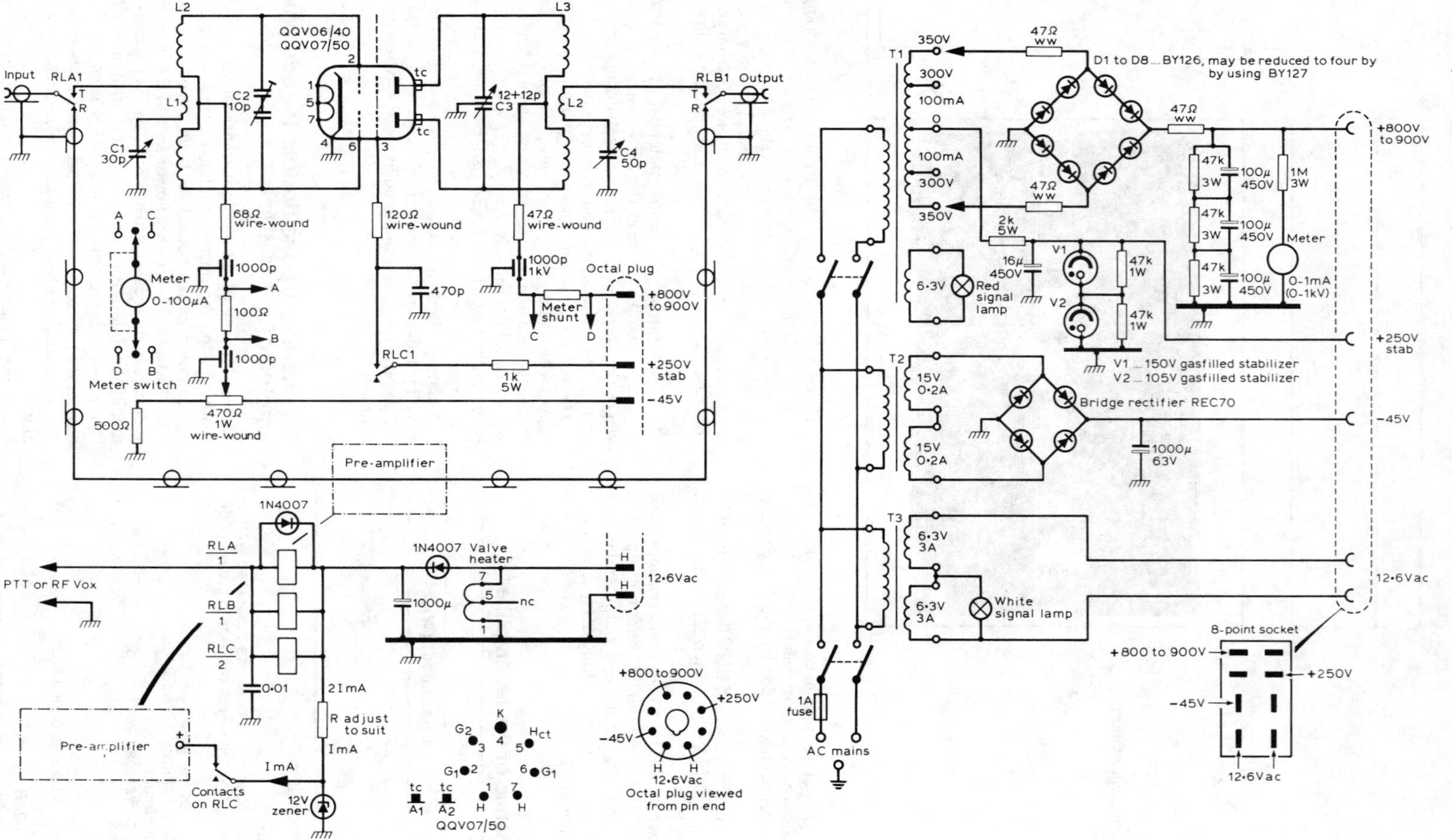

Fig 159. General-purpose 144MHz amplifier using QQV06-40

Fig 160. Power supply unit

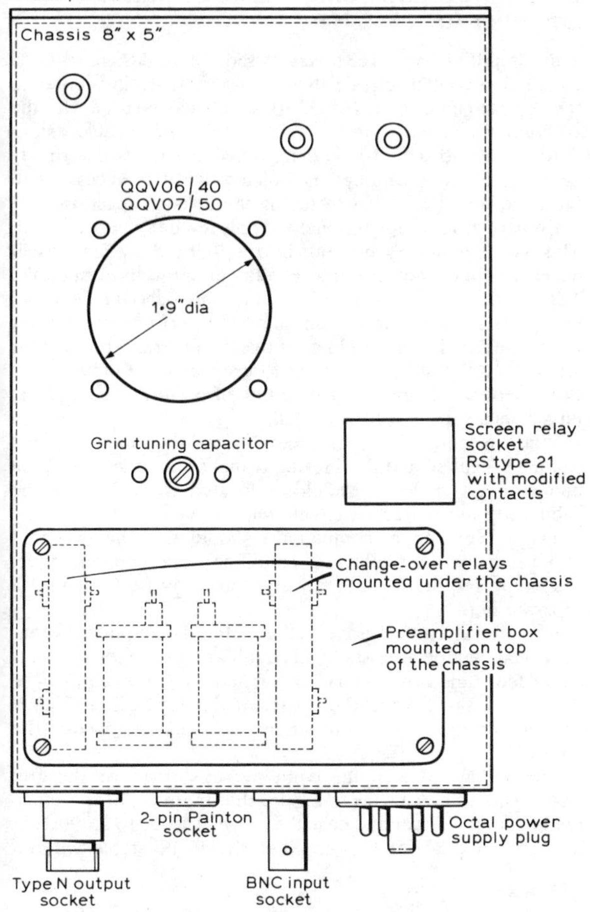

Fig 161. Layout of amplifier (top view)

Front panel 5¾" x 5"

ANTENNA

ANODE TUNE

Ia Ig

BIAS ADJUST

INPUT TUNE

ANODE-GRID CURRENT SWITCH

Switch, double-pole, two-position, with 60° spacing or or three-position, 30° spacing, with centre contacts blank. Contacts should break-before-make

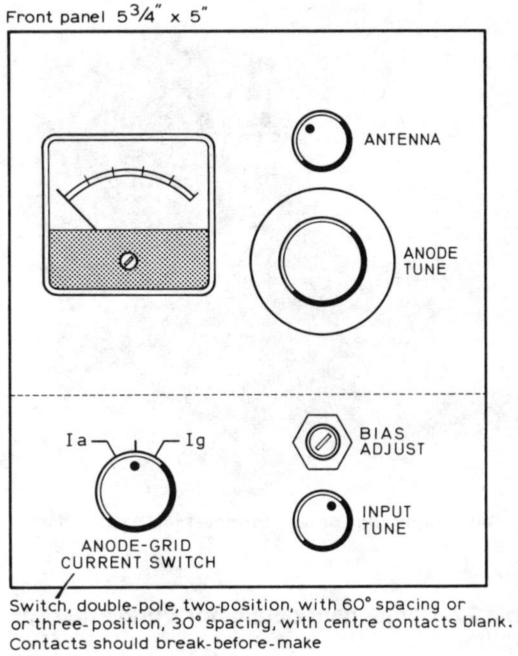

Fig 162. Layout of front panel

operated in linear or Class C modes with appropriate grid bias voltage and drive power.

The complete circuit is shown in Fig 159 from which it can be ssen that provision is made for matching the input and output circuits. Both the grid and anode circuits are tuned by normal butterfly capacitors. Some small improvement in efficiency can be obtained using line circuits but the improvement is not worth the increase in overall size.

Switching from transmit to receive is accomplished by coaxial relays in the standard manner. On receive the amplifier screen grid is disconnected, rendering it inoperative. This method is more reliable than block biasing and ensures that the valve does not generate noise under receive conditions.

The screen and bias voltage supplies should be well regulated to prevent voltage variation, during voice operation with ssb. The screen voltage in this case is stabilized by the use of a standard shunt stabilizer using two gas-filled stabilizers in series to obtain 250V. A number of appropriate zener diodes in series could be used if preferred. The grid bias supply for AB1 operation should have a standing bleed current of at least 10mA, the control being a potentiometer with a series resistor in the lower end to ensure that the voltage cannot be reduced below about 20V.

Under normal conditions for Class AB1, with the anode voltage between 700 and 900V and the screen voltage 250V, the bias required to set the anode current to a suitable value (35mA) will be between 27 and 30V. Under these conditions an output power of around 70–90W is attainable. The conversion efficiency is at least 50 per cent and the anode current peaks to about 250mA. If Class C operation is required the bias voltage will need to be considerably increased. Normally this voltage is set at between two and three times the cut-off (anode current) voltage. Input power will also be increased with approximately 6–10W input when an output of the order of 130W may be expected.

When using a power amplifier of the level of 100W it is usually necessary to include a preamplifier for the receiver to keep the receive and transmit ranges similar.

As shown in the circuit diagram the relay switching is by ptt switch extension from the driving transceiver; rf switching may be used as an alternative if preferred.

In Fig 160 is shown details of a suitable power supply unit. It should be noted that the ht transformer has a conventional centre tapping point normally used in biphase half-wave rectifier circuits. In this case it is used with a full-wave bridge rectifier and the "half volts" point (centre tap) is used to supply the screen voltage. For a transformer used in this manner the current rating should be half of that normally designated for the biphase half-wave operation.

The bias supply as shown is only suitable for linear Class AB1 operation. If the full advantage of Class C operation is desired the voltage should be increased to −100V.

Very little need be said about construction. The details given in Figs 161 and 162 and the photograph clearly illustrate the unit. In the circuit diagram separate meters are shown for anode and grid current. These were combined with a suitable switch in the prototype.

General-purpose double-tetrode 144MHz amplifier

Table 22. Component details for double-tetrode amplifier

L1	1½t 5/16in i.d. 16swg insulated
L2	2 + 2t 5/16in i.d. 5/16in gap. 1·1in long 15swg
L3	2 + 2t 5/8in i.d. 5/16in gap 1in long 1/8in copper
L4	1t 5/8in i.d. 16swg well insulated
C1	30pF Polar type G31
C2	10pF split stator Polar type G8-52/1
C3	12 + 12pF split stator
C4	50pF Polar C8-04
RL1, RL2	coaxial (Magnetic Devices)
RL3	RS type 21 modified

General-purpose single-tetrode power amplifier for 144MHz

This amplifier (Fig 163) was based on a design using a conduction-cooled tetrode that is characteristically similar to the standard air-cooled 4CX250B, which may be used with the addition of a suitable blower. With the air-cooled valve a standard socket with a built-in screen bypass capacitor will normally be used. For the conduction-cooled valve it is necessary to fabricate suitable fittings including the bypass capacitor.

Construction is conventional and only few details are needed. The whole unit may be built into a 17 by 5 by 5in case if necessary, but for most purposes a larger unit is more suitable. The anode circuit together with the valve should be in an enclosure 12in by 5in by 4in deep and performance figures given later are for an amplifier of this larger size. If the smaller size is used the anode circuit enclosure may be 10in by 3in by 2½in deep; this does cause some loss of performance and the larger enclosure is recommended.

Where a conduction-cooled valve is used then adequate heat sinking is needed and this inevitably means that the rear of the anode circuit enclosure should be located at the back of the cabinet, to avoid free air circulation.

The power supply components should then be mounted either in front of, or below the amplifier proper, depending on the shape required. Alternatively, they may be built into a separate unit.

From the circuit diagram it is seen that the amplifier is conventional, having a passive grid circuit and the anode circuit is shunt fed, tuned by a capacitor tapped on the inductor. The output is tapped on to the corner of this for 50Ω; if 75Ω is needed the tap will be further up the inductor towards the anode.

The actual value of the damping resistor across the grid circuit should be such as to ensure that there is not too much loading on the driver and be in the range of 1,000 to 2,000Ω. In a satisfactory layout the amplifier should be stable without

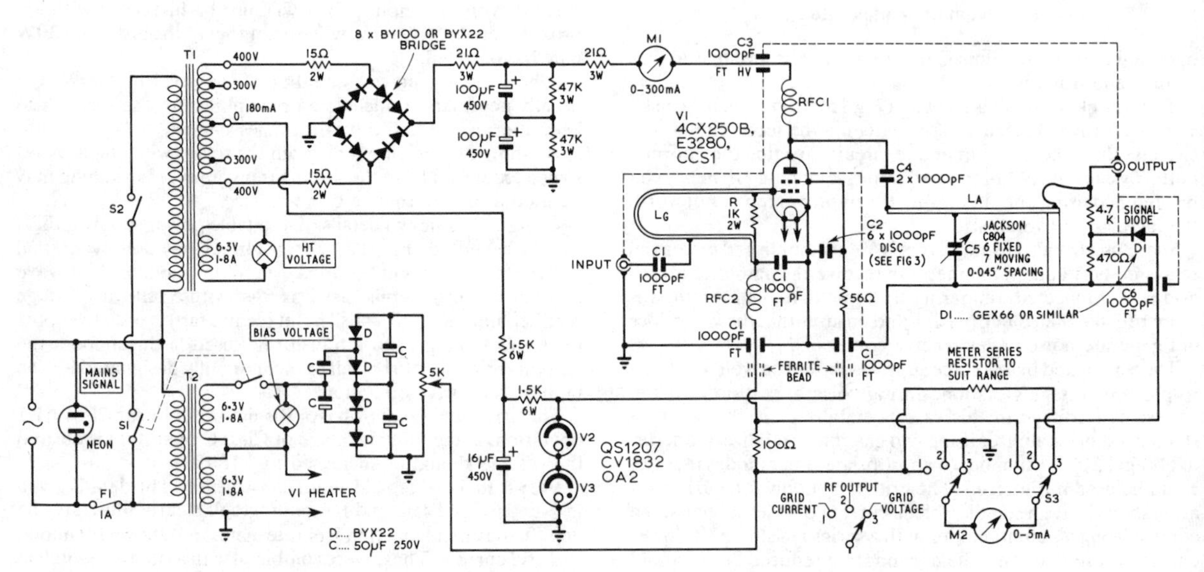

Fig 163. Circuit of 144MHz general-purpose amplifier using a 4CX250B

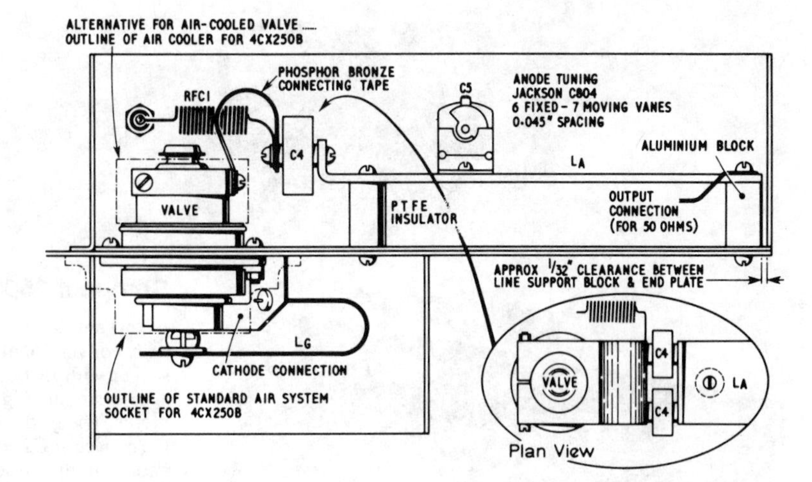

Fig 164. General layout of the grid and anode circuits

reliance on the damping. To minimize the drive required, it is an advantage for the grid circuit to be resonant at the operation frequency.

With low drive power, this circuit may be made tunable, but for most purposes the passive arrangement is to be preferred.

In Fig 164 the component arrangement of the tuned circuit is shown for the small anode circuit enclosure. With the larger enclosure recommended earlier, there is more room to space the valve further from the capacitors C4 and the end plate.

With an air-cooled valve probably the most convenient arrangement for enclosing the grid, where it needs to be fairly airtight, is a 4½ by 3¾ by 2in cast box.

Details of the grid and anode inductors are given in Fig 165(b) and (d) respectively, together with a suitable low-inductance cathode lead and screen bypass capacitor for the conduction-cooled valve.

Typical performance

The actual performance that may be obtained is, of course, dependent upon the anode voltage and current input used, but for convenience the prototype uses a commonly available transformer 400V + 400V with a full-wave bridge rectifier, the screen supply being taken from the centre tap and stabilized by two series-connected 150V stabilizers V2 and V3.

The grid bias voltage is obtained from two series-connected

Table 23. Component details

T1	400 + 400V 180mA
T2	6·3 + 6·3V 1·8A
C	50μF
C1	1,000pF feedthrough (discoidal type)
C2	6, 1,000pF disc
C3	1,000pF hv leadthrough
C4	Hunts type C25375 1,000pF 3·5kV wkg
C5	C804, 6 fixed 7 moving 0·045in spacing
C6	1,000pF feedthrough (screw fixing)
D	BYX22
D1	GEX66 or similar
V1	4CX250B or E3280 or CCS1
V2	QS1207 or CV1832 or OA2
V3	QS1207 or CV1832 or OA2
LG, LA	see separate detail
RFC1	21t 18swg ⅜in i.d. 1in long
RFC2	3 pie 2·5mH

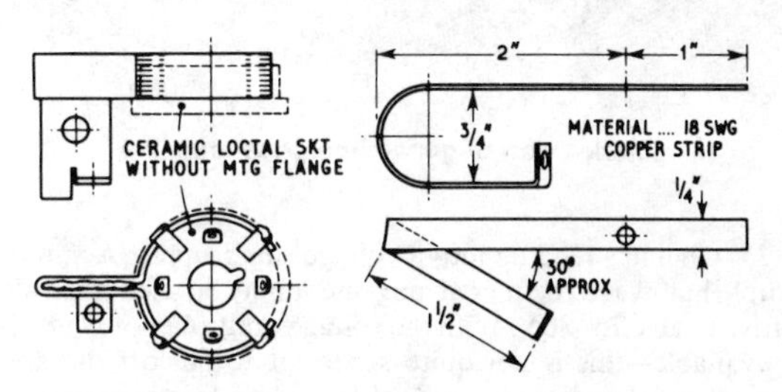

(a) Cathode connection (b) Grid inductor LG

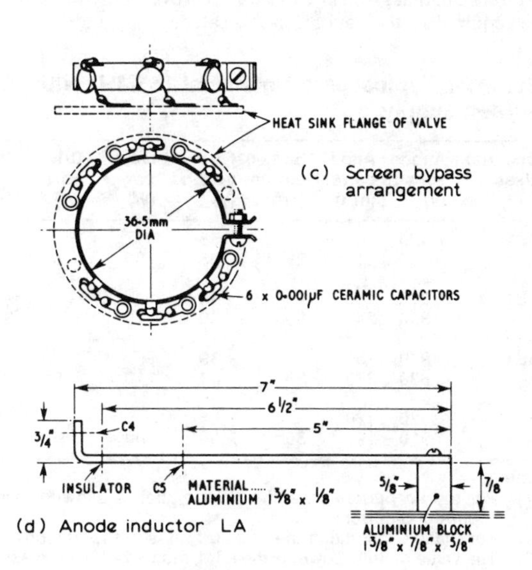

(c) Screen bypass arrangement

(d) Anode inductor LA

Fig 165. Circuit component parts

Front-panel layout of general-purpose amplifier

Interior view of general-purpose amplifier

6·3V windings feeding into a voltage quadrupler. A standard simple half-wave rectifier arrangement may be used as an alternative to give 75–80V. With the voltage multiplier only 68–70V is available—this is not quite sufficient to cut off the anode current and the efficiency under Class C conditions is somewhat poorer than that given in Table 24. However more drive would be required so the data given is a satisfactory guide.

Table 24. Typical performance at 145MHz with 300V screen supply

Operation class	Anode voltage (V)	Anode current (mA)	Screen current (mA)	Grid voltage (V)	Output power (W)	Drive power (W)	IM (−dB)
AB1	1,020	50	–	−58	–	–	–
	900	210	28	−58	100	4·5	24
AB1	1,010	100	–	−46	–	–	–
	860	245	30	−46	110	3·5	34
AB1	970	150	–	−39	–	–	–
	830	270	28	−39	110	2·8	37
C	1,020	120	–	−68	–	–	–
	910	190	35	−68	100	6	–

Note:
(1) For the im performance the peak signal is allowed to reach 0·5mA grid current.
(2) For Class C operation the grid current is not restricted.
(3) The value of drive power is the total, most of which is dissipated in the damping resistor.

Compact 150W amplifier for 144MHz

In this amplifier a 4CX250B forced air-cooled tetrode is used with conventional circuit components and a standard valve socket with its built-in screen bypass capacitor.

The circuit, Fig 166, shows the simplicity of the arrangements. The grid inductor L1 consists of a copper loop tuned to the capacitor C2 with the input tapped down from the grid. The anode circuit is a series-tuned half-wave circuit with the ht feed joint at the centre of the inductor L2. The output coupling consists of a well-insulated single turn, which is adjustable. It should be noted the frequently used series tuning capacitor has not been used in this case.

Construction and the method of fitting the blower are clearly shown in the drawings and photographs. The grid and input circuit below the chassis must be fully enclosed to ensure the cooling air passes through the valve cooler. The valve and its anode circuit are enclosed by the box above the chassis with its top left open. If the amplifier is to be built into a cabinet, free airflow from the top of the valve must be provided. An adequate air inlet is also necessary.

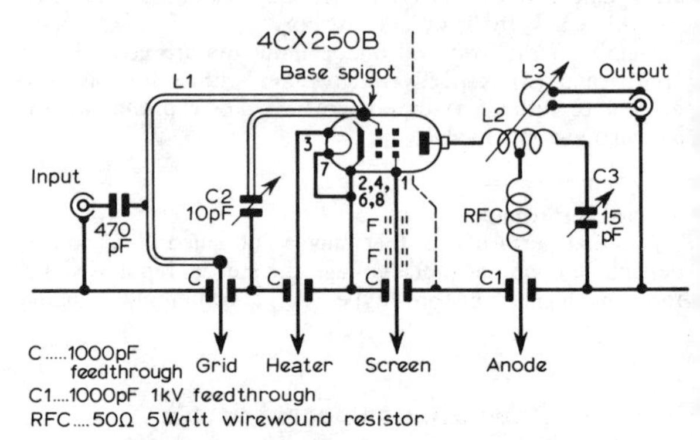

Fig 166. Circuit of compact 150W amplifier for 144MHz

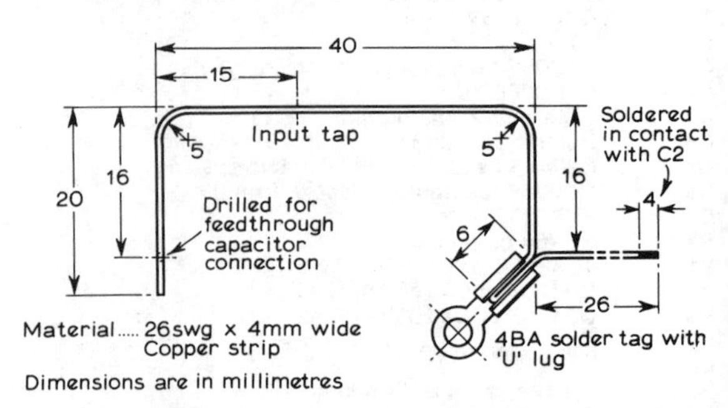

Fig 167. Details of grid inductor

Compact amplifier for 144MHz

Underside view of compact amplifier for 144MHz

The blower used in the prototype causes very little vibration, and no shock absorbent mounting is needed. It is mounted so that the air inlet is directly into the grid circuit enclosure under the chassis, by a suitable cutout in the chassis. The blower is then mounted by a simple U-shaped strap around its motor.

The input socket used is a standard tv type but that used for the output is a bulkhead mounting BNC.

Table 25. Components for 150W amplifier

C	1,000pF feedthrough
C1	1,000pF feedthrough 1kV type
C2	10pF C804 Jackson
C3	15pF C804 Jackson
F	Ferrite bead
RFC	50Ω 5W wirewound
L1	Copper strip loop (see Fig 167)
L2	3½t ¾in i.d. ⅛in diam copper
L3	1t ¾in i.d. insulated
Valve socket	Eimac or AEI
Blower	Plannair Type 2PL 321-284C Mk3

Table 26. Performance of 150W amplifier

Anode voltage (V)	750	800
Anode current (mA)	200	200
Screen voltage (V)	250	250
Screen current (mA)	5	8
Grid voltage (V)	−100	−100
Grid current (mA)	6·6	8
Drive power (W)	2·6	3·0
Output power (load) (W)	90	100

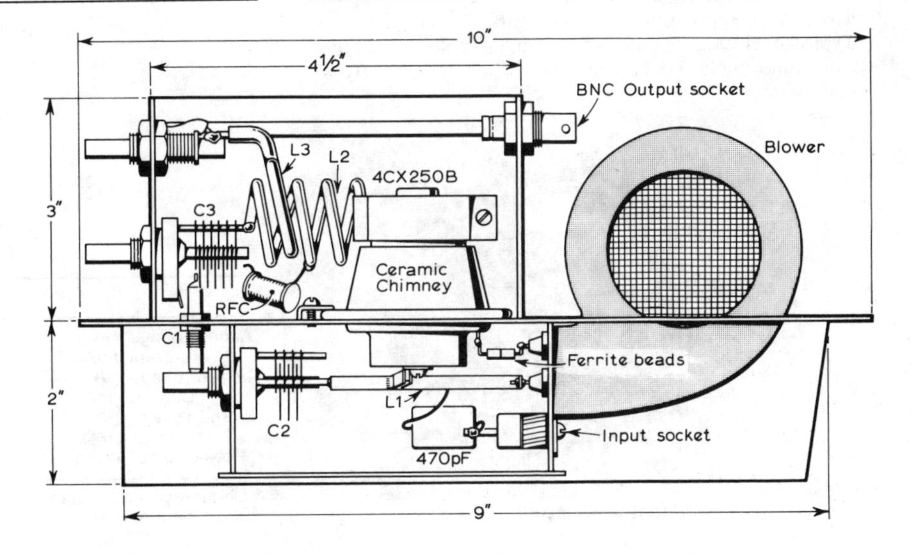

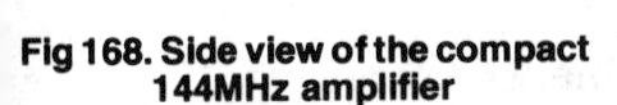

Fig 168. Side view of the compact 144MHz amplifier

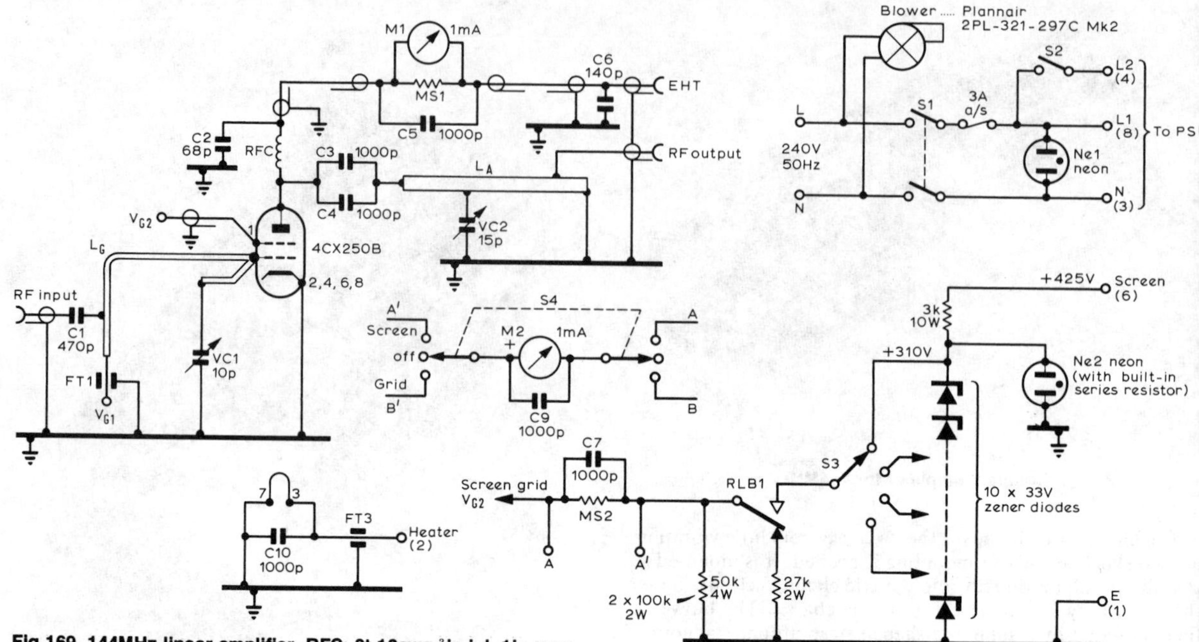

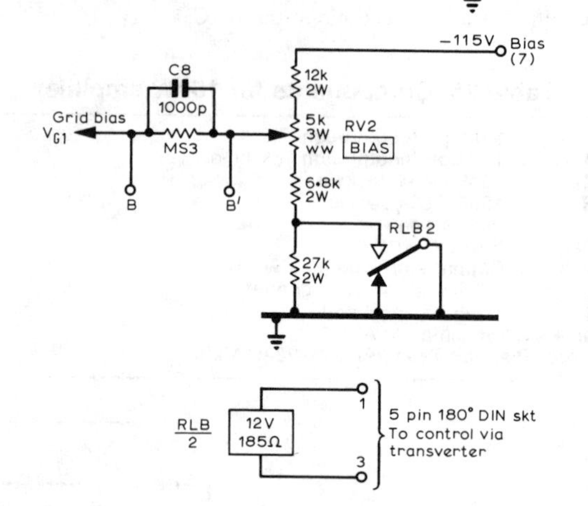

Fig 169. 144MHz linear amplifier. RFC: 2t 18swg ⅜in i.d. 1in long. Note that C2 should be 680pF not 68pF as shown. Alternatively a high-voltage 1,000pF feedthrough can be used if available

Alternative design

A further design of these amplifiers uses the strip anode circuit and the tuned grid with an air-cooled 4CX250B, and for many purposes may be preferred to either of the previously described amplifiers.

Mechanical and electrical details are given in Figs 169–173 and as can be seen from the photographs the amplifier is housed in a cabinet which encloses the blower. The actual tuned circuits, grid and anode, are separately enclosed, the grid in a die-cast box so that the air from the blower is directed through the socket into the anode cooler.

The power supply is in a separate unit.

Typical operating conditions are given in Table 27, and they are of course applicable also to either of the earlier designs.

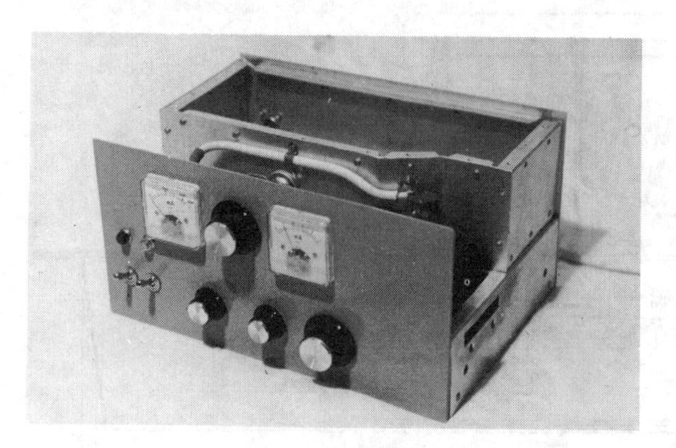

Front-panel layout

Table 27

		No signal	Single tone
Anode voltage	(V)	1,350	1,200
current	(mA)	100	200
Screen voltage	(V)	315	315
Current	(mA)	—	10
Grid voltage	(V)	−32	−32*
current	(μA)	—	less than 100
Power output	(W)	—	150–170

* Under receiving or standby conditions this is increased to −80V to cut off the amplifier.

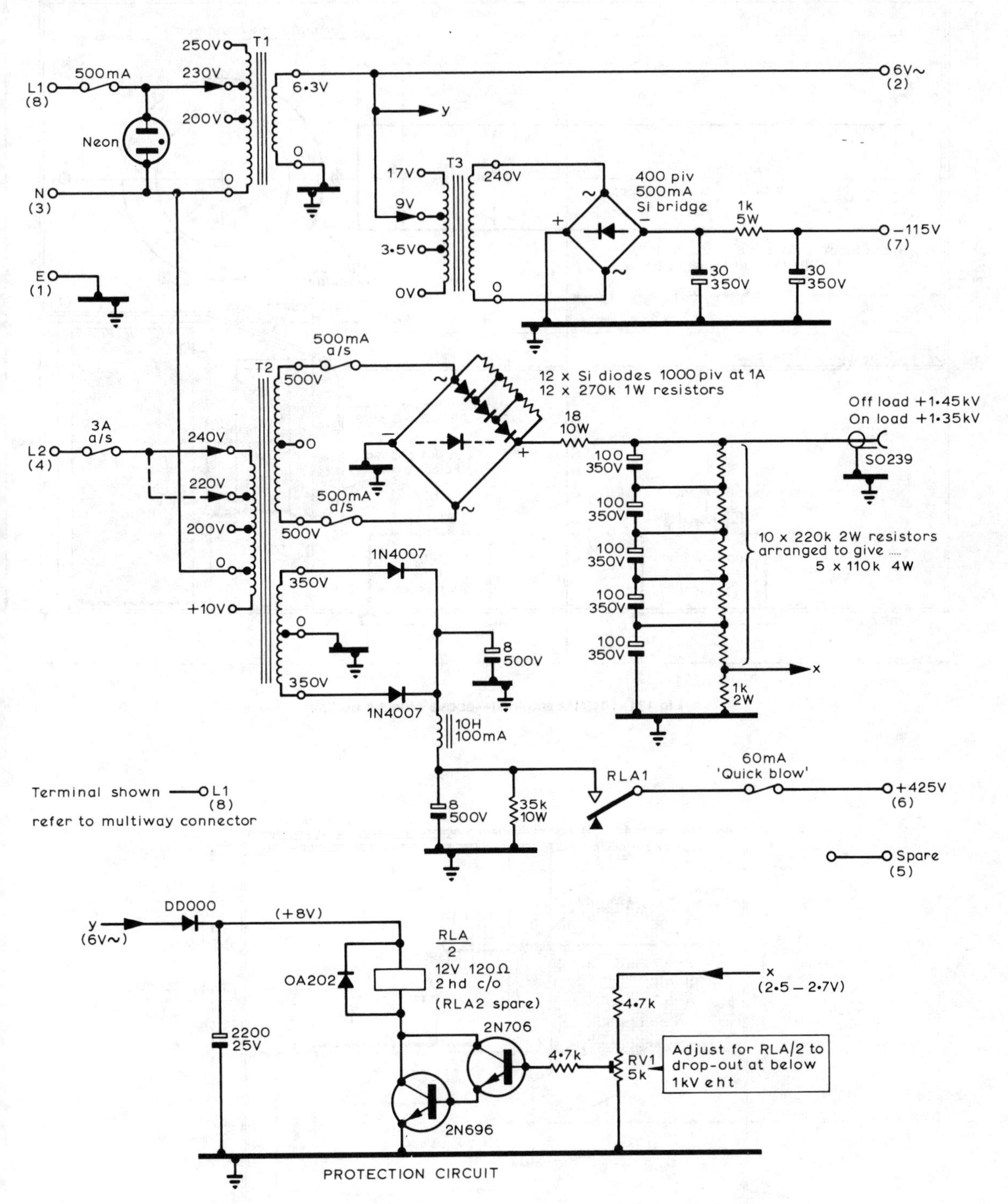

Fig 170. 144MHz linear amplifier–circuit diagram for remote power supply unit

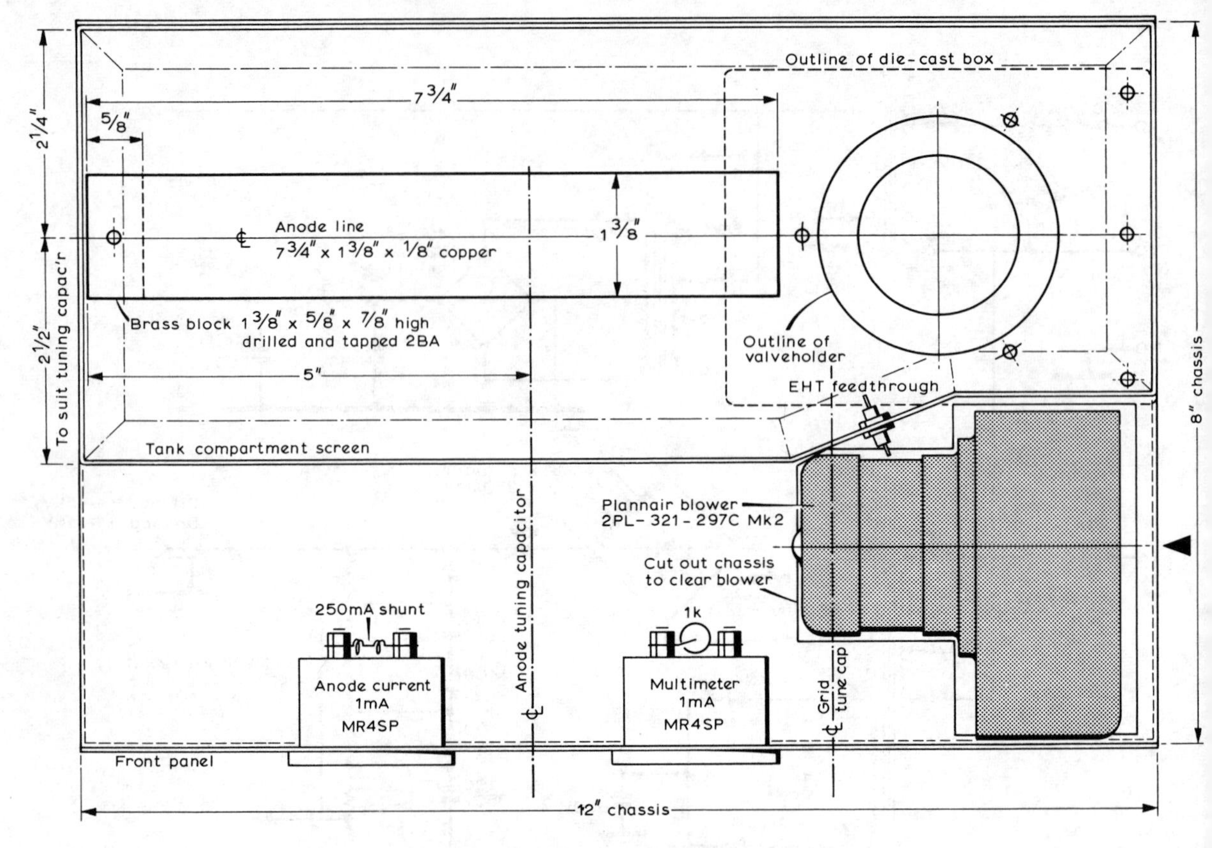

Fig 171. 144MHz amplifier—above-chassis outline

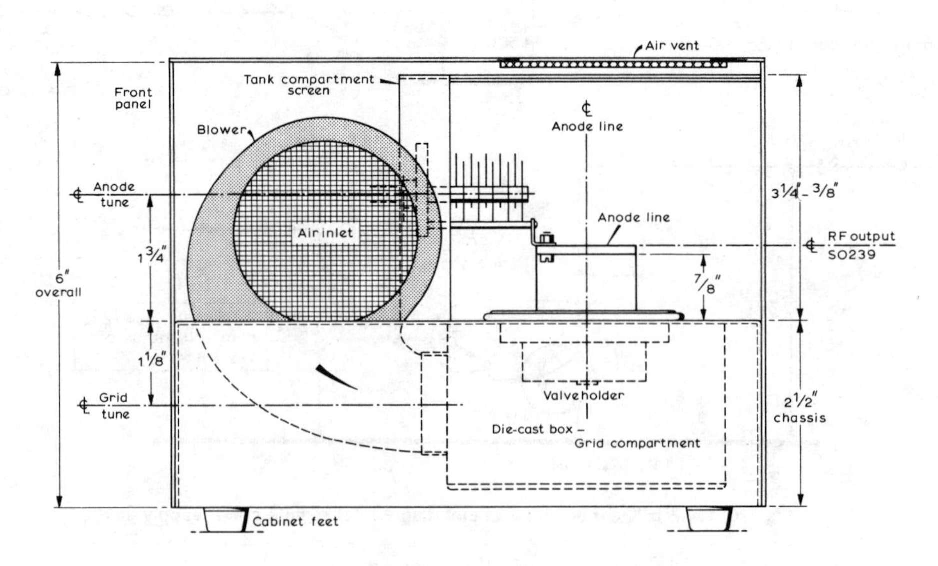

Fig 172. 144MHz linear amplifier—side elevation

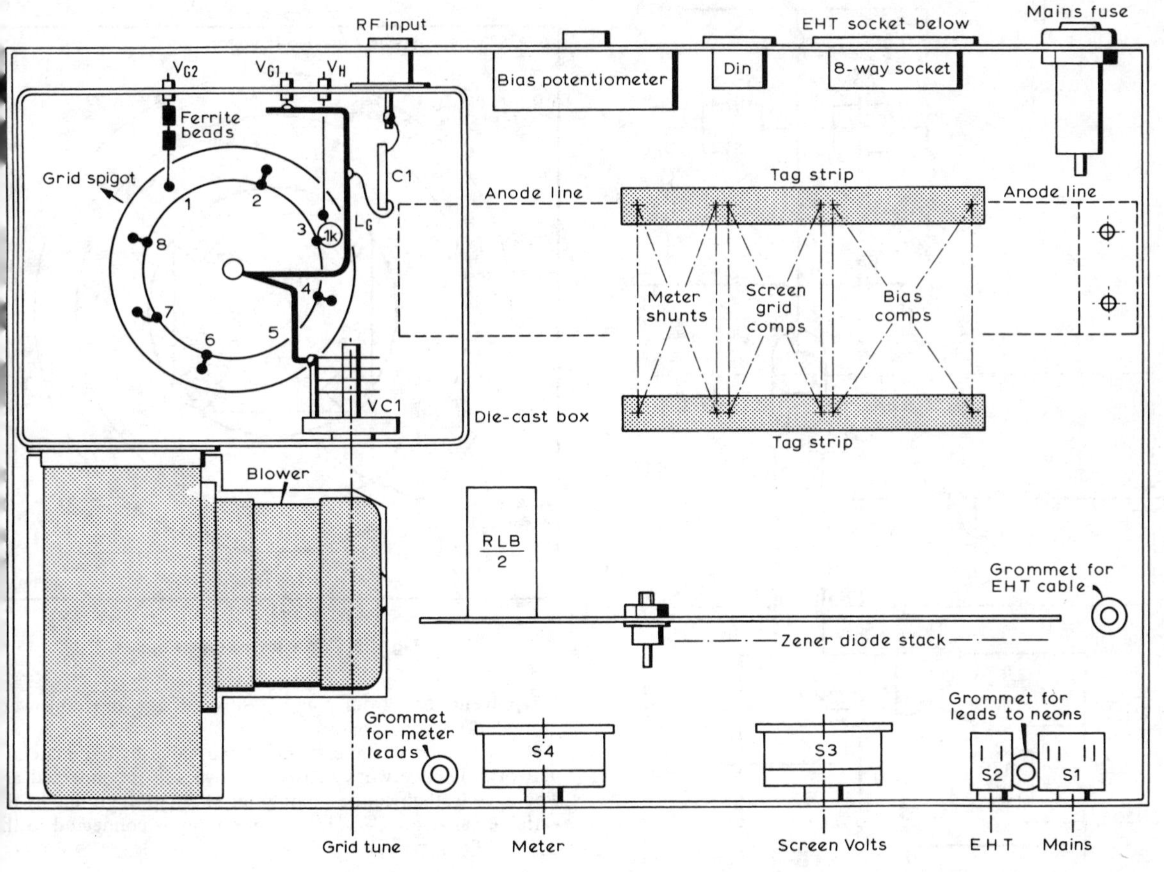

Fig 173. 144MHz linear amplifier—below-chassis outline

Interior showing fan, strip line and tuning capacitor

Underside view

High-power grounded-grid amplifier for 144MHz

The use of triodes as grounded-grid linear amplifiers for vhf has very largely been neglected. Most amateurs have preferred to use the higher gain (or at least lower-drive) valves such as the 4CX250B or similar.

The triode has a great deal of merit, especially in regard to linearity, though of course the only circuit arrangement that will meet the stability required is the grounded-grid connection. The choice of valves is limited as it is for tetrodes, though the latter are used in considerable quantities in many applications and are therefore seen more often than the triodes. Triodes

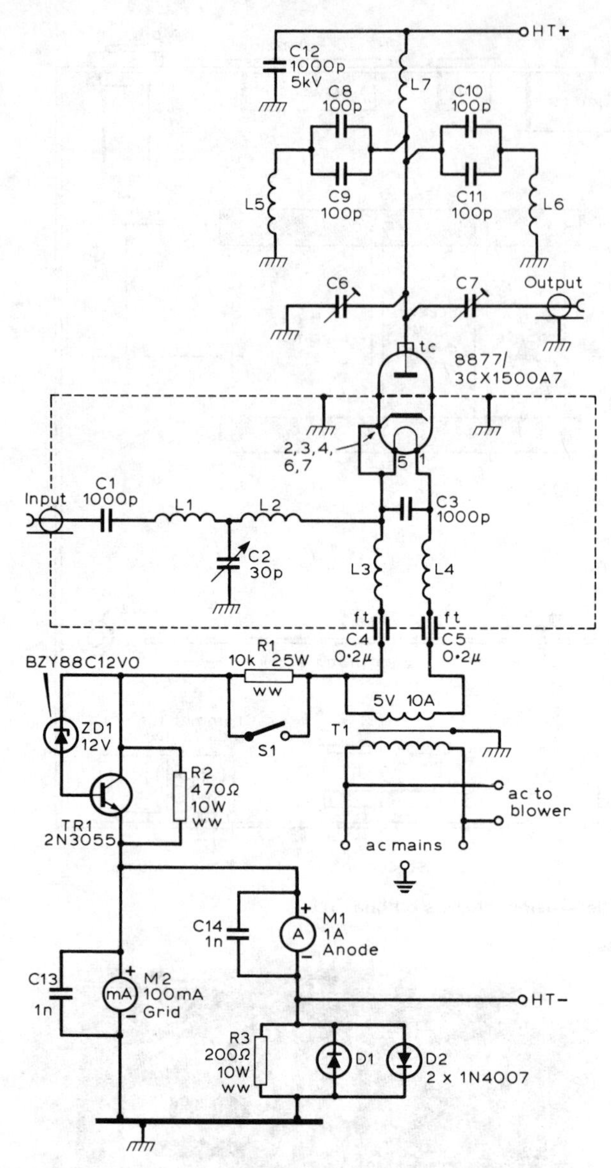

Fig 174. Grounded-grid amplifier circuit

have the considerable advantage that there is no stabilized screen supply needed.

Circuit description (Fig 174)

In this design by GW4BXE the 8877 triode is operated in a grounded-grid cathode-driven configuration with the operating bias being provided by a low-power zener diode and power transistor. These bias components, along with the metering components, are placed in the negative return lead. Both meters are protected by diodes D1 and D2. The 10kΩ resistor R1 effectively shuts off the valve when in standby position and, when shorted out for transmit, allows the valve to function normally. Resistor R2 is shunted across the power transistor TR1 to prevent a voltage rise should TR1 burn open. Resistor

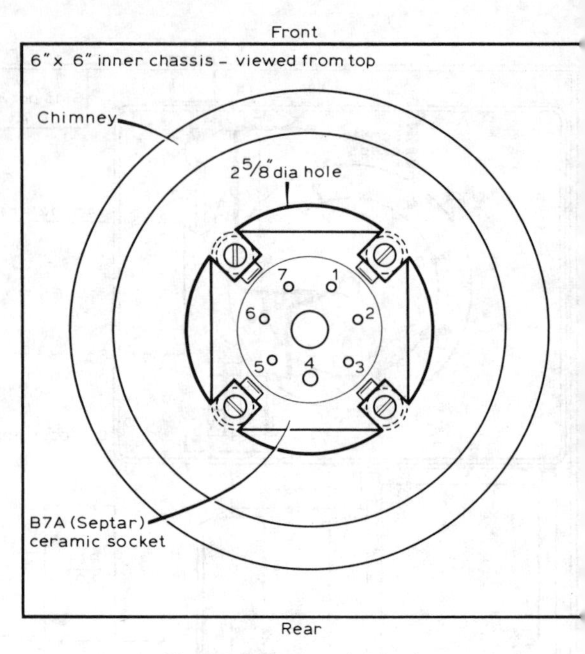

Fig 175. Top view of valve base

R3 prevents ht− from going positive, if the ht+ line were grounded for some reason.

RF is applied to the cathode of the valve by a T matching network. This network consists of two series-connected air-wound coils, their centre point being shunted to ground by the variable capacitor C2. The heater supply is connected to the

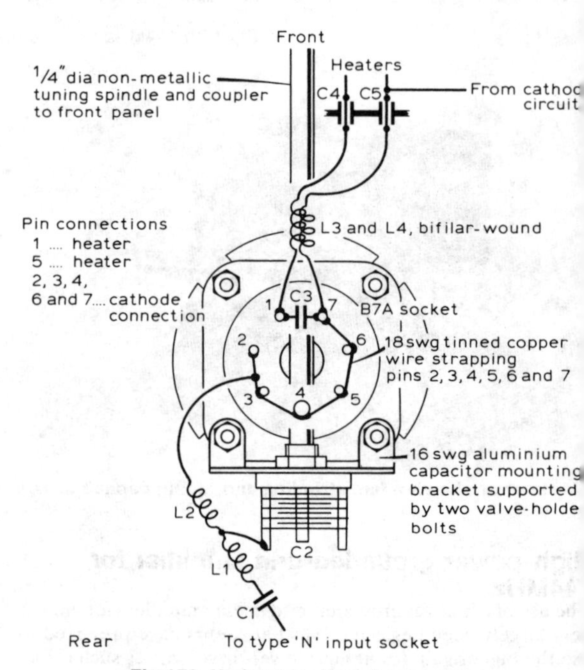

Fig 176. Underside view of valve base

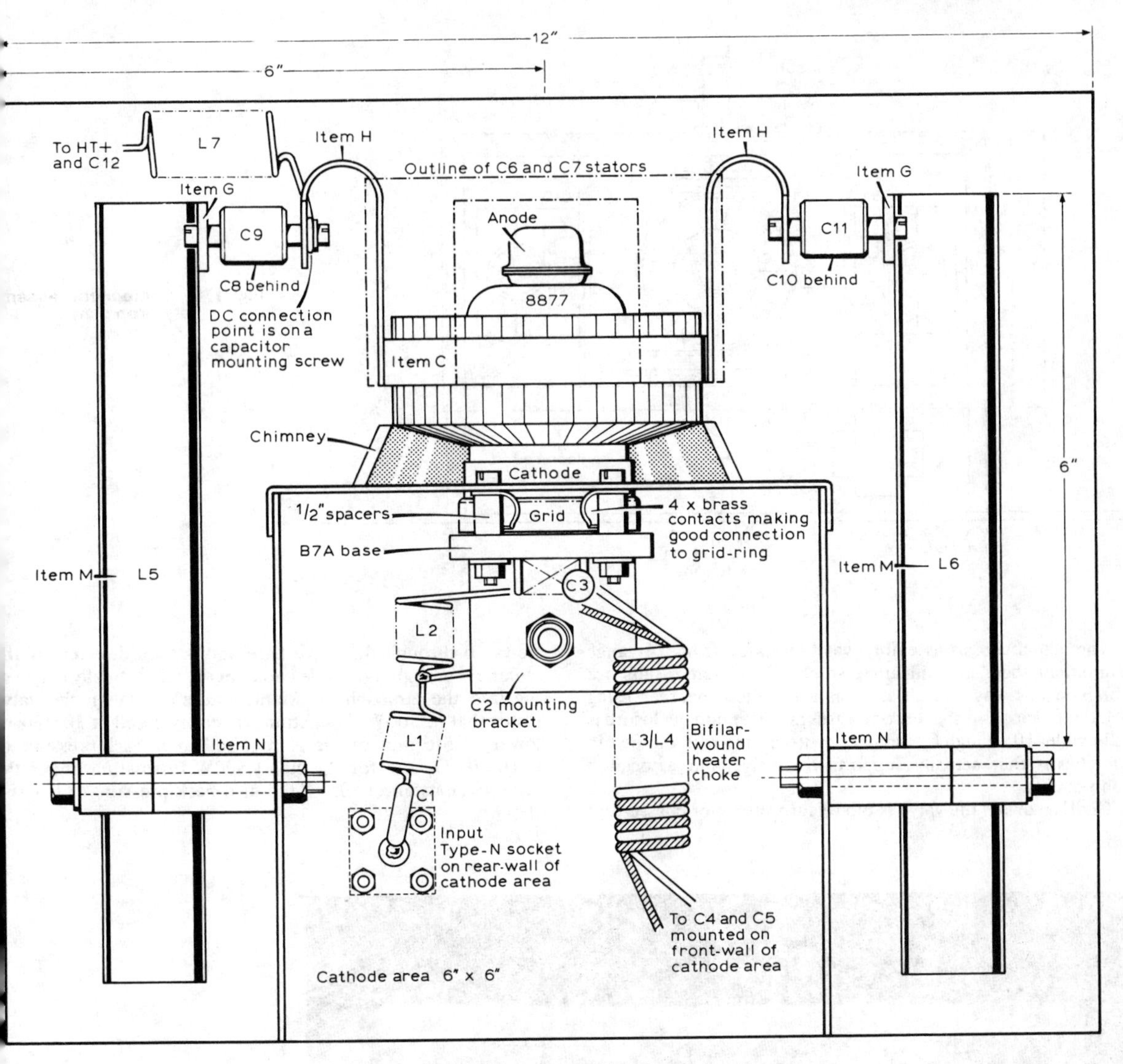

Fig 177. Component assembly—front elevation

alve base via an air-wound bifilar choke and high-current edthroughs C4, C5.

The valve base used is a standard ceramic B7A and is ounted ½in below chassis level by four spacers. These spacers lso serve to hold four grid-grounding clips made from small -shaped brass shims. These clips are sandwiched between the n spacers and the chassis underside.

The heater transformer T1 is bolted to the outer chassis wall s close as possible to C4 and C5.

The anode tuned circuit consists of two symmetrical iametrically-opposed $\lambda/4$ lines. This configuration may be egarded as a $\lambda/2$ line (L5 plus L6) with the valve, anode-tuning apacitor and loading capacitor at the electrical centre. Stanard copper water pipe is used for the lines. The loading apacitor, for example, could be fabricated from existing brass or copper tube-stock, the moving portion forming a sliding fit inside the fixed one. The fixed portion has sawcuts on its end and this enables a small clip to clamp both pieces solidly after adjustment. The N socket used for rf output has had its mounting flange removed and is soldered to the moving portion *after* the ¼in diam inner conductor has been soldered to the centre spigot of the N socket.

The anode shorting blocks need not be machined items and any sort of arrangement that clamps the anode lines positively could be reliably substituted. Both clamps should be of identical size, however, to maintain circuit symmetry. The lines should be clamped to the side chassis walls with 6in of line protruding upwards on each half.

The anode tuning capacitor C6 should be controlled by a suitable slow-motion drive.

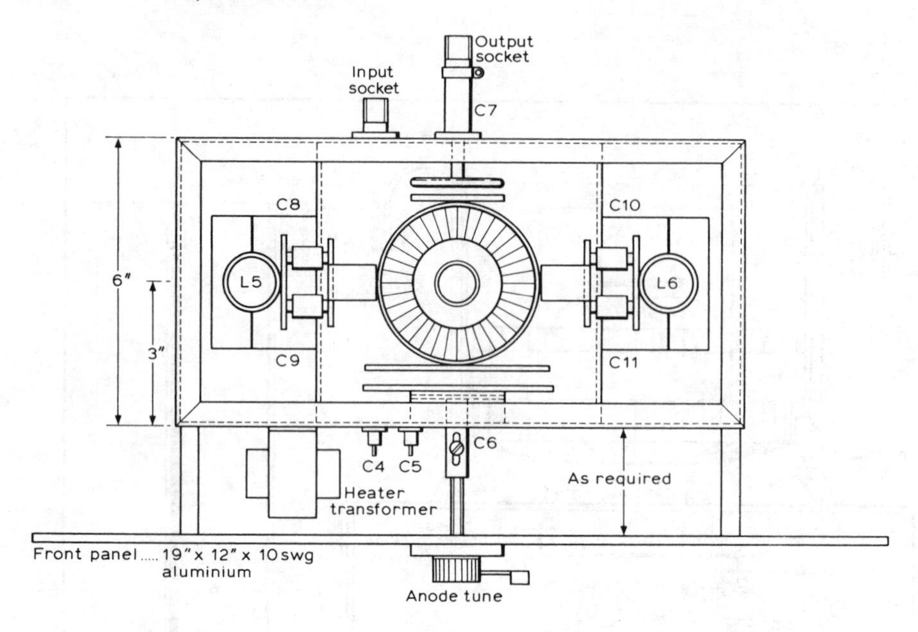

Fig 178. Component assembly—top view

The actual chassis assembly was fabricated from 16 gauge aluminium sheet and ½in angle stock. Very neat results are obtained this way and all sections are bolted together using 4BA hardware and shakeproof washers. The main enclosure is 12in wide, 10¼in high by 6in deep, with an internal 6in by 6in sub-chassis that actually supports the valve and associated components.

Cooling air for the valve is blown into the inner chassis and flows up through the valve base and is then directed by the chimney through the anode cooler of the valve, finally exhausting into the atmosphere. Manufacturer's data on the valve states that at 500W dissipation, at sea level and at 30MHz or lower, 7·5ft³/min of air is required at a back-pressure of 0·10in/H_2O, and for the full 1,500W dissipation under the same circumstances, 35ft³/min at a back-pressure of 0·41in/H_2O.

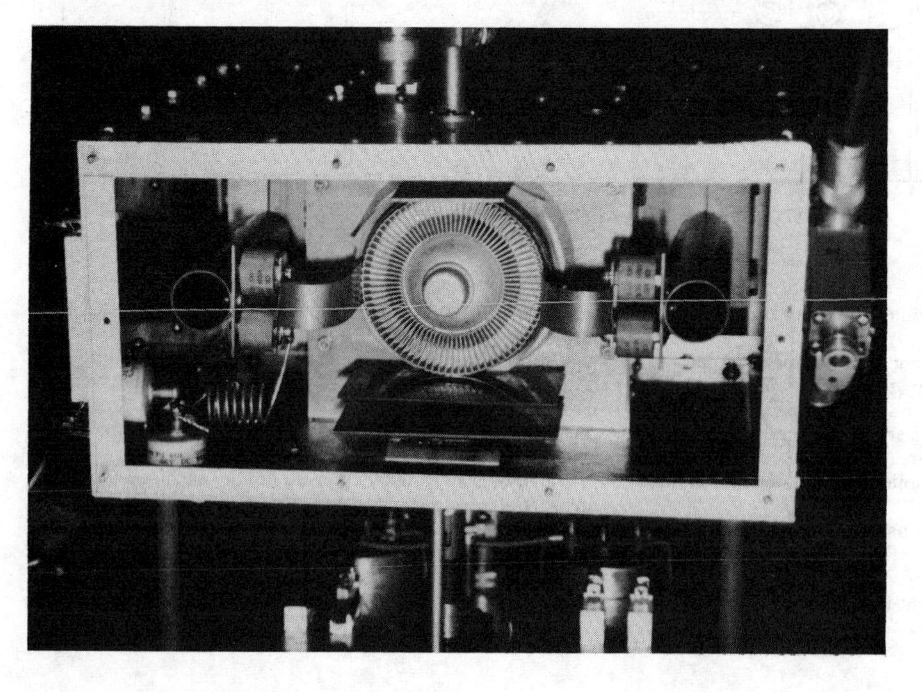

View of anode compartment with perforated top cover removed clearly showing major components. HT entry is via a ptfe plate close to the paralleled 500pF capacitors. The horizontal lines in these and the other photos are blemishes on the negatives

Table 28. Components list

1	1,000pF mica
2	30pF var Jackson C804
3	1,000pF mica
4	0·2μF 10A feedthrough
5	As C4
6	Special
7	Special
8,9,10,11	100pF mica tx quality
12	1,000pF 5kV minimum
1, D2	1N4007 or similar
D1	BZY88C12VO 12V zener 400mW
11, M2	1A and 100mA meters
1	5t 16swg tinned copper ½in diam ¾in long
2	4t 16swg tinned copper ½in diam ¾in long
3, L4	Each 10t 14swg en ⅝in diam bifilar
5, L6	Each 8½in of 1in bore copper water pipe (approx 1⅛in o.d.
7	7t 16swg tinned copper ⅝in diam 1⅜in long
1	10kΩ 25W ww
2	470Ω 10W ww
3	200Ω 10W ww
R1	2N3055 or similar
1	Heater transformer 5V 10A secondary

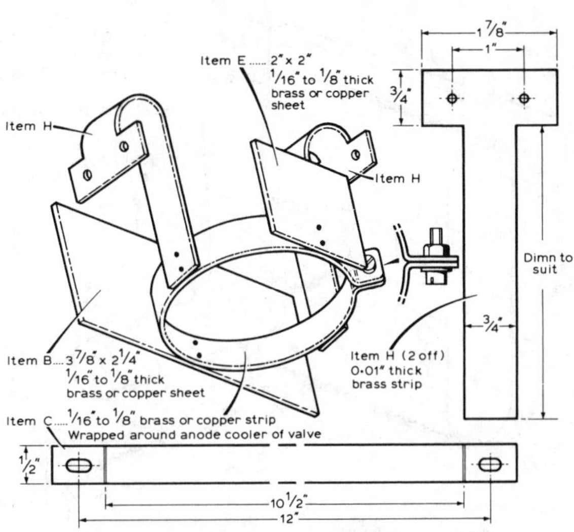

Fig 179. Anode clamp assembly (complete)

Operation

1. Establish blower and heater supplies. Allow 3min for warm-up.
2. Short out R1 and check standing current (should be in the order of between 50 and 100mA depending on the value of ht).
3. Apply a few watts of drive and quickly tune cathode, anode and loading for maximum output. Repeat this procedure until drive is at maximum, always tuning for maximum output. Loading heavily will increase dc input at the expense of output. The tuning and loading controls are to a large extent inter-dependent. A good power meter/dummy load is essential.

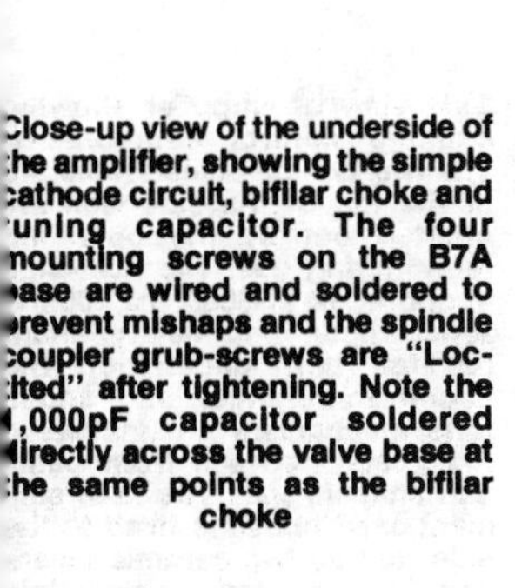
Close-up view of the underside of the amplifier, showing the simple cathode circuit, bifilar choke and tuning capacitor. The four mounting screws on the B7A base are wired and soldered to prevent mishaps and the spindle coupler grub-screws are "Loc-tited" after tightening. Note the 1,000pF capacitor soldered directly across the valve base at the same points as the bifilar choke

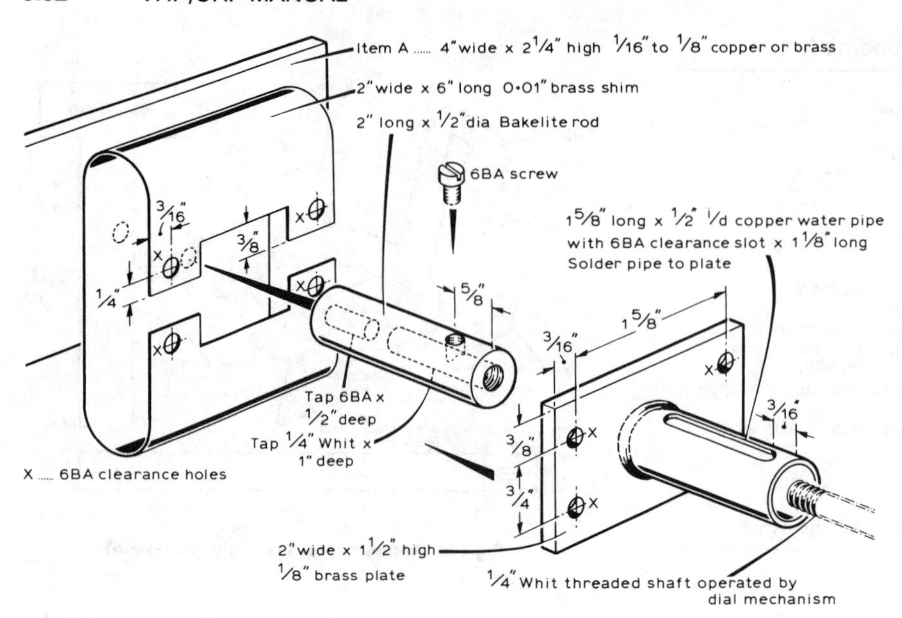

Fig 180. Anode tuning assembly (moving plate)

Side view of amplifier showing cathode control components. The two 22Ω paralleled resistors at the top of the side wall are shorted out by the operating relay during use. The heat sink supports the 2N3055, the 400mW zener diode and safety shunt resistor (both underside). The heater transformer and anode tune mechanism are visible in the space between front panel and chassis wall. The heat sink mentioned above is fixed to the side wall by two ceramic pillars and is mounted immediately above the pair of octal-based relays that are controlled by the ptt. The flying lead is vehicle ignition cable and carries ht to the anode compartment.

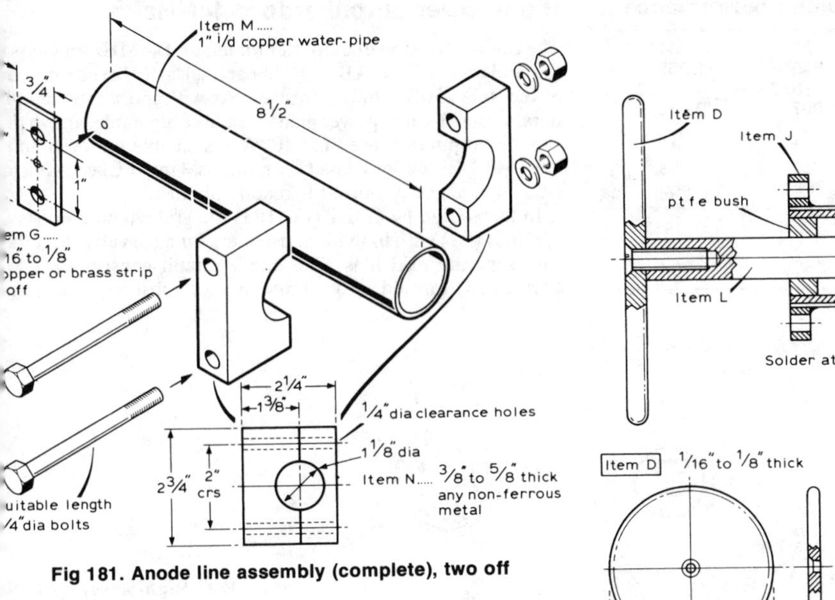

Fig 181. Anode line assembly (complete), two off

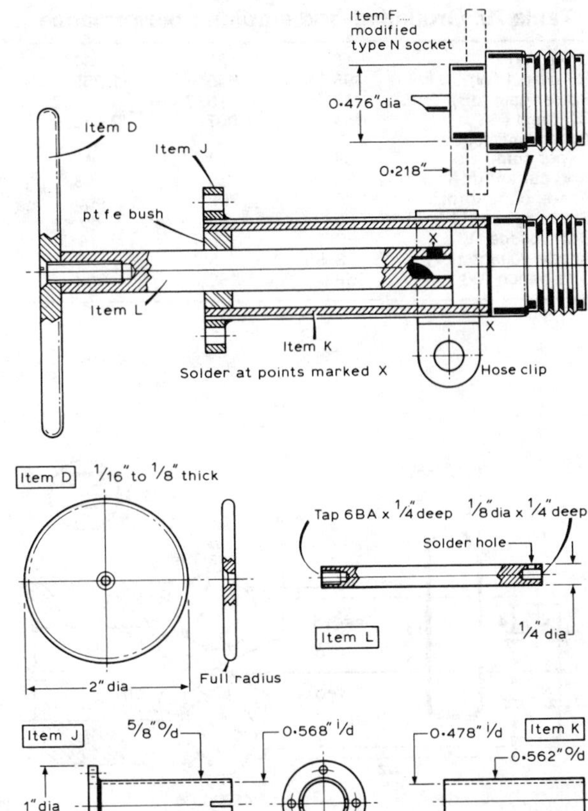

Fig 182. Capacitor assembly

Performance

During initial tests, a popular 15W transceiver was used as the driver and the amplifier was terminated into a commercial dummy load with its associated power meter of certified accuracy. The results shown in Table 29 were obtained.

All tests were carried out under single-tone conditions. An additional amplifier was used as an intermediate stage for the 25W and 60W tests and consisted of a pair of 2N5643 power transistors in parallel, with a 25V collector line, delivering up to 35W of rf.

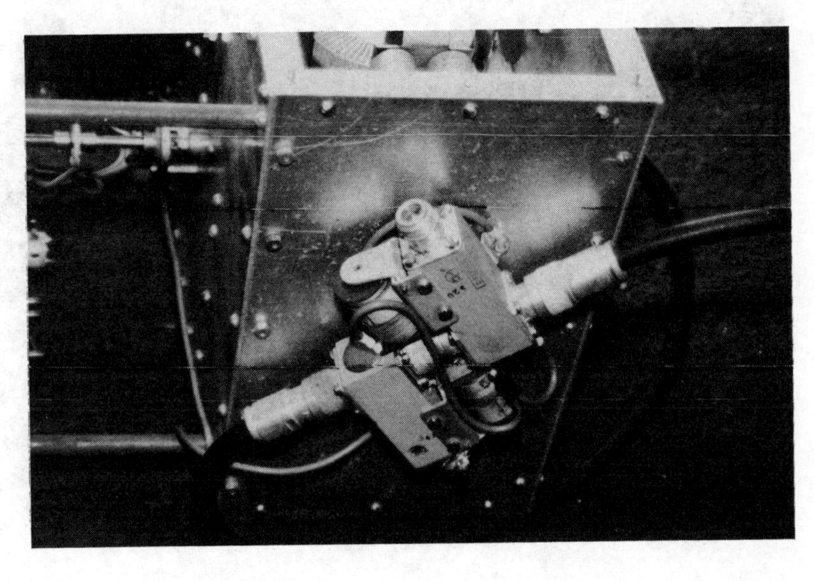

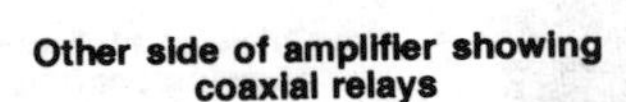

Other side of amplifier showing coaxial relays

Table 29. Grounded-grid amplifier performance

Drive (W)	15	25	60
RF output (W)	495	645	1,255
Power gain (dB)	15·2	13·7	13·2
DC input (W)	854	1,007	2,058
Approx efficiency (per cent)	58	64	61
Grid current (mA)	22	39	53
Anode current (mA)	240	308	465
Standing current (mA)	85	85	85
Grid voltage (V)	−9·7	−9·7	−9·7
Anode voltage (kV)	3·55	3·27	2·7
Dissipation (W)	359	362	803

High-power amplifier for 144MHz

The classic high-power amplifier for use on 144MHz for Class C (cw and fm) or Class AB1 (ssb linear) is usually based on a pair of the 4CX250B family of valves. As with most valve amplifiers, a considerable power gain is readily obtainable, and in this case an output of more than 400W is available for an input of less than 10W under Class C conditions. Under Class AB1 for ssb a similar p.e.p. output is readily obtained.

In this design by G8LT (Fig 183) the grid circuit consists of λ/2 lines (L2) with individual trimmers for each valve, together with separate grid bias. The anode circuit consists of a λ/4 circuit (L3) formed into a horseshoe of substantial size, and

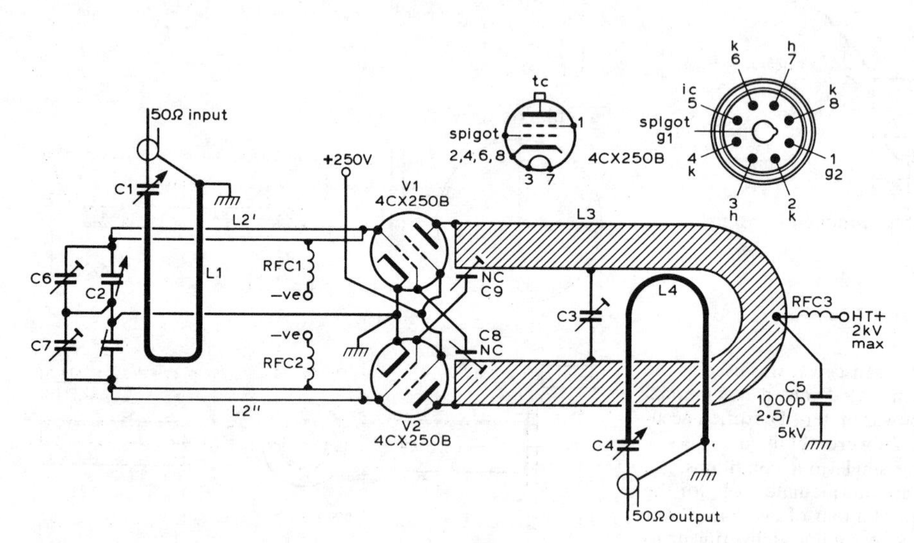

Fig 183. High-power 144MHz amplifier using pair of 4CX250B valves

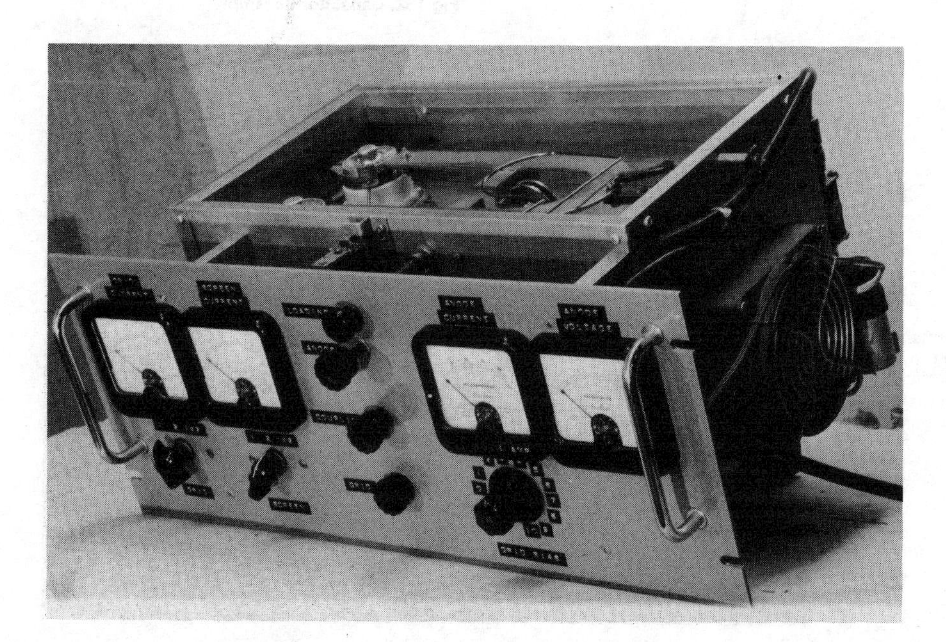

Front view of high-power amplifier showing controls and metering. The fan can be seen on the right of the rf compartment

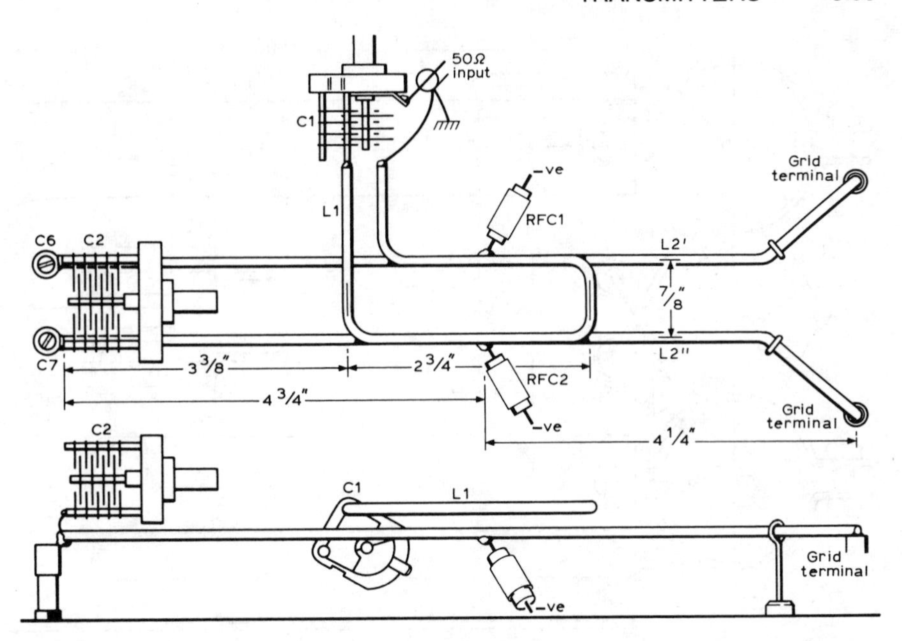

Fig 184. Grid circuit

tuning is by disc capacitor which is positioned so that coverage of the whole band 144–146MHz is obtained. The output is by a simple tuned coupling loop.

In order to obtain the full gain it is necessary to neutralize the valves. This accomplished by the conventional "cross wire" method, using stiff wires connected to the grid below the chassis and fed through the chassis. They are attached to a copper (brass) flag which is positioned near the opposite valve anode (cooler).

The 4CX250B class of valves depend on the maintenance of an adequate supply of air, and it is an advantage for some positive form of air-flow switch that switches off the anode and screen supplies in the event of a failure of the air supply. This may be a small vane fitted in the air duct which actuates a microswitch in the primary of the ht supply. The chimney normally used with the special air-flow socket must be used and in position when operating, otherwise the air will not pass through the anode cooler, and it will also significantly change the tuning of the anode circuit.

As mentioned earlier, the grid circuit consists of $\lambda/2$ lines, tuned at the remote end from the valves. In order to keep the length to a reasonable size the tuning capacitor, a butterfly type, has a fairly high value. So as to be able to make individual adjustments for variations of valves, a separate trimmer is attached to each of the lines.

Table 30. Components for high-power amplifier

C1,C4	50pF	Polar C4.04
C2	15+15pF	Polar C8.52/1
C6, C7	10pF	Piston trimmer
C3	Disc	1½in diam
C5	1,000pF	2·5–5kV bypass
C8, C9	NC	Plate attached to 16swg wire
L1	Input coupling loop	see Fig 184
L2′, L2″	⅛in diam copper 9in long	see Fig 184
L3	1in × ⅙in copper strip (see Fig 185)	

The input loop L1, C1 and the output loop L4, C4 are series tuned in the conventional manner. To avoid short-circuiting the supplies the actual loops should be insulated with suitable sleeving, and this is particularly important for the output loop.

The grid tuning capacitor is connected by a flexible shaft to allow the control, which is at right-angles to the front panel, to be fitted to it.

Low-power transistor transmitters for 144MHz

Exciter for 144MHz

This unit is suitable either as an exciter or a low-power transmitter. The design was prepared by the Mullard Co using their silicon transistors.

The circuit shown in Fig 186 is conventional and may be constructed in any form convenient to individual requirements.

Close-up view of grid circuit with components labelled

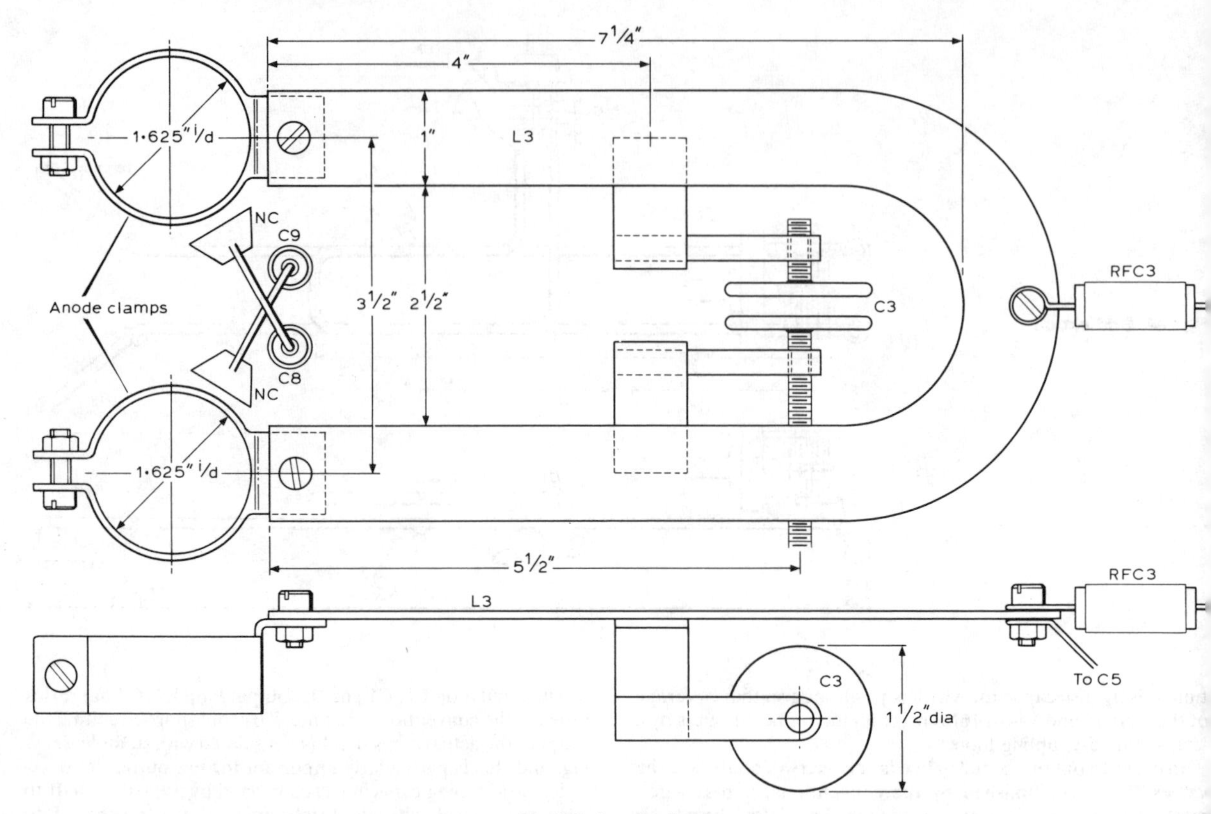

Fig 185. Anode circuit

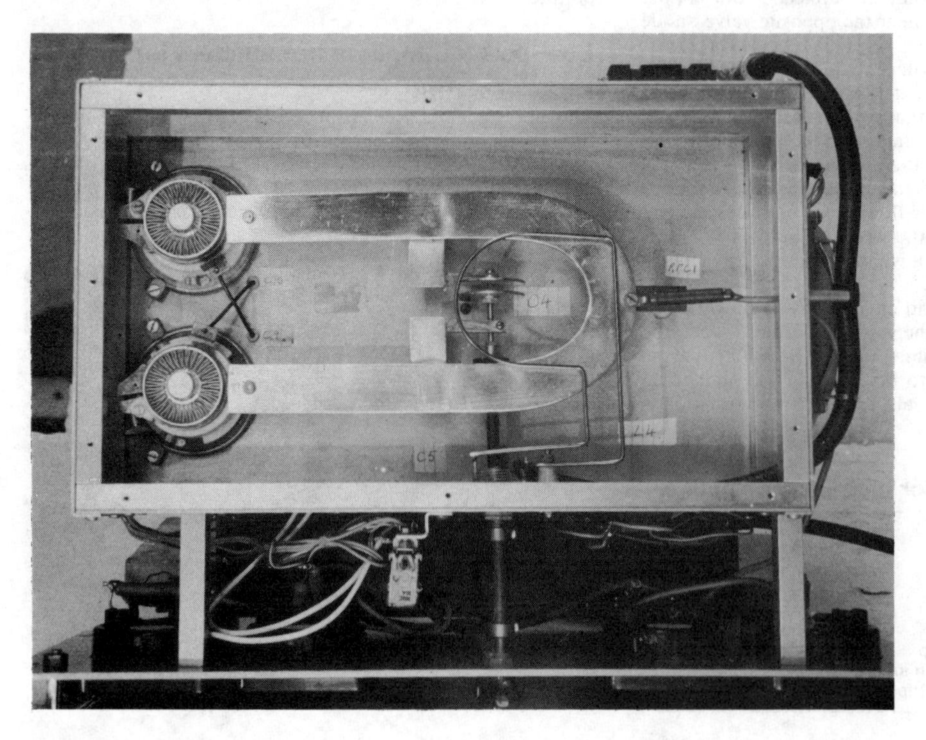

Top view of amplifier. Component numbers do not correspond to Fig 183

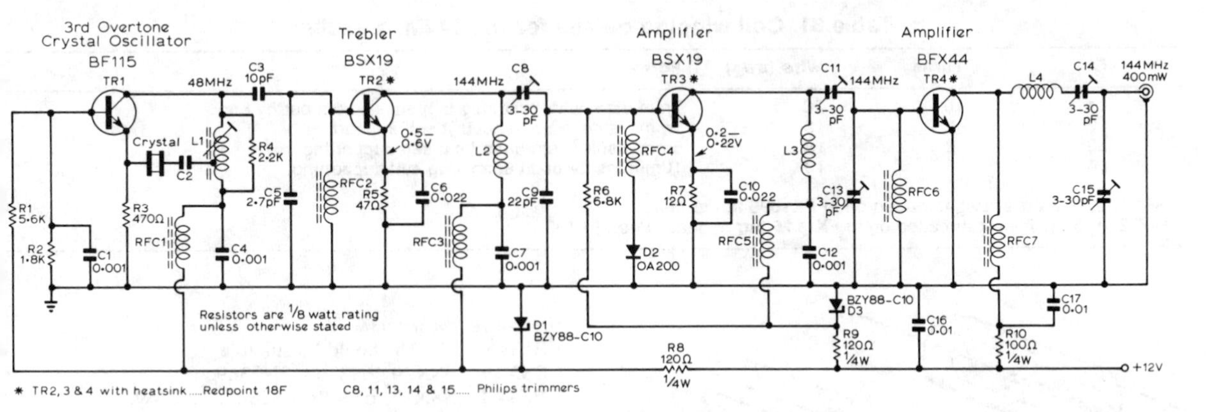

Fig 186. Circuit diagram of the 144MHz 400mW exciter

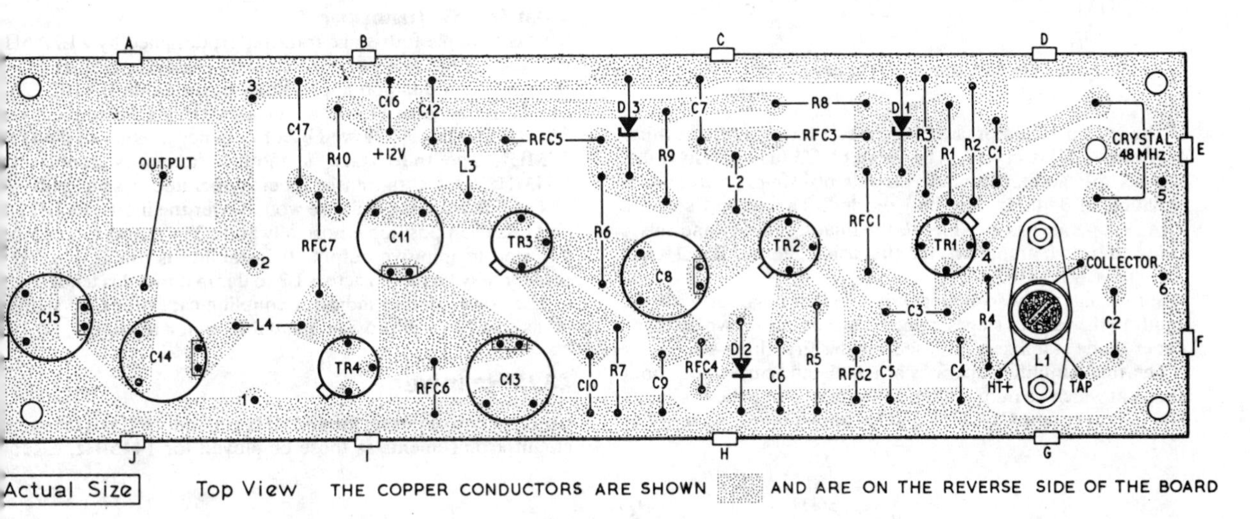

Fig 187. Component layout

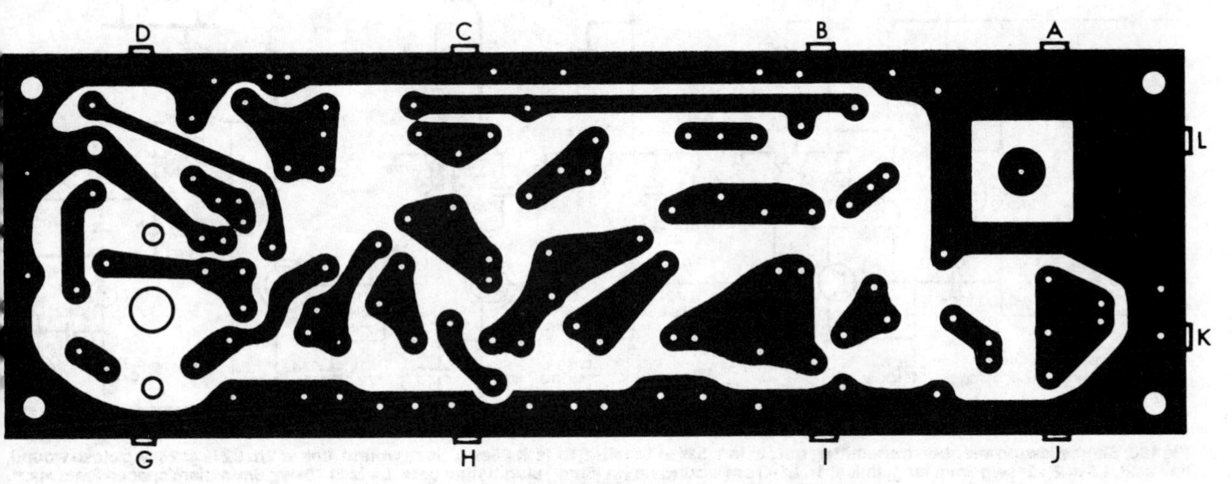

Fig 188. Underside of pcb

Table 31. Coil winding details for the 144MHz exciter

Coil	Turns	Wire (swg)	Former
L1	10	26	7mm diam with dust slug tapped 1½t from earthy end.
L2	3	18	7mm inside diam spaced ½t self supporting
L3	2	18	5mm inside diam 5mm long self supporting
L4	4	18	10mm inside diam 8mm long self supporting.

RFC1, 3, 5, 7 2½t 20swg threaded on to FX1898 ferrite bead.
RFC2, 4, 6 2½t 26swg threaded on to FX1115 ferrite bead. See Fig 189.

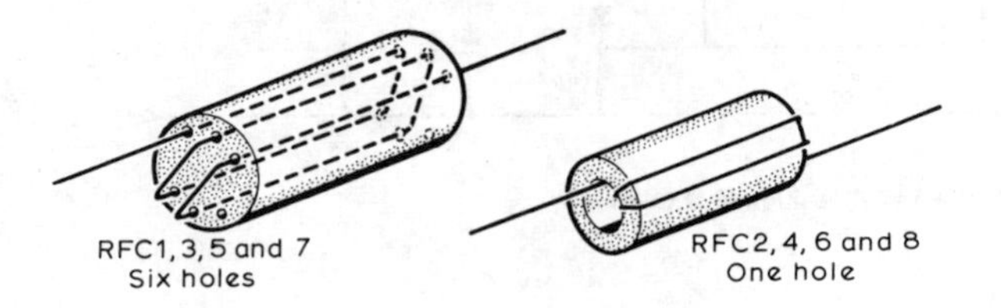

Fig 189. Detail of rf chokes

The crystal oscillator, a BF115, uses a series-resonant third-overtone 48MHz crystal. The value of C2 may be any value above 10pF, and if it is made variable 60–100pF, a frequency variation of 3–4kHz may be expected. The second stage, a BSX19, operates as a trebler to the final frequency and this is followed by two amplifiers, the first using another BSX19 and the final stage a BFX44.

Simple interstage couplings are used throughout with the inputs to the various stages tapped down by capacitive dividers. Zener diode stabilizers are used for the first three stages.

The final amplifier operates at a collector current of about 55mA at which an output of up to 400mW should be available. The output circuit C14, C15 and L4 allows matching to 50 or 75Ω.

Alternative transistors

BF115 2N918 should be suitable
BSX19 BSX20, 2N2368, 2N2369.
BFX44 BSX19, BSX20, 2N2368, 2N2369.
BZY88-C10 Any 10V 400mW type.

144MHz 1·5W transmitter

This is a simple four-stage transmitter, designed by ZL2AMJ, and consisting of a switched-crystals (separate board) oscillator, with modulation applied to varicap diode BA102. The oscillator transistor TIS44 or equivalent triples the frequency to 36MHz and this is followed by a frequency doubler (TIS44) to 72MHz. The third stage is another frequency doubler to 144MHz, the fourth transistor being operated as an amplifier.

The link coupling coils are wound over the inductors L1, L2 and L3. Their position is normally at the low rf end, but may be adjusted to improve output. If instability is found, a 4·7kΩ resistor may be placed across L2 to damp down this tendency.

The power output indicator coupling capacitor C20 should be as small as will provide a suitable meter reading.

432MHz mixer

Construction of mixers for 432MHz generally follows the same circuit arrangements as those employed for 144MHz, except

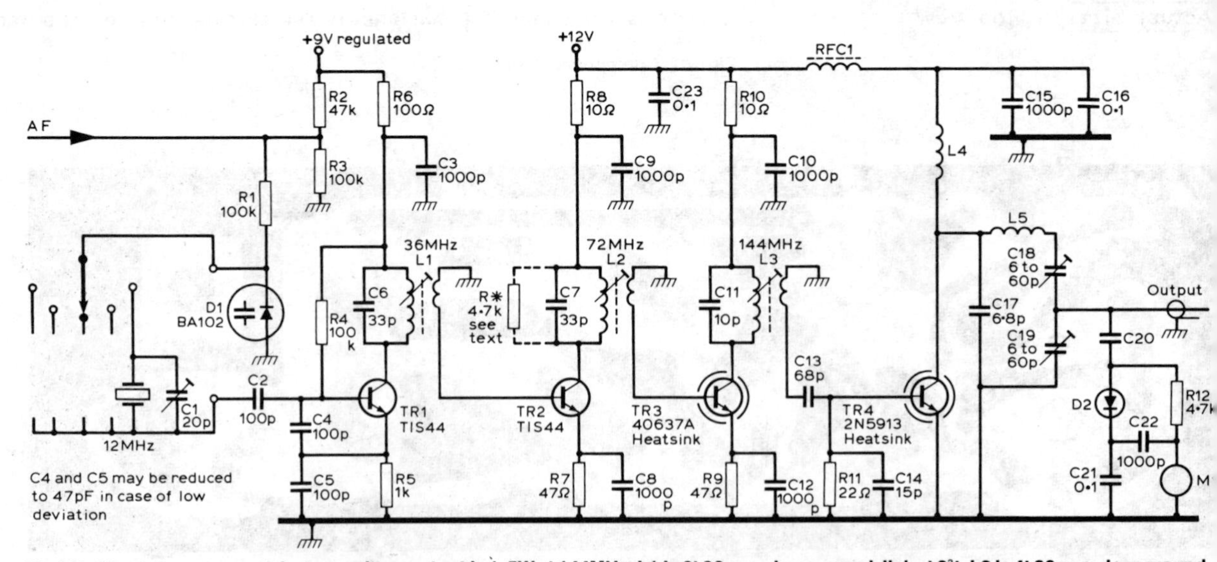

Fig 190. Simple low-power nbfm transmitter; output is 1·5W at 144MHz. L1 is 8t 26swg close wound, link at 2¾t. L2 is 4t 26swg close wound, link at 2t. L3 is 2½t 26swg 3mm long, link at 1t. L1–3 are wound on ¼in (6mm) slug tuning core. L4 is 2t 18swg 6mm diam spaced 3mm apart, 3mm above pcb. L5 4t 18swg 6mm diam 12mm long. RFC is 3t 26swg on ferrite bead

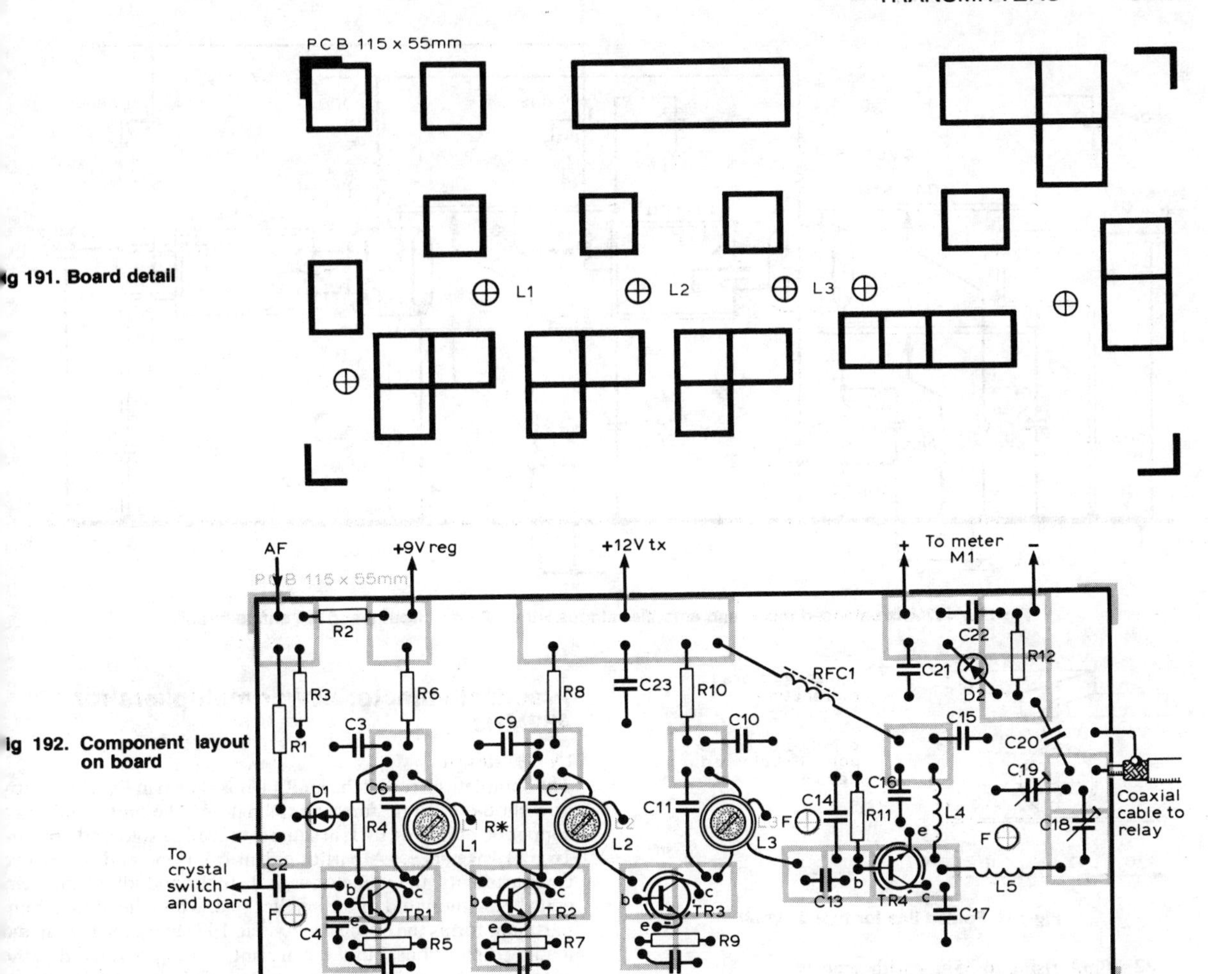

Fig 191. Board detail

Fig 192. Component layout on board

that the inductors are usually linear or single-turn loops of low-inductance material such as copper (or brass) ribbon.

The local oscillator chain will need to have a final frequency suitable to mix with the 28–30MHz ssb signal to 432MHz.

Some form of balanced mixer is desirable; although of course a simple single-end type may be used it is likely to be much more difficult to remove the unwanted signals.

In the case of valve design, probably the most suitable valve for this application is the QQV02-6, or two separate valves of similar grid input capacitance. In either case it is usually convenient to use λ/2 grid circuits, while for the anode tuned circuit λ/4 is suitable.

In Fig 193 a generic design of a suitable balanced mixer and following amplifier is shown, the output from which is sufficient to drive a high-power amplifier stage.

For semiconductor transverters, the choice of balanced mixer is either:

(a) pair of similar devices (fets); or
(b) a diode ring of matched diodes either in the form of separate diodes or a complete module; the latter is to be preferred.

The circuits for all the final frequencies are best of the linear type with end tuning. These λ/4 circuits may be shortened to a suitable length such as 65 to 90mm of 4–6mm diameter. Alternatively, single loops or ribbon may be used for more compact assemblies, see Fig 194. The use of linear circuits allows easy access for attachment of impedance matching connections between stages. The use of inductive coupling between driver and output amplifier will significantly improve the frequency discrimination, improving the attenuation of unwanted frequencies from the output.

Fig 195 shows details of a balanced circuit suitable for the output of the balanced mixer. In Fig 193, the various tuned circuits are made of short lines, and those for the input circuits are λ/2 with the RFC chokes tapped at the electrical centre (usually close to the valve connections). The anode circuits are λ/4 tuned by small butterfly capacitors with the rotor left free.

The input inductors are typically 2in long, wound from 14swg copper. As shown, the 28MHz input relies on a dc return in the coupling coil.

Typical anode currents are

V1 28mA

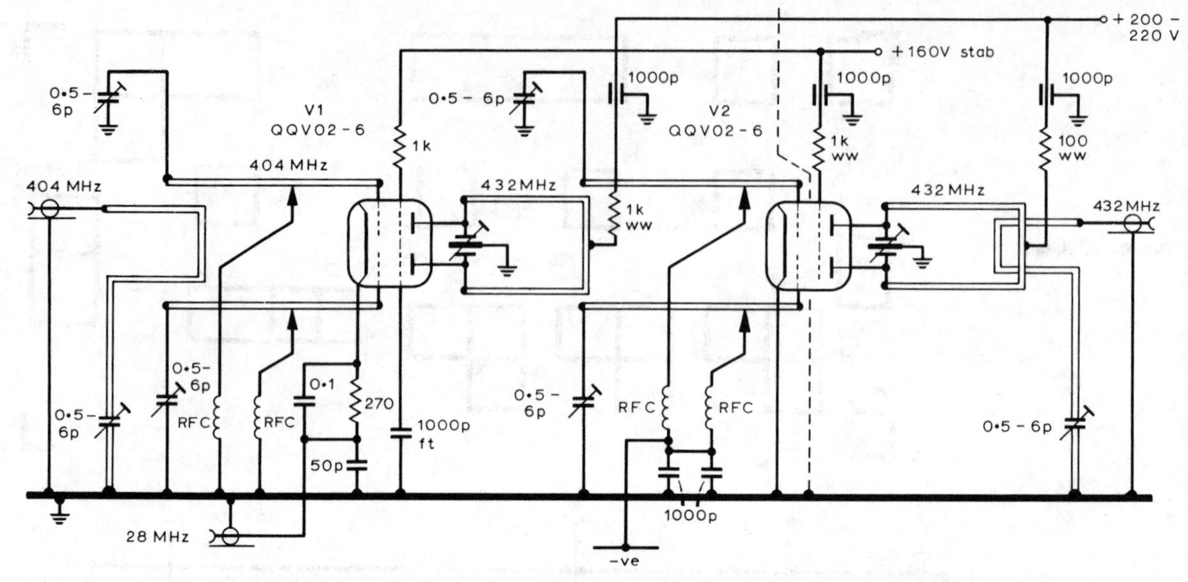

Fig 193. 432MHz balanced mixer and amplifier stages with λ/2 grid circuits and λ/4 anode circuits

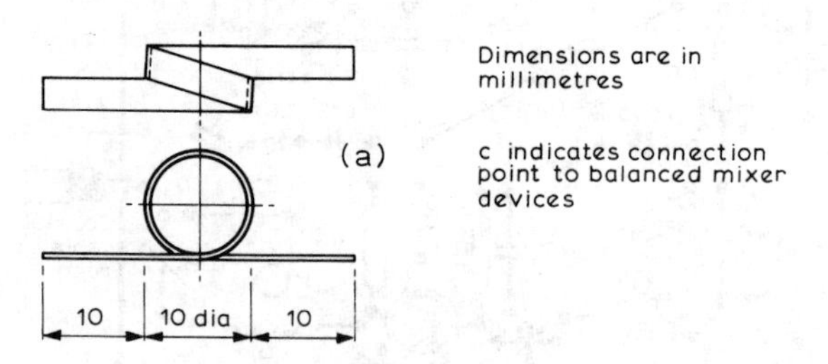

Fig 194. Folded line for tuned circuit

V2 20mA rising to 35mA with speech.

Bias to V2 will be about −6V, this should be a variable.

The amplifiers detailed later may be set up for linear operation to follow this mixer.

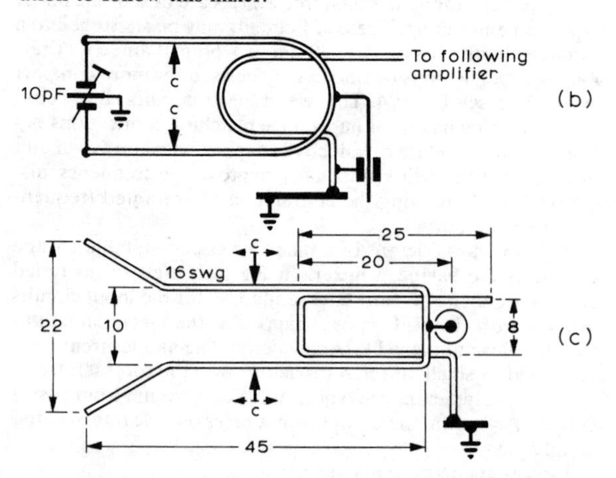

Fig 195. Theoretical and practical circuit for 432MHz balanced mixer

Practical varactor power multipliers for 432MHz

1N4387 design

The complete circuit of the multiplier is shown in Fig 196 and by now should need no further explanation. The unit is built in a copper box 6in long by 1½in square, brazed or soldered up from 16 to 18swg sheet. A partition 2¼in from one end forms two compartments, the varactor with its input and idler tuned circuits being mounted in the smaller one, while the longer compartment forms the output cavity. Fig 197 shows the layout and leading dimensions, but these are not critical provided that the output cavity dimensions are not varied too much, consequently a detailed metalwork drawing is not given. A 4½in by 3½in by 2in Eddystone die-cast box with the cavity formed by a copper partition would undoubtedly work just as well.

Setting up the multiplier requires, in addition to a source of rf at 144MHz, an absorption wavemeter to cover 288 and

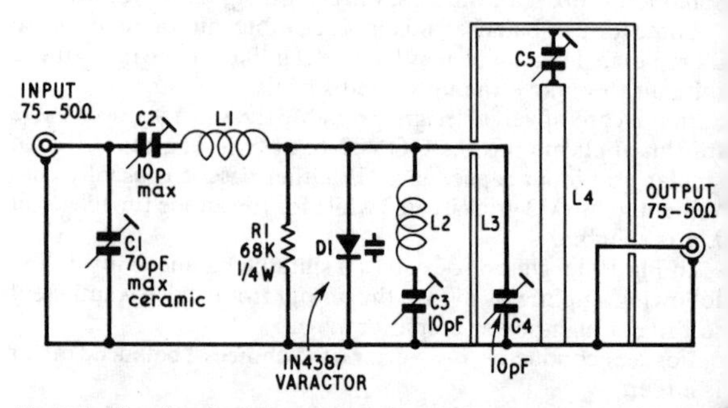

Fig 196. The circuit of the tripler. C1: 70pF max ceramic. C2: 10pF max. C3, C4: 10pF beehive. C5: two 1in diam discs, approx $\frac{1}{16}$in apart. D1: 1N4387 varactor diode. L1: 3½t 16swg ½in diam (0·2μH). L2: 2t 16swg ⅜in diam (0·06μH). L3: 2in 16swg. L4: 3⅛in ⅛ od brass tube. R1: 68KΩ ¼W

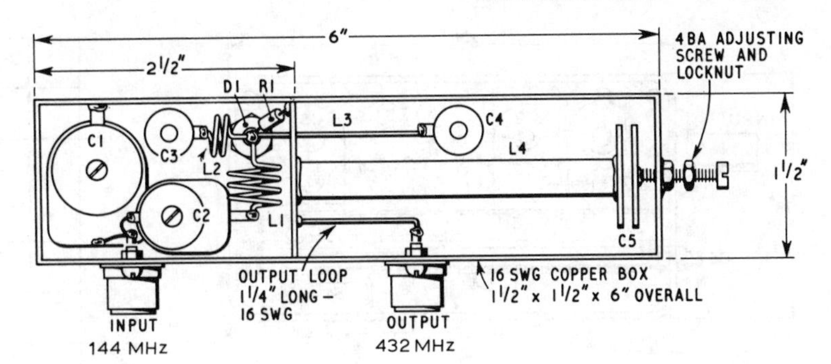

g 197. Layout and principal dimensions of the 432MHz varactor tripler

32MHz, and a good dummy load or rf power meter. With the ɔad connected to the varactor output, apply about 10W of rf to ne input and peak up the input circuit (C2, L1 and C1) for naximum absorbed power, using the 144MHz transmitter pa node current meter as an indicator. Next set the wavemeter to 88MHz and bring a probe, loosely coupled to it, near to the unction of L2, C3 and adjust C3 for maximum idler voltage at nis point (ie L2, C3 in series resonance). These first two steps an be carried out more rapidly if a gdo is used initially to set the nput and idler to the correct frequencies.

Next, peak up C4 and C5 for maximum rf out, using the vavemeter to confirm that this is on 432MHz and not 576MHz. With the cavity dimensions shown, the plates of C5 will be bout $\frac{1}{16}$in apart. Now increase the power level in steps, re-adjusting the trimmers each time because of the changing var-actor capacitance which forms part of the input, idler and first output tuned circuits. It will be found that correct adjustment of he idler circuit produces a peak in the output power, but this is ot a reliable way of adjusting the idler since a number of purious peaks will occur if C3 is varied over its range, owing to nteraction between the various tuned circuits.

Having set the idler to series resonance by the method sug-gested above, it is best left alone, and subsequent alignment onfined to the input and output circuits. If a reflectometer is vailable, it may be used to adjust C1 for optimum match to the eeder cable, again at the proper power. In practice, adjustment f C1 so that the 144MHz transmitter pa does not detune as the oupling loop is brought in, seems to be satisfactory.

After a short period of operation at full power, check the varactor stud temperature. At the maximum allowable rf input evel of 40W, the 1N4387 will produce about 25W of rf output nd will therefore be dissipating 15W as heat; at this dissipation he maximum permissible stud temperature is 100°C. The box hown in Fig 197, if made of 16swg copper, will have a thermal esistance of about 5°C/W in free air, and at 15W will therefore old the varactor stud at 100°C in an ambient temperature of 25°C. This, of course, is on the limit of the device rating and is uncomfortably hot in any case, so it is recommended that the ripler unit be mounted to a thick copper or brass bracket bolted lirectly on the varactor stud.

The power levels quoted above are cw and in fact the varactor nay limit, due to reverse voltage breakdown, at a power level lightly above the manufacturer's rated maximum. This means hat although the 1N4387 or BAY96 will produce 25W of cw ɔower, the peak power level attainable will not be much more han this. With the 1N4387 it is necessary to reduce the input ɔower from 40 to 20W in order to produce reasonably symmet-rical 100 per cent a.m. This diode, which is a graded-junction step-recovery device, will, in fact, multiply an a.m. signal very well with good linearity, but the abrupt-junction types, such as the BAY66, detune more rapidly with changes of drive level, and would probably be slightly less satisfactory for a.m. use.

Phase or frequency modulation is cheaper to achieve and more suitable (because of voltage breakdown and hence peak power limitations) for varactor and transistor transmitters. If it is necessary to use a.m. with a varactor tripler, it is advisable to tune it up with a 100 per cent sinewave modulated signal at the normal power level while watching the demodulated envelope on an oscilloscope. Look for peak clipping, and for discon-tinuities in the scope pattern due to dynamic detuning as the applied power varies over the modulation cycle. These can be eliminated by adjusting the input power level and finding a compromise setting for the input tuned circuit. These complica-tions are unnecessary, of course, with nbfm.

An alternative design

Another type to that just described is based on a standard die-cast box. The circuit is very similar, except that the high-Q filter consists of a tuned $\lambda/4$ line, shown as L4 in the diagram (Fig 198). The varactor used is a BAY96 and with 15W input; 9W output can be expected when properly adjusted.

Good-quality a.m. speech can be passed through this multi-plier provided the peak percentage modulation of the drive is

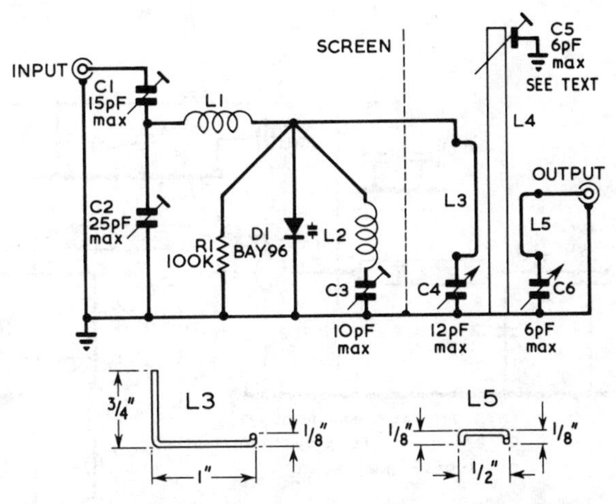

Fig 198. The 432MHz tripler circuit. L1: 6t 18swg $\frac{3}{16}$in diam $\frac{1}{2}$in long. L2: 3t 14swg $\frac{3}{16}$in diam $\frac{3}{4}$in long. L3: 18swg shaped as shown and spaced $\frac{3}{32}$in from L4, $\frac{1}{4}$in od, $\frac{3}{16}$in i.d. copper tube, $4\frac{1}{8}$in long. L5: 18swg as drawing, spaced $\frac{3}{16}$in from L4

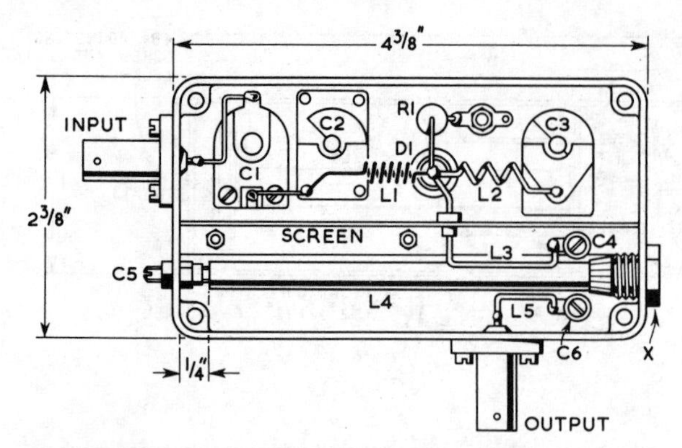

Fig 199. Layout of tripler in die-cast box. The diode is bolted directly to the base. D1 shows position of the diode

held to about 80 per cent maximum. The procedure for setting up and alignment is the same as for the previous unit.

432MHz 3–4W power amplifier

A useful low-power amplifier providing 10dB gain can be built using strip-line circuits on double-sided copper-clad glassfibre board. The circuit, first described in *Break-In* August 1978, is shown in Fig 201.

Tuning of the circuits is by foil-insulated trimmers (air types may be used provided they are dimensionally similar). During tune-up it is advisable to reduce the supply voltage. The inclusion of a resistor (2·2kΩ) at the output is to prevent the transistor from being unloaded and it can be removed later.

Included in the circuit is a simple pi filter to reduce unwanted harmonics to a satisfactory level.

An output of 3W can be obtained at 12V with a collector current of about 450mA. At 14V 4W a collector current of 600mA is obtained. Tuning for maximum output should be done using a suitable power meter and reliable dummy load.

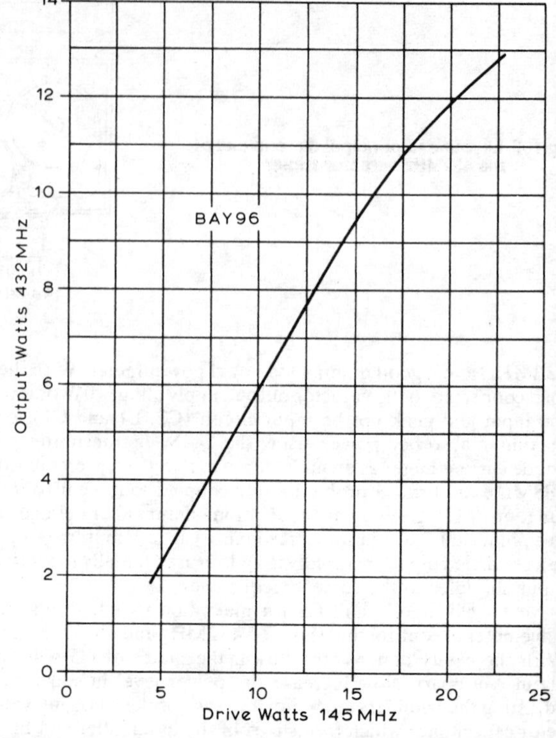

Fig 200. Typical varactor tripler. Input 145MHz, output 432MHz

432MHz 2W linear amplifier

This is a simple two-stage 10dB gain linear amplifier (*Radio Communication* June 1977) suitable for use on ssb or atv using lumped-circuit inductors (Fig 204). Although no pcb layout is given for this amplifier, a pcb may of course be used. Screens are required to isolate the various parts of the circuit as indicated in the circuit diagram. The pi filter shown in the previou

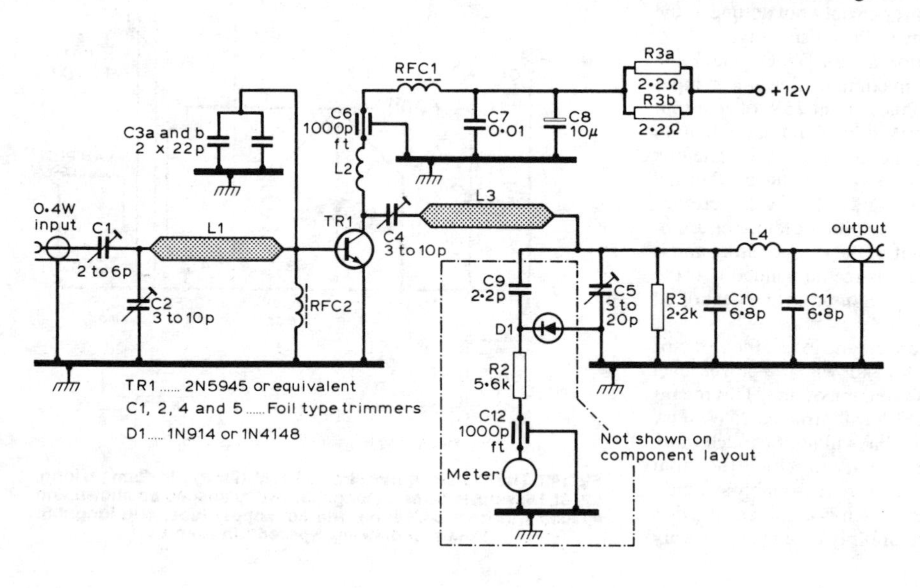

Fig 201. 432MHz power amplifier giving 3–4W output. L1 strip line. L2 7t 6mm diam 22swg wound. L3 strip line. L4 1t 7mm diam 18swg. RFC1 2t 22swg ferrite bead. RFC 3t 20swg large ferrite bead

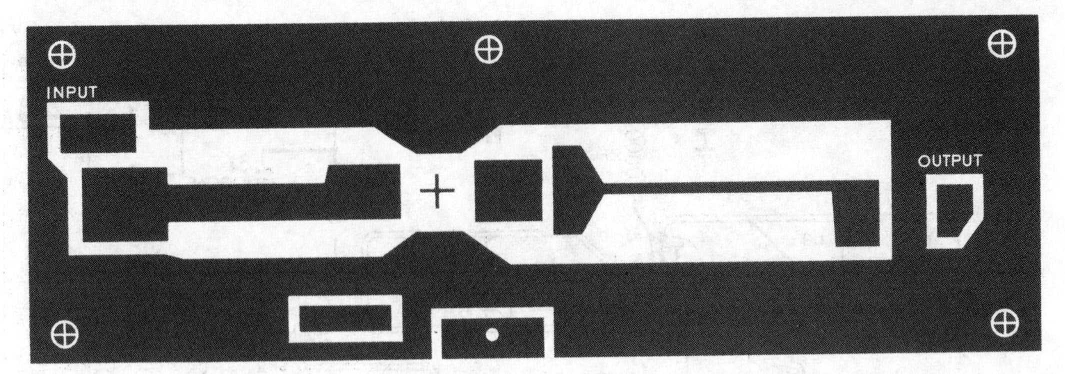

Fig 202. Transmitter pa board, actual size. This board is double-sided (see text)

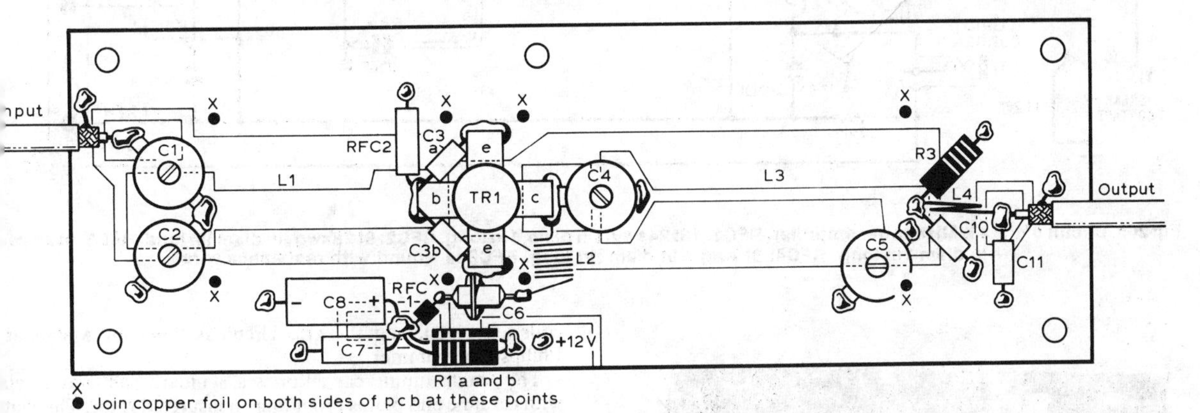

Fig 203. Component layout

mplifier is also suitable for use with this or any other low-ower amplifier.

Medium-power linear amplifier for 432MHz

his is a power amplifier for 432MHz using a QQV03-20A or imilar valve. Both the grid and anode circuits are of the tuned line type. Although the prototype was designed as a linear amplifier, it may of course be used as a Class C amplifier if desired by changed operating conditions.

As can be seen from the photos, the amplifier itself is fully screened and the front panel to which anode and screen current meters are attached is fixed to the amplifier box.

Details of the anode and grid lines together with the coupling

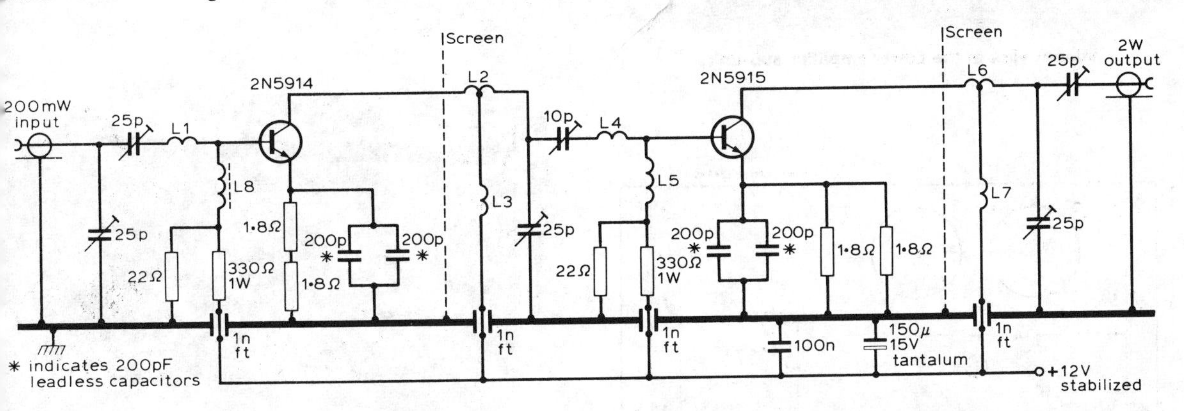

ig 204. 432MHz linear amplifier providing 10dB gain and using lumped-circuit inductors. L1, L4 1t 3mm diam 20swg length 3mm. L2, L6 1t 5mm diam 18swg length 3mm, tap ¼t from collector. L3, L7 1t 6mm diam 20swg 3mm length. L5 3t 5mm diam 20swg length 5mm. L8 2½t 26swg FX1115

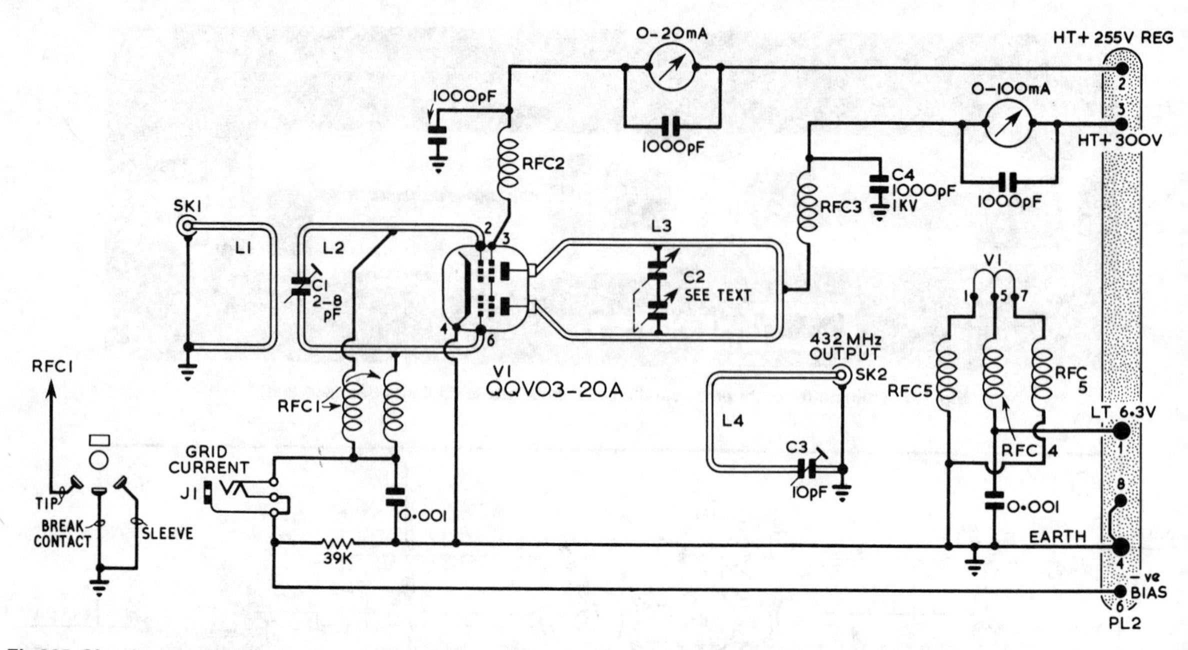

Fig 205. Circuit of the 432MHz power amplifier. RFC1: 13t 24swg, ⅛in diam, 1in long. RFC2: 9t 28swg ¼in diam ⅝in long. RFC3: 9t 22sw 3/16in diam 1in long. RFC4: 9t swg 3/16in diam ¾in long. RFC2 is wound with resistance wire

Interior view of the power amplifier sub-unit

coils are given, and the grid circuit is tuned by a standar Philips-type trimmer.

The anode tuning capacitor is a standard split-stator typ with ceramic end plates providing an insulated rotor. The plat spacing is 0·045in (double spaced) with only two fixed and tw moving plates per section. Connection to the anode line is mad by copper or phosphor bronze foil; the position should b adjustable.

An insulated coupling is used to connect to the control sha to leave the capacitor above earth.

The capacitor tunes the output coupling loop with a max mum value of 10pF, and is located alongside the output coaxia socket.

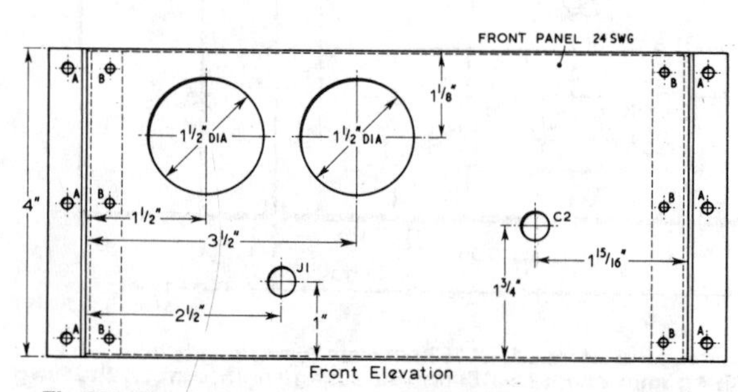

Fig 206. Front-panel layout of the 432MHz power amplifier

The power amplifier

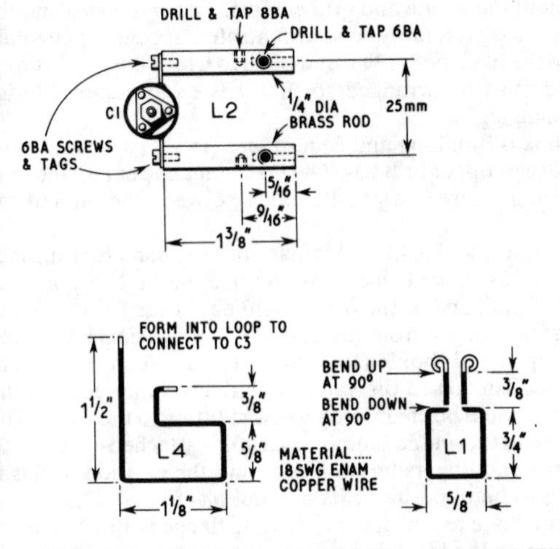

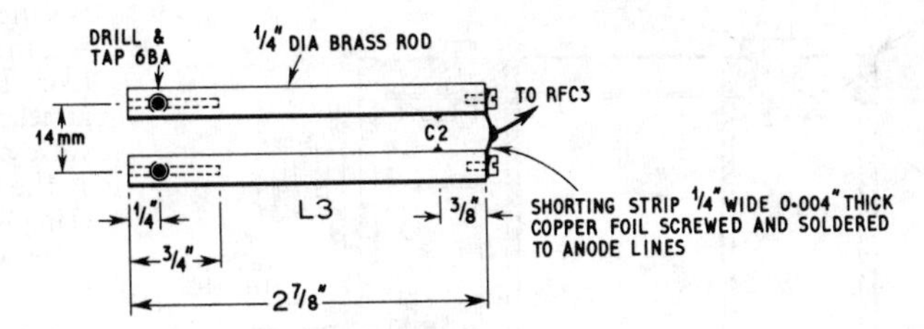

Fig 207. Tuned circuits for 432MHz power amplifier

Coaxial cavity for 432MHz

As an alternative to the box-type cavity a tubular or coaxial type offers a considerable space saving, but of course a significant amount of machine work will be needed.

Fig 209 shows the general arrangement of the anode circuit and Fig 210 gives the mechanical details of the various component parts. Detail (A) gives dimensions for either a 4X150A or 4CX250B valve.

The grid circuit may be similar to that previously described and built into a cast box. Above this a plate is mounted and spaced to provide the necessary room for the supply leads.

A flange (detail L) is made to fit into the lower rim of the valve socket skirt. This is fixed to the cast box and completely isolates the input and output circuits, as well as providing a suitable air duct for the cooling air which must be blown up from the underside of the valve socket and through the anode cooling fins. The valve socket is attached to the extra top plate by the normal clips.

The anode circuit outer, detail A, is attached to the top plate by four eyebolts at the bottom and then the inner tube assembly consisting of the anode line (C) is soldered or brazed to the inner top disc (D) which is bolted to the outer top disc (B) and isolated from it by the ptfe washer (E). The fixing bolts of the two top discs are insulated from the outer top disc by ptfe bushes (F). The whole assembly is then attached to the outer tube by four lugs into which eyebolts at the top end of the tube locate.

Tuning of the cavity is provided by a disc-type capacitor as detail H and G. The adjustable element (G) should be provided with some tensioning device such as a spring locating into the screw thread. Since there is the full ht between these two plates one of them should be covered with suitable insulating material to prevent a possible short circuit.

Output from the cavity is by the conventional series-tuned

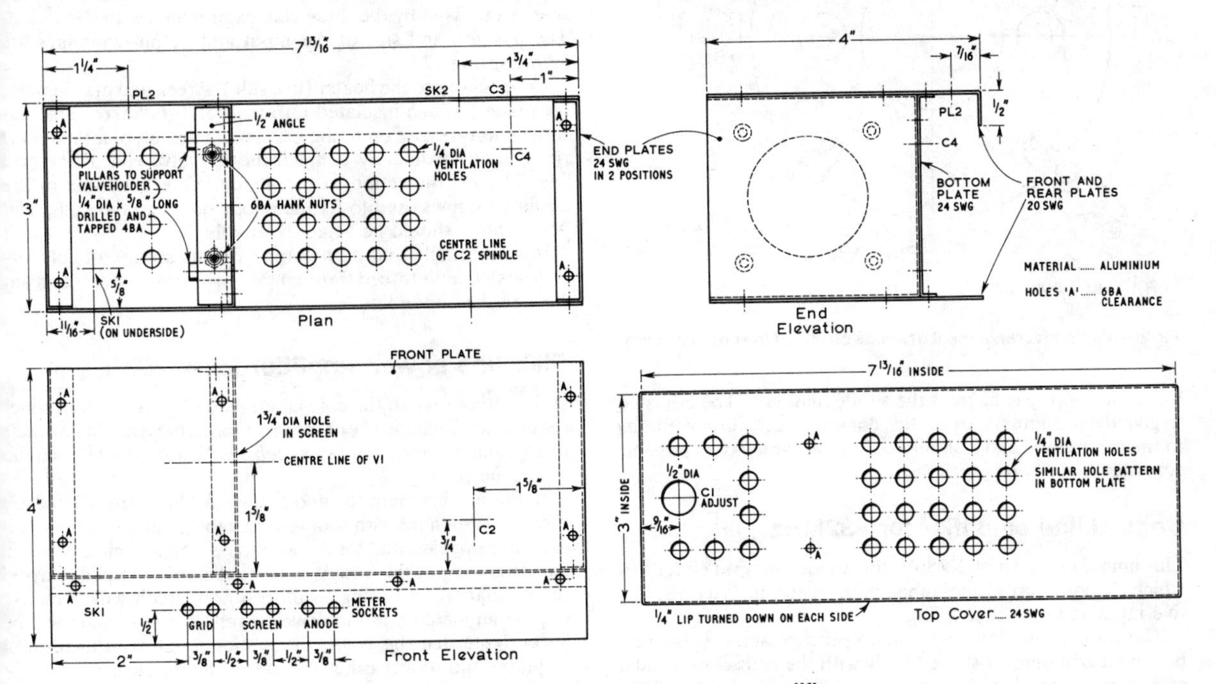

Fig 208. Drilling details of the 432MHz power amplifier

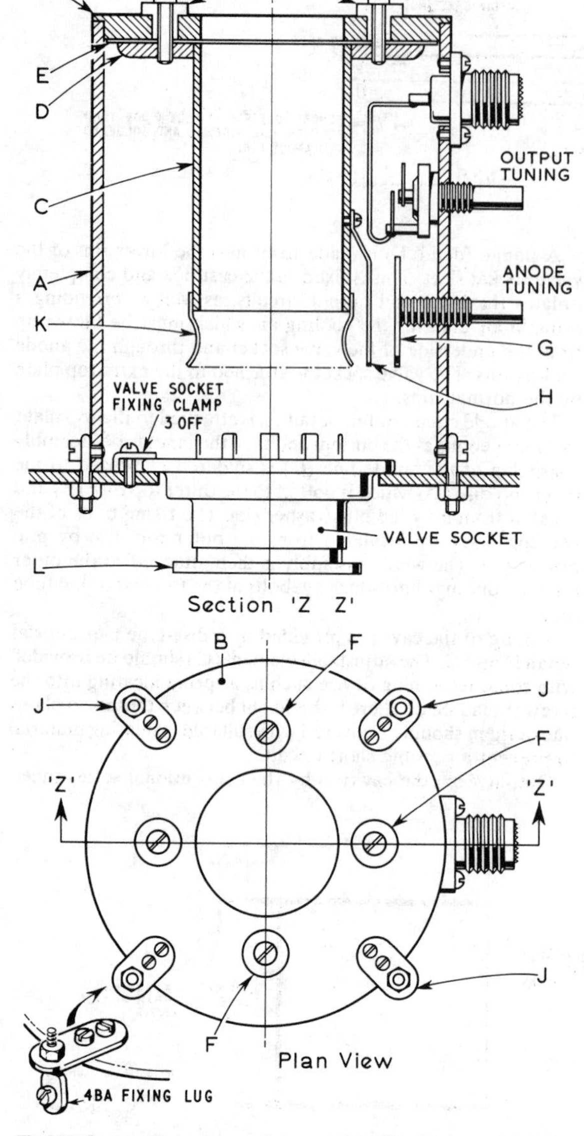

Fig 209. General arrangement of anode circuit of the coaxial cavity

loop. The loop spacing from the anode line should be adjusted to give the maximum output; this does not need close coupling to the centre tube and it should be kept as far away as possible consistent with good efficiency.

Coaxial line amplifier for 432MHz

This amplifier uses a 4CX250B, the anode and grid circuits of which are both coaxial lines tuned by disc capacitors with inductive input and output coupling.

The construction follows standard practice and consists of a box made of a main U-shaped body with the ends closed and a screen across the box for mounting the valve socket and for isolation of the anode and grid circuits. The end plates and the screen should preferably bend around all four edges to facilitate fixing to the main body. The end plate to which the anode line is attached must be arranged so that it is easily removable for valve changing.

The box is $8\frac{1}{4}$in long and $3\frac{1}{2}$in square (inside) across section using 18swg copper or brass. The lid should be bent on the long sides so that there is a good contact between the lid and the body.

The anode line, Fig 212(a) is made of $1\frac{3}{4}$in diameter (outside) tube with 20swg wall thickness. At one end a $2\frac{3}{4}$in diameter flange is fitted, and at the other eight equidistant slots are cut for a distance of 1in from the end. After these slots have been cut, the open end should close down to a diameter of 1·6in to make good contact to the valve cooler. The inner edge of the "fingers" should be chamfered to assist fitting to the valve. The fixed plate of the anode tuning capacitor is attached centrally to one of the end fingers by soldering, and the position of this is arranged to be opposite to its moving plate.

The end plate to which the mounting flange is attached has a hole to match the inside diameter of the anode line for the air outlet. Insulation between the line and the end plate should be a mica ring, which, with its high dielectric constant, will provide a substantial bypass capacitor. For safety it is desirable to cover the hole in the end plate with an open mesh to prevent accidental contact with the live anode line.

The grid line is made of $\frac{7}{8}$in diameter tube of 20swg wall. One end is closed by a disc soldered into the tube and a clearance in the centre of this is needed so that the line can be directly attached to the grid connection of the valve socket. As with the anode line, the fixed plate of the grid tuning capacitor is fixed directly on to the tube at $2\frac{1}{16}$in from the valve end of the line, see Fig 212(b).

The valve socket is fitted to the central screen, with the screen bypass capacitor flange for the socket on the anode side of the screen and fixed by the three clamps provided with the socket. The position and size of the input and output couplings are shown in Fig 213.

Connections to the heater (live side), screen and bias supplies are made through insulated terminals and rf chokes. The bias connection is made on to the grid line at a point of minimum rf voltage, approximately 0·8in from the valve end of the grid line. The ht connection to the anode is taken by one of the insulated screws used to fix the anode flange to the end plate. An rf choke should be fitted externally.

It is essentially that both compartments are reasonably air-tight so that air is forced through the valve anode cooler and out through the anode line.

Slab-line power amplifier for 432MHz

As an alternative to the coaxial method of construction, which requires appreciable use of machine tools, the use of a flat-plate line (usually referred to as a *slab line*) can provide a similar performance.

In this arrangement the anode and grid lines are $\lambda/2$ and are tuned to resonance with simple adjustable plate capacitors. It is of course not essential for the grid to be a high-Q circuit; it is in fact desirable for this circuit to be reasonably damped to avoid self-oscillation, but using a damped grid circuit will of course require an increase in the drive power—the stage gain will be lower. Note that this comment applies equally to this form of amplifier and to any other for use at this frequency.

Such a design was described by L. Williams, G8AVX, in

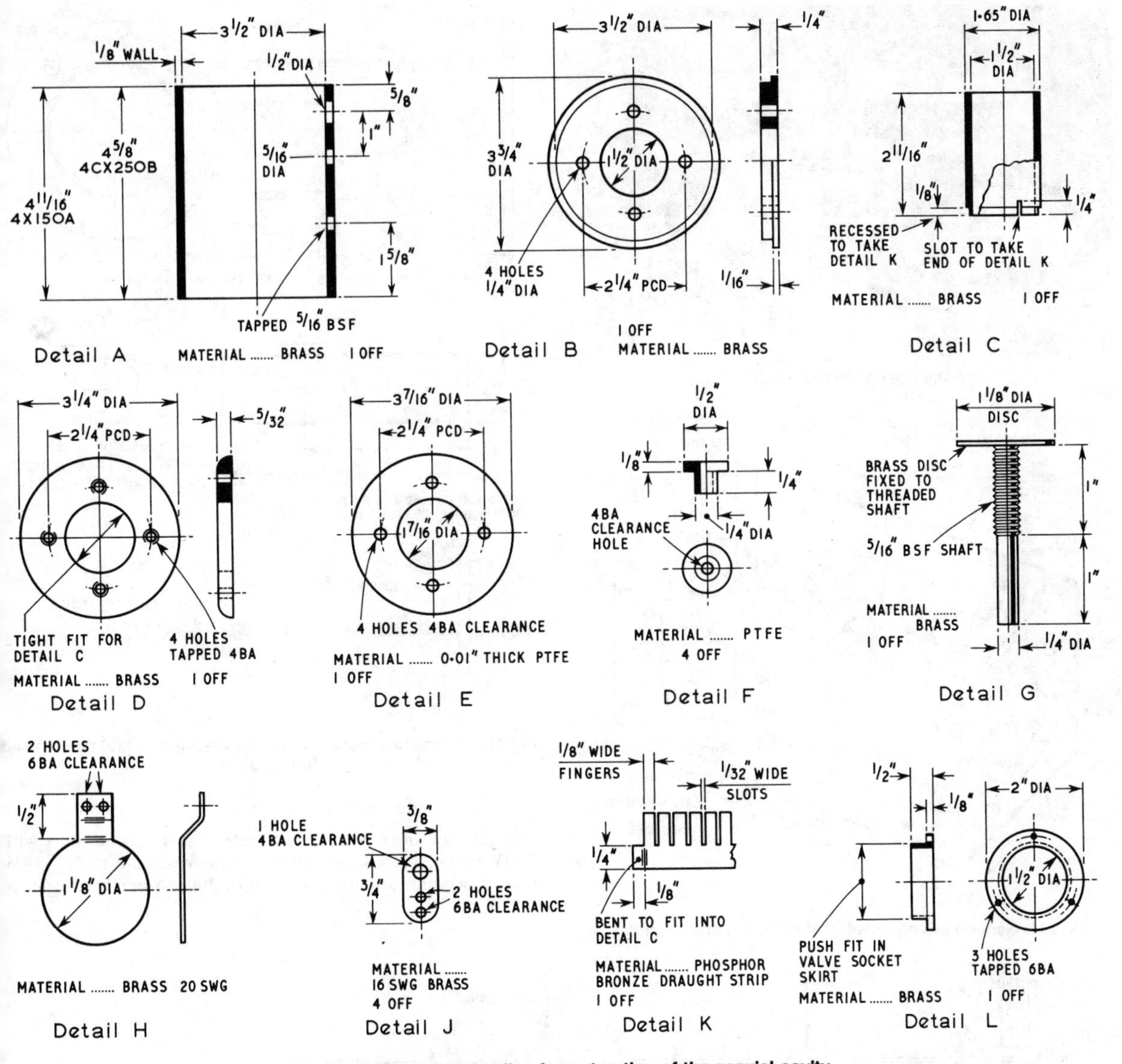

Fig 210. Mechanical details of construction of the coaxial cavity

Radio Communication October 1976 and Fig 214 shows the general arrangement of the main components. As can be seen the anode and grid circuits are each enclosed in a cast aluminium box connected together with a rf dead-space box in which the valve socket is contained. The valve socket, which contains an appropriate screen bypass capacitor, must be an SK620A or its direct equivalent. The screen and heater supplies are fed through the rf dead-space box using feedthrough capacitors.

Construction of this form of amplifier can be clearly seen in Figs 214 and 215. The following comments will be of assistance:

(a) The finger contacts to the anode need to be carefully formed, so that each make a good contact to the anode cooler cylinder. If this is not done considerable rf arcing (fizzing) will occur, causing both local heating and appreciable loss of power.

(b) Provision for positive limitation of the movement of the grid and anode plate trimmers to ensure that no contact with the relevant line can occur.

(c) The anode bypass/feed through capacitor is made from $1\frac{1}{2}$in diameter or square plates insulated by either polythene, Teflon or mica. 0·01in thick material is suitable. The edges of the plates should be "rounded" to prevent potential breakdown and the insulation should be not less than $\frac{1}{4}$in larger all round than the plates.

(d) The anode rf choke should for preference consist of a 10–15Ω 3–5W wire wound resistor.

The coaxial line amplifier

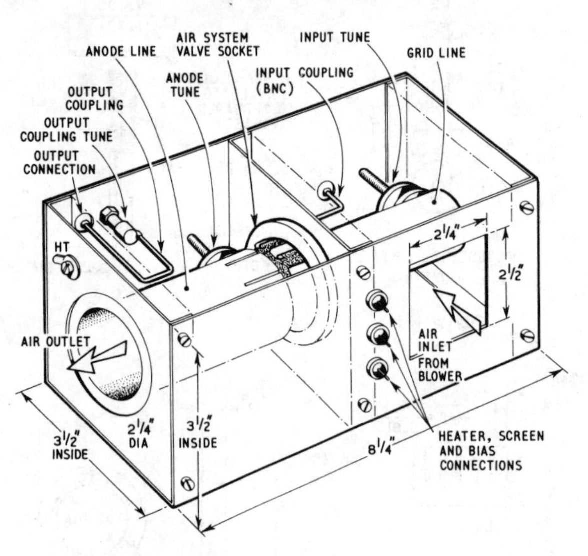

Fig 211. General arrangement of the coaxial line amplifier

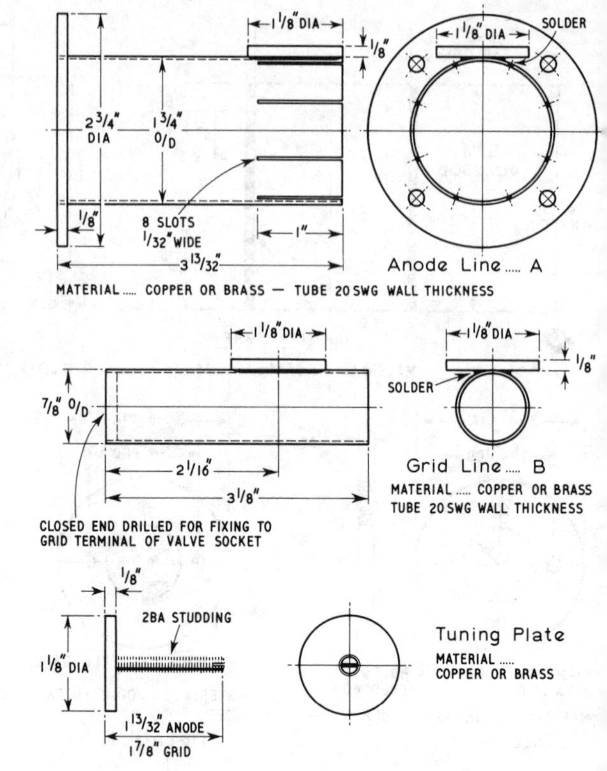

Fig 212. Mechanical details of the anode line (A), grid line (B) and tuning plate

If this amplifier is operated under Class C conditions with 750V anode, 250V screen and 90V grid bias, a drive of 12–14W should produce an anode current of 200mA and an output of 100W.

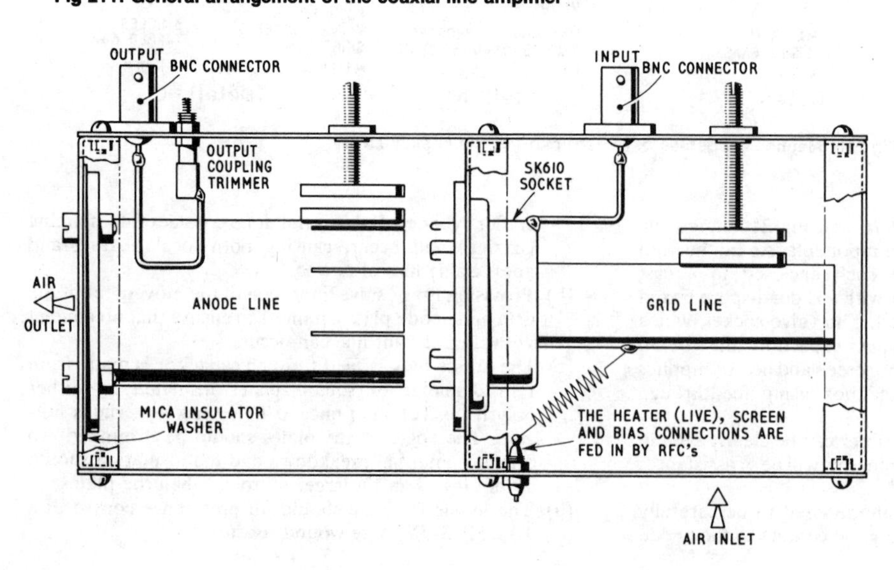

Fig 213. Layout of the amplifier

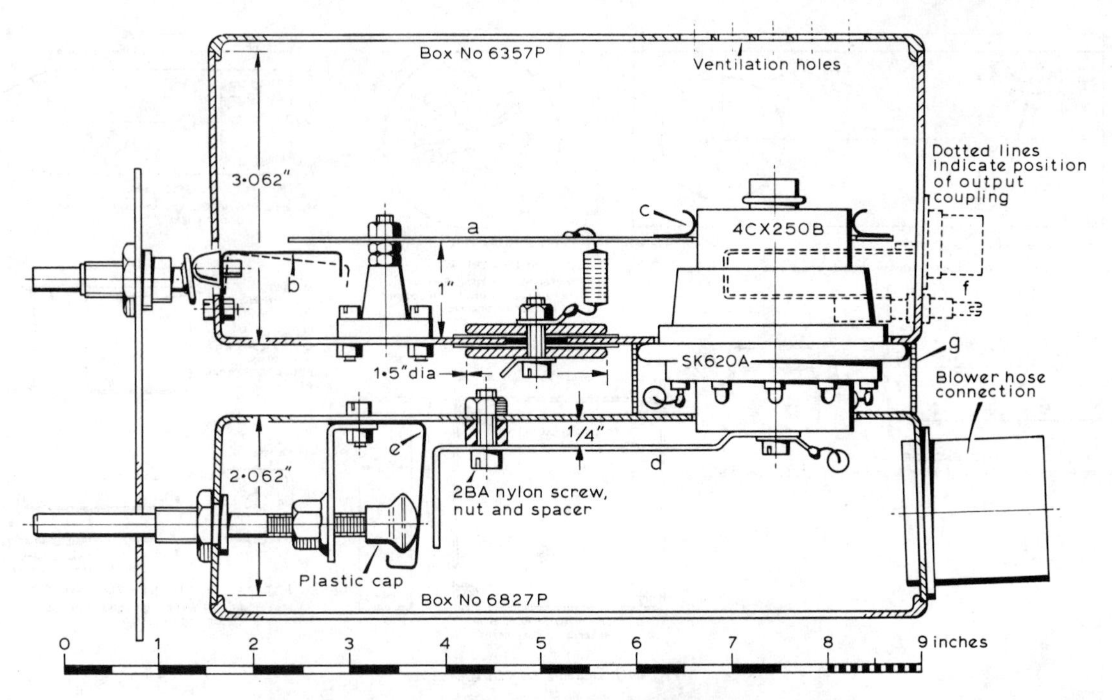

Fig 214. Section of complete assembly showing principal components

Close-up showing the anode in its holder and the output loop

The grid box showing the grid line, input coupling loop and blower-hose connection

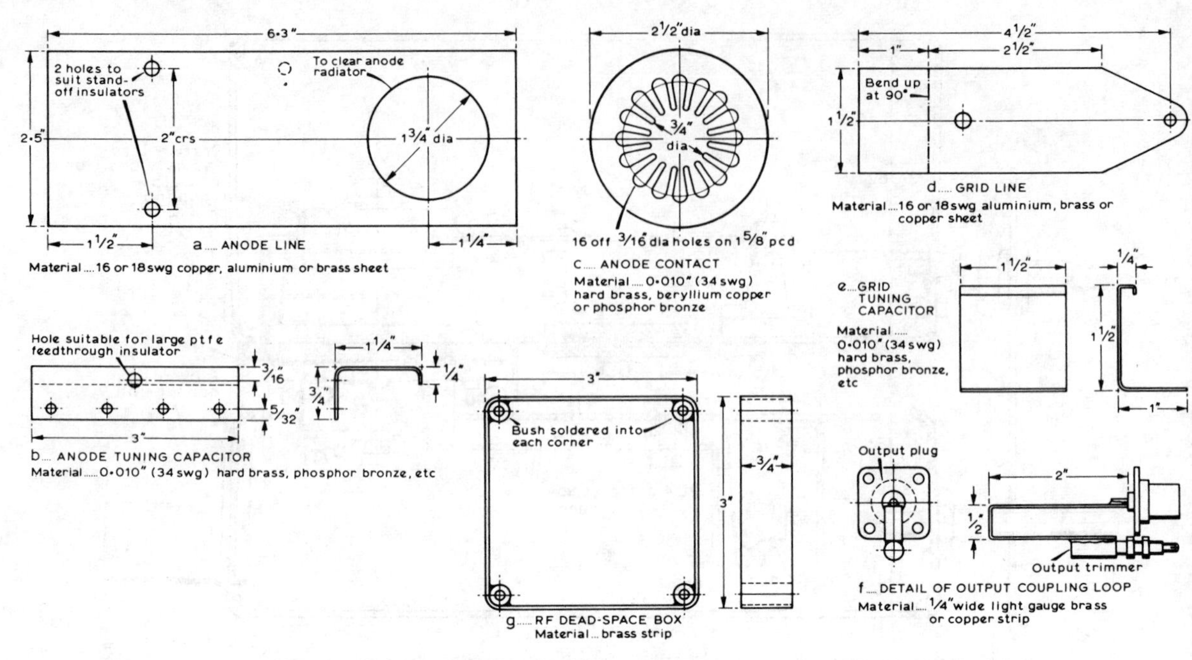
6·3"
2 holes to suit stand-off insulators
To clear anode radiator
2·5"
2"crs
1 3/4 dia
1 1/2"
1 1/4"
a.... ANODE LINE
Material....16 or 18swg copper, aluminium or brass sheet
2 1/2"dia
3/4" dia
16 off 3/16" dia holes on 1 5/8" pcd
c..... ANODE CONTACT
Material..... 0·010" (34 swg) hard brass, beryllium copper or phosphor bronze
4 1/2"
1"
2 1/2"
Bend up at 90°
1 1/2"
d..... GRID LINE
Material....16 or 18swg aluminium, brass or copper sheet
Hole suitable for large ptfe feedthrough insulator
3/16"
5/32"
3"
1 1/4"
3/4"
1/4"
b.... ANODE TUNING CAPACITOR
Material.....0·010" (34swg) hard brass, phosphor bronze, etc
e....GRID TUNING CAPACITOR
Material..... 0·010" (34 swg) hard brass, phosphor bronze, etc
1 1/2"
1/4"
1"
3"
Bush soldered into each corner
3/4"
g..... RF DEAD-SPACE BOX
Material... brass strip
Output plug
2"
1/2"
Output trimmer
f.... DETAIL OF OUTPUT COUPLING LOOP
Material..... 1/4"wide light gauge brass or copper strip

Fig 215. Details of components

CHAPTER 6

Integrated equipment

Although much of the foregoing material is given under the general headings of receivers and transmitters, these have at some stage to be co-operational. Such equipments may be either of the form of an additional transverter or a complete transmitter/receiver with all the attendant switching to facilitate the change from receive to transmit while feeding a common antenna. The term *transverter* is generally accepted as meaning a transmitting converter and a receiving converter combined into one unit for attachment to an existing transceiver; such devices may be constructed for any of the vhf/uhf bands.

The output frequency of the transceiver may play an important part in the second-channel performance of a transverter. For this reason it is an advantage to use a 144MHz transceiver for the higher frequencies such as 1·3GHz whereas a 144MHz transverter will successfully feed into an hf band transceiver. For 432MHz either type of transceiver can be used, though the higher frequency has some advantage.

Care must be exercised to ensure that the oscillator used in the transverter does not produce an unwanted signal in the pass band required. For this reason it is preferable to use a high-frequency crystal, normally a fifth-overtone type operating at 116MHz for a 28MHz input/output to the hf band transceiver. Similar precautions should be taken for the other bands.

In the case of transmitter/receivers the whole units are normally complete in themselves with switching to disable the receiver when the transmitter is operating and vice versa. Most transmitter/receivers, unlike the hf band transceivers, are generally of relatively low power output, usually around 10–15W, which makes them very suitable for driving high-power amplifiers. If this is to be done, provision for switching any add-on amplifier should be made.

When an additional high-power amplifier is attached to a transmitter/receiver it is important to ensure that the increased transmitter capability is matched by the receiver performance. A receiver preamplifier may be needed to equalize the transmit and receive performances.

Signal-path switching

As mentioned elsewhere, semiconductor diodes may be used for switching. They offer advantages over mechanically operated types because they can be fitted close to the circuit and the actuating switch or relay positioned where most convenient.

In Fig 1(a) the resistors R1 and R2 provide the bias voltage for the diode D. R3 is connected to the other side of the diode and provides rf isolation and allows the diode to be forward or back biased, thereby causing the diode conductance to be either high or low, cutting out the circuit or leaving it in operation.

The actual value of the resistors is not important and values between 10 and 100Ω are suitable. The fixed bias should be such that it is unlikely to be exceeded by the signals involved.

Fig 1(b) shows a double pole changeover, applied to two circuits. If only single-pole changeover is required, then either the right- or left-hand half of this circuit may be used.

Diodes suitable for this type of application should have a high forward conductance, low reverse conductance, and low capacitance. Most types known as *gold bonded diodes* will be suitable for use as switches.

Carrier-operated switching

The use of some form of carrier-operated switching is of particular value for add-on power amplifiers for use with transceivers. By this means the basic transceiver switching arrangements need not be changed, only the presence of rf power being needed to activate the amplifier.

The usual forms use either a sensitive active device to actuate an ordinary relay(s) or alternatively a passive system of λ/4 cables and switching diodes.

Transistor-operated relay switch

In Fig 2 a basic circuit arrangement is shown. In this the input is voltage doubled by two diode rectifiers and the output is fed into a fast switching transistor or preferably a Darlington pair capable of operating a changeover relay.

Ideally a pair of relays, one for the input and another for the output, would give good isolation but with care a single four-way changeover type may be used, provided the usual long

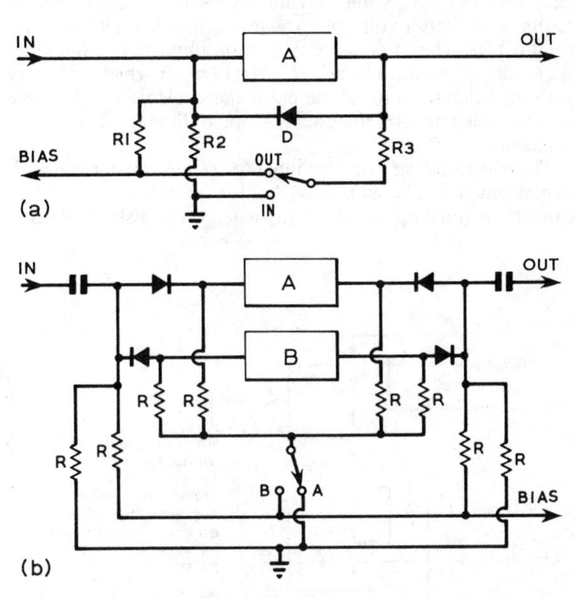

Fig 1. Two circuits illustrating the use of diodes as switches

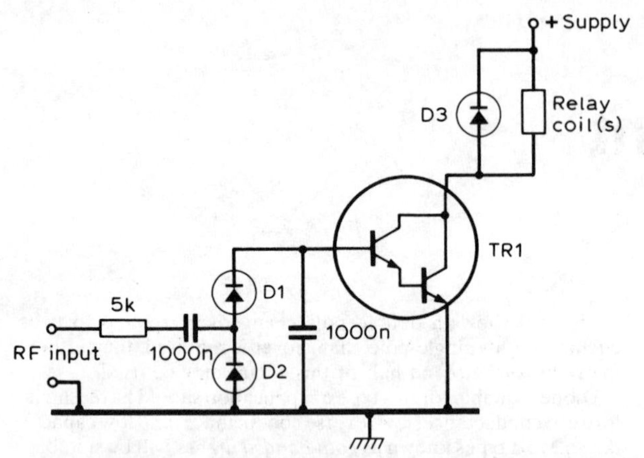

Fig 2. Carrier-operated switch. D1, D2: 100V fast switching diode. D3: 100V 500mA diode (IN4001 or equiv). TR1: silicon Darlington-pair transistor (eg Motorola MPS-A13) or two separate devices

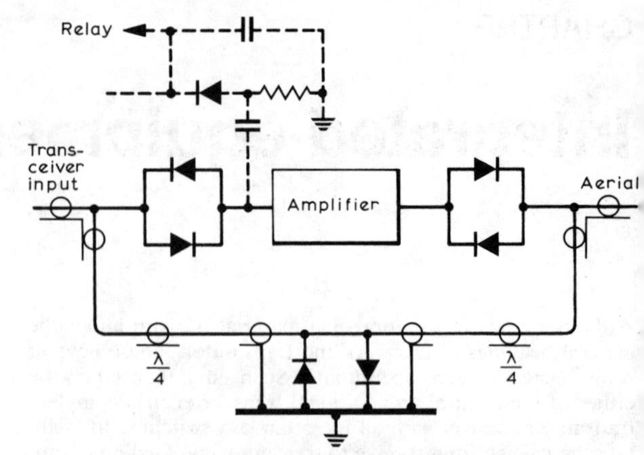

Fig 4. Diagram illustrating the use of diodes in place of relays to switch in and out an amplifier for an fm transceiver. Also shown is the additional rf rectifier for operating a relay to break the ht supply if a valve amplifier is used. This is often necessary to avoid noise generation

flexible leads to the moving blades are removed and direct connections are made between relevant pairs of contacts as shown in Fig 3.

λ/4 coaxial cable and diode switch

The use of λ/4 coaxial cables together with suitable diodes as shown in Fig 4 provides a purely static method of switching. In this application use is made of the impedance characteristic of a λ/4 length of feeder. When one end is short-circuited, the impedance at the other end is high. The diodes are switching elements and are normally non-conducting, allowing signals from the antenna to pass without loss to the transceiver. When the transmitter is switched on the diodes conduct, short-circuiting the λ/4 cables and connecting the amplifier into circuit. For this use, cable having a closely woven sheath is required or, better still, solid sheath such as is found in semi-rigid cables. The impedance is of little importance, the chief requirement being accurate electrical length which will vary with the velocity factor of the particular cable used. The cable may be coiled or formed into any shape to fit into the amplifier enclosure.

These methods are only suitable for steady-carrier use such as a.m and fm (and possibly cw), but for ssb the control must be capable of voice operation—fast switch on and slow release.

RF vox

Fig 5 shows the circuit of an rf switching unit suitable for use with ssb. The arrangement comprises an rf detector feeding into a high-gain integrated circuit amplifier (LM741). This drives the emitter-follower transistor (BC108), the relays forming the emitter load.

In some cases it may be useful to use a slave relay to actuate the changeover relays. The sensitivity of this unit is sufficiently high in some cases to operate on the suppressed carrier.

PIN diodes as transmit/receive switches

The pin diode offers an attractive alternative to the conventional coaxial relay especially in vhf and uhf applications. It is available for power dissipations up to 10W (corresponding to a transmitter power of 625W into a 50Ω load).

A comparison by ZL1BCG (*Break-In*, January 1980) of various types of diode at 150MHz shows why pin diodes are suitable for rf switching—see Table 1.

A practical application of these diodes is shown in Figs 6, 7 and 8. In this circuit, when voltage is applied to the diodes D1 connects the transmitter to the antenna while D2 (and D3) virtually short-circuits the input to the receiver. A typical total insertion loss due to both diodes will be about 0·4dB (0·2dB in respect to each diode, D1 due to its dissipation and D2 due to it

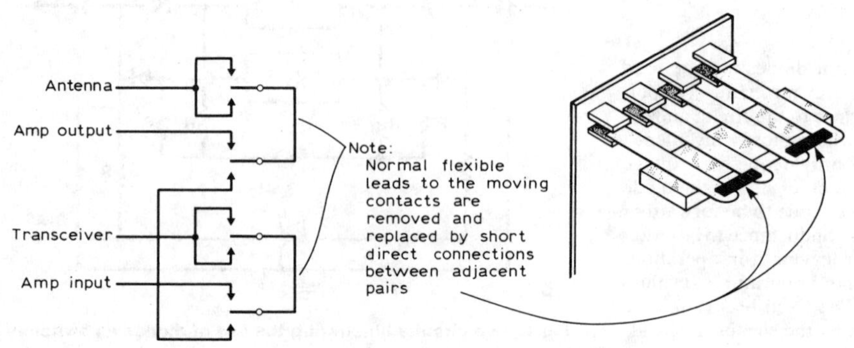

Fig 3. Connections for single relay

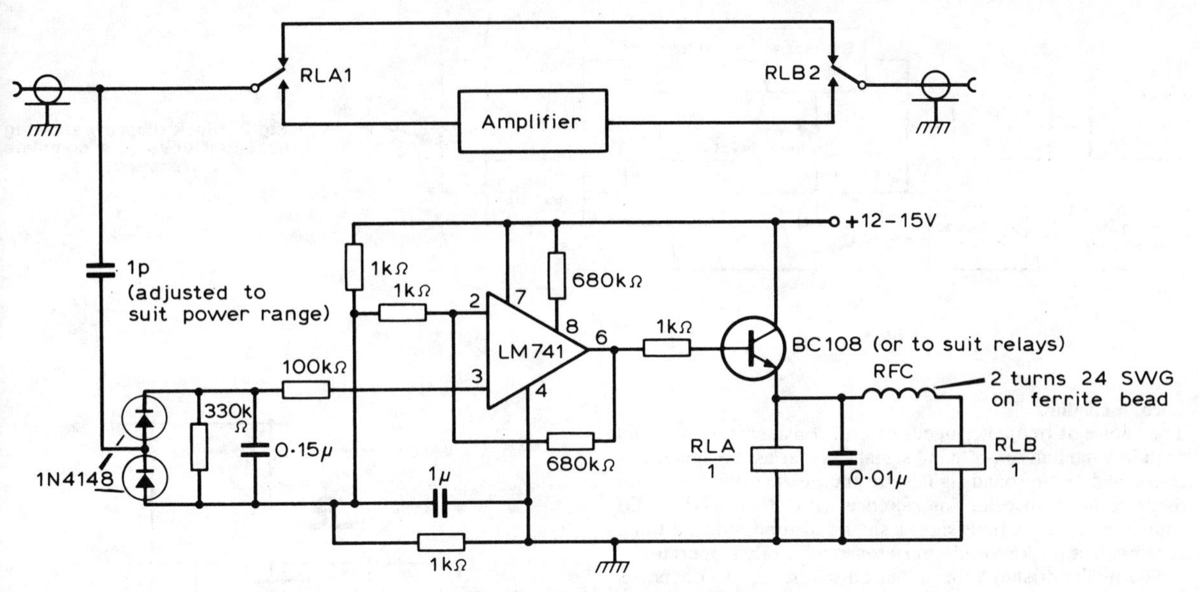

Fig 5. RF vox suitable for use with ssb

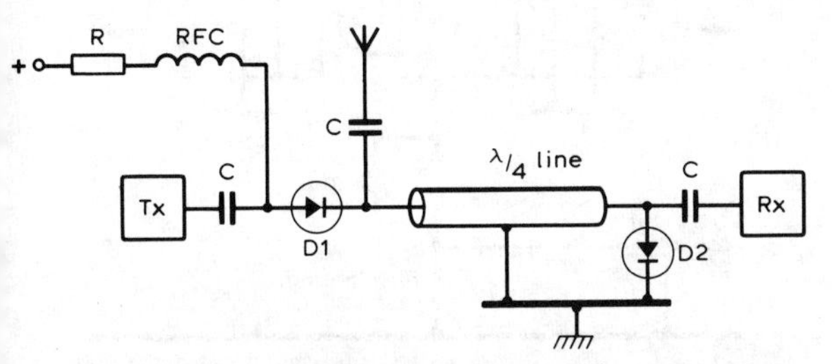

Fig 6. PIN diode t/r switch. The λ/4 line may be coaxial or stripline, C: 0·01μF isolating capacitors. R: limiting resistor to set diode current. RFC: choke suitable for particular frequency. D1, D2: UM9401 or similar

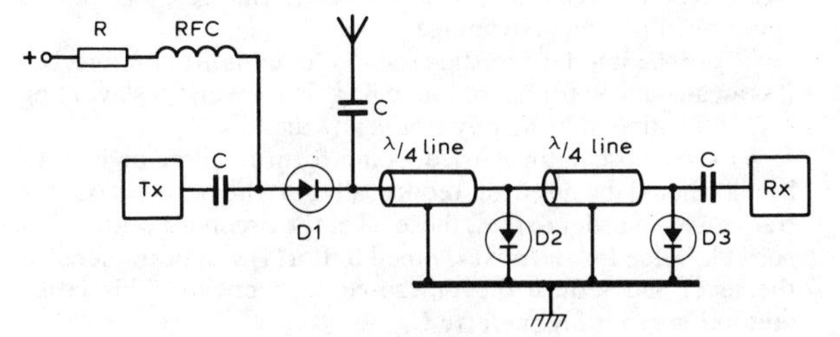

Fig 7. PIN diode t/r switch with increased isolation

not being a perfect short-circuit). Typical isolation of 30–35dB may be expected, while using the double circuit arrangement shown in Fig 7 should provide up to 10dB additional isolation.

The actual transmitter (voltage) that appears at the receiver input connection may be measured across a terminating resistor of 50Ω. The diodes need to be fitted into the circuit with the absolute minimum of lead length.

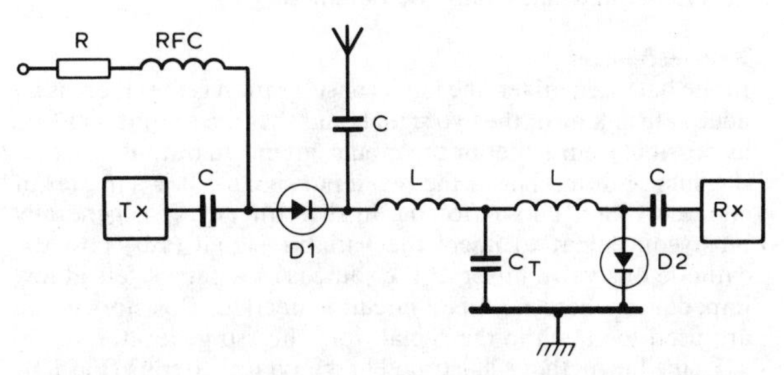

Fig 8. PIN diode t/r switch with lumped circuit L and C_T which is suitable for lower frequencies

Table 1. Comparison of rf switching diodes

Diode	ON resistance (Ω) at I = 50mA or V = 1V	OFF resistance (Ω) at V = 10V	Capacitance (pF) at V = 0V
Germanium (point contact signal diode)	20–200	10,000	10–20
Silicon (junction)	5–20	50,000	10
Silicon (high speed)	3–5	50,000	1–5
PIN	0·8	10,000	1

Transverters

In most transverters both the functions of transmitter and receiver conversions are performed, using a common local oscillator for both upward (transmitter) and downward (receiver) frequency conversions.

The block diagram of Fig 9 shows the essential units involved in the operation (see also Chapter 5).

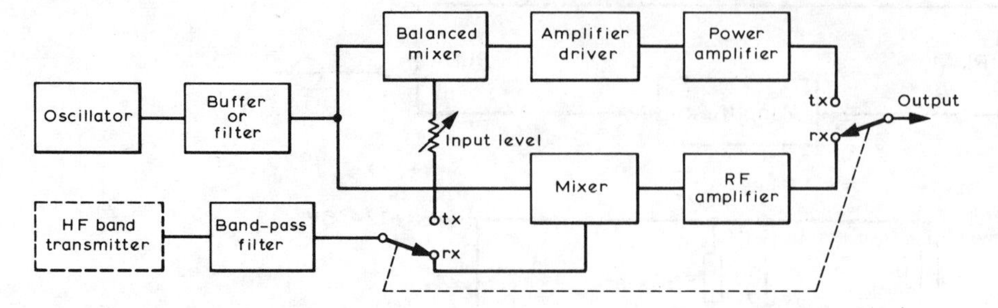

Fig 9. Block diagram showing essential units of a complete transverter

Local oscillator

The choice of frequency needs careful consideration to avoid both in-band and out-of-band signals. As far as the amateur is concerned, out-of-band signals are the most serious, because they are likely to cause interference with other services. Of course, in-band spurious signals should also be reduced to an acceptable level, to avoid interference with other operators.

The oscillator should be stabilized so that the frequency is maintained to 130Hz for short periods (up to 5min) and ± 200Hz for long periods (more than 5min). In equipment likely to be subjected to wide temperature changes, the use of a small oven is a real advantage.

Any of the standard crystal oscillator circuits are suitable, but it is an advantage for operation to be at low level, thus avoiding crystal heating and thereby frequency drift.

Whatever oscillator is used, some form of filter or high-*Q* break should be used to reduce all but the wanted output frequency. In order to raise the level of the oscillator output to a suitable value for the mixer, tuned buffer(s) will both increase the level and reduce the unwanted frequencies. This latter method is generally preferred.

The actual level required will be decided by the transmitter mixer—the amount needed for the receiver mixer will always be smaller and can readily be obtained.

Balanced mixer

In the balanced mixer, the main consideration is that there is an adequate mixing of the two signals and that the output is as free as possible from either of the inputs, giving an output of either the sum or difference of the two input signals. It is a matter of choice which is chosen for the final frequency. It is generally most convenient to inject the variable signal (ssb) into the cathode of a valve mixer or the sources of a pair of fets at low impedance where no tuned circuit is needed. Resistors alone are used to match in the signal from the ssb generator.

Using the methods illustrated in the typical circuits (Fig 10), it is important to note that the ssb input and any harmonics or other unwanted signals are attenuated by the balancing action of the symmetrical arrangement relative to the anode circuit which is push-pull compared to the push-push of the ssb input.

It is important in any mixer that the correct levels should be observed in order to minimize intermodulation products. A 10dB ratio between the local oscillator and the ssb input is generally suitable for amateur operation, and care must be taken not to exceed this ratio in an attempt to obtain greater output. Obtaining the cleanest possible signal should be the main objective, and raising the level of output should be confined to following linear amplifiers.

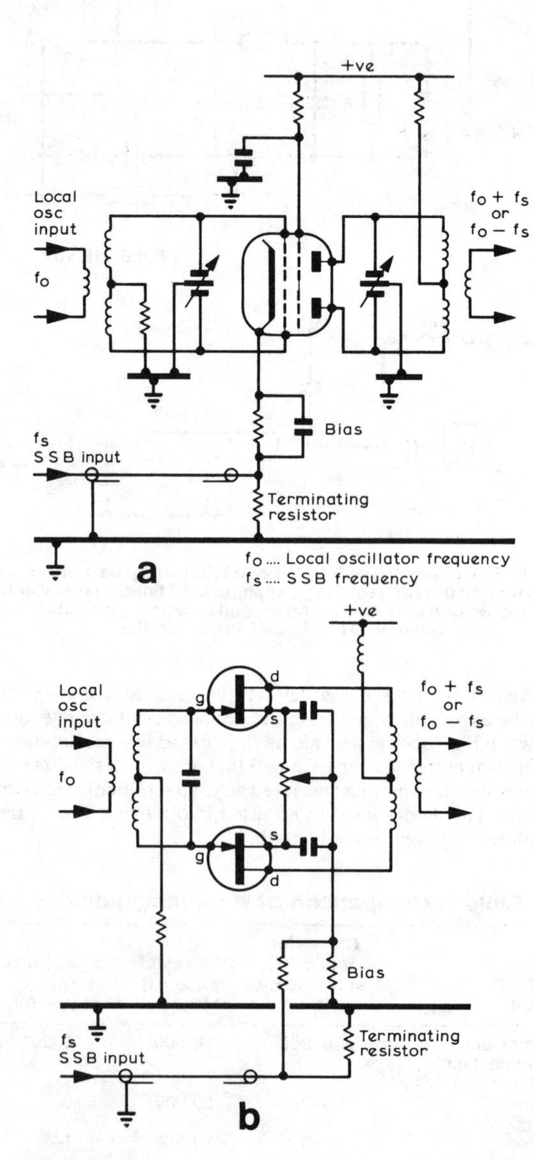

Fig 10. Typical balanced mixers. (a) Double tetrode. (b) Pair fets

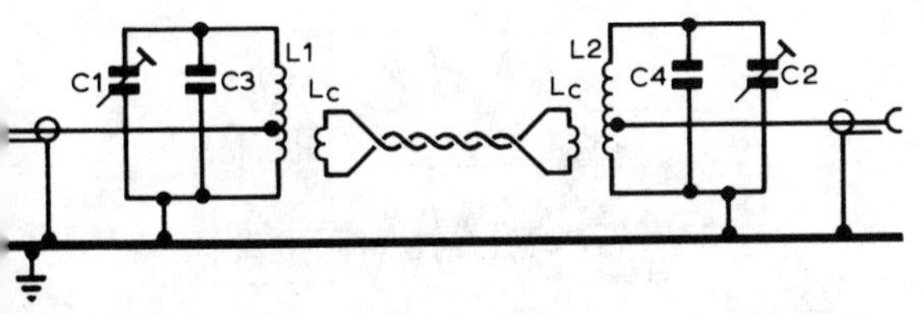

ig 11. High-Q bandpass filter for 28MHz. L1, L2: 8t 20swg 0·5in iam 0·5–0·6in long. L_C: 1t link coupling coil 20 swg insulated. 1, C2: 50pF max air trimmer. C3, C4: 47pF sm or other stable type

Buffer amplifier-driver-power amplifier

Following the mixer, the power level should be raised by a linear amplifier, which may be of one or more stages depending on the drive requirements of the final amplifier. Generally this stage is operated under Class A or AB1 conditions, the latter is most usual. A facility to observe the grid current should be provided. Although it has often been stated that there should be no grid current, some slight improvement in intermodulation product results from a small amount—a few tens of microamps in the case of buffer and driver amplifiers and up to 100–150μA for the power amplifier such as a 4CX250B.

Interstage couplings

All couplings between the mixer anode and each of the succeeding stages should be inductive, in the form of simple coupled circuits or more elaborate low-impedance links.

Considerable care in circuit arrangements for semiconductors is needed where their impedances are usually very low compared to valves, and matching is by tapping down the tuned circuit of the preceding stage.

It is probably best to resort to valve amplifiers once the power has reached 2 to 5W, thus enabling the use of more satisfactory couplings.

Output filters

A desirable feature of any well-designed equipment will be a bandpass filter, to significantly attenuate all out-of-band signals. This will not only reduce the likely interference with other services on adjacent frequencies but also reduce the chances of television interference.

SSB input filter and level control

The output from the ssb generator, whether this is a specially designed or hf band transceiver, should supply the input to the transverter at a suitably low level, which is more suitable than taking the output from the power stage and then absorbing the unwanted power in some form of load/attenuator. It is usually fairly simple to arrange for an alternative output from the driver stage, and some transceivers already have this facility.

The output from the ssb unit will inevitably contain not only the wanted signal, but also others at some level or other, and it is therefore an advantage to introduce a bandpass filter for the chosen frequency. Such a filter, shown in Fig 11, may consist of two tuned circuits coupled by a link or low-impedance taps.

In Fig 12 are shown methods of controlling the ssb input from the exciter transceiver (low power level) to the transverter mixer. The coupling coil L1 is resonated at the operating frequency, and using a two-turn link the connecting coaxial cable may be of any reasonable length. A variable wirewound or tapped potentiometer (or attenuator) can be imposed in this line as a drive level control. It should be noted that multiple

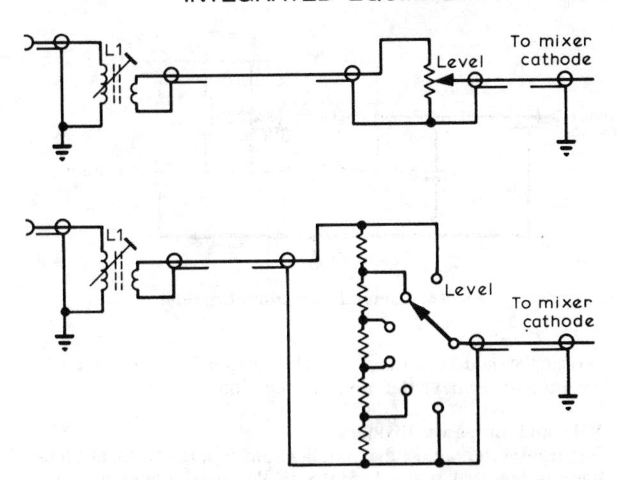

Fig 12. Methods of obtaining drive control between ssb exciter and transverter mixer. L1 is resonated to output frequency for use.

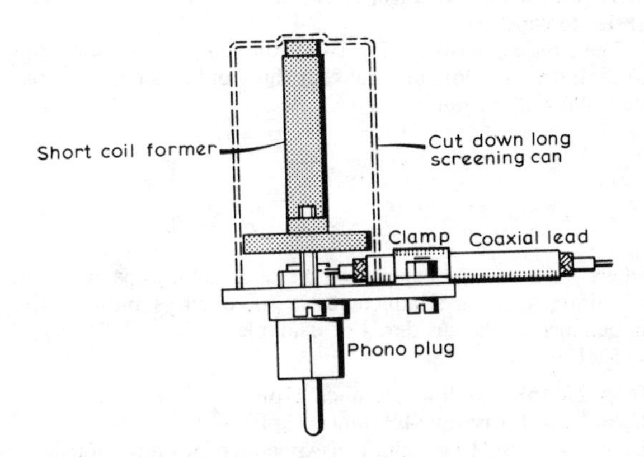

Fig 13. General arrangement of coupling unit L1 to feed transverter of Fig 12

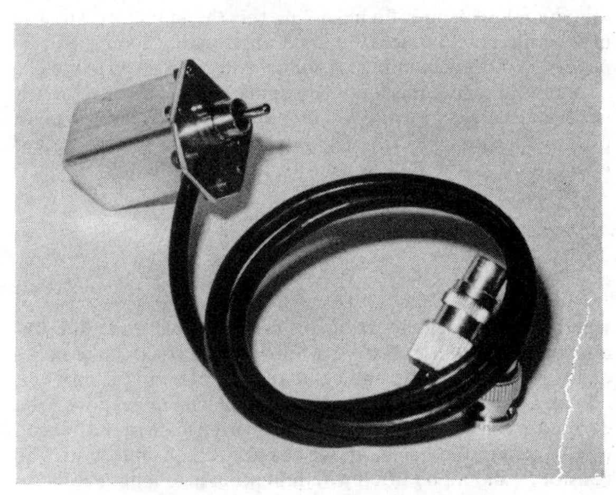

Coupling unit for feeding the transverter

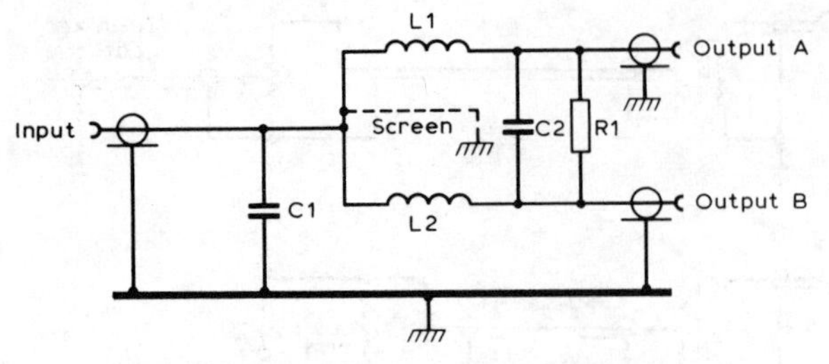

Fig 14. Lumped component divider

earthing should be avoided and the earth is best connected at the transverter near the mixer connection.

VHF and uhf power dividers

For transverters and other applications where the local oscillator is required to feed into both the receive and transmit sections, the oscillator may be switched from one to the other by a relay, preferably a coaxial type. Alternatively a power divider can be successfully used. In the vhf region a lumped-circuit arrangement can be constructed, but at uhf a coaxial line is easier to construct.

The circuit is shown in Fig 14 for the lumped-circuit configuration; the component values for this can be calculated from the following formulae:

$$C_1 = \frac{1}{2\pi f.R_0} \qquad C_2 = \frac{C_1}{2}$$

$$L_1L_2 = \frac{R_0}{2\pi f} \qquad R_1 = 2R_0$$

where f is the frequency in megahertz, C is the capacitance in microfarads, L is the inductance in microhenrys and R_0 is the impedance of the divider. For example, if $R_0 = 50\Omega$ at $f =$ 115MHz:

$C_1 = 27{\cdot}4$pF (use low-tolerance 27pF)
$C_2 = 13{\cdot}7$pF (use low-tolerance 13pF)
$L_1, L_2 = 68{\cdot}6$nH (see chart in Appendix for dimensions)
$R_1 = 100\Omega$

Construction of a unit should be arranged so that the output connections are close together with resistor R_1 being fitted with minimum lead length. In achieving this the inductors will also necessarily be close together and an isolating screen will be needed to prevent coupling. A suitable layout is given in Fig 15.

In the uhf region the circuit elements become inconveniently small and it is easier to use $\lambda/4$ sections of coaxial cable in place of the inductors (Fig 16). The impedance of a suitable line is given by $Z_{\text{line}} = 1{\cdot}414\ R_0$ and its mechanical length

$$= \frac{2{,}950V}{f} \text{ inches}$$

$$\text{or } \frac{7{,}495V}{f} \text{ centimetres}$$

where V is the velocity factor of coaxial cable and f the frequency in megahertz. For a 50Ω divider the coaxial line impedance becomes 70·7Ω and cable of 70–75Ω will be suitable.

In construction it is essential for the coaxial line sections to be earthed at each end and the connectors used to be of the flanged type to reduce the height above chassis of the connection. The resistor R_1 should be fitted with minimum lead length and also down on the ground plane.

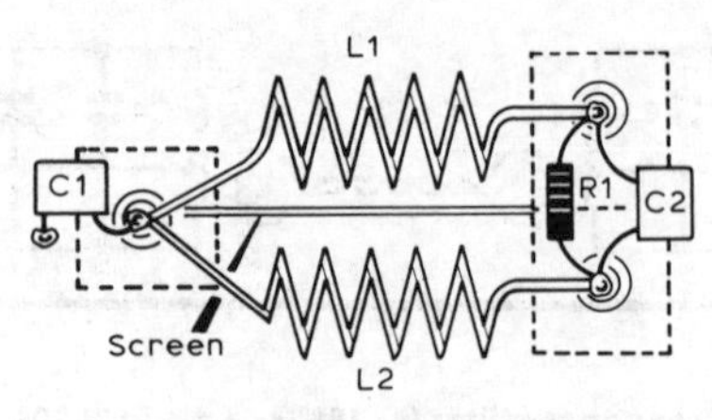

Fig 15. Component layout

At frequencies above 1GHz it is likely to be easier to construct the unit using microstrip lines in place of coaxial cable sections. For such lines the material must be of a low-loss type.

With either the lumped-circuit or coaxial-line dividers, isolation of more than 20dB between the two outputs should be readily obtained, with power level difference less than 0·25dB between the two outputs.

A 70MHz transverter

This design was originally described by D. F. Harvey, G3XBY, and C. S. Gare, G3WOS, in *Radio Communication* February 1977.

Local oscillator, receiver, rf amplifier and mixer (Figs 17 and 18)

The crystal oscillator uses a third-overtone HC18/U 42MHz crystal. A capacitive divider feeds the buffer TR2, which provides signal isolation between the oscillator and the two mixers.

The rf amplifier and mixer stages utilize 40673 dual-gate mosfets, the current through each being set to 2mA by the source resistors for optimum noise performance. The 50Ω antenna input is tapped down the tuned circuit to provide matching to the input of the amplifier stage; fine adjustment of this tap should produce an overall noise figure in the order of 2–3dB. L8 and L9 are critically coupled to provide maximum gain. The mixer provides about 10dB of gain; this, together with 20dB in the rf amplifier, gives the receiver an overall gain of 30dB. A link winding on the toroid L10 transfers the signals to the 28MHz receiver.

Transmit mixer, buffers and low-power amplifier (Fig 19)

The 28MHz ssb input to the transverter is filtered by a double-section bandpass filter to remove the out-of-band spurii generated by the exciting transceiver. The drive level to the mixer is controlled by the resistive attenuator following the 50Ω input load. L14 is overwound on L13 to provide the two anti-phase

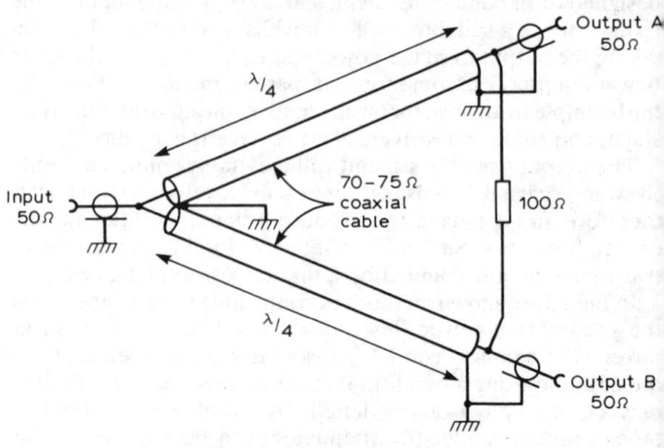

Fig 16. Coaxial line divider

eneral view of the transverter. eft: unit 1 with unit 4 below. ight: heat sink with units 2 and 3 below

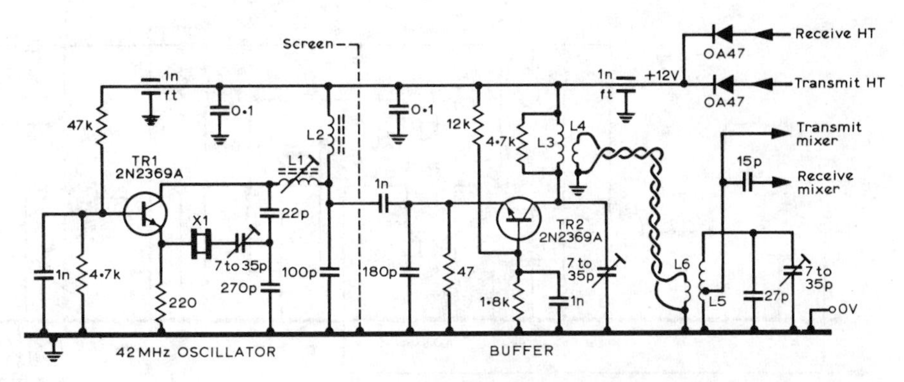

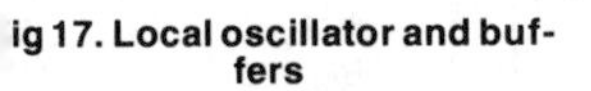

ig 17. Local oscillator and buffers

ignals needed to drive the balanced mixer. The 42MHz local oscillator injection is fed, in phase, to the emitters of the mixer ransistors. No balancing potentiometer was necessary but mall adjustments may be made by the relative positions of the ndependent trimmers in the mixer tank circuit. Any tendency o oscillation is suppressed by RFC1 and the 1kΩ resistor onnected to earth.

To prevent unwanted loading of the mixer a buffer stage TR8 s provided. A link winding is used to couple into the first power mplifier stage TR9. Ferrite beads are used on the input and utput of this amplifier to ensure stability. TR9 provides 0–30mW output on 70MHz.

The output matching network provides good transfer of ower to the following state. Although no attempt has een made to match to 50Ω, coaxial cable may be used for

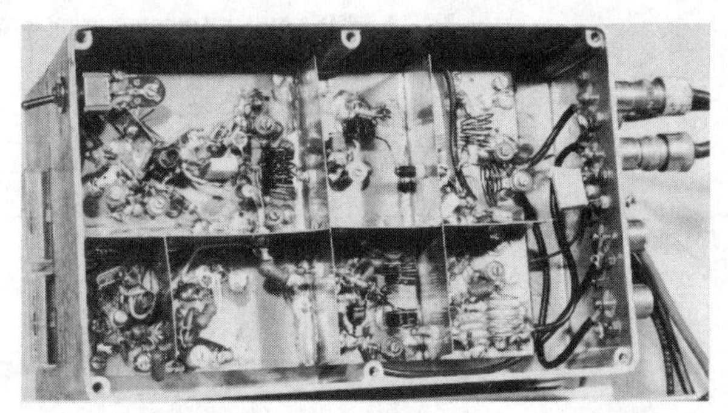

Unit 1

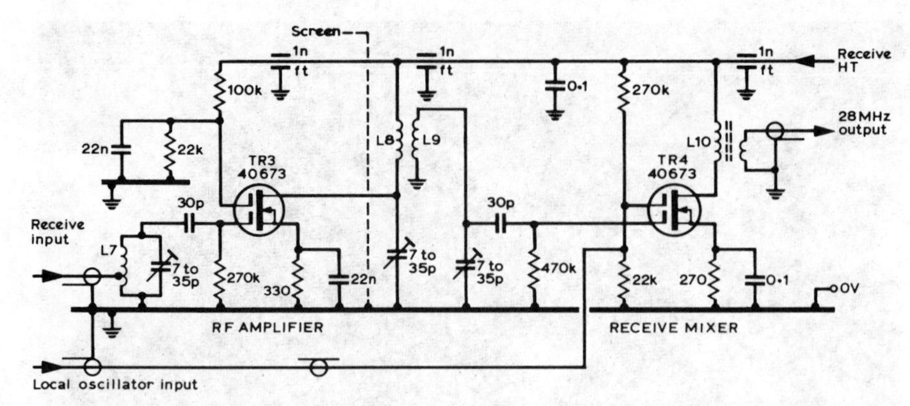

Fig 18. The receiver rf amplifier and mixer (unit 1)

interconnection with only minimal losses provided the cable run is kept short.

A high/low power switch is provided for operation in the cw mode. This may also be used for low-power ssb operation to avoid excessive interference to other stations when working locally.

20mW–25W linear power amplifier (Fig 20)

TRs10, 11 and 12 are biased into Class AB and each stage should have its respective base resistor adjusted for 30mA standing current. The outputs to be expected from each stage are as follows:

TR10—600mW; TR11—4–5W; TR12—20–30W.

The chokes isolating the bases of the transistors from the bias networks are not critical and although Mullard FX1898 six hole beads wound with 22swg enamelled wire are specified, ½in toroids or air-cored coils have been substituted and found to be satisfactory.

The amplifier (Fig 21)

The amplifier utilizes two Motorola soe (stripline-opposed emitter) transistors operating in parallel mode to produce 100W rms into a 50Ω load. To simplify the alignment procedure only one tuning network is used on the input and output. Drive balance is maintained by strapping both collectors and both bases together with low-value resistors.

The 50Ω coaxial input is matched to the very low base input impedance by the use of a combined L-network; drive power is

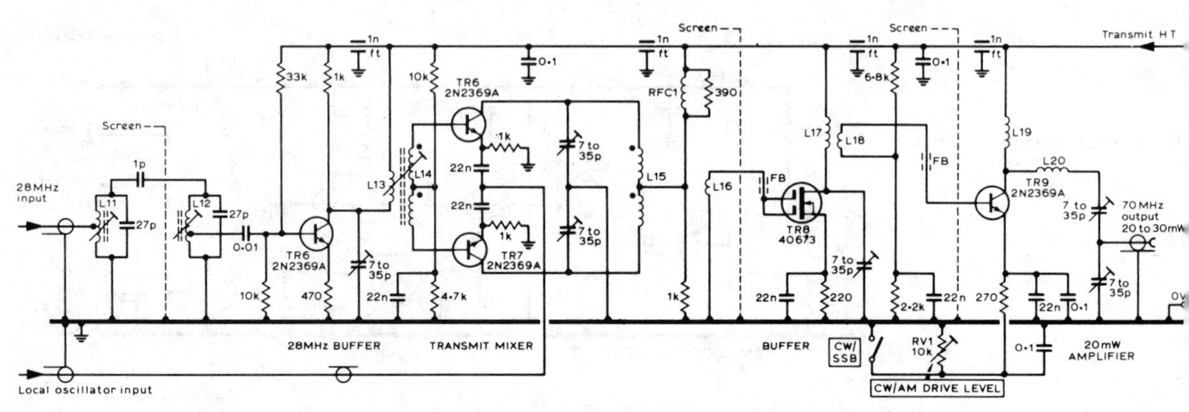

Fig 19. 28MHz buffer, transmitter mixer, buffer and first transmit amplifier (unit 1)

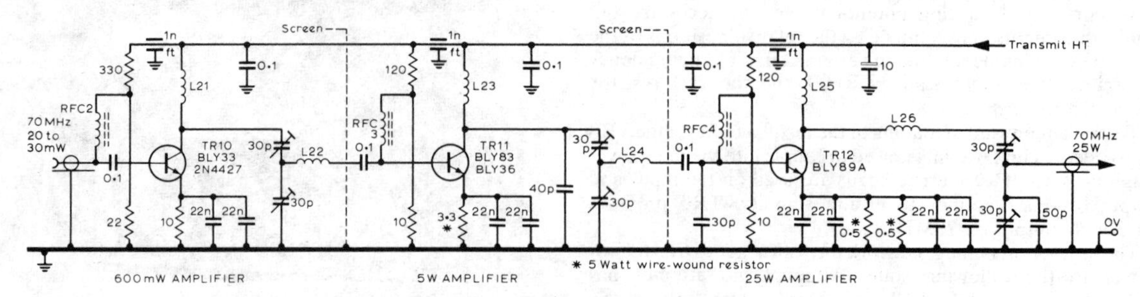

Fig 20. 20/30mW to 25W transmit amplifier (unit 2)

Unit 2

Unit 3

hared equally between both bases by splitting the inductor in wo. Two 100pF silver mica capacitors are placed across each ase to earth for partial neutralization of the parametric input apacitance of the transistors. Bias is applied to both bases hrough a ferrite-cored choke to isolate the bias generator from he signal.

he biasing network (Fig 22)

or good amplifier linearity the bases of the pa transistors must e forward biased to generate a standing current greater than 0mA. The emitter of TR16 drives the bases of the two power ransistors. The standing currents of the pa transistors are set to 0mA each by suitable adjustment of RV2. The level of com-ensation is set by the current through the compensation diode; vercompensation occurs when the diode current is greater han the transistor base current, undercompensation occurs hen the diode current is less than the base current. The bias urrent (with no drive) for the 2N6084 is in the order of –5mA. In the prototype units, with the standing currents set to 5mA at ambient (25°C), the collector current increases to 7·5mA at a heatsink temperature of 70°C.

Control circuitry

Reverse-polarity protection to the receiver +12V line is afforded by a 1A fuse and parallel diode. This method is not satisfactory for protection of the transmit line, where unacceptable losses occur in standard fuseholders at currents of 15A or so. Instead a diode is wired in series with the power relay, completely preventing operation in the event of accidental supply reversal.

A 20A fuse in an automobile-type holder is placed in the main positive feed. Although 0·2V is lost at full power its inclusion is desirable for supply protection.

Construction

Inter-unit connections are by coaxial plugs and sockets for all leads carrying rf, and by ptfe feedthroughs and wire for power distribution. Input/output, power and bias leads for the pa unit are passed through holes drilled in adjoining boxes, for interconnection using the shortest possible leads.

Unit 1 uses a single-sided copper-clad board as a ground plane. This is mounted on ⅛in brass pillars tapped 6BA. Countersunk screws attach the pillars to the base of a 6827P die-cast

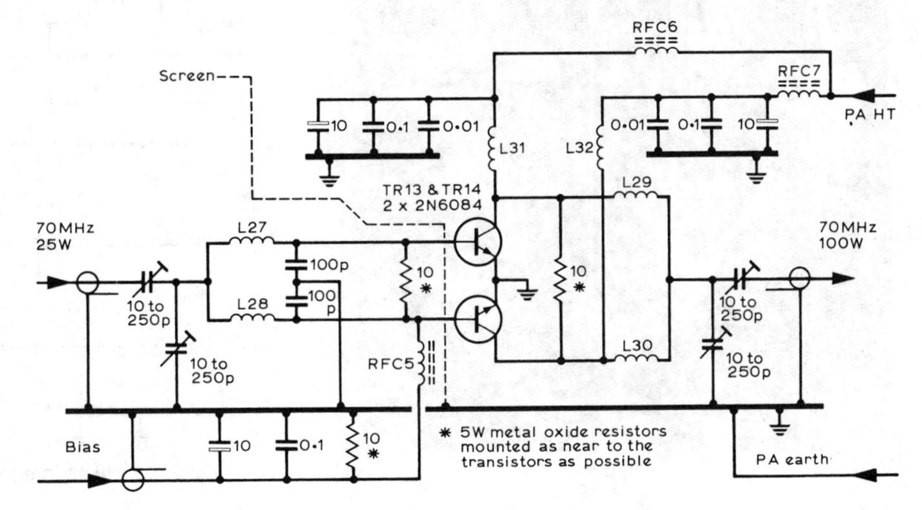

Fig 21. 100W transmit amplifier (unit 3)

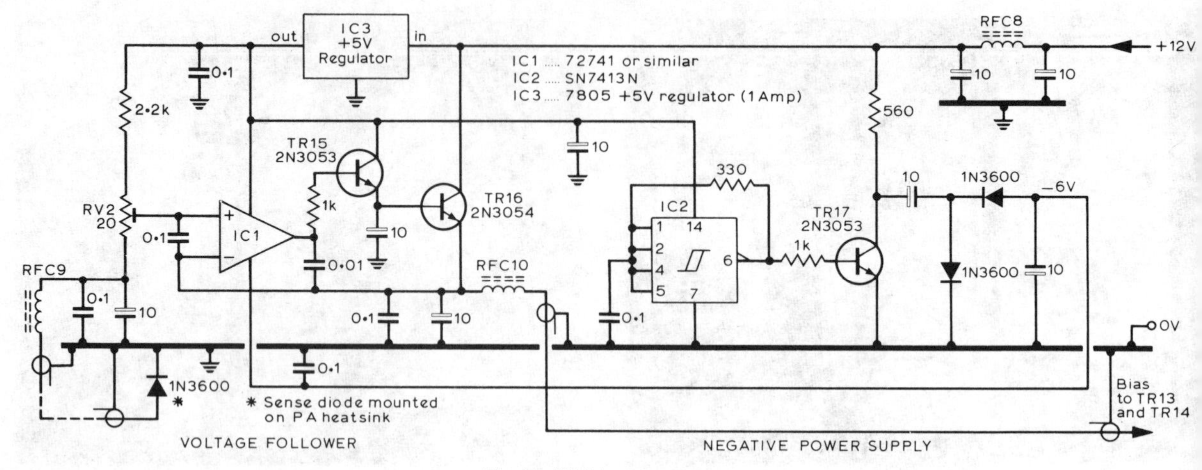

Fig 22. PA bias generator

Unit 4

box. Thin brass screens 1¼in high are soldered to the ground plane and solder-in feedthroughs are mounted in each of the compartments thus formed. Power wiring is on the reverse side of the board. PTFE feedthroughs carry rf between compartments and, where appropriate, support components. Components soldered to the ground plane are used as stand-offs for circuit connections.

Unit 2 uses a ⅛in-thick brass plate cut to fit the internal dimensions of a 6908P die-cast box. This is mounted in the same manner as unit 1. Feedthrough capacitors again carry

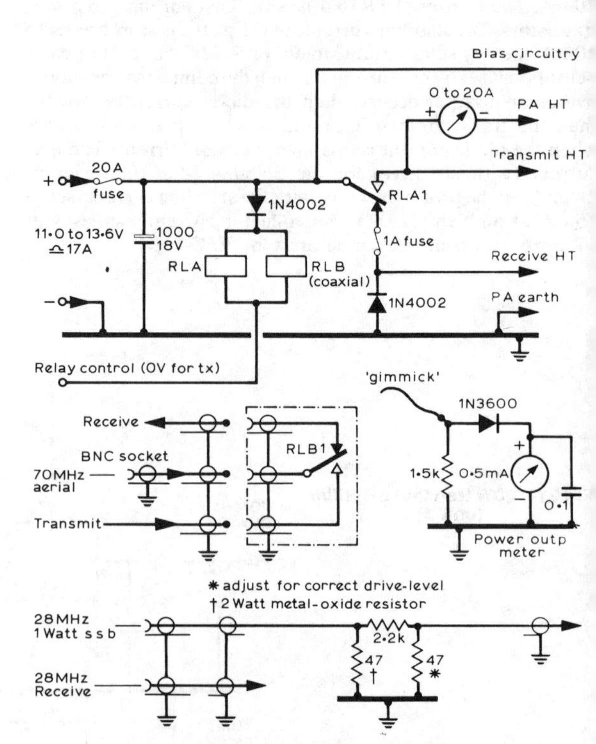

Fig 23. Control unit (unit 4)

nderside view of transverter. Left: top, unit 2; bottom, unit 3. Right: unit 4

ower to each compartment in the same way as unit 1. Due to he thermal inertia of the chassis, soldering is difficult and more ormal wiring techniques have been used—solder tags forming arth connections and other components screwed down where ossible. TRs11, 12 are bolted to the chassis which acts as a eatsink.

Unit 3 uses a single-sided copper-clad board mounted flush vith the base of a 6908P die-cast box. Clearance holes in board nd box ensure that the metallic under-surfaces of TRs13, 14 re in direct contact with the heat sink. Small pads of copper-lad board are fixed to the base-board with Araldite to form solid anchor points for the bases and collectors of TRs13, 14 and other components.

It is not possible to use feedthrough capacitors with this form of construction, but standard polyester and ceramic capacitors provide adequate bypassing. A screen soldered across the board provides complete isolation of input from output. The four 250pF mica trimmers used have mounting studs isolated from both connections. These are mounted on the board only; the box and heat sink are drilled ⅜in to provide clearance. The complete board is attached only by the two transistors' studs and nuts, thus ensuring easy access.

The heat sink used is a 200mm length of Marston type 63DN (unblackened); this will dissipate >60W continuously for a 40°C rise in temperature above ambient. This would be the worst case of continuous transmission, 120W output. The heat sink base thickness of 0·594in exceeds the length of stud available on the 2N6084 and BLY90. The finned side of the heat sink must therefore be end-milled to a suitable depth to provide sufficient clearance for the mounting nuts. The surfaces must be truly square to ensure that the stud is not strained. To permit maximum heat transfer to the heat sink, no edges should be chamfered.

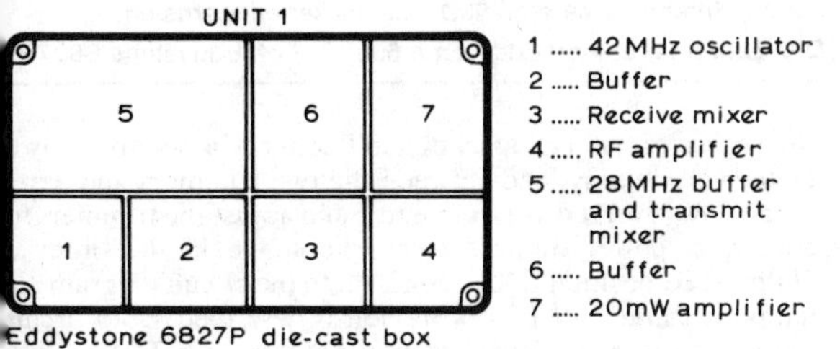

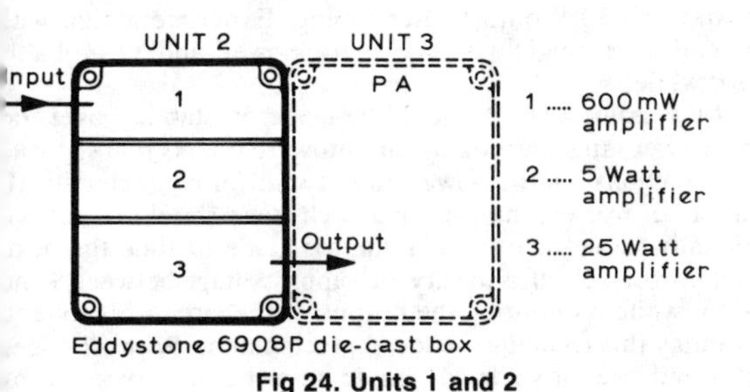

Fig 24. Units 1 and 2

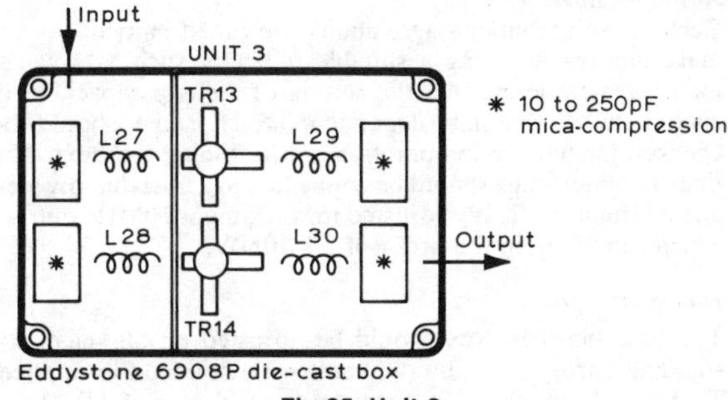

Fig 25. Unit 3

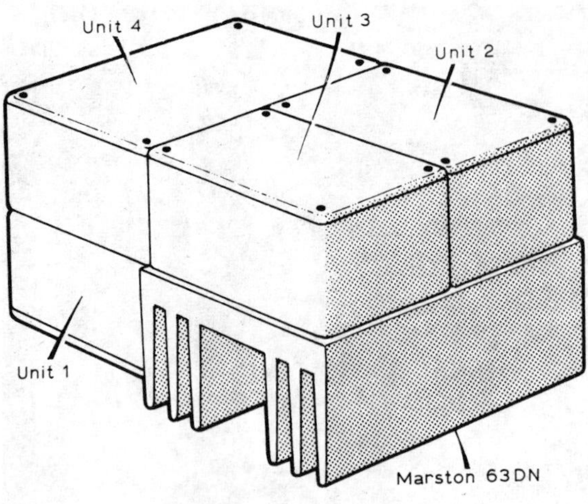

Fig 26. Box assembly

Suggested alignment procedure

Local oscillator and buffers (Fig 17)
L1 should be set approximately to the correct frequency with no supply voltage by shorting the crystal and dipping L1 with a gdo. After this has been done the short should be removed and the oscillator checked for correct operation on 42MHz. If necessary L1 should be trimmed for reliable and consistent start-up on the application of power. L4 and L5 should be resonated for maximum output and the coupling link adjusted for approximately 700mV output to the tx mixer.

Receiver rf amplifier and mixer (Fig 18)
All the trimmers in the receiver section should be adjusted for maximum output into the 28MHz receiver. The relative positions of L8 and L9 should be adjusted to achieve the critical coupling needed for optimum performance. Minor adjustments of the antenna tap position on L7, made in conjunction with a noise generator, can optimize the noise factor but this will probably not be of significance due to the high ambient noise always encountered on 70MHz.

28MHz bandpass filter (Fig 19)
Disconnect the top coupling capacitor and tune each of the two parallel-tuned circuits separately to 28·3MHz with a gdo. When this has been done reconnect the capacitor and re-resonate one of the tuned circuits to maximize the output.

Amplifier stages (Fig 19)
Each of the amplifier stages should be tuned individually for maximum output using a suitable indicator such as a wave-meter, remembering that the setting of the two capacitors in each network are interdependent. Each stage should be checked for full stable operation before tuning the next. The final amplifier stage should be connected to a 50Ω dummy load and all trimmers finally adjusted for maximum 70MHz output, which should be in the order of 20–30mW.

Unit 2 (Fig 20)
The base bias resistors should be adjusted on all stages for standing currents of about 30mA with no rf drive applied. Temporarily connect L22 between the collector of TR10 and the series trimming capacitor, and connect a suitable power meter and dummy load between the two trimmers and earth. Apply low-level rf drive from unit 1 and adjust the trimmers for maximum power output, which should be in the order of 600mW. Reposition L22 to conform to the circuit diagram and temporarily relocate L24 as previously described. Both circuits should now be re-peaked. The power output from TR11 should be about 4–5W. With L18 correctly positioned TR12 should produce 25–30W output after tuning. Experimentation with the coil sizes might produce extra power and is probably worthwhile.

At this point a check should be made on stability over the total power range by looking for untoward effects that show up as "inflections" in the power output transfer characteristic. It cannot be over-emphasized that each stage should be unconditionally stable before an attempt is made to tune the next. Another good check is to vary the supply voltage between 9 and 13·5V while monitoring the output. If the circuit is prone to instability this technique tends to precipitate it. With all stages optimized the drive level should now be set correctly by

Table 2. Components for 70MHz transverter

L1	9 turns, ¼in former, slug tuned 28swg
L2	50nH choke
L3	8 turns, 18swg, ⅜in i.d., close wound, ⅝in long
L4	1 turn link in L3
L5	8 turns, 18swg, ⅜in i.d., close wound, ⅝in long, tap 1t from cold end
L6	1 turn link in L5, joined to L4
L7	5 turns 18swg, ⅜in i.d., length ¾in, tap 1t from cold end
L8	5½ turns 22swg, ⅜in i.d., close wound
L9	5 turns 22swg, ⅜in i.d., close wound, coupled to L8
L10	9 turns 36swg wound on ferrite bead. 2 turns secondary
L11	10 turns 28swg on ¼in slug tuned former. Tap [illegible] turn from cold end
L12	10 turns 28swg on ¼in slug tuned former. Tap [illegible] turn from cold end
L13	16 turns 28swg on ¼in former, slug tuned
L14	3 + 3 turns, 22swg, bifilar wound, on L13
L15	5 + 5 turns, 22swg, ⅜in i.d., close wound
L16	1½ turns, interwound in the centre of L15
L17	5 turns, 22swg ⅜in i.d., length ½in
L18	3 turns, 22swg, ⅜in i.d. interwound in L17
L19	6 turns 22swg ⅜in i.d., length ½in
L20	4 turns 22swg ⅜in i.d., length ¼in
L21	6 turns 18swg ⅜in i.d., length ⅝in
L22	5½ turns 18swg ⅜in i.d., length ½in
L23	7 turns 18swg ⅜in i.d., length ¾in
L24	3 turns 18swg ⅜in i.d., length ⅜in
L25	7 turns 16swg ⅜in i.d., close wound
L26	6 turns 16swg ⅜in i.d., close wound
L27, 28	2 turns 16swg ½in i.d., ¼in leads
L29, 30	1 turn 16swg ½in i.d., ¼in leads
L31, 32	5 turns 16swg ½in i.d., close wound
RFC1	14 turns 22swg on 390Ω resistor
RFC2, 3, 4, 5, 10	6 turns on Mullard FX1898 6-hole ferrite bead
RFC6, 7, 8	10 turns 18swg on ⅝in diameter toroid
RFC9	1·5mH choke

Trimmers in unit 1 are 7/35pF ceramic items intended for pcb mounting. Bend rotor legs at right angles and solder to earth plane.
Unit 2 trimmers are 30pF maximum air spaced.
Unit 3 uses 10/250pF mica-compression trimmers, nut-fixing.

RV1	10kΩ 270° variable resistor
RV2	20Ω 10 turn potentiometer

200mm length of Marston 63DN unblackened extrusion.

Die-cast boxes: 2 off Eddystone 6908P, 2 off Eddystone 6827P.

adjustment of the 28MHz attenuator to ensure correct linear operation of the mixer. The post-mixer drive level may be set by alteration of the coupling between L15 and L16. This procedure is most important if adequate spurii and carrier suppression is to be maintained.

Unit 3 (Fig 21 and 22)
Build and test the bias circuitry first by connecting its output to a silicon diode instead of the bases of TR13 and TR14. Ensure that the multi-turn potentiometer is turned for minimum bias voltage ($\approx 0 \cdot 5$V) and connect to the pa transistors. Connect a 10Ω resistor in series with the pa supply lead and adjust the bias for 60mA collector current (30mA per transistor). Remove the resistor and readjust as necessary. Connect the pa output to a dummy load capable of dissipating 100W at 100 per cent duty cycle via a suitable power meter. Apply drive from unit 2 and resonate the output circuitry, noting that a peak in collector current very nearly corresponds to maximum power output. At this stage always limit the total collector current to 4A. Now resonate the input circuitry, reducing the drive as necessary. After both circuits have been tuned the drive should be increased in steps, retuning the input and output at each stage. Any imbalance due to errors in construction or mismatched devices will be indicated by excessive heating of the strapping resistors. When 12A has been reached, 100W of power should be obtained.

The alignment is now completed by the possible readjustment of the post-mixer drive level as before. The a.m./cw drive level can be set to 50W input by suitable adjustment of the front-panel drive potentiometer RV1. Because of mistuning at low power levels the efficiency is reduced and will be typically about 40 per cent. To improve this situation a compromise may be made by tuning the pa at an intermediate power level at the expense of maximum output power.

Typical transverters for 144MHz

Circuit details are given for a valve and a semiconductor transverter, and there is of course no reason why a hybrid design should not be used. For example, the receiver and local oscillator sections of the semiconductor version could be used with valve mixer and amplifier stages. Such a design probably offers the best compromise and has the merit of using semiconductors where they are most effective in this application.

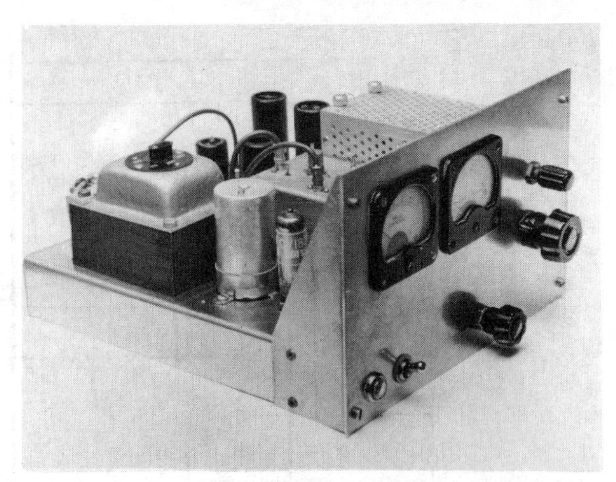

Valve transverter for 144MHz

There is little doubt that it is simpler in the valve stages, where loose-coupled circuits offer a higher degree of frequency discrimination than is possible with the direct couplings typical in semiconductor arrangements.

Of course, a clean signal can be produced by the semiconductor circuit, but this often requires that there is positive action to "suck out" known frequencies such as is illustrated in the semiconductor design, where a series-tuned circuit to the local oscillator frequency (116MHz) is included in the input to the driver stage.

It is very important that there are no out-of-band radiations and it is not good enough to assume that the multiplicity of tuned circuits will always remove harmonics. It is a distinct advantage to include a bandpass filter, in which case the insertion loss can be made quite small—of the order of $0 \cdot 5$dB max.

Construction of the transverter may take any form convenient to the constructor, but it is desirable that both the

Table 3. Details of inductors, etc for valve transverter

Coil	Frequency (MHz)	Detail
L1	38·66	15 turns 28swg close wound $\frac{1}{4}$in dia dust core
L2	38·66	15 turns 28swg close wound $\frac{1}{4}$in dia dust core
L3	116	5 turns 18swg $\frac{7}{8}$in long $\frac{1}{2}$in dia centre tapped
L4	116	
L5	144	6 turns 18swg $\frac{5}{16}$in dia spaced 1d centre tapped
L6	144	2 + 2 turns 18swg $\frac{5}{16}$in dia coupled to outer ends of L15
L7	144	6 turns 18swg $\frac{5}{16}$in dia spaced 1d centre tapped
L8	144	2 + 2 turns 16swg $\frac{3}{8}$in dia coupled to outer ends of L7
L9	144	4 turns $\frac{1}{8}$in copper 1in long $\frac{3}{4}$in dia centre tapped
L10	144	1 turn 14swg $\frac{3}{4}$in insulated
L11	144	6 turns $\frac{1}{4}$in dia
L12	144	
L13	144	6 turns $\frac{1}{4}$in dia
L14	28	
LM & C	—	2 turns insulated wire coupling coils
M1	0–500μA	
M2	0–200mA	
V1	6CW4 } or ECF80 or equivalent	
V2	EF91 } or ECF80 or equivalent	
RFC1	50–100Ω, 3W, wire wound resistor	
RFC2	100Ω 3W wire wound resistor	
RFC3	50Ω 5W wire wound resistor	

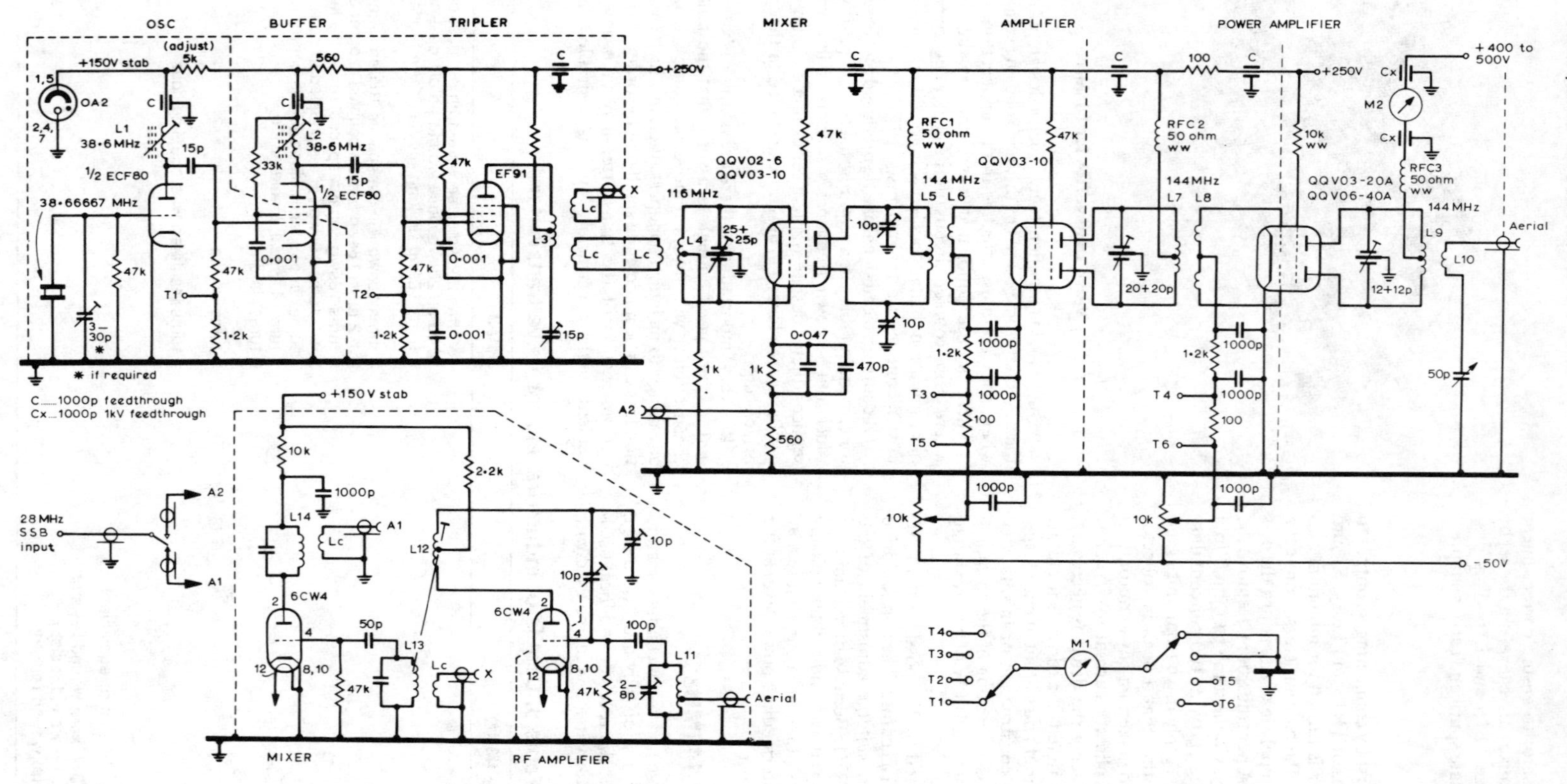

Fig 27. Valve transverter for 144MHz

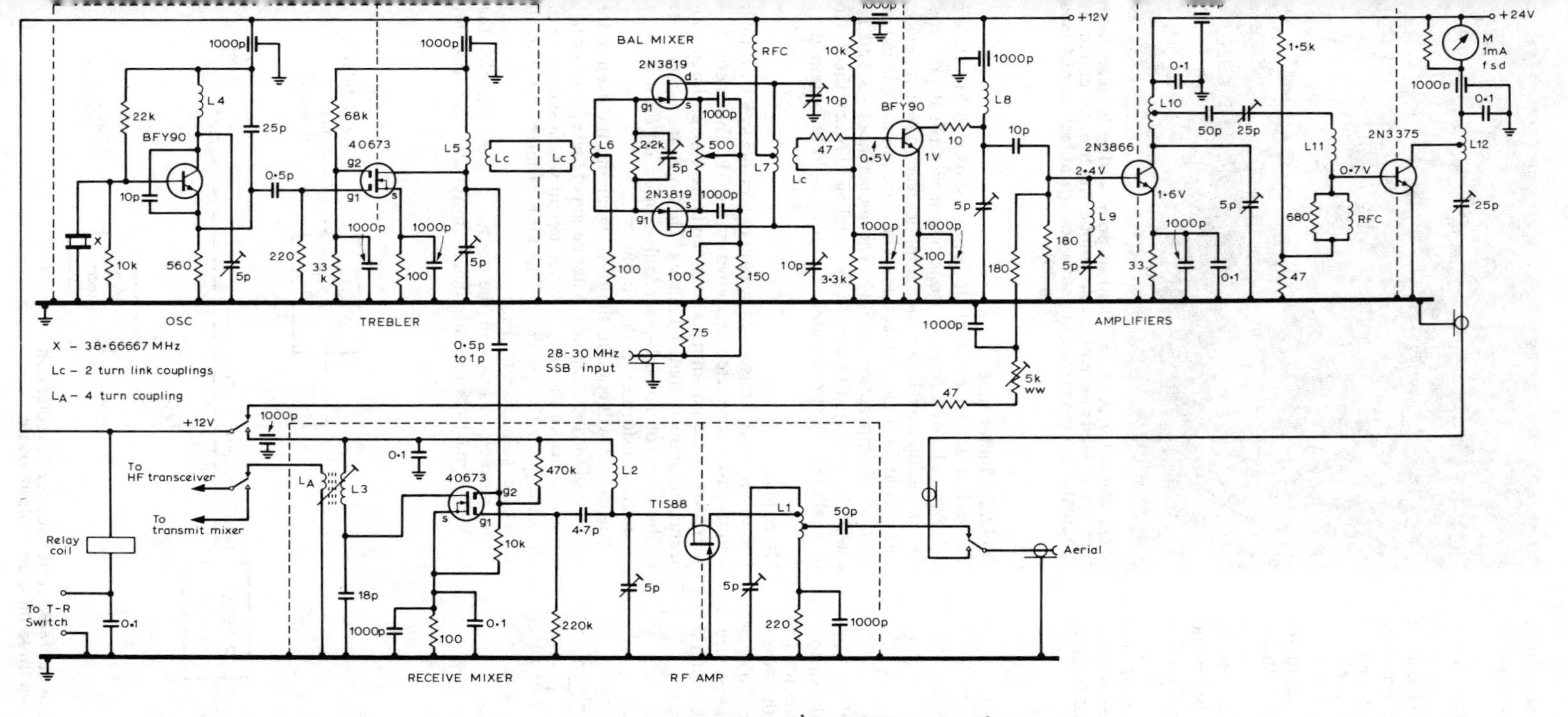

Fig 28. Typical semiconductor 144MHz transverter

Table 4. Details of inductors for transistor transverter

Coil	Frequency (MHz)	Detail
L1	144	9 turns 22swg ¼in dia ½in long tapped 3 turns and 5 turns
L2	144	8 turns 22swg ¼in dia 0·45in
L3	28	22 turns 28swg 0·45in dust core
L4	38·6	7 turns 22swg ¼in dia 0·45in
L5	116	7 turns 22swg ¼in dia 0·4in
L6	116	8 turns 22swg ¼in dia ½in centre tapped
L7	144	7 turns 22swg ¼in dia ½in
L8	144	4 turns 22swg ¼in dia 0·45in
L9	116	8 turns 22swg ¼in dia 0·45in
L10	144	5 turns 18swg ¼in dia 0·4 centre tapped
L11	144	4 turns 18swg ¼in dia 0·5in
L12	144	5 turns 16swg ¼in dia 0·45in centre tapped
LC		2 turns insulated wire 0·45in
RFC	18-19in	32–34swg wound ⅛in dia former

receiver and local oscillator sections should be separately screened and normal interstage screening should be included in the amplifier stages.

Relay switching should be co-ordinated with the transceiver to achieve reasonable operating convenience.

The most important stage in the transverter is the balanced transmitter mixer. It is essential that the output is properly balanced, and for this reason both designs have separate trimmers at each end of the output tuned circuit to assist this.

When a 28MHz signal is used, it should be realized that the fifth harmonic tunes between 140 and 150MHz and can therefore produce an in-band signal unless it is adequately attenuated by balancing.

The 116MHz signal will normally be attenuated satisfactorily by loose-coupled tuned circuits in the valve design, but in the semiconductor design a series-tuned circuit is included for this purpose.

As mentioned earlier, out-of-band signals, such as the second harmonic of 116 and 144MHz, should be suitably attenuated to prevent interference with other services. This can best be done by the addition of a narrow bandpass filter.

Typical operating conditions for a QQV03-10 are:

Set up I_a to 23 to 25mA
increase in I_a by 4 to 5mA with 116MHz drive
increase in I_a by 1mA with ssb 28MHz.

Power-fet transverter for 144MHz

This transverter, originally described by WB6BPI in *Ham Radio*, illustrates a number of features employed in the various individual stages, in particular the use of power fets for the amplifiers. Because these devices operate at higher-than-usual voltages, all the stages are operated from this voltage (30V). A block diagram of the transverter is shown in Fig 29. The particular characteristics of the power fets are dealt with in Chapter 5.

Local oscillator module. Point-to-point wiring is used, with component leads serving as tie points. The trimmer capacitor is adjusted for maximum negative voltage at test point 1 (see Fig 30)

Oscillator/buffer unit

The circuit arrangement of this unit is shown in Fig 30 and employs a 116MHz fifth-overtone crystal with a dual-gate mosfet. This is followed by a buffer amplifier using a similar device. The output has dual connections which are mutually independent at an impedance of 50Ω. The inductances L3 and L4 should be arranged to avoid any coupling between them. An output level of approximately 1V rms should be obtained.

Mixer unit

The mixer stage consists of a pair of jfet devices with their sources cross-connected as shown in Fig 31. This method of operation offers advantages over the more conventional connection of double-balanced mixers. They operate in a manner similar to that of the push-push doubler, avoiding the need for a balanced transformer in the output.

The output will contain the beat signal and the even-order products of the input signals. Attenuation of these latter signals will take place in the output tuned circuit which should be of adequate Q for this purpose. This form of mixer has a small conversion gain, about 1dB.

The variable resistor in the source of TR1 enables the 116MHz signal to be minimized in the mixer output. The buffer

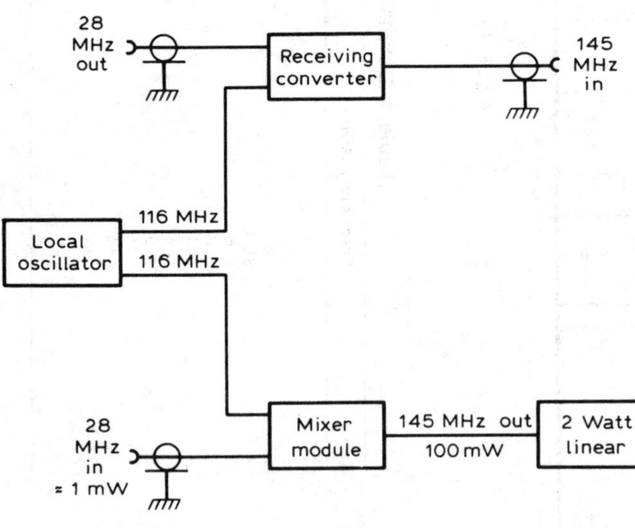

Fig 29. Block diagram of the 144MHz transverter. Modular construction allows three different output levels

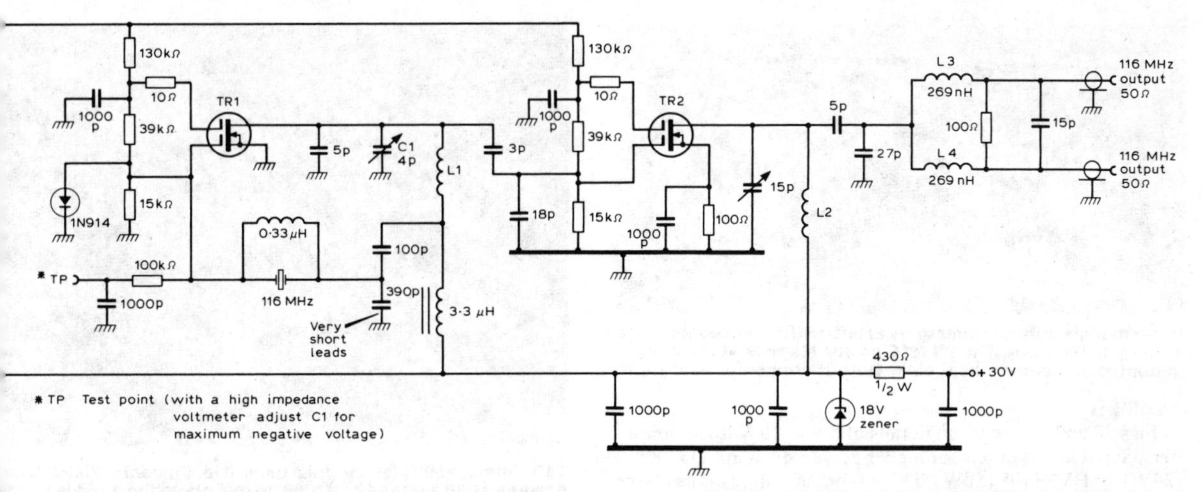

Fig 30. Local oscillator module provides two mutually independent outputs at 116MHz. L1: 5t ½in i.d. L2: 7t ⅛in i.d. L3, L4: 4½t ⅛in i.d. All are close wound using 20awg enam copper wire. TR1, TR2: Fairchild FT0601 or RCA40673

mplifier, a 2N3866 in this application, runs at 40mA and needs some form of small heat sink such as a clip-on type. The output circuit of this stage is arranged to attenuate the second harmonic of the 116MHz fed through the mixer.

If preferred, a bandpass filter could be imposed between this stage and the following amplifier to still further reduce any second harmonic of the 116MHz signal, but under normal circumstances this should not be necessary.

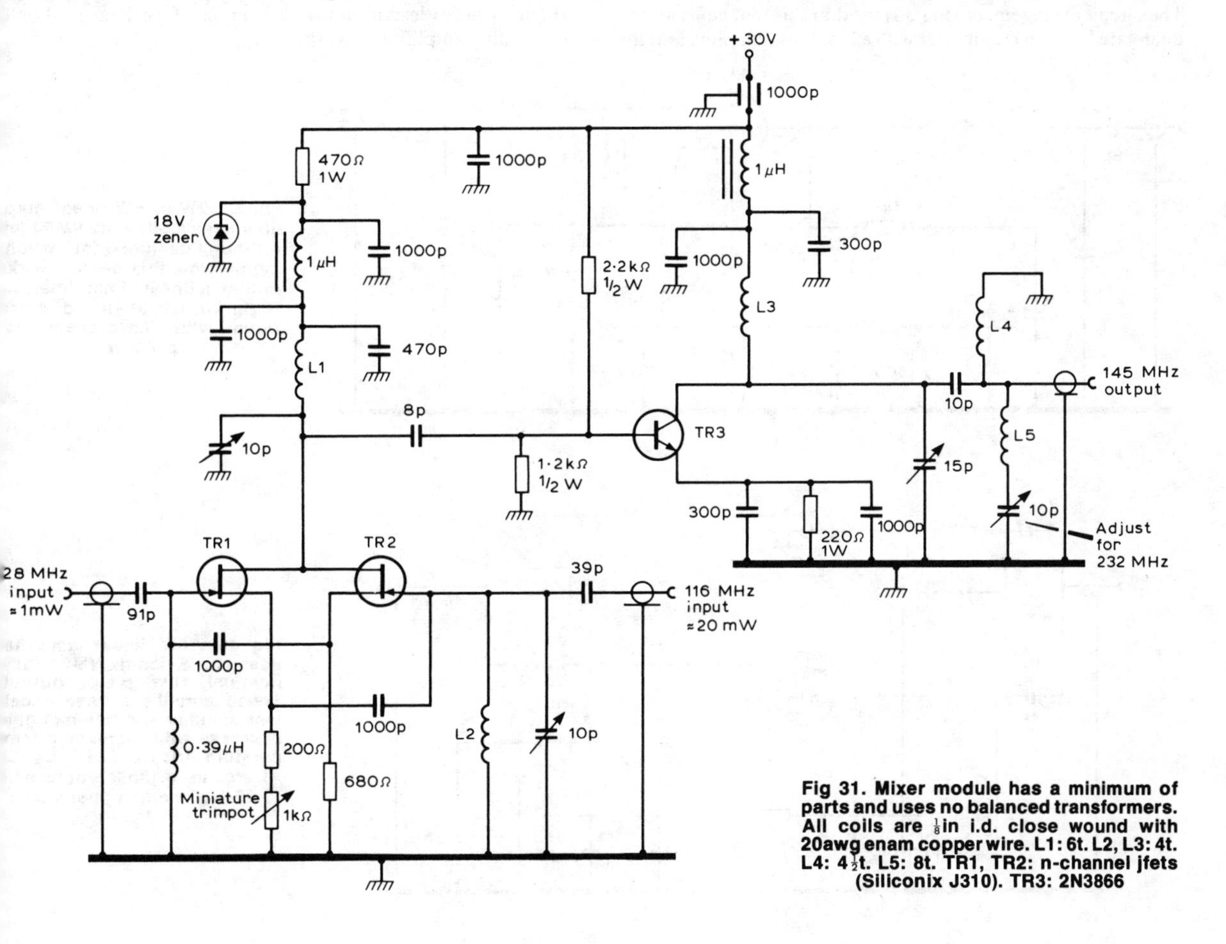

Fig 31. Mixer module has a minimum of parts and uses no balanced transformers. All coils are ⅛in i.d. close wound with 20awg enam copper wire. L1: 6t. L2, L3: 4t. L4: 4½t. L5: 8t. TR1, TR2: n-channel jfets (Siliconix J310). TR3: 2N3866

Mixer module. Input connector is at left, with balanced fet stage slightly to the right. The 2N3866 power stage is at the centre, mounted in a clip-on heat sink. Output connector is at right

Amplifiers

In Figs 32 and 33 are given details of 5 and 10W linear amplifiers. Suitable power fets for higher power levels are DV2820S (24W), or DV2840S (50W). These types are rated at the above output powers for frequencies up to 175MHz.

The amplifiers shown Figs 32 and 33 are adjusted to a quiescent drain current of 150mA by forward positive bias. Incidentally, failure of the bias will cause the drain current to fall to a low safe value.

Receiver converter

The circuit arrangement (Fig 34) used in this unit consists of a dual-gate fet as an rf amplifier with a bandpass coupling into the mixer, which is of the same form as that used for the transmit mixer. If preferred a dual-gate device could be used.

10W linear amplifier module uses two Siliconix VMP4 Mospower fets on a finned heat sink. In this photo the input is at left, output at right. Bias adjust pots are at left

Construction

As illustrated, the construction was without pc boards and requires little description—substitution of pc boards should materially simplify the work.

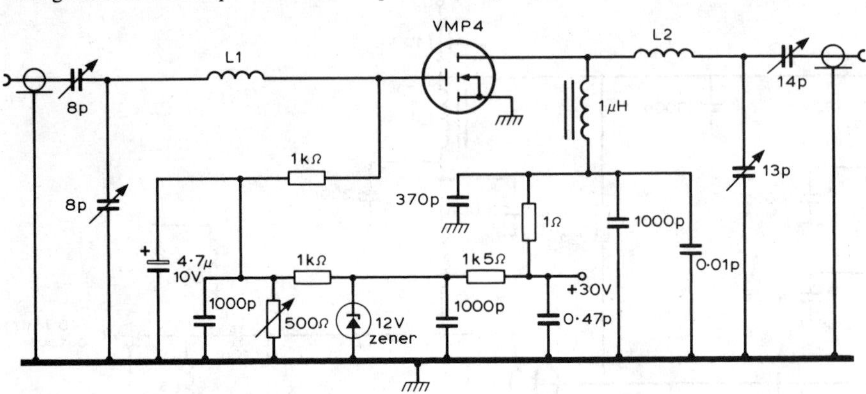

Fig 32. 2W or 5W linear amplifier uses a Siliconix VMP4 fet. Although designed for switching service, this device works well as a linear rf amplifier. L1 8t 1/8in i.d. L2: 5t 1/8in i.d. close wound with 20awg enam copper wire

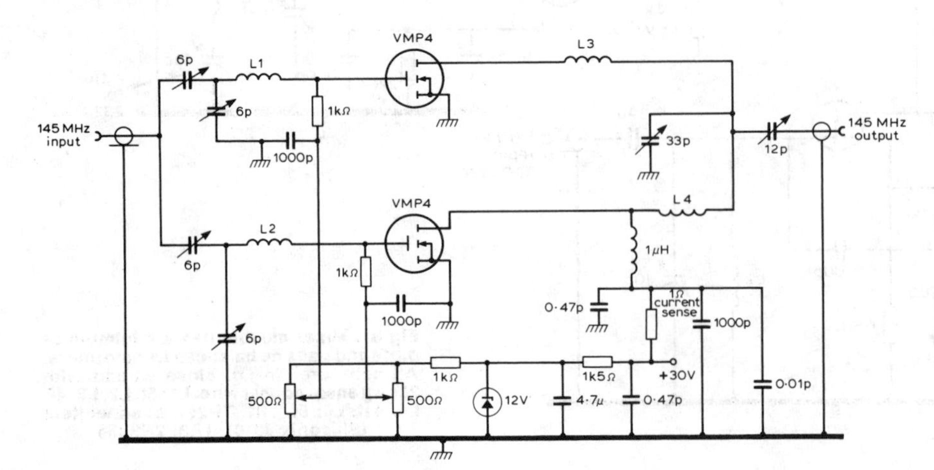

Fig 33. 10W linear amplifier uses two Siliconix VMP4 for a nominal 10W p.e.p. output. These amplifiers have excellent stability and minimal gain decrease with increasing temperature. L1, L2: 8t L3, L4: 5t All are, 1/8in i.d. close wound with 20awg enam copper wire

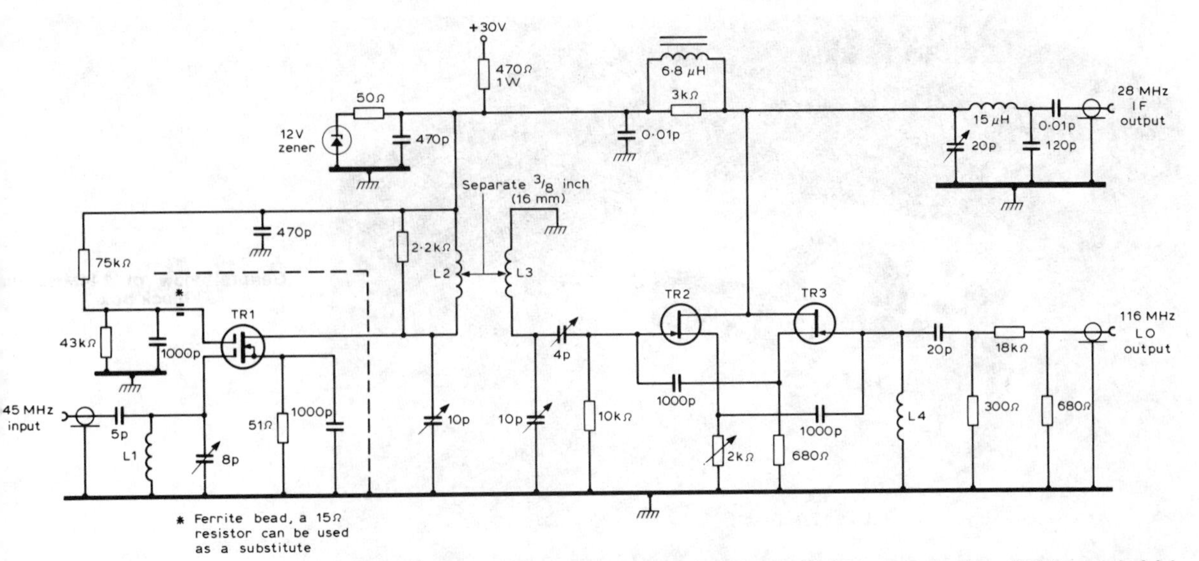

Fig 34. Receiving converter is relatively narrow-band. For full coverage of the 144MHz band, L2 and L3 should be tightly coupled. L1, L4: 6t. L2, L3: 8t. All are ¼in i.d. close wound with 20awg enam copper wire. TR1: Fairchild FT0601 or RCA 40673. TRs, TR3: n-channel jfets (Siliconix E300, J310 or 2N5485, 2N5486)

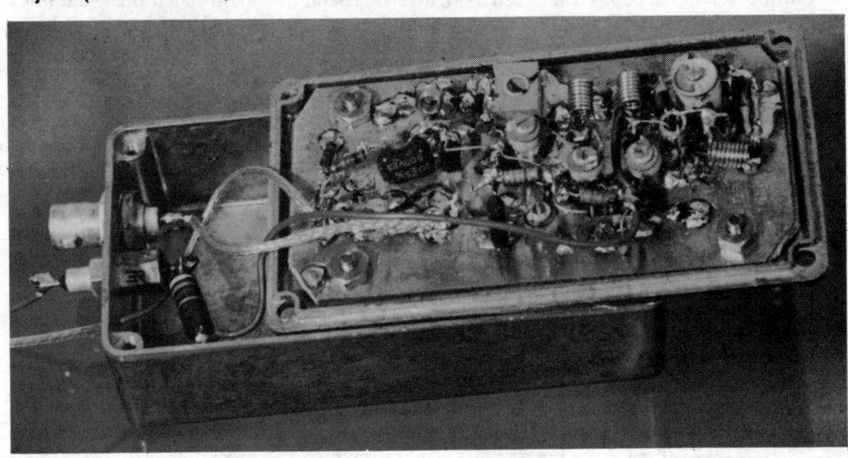

Receiving converter module uses point-to-point wiring and is mounted in small die-cast box

A 144MHz fm black box

This design was originally described by J. R. Hey, G3TDZ, in *Radio Communication* March 1978.

Receiver

A dual-gate mosfet rf stage followed by a fet mixer take familiar lines, injection being developed from a bipolar overtone oscillator and tripler. The oscillator crystals may be 52 or 44MHz.

A home-made i.f. transformer at 10·7MHz, consisting of two coils of only 16 turns at a suitable spacing, 0·45in, couples the mixer to the second mixer, a further fet. A single BC109 crystal oscillator operates at 11·155MHz to produce a 455kHz second i.f.

The printed circuit has provision for either the Mu-Rata CFR-455 middle-class ladder filter, or the less expensive CFM-455 popular-class filter; these are widely employed in Japanese fm black boxes. Types CFM-455E, CFM-455F, CFR-455E or CFR-455F are recommended.

The main i.f. amplifier is designed around the TBA120 ic which has a built-in coincidence detector. The TBA120, along with almost all similar devices, has a high current consumption. Siemens, however, produce a low-current version, the S-041-P, which only consumes about 6mA.

The TBA120 alone has insufficient gain and an i.f. preamplifier is required in front of the ic. This is a cascode amplifier using bipolar transistors and operates with only 2mA. The coupling i.f. transformer is a standard 10mm type.

The quadrature detector tuned circuit needs to be as good as possible, because the recovered audio depends on it.

The basic receiver requirements are completed by an LM380 audio power ic which has low quiescent current.

Where the audio is taken from the TBA120, prior to the volume control, a high-pass filter, TR8, separates the noise from wanted audio for driving the squelch circuit.

One section of IC3 is biased for linear amplification of the noise signal following the high-pass filter. The amplified noise is

General view of 144MHz fm "black box"

rectified by D1 (Fig 36) and the resultant positive-going voltage applied across the squelch control, RV2.

A further section of IC3 is connected as an inverting Schmitt trigger: where interstation noise is present, the voltage from the squelch control causes a current to flow into the inverting input, pin 6, via the series resistor R33. No bias is applied to the opposite input pin 1, and the resulting output is at earth or logic 0. However, when a signal is received the noise dies away: there is no bias available for pin 6 and the output rapidly switches to full ht, or logic 1. The switch now supplies current to the current amplifier TR12, TR13 which in turn powers the audio amplifier IC4. Instead of actual audio gating, the audio power amplifier is switched off when not required, a saving in battery power.

Two sections of IC2, another LM3900, form a free-running multivibrator or astable. The circuit will operate without any biasing but was found to be very ht conscious; linear biasing lowered its sensitivity to ht line variations. This forms the battery economizer timer circuit which is left running continuously with a 6:1 ratio. Its output on pin 5 feeds a further section of IC2 connected as a non-inverting Schmitt circuit. Here the

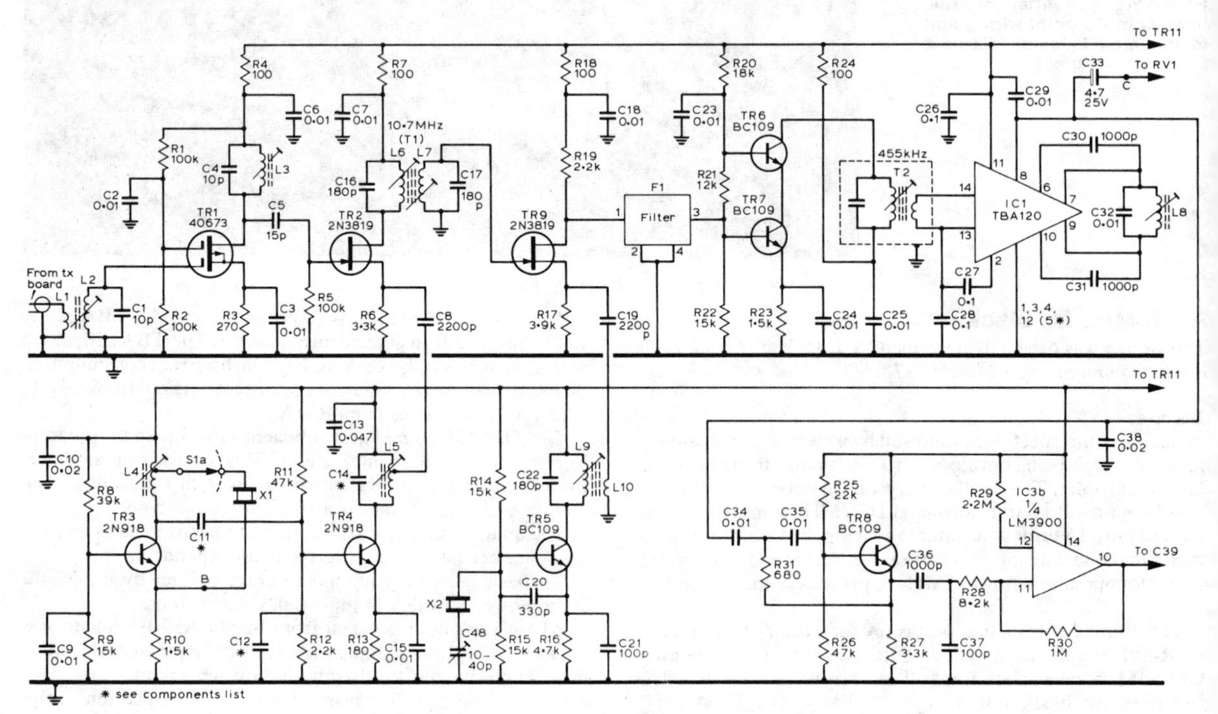

Fig 35. Receiver theoretical circuit rf sections

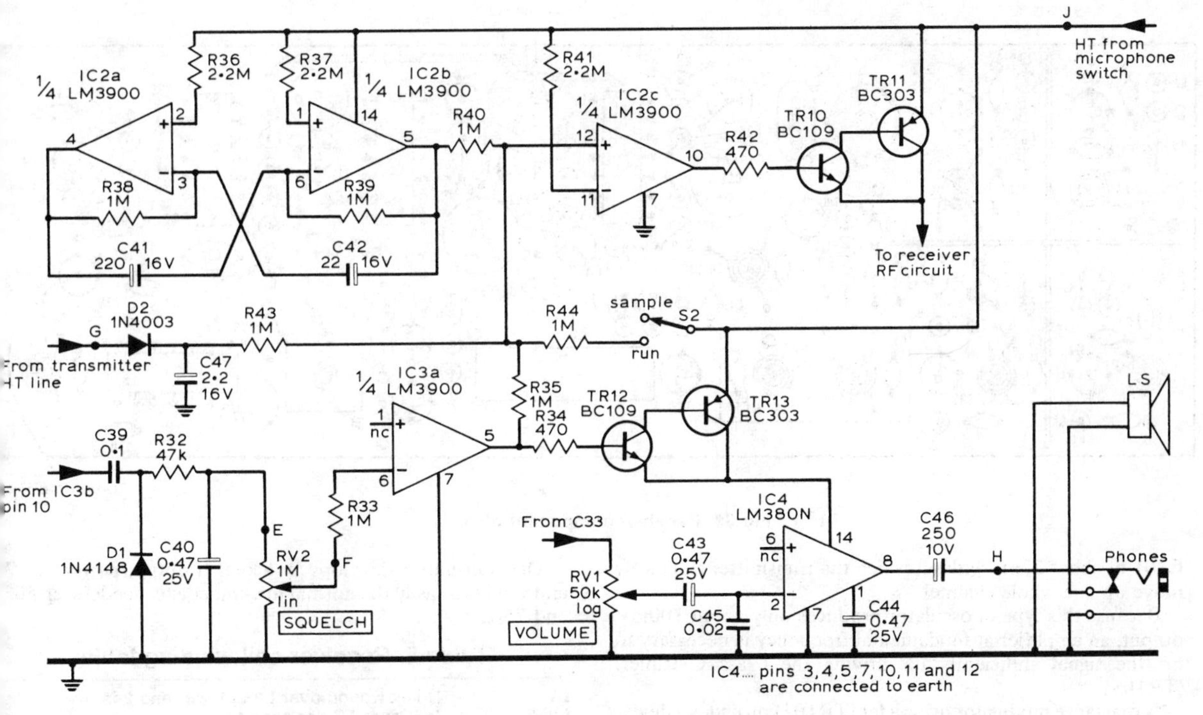

Fig 36. Receiver "logic" and af sections theoretical circuit

nverting input pin 11 is permanently biased, which holds the output at logic 0. When the timer supplies current to the non-inverting input pin 12, the output pin 10 switches up to ht or logic 1, in turn allowing current amplifiers TR10 and TR11 to supply voltage to all the receiver rf circuits.

Only IC2 and the two current amplifiers connect to the manually switched ht line. As the timer turns on the receiver to sample the channel, absence of a signal holds off connection of ht to the audio stage. When a signal is present, not only is ht supplied to the af amplifier but the switching signal is applied to the non-inverting Schmitt. This holds the receiver in the ON state regardless of timer switching signal.

In order to prevent too fast operation D2 C47 fed from the transmitter ht line holds the receiver open for a few seconds after transmission.

The "battery-saver" is not always needed; the front panel switch S2 allows the receiver to remain open by applying a further switching current to IC2 pin 12 through R44.

Transmitter

A 12MHz Clapp circuit was chosen with the crystals selected by a further section of S1, S1b in Fig 39. It is necessary to include a crystal trimmer for each channel: C140 therefore is duplicated for the number of channels demanded with a fixed capacitor

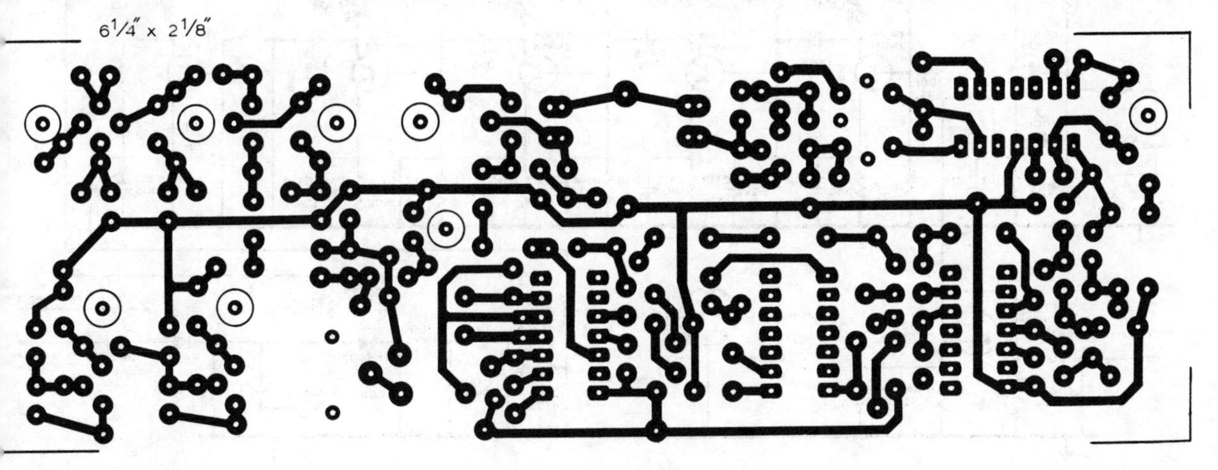

Fig 37. Receiver pcb

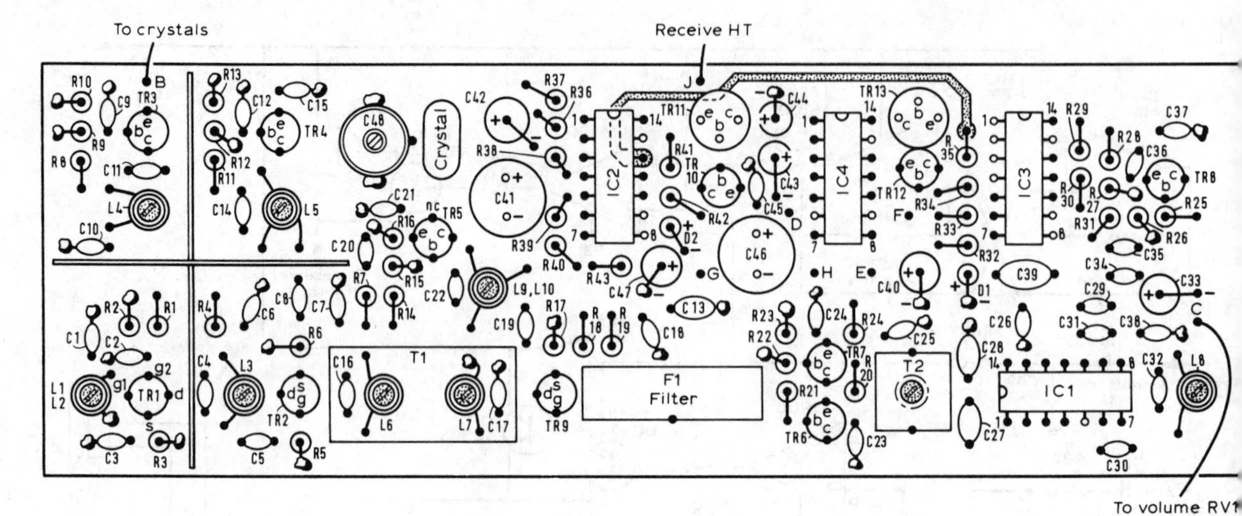

Fig 38. Receiver component plan

C101 of about 27pF, without which the transmitter can easily move up one whole channel.

Because this type of oscillator produces only about 100mV output, an amplifier at fundamental frequency is necessary to lift the signal sufficiently for driving the Class C tripler. (TR103).

A reactance modulator using a fet (TR102) provides a deviation of 6kHz with an audio input of 600mV.

From TR103 onwards, there is a tripler TR104 to 36MHz; a doubler TR105 to 72MHz, both using 2N918; a doubler TR106, a 2N3866, to 145MHz. Capacitive divider networks form the interstage couplings up to the final doubler.

Coils L101 to L104 have been wound on $\frac{3}{16}$in formers and slug tuned (Figs 40 and 41); L105 onward are self-supported coils of 20swg with tuning adjusted by airspaced trimmers. The L-pi output network acts as its own low-pass filter.

The transmitter develops an actual rf output power of 1W and will load easily the normal low-impedance feeders, eg 50Ω and 75Ω.

Table 5. Receiver coil winding table

L1	1t link wound over L2 at lower end 24s pvc
L2, 3	4t 22swg TCu spaced $\frac{1}{4}$in
L4	For 44MHz crystals: 7t 22swg TCu tap one turn down For 52MHz crystals: 6t 22swg TCu tap one turn down
L5	Low side: 4t 22swg TCu High side: 3t 22swg TCu
L6, 7	16t 28–20swg enamel close wound
L8	50t 32–36swg enamel close wound over two layers
L9	15t 28–30swg enamel close wound
L10	3t 24–26swg wound over cold end of L9

All coils are wound on $\frac{3}{16}$in Aladdin 8A-6259-02 and fitted with iron dust cores. Filter and i.f. transformers—see text.

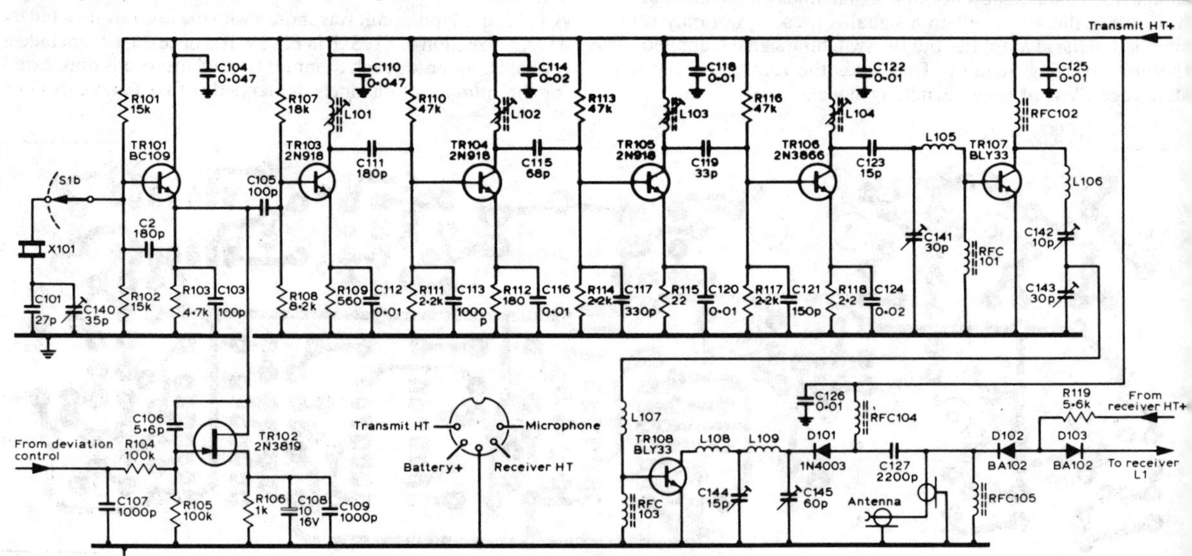

Fig 39. Transmitter rf and modulator section theoretical circuit

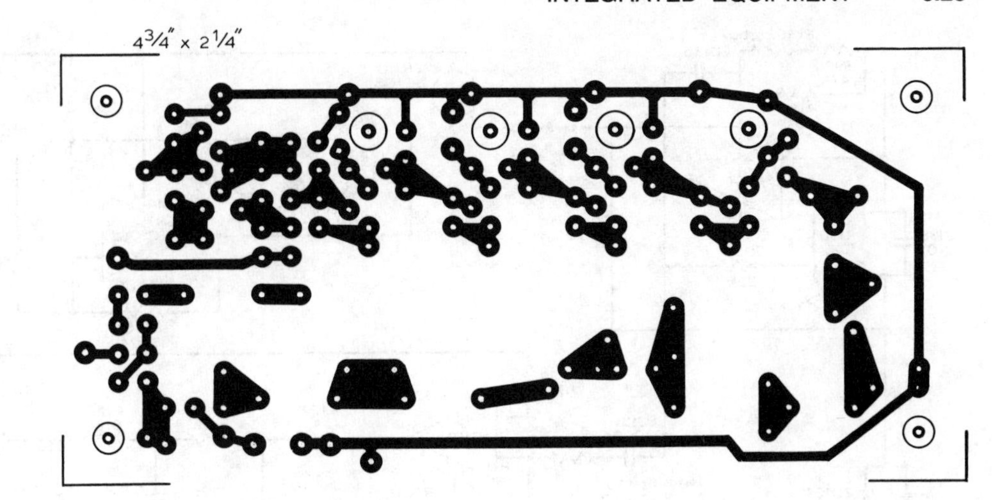

ig 40. Transmitter pcb

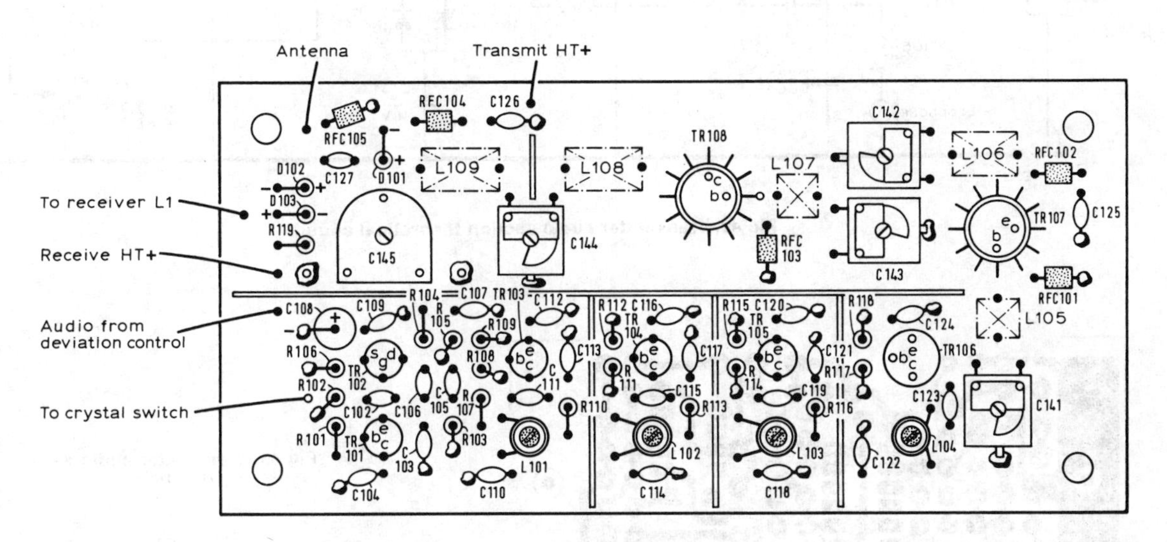

Fig 41. Transmitter component plan

Table 6. Transmitter coil winding table

.101	12t 26–28swg enamel close wound
.102	7t 22swg 3/16in i.d. TCu spaced about 3/8in
.103, 104	5t 22swg 3/16in i.d. TCu spaced about 1/4in
.105, 107	3t 20swg 1/4in i.d. plain copper or enamel
.106	6t 20swg 1/4in i.d. plain copper or enamel spaced to fit board
.108	8t 20swg 1/4in i.d. plain copper or enamel spaced to fit board
.109	9t 20swg 1/4in i.d. plain copper or enamel spaced to fit board

.101 to 104 are wound on 3/16in Aladdin 8A-6259-02 and fitted with ron dust cores. Coils L105 to 109 are wound 1/4in i.d. self supporting

RFC101	1t 28swg enamel
RFC102	2t 28swg enamel
RFC103	1t 26swg enamel
RFC104	2t 26swg enamel
RFC105, 106	3t 28swg enamel

ll RFCs are wound on FX1115 ferrite beads.

The audio section

A separate pc board houses the transmitter's audio section (Figs 42, 43 and 44). As in the receiver, both the linear and digital qualities of the LM3900 are exploited. With phase modulation, fm pre-emphasis is unnecessary; however, some bass roll-off is provided by choice of C129, R120.

One section of IC101 is biased for linear operation with the gain set to 100 by R120, R123. RFC106 and C128 prevent rf from entering the speech channel. Fitted fundamentally as a deviation limiter, the simple amplitude clipper, together with the bass roll-off and followed by a low-pass filter, produces very respectable modulation reports.

A second section of IC101 performs as a monostable for gating the access tone generator. It is triggered into operation by a pulse through the small capacitor C139 upon application of ht. The duration of the ON condition is set by C138, in this case 470ms.

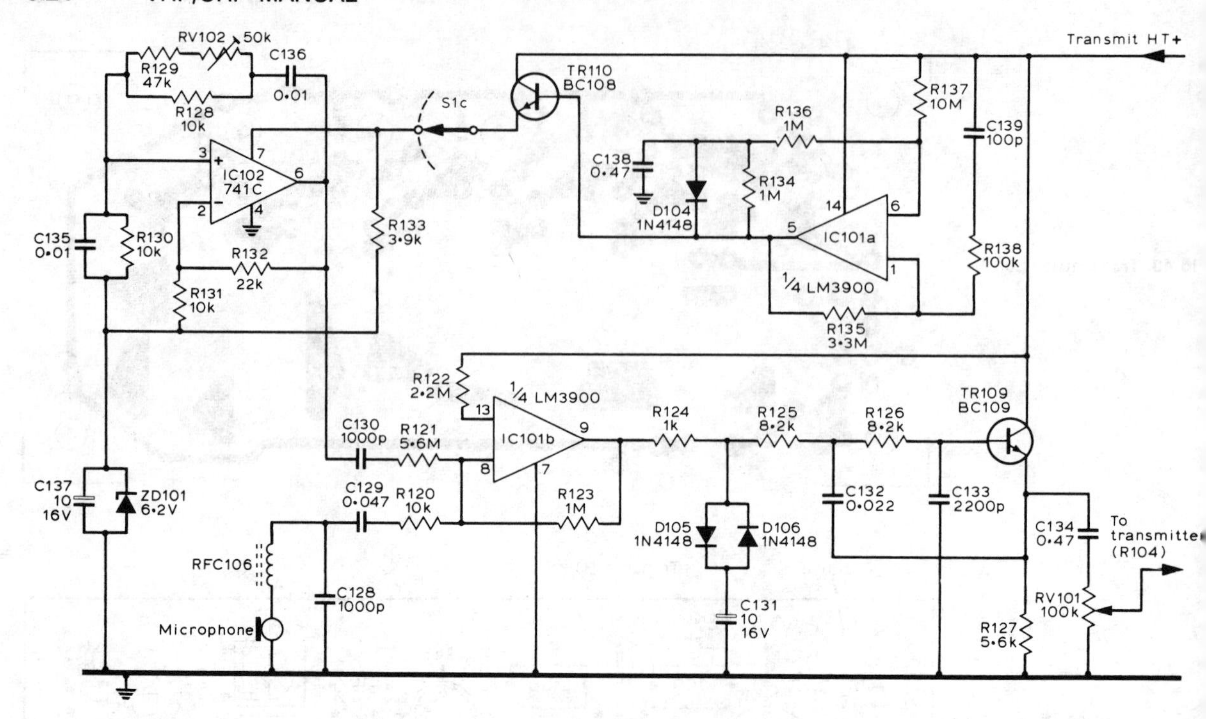

Fig 42. Transmitter audio section theoretical circuit

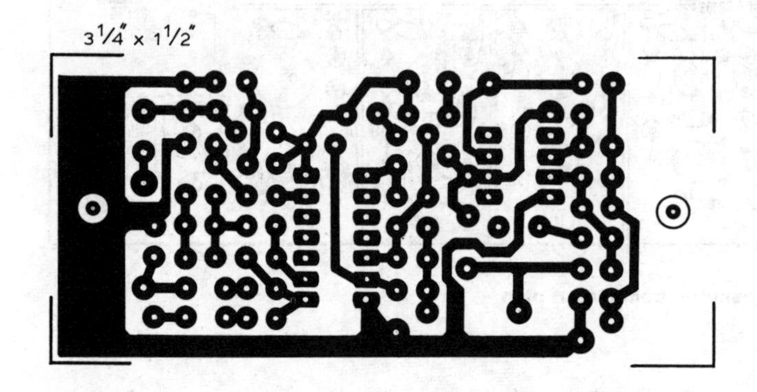

Fig 43. Transmitter audio section pcb

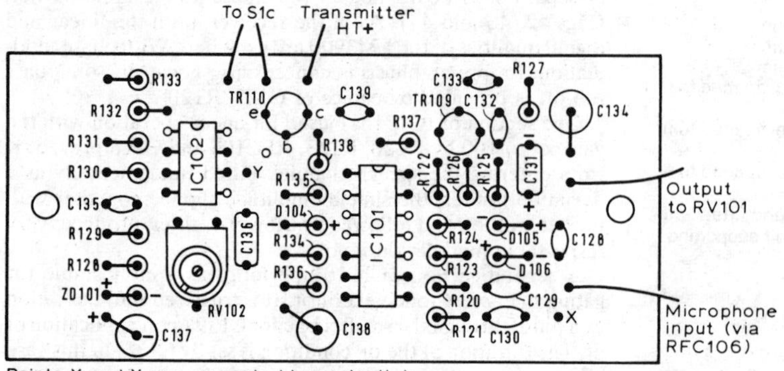

Fig 44. Transmitter audio section component plan

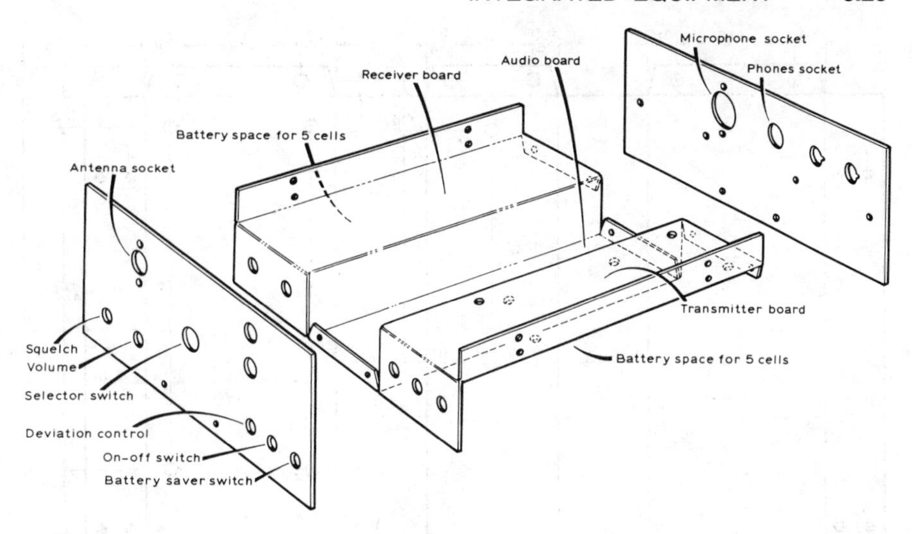

g 45. Basic chassis design

A third wafer or set of contacts S1c connects the timer to the ccess tone generator as required for repeater channels. A eparate 741, IC2, forms a Wien bridge oscillator which posses-s good immunity to the effects of ht variation; its frequency an be set to exactly 1,750Hz by RV102, a small preset on the c board (Fig 44). The high-amplitude output from the tone scillator is attenuated by the action of R121, a 5·6MΩ resistor orking against R123.

he chassis

n Fig 45 a suggested chassis form is shown. The seemingly omplicated central chassis member is redrawn more simply in ig 46(a) where the unbent dimensions are indicated. By dding a simple front and rear plate, a sturdy chassis results.

The receiver board is mounted on to the left-hand platform nd the transmitter rf board on the right, with the audio oard down in the channel close to the rear plate. RFC6 con-ects between the board's input at C28, 29, and the DIN socket nounted in the rear plate.

A two-piece wrap-round shell case is required to enclose the nit; the lower half should be fitted so that the batteries are held n position.

The power supply is 10 U11 size cells, 1·6Ah or 1·8Ah epending on manufacturer; five cells wired in series and wrap-ed in a cardboard package fit under the two platforms.

A small 8Ω 2½in type loudspeaker is fitted into the upper hassis shell or lid, its magnet assembly entering the trough bove the audio board. The two shells are retained by self-apping screws into the side pieces (Fig 45). To the front of the udio board there should be ample room for the channel switch nd the crystal banks. A suggested layout for the transmitter rystals with their trimmers is shown in Fig 48. In the working nodel a slotted piece of plastic was glued to one side of the hannel, the crystal bank then being fitted in and retained at the ther side by self-tapping screws to form a bridge. This enables asy access for adjusting fixed value capacitors C1 soldered cross each trimmer.

The position of all sundry components is shown in Fig 45. For hose who might question the siting of RV1, the deviation ontrol on the front panel: it was for no better reason than some ind person presented a fine miniature panel mounting pot made by Allen Bradley. An ordinary control or pre-set may of course be mounted anywhere within, even its value is not too important, 10kΩ to 100kΩ will do nicely.

Construction

The receiver is housed on one printed board made from double-sided laminate. Fig 37 shows the underside; the upper side remains a continuous copper earth plate. Where components pass through holes to be soldered to underside conductor tracks, a clearance is made in the upper foil either by a small drill or by etching. There is one conductor track to be laid on the upper surface between pin 12 of IC2 and R35, see Fig 38.

Inside top view

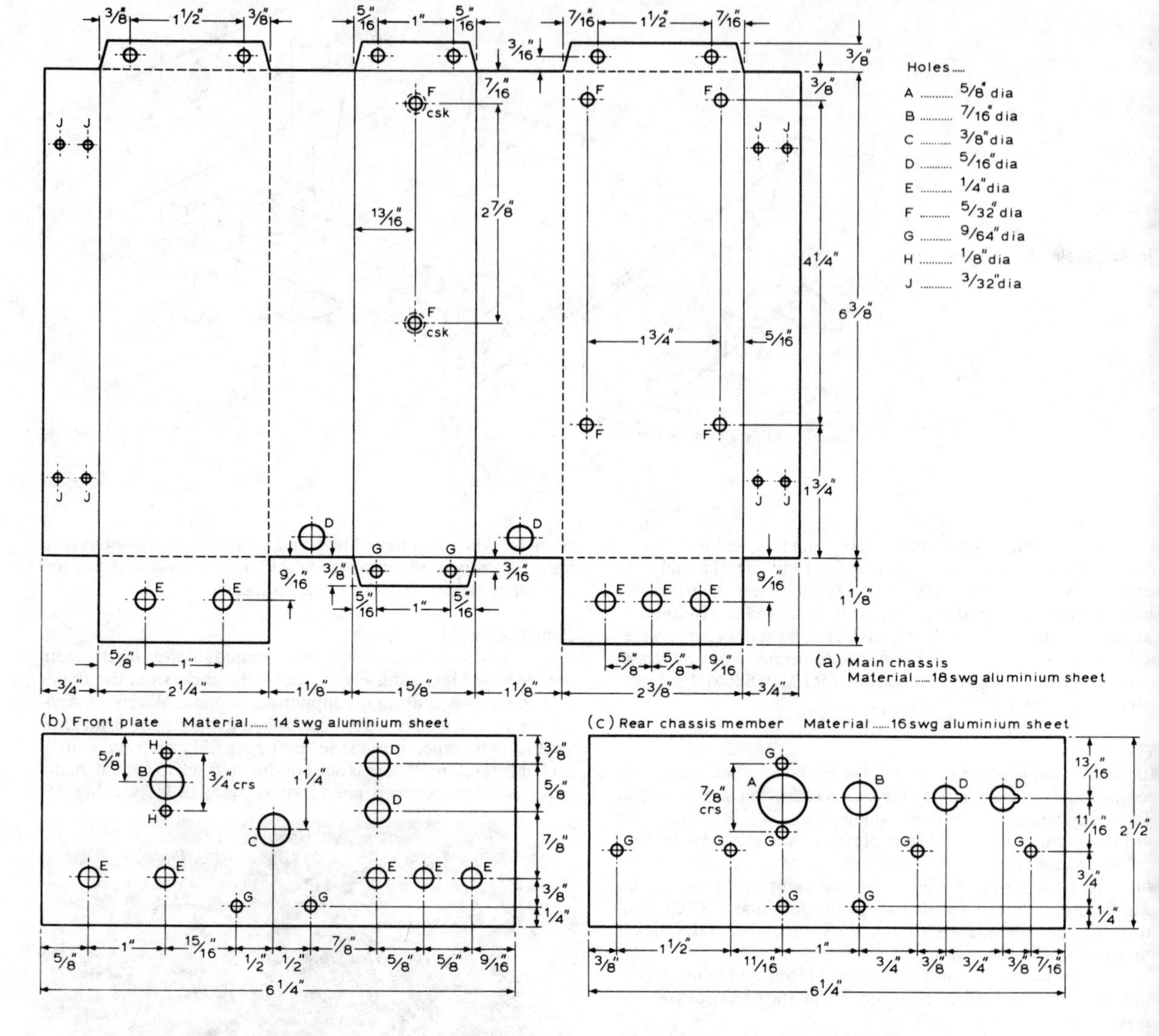

Fig 46. (a) Chassis main member blank. (b) Front plate dimensions. (c) Rear plate dimensions

Where components connect to earth, their wires solder on to the upper foil.

The screens between rf, mixer and the oscillator stages, also the screen round L6, L7 forming T1, are made from a ½in strip of tinplate soldered to the upper earth copper foil.

Not all the ic pins are connected: clearance should be made even if the underside contacts go nowhere. Those to which this applies are IC2 pins 8 and 9; IC3 pins 1, 2, 3, 4, 8, 9 and 13; IC4 pins 6, 9 and 13. Some ic pins are soldered to the upper foil; their holes should be drilled but the upper copper not cleared around the pins, the pins being soldered directly to the foil. These are IC2 pin 7, IC3 pin 7, IC4 pins 3, 4, 5, 7, 10, 11 and 12. If a TBA120 is fitted for IC1, pins 1, 3, 4 and 12 are earthed as described, but pin 5 is left unearthed and disconnected, with copper clearance. If an S-041-P is fitted for IC1, pin 5 should be earthed along with 1, 3, 4 and 12.

Coils with a large number of turns, such as L6, 7, 8 and 9, are better wound and doped with cellulose varnish, then left to harden before fitting. The Aladdin formers make a tight fit into the $\frac{3}{16}$in holes but may be glued for extra strength. Where coils have only a few turns of a heavier gauge, such as L2 to L5, it is easier to fit the formers, wind the coils on, say, a $\frac{3}{16}$in drill shank, form the leads, then drop into place over the formers and solder.

The number of channels fitted is a matter of personal choice; in the prototype provision has been made for nine channels.

Trimming should not be required once C48 has been set for one channel. The crystal sockets are fitted to a strip of metal which is attached to the front panel, stood off by spacers.

Two wires from the board connect to the crystal bank and its switch: one from the tap on L4 (one turn from the cold end) and one from point "B", the emitter of TR3.

A $2\frac{1}{2}$in 8Ω speaker is fitted into the cabinet lid and connected via a switched phone jack.

The volume control RV1, a 50kΩ log, and the squelch control RV2, a 1MΩ lin, both miniature types, are fitted into the front panel.

It was suggested earlier that as Mu-Rata filters might be difficult to obtain, it should be possible to fit one of the cheaper and readily available Toko range such as CFT, CFU or the CFX. Fig 47 shows how it is possible to modify Fig 37 to accommodate the CFU-455 type filter. The area of circuit between TR9 and TR6, 7 is involved: only R19 is removed, all other components remain in their original positions. There is one addition, a 0·01μF disc ceramic capacitor connected from the new hole adjacent to R23 to earth.

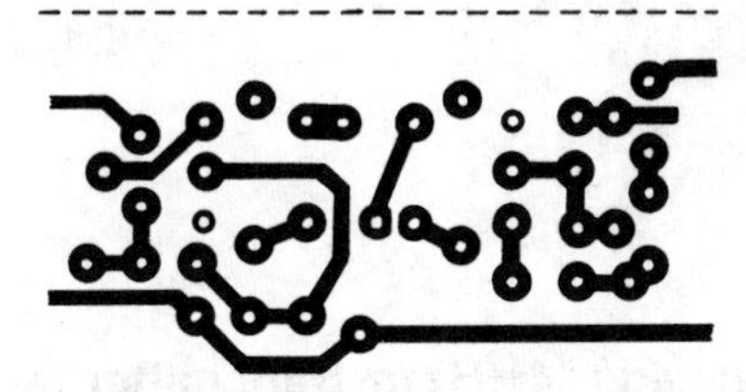

Fig 47. Modifications to Fig 37 for CFU455 filter

The transmitter rf board, Fig 40, is built on double-sided copper laminate but, unlike the receiver, the upper copper area is used entirely as an earth plate. It is advisable to clear round all the holes in the top foil before commencing assembly, except for the two holes, one either side of C145. Screens made from $\frac{1}{2}$in tinplate strips are soldered to the upper surface as shown in Fig 41; start by fitting the long central screen, then add the three dividers left to right. TR106 and TR107 emitter leads should not be more than 2mm long soldered directly to the upper copper earth foil, by bending carefully 1mm from the header to form an "L".

Alignment

There is little in the receiver alignment unfamiliar to constructors. Some form of rf indication, such as a one-turn pickup loop and meter or vvm, is useful in setting up the crystal oscillator and multiplier, and the second oscillator TR5. The onset of oscillation in L4 is quite abrupt and will only be maintained over about one turn of the slug.

Discriminator alignment requires a signal generator set to 455kHz at −40dB applied to IC1 pin 14 through an isolation capacitor, and a vvm connected to pin 8. The voltage at pin 8 should be noted before signal is applied; a reading of about 7V can be expected. With signal now applied and L8 adjusted, the needle will deflect slowly one way, say up to 10V, then swing rapidly but linearly to the other extreme, about 4V, finally returning towards its original reading. The slug should be adjusted so that the needle reads mid-way between the two extremes; that is the original voltage, 7V in our example. The actual voltage will vary a little from ic to ic; the S-041-P will be about 5V.

Once the detector and T2 have been set up at exactly 455kHz and T1 peaked at 10·7MHz, all the other coils can be tuned for maximum output on either an actual station or the signal generator set to a known channel number. Once a station is received, C140 can be adjusted for accurate tuning and will not require further adjustment on other stations.

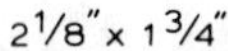

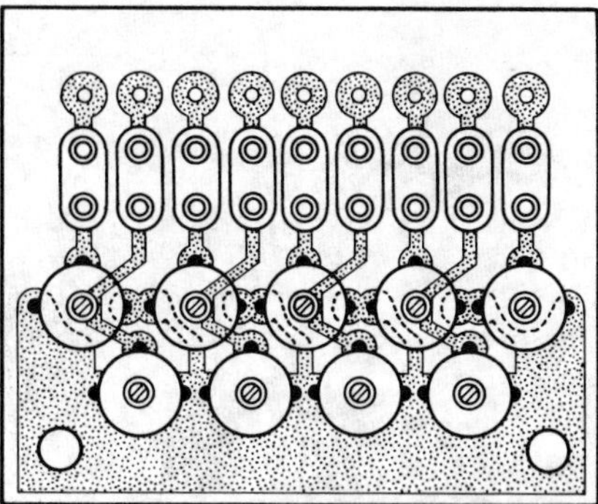

48. Transmitter crystal bank layout

When aligning the transmitter a wavemeter, rf pick-up loop and indicator are essential. The oscillator will start without problem. Place loop over L101 and tune up for maximum; this will not be its final setting as further adjustment is required later. Place pick-up loop over L102 and also pickup from wavemeter. As L102 is peaked for maximum, make very sure the frequency is actually 36MHz as false readings are possible. Bring L103 into line similarly at 72MHz, again checking for true frequency. Examine for output at 48MHz and 84MHz; the 36MHz and 72MHz selection is quite clear but easily mistaken.

Some form of load is now important if not already connected. An 8V or 12V 0·15A dial bulb mounted into a coaxial plug is a useful aid. Adjust L104 using pickup loop, then transfer to L106 and adjust C141 and L104 again. Move the loop to L108, adjusting C144 for some indication. All adjustments between L104 and C144, that is L104, C141, C142, C143 and C144, should be repeated over and over again as inter-electrode capacitances vary with increasing power; constant re-adjustment is necessary. By this time the bulb will have started to glow; adjust C145 for maximum brightness.

There are three more important final adjustments. Return to L102 and with the lightest coupling possible which will produce a full-scale indication on the wavemeter, adjust for 36MHz, watching the output on the bulb. Similarly carefully set L103 for 72MHz and then peak L104. These can now be regarded as set and one must reject the temptation to keep giving them a tweak. Replace the bulb with a load whose impedance is nearer to that expected in use. Some form of indication will be needed, so one may either feed a dummy 50Ω or 75Ω load via an swr bridge or feed an actual antenna set up in the shack where a field strength reading may be taken. Whichever method is adopted, tune C145 for greatest output, then re-peak C144 carefully for maximum. C141, 142, and 143 may be gently adjusted but use a well-insulated trimming tool to prevent stray pickup.

The final adjustment requires someone else's receiver. As L101 acts as a phasing control, linear modulation depends on its accurate setting, regardless of the deviation setting. It is simple to connect an oscilloscope to the other receiver loudspeaker and apply a sine wave to the microphone socket. Advance the deviation control to about half-way and observe the waveform. Carefully adjust the L101 slug either way. Although already peaked for maximum drive, there will be a fairly fine setting where the waveform is perfect, assuming the receiver is OK anyway; all other settings will produce little moduation and heavy distortion.

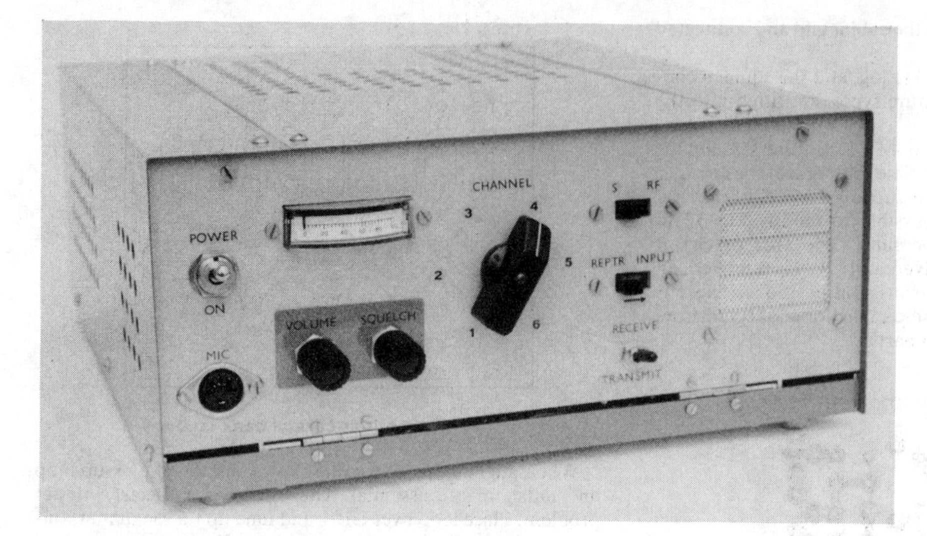

General view of the channelized 144MHz fm transmitter/receiver

The crystal trimmer C140 will require setting for every channel where a crystal is fitted. If the other chap's receiver has an S-meter, the job becomes simpler.

As the audio circuit has a speech clipper, audio gain must not be mistaken for deviation. An oscilloscope check at the R124/R125 junction will show the onset of clipping from the microphone to be used. If gain adjustment is in fact necessary, this can only be done by changing R120. It is a good plan therefore to check the audio circuit before the rf board is connected or before fitting it into the chassis. It is not intended that the clipper be used as full speech processing but only as a safeguard against over-deviation when raising the voice, etc. Deviation is set either with a deviation meter if available or against a known receiver. The deviation control is finally set to just short of full rotation. This completes the testing and alignment.

Channelized 144MHz fm transmitter/receiver

This design was originally described by N. G. Hyde, G2AIH, in *Radio Communication* May 1978. The receiver is a single conversion superhet with an i.f. of 10·7MHz. Phase modulation is employed in the transmitter, which has a maximum input to the pa stage of 20W. Operation is from a 12V dc supply, with the maximum current consumption (on transmit) being of the order of 2A. Modular construction on printed circuit boards has been adopted for both receiver and transmitter.

During development of the receiver, strong interference on channel R5 was experienced from a local business radio transmitter. This was eliminated by the addition of a helical filter at the antenna input, constructed in accordance with the information given in Chapter 7. The filter was found to be so effective that it has been incorporated permanently in the antenna feeder

Receiver local oscillator (earlier six-crystal version shown)

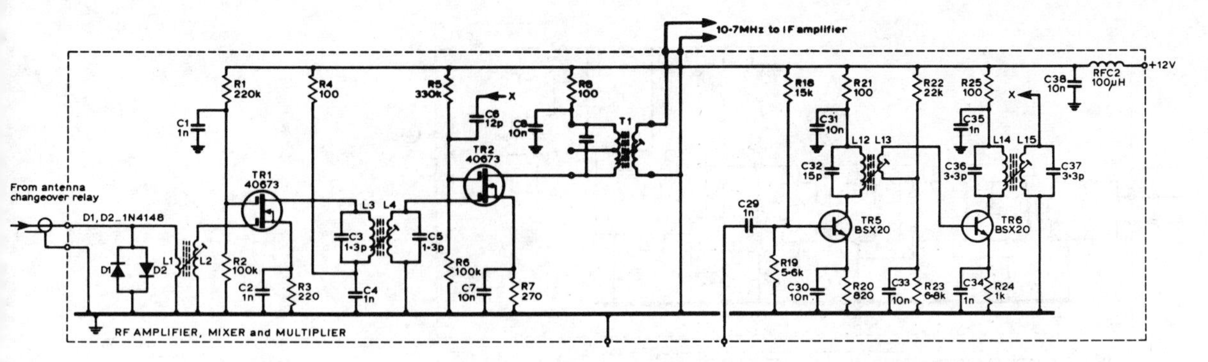

Fig 49(a). RF amplifier, mixer and multiplier. C29 is connected to C27 of Fig 49(b)

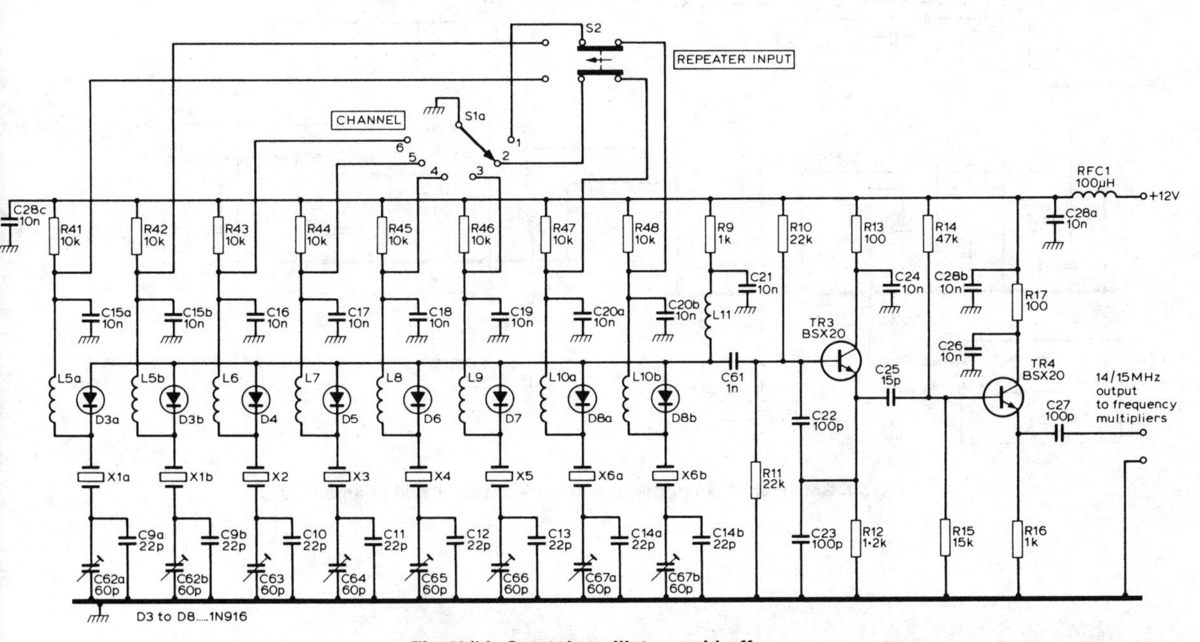

Fig 49(b). Crystal oscillator and buffer

subsequent to the changeover relay; for this reason a harmonic filter has not been included in the transmitter pa stage.

Receiver (Figs 49 and 50)

The converter (Fig 49) consists of two circuit boards, one for the crystal oscillator and buffer, while the second carries the rf amplifier, mixer and frequency multiplier circuitry.

The receiver front-end is conventional and employs dual-gate mosfets TR1 and TR2 as rf amplifier and mixer respectively, with the input to TR1 protected by back-to-back shunt diodes D1 and D2. The two stages are coupled through a bandpass circuit L3, C3 and L4, C5.

Fundamental frequency parallel-resonance crystals in the 14 to 15MHz range are employed in the local oscillator. Eight crystals in the base circuit of TR3 are connected through series diodes D3 to D8, and 12V dc is applied via R9 and L11 to their commoned anodes. Any one crystal is selected by S1a (CHANNEL) which earths the cathode of the particular diode through a series inductor (L5 to L10). This diode then conducts and presents a very low resistance in series with the crystal; all other crystals are isolated from the circuit by the high series resistance of the five non-conducting diodes.

Positions 1 and 2 of S1 are allocated to repeater channels with the four simplex channels occupying positions 3 to 6. With S1 set to position 1 or 2, operation of the slide switch S2 changes the crystal in circuit from the repeater output channel to the input channel, to permit monitoring on the input frequency.

Crystal frequencies are set to the exact sub-multiple of the oscillator injection frequency by the film-dielectric trimmers C62-67 in series with the crystals.

Output from the emitter-follower buffer TR4 is coupled to the frequency tripler stages TR5 and TR6 on the mixer board. The local oscillator injection frequency, in the 134MHz range (f_s–10·7) is applied via a bandpass circuit L14, C36, L15, C37 to gate 2 of the mixer TR2.

Fig 50 shows the circuitry of the i.f. amplifier, quadrature

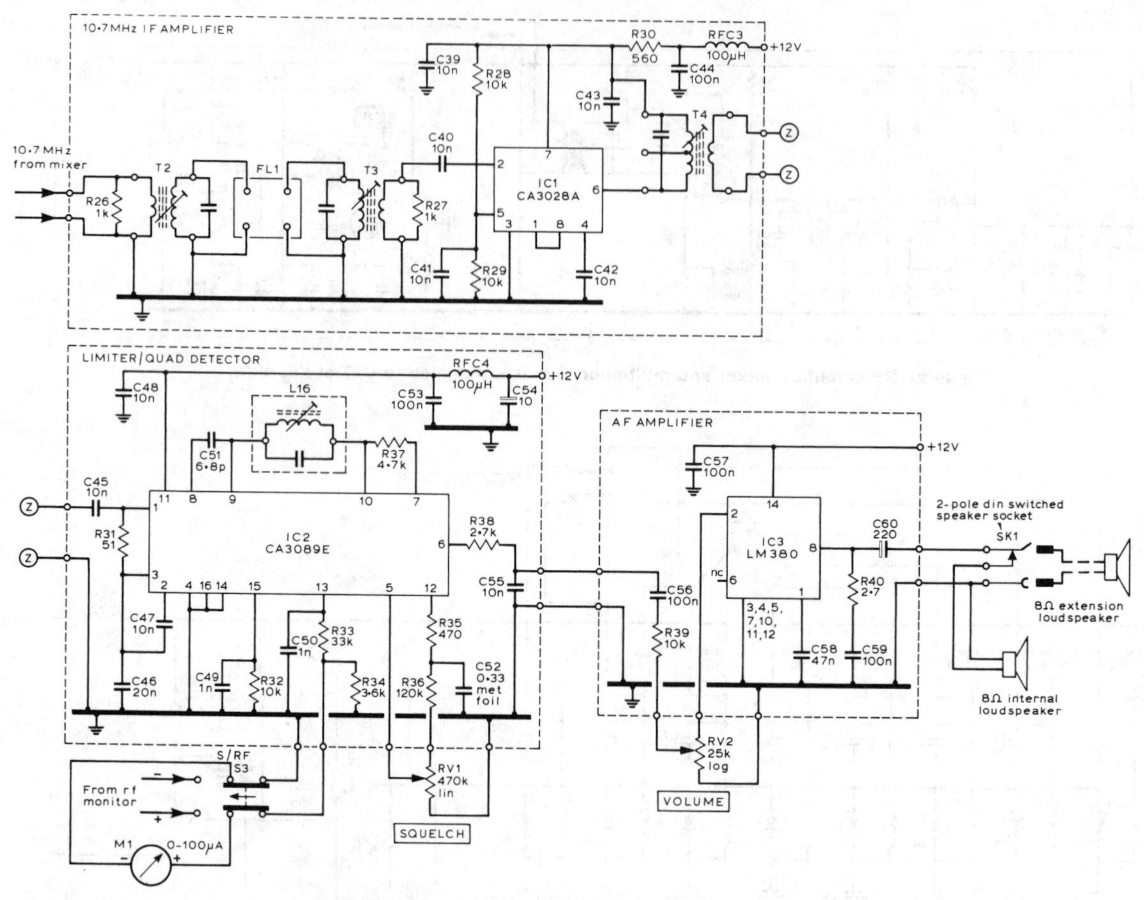

Fig 50. Receiver i.f. amplifier, quadrature detector and af amplifier

Receiver (r to l): mixer, i.f amplifier and quadrature detector with af amplifier at rear

letector and audio-frequency amplifier. Intermediate fre-quency output at 10·7MHz from T1 on the mixer board is ipplied to the crystal filter FL1; T2 and T3 are the filter input and output matching transformers, terminated by R26 and R27 espectively. IC1, a CA3028A connected in cascode configura-ion, functions as a 10·7MHz i.f. amplifier; the output of this ic s coupled via T4 to IC2, a CA3089E which combines the unctions of limiter, quadrature detector and low-level af amp-ifier. Circuitry associated with this ic follows the recommenda-ions given by RCA Ltd in their application note. L16, with its issociated parallel capacitance, forms the quadrature detector uned circuit.

The CA3089E also incorporates a squelch facility, controlled by RV1 (SQUELCH). It also provides a voltage for operating an external tuning meter (M1) which is connected into circuit hrough a double-pole slide switch S3, allowing the meter to be used to monitor the rf output of the transmitter. The meter employed in this application is a 0–100 microammeter shunted by R34 to give an fsd of 150μA; if the meter used has an nternal resistance different from the one specified, it will be necessary to change the value of R34.

Recovered audio from the CA3089E is applied via RV2 (VOLUME) to IC3, an LM380 af amplifier which drives an nternal 8Ω 1¾in diameter monitor speaker, or an external speaker plugged into the 2-pole DIN switched socket SK1. The LM380 has a rated af output of approximately 1·5W; this is adequate for fixed station use, but in situations having a high ambient noise level, eg mobile operations, it would be an advantage to include a single-transistor amplifier stage after the CA3089E, and to substitute an ic having a higher audio rating, eg a TBA810AS, for the LM380.

Table 7. Receiver components list

R1	220kΩ	R20	820Ω
R2, 6	100kΩ	R23	6·8kΩ
R3	220Ω	R28, 29, 32, 39, 41 to 48	10kΩ
R4, 8, 13, 17, 21, 25	100Ω	R30	560Ω
R7	270Ω	R31	51Ω
R9, 16, 24, 26, 27	1kΩ	R33	33kΩ
R10, 11, 22	22kΩ	R34	3·6kΩ
R12	1·2kΩ	R35	470Ω
R14	47kΩ	R36	120kΩ
R15, 18	15kΩ	R37	4·7kΩ
R19	5·6kΩ	R38	2·7kΩ
		R40	2·7Ω
All fixed resistors are ⅛W carbon film			
RV1	470kΩ linear	RV2	25kΩ log
C1, 2, 4, 29, 34, 35, 49, 50, 61	1nF	C22, 23, 27	100pF
C3, 5	1·3pF	C25, 32	15pF
C6	12pF	C36, 37	3·3pF
C7, 8, 15, 16, 17, 18, 19, 20, 21, 24, 26, 28, 30, 31, 33, 38, 39, 40, 41, 42, 43, 45, 47, 48, 55	10nF	C44, 53, 56, 57, 59	100nF
C9, 10, 11, 12, 13, 14	22pF	C46	20nF
		C51	6·8pF
		C52	0·33μF met foil
		C54	10μF elect
		C58	47nF
		C60	220μF elect
		C62, 63, 64, 65, 66, 67	60pF max preset
All capacitors except electrolytics are miniature 50V ceramics.			
D1, 2	1N4148	IC1	CA3028A
D3 to D8	1N916	IC2	CA3089E
TR1, 2	40673	IC3	LM380
TR3, 4, 5, 6	BSX20		
L1	2t 22swg enam	Wound on 4mm diam formers, with dust-iron cores	
L2, 3, 14	4t 22swg enam		
L4, 15	5t 22swg enam		
L12	15t 26swg enam		
L13	2t 24swg enam		
L5 to L11	Toko Type 7BA		
L16	Toko K586 10·7MHz quad detector coil		
RFC1, 2, 3, 4	Toko Type 7BA		
T1, 4	Toko KALS 1506 10·7MHz i.f. transformer		
T2, 3	Toyocom 10B-10 filter matching transformer		
FL1	Toyocom 10M-5B-1 or 10M-4B-1 10·7MHz crystal filter		
X1 to X6	14/15MHz range fundamental frequency parallel resonance, 30pF capacitance, HC25U holder		
SK1	2-pin DIN switched speaker socket		
S1	3-pole 6-way wafer switch		
S2, 3	DPCO slide switch		
M1	100μA fsd Ernest Turner edgewise meter		

Transmitter (Figs 51 and 52)

The circuit and method of channel switching used in the trans-mitter crystal oscillator are similar to that employed in the receiver local oscillator with the exception that the supply vol-tage to the oscillator (TR1) is stabilized at 10V by ZD1. Cryst-als are in the 12MHz range, the transmitter having a multiplica-tion factor of 12 to reach the final radiated frequency.

The 12MHz output from the emitter of TR1 is applied to the phase modulator, which consists basically of the capacitance-coupled inductors L8 and L9, and the two biased variable-capacitance diodes D7 and D8. L8 and L9 are individually screened, and coupling between the tuned circuits is by C22 only. Bias voltage for D7 and D8 is stabilized by ZD2.

The speech amplifier TR4, TR5 and TR6, is suitable for use with a crystal microphone. TR5 is followed by a speech clipper consisting of D9 and D10 connected back-to-back across the output circuit of the transistor. Input to the clipper is adjusted by a preset control RV1, while R29 and C41 form a filter to minimize harmonics of the speech waveform generated by the clipping action. Clipped audio is amplified by TR6 and applied to the phase modulator diodes via a potential divider R6, R7 and R8. The present control RV2 sets the deviation level.

The 1,750Hz access tone generator employs a dual NAND Schmitt trigger SN7413 (IC1). Frequency of oscillation is determined by RV3 in conjunction with R35 and R36, the function of the two fixed resistors being to provide a fine adjustment by the preset control RV3. Duration of the toneburst is dependent on the values of C45 and R34; increas-ing the value of capacitance and decreasing the resistance results in an increased length of toneburst. Power supply to the generator is stabilized at 5·1V by ZD3, and this is applied only when Slc is set to positions 1 and 2, to give automatic toneburst on repeater channels. Output is taken through C47 and the preset variable resistor RV4, which controls the deviation level, to the phase modulator.

Phase-modulated rf at 12MHz is applied to the emitter-follower buffer TR2. The next stage, TR3, is a frequency tre-bler with L10, C30 tuned to the third harmonic (36MHz).

Fig 52 shows the circuit of the frequency multiplier and amplifier boards. The 36MHz output from the first multiplier is fed through a 50Ω coaxial link and capacitive tap on the input tuned circuit to the doubler stage TR7. Both TR7 and TR8 are frequency doublers. Interstage and output coupling is by loosely-coupled tuned circuits with capacitive dividers for

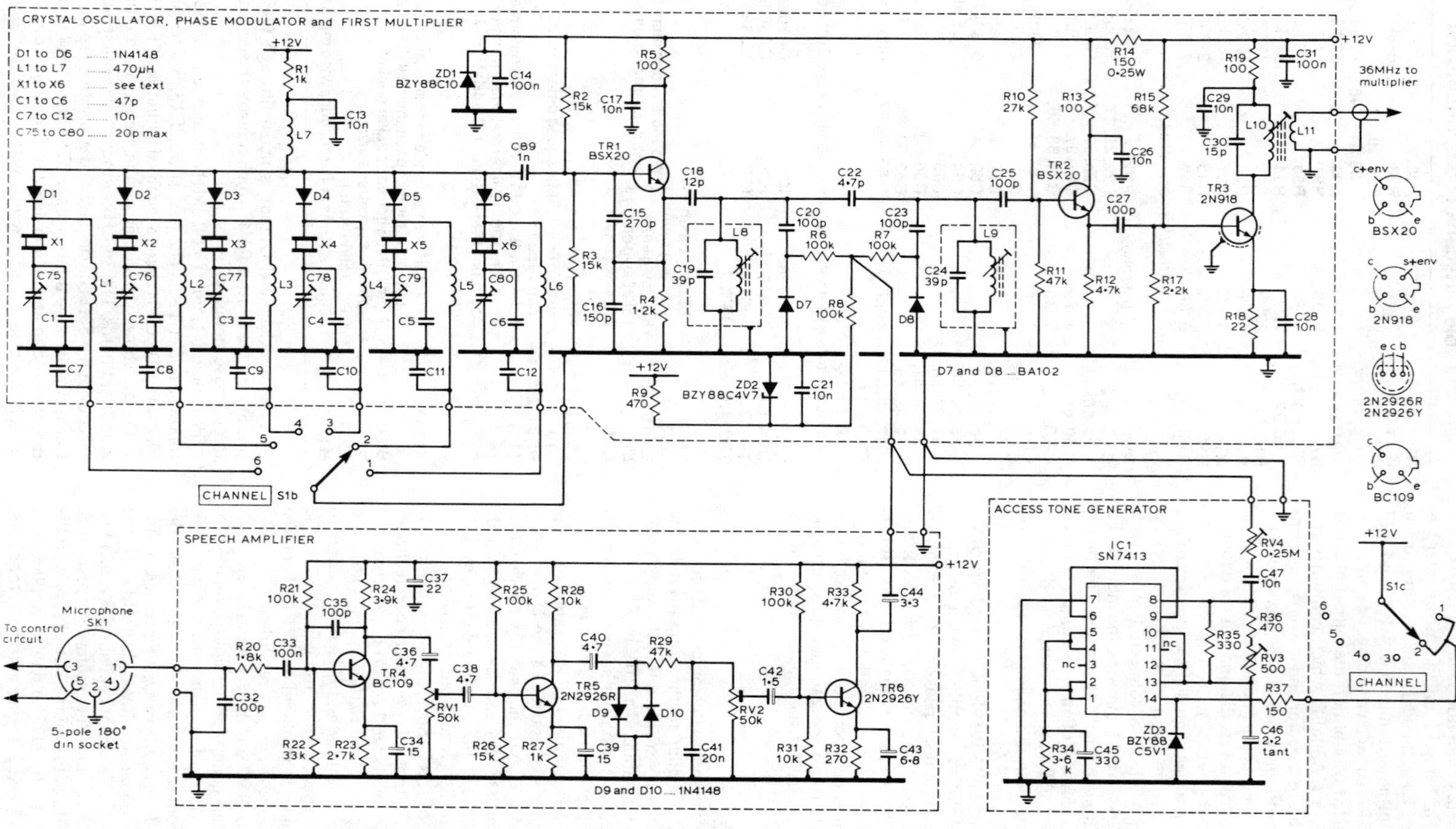

Fig 51. Transmitter oscillator and phase modulator, speech amplifier and access tone generator

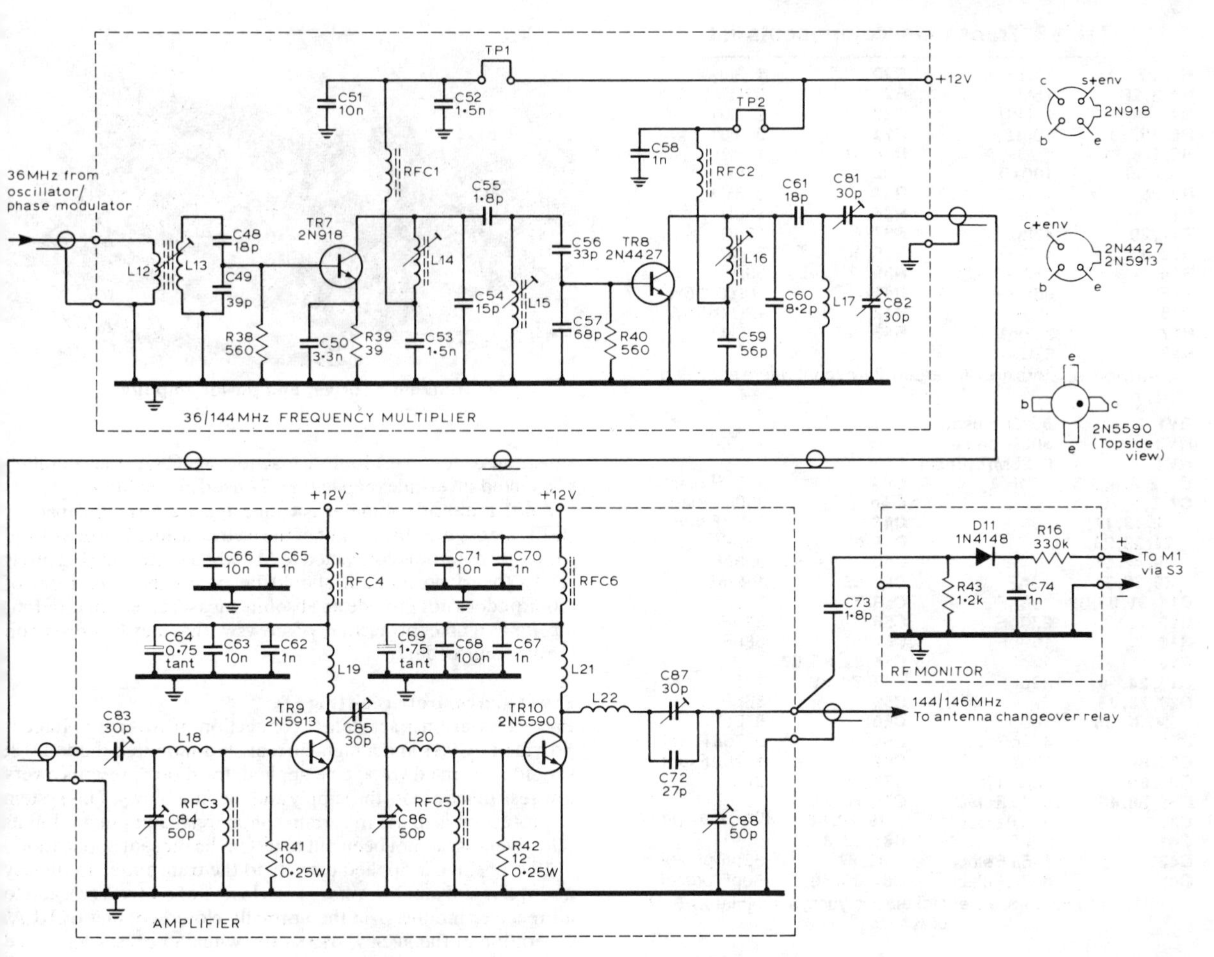

Fig 52. Transmitter frequency multiplier and power amplifier

impedance matching, the 50Ω output line being matched to TR8 by preset air-spaced trimmers C81 and C82. Test points TP1 and TP2 allow the collector current of the doubler stages to be monitored during alignment.

The 145MHz amplifier consists of two zero-biased Class C stages, of which TR9 is a driver and TR10 is the final power amplifier. Interstage matching circuits are employed at the input to TR9 and between the two stages, the base circuits of the transistors being slightly damped by R41 and R42. Matching between the collector tuned circuit of TR10 and the 50Ω output line is achieved by C87 and C88. All variable capacitors in the amplifer are preset air-dielectric types; if a 50pF preset is

Transmitter oscillator, phase modulator and first multiplier, with access tone generator on right

36/144MHz frequency multiplier

Table 8. Transmitter components list

R1, 27	1kΩ	R20	1·8kΩ
R2, 3, 26	15kΩ	R22	33kΩ
R4	1·2kΩ	R23	2·7kΩ
R5, 13, 19	100Ω	R24	3·9kΩ
R6, 7, 8, 21,		R28, 31	10kΩ
25, 30	100kΩ	R32	270Ω
R9, 36	470Ω	R34	3·6kΩ
R10	27kΩ	R35	330Ω
R11, 29	47kΩ	R37	150Ω
R12, 33	4·7kΩ	R38, 40	560Ω
R14	150Ω 0·25W	R39	39Ω
R15	68kΩ	R41	10Ω 0·25W
R16	330kΩ	R42	12Ω 0·25W
R17	2·2kΩ	R43	1·2kΩ
R18	22Ω		

All fixed resistors are ⅛W carbon film except where specified

RV1, 2	50kΩ preset		
RV3	500Ω preset		
RV4	0·25MΩ preset		
C1, 2, 3, 4, 5, 6	47pF	C44	3·3µF elect
C7, 8, 9, 10, 11,		C45	330µF elect
12, 13, 17,		C46	2·2µF tant
21, 26, 28,		C48, 61	18pF
29, 47, 51,		C50	3·3nF
63, 66, 71	10nF	C52, 53	1·5nF
C14, 31, 33, 68	100nF	C55, 73	1·8pF
C15	270pF	C56	33pF
C16	150pF	C57	68pF
C18	12pF	C58, 62, 65, 67,	
C19, 24, 49	39pF	70, 74, 89	1nF
C20, 23, 25,		C59	56pF
27, 32, 35	100pF	C60	8·2pF
C22	4·7pF	C64	0·75µF tant
C30, 54	15pF	C69	1·75µF tant
C34, 39	15µF elect	C72	27pF
C36, 38, 40	4·7µF elect	C75, 76, 77,	
C37	22µF elect	78, 79, 80	20pF max preset
C41	20nF	C81, 82, 83,	
C42	1·5µF elect	85, 87	30pF preset
C43	6·8µF elect	C84, 86, 88	50pF preset

All fixed capacitors, except for electrolytics, are miniature 50V ceramics

D1, 2, 3, 4, 5,		TR1, 2	BSX20
6, 9, 10, 11	1N4148	TR3, 7	2N918
D7, 8	BA102	TR4	BC109
ZD1	BZY88C10	TR5	2N2926R
ZD2	BZY88C4V7	TR6	2N2926Y
ZD3	BZY88C5V1	TR8	2N4427
		TR9	2N5913
IC1	SN7413	TR10	2N5590

L1 to L7	Toko Type 7BA
L8, 9	17½t 28swg enam, 4mm former, ferrite core
L10	12½t 28swg enam, 4mm former, ferrite core
L11	4½t 28swg enam
L12	3½t 28swg enam
L13	12½t 28swg enam, 4mm former, dust-iron core
L14	6½t 26swg enam, 4mm former, dust-iron core
L15	4½t 26swg enam, 4mm former, dust-iron core
L16	2½t 20swg enam, 4mm former, dust-iron core
L17	3t 20swg enam, 6·4mm i.d.
L18, 20	3t 20swg enam, 5mm i.d
L19	4t 20swg enam, 5mm i.d.
L21	2t 20swg enam, 5mm i.d.
L22	3t 18swg enam, 5mm i.d.
RFC1, 2	2½t 28swg enam on FX1898 ferrite bead
RFC3, 5	2½t 26swg enam on FX1115 ferrite bead
RFC4, 6	2½t 26swg enam on FX1898 ferrite bead
X1 to X6	12MHz range fundamental frequency parallel resonance, 40pF capacitance, HC25U holder
SK1	5-pin 180° DIN socket

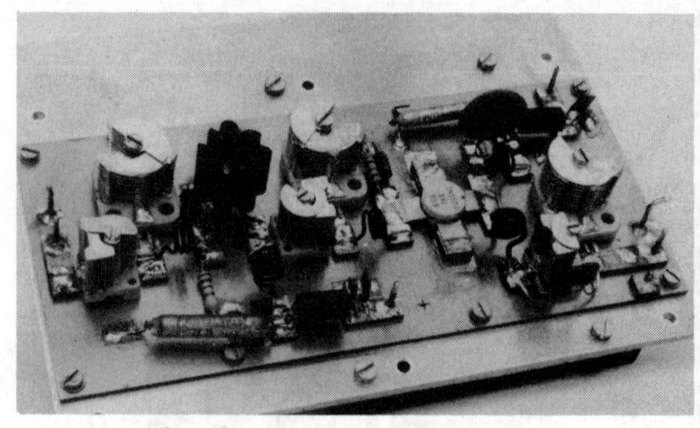

Transmitter driver and power amplifier

substituted for the 30pF capacitor at C87, the parallel-connected silver-mica capacitor C72 need not be fitted.

An rf monitor voltmeter is connected via a small capacitor (C73) across the 50Ω output of the pa transistor. The dc voltage from the monitor is connected to M1 when switch S3 (Fig 50) is set to the rf position. It should be noted that this form of monitor does not provide an absolute measurement of rf output insofar as it takes no account of any vswr that may be present on the antenna feeder.

Power and control circuit (Fig 53)

Protection against accidental connection of reverse voltage is provided by FS1 and a high-current stud-mounted diode D12; should a reversed voltage be applied, the diode presents a very low resistance across the supply and the fuse blows. This system of protection is in use in certain commercial equipment, but its effectiveness has not been put to test in the present application.

12V positive is applied directly to the transmitter frequency multiplier and amplifier stages on closure of S4 (POWER), and to all receiver modules via the normally-closed contact of RLA. Operation of the RECEIVE-TRANSMIT switch S5 causes RLA and the coaxial antenna change-over relay RLB to operate; RLA switches the 12V supply from the receiver to the transmitter oscillator/modulator, access tone generator and speech amplifier, and RLB switches the antenna from receiver input to transmitter output.

Provision is also made for receive-to-transmit change-over by a press-to-talk switch on the microphone through pins 3 and 5 of the microphone socket SK1 (Fig 51), these pins being connected in parallel with S5.

The power control relay RLA is a double-pole changeover type, with the two contact sets connected in parallel. As the contacts of the relay specified are rated to carry 1A, and in this equipment are only required to pass 100mA, the second contact set could be used to switch the monitor meter M1 in lieu of the manual changeover switch S3.

Constructional notes

The complete equipment is housed in a case measuring 10in wide by 4⅝in high by 11in deep; this is larger than necessary for the present application, but increased depth has been allowed

Table 9. Power and control unit components

RLA	Keyswitch Type SMP dpco relay, 12V coil
RLB	Magnetic Devices coaxial relay 50Ω, 12V coil

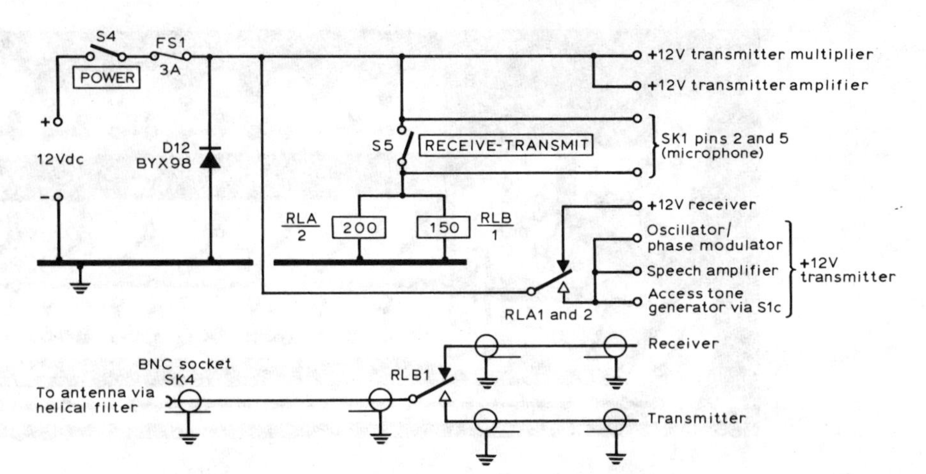

Fig 53. Power and control unit

to incorporate a higher power pa stage, eg 50W, which would be mounted towards the rear with an external heat sink. Space has also been allowed for inclusion of a low-noise rf preamplifier to improve the receiver performance. Top and side dust covers are detachable, and the front and rear panels are hinged to allow easy access for alignment and servicing.

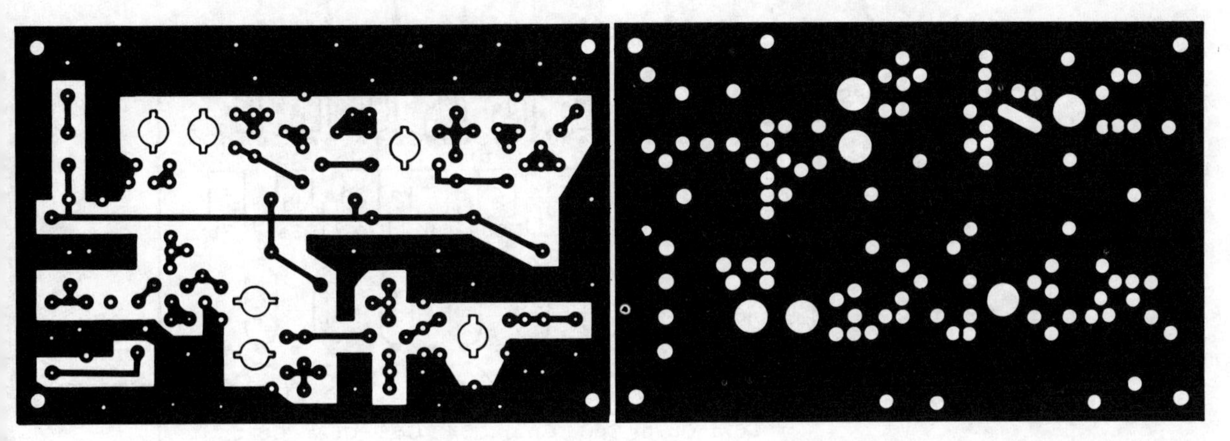

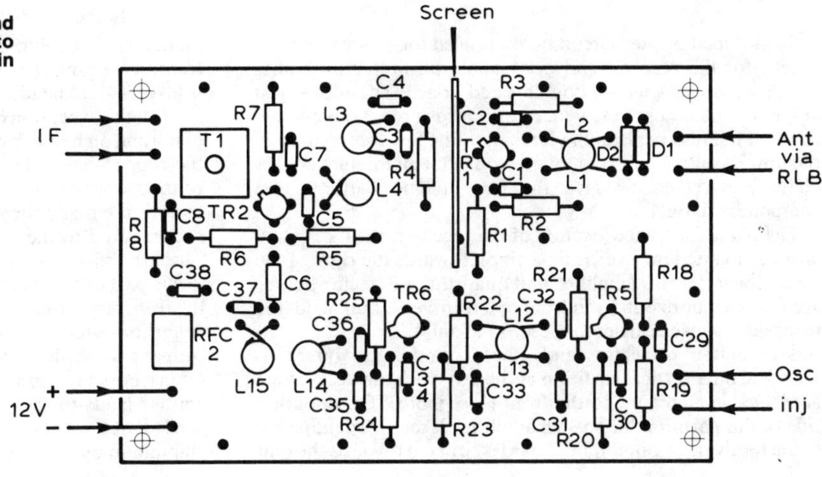

Fig 54. Receiver rf amplifier, mixer and multiplier board. Note that connectors to L4 and L15 are transposed to maintain correct phase relationship

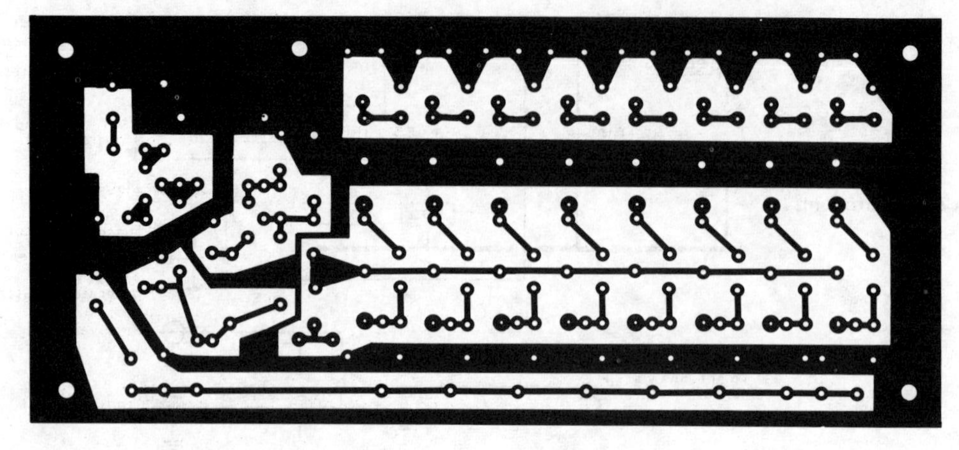

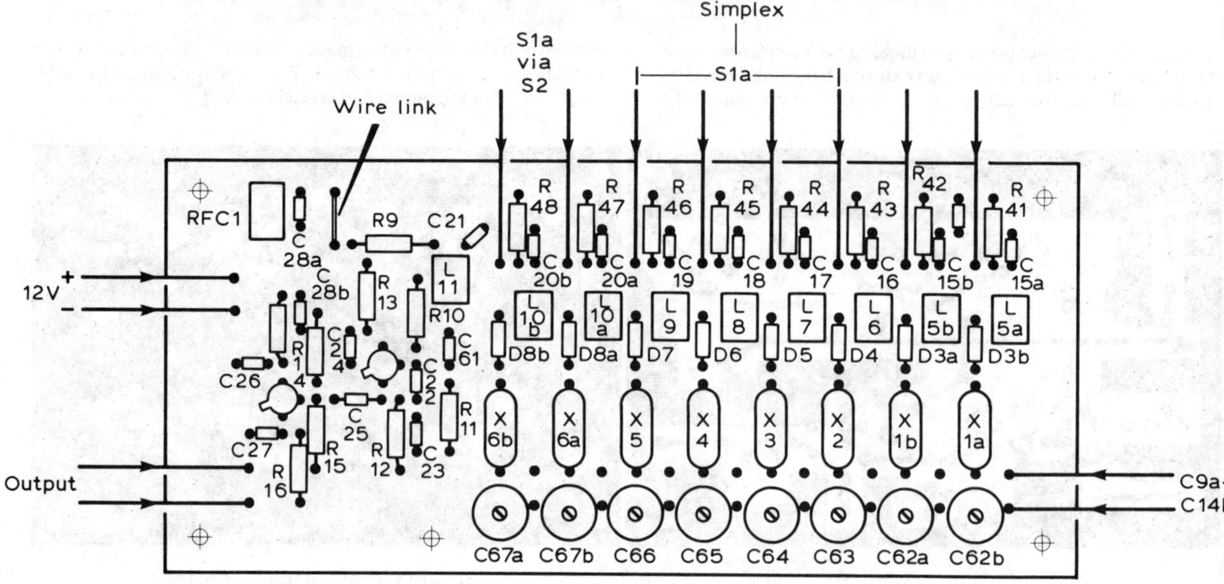

Fig 55. Receiver crystal oscillator and buffer amplifier pcb

Single-sided printed circuit board is used for sub-assemblies, except for the receiver converter and transmitter multiplier which are constructed on double-sided board. The receiver af amplifier and access tone generator boards are srbp laminate, all other boards are glassfibre laminate. The few components in the power control unit are mounted on a flat aluminium chassis plate. Figs 54 to 64 give the pcb etching patterns and component layouts.

The photos show the location of the receiver; the local oscillator is mounted on a vertical partition towards the right of the case. Converter, i.f. amplifier and quadrature detector boards are mounted horizontally in front of a transverse bulkhead, the front side of which carries the receiver af amplifier.

Transmitter oscillator and phase modulator board is mounted on a vertical partition at the left, with the access tone generator immediately to the front (see photo). On the other side of this partition the speech amplifier is mounted, adjacent to the receiver. The multiplier board is situated towards the rear immediately behind the oscillator/phase modulator, and the transmitter amplifier is mounted vertically on the rear of the transverse bulkhead.

With the exception of the transmitter amplifier, all boards are of normal etched pcb construction. For the amplifier, however, the copper-clad laminate serves as a ground plane only; interconnections between circuit elements, input and output terminations are made through small pads of $\frac{1}{16}$in copper-clad laminate secured to the ground plane by an epoxy resin adhesive. The ground plane is backed by $\frac{3}{32}$in aluminium sheet which forms part of the pa heat sink, and to which the pa transistor is fixed through a clearance hole in the ground plane. Emitter connections to this transistor are made through small $\frac{3}{32}$in thick copper pads soldered to the ground plane as close to the transistor as possible; considerable heat is required to solder the emitter leads to the copper pads, and this operation must be carried out with some care. An additional heat sink of $\frac{1}{4}$in aluminium plate, painted matt black, is bolted to the first heat

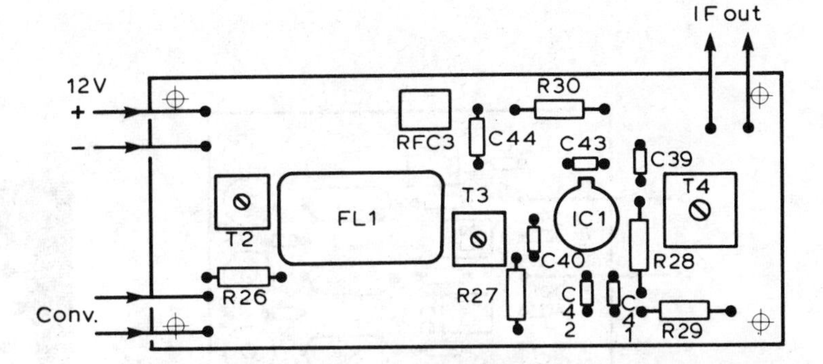

Fig 56. I.F. amplifier pcb

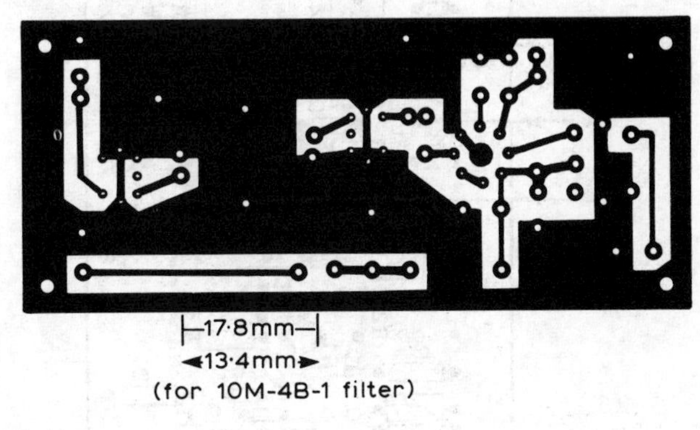

sink immediately behind the pa transistor (Fig 65). Silicon heat-sink grease (Thermaflow) is applied to the transistor mounting stud and between both parts of the heat sink before assembly.

Alignment

Alignment of both receiver and transmitter is straightforward and follows normal procedure. The only critical adjustment in receiver alignment is to the quadrature detector coil L16; the core of this inductor should first be tuned for maximum af output and then re-adjusted slightly to obtain the best speech quality. These two conditions may not be co-incident.

The two inductors L8 and L9 associated with the phase modulator should be adjusted for maximum rf output. Tuning of these circuits interacts to a certain extent, and adjustments to the cores should be made repetitively until the optimum condition is obtained.

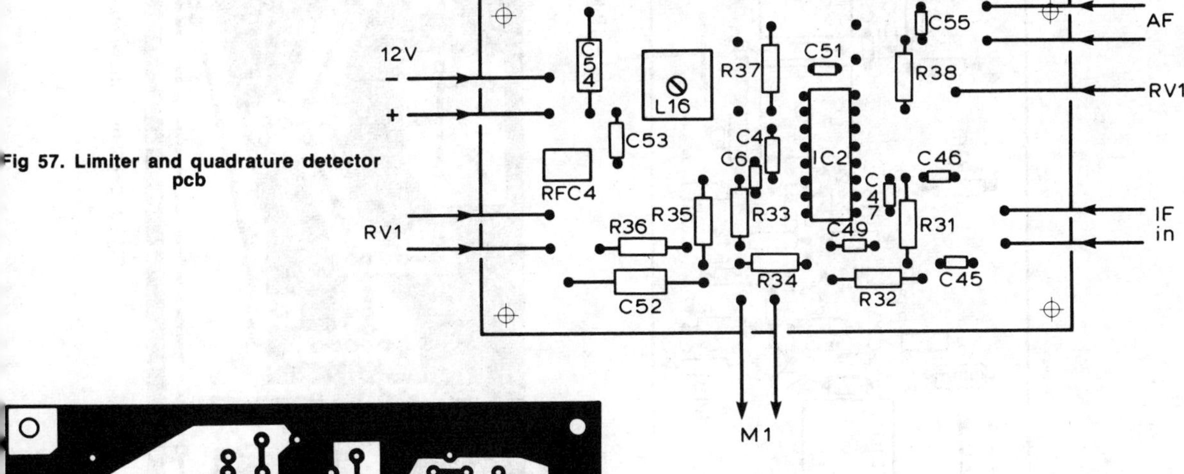

Fig 57. Limiter and quadrature detector pcb

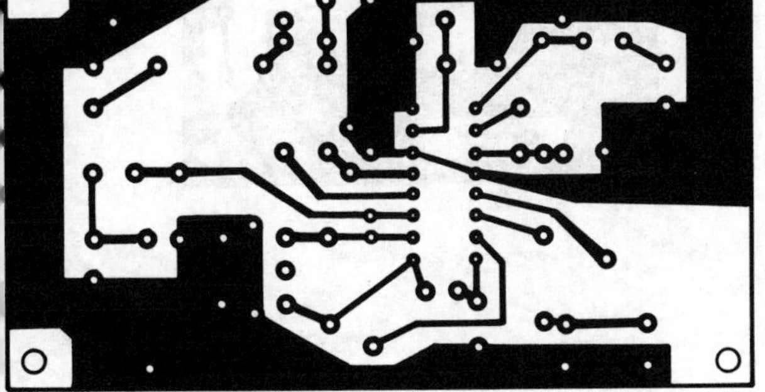

Table 10. Typical current readings (12V supply)

Receiver (no signal)		65mA
Access tone generator		50mA
Transmitter oscillator phase modulator		50mA
Transmitter multiplier	TR7	21mA
	TR8	65mA
Transmitter amplifier	TR9	150–200mA
	TR10	1·3–1·6A

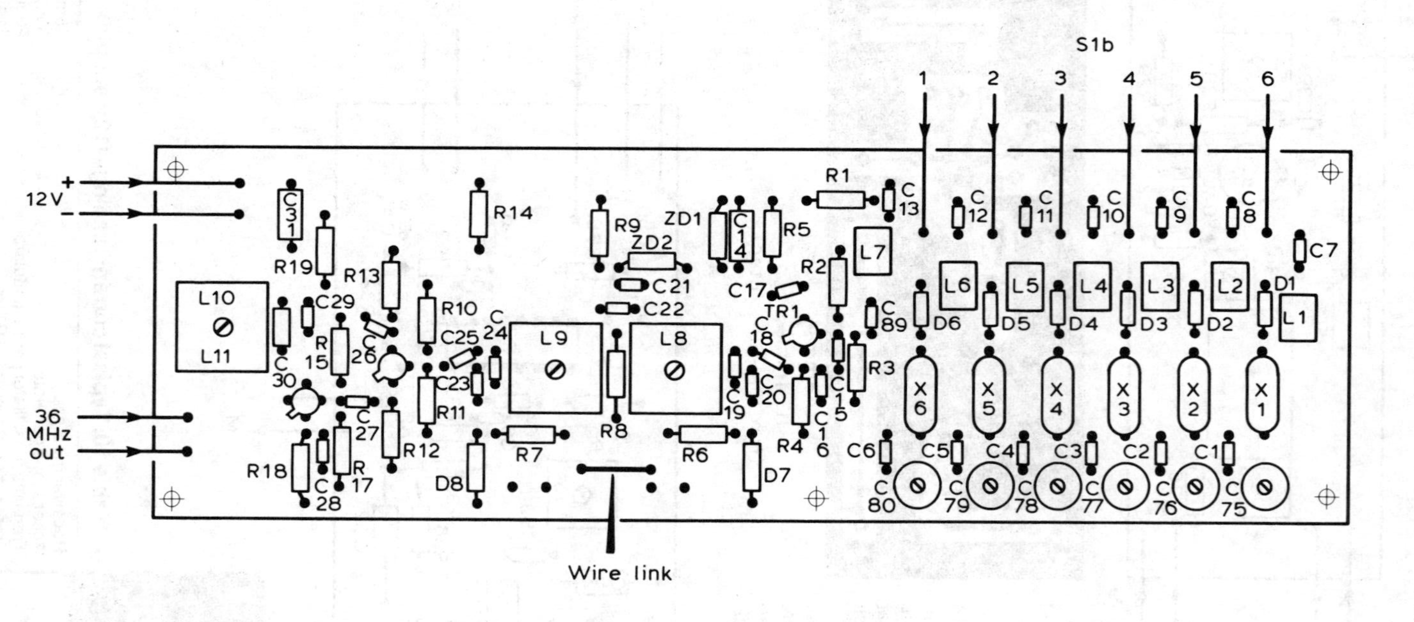

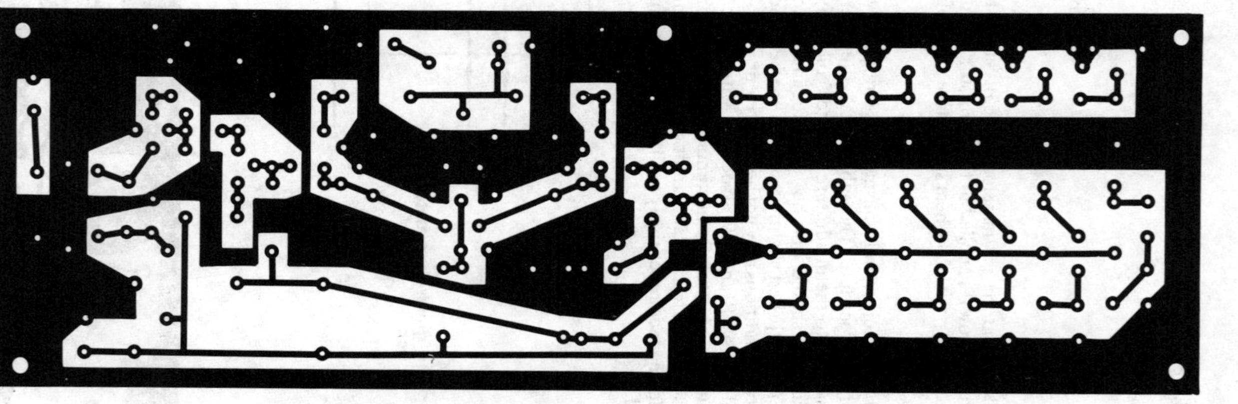

Fig 58. Oscillator, phase modulator and first multiplier pcb

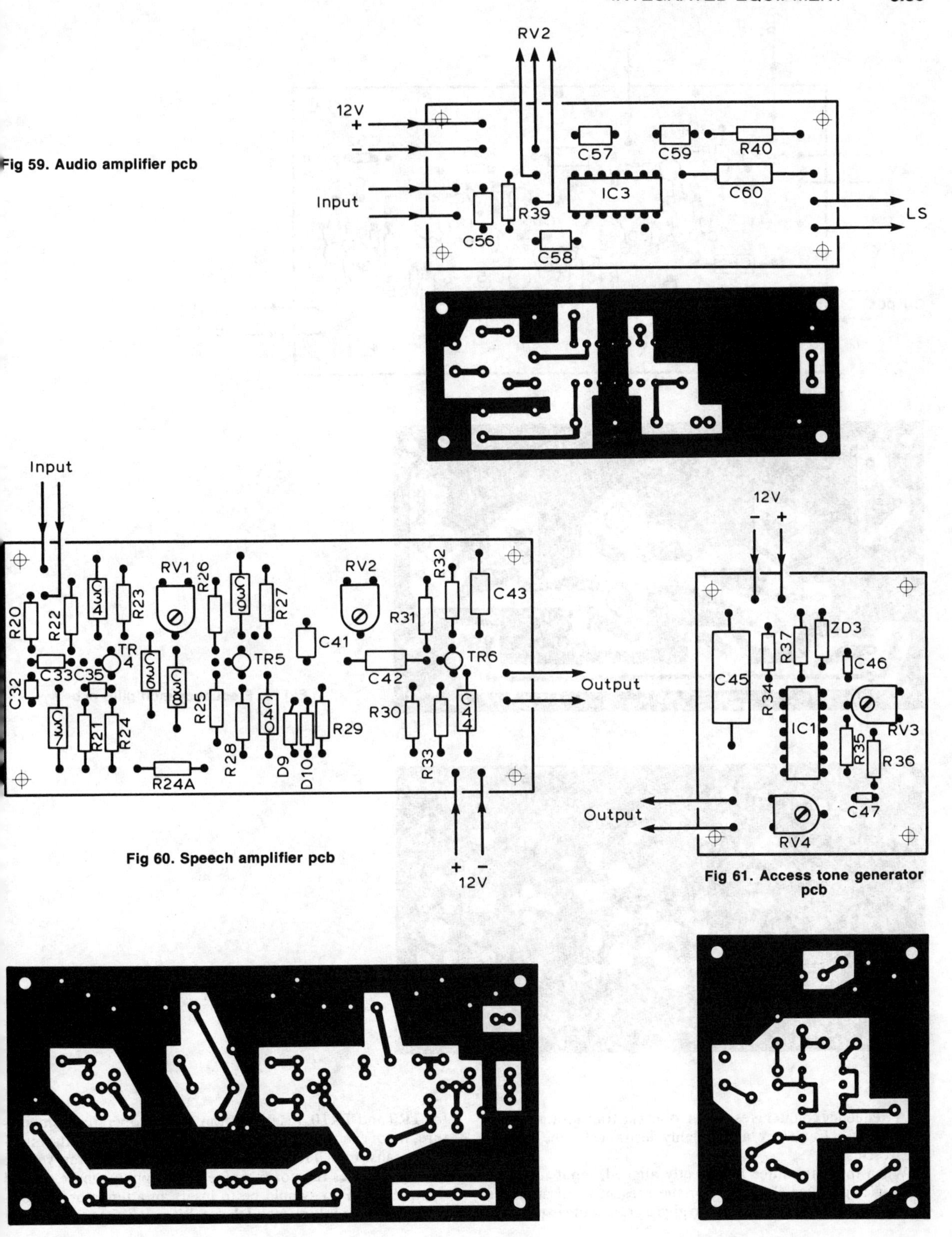

Fig 59. Audio amplifier pcb

Fig 60. Speech amplifier pcb

Fig 61. Access tone generator pcb

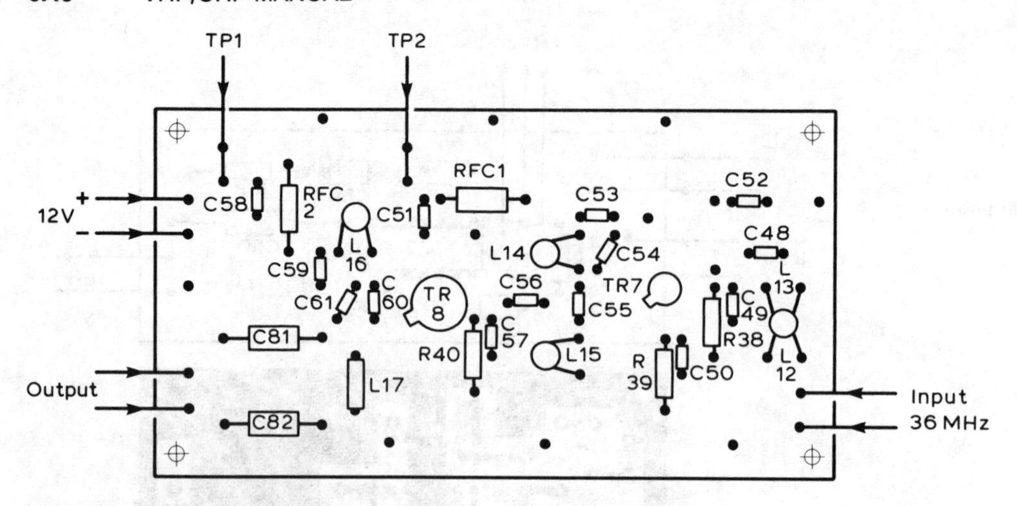

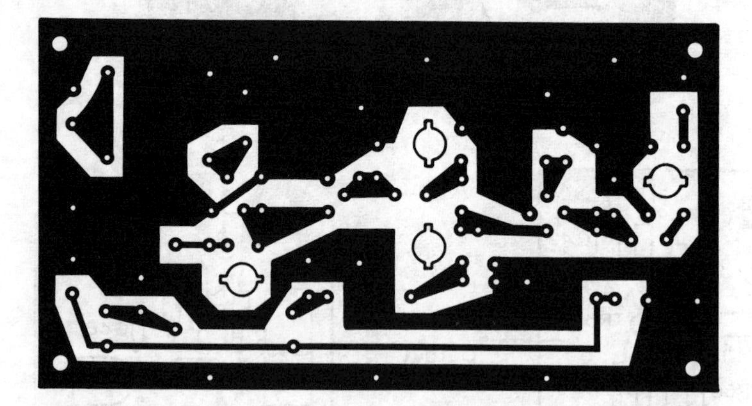

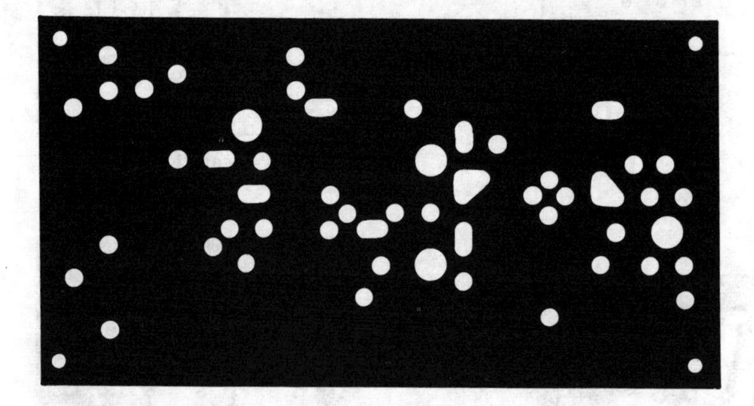

Fig 62. Frequency multiplier pcb

A frequency counter is essential to set the transmitter crystals to the correct frequency, and is highly desirable for the receiver local oscillator.

When the transmitter is correctly aligned, input to the pa stage is approximately 20W. For the present application this has been reduced to about 15W to give a greater life expectancy for TR9 and TR10, resulting from a lower operating temperature. Input can conveniently be reduced by operating the multiplier transistors TR7 and TR8 at a slightly lower voltage through a series resistor from the 12V supply; a more elegant method, however, would be to insert an attenuator pad between the final multiplier and the pa driver transistor.

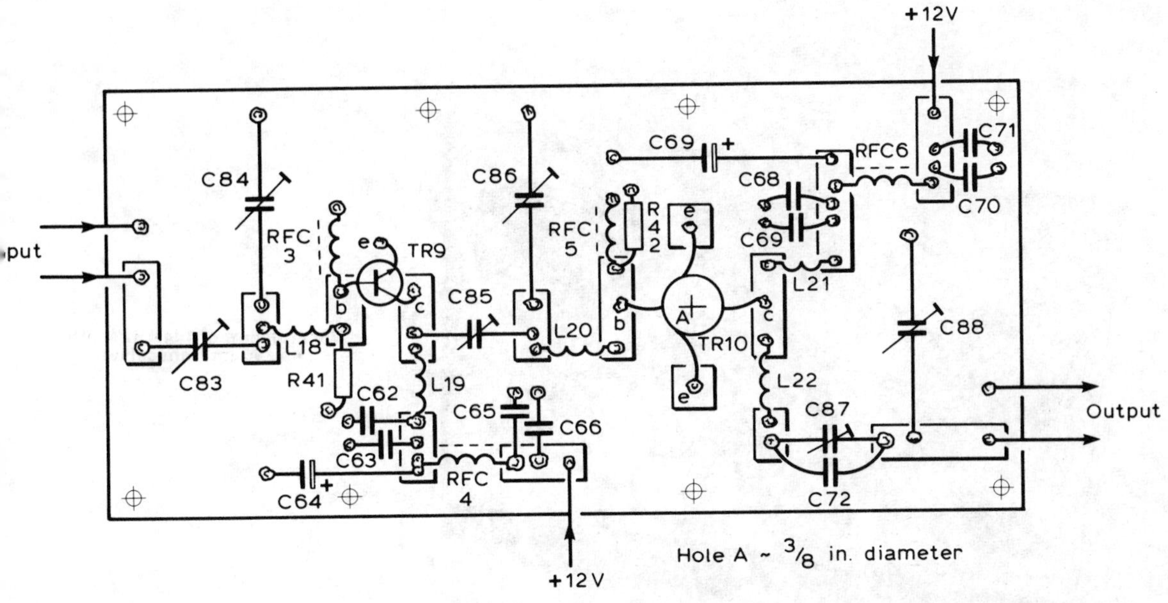

Fig 63. Amplifier board layout

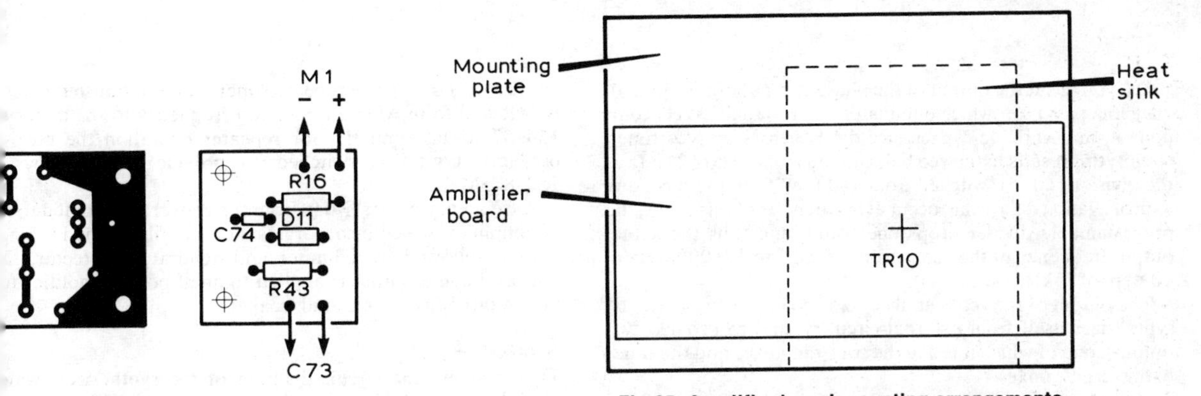

Fig 64. RF monitor pcb

Fig 65. Amplifier board mounting arrangements

144MHz synthesized fm transceiver

'his equipment, originally described by G2AIH in *Radio 'ommunication* April 1980, covers the fm portion of the band rom 145 to 146MHz in 25kHz steps. Provision is made for implex, repeater and reverse repeater operation, with automa-ic toneburst on the repeater channels. Indication of the particu-ar channel in use is given by a seven-segment led display ontrolled by the channel switches.

Phase modulation of the transmitter is employed, and the ower output is continuously variable from approximately 1W o a maximum of 12W. The receiver is a single-conversion uperhet, in which provision has been made for S-meter and quelch facilities, although these have not been incorporated at he time of writing.

A block diagram of the complete transceiver is shown in Fig 6. The 1MHz reference oscillator frequency is divided by a actor of 40 to produce a 25kHz signal which determines the channel spacing and is applied to one port of a phase comparator. Another signal from a voltage-controlled oscillator (vco) in the 11 to 12MHz range is applied via a programmable divider to the other port of the phase comparator. The programmable divider is controlled by channel switches to provide division ratios from 440 to 479, which results in a frequency of 25kHz at the output of the divider for frequencies between 11 and 12MHz from the vco.

By the action of the phase comparator this 25kHz frequency is locked in frequency and phase with the 25kHz reference frequency, and the resultant output from the phase comparator is a dc voltage of a magnitude dependent on the division ratio of the programmable divider.

The switched data input lines of the programmable divider are connected to two BCD-to-seven-segment decoder-drivers which operate seven-segment displays giving channel indication; repeater channels are indicated as 00 to 09, and simplex channels appear as 10 to 39.

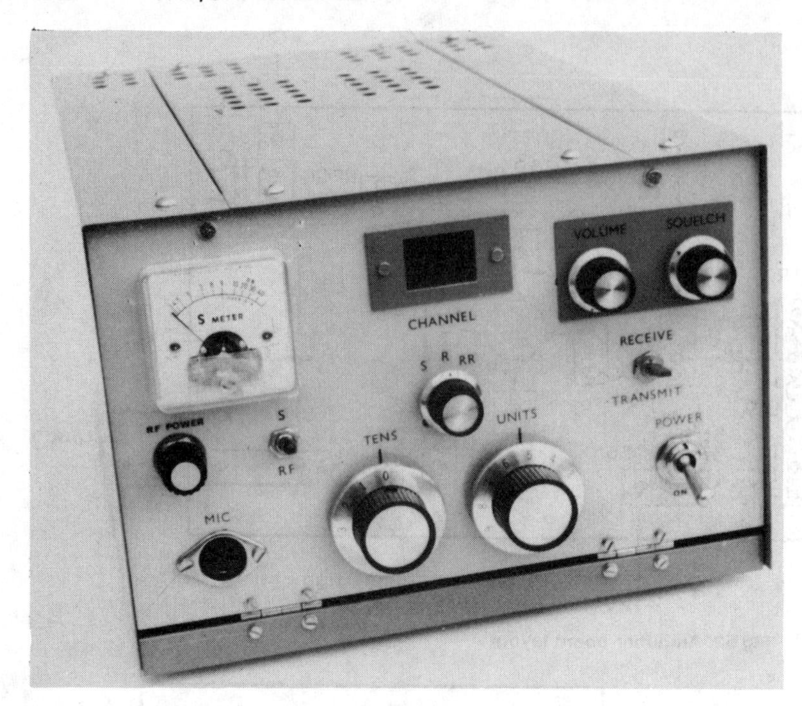

General view of 144MHz synthesized fm transceiver

DC voltage at the output of the phase comparator is applied, via a low-pass filter which eliminates any residual 25kHz component, to a variable-capacitance diode across the vco tuned circuit; this results in the vco being tuned from 11 to 12MHz as the division ratio is switched from 440 to 479. In practice, due to propagation delays that occur at frequencies of this order, the programmable divider drops one count, and thus the actual output frequency of the vco is from 11·025 to 12·000MHz in 40 steps of 25kHz each.

The output of the vco is applied to a vco buffer to isolate the synthesizer itself from external circuitry, and to provide two outputs, one of which is fed to the transmit mixer and the other to the receive mixer.

Considering first the transmitter: in addition to the 11·025 to 12MHz applied to one port of the transmit mixer, a signal at 133·975MHz is applied to the other port; this signal is derived from the transmit heterodyne oscillator-multiplier which also incorporates the phase modulator. The sum of the two frequencies (145 to 146MHz) is selected at the output of the mixer, amplified and applied through the transmit driver to the power amplifier stage.

Audio voltage from a speech processor, together with the output of the repeater access tone generator, is applied to the phase modulator associated with the heterodyne oscillator.

A similar process is employed to generate the receiver heterodyne frequency. A frequency of 11·025 to 12MHz from the vco buffer is applied to the receive mixer together with a frequency of 123·275MHz from a heterodyne oscillator-multiplier. Again, the sum frequencies of 134·3 to 135·3MHz are selected by the mixer and applied to a second mixer in the receiver converter. The output of the converter is thus 10·7MHz over the signal frequency range of 145 to 146MHz.

A 600kHz upshift for repeater and reverse repeater operation is achieved by switching crystals in the two heterodyne oscillators. For reverse repeater operation the transmit cryst is switched to provide an injection frequency to the mixer 134·575MHz. Similarly, for repeater operation the receiv oscillator crystal is switched to provide a frequency 123·875MHz.

A frequency of 10·7MHz from the converter is routed to a i.f. amplifier, which incorporates a crystal filter. The i.f. amp lifier is followed by a limiter and quadrature detector, th low-level audio output is applied to an af power amplifier fo operation of an external loudspeaker.

Synthesizer

Fig 67 shows the circuit diagram of the synthesizer, whi uses low-power Schottky ttl for digital functions, and peripheral elements. Three gates of a 74LS04 hex invert (IC1) are employed as the 1MHz reference frequency osci lator; the first two gates forming the oscillator proper, with th third gate acting as a buffer. The value of resistors R1 and R2 the feedback circuit of the oscillator is fairly critical; if th resistance is too low there is a tendency to self-oscillation whe the crystal is removed, while too high a resistance results sluggish startup. The oscillator is followed by two 74LS9 decade counters (IC2 and IC3) which are connected in ÷ 1 and ÷ 4 configurations respectively, giving a resultant refe ence output of 25kHz.

The 5V supply line to the reference oscillator and dividers derived through a voltage regulator (IC4), input and output which is decoupled by C7, C6 and C5. In a similar manner th power supply to each of the other circuits forming the phas lock-loop is derived through individual regulators (IC6, IC and IC13) to minimize any possibility of feedback around th loop.

A 25kHz reference frequency is applied to one input port the MC4044 phase comparator (IC5). The 25kHz sign

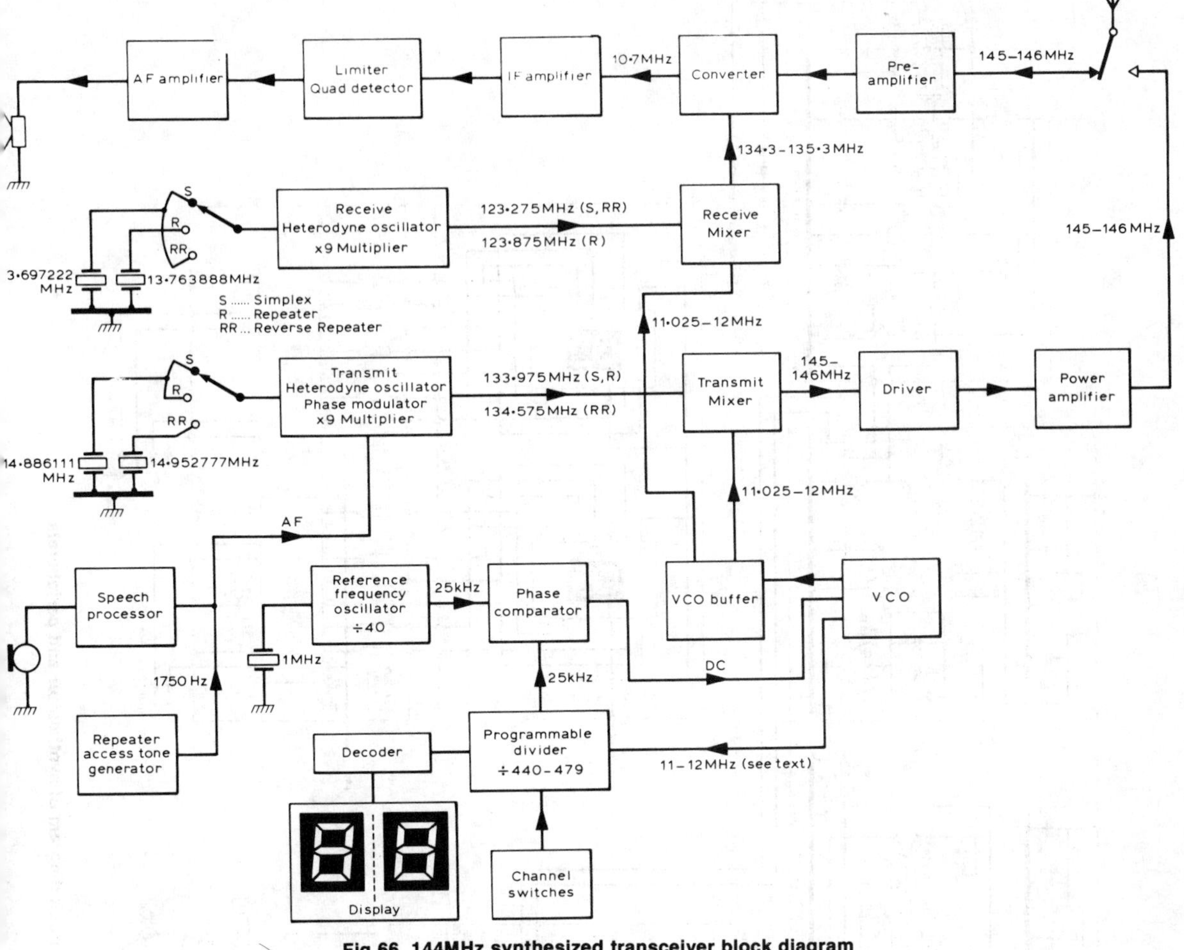

Fig 66. 144MHz synthesized transceiver block diagram

appearing at the output of the programmable divider is applied to the other input port of this ic, the action of the phase comparator being such that this frequency is maintained in phase relationship with the accurate 25kHz signal derived from the reference oscillator. The MC4044 consists of a frequency/phase comparator, a charge pump and an amplifier. The resultant output from the device, consequent upon the two 25kHz signals applied to the input ports, is a dc voltage of a value dependent on the division ratio of the programmable divider.

A tunable low-pass filter consisting of C8 and RV1 is connected through an emitter-follower (TR1) between the charge pump and amplifier of the phase comparator. This suppresses any residual 25kHz component that may appear at this point; additional filtering is provided by C9 connected across the dc output line.

Filtered dc from the output of the phase comparator is applied via isolating resistors R5 and R6 to a variable-capacitance diode (D1), which is effectively connected in parallel across the vco tuned circuit L1, C15 and C16. The vco employs an MC1648L emitter-coupled oscillator (IC7) which in the present application tunes over a frequency range of 11·025 through 12MHz. Output of the vco is buffered by a pnp transistor (TR2); a diode D2 in the emitter circuit of the transistor provides a constant bias of approximately 0·6V to interface correctly between IC7 and TR2.

The vco has two output ports, one of which is connected to the vco buffer and the second to the programmable divider. This divider consists of three synchronous reversible counters (IC10, IC11 and IC12) which function as hundreds, tens and units dividers respectively. In the present application the circuit is arranged to divide by integers from 440 to 479. Normally the data input lines to the counters are held at logic "0" level (earth) by the pull-down resistors R13 to R24, and division is achieved by applying a logic "1" level (+5V) to the appropriate data input. The divider is preset to divide by 440 through the application of logic "1" to data input C of both the hundreds and tens dividers, this being derived from the +5V termination designated "1" on the circuit diagram. Division from 440 to 479 is then achieved by the setting of the two channel switches S1a, S2a and S2b, which apply a logic "1" level to the appropriate data inputs of the tens and units dividers, either directly or through diodes D3, D4, D5 and D6. The +5V level to the two channel switches is derived from the 5V termination "3" on the

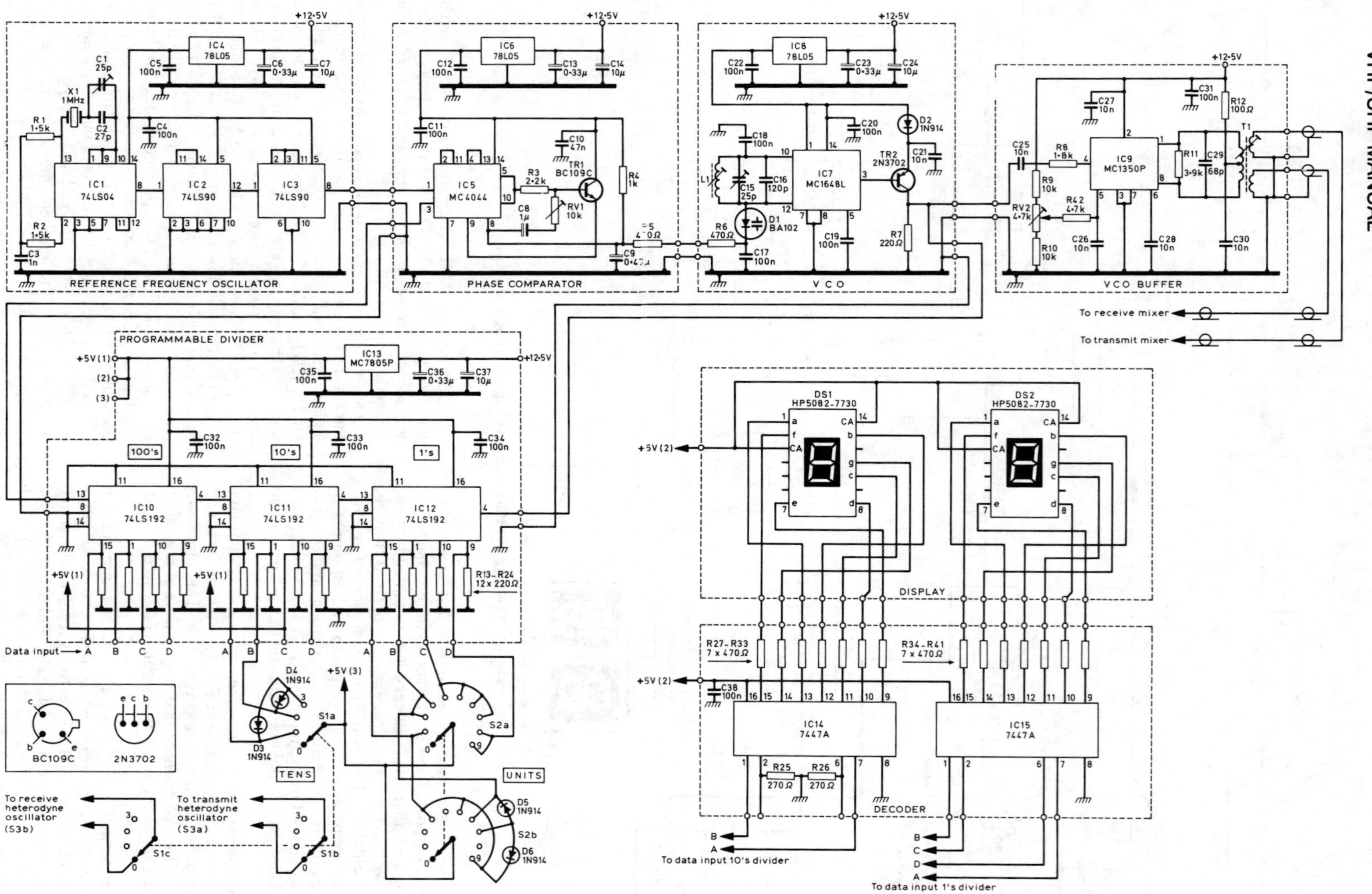

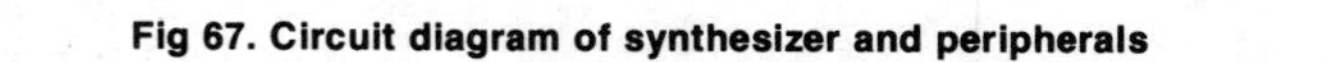
Fig 67. Circuit diagram of synthesizer and peripherals

Table 11. Synthesizer components list

1, 2	1·5kΩ
3	2·2kΩ
4	1kΩ
5, 6, 24–41	470Ω
7	220Ω
8	1·8kΩ
9, 10	10kΩ
11	3·9kΩ
12	100Ω
13–24	220Ω ½W
25, 26	270Ω
42	4·7kΩ
V1	10kΩ trimpot
V2	4·7Ω 0·1W horizontal preset pot
1, 15	25pF film dielectric trimmer
2	27pF 63V cp
3	1nF 50V c
4, 5, 11, 12, 17, 18, 19, 20, 22, 31, 32, 33, 34, 35, 38	100nF 25V c
6, 13, 23, 36	0·33μF 35V tb
7, 14, 24, 37	10μF 35V tb
8	1μF 35V tb
9	0·47μF tb
10	47nF 50V c
16	120pF 160V p
21, 25, 26, 27, 28, 30	10nF 50V c
29	68pF 63V cp
C1	74LS04
C2, 3	74LS90
C4, 6, 8	78L05
C5	MC4044 Motorola
C7	MC1648L Motorola
C9	MC1350P Motorola
C10, 11, 12	74LS192
C13	MC7805P
C14, 15	7447A
S1, 2	HP5082–7730 Hewlett-Packard
R1	BC109C
R2	2N3702
1	BA102
2	1N914
1	Three-pole four-way rotary
2	Two-pole 10-way rotary
1	1MHz crystal 30pF parallel resonance HC6U
1	20t 28swg enam 5mm i.d. dust-core tuned
1	Primary 22½t 28swg enam 5mm i.d. dust-core tuned Secondaries 4½t 28swg enam each side of centre of primary

ll resistors ⅓W 5% carbon film unless otherwise stated.
apacitors: c = ceramic, cp = ceramic plate, tb = tantalum bead,
= polystyrene

ircuit diagram. Power supply to each of the three programm-ble dividers is decoupled by C32, C33 and C34.

Output from the first port of the vco at frequencies of 11·025 o 12MHz in discrete steps of 25kHz each is applied to the AC1350P buffer (IC9). This amplifier has a variable gain, with V2 controlling the bias applied to the agc section of the ic. The ush-pull output circuit formed by T1 primary and C29 is lamped by R11 to give a flat response over the frequency ange. T1 has two low-impedance secondary windings which rovide independent outputs for application of the 11·025 to 2MHz signal to the transmit and receive mixers (Figs 68 and 9).

Operation of the two seven-segment displays DS1 and DS2, which provide channel indication, is achieved through two 7447A BCD-to-seven-segment decoder-drivers IC14 and IC15. The decoder inputs are connected to the corresponding data inputs of the programmable divider, and operate the displays through current-limiting resistors R27 to R41. R25 and R26, connected to the data input lines of the tens decoder (IC11), function as pull-down resistors and eliminate the need for these two points to be connected to the programmable divider. Power for operation of the decoders and displays is derived from the +5V termination "2" on the programmable divider board.

Transmitter (Fig 68)

The final radiated frequency is derived by mixing the output of the vco buffer with a second higher frequency from a heterodyne oscillator-multiplier. The oscillator (TR1) is a Colpitts circuit, with one switch bank (S3a) selecting one of two crystals (X1 and X2) to obtain either simplex or reverse repeater operation. Crystal switching is accomplished through the use of biassed diodes.

RF output from the TR1 emitter circuit is applied via C13 to the base of TR2 which functions as a reactance device to provide phase modulation.

The crystal oscillator and phase modulator are followed by two ×3 multiplier stages (TR3 and TR4). Coupling between the two transistors is through a bandpass tuned circuit (L3, C24, C26 and L4, C27, C28), tuned to the third harmonic of the oscillator frequency, ie approximately 44MHz. An impedance match to the base of the second multiplier is achieved by a capacitance tap formed by C27 and C28. Similarly the tuned circuit associated with TR4 is a bandpass configuration; an output impedance of 50Ω at 134MHz being obtained by the preset tuning capacitors C33 and C34. Bandpass circuits are used extensively throughout the equipment to reduce the level of unwanted frequencies.

For simplex and repeater working, S3a switches a 14·886111MHz crystal (X1) into circuit, which results in a heterodyne frequency of 133·975MHz. A 600kHz upshift for reverse repeater operation is obtained from a 14·952777MHz crystal (X2), this giving an output frequency of 134·575MHz. When X2 is activated it would be possible for frequencies outside the 144MHz band to be radiated at certain settings of the channel switches S1 and S2; to prevent this the oscillator is linked by its switching circuit with S1c, so that reverse repeater operation is possible only when the TENS channel switch is set to the "0" position.

The output of the heterodyne oscillator-multiplier is applied to the lo port of an MD108 double-balanced mixer (MX1). One output of the vco buffer is applied to the rf port resulting in the sum of the two input frequencies, 145 to 146MHz, appearing at the i.f. port. R19 is a terminating resistor at the output port of the mixer, which is followed by two stages of amplification (TR5 and TR6), the latter stage employing bandpass coupling in the input and output circuits.

Output from the mixer at a level of approximately 30mW is applied to a two-stage driver amplifier (TR7 and TR8). Power output from TR8 can be varied by adjustment of RV1 (RF POWER) in the supply line to TR7. When set to zero resistance, a power of approximately 2·5W is available at the input of the power amplifier stage (TR9). The pa output tuned circuit C72, C73, L19 and C74 form a low-pass filter to reduce radiation of harmonics generated by the transistor amplifier stages.

The speech processor is a three-stage af amplifier (TR10,

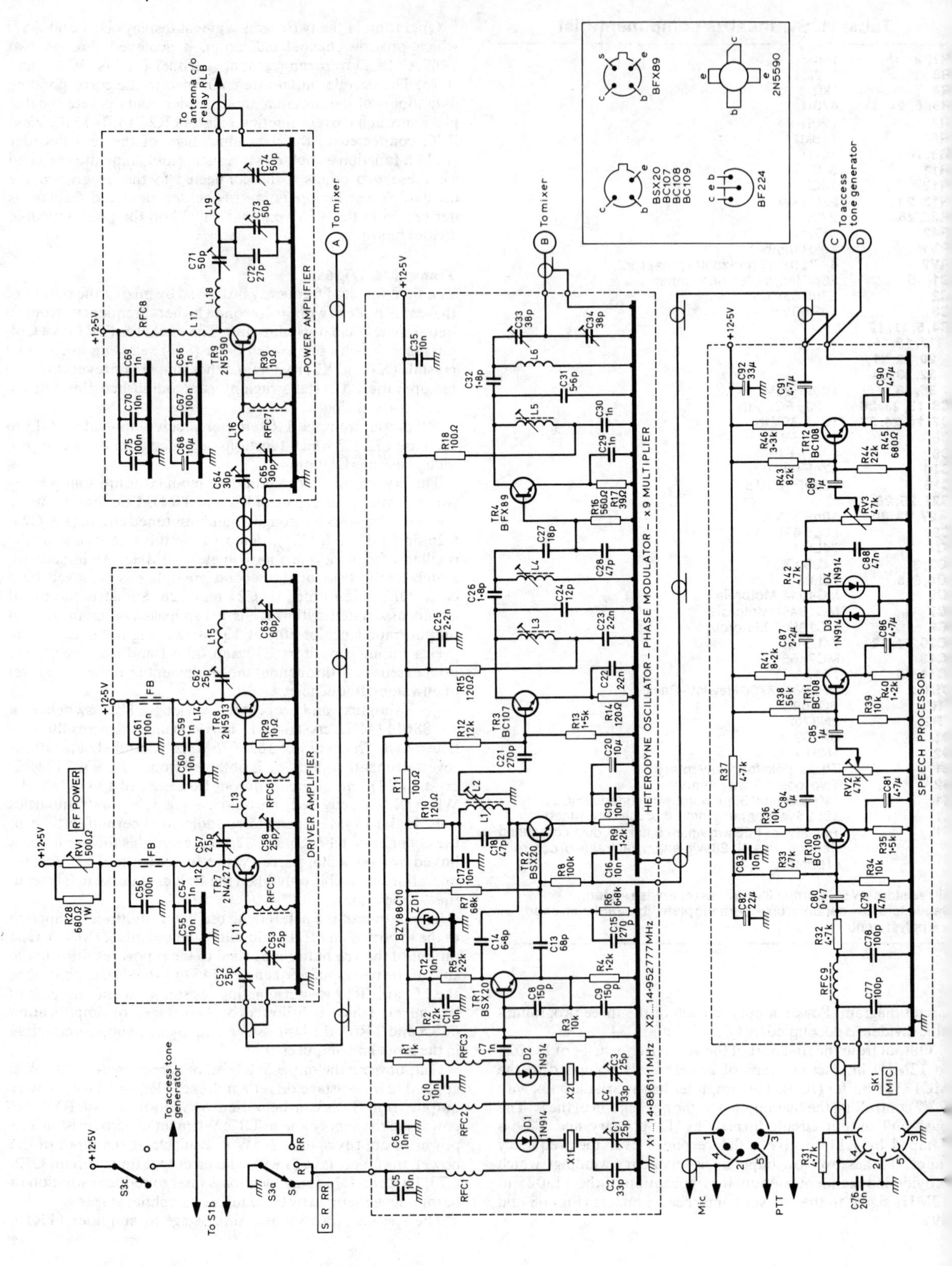
To antenna c/o relay RLB
POWER AMPLIFIER
DRIVER AMPLIFIER
RF POWER
To mixer
HETERODYNE OSCILLATOR – PHASE MODULATOR – x9 MULTIPLIER
X1 ...14·886111 MHz
X2 ...14·952777 MHz
To access tone generator
SPEECH PROCESSOR
To S1b
S R RR
SK1
MIC
Mic
PTT

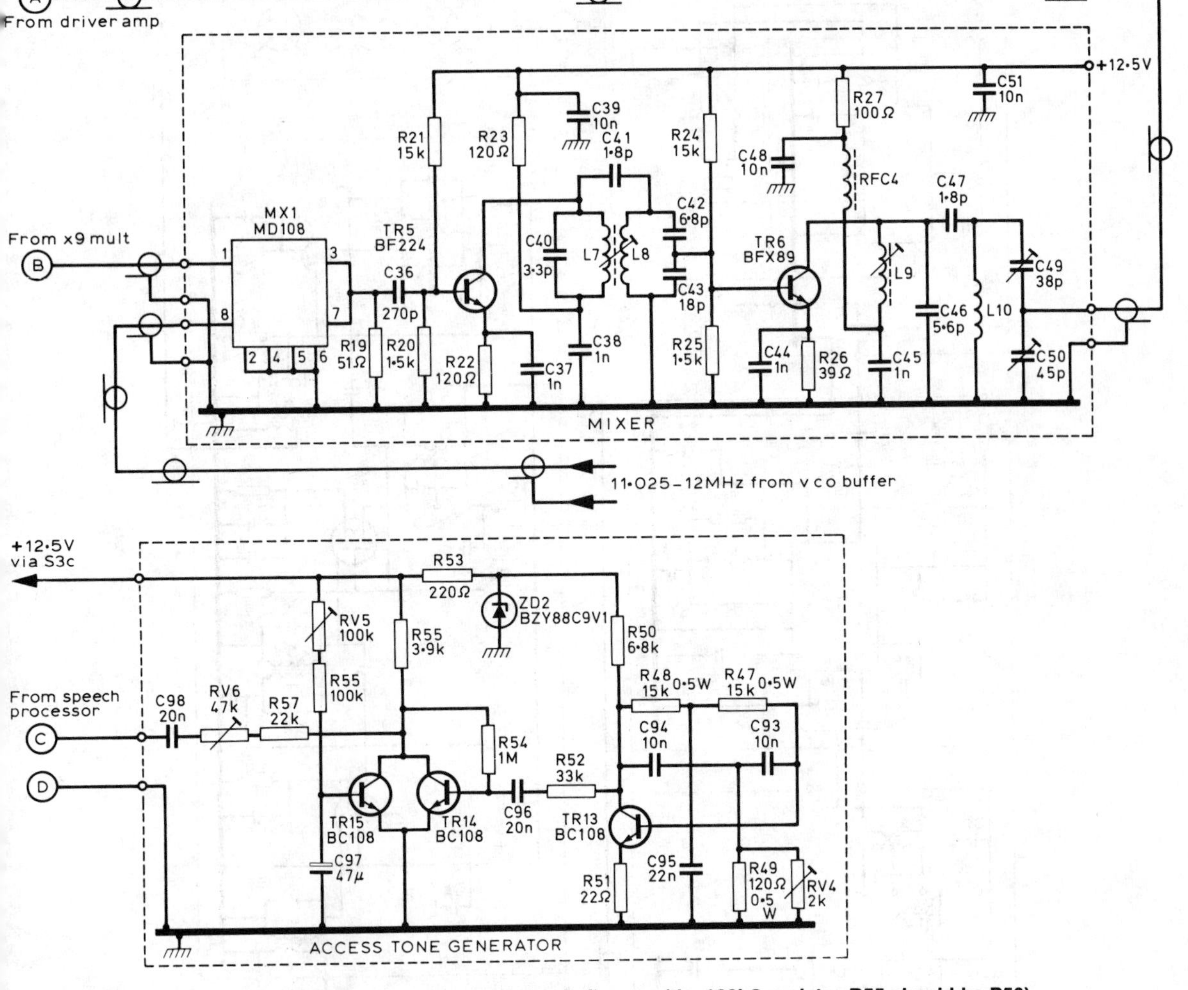

Fig 68 (facing page and above). Transmitter circuit diagram (the 100kΩ resistor R55 should be R56)

TR11 and TR12) incorporating clipping and filtering to achieve optimum audio characteristics. R31 and C76 are mounted directly on the microphone socket (MIC SK1). C77, RFC9 and C78 form an rf filter to eliminate rf feedback into the processor. R32 and C79 constitute a low-pass filter which attenuates the upper audio frequencies to compensate for the rising high-frequency characteristic of the phase modulator.

TR11 is followed by a shunt diode clipper (D3, D4), with the clipping level set by RV2. Harmonics generated by the clipping action are reduced by a filter consisting of R42 and C48. RV3 connected between the output of the clipper and TR3 functions as a deviation control.

RV4 controls the oscillator frequency, with the output buffered by TR14 followed by a timer consisting of TR15, RV5, R56 and C97. At switch-on C97 is discharged, the base of TR15 is at earth potential and the transistor, being cut-off, has no effect on the operation of the circuit; 1,750Hz tone is therefore passed to the output. C97 now commences to charge through RV5 and R56, and when the potential at the base of TR15 reaches a value of approximately 0·6V the transistor conducts, effectively short-circuiting the output and cutting off the tone. Toneburst duration is determined by RV5. Supply voltage to the tone generator is applied via S3c, so that it is only operative when S3 is switched to the repeater position.

Receiver (Fig 69)

A low-noise mosfet Type BF900 (TR1), having a reputed nf of less than 2dB at 200MHz, is employed as rf amplifier. This stage is coupled to a second rf amplifier (TR2) on the converter board. The second amplifier is bandpass-coupled to the second mixer (TR3); both these stages employ dual-gate mosfets.

The circuitry associated with the receive heterodyne oscillator is similar to the corresponding unit in the transmitter. For simplex operation S3b switches a 13·697222MHz crystal (X1) into circuit; to operate on repeater channels a 600kHz upshift is obtained by a 13·763888MHz crystal (X2). When S3 is set to the repeater position, out-of-band signals could be received at certain settings of the TENS channel switch S1, and so in a

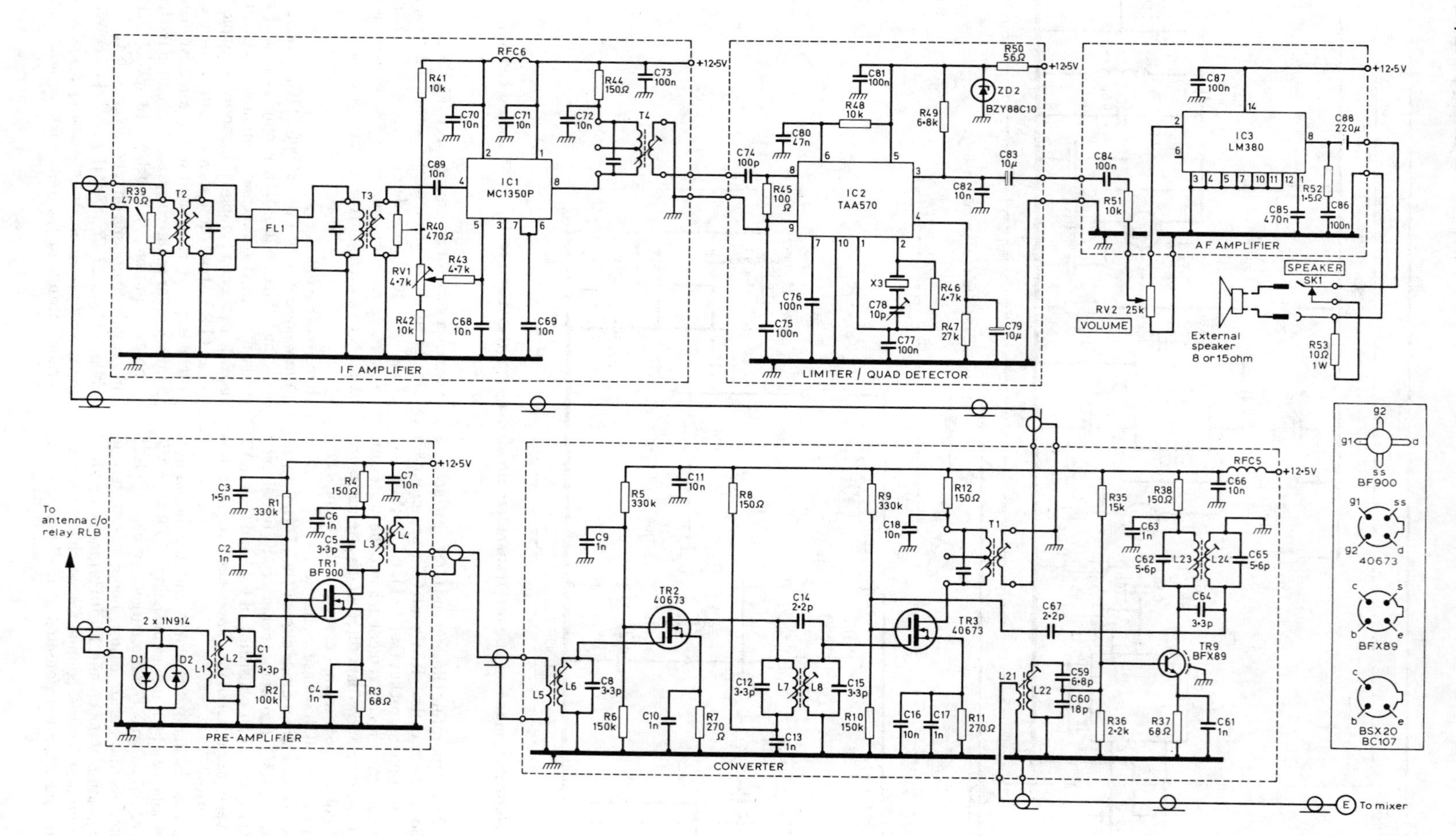
IF AMPLIFIER
IC1 MC1350P
FL1
LIMITER / QUAD DETECTOR
IC2 TAA570
ZD2 BZY88C10
AF AMPLIFIER
IC3 LM380
RV2 25k
VOLUME
SPEAKER
SK1
External speaker 8 or 15ohm
R53 10Ω 1W
+12·5V
To antenna c/o relay RLB
2 x 1N914
TR1 BF900
PRE-AMPLIFIER
TR2 40673
TR3 40673
TR9 BFX89
CONVERTER
To mixer
BF900
40673
BFX89
BSX20 BC107

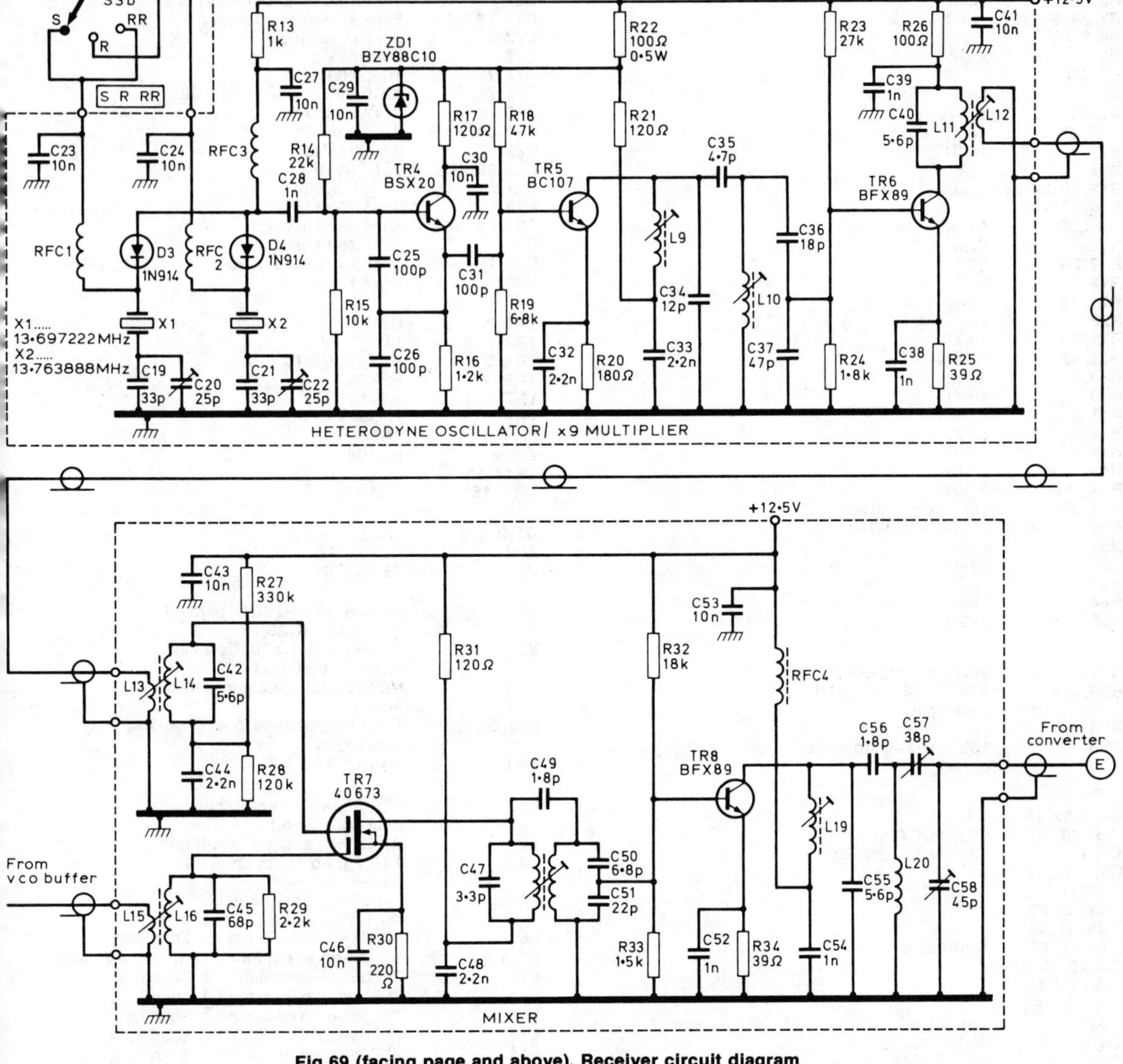

Fig 69 (facing page and above). Receiver circuit diagram

manner similar to that employed in the transmitter, repeater operation is possible only when S1 is in the "0" position, by linking the crystal switch with S1c.

TR4, the crystal oscillator, is followed by two ×3 multiplier stages (TR5 and TR6). For simplex operation the resultant output frequency from TR6 is thus 123·275MHz, which is applied to gate 2 of TR7 as first mixer. To gate 1 of TR7, 11·025 to 12MHz from the vco buffer is applied, the resultant output from the mixer being the sum of these, namely the final heterodyne frequency of 134·3 to 135·3MHz. The mixer is followed by an amplifier stage (TR8) which is coupled to a second amplifier (TR9) located on the converter board and this raises the injection voltage to a level adequate to secure optimum conversion gain from the second mixer (TR3).

The 10·7MHz i.f. at the output of the second mixer is routed to the input of the i.f. amplifier. The receiver selectivity is obtained by the eight-pole crystal filter (FL1). Input and output of the filter are coupled through matching transformers T2, T3 and terminating resistors R39 and R40 respectively.

Output from the i.f. amplifier is coupled to the limiter and quadrature IC2. A crystal quadrature element is employed, the crystal having an actual frequency of 10·698MHz which is set to 10·7MHz by a series trimmer C78. Supply voltage to the ic is reduced to 10V by ZD2.

Table 12. Transmitter components list

R1	1kΩ ½W
R2	12kΩ
R3, 34, 36, 39	10kΩ
R4, 9, 40	1·2kΩ
R5	2·2kΩ
R6, 50	6·8kΩ
R7	68kΩ
R8, 56	100kΩ
R18, 27	100Ω
R11	100Ω ½W
R12	12kΩ
R13, 20, 25, 35	1·5kΩ
R10, 14, 15, 22, 23	120Ω
R16	560Ω
R17, 26	39Ω
R19	51Ω
R21, 24	15kΩ
R28	680Ω 1W
R29, 30	10Ω
R31, 32, 37	4·7kΩ
R33, 42	47kΩ
R38	56kΩ
R41	8·2kΩ
R43	82kΩ
R44, 57	22kΩ
R45	680Ω
R46	3·3kΩ
R47, 48	15kΩ ½W metal film
R49	120Ω ½W metal film
R51	22Ω
R52	33kΩ
R53	220Ω
R54	1MΩ
R55	3·9kΩ
RV1	500Ω 3W wire-wound pot
RV2, 3, 6	47kΩ 0·1W horizontal preset pot
RV4	2kΩ trimpot
RV5	100kΩ 0·1W horizontal preset pot
C1, 3, 52, 53, 57, 58, 62	25pF fdt DAU
C2, 4	33pF 100V cp N750
C5, 6, 10, 11, 12, 16, 17, 19, 35, 39, 48, 51, 55, 60, 70, 83	10nF 50V c
C7, 29, 30, 37, 38, 44, 45, 54, 59, 66, 69	1nF 50V c
C8, 9	150pF 63V cp
C13	68pF 63V cp
C14	6·8pF 63V cp
C15, 21, 36	270pF 63V cp
C18, 28	47pF 63V cp
C20	10μF 25V e
C22, 23, 25	2·2nF 50V c
C24	12pF 63V cp
C26, 32, 41, 47	1·8pF 63V cp
C27, 43	18pF 63V cp
C31, 46	5·6pF 63V cp
C33, 34, 49	38pF fdt DAU
C40	3·3pF 63V cp
C42	6·8pF 63V cp
C50	45pF fdt DAU
C56, 61, 67, 75	100nF 25V c
C63	60pF fdt Mullard
C64, 65	30pF min air-spaced trimmer Oxley
C68	10μF 20V tantalum metal-cased
C71, 73, 74	50pF air-spaced trimmer
C72	27pF silver mica
C76	20nF 50V c
C77, 78	100pF 63V cp
C79, 88	47nF 50V c
C80	0·47μF 35V tb
C81, 88, 90, 91	4·7μF 35V tb
C82	22μF 16V tb
C84, 85, 89	1μF 35V tb
C87	2·2μF 35Vtb
C92	33μF 25V tb
C93, 94	10nF 250V petp mf
C95	22nF 250V petp mf
C96, 98	20nF 100V mylar film
C97	47μF 16V e
TR1, 2	BSX20
TR3	BC107
TR4, 6	BFX89, 2N918
TR5	BF224
TR7	2N4427
TR8	2N5913
TR9	2N5590
TR10	BC109
TR11, 12, 13, 14, 15	BC108
D1, 2, 3, 4	1N914
ZD1	BZY—C10
ZD2	BZY88C9V1
X1	14·886111MHz 30pF parallel resonance HC25U
X2	14·952777MHz 30pF parallel resonance HC25U
MX1	MD108 double-balanced mixer Anzac
S3a, S3c	Two banks of three-pole three-way rotary switch
SK1	Five-pin 180° DIN socket
L1	29½t 28swg enam 5mm i.d. dust-core tuned
L2	4½t 28swg enam at earth end of L1
L3, 4	13½t 26swg enam 5mm i.d. dust-core tuned
L5	3½t 20swg enam 5mm i.d. dust-core tuned
L6	3t 20swg enam 6mm i.d. 7mm long
L7, 8, 9	3½t 20swg enam 5mm i.d. dust-core tuned
L10	3t 20swg enam 6mm i.d. 7mm long
L11	2t 20swg enam 6mm i.d. 4mm long
L12	2t 20swg enam 5mm i.d. 5mm long
L13	2t 20swg enam 6mm i.d. 5mm long
L14	4t 20swg enam 5mm i.d. 6mm long
L15	3t 18swg enam 6mm i.d. 8mm long
L16	2t 20swg enam 6mm i.d. 7mm long
L17	4t 20swg enam 5mm i.d. 6mm long
L18	3t 18swg enam 7mm i.d. 7mm long
L19	2t 18swg enam 7mm i.d. 6mm long
RFC1, 2, 3	470μH Toko 7BA
RFC4, 5, 6, 7	2½t 28swg enam FX1115 ferrite bead
RFC8	2½t 26swg enam FX1898 ferrite bead
RFC9	17·5μH dust-iron core
FB	Two FX1115 ferrite beads

All resistors ½W 5% carbon film unless stated
Capacitors: fdt = film dielectric trimmer, cp = ceramic plate, c = ceramic, e = electrolytic, tb = tantalum bead, mf = metallized film.

Table 13. Receiver components list

1, 5, 9, 27	330kΩ
2	100kΩ
3, 37	68Ω
4, 8, 12, 38, 44	150Ω
6, 10	150kΩ
7, 11	270Ω
13	1kΩ
14	22kΩ
15, 41, 42, 48, 51	10kΩ
16	1·2kΩ
17, 21, 31	120Ω
18	47kΩ
19, 49	6·8kΩ
20	180Ω
22	100Ω ½W
23, 47	27kΩ
24	1·8kΩ
25, 34	39Ω
26, 45	100Ω
28	120kΩ
29, 36	2·2kΩ
30	220Ω
32	18kΩ
33	1·5kΩ
35	15kΩ
39, 40	470Ω
43, 46	4·7kΩ
50	56Ω
52	1·5Ω
53	10Ω 1W
V1	4·7kΩ 0·1W horizontal preset pot
V2	25kΩ logarithmic pot
1, 5, 8, 12, 15, 47, 64	3·3pF 63V cp
2, 4, 6, 9, 10, 13, 17, 28, 38, 39, 52, 54, 61, 63	1nF 50V c
7, 11, 16, 18, 23, 24, 27, 29, 30, 41, 43, 46, 53, 66, 68, 69, 70, 71, 72, 82, 89	10nF 50V c
14, 67	2·2pF 63V cp
19, 21	33pF 100V cp N750
20, 22	25pF fdt DAU
25, 26, 31, 74	100pF 63V cp
3	1·5nF 50V c
32, 33, 44, 48	2·2nF 50 V c
34	12pF 63V cp
35	4·7pF 63V cp
36, 60	18pF 63V cp
37	47pF 63V cp

C40, 42, 55, 62, 65	5·6pF 63V cp
C45	68pF 63V cp
C49, 56	1·8pF 63V cp
C50, 59	6·8pF 63V cp
C51	22pF 63V cp
C57	38pF fdt DAU
C58	45pF fdt DAU
C73, 75, 76, 77, 81, 84, 86, 87	100nF 25V c
C78	10pF fdt
C79, 83	10μF 25V e
C80	47nF 50V c
C85	470nF 3V c
C88	220μF 16V e
IC1	MC1350P Motorola
IC2	TAA570
IC3	LM380
TR1	BF900
TR2, 3, 7	40673
TR4	BSX20
TR5	BC107
TR6, 8, 9	BFX89, 2N918
D1, 2, 3, 4	1N914
ZD1, 2	BZY88C10
X1	13·697222MHz 30pF parallel resonance HC25U
X2	13·763888MHz 30pF parallel resonance HC25U
X3	10·698MHz
FL1	10·7MHz crystal filter Toyocom 10M-4B-1
T1, 4	10·7MHz i.f. transformer Toko KALS 1506A
T2, 3	10·7MHz i.f. transformer Toko 119LC30099N
SK1	Two-pin DIN switched speaker socket
S3b	One bank of three-pole three-way rotary switch
L2, 3	4½t 22swg enam 4mm i.d. dust-core tuned
L1, 4	1½t 22swg enam at earth end of L2, L3
L6	3½t 22swg enam 5mm i.d. dust-core tuned
L5	1½t 22swg enam at earth end of L6
L7, 8	3½t 22swg enam 5mm i.d. dust-core tuned
L9, 10	13½t 26swg enam 5mm i.d. dust-core tuned
L11	3½t 22swg enam 5mm i.d. dust-core tuned
L12	1½t 22swg enam at earth end of L11
L13	1½t 26swg enam at earth end of L14
L14	4½t 26swg enam 5mm i.d. dust-core tuned
L15	4½t 28swg enam at earth end of L16
L16	22½t 28swg enam 5mm i.d. dust-core tuned
L17, 18, 23, 24	3½t 22swg enam 5mm i.d. dust-core tuned
L19	3½t 22swg enam 5mm i.d. dust-core tuned
L20	3t 22 swg enam 6mm i.d. 7mm long no former
L21	1½t 22swg enam at earth end of L22
L22	3½t 22swg enam 5mm i.d. dust-core tuned
RFC1, 2, 3	470μH Toko 7BA
RFC4	2½t 28swg enam FX1115 ferrite bead
RFC5, 6	100μH Toko 7BA

All resistors ⅓W 5% carbon film unless otherwise stated.
Capacitors: cp=ceramic plate, c=ceramic, fdt=film dielectric trimmer, e=electrolytic.

In the mechanical design of the equipment, provision has been made for inclusion of an S-meter and squelch control. The TAA570 device at present fitted as limiter and quad detector does not provide either of these facilities, and it is proposed to replace this circuit board by one using a more sophisticated ic that will provide these refinements.

A conventional low-power audio amplifier (IC3) follows the quadrature detector, giving an af output of approximately 1·5W. R52 and C86 constitute a Zobel network to suppress any high-frequency oscillation. The external speaker is connected via a two-pole DIN switched socket; removal of the speaker automatically substitutes a 10Ω resistor as the amplifier output load.

Power and control circuitry (Fig 70)

Protection against accidental connection of reversed voltage to PL1 is provided by a shunt diode D1, a high-current device with its stud anode connected to chassis.

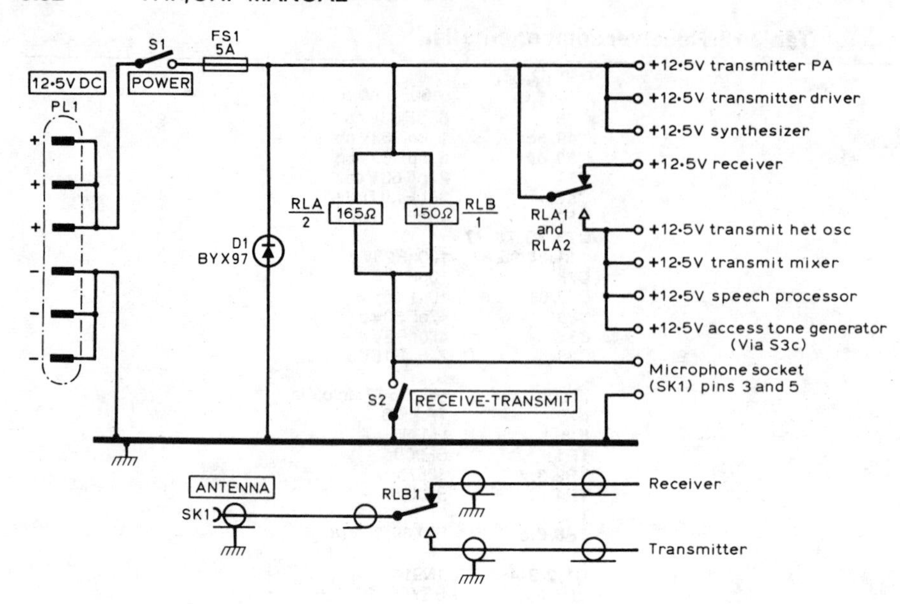

Fig 70. Power and control circuit diagram

In the receive condition, power is applied to all sub-assemblies forming the receiver through the normally closed contacts of RLA; this is a dpco relay with its contact sets connected in parallel to increase the current rating. Power is also applied continuously to all elements of the synthesizer, the transmitter driver amplifier and the power amplifier.

On operation of the RECEIVE-TRANSMIT switch S2, RLA changes over, the receiver is de-energized, and power is applied to the transmit heterodyne oscillator-multiplier, mixer, speech processor and (through S3, Fig 68) to the access tone generator. The press-to-talk switch on the microphone performs the same function as S2, being connected in parallel with the panel-mounted switch via pins 3 and 5 of the MIC socket SK2 (Fig 68). Operation of S2 or the ptt switch also energizes the antenna changeover relay RLB.

Construction

External dimensions of the equipment (excluding pa heat sink) are 8in wide by 5½in high by 11¼in deep, and the photos show views of the transceiver with the three-section dust cover removed. Sub-assemblies forming the synthesizer (Fig 67) are mounted on both sides of a central fixed vertical plate running from front to rear. Screening covers, secured in position by clips, are fitted to the phase comparator, vco and programmable divider. The short connections between the synthesizer pcbs are made through single pvc-covered wire.

The transmitter driver, ie all sub-assemblies shown in Fig 68 with the exception of the pa, and the receiver (Fig 69) are likewise fitted to both sides of vertical mounting plates to the left and right of the synthesizer respectively. Each of these plates is, however, hinged at the lower edge which, after removing securing screws at the rear, permits them to be lowered to a horizontal position, giving access to the interior-mounted sub-assemblies. In a similar manner the front panel, and the back plate on which the transmitter pa and antenna changeover relay are mounted, are hinged and may be lowered to a horizontal position.

In the transmitter driver the heterodyne oscillator-multiplier, speech processor, access tone generator and mixer are fitted with screening covers, with the speech processor and tone

Table 14. Power and control components list

PL1	Six-pole miniature panel-mounting plug P427
S1	SPST switch 24VDC 17A rating
S2	SPST miniature toggle switch
FS1	5A 1·25in fuse
D1	BYX97-C2 (stud anode)
RLA	DPCO relay 12V coil
RLB	50Ω coaxial relay 12V coil (Magnetic Devices 951-170)
SK1	BNC 50Ω bulkhead socket

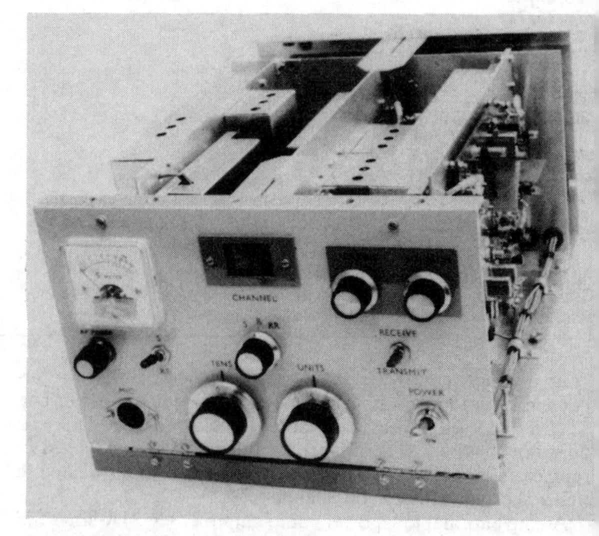

Transceiver with cover removed. L to r: transmitter driver, synthesizer and receiver

Left-hand side view. Transmit heterodyne oscillator-multiplier (above) and driver amplifier (below)

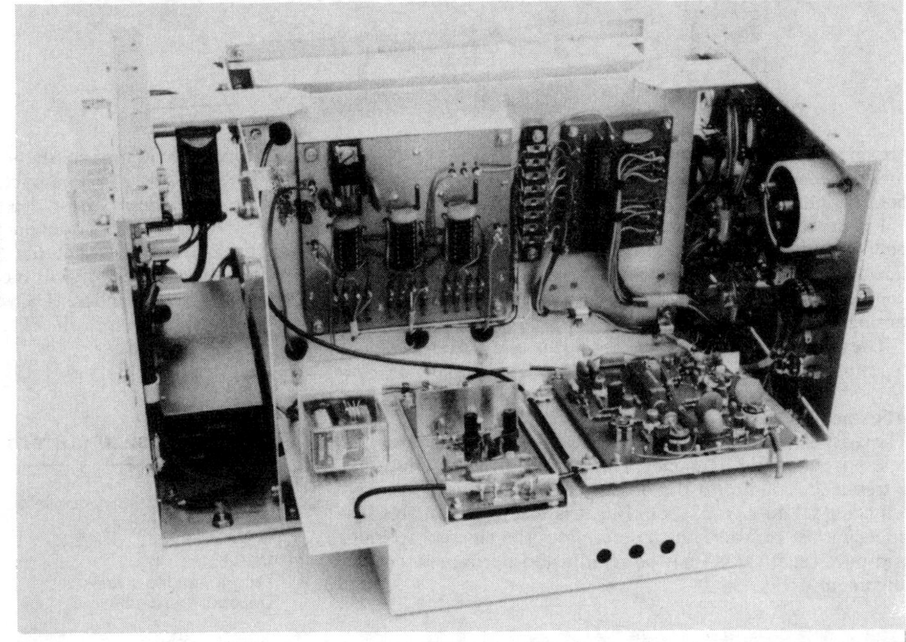

Left-hand side view. Programmable divider and display decoder (rear), speech processor, access tone generator and transmit mixer (front)

generator having a common cover for both sub-assemblies. The power changeover relay RLA is mounted on a plate adjacent to the mixer. At the rear, from left to right, are the programmable divider and display decoder. In the photos the screening cans have been removed from the relevant sub-assemblies.

The receiver, mounted at the right-hand side of the equipment is also shown in the photos. One shows the mixer with the oscillator-multiplier immediately beneath. At the right-hand side is the pre-amplifier; none of these units is fitted with screening covers, but both mixer and pre-amplifier have vertical copper screens soldered to the pcb earth plane between input and output circuits of the amplifiers. In another photo the mounting plate has been lowered to the horizontal, and the remainder of the receiver, with its cover removed, can be seen in the foreground; these are, from right to left, converter, i.f. amplifier, quadrature detector and af amplifier. At the rear, mounted on the central fixed plate, are the reference frequency oscillator at the left, followed by the phase comparator, vco and vco buffer.

One photo shows the transmitter power amplifier with the antenna changeover relay RLB at the left. A heat sink (DAU 4·2°C/W 4½ by 2in) is secured external to the backplate and centred on the transistor mounting stud.

With the exception of the transmitter pa, decoder, receiver quadrature detector and af amplifier, all sub-assemblies are constructed on double-sided pcb with the topside acting as earth plane. The pa is assembled on a single-sided board with interconnections made through insulated islands formed by small pieces of pcb, copper-side up, secured to the copper-foil ground plane by an epoxy adhesive.

The backplate also carries a miniature BNC socket connected internally to a wire loop adjacent to the pa output; this

Right-hand side view. At rear, l to r: reference frequency oscillator, phase comparator, vco and vco buffer. Receiver at front

provides rf pickup so that the radiated frequency may be monitored on a counter when setting the frequency of the transmit heterodyne oscillators.

RF interconnections between receiver sub-assemblies, and between low-level sub-assemblies in the transmitter, are made through UR95 miniature coaxial cable; connections between pa input, output and antenna changeover relay are made through UR43.

The power input plug (SK1, Fig 70) is a miniature six-pole type with two pairs of three poles connected in parallel.

Alignment and test

The first step in alignment of the synthesizer is to set the reference oscillator frequency. This is carried out by connecting a frequency counter to the output of the second divider and adjusting C1 to give 25·000kHz. It is essential that this frequency is set accurately as it determines the channel spacing, and once set it should not be re-adjusted during subsequent alignment.

Right-hand side view. L to r: receive mixer (above), receive heterodyne oscillator-multiplier. RF preamplifier at right

Adjustment of the vco frequency is made by disconnecting its output from the programmable divider and setting the free-running oscillator to a frequency around mid-band, ie 11·5MHz. The actual frequency to which the oscillator is set is not critical, because when the programmable divider is reconnected the synthesizer will lock to the relevant channels, as determined by S1 and S2. The vco buffer tuned circuit is aligned by adjusting the core of T1 to give maximum rf output at mid-band frequency.

Table 15. Typical current readings (V_{cc} = 12·5V)

Synthesizer	
Reference frequency oscillator	24·5mA
Phase comparator	30mA
VCO	35mA
VCO buffer	15mA
Programmable divider	120mA
Decoder and display	Approx 200mA
Transmitter	
Heterodyne oscillator	59mA
Mixer	11·5mA
Driver TR7	100mA
TR8	400mA
Power amplifier	2A max
Speech processor	5mA
Access tone generator	17mA
Receiver	
Heterodyne oscillator	60mA
Mixer	12mA
RF amplifier	2·5mA
Converter	13·5mA
IF amplifier	12·5mA
Limiter-quad detector	45mA
AF amplifier (quiescent)	6·5mA

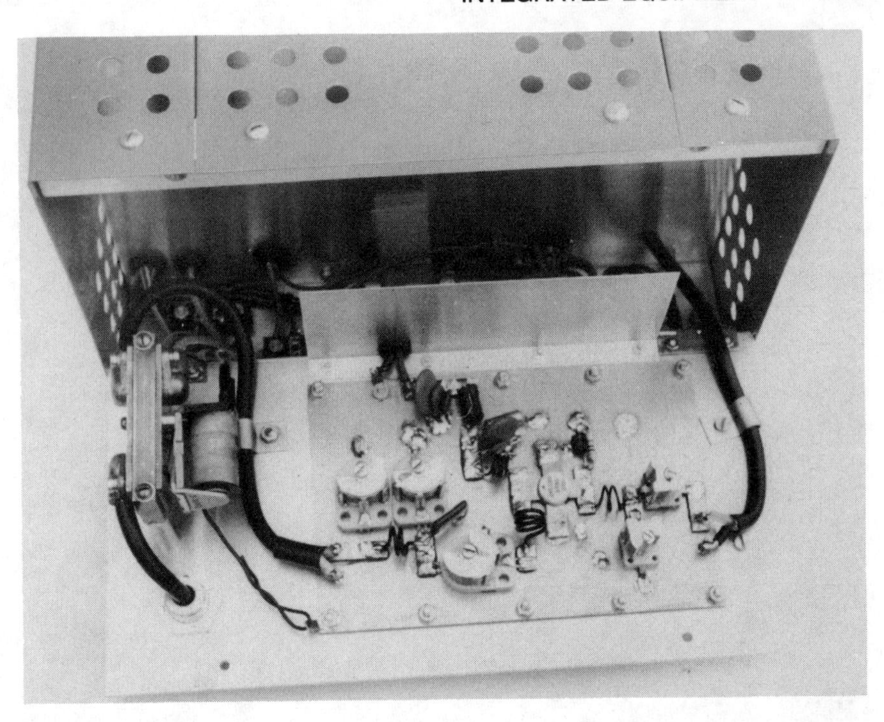

Rear view showing transmitter power amplifier. Antenna changeover relay at left

After the above procedures have been carried out the synthesizer will maintain lock over its range of 11·025 to 12MHz.

The final step is to adjust the loop filter to minimize any 25kHz reference frequency component that may be present in the output, which will appear as upper and lower sidebands spaced 25kHz from the selected frequency. This adjustment is carried out by listening to the synthesizer output on an hf receiver with the bfo switched on, and loosely-coupled through screened cable to the output of the vco buffer. The receiver is then detuned 25kHz either side of the selected frequency (which will appear as a pure cw note) to detect one of the sidebands, and RV1 is adjusted until the sideband is at minimum level. When RV1 is correctly adjusted the sideband will be either undetectable or at a very low level; this condition obtains when RV1 is set to a resistance of approximately 8kΩ.

Adequate output from the vco buffer to drive both transmit and receive mixers is obtained with the gain control RV2 set to approximately mid-position.

CHAPTER 7

Filters

A look at the frequency allocations in the uhf and vhf portions of the spectrum shows that the amateur bands lie in between various tv and fm broadcast bands, and this almost inevitably leads to some interference. Fig 1 indicates the most likely causes by showing the relative positions of the tv bands and harmonics of the vhf and uhf amateur bands.

The approach to overcome this problem will have to be rather different from that normally applied to hf band equipment, where often the matter can be resolved by use of a low-pass filter at the transmitter and a high-pass filter in the receiver input.

The most satisfactory method is to use some form of band-pass filter suitable for each of the bands concerned. The filter may be either a multi-element type with a relatively wide band, say 5 to 7 per cent of the frequency being used, or a narrow band, high-*Q* stripline type which is tuned to the frequency in use.

The former is the more elegant approach but the design, and especially the setting up, of such a filter without fairly elaborate test equipment is not easy if the insertion loss is to be kept down to a maximum of 1dB.

The high-*Q* strip or tube line filter on the other hand is readily made and tuned, but will also have to be adjusted for any appreciable change in operating frequency. This can be a problem when a vfo is used.

Either method will provide a very considerable measure of protection against out-of-band radiation such as harmonics and spurious emissions from transmitters.

Low-power bandpass filter

A simple bandpass filter can be made by overcoupling two pairs of tuned circuits and then coupling them together through a suitably small capacitor. A screen is fitted between the pairs to reduce stray coupling (Fig 2).

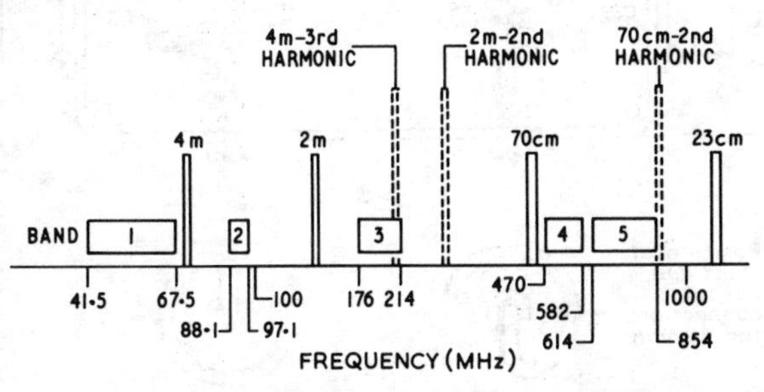

Fig 1. Chart illustrating relationship between the bands and harmonics from the amateur vhf and uhf bands

Small bandpass filter for 144MHz

The bandpass filter shown in Fig 4 is suitable for use either with receivers or low-power transmitters.

It consists of two tuned circuits, the inductors of which are substantially coils of relatively small dimensions, with a long tail that enables convenient connections to be available for matching into a 50 or 75Ω system.

Coupling between the tuned circuits may be either by a small capacitance (wire as shown in the diagram) or inductance. The latter will require an appropriate aperture cut in the central screen and once fixed in position, it is difficult to make adjustments unless the screen is made moveable. The bandwidth that may be obtained with this filter is 0·5MHz to 2MHz.

If a filter less than 2¾in long is needed, then the long tail can be omitted, making the connections on to the lower turn of each coil. This tends to be difficult unless the coil can be rotated about its axis.

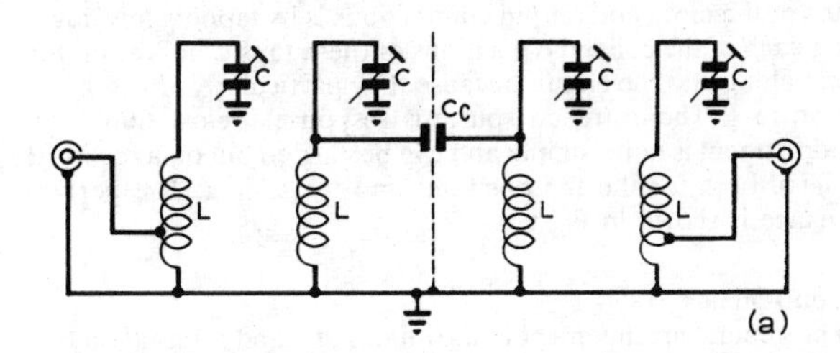

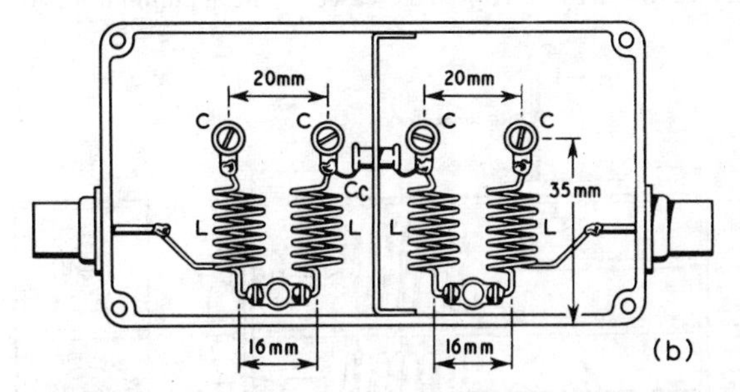

Fig 2. (a) Filter circuit Cc = 0·5pF, C = 6·0pF max, L = 6½ turns of 18swg ⅜in dia, spaced one turn. Tap at one turn up on end coils. As can be seen from the layout (b) the whole unit can be built into a small die-cast box. In the prototype, concentric ceramic trimmers were used but there is space for small air trimmers which are necessary if high-power operation is required. In any case air trimmers are desirable to avoid heating of the dielectric and to avoid breakdown due to the high voltage which will develop in a high-*Q* circuit

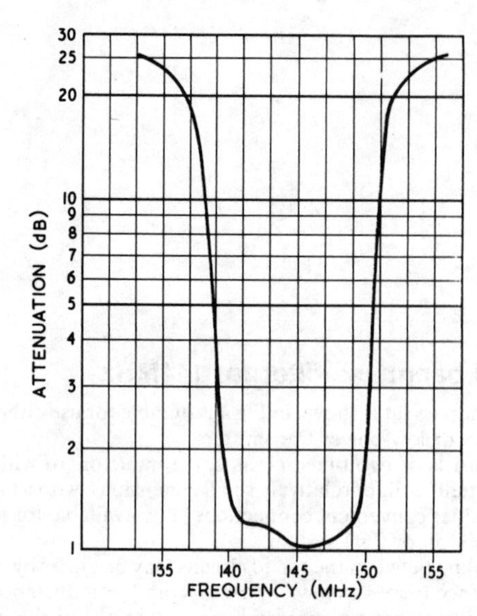

Fig 3. Performance curve of the filter described and shown in Fig 2

A compact bandpass filter for 144MHz

In this filter, the tuned circuits consist of a simple helix tuned by a small top capacitor. The two tuned circuits are arranged so that they are slightly over-coupled in order to provide an adequate bandwidth, which in this case is 4MHz wide with a maximum variation of 0·1dB and an insertion loss of 0·4dB. Coupling of the input and output connections is by tapping low down on each of the coils; the positions of these taps is important for matching into the circuit because they particularly affect insertion loss. There are no spurious responses below 600MHz, adjustment is quite simple and can be carried out on a received signal both for the tap positions and the tuning. The performance is shown in Fig 5.

Construction

The general arrangement is shown in Fig 6 and is based on the standard $4\frac{3}{4}$in by $3\frac{3}{4}$in by 2in die-cast box; the aluminium version

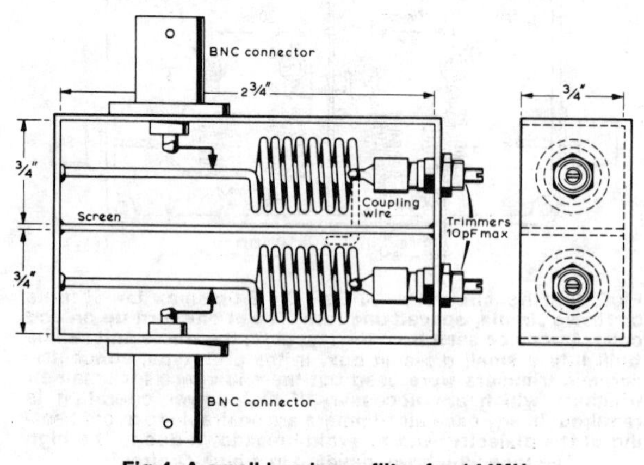

Fig 4. A small bandpass filter for 144MHz

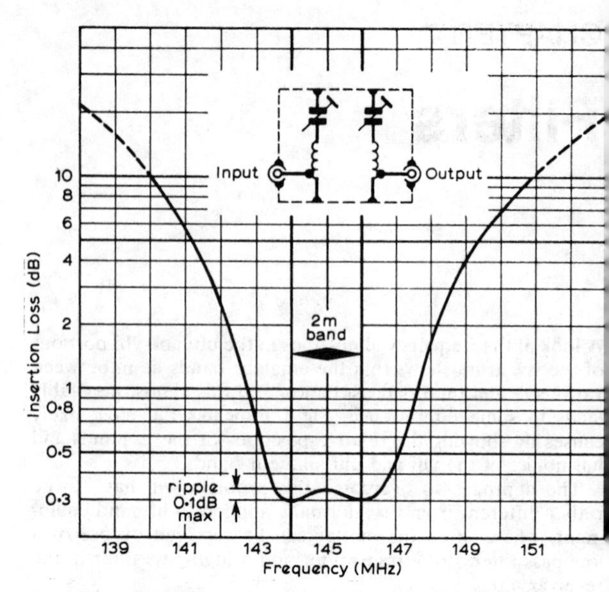

Fig 5. Performance of the 144MHz bandpass filter

of which is preferred. In the prototype, type N connections have been used, but any of the usual alternatives may be substituted.

The tuning capacitors used are not ideal, but it is doubtful if there is a readily available cheap alternative. With capacitors of lower minimum capacitance it would be possible to increase the value of the inductor, but is not thought there would be any significant improvement in performance. If a different type of

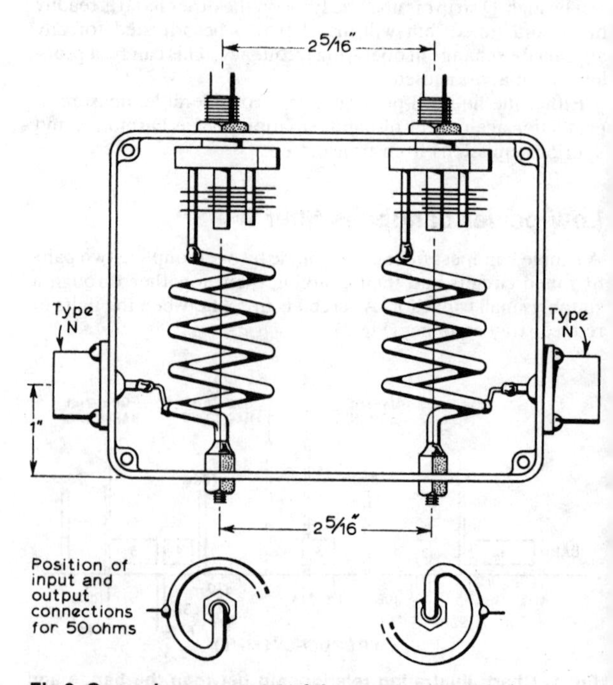

Fig 6. General arrangement of the compact 144MHz bandpass filter

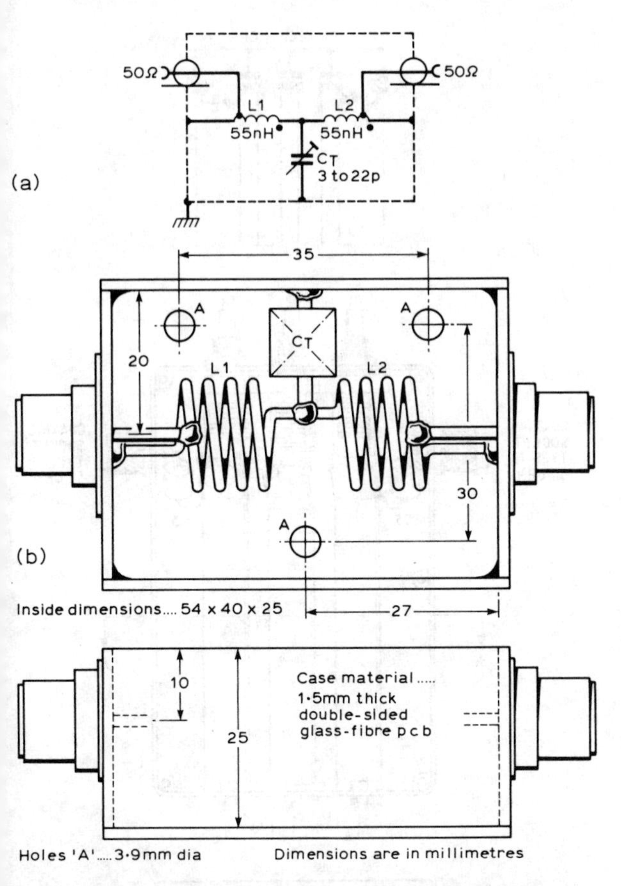

Fig 7. (a) Filter circuit. The junction of L1, L2 and C_T is suspended freely, supported only by the tag of C_T. The earth end of L1 and L2 is on the base of the enclosure directly under the end of the coil. All joints of encasing pcb strips are soldered. Coil details, L1 and L2: 4t 16swg tcw, 12·5mm i.d., 12·5mm long, separation 10mm, taps ½t from earth. (b) Typical construction, plan and side views.

capacitor is used it should be remembered that the voltage across it will be relatively high.

The inductors are made from $\frac{7}{8}$in diameter copper wound on a $\frac{7}{8}$in mandrel; they consist of four full turns plus that required at the lower end to reach the central fixing. Care is needed to ensure that the coil spacing is correct; with the dimension given there is sufficient overcoupling to give a small ripple at the nose of the response curve. The method of fixing adopted in the prototype was to solder the $\frac{1}{8}$in diameter copper into a socket as used for the Erie type K1700 stand-off capacitor (see Fig 6) with the capacitor removed. Any alternative method of making a good electrical contact to the box would be suitable, bearing in mind the relatively high circulating current involved.

The tuning capacitors are Jackson type C804 trimmers (3·5–15pF) with two plates removed from both the rotor and stator, leaving three fixed and three moving.

When the capacitor and coil are mounted and soldered together, the circuits should be rotated so that the tap point is opposite the input and output connectors; the connections being made of 16swg copper wire.

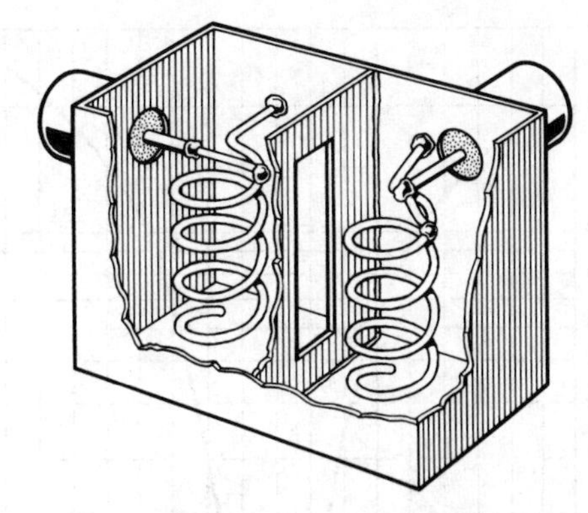

Fig 8. General arrangement of the 432MHz helical filter

A simple modified T filter for 144MHz

A simple filter designed by G8IPQ and shown in Fig 7 has bandpass characteristics and can be matched for its input and output impedances. It will provide significant second harmonic (288MHz) attenuation. There is little detail needing description. Adjustment of the taps is quite straightforward and may be carried out with either a signal generator or by receiving a beacon. On transmit the tuning should be carried out using a terminated power output meter.

When correctly adjusted, the insertion loss should be less than 1dB and second harmonic suppression should be −35dB.

432MHz helical resonator filter

This is a practical bandpass filter for the 432MHz band using two helical resonators coupled by an iris in the separating screen, see Figs 8 and 9. It has an insertion loss of less than 1dB with more than 20dB attenuation outside the pass band, as shown in Fig 10.

High-power bandpass filter

Filters for use with transmitters of output powers up to 100–120W can readily be constructed using stripline tuned circuits. The design to be described here features three tuned circuits; a simplified version for 144MHz using only two tuned circuits is described later.

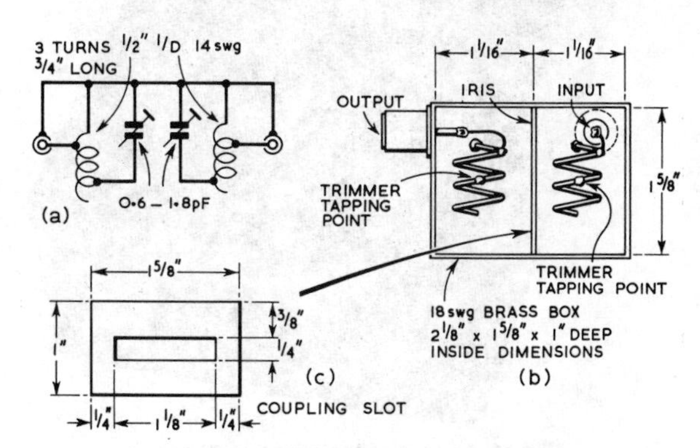

Fig 9. Layout of the 432MHz helical filter

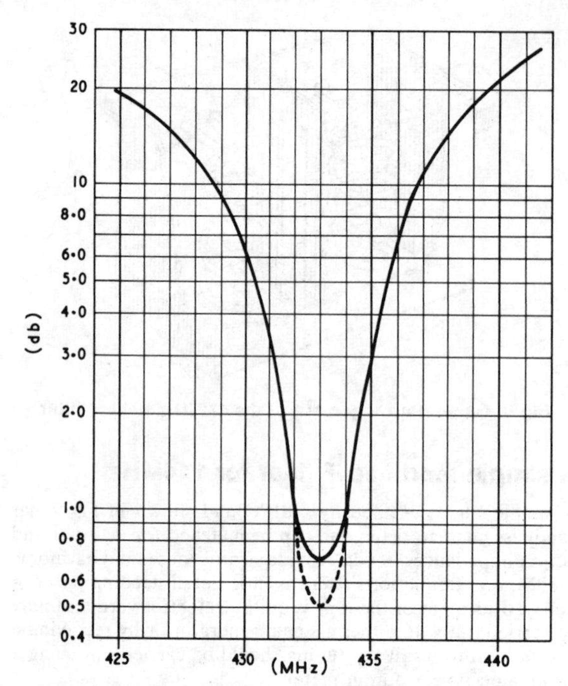

Fig 10. Performance curve of the 432MHz helical filter

The arrangement is of three shortened striplines tuned by capacitors at the top end. Input and output coupling is through small fixed capacitors to the top end of the outer lines; the third (central) line is free and couples the input and output circuits.

The striplines are made of 1in wide copper and in order to get these large units into the box without overcoupling they are set

Fig 11. Layout of the stripline filter

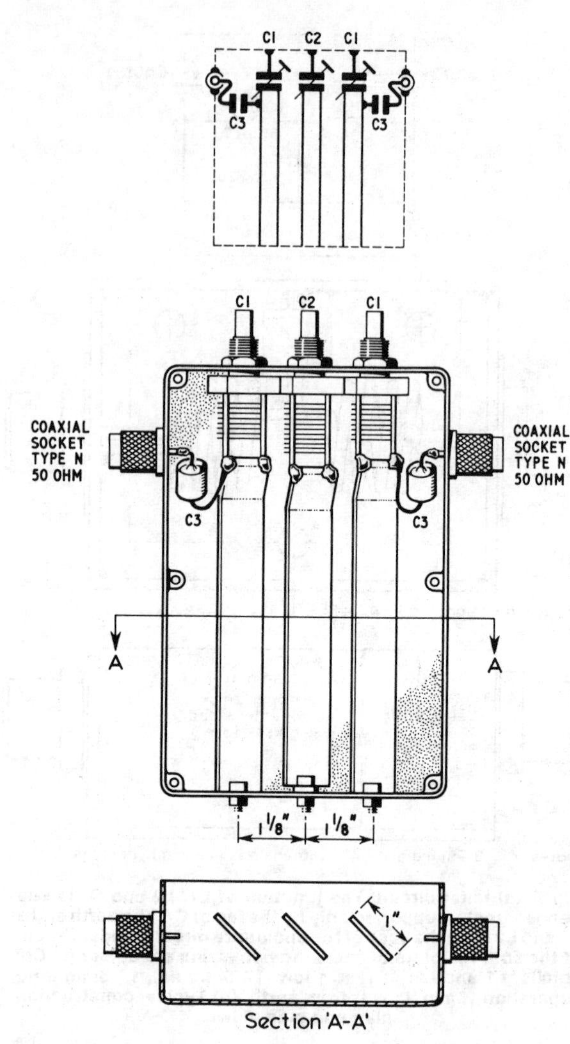

Fig 12. Mechanical layout and electrical circuit of the 144MHz filter. For 432MHz a smaller, 4¾in by 3¾in box is used

	144MHz	432MHz
Line length (in)	6⅛*	2½
Line size (in)	1×1/16	1×1/32
Line centres (in)	1⅛	1¼
C1 pF (Jackson C804)	50	50
C2 pF (Jackson C804)	60	15–0·045in spacing
C3 pF	4·4 (see text)	5
Insertion loss (dB)	0·6	1·2
Bandwidth (MHz)	6	10
Out of band attenuation (dB)	26	26
VSWR-50Ω	1·1	1·1
Connectors	Type N	Type N

* Central line approx 3/16in shorter to allow for rib in cast box and longer capacitor.

at an angle of 45° (incidentally this angle will be provided naturally if the standard type of trimmer is used with the centres given). Fixing of the line to the end wall of the box is provided by 0BA brass cheesehead bolts with saw cut opened to allow the line to be brazed centrally to the end.

The top end of the line is bent to make contact with both the capacitor stator pillars, which are soldered directly to the line

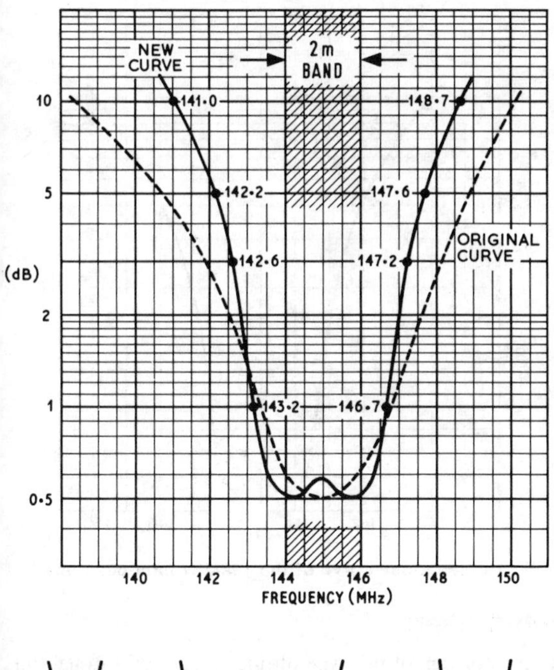

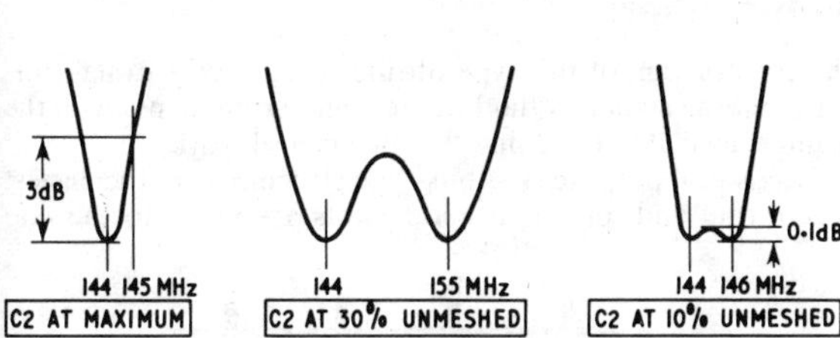

Fig 13. Performance curve of the 144MHz strip line filter

after assembly—a fairly large soldering iron will be needed for this.

Input and output capacitors are taken directly from the connectors to the top of the respective line. Setting up is straightforward provided an output power measuring device of some form is available. Initially, C2 should be set near maximum capacitance, this and the C1s are then adjusted for maximum output, taking care to keep the C1s value similar. If this is not done an asymmetrical response will result.

In the 432MHz filter there is a response at 288MHz, and although this is some 13dB down on the wanted frequency it should be borne in mind in cases where this frequency is likely to appear in the transmitter output, such as in the case of a varactor tripler directly feeding the antenna.

From the curve of the 144MHz filter the insertion loss (at the band centre) is less than 1dB. On actual power measurement this was found to be a loss of approximately 10 per cent (or 0·5dB) which is a small price to pay for keeping the harmonics under control.

Although the 144MHz unit was intended for this one band only, it is also suitable with the present mechanical details for use up to about 175MHz.

The original dimension (C3) is for 50Ω line; for use with 75Ω line the value of this component should be reduced to 3·2–3·4pF.

However, the insertion loss is in fact sufficiently low for its

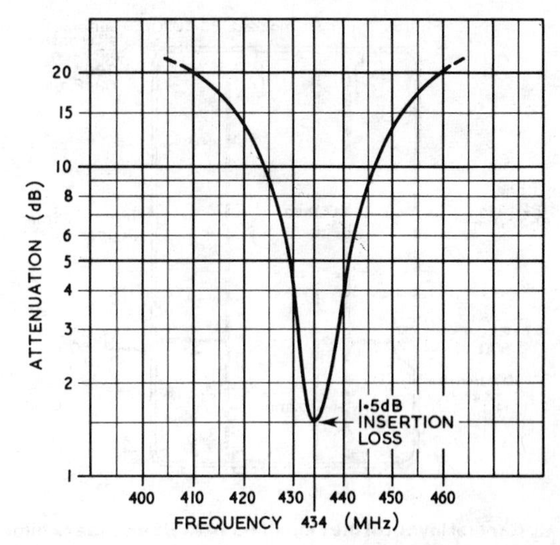

Fig 14. Performance curve of the 432MHz stripline filter

use in feeders of either impedance. The capacitors C3 should preferably be made adjustable and standard Philips type trimmers of 2–8pF are suitable. They should be about ⅛in mesh for 50Ω.

This filter will also be of use for a receiver which is subject to adjacent high-strength signals such as from tv transmitters.

The centre line with C2 set at maximum tunes to about 144MHz. Hence, when the input and output lines are tuned to resonance with it the overall response is quite sharp and is about 3dB down at ±1MHz. However, as C2 is decreased in value the higher frequency cut-off moves upwards and a double humped response develops. With C2 at about 10 per cent unmeshed there is an almost square-shaped response 2MHz wide with a slight dip in the middle of around 0·1dB.

Alignment procedure

Set the coupling capacitors (C3 Philips 2–8pF trimmers) meshed by ⅛in and C2 at 10 per cent unmeshed. Apply a signal and peak the output by adjustment of C1. Slightly readjust the coupling capacitors in step, retuning C1 until maximum power transfer is achieved.

Replace and fix the box lid before the final adjustment of the capacitors C1. If transmitter output at several frequencies in the band is available, make the adjustments at the centre of the wanted range. If after this the higher frequencies show reduced output, reduce the capacitance of C2 slightly. If, however, there is some loss at the lower frequencies, retune both C1 to optimize the lower frequencies and adjust C2 to maintain output at the higher frequency.

Simplified high power bandpass filter for 144MHz

In this design, only two tuned high-Q linear circuits are used, with direct connection to the striplines for input and output matching. The spacing between the lines has been set at the critical distance.

The striplines are made of 25mm by 1mm thick and 173mm long copper or brass, with allowance for the bend over (10mm) for fixing the line to the box.

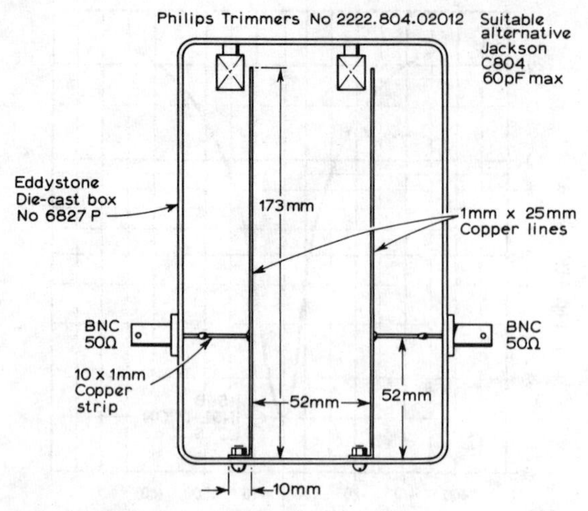

Fig 15. General layout of the simplified 144MHz bandpass filter

In Fig 15 the positions of the lines and the input and output connections are for 50Ω. For 75Ω (or any other impedance) these must be adjusted accordingly.

The mounted position of the lines is substantially central between the bottom of the die-cast box and the lid. Care should be taken to ensure a good contact between the striplines and the box.

The response curve shown in Fig 16 shows that the insertion loss is less than 0·5dB and the bandwidth is 3MHz at −1dB.

The tuning capacitors used in the original unit were Philips type 2222.804.2012 having a capacitance range of 5–64pF, but standard air-spaced units may be used as an alternative.

Trap filter for 144MHz

This type of filter is useful for duplex operation or in a repeater station, where the transmitter is likely to cause considerable desensitization of the receiver.

Basically this type of filter is connected in the receiver antenna feeder with circuits tuned to the transmitter frequency, coupled to them to "suck out" the transmitter signal. These filters are single-frequency devices and assist in operating a receiver within about 500kHz of the transmitter frequency. It should, however, be recognized that a filter alone will not permit such small frequency separation. Relative antenna positioning will have a considerable effect on the amount of transmitter signal that is present at the receiver antenna.

In order to obtain suitably high performance in a simple filter, the tuned circuits must be of high-Q and the simplest method of obtaining a suitable value is to use line circuits in which the inductor is at least 85 per cent of $\lambda/4$ tuned with a minimum amount of top capacitance.

As shown in the general arrangement, Fig 17, the four linear circuits are tuned by top disc-type trimmers. Circuits A and D are tuned to the transmitter frequency, and B and C to the receiver frequency. Coupling between circuits is restricted to the gaps in the inter-circuit screening.

It is important that there is good bonding between all the joints of the enclosure and inter-circuit screens if the performance is to be good.

Although this type of filter has a very significant performance, it is unlikely that sufficient signal isolation will be provided by use of the filter alone.

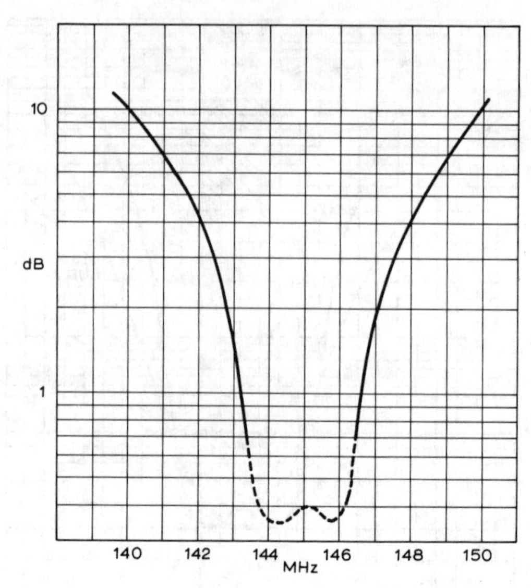

Fig 16. Response curve of the 144MHz bandpass filter

High-Q filters

The construction of this type of filter is relatively straightforward, but the actual method will to some extent depend on the facilities available for doing the mechanical work.

For general purposes the box-type structures are the easiest to fabricate and, provided good joints are made to the end

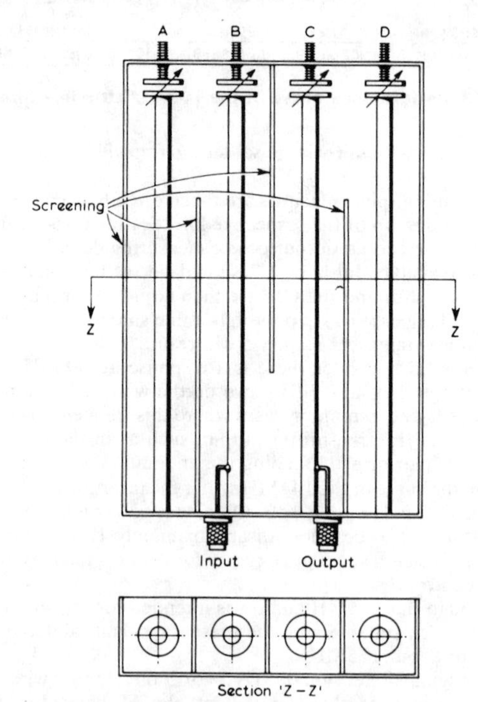

Fig 17. General arrangement of the 144MHz trap filter. The lines should be of ½ to ⅝in dia tube. The top capacitors consist of 1in dia discs. A suitable box size is 8in by 17in by 2in deep

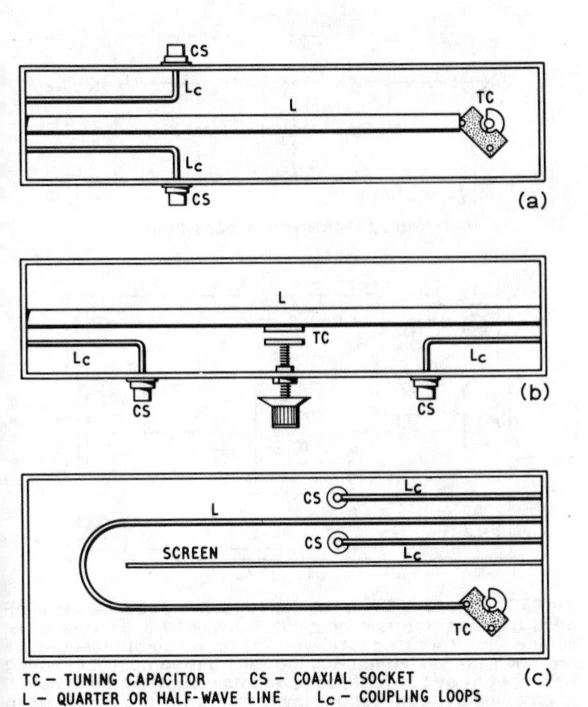

Fig 18. Typical forms of high-*Q* filter. (a) $\lambda/4$ line with tuning capacitor at one end. It is suitable for any of the bands, but at 70MHz is likely to be inconvenient. (b) $\lambda/2$ line with centre tuning capacitor. Particularly suitable for 432MHz and 1·3GHz. (c) $\lambda/4$ line folded into U-shape with a screen between the legs of the U-line. May be suitable for 70MHz

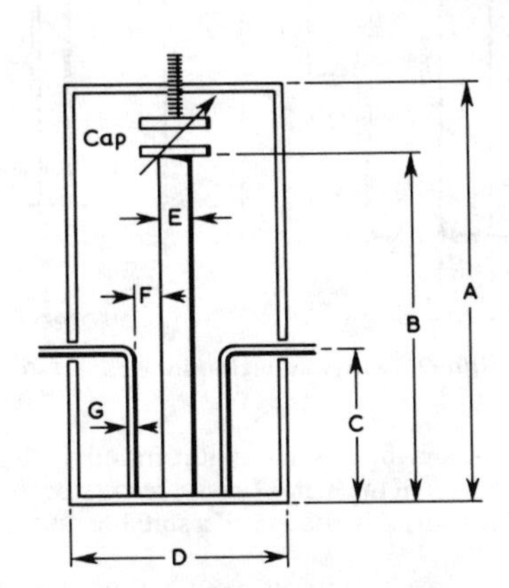

Fig 19. Showing a high-*Q* filter. The end capacitor may be a disc or conventional type, except at 432MHz or 1·3GHz when a disc must be used. The dimensions for each amateur band are given in the following table

Dimensions (in)	70MHz	144MHz	144MHz	144MHz	432MHz
A	39	19	14	12	$6\frac{1}{2}$
B	36	17	$12\frac{1}{2}$	10	6
C	16	8	$3\frac{1}{2}$	3	$1\frac{1}{4}$
D	3	3	4	$2\frac{1}{2}$	$1\frac{1}{2}$
E	$\frac{1}{2}$	$\frac{1}{2}$	$\frac{7}{8}$	$\frac{1}{2}$	$\frac{1}{2}$
F	$\frac{1}{4}$	$\frac{1}{4}$	16	$\frac{1}{8}$	$\frac{1}{8}$
G (swg)	12/14	12/14	14	14	14
Cap (pF)	15	15	15	15	7·5

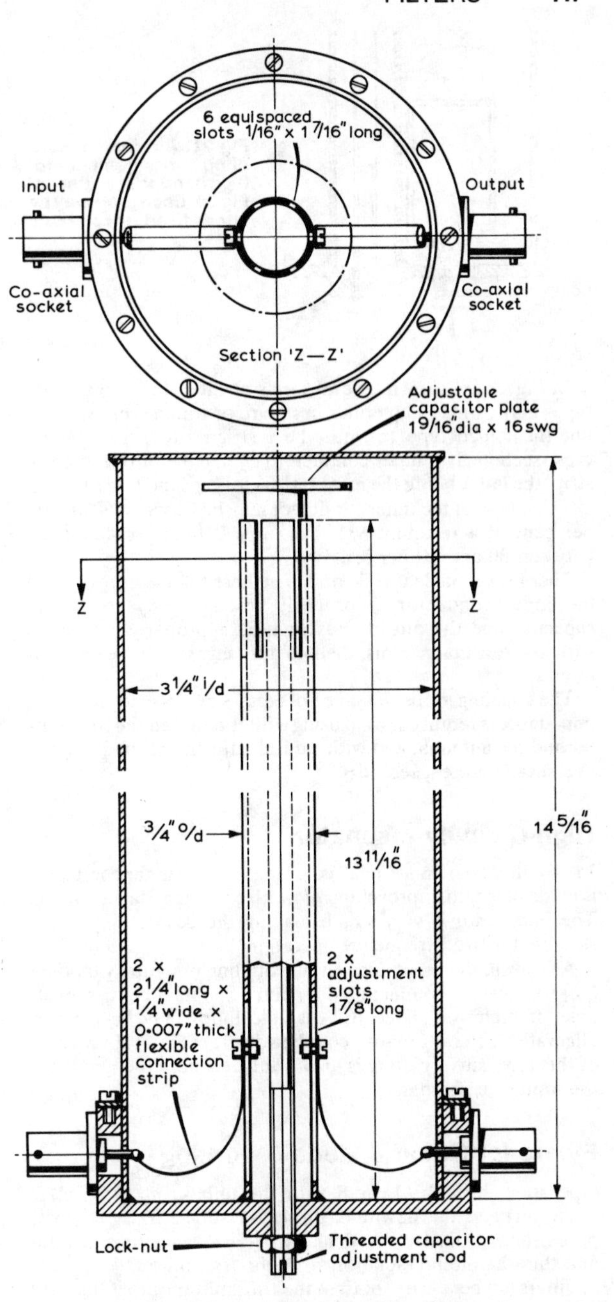

Fig 20. High-*Q* cavity resonator filter for 144MHz. Material is silver-plated copper or brass throughout

plates by screwing together or soldering, a satisfactorily high *Q* will be obtained.

The form of the circuit will generally be of near $\lambda/4$ long strip or tube tuned at one end or, for the higher frequencies, $\lambda/2$ lines tuned at the centre. In the case of the lowest frequency band (70MHz) the length of the filter may be inconveniently long and in this case the line may be folded provided the two legs are screened from one another.

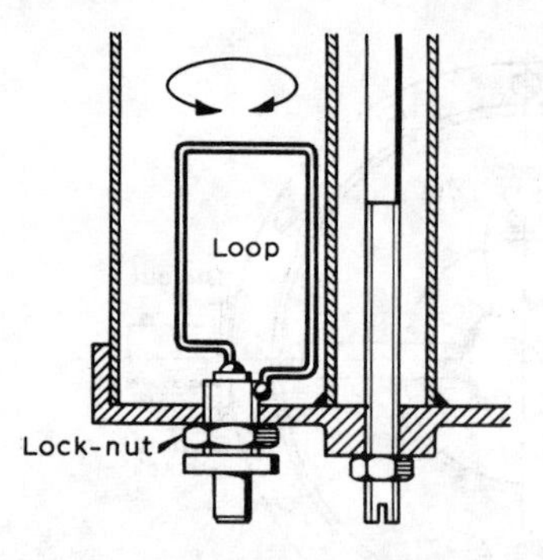

Fig 21. Alternative coupling arrangement for the bandpass filter of Fig 20. Each loop may be either fixed or rotatable

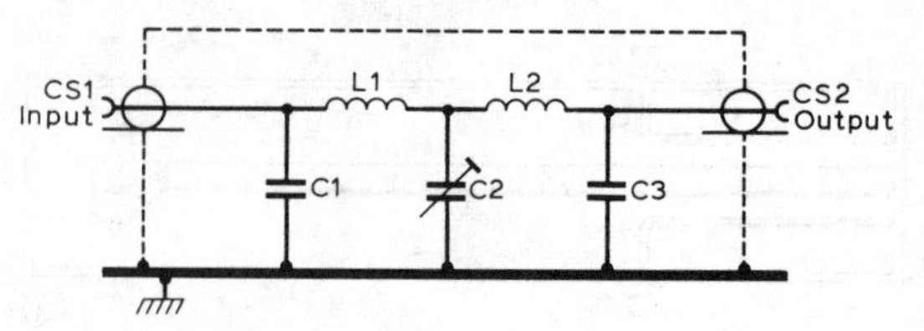

Fig 22. 148MHz low-pass filter

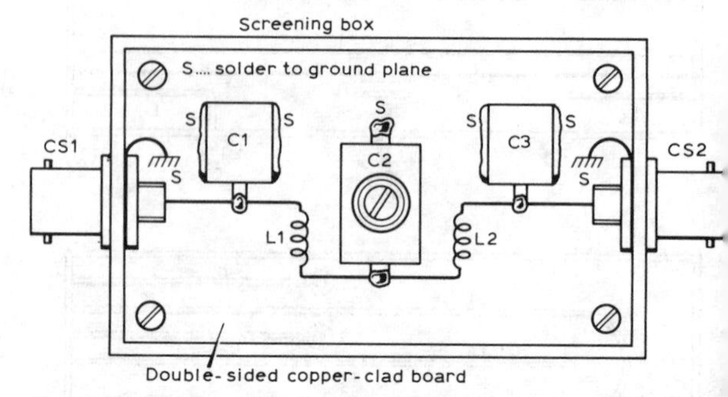

Fig 23. C1/C3, 22pF low-loss mica capacitor, 300V. C2, 10–60pF mica trimmer, shortest possible leads. L1/L2, 3 turns close wound $\frac{1}{4}$in (6mm) i.d., 16swg. These inductors should be arranged for minimum coupling (at right-angles). Screening box, $2\frac{1}{2}$ by $1\frac{1}{2}$ by $1\frac{1}{4}$in high, components mounted on pcb bolted to box, positive connections made from coaxial connectors to the pcb

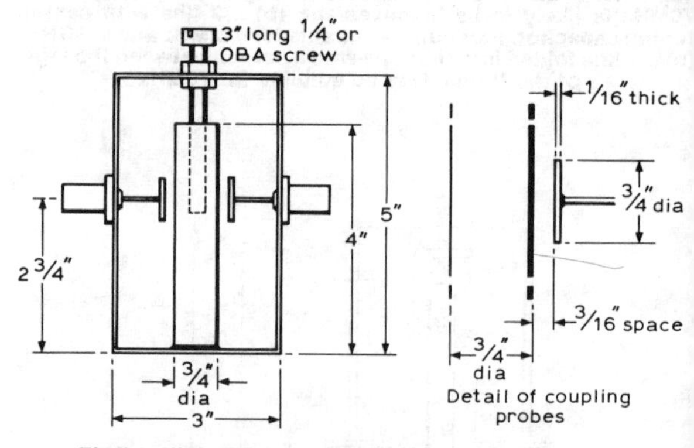

Fig 24. High-*Q* cavity. Insertion loss is 0·4–0·5dB

In Fig 18 are shown several forms of filter, the two straight types may be made up either in square or round cross-section, but the folded type (c) must be restricted to a rectangular cross-section. The inner conductor (L) may be of rod, tube or strip, the latter being the most satisfactory for the folded type.

The length of the inner conductor may be between 60 and 90 per cent of a resonant $\lambda/4$, but for $\lambda/2$ filters it should be between 80 and 90 per cent.

There is a good deal of flexibility in these filters and, provided the inner conductor is properly resonated by its tuning capacitor and the outside box or tube is properly connected with low-resistance joints, then no difficulty should be encountered.

The coupling loops should be of equal size since no change in impedance is required when using a filter between the transmitter and the antenna, and with careful adjustment the insertion loss should not exceed 1dB.

High-*Q* cavity resonator

In this filter (shown in Fig 20) the length of the inner conductor is made of length approaching $\lambda/4$ with end-capacitance tuning. The bandwidth is very small, making the device only really suitable for fixed-frequency operation.

As shown, the input and output coupling is made by tapping on to the centre conductor, the point of contact being adjustable. If preferred, fixed or rotatable loops may be used as illustrated in the alternative coupling diagram Fig 21. In cavities of this type, silver plating is an advantage where the aim is for the utmost performance.

Filters for Oscar 8 Mode J working

Operation through Oscar 8 with the uplink on 145·9MHz (transmit) and the downlink on 435·1–435·2MHz (receive) poses some problems, particularly of receiver desensitization and third-harmonic radiation from the transmitter.

Filters are necessary, both in the transmitter output line and in front of the receiver, to give adequate isolation.

The bandpass filters described earlier are very suitable for transmitter output, though as an alternative, a $\lambda/2$ low-pass filter may be used. Details of such a filter are given in Figs 22 and 23. This filter is basically similar to a Chebyshev design having a 1–2dB ripple over a 130–150MHz band, with a cut-off frequency of 250–275MHz, having a second harmonic attenuation (292MHz) of more than 10dB and greater than 50dB on the third harmonic (437·7MHz).

On the receiver side (435MHz downlink) an effective protection from the 145MHz transmission can be provided by a high-*Q* narrow-band filter such as illustrated in Fig 19 or a scaled down version of the high-*Q* cavity resonator shown in Fig 20. As a further alternative details of a suitable unit are given in Fig 24.

The body is 3in id thin-wall copper tube, and the inner conductor is $\frac{3}{4}$in id thin-wall copper tube. Coupling discs are $\frac{3}{4}$in diameter, $\frac{1}{6}$in thick, attached by 16swg wire to the inner of the coaxial sockets.

The body, inner tube and coupling are fitted together, and then the base copper is soldered to the tube. The top plate with trimmer screw $\frac{1}{4}$in or 0BA has a nut each side of the plate which is then soldered and the thread cleared if necessary. The top plate (copper sheet) is soldered around the edge. Some advantage will be found by punching a hole in the base to assist centralizing the inner tube.

CHAPTER 8

Antennas

The antenna is the connecting link between free space and the transmitter or receiver. As such, it plays an essential part in determining the characteristics of the system in which it is used. Both the design of the antenna and its working environment will determine its effectiveness in any particular system.

In many amateur systems the requirement is for a highly directive pattern to achieve increased gain and interference reduction. However, for such systems as repeaters and mobile communication it is often necessary to radiate energy in an omnidirectional pattern in order to provide a broadcast type of coverage.

Regardless of the system's application, all antennas have certain basic properties which can be well defined. The characteristics which are of most interest to the amateur and professional designer alike are the radiation pattern, polarization, gain and impedance.

The radiation pattern of an antenna is generally its most basic requirement since it determines the spatial distribution of the radiated energy, that is the direction in which the signal is transmitted or whence it is received. With amateur antennas, which normally have radiation patterns of a simple shape, the important characteristics of the patterns can be specified by the beamwidth and sidelobe level in the two principal planes, usually taken as the E (or vertical) plane and the H (or horizontal) plane.

The beamwidth in a principal plane of the radiation pattern is defined by the pattern's angular width at a level which is 3dB down from the beam maximum. This is also known as the *half-power beamwidth*.

Sidelobes (radiation in any direction other than that required) and the front-to-back ratio with directional beam antennas (the ratio of the energy radiated in the required direction to that radiated in the diametrically opposite direction) are both expressed as the number of decibels down with respect to the maximum radiation of the main beam.

Polarization

The polarization of an antenna is usually defined in terms of the orientation of the electric-field vector in the direction of maximum radiation. In simple terms a vertical dipole above ground will radiate vertically polarized signals, while a horizontal dipole above ground will radiate horizontally polarized signals.

Radio waves are constituted from electric and magnetic fields mutually coupled at right-angles and also at right-angles to the direction of propagation. The ratio of the electric component E to the magnetic component H in free space ($E/H = Z$) is known as the "impedance of free space" and has a value of approximately 377Ω. It can be seen from this statement that an antenna can also be considered as a matching device or transformer between the transmission line and free space.

In addition to linearly polarized antennas, the use of circular polarization has become quite common for receiving signals from rotating amateur satellites, or where polarization has changed due to propagation or terrain effects. Circular polarization can be produced by the helix antenna or can be produced by two perpendicular linearly polarized radiation patterns which have a 90° phase difference. Depending on the sense of rotation, circular polarization may be either right-handed or left-handed. To be compatible the signal must be of the same sense as that transmitted when it reaches the receiving antenna.

A dipole will receive an equal signal from a circularly polarized wave irrespective of whether it is mounted horizontally, vertically or in an intermediate position, but the signal strength will be 3dB less than if an antenna designed for circular polarization of the same sense is used. This means that the full gain of a helix, for example, will only be realized when received by a similar antenna of the same sense of rotation.

An antenna may radiate unwanted energy in a polarization which is different from the polarization in which the antenna was intended to be used. This unwanted radiation is known as *cross-polarization*. For linearly polarized antennas, the cross-polarization is perpendicular to the intended polarization. For circular polarization the cross-polarization may be considered as the component which has the sense of rotation opposite to that of the intended sense. This is commonly expressed as the deviation from the perfect circular polarization in terms of the axial ratio or the ellipticity. It is worth noting that with linearly polarized antennas, particularly beams, radiated energy from the side of the beam can be of the opposite polarization to that of the main lobe and can be of a complex or elliptical nature. This often has the effect with a cross-polarized system of giving a maximum received signal in a direction other than that in which the beam is pointing!

Gain

The gain of an antenna is a basic property which is frequently used as a figure of merit. Gain is closely associated with directivity, which in turn is dependent upon the radiation patterns of an antenna. The gain is defined as the ratio of the maximum radiation signal in a given direction to the maximum radiation signal produced in the same direction from a reference antenna with the same power input. The reference antenna is normally an *isotropic radiator*, a hypothetical lossless antenna which radiates uniformly in all directions. One way to appreciate the meaning of antenna gain is to imagine the radiator to be totally enclosed in a hollow sphere, as indicated in Fig 1. If the radiation is distributed uniformly over the interior surface of the sphere the radiator is said to be *isotropic.* An antenna which causes the radiation to be concentrated into any particular area of the inside surface of the sphere, and which thereby produces a greater intensity than that produced by an isotropic radiator

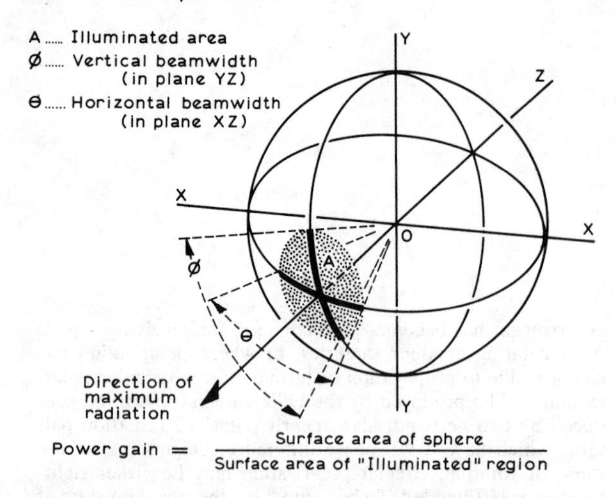

Fig 1. Radiation from an antenna. An isotropic radiator at point O will give uniform illumination over the inner surface of the sphere. A directional radiator will concentrate the energy into a beam which will illuminate only a portion of the sphere, as shown shaded

fed with equal power, is said to have *gain*. This gain is inversely proportional to the fraction of the total interior surface area which receives the concentrated radiation.

The gain of an antenna is usually expressed as a power ratio, either as a multiple of so many "times", or in decibel units. For example, a power gain of 20 times could be represented as 13dB (ie $10 \log_{10} 20$).

The truly isotropic radiator is a purely theoretical concept, and in practice the gain of beam antennas is usually compared with the radiation from a single $\lambda/2$ dipole fed with an equal amount of power. The radiation pattern of even a single $\lambda/2$ dipole is markedly non-uniform, and in consequence the power gain of such an antenna compared with the hypothetical isotropic radiator is 1·64 times or 2·15dB. Since the $\lambda/2$ dipole is the simplest practical form of radiator it is generally accepted as a basis of comparison.

The area of "illumination" is not sharply defined as shown by the shaded region in Fig 1 but falls away gradually from the centre of the area. The boundaries of the illuminated area are determined by joining together all points where the radiation intensity has fallen by half (ie 3dB) (the *half-power points*). The gain of the antenna can then be determined by dividing the total surface area of the sphere by the illuminated area: eg if the total surface area were 100cm² and the illuminated area bounded by the half-power points were 20cm², the gain of the antenna would be five times or 7dB.

This concept of gain measurement can be rationalized to a

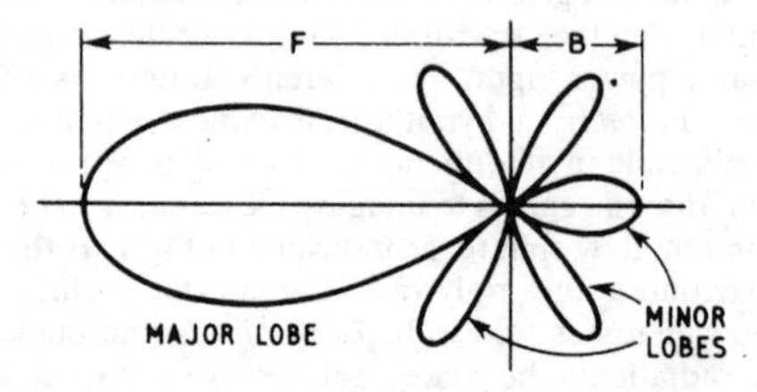

Fig 2. Typical polar diagram of a vhf antenna. The front-to-back ratio is indicated by the ratio of F to B, ie F/B

simple formula and compared to the more practical $\lambda/2$ dipole to give a close estimate of antenna gain (normally better than within 1dB if the lobe structure is simple and of a low level). By measuring the half-power points in both of the principal planes the following relationships can be used.

$$\text{Gain relative to } \lambda/2 \text{ dipole} = \frac{27{,}000}{\theta_E \theta_H}$$

where θ_E is the angular width in degrees at the half-power points in the E or vertical plane and θ_H is the angular width in degrees at the half-power points in the H or horizontal plane.

$$\text{So gain in decibels relative to dipole (dBD)} = 10 \log_{10} \left[\frac{27{,}000}{\theta_E \theta_H}\right]$$

Besides examining the action of a transmitting antenna array in concentrating the radiated power into a beam it is also helpful to examine the way in which the same antenna structure will affect the reception of an incoming signal. In this study it is convenient to introduce the concept of *capture area* or *aperture* of the antenna. This concept is frequently misunderstood, probably because it may appear to relate to the cross-sectional area of the beam (as represented by A in Fig 1). It is in fact related to the *inverse* of the cross-sectional area of the beam inasmuch as an antenna which has a high gain usually has a sharply focused beam (ie one small cross-sectional area) but at the same time the capture area of the antenna is large. The larger the capture area, the more effective is the antenna as compared with a simple dipole.

The actual size of the antenna system does not always give a reliable indication of the capture area. A high-gain array may have a capture area considerably greater than its frontal area as determined by its physical dimensions. The fundamental relationship between the capture area and the power gain of an antenna system is

$$A = \frac{G_I \lambda^2}{4\pi}$$

where A is the capture area and λ is the wavelength (measured in the same units as A) and G_I is the power gain relative to an isotropic radiator. A $\lambda/2$ dipole has a gain of 1·64 relative to an isotropic radiator, and therefore this formula can be modified so as to give the capture area in terms of the gain of a $\lambda/2$ dipole G_D instead of G_I simply by introducing the factor 1·64, thus:

$$A = \frac{1 \cdot 64 \times G_D \lambda^2}{4\pi} = \frac{0 \cdot 13\, G_D \lambda^2}{\pi} = 0 \cdot 041\, G_D \lambda^2$$

Note that for a dipole, since $G_D = 1$, the capture area is approximately $\lambda^2/8$.

This formula shows that if the wavelength is kept constant the capture area of an antenna is proportional to its gain, and therefore if an increase in gain results in a narrower beamwidth, this corresponds to a greater capture area (the term *beamwidth* being used here to signify both horizontal and vertical dimensions, ie in effect the cross-sectional area).

The formula also shows that for any given power gain the capture area is proportional to the square of the wavelength. For example, an antenna with a power gain of, say, 10 times relative to a dipole at 600MHz (0·5m) would have a capture area one-sixteenth of that of an antenna having a similar power gain at 150MHz (2m), and to achieve equal capture area the gain of the 600MHz antenna would thus have to be 16 times greater than that of the 150MHz one, ie 160 times relative to a dipole. This is unfortunate because it is the capture area of the antenna that determines its effectiveness in absorbing the

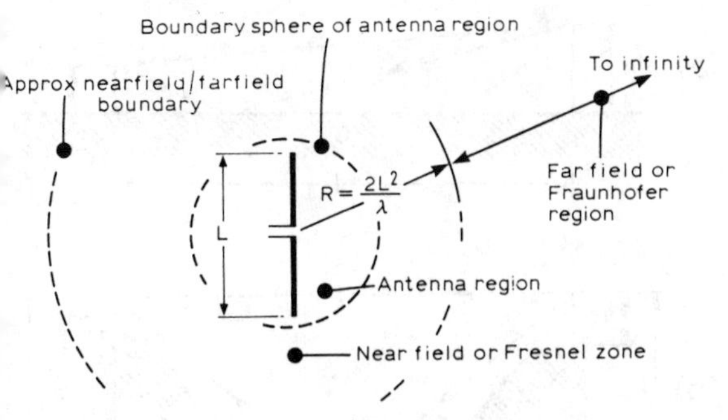

Fig 3. The near and far fields of an antenna

incoming radiation: it means that as the wavelength is reduced it becomes increasingly important to design an antenna to have greater gain.

Antenna height gain

A very important factor, which is often a rather "grey" region for many amateurs and professionals alike, is the effect of an antenna's height on its performance above ground. Similarly of interest are the effects that may be apparent due to surrounding terrain or nearby structures.

Apart from the changes of pattern due to ground reflections, adding or cancelling signals at various wavelength distances from the antenna, there is one other important mechanism to consider. It was previously mentioned that an antenna has an electric and magnetic field radiating from it. The electric field is the one normally considered the link between antennas as the magnetic field strength decreases with distance more rapidly than the electric field. Any object in the radiated fields will disrupt them, even the distant receiving antennas. However, there is a region of maximum electromagnetic intensity called the "near field" where an object has the most effect. Nearby structures, including the antenna mounting itself, will have an effect on the radiation pattern and often the impedance of the antenna.

A simple formula which gives an approximate distance outside of which measurements of the radiation patterns will have some sense is

$$R = \frac{2L^2}{\lambda}$$

where R is the distance, L is the largest linear dimension of the receiving or transmitting antenna and λ is the wavelength. All dimensions should be in the same units of measurements.

Referring to Fig 3, under ideal conditions in the Fraunhofer region measured field components are transverse and the shape of the field pattern is independent of the distance at which it is measured. However, in the Fresnel region the radial field may be appreciable and the shape of the field pattern is, in general, different as a function of distance from the antenna and is also changed by the measuring device.

Both the height above ground and disruption of the near field pattern will give an apparent or actual change of the received or transmitted signal. Assuming the antenna is mounted such that there is minimal change of the near field, the main consideration will be addition or cancellation of the field pattern due to ground reflections.

Several considerations then apply when deciding the height of the antenna above ground for optimum performance. The antenna should be above local screening from buildings and other obstacles. In addition, the rule-of-thumb figure of approximately 12m (40ft) is worth considering as in general this raises the antenna above the layer of electrical interference and signal variations caused by the heat layer above buildings.

If there is no screening and assuming the antenna is on a mast on a ground area reasonably flat for several miles, at low levels the radiation from it will tend to be raised in the vertical plane. As the height increases above ground the pattern will tend to level off, giving the main radiation in the required horizontal plane. However, secondary lobe structures will be present and it is rare that the antenna manufacturer's pattern will be obtained unless mounted under the same conditions as those used by the manufacturer.

In general, however, as height increases the pattern directivity improves and an additional gain of 6dB is obtained each time the mast height is doubled. Fig 5 gives approximate height gains obtained at various frequencies for various heights above ground. Over 12m above ground, assuming all obstacles have been cleared, a 24m (80ft) mast will be required to increase the gain a further 6dB. The additional expense for the mast is rarely justified by the 6dB gain improvement.

Should the station be well-sited, on a hill for instance, doubling the mast height may make little or no improvement as the effective height above ground can relate to a point at the bottom of the hill, not the base of the mast. Conversely, a station in a valley or behind a hill may find over a certain mast height a considerable increase in gain, much in excess of the 6dB, as a more favourable angle to the hilltop or actually looking over it is achieved. Often a change of the antenna's vertical mounting angle or polarization in this situation can give a gain improvement.

The three basic arrangements for receiving and transmitting antennas, and the intervening ground, are illustrated in Fig 6. The classic plane-earth case is shown in Fig 6(a), and under such conditions the signal received at the distant antenna is given by the relationship:

$$e = \text{constant} \times \frac{h_T\, h_R}{\lambda d^2}$$

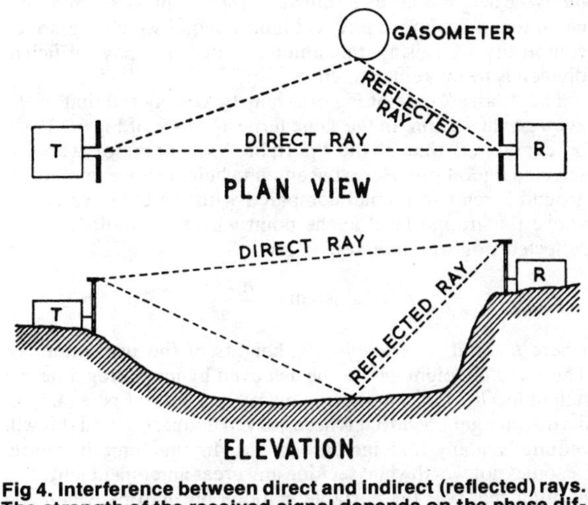

Fig 4. Interference between direct and indirect (reflected) rays. The strength of the received signal depends on the phase difference between the two rays when they arrive at the receiver, and on their respective intensities

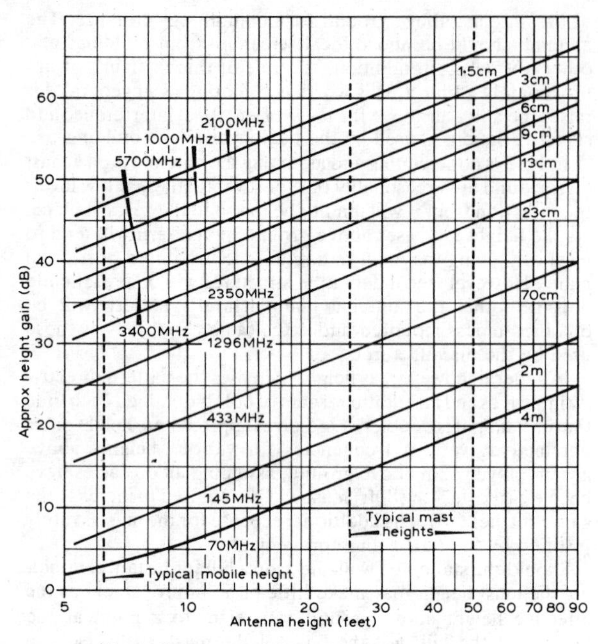

Fig 5. Antenna height gain correction factor

where h_T = Height of transmitting antenna
h_R = height of receiving antenna
λ = wavelength
d = distance between antenna

In this expression h_T, h_R and d must all be in the same units, and d must be much larger than either h_T or h_R (by a factor of at least 10): this is usually the case in practice.

From this expression it is clear that an increase in either h_T or h_R will result in a corresponding increase in e, and doubling the height will give an increase of 6dB. This is the 6dB "height gain" rule. It is worthwhile noting that for each 6dB improvement the height must be doubled, so there soon arises in practical antenna systems a physical limit beyond which the added complexity of raising the antenna does not pay sufficient dividends to make it attractive.

The "classic" case of Fig 6(a) may be considered that of the average vhf station. In the same terms the case of Fig 6(b) may be considered that of the "portable" vhf operator who has selected a good site. Here, the antenna height above immediate ground is relatively small compared with the effective height above the ground level at the point where the indirect ray is reflected from the intervening ground.

$$e = \text{constant} \times \frac{h'_T \cdot h'_R}{d^2}$$

where h'_T and h'_R are *effective* heights of the two antennas. There is still height gain to be achieved by increasing antenna height locally, but not at the same rate as in the first example. To obtain a gain of 6dB it is necessary to double h'_R, and this will require a many-fold increase in h_R. In the limit it clearly becomes not worthwhile seeking any great antenna height: this is often the case for portable stations on hilltops, when the increased loss in the feeders is less than offset by the small additional signal to be obtained by raising the antenna.

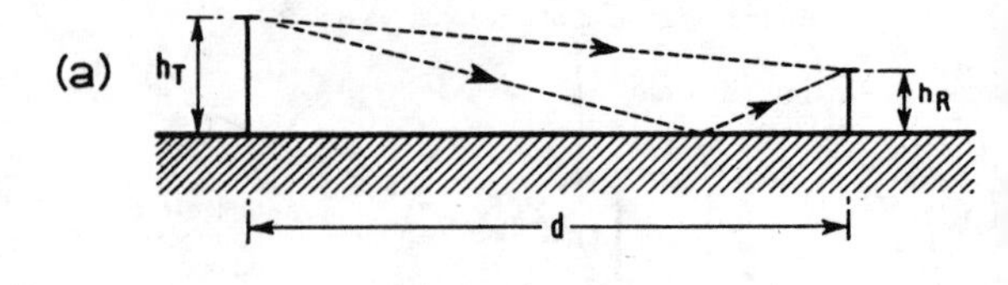

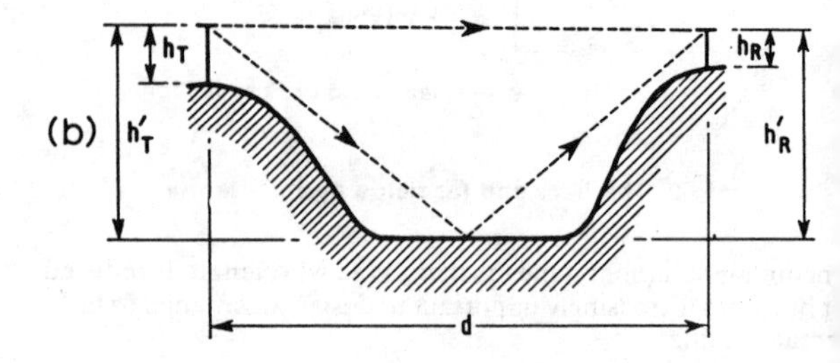

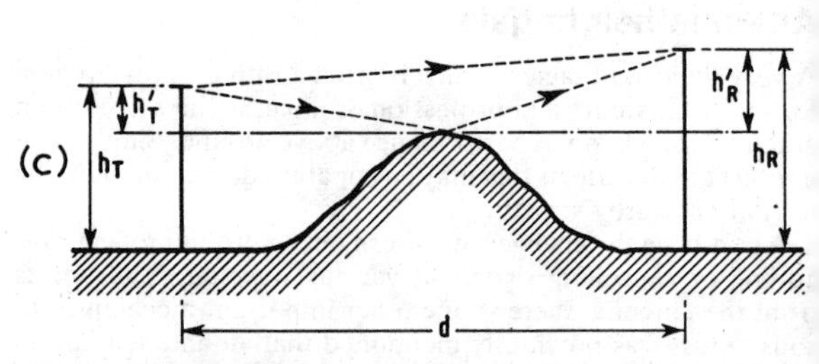

Fig 6. The effect of ground profile on direct and indirect rays. (a) Linear height gain. (b) Marginal height gain. (c) Rapid height gain. (The vertical scale has been exaggerated in each case.)

In the third case, that of the poorly sited station whose antenna is just able to see over the surrounding higher ground the reverse of case (b) applies. The effective height h'_R is much *less* than h_R, and a small increase in the height of the antenna is required to bring massive improvements in signal level.

Bandwidth

Unlike some of the properties previously discussed, the bandwidth of an antenna or antenna system does not have a unique definition. Depending upon the operational requirement of the system with which the antenna is to be used, its functional bandwidth may be limited by any one of several parameters. These can be the change of pattern shape or direction, increase in sidelobe level, loss of gain, change of polarization or deterioration of impedance.

Amateurs usually consider the impedance match and gain as the main criteria when quoting bandwidth. Fortunately with the relatively limited frequency range of the vhf and uhf bands used by amateurs the gain normally does not change too radically, so the impedance bandwidth is normally quoted. However, this is not always the case with high-gain systems where the gain and the pattern shape or direction of radiation may change quite considerably with bandwidth.

For antennas of relatively small dimensions (ie when the linear dimensions are of the order of $\lambda/2$ or less) the limiting factor is normally the impedance performance. With circular polarization, however, the change of the polarization characteristics prove to be the limiting factor on bandwidth. For

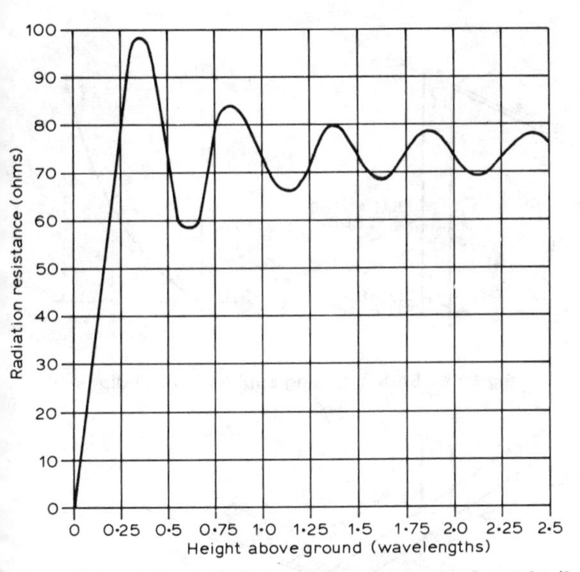

Fig 7. Variation in radiation resistance of a horizontal λ/2 antenna with height above a perfectly conducting ground (*ARRL Antenna Book*)

endfire linear arrays, collinears and the like, the pattern direction can deviate considerably before the actual pattern shape, gain or impedance characteristic deteriorates substantially.

It should be noted that the bandwidth of the antenna is very dependent on its value of Q. The higher the Q, the less the bandwidth.

Impedance

The input impedance of an antenna system is of importance since it directly affects the efficiency of energy transfer to or from the antenna. Radiation from transmission lines and cables can also modify the antenna's pattern and can also lead to interference between co-located systems. The overall input impedance of an antenna system depends not only on the impedance of individual antenna elements but also on the mutual impedance between elements, as well as the transmission lines and transmission-line components which are used to interconnect them. The overall design of a complex antenna system will therefore be governed as much by the interconnections of the transmission lines as by the characteristics of the individual antenna elements.

Impedance matching

For a feeder to deliver power to the antenna with minimum loss, it is necessary for the load to behave as a pure resistance equal in value to the characteristic impedance of the line. Under these conditions no energy is reflected from the point where the feeder is joined to the antenna, and in consequence no adverse standing waves appear on the line.

When the correct terminating resistance is connected to any feeder, the voltage and current distribution along the line will be uniform. This may be checked by using a device to explore either the magnetic field (H) or the electric field (E) along the line. One such device, suitable for use with a coaxial feeder, is a section of coaxial line with a longitudinal slot cut in the wall

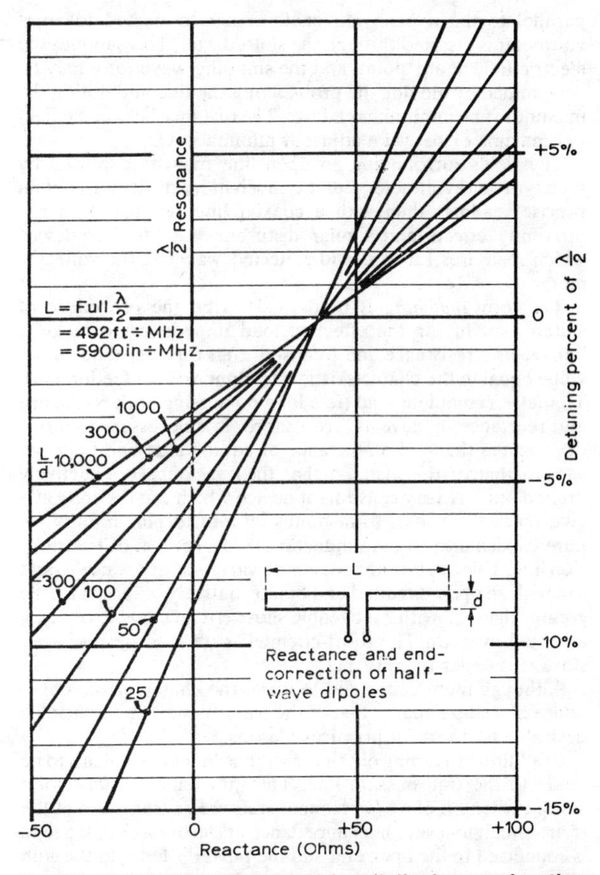

Fig 8. Tuning and reactance chart for λ/2 dipoles, as a function of the length/diameter ratio. A radiator exactly λ/2 long is "overtuned" by 42Ω, and "end correction", given as a percentage of the length, is necessary to bring it to resonance (zero reactance). The chart is useful for the construction of parasitic arrays and vhf dipoles. Each 1 per cent of length corresponds to 5 units in the factor 492/f or 60 in 5,900/f (f is in megahertz)

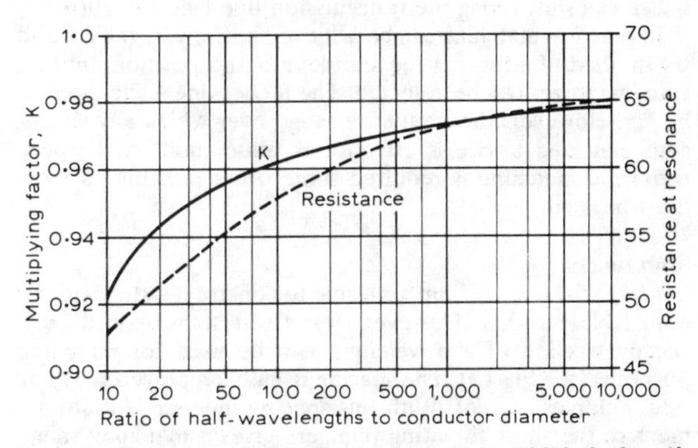

Fig 9. The solid curve shows the factor, *K*, by which the length of a half-wave in free space should be multiplied to obtain the physical length of a resonant λ/2 antenna having the length/diameter ratio shown along the horizontal axis. The broken curve shows how the radiation resistance of a λ/2 antenna varies with the length/diameter ratio (*ARRL Antenna Book*)

parallel to the line. A moveable probe connected to an rf voltmeter is inserted through the slotted wall. This samples the electric field at any point, and the standing-wave ratio may be determined by moving the probe along the line and noting the maximum and minimum readings. The distance between adjacent maxima or between adjacent minima is $\lambda/2$.

The fields surrounding an open line may be explored by means of an rf voltmeter, but it is much more difficult to obtain precise readings than with a coaxial line because of hand-proximity effects and similar disturbances. Another device which measures forward and reflected waves is the reflectometer.

The term *matching* is used to describe the procedure of suitably modifying the effective load impedance to make it behave as a resistance and to ensure that this resistance has a value equal to the characteristic impedance of the feeder used. To make a complete load (ie a load possessing both resistance and reactance) behave as a resistance, it is necessary to introduce across the load a reactance of equal value and opposite sign to that of the load, so that the reactance is effectively "tuned out". A very convenient device which can theoretically give reactance values from minus infinity to plus infinity (ie pure capacitance to pure inductance) is a section of transmission line. This can be either of length variable between zero and $\lambda/2$ with an open-circuited end or alternatively of length a little greater than $\lambda/2$ with a moveable short-circuit capable of being adjusted over 1λ. The short-circuited stub is to be preferred since it is easier to construct.

Although there is no need to make the characteristic impedance of a stub equal to that of the transmission line, it may be desirable to do so for practical reasons.

In addition to tuning out the reactance, a match still has to be made to the transmission line. The impedance at any point along the length of a $\lambda/4$ resonant stub varies from zero at the short-circuit to a very high impedance at the open end. If a load is connected to the open end and the power is fed into the stub at some point along its length, the stub may be used as an auto-transformer to give various values of impedance according to the position of the feed point. This is shown in Fig 10(a). The distance L is adjusted to tune the antenna to resonance and will be $\lambda/4$ long if the antenna is already resonant. The distance l is adjusted to obtain a match to the line. However, it is usually more convenient to have a stub with an adjustable short-circuit which can slide along the transmission line (see Fig 10(b)).

In practice, matching can be achieved entirely by the cut and try method of adjusting the stub length and position until no standing waves can be detected. The feeder line is then said to be *flat*. However, the frequency range over which any single-stub matching device is effective is quite small, and where wideband matching is required some other matching system must be used.

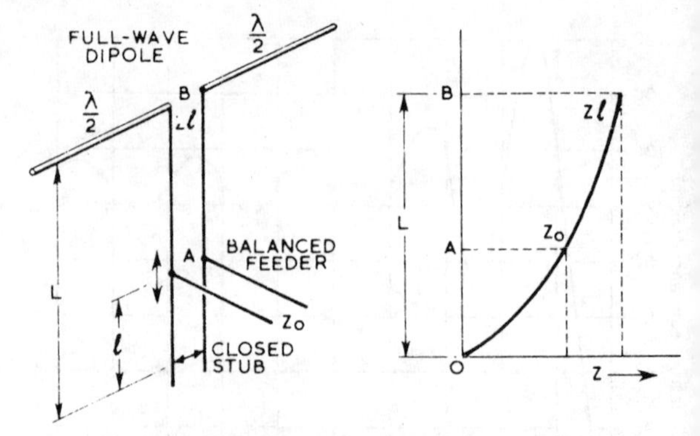

Fig 10(a). Stub matching applied to a $\lambda/2$ dipole

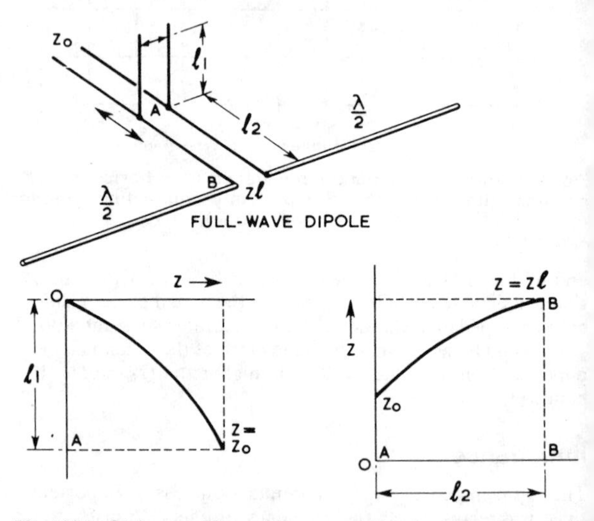

Fig 10(b). Stub matching with a movable short-circuited stub

Stub tuners

On a coaxial line it is impracticable to construct a stub with an adjustable position. However, two fixed stubs spaced by a certain fraction of a wavelength can be used for matching purposes (see Fig 12). The spacing usually employed is $\lambda/8$ or odd multiples thereof. With this spacing independent adjustment of the short-circuiting plungers gives a matching range from 0·5 times the characteristic impedance (Z_0) of the transmission line upwards. As the spacing is increased towards $\lambda/2$ or decreased towards zero, the matching range increases, but the adjustments then become extremely critical and the bandwidth very narrow. The theoretical limit of matching range cannot be achieved owing to the resistance of the conductors and the dielectric loss, ie the Q is limited. To obtain the highest Q the ratio of outer-to-inner conductor diameters should be in the range 2:1 to 4:1 (as for coaxial baluns). An important mechanical detail is the provision of reliable short-circuiting plungers which will have negligible inductance and also ensure low-resistance contact. These can be constructed of short lengths of thin-walled brass tubing, with diameters chosen so that when they are slotted and sprung they make a smooth sliding contact with both inner and outer conductors.

The two-stub tuner may be applied to open transmission lines if it is inconvenient to have a movable stub. In this case the stubs must be mounted laterally opposite to each other to prevent mutual coupling (see Fig 12).

This type of tuner may, of course, be used for other purposes than to feed an antenna. For example, it will serve to match an antenna feeder into a receiver, or a transmitter into a dummy load. A greater matching range can be obtained by using a three-stub tuner, with stubs at intervals of $\lambda/4$, as shown in Fig 13. The first and third stubs are usually ganged together to avoid the long and tedious matching operation which becomes necessary when adjustments are made to three infinitely variable stubs.

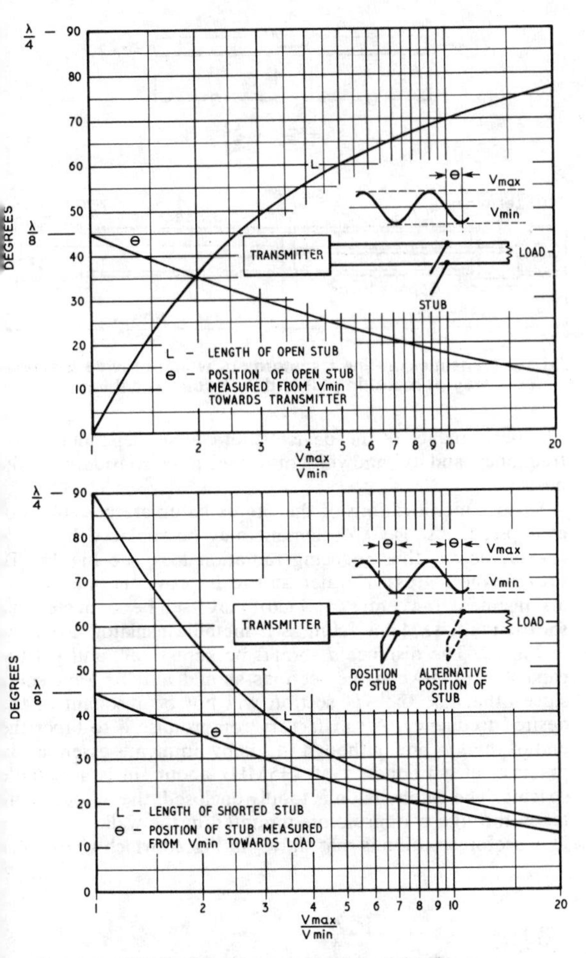

Fig 11. Impedance matching charts

Quarter-wave lines

An impedance transformation can be effected by using a certain length of transmission line of a different characteristic impedance from the feeder, and this is a technique which may be used to match a load to a transmission line. A special condition occurs when the length of the section of line is an odd number of λ/4 units and the following formula then applies:

$$Z_t = \sqrt{Z_0 . Z_1}$$

where Z_t is the characteristic impedance of the section of λ/4 line and Z_0 and Z_1 are the feeder and load impedance respectively. For example, if Z_0 is 80Ω and Z_1 is 600Ω

$$Z_t = \sqrt{80 \times 600} = 251\Omega$$

This matching section is useful for transforming impedance and is called a quarter-wave transformer (see Fig 15).

A section of tapered line can also be used to effect an impedance transformation. Again, a λ/4 section is only a special case, and to achieve a match in a particular installation the line length and the angle of taper should be varied until a perfect match is achieved. This form of matching device is often called a *delta match.*

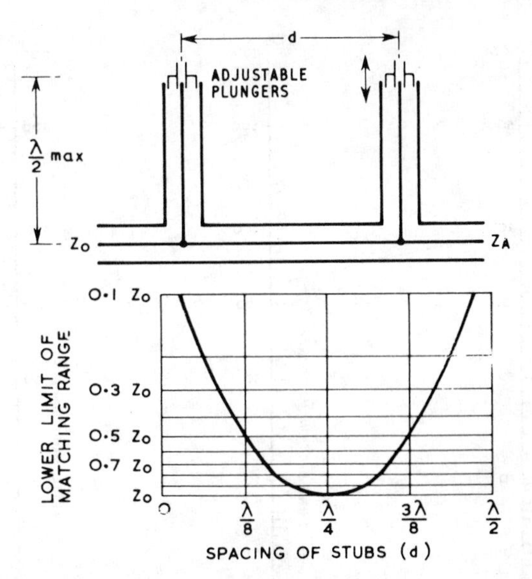

Fig 12. Two-stub coaxial tuner. The graph shows the lower limit of the matching range: the upper limit is determined by the *Q* of the stubs (ie it is dependent on the losses in the stubs). Z_0 is the characteristic impedance of the feeder

Cot (linear transformer) matching

An alternative method of matching is shown in Fig 16. It permits any two cables of different impedance to be matched together by using appropriate lengths of the cables as shown, so avoiding the need for a cable at the geometric mean impedance. G3KYH simplified the original formula to that shown and noted that "for a 50/75Ω transformer this works out to an electrical length of 29·3° for each section of cable. The physical length must of course take into account the velocity factor of the cables (typically about 0·66–0·80)".

Balance-to-unbalance transformers

In most cases an antenna requires a balanced feed with respect to ground, and therefore it is necessary to use a device which converts the unbalanced output of a coaxial cable to a balanced output as required by the antenna. This device also prevents the wave which has been contained within the cable from tending to "spill over" the extreme end and travel back over the surface of the cable. Whenever this occurs there are two important undesired effects; first, the re-radiated wave modifies the polar diagram of the attached antenna, and second the outer surface of the cable is found to have an rf voltage on it.

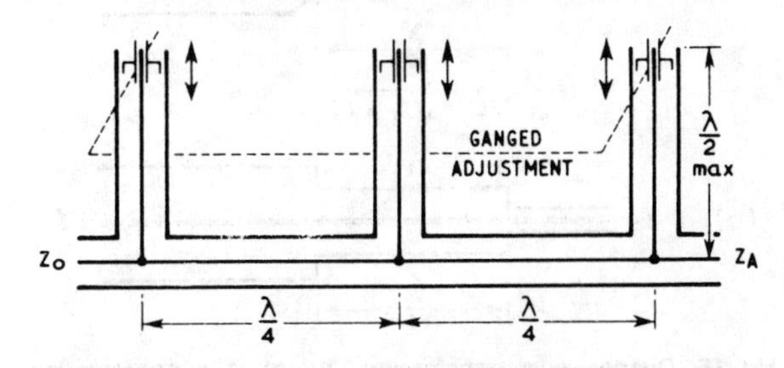

Fig 13. Three-stub tuner. This provides a greater matching range than a two-stub tuner. Z_0 is the characteristic impedance of the feeder

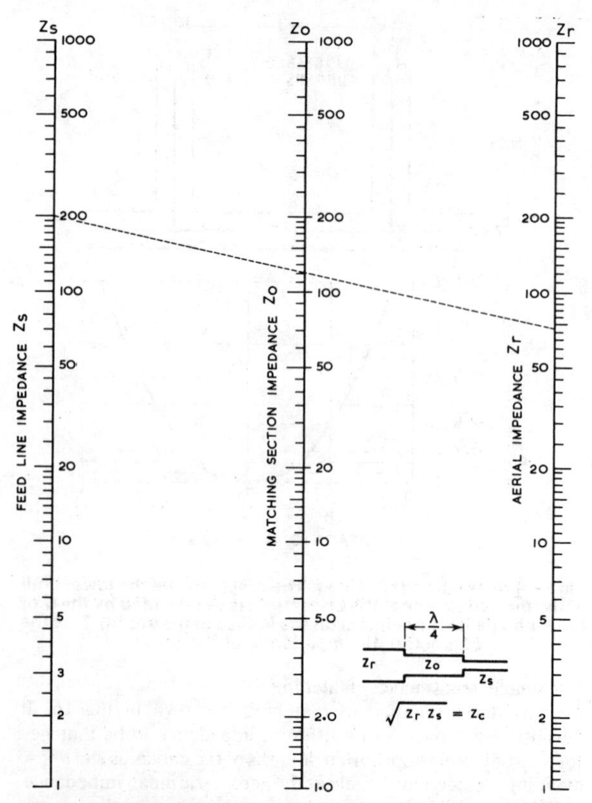

Fig 14. Matching section chart. This chart may be used to obtain the surge impedance of a λ/4 matching section used as an impedance transformer from one real impedance to another. In the example shown, Z_r is 72Ω and Z_s is 200Ω, indicating that a λ/4 matching section of 120Ω is needed

To prevent this, a balance-to-unbalance transformer (abbreviated to *balun*) is connected between the feeder cable and the antenna. The simplest balun consists of a short-circuited λ/4 section of transmission line attached to the outer braiding of the cable as shown in Fig 17. This is often known as a *Pawsey stub*. At the point A the λ/4 section presents a very high impedance which prevents the wave from travelling over the surface.

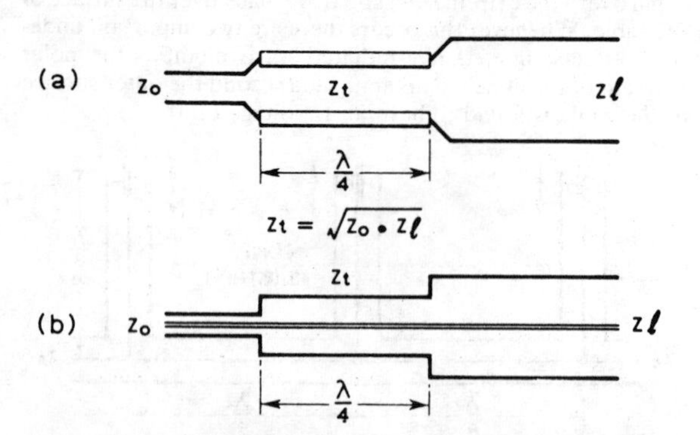

Fig 15. Quarter-wave transformers. In (a) is a construction suitable for open-wire lines, and (b) is the corresponding method for coaxial cables. Where a solid dielectric section is used, due allowance must be made for the velocity factor

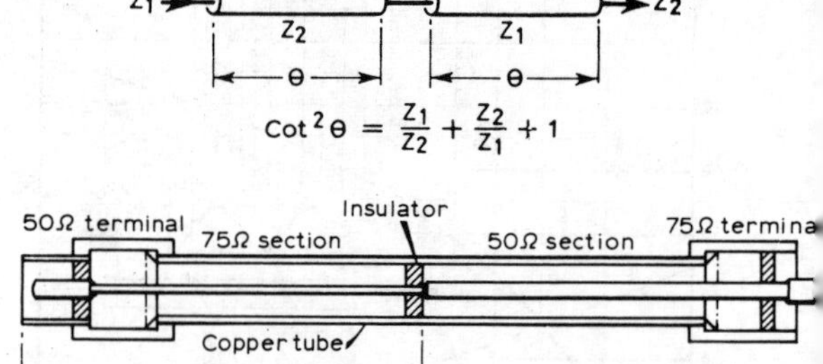

Fig 16. Transmission-line transformers which provide a simple way of matching 50 and 70Ω coaxial cables

The performance of this device is, of course, dependent upon frequency, and its bandwidth may have to be considered in the design.

Several modifications of the simple balun are possible. For example, the single λ/4 element may be replaced by a λ/4 coaxial sleeve, thus reducing radiation loss, see Fig 18. To prevent the ingress of water and to improve the mechanical arrangement, the centre conductor may itself be connected to a short-circuited λ/4 line acting as a "metallic insulator" as shown in Fig 19. The distance *d* should be kept small, and yet the capacitance between the sections should also be kept small since otherwise the λ/4 section will not be resonant at the desired frequency. A satisfactory compromise is to taper the end of the λ/4 line, although this is by no means essential. In practice, at a frequency of 435MHz about ⅛in is a suitable spacing. The whole balun is totally enclosed, the output being taken through two insulators mounted in the wall.

A useful variation is that shown in Fig 20 which gives a 4:1

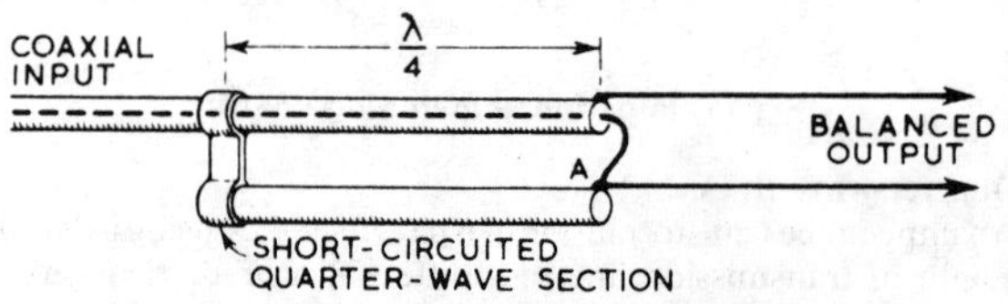

Fig 17. Quarter-wave open balun or Pawsey stub

Fig 18. Coaxial sleeve balun

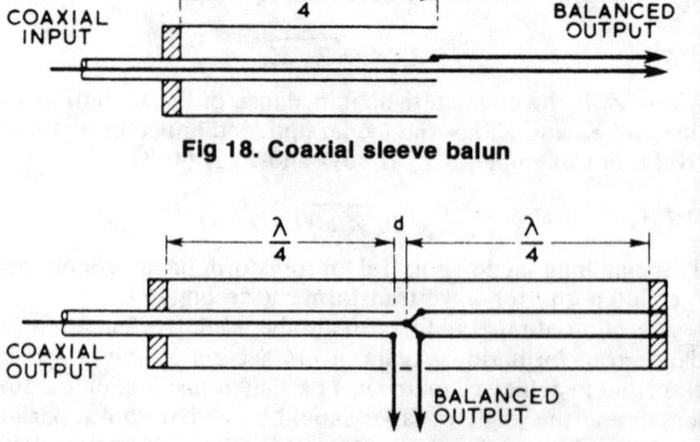

Fig 19. Totally enclosed coaxial balun. The right-hand section acts as a metal insulator

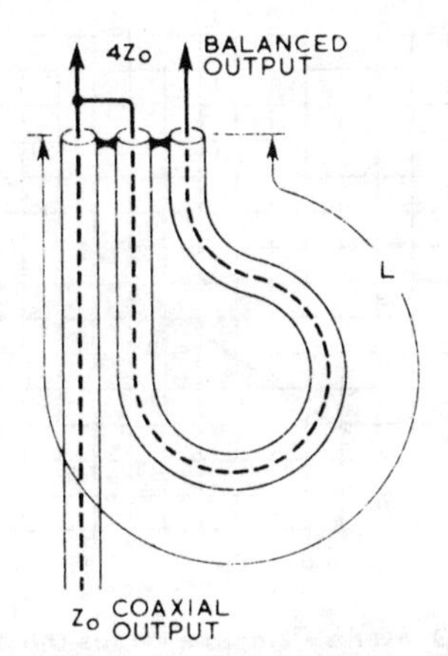

Fig 20. A coaxial balun giving a 4:1 impedance step-up. The length L should be $\lambda/2$, allowing for the velocity factor of the cable. The outer braiding may be joined at the points indicated

step-up of impedance. The $\lambda/2$ loop is usually made from flexible coaxial cable, and allowance must be made for the velocity factor of the cable when calculating a half-wavelength.

Coaxial-sleeve baluns should have an outer-to-inner diameter ratio of between 2:1 and 4:1.

Although the type of balun illustrated in Fig 19 has a larger effective bandwidth than the other types described here, they are all suitable for the restricted frequency ranges in common use in the vhf amateur bands.

The Yagi and its derivatives

It has been said that if you take a dozen variables and fit them in line along a supporting boom you will produce a Yagi antenna. This system, consisting of a driven element combined with an in-line parasitic array, was first conceived by Uda and constructed by Yagi in a form similar to that shown in Fig 21. Since this original there have been many variations of the basic concept including its combination with log periodic and backward-wave techniques.

To cover all variations of the Yagi is beyond the scope of this antenna chapter. In fact, just to cover the "dozen variables" of the standard Yagi form would not only be complex but would not make it possible for the average amateur to construct and use a Yagi producing parameters most suitable to his requirements. To overcome this problem, three design concepts are considered for the basic Yagi. One design is from a study by Greenblum in the USA and re-confirmed by Powers in the UK in 1978. The second study is from Chen and Cheng who produced an analytical study ("Yagi-Uda Arrays", *Proc IEEE*, 1975) to maximize the directivity of the Yagi-Uda array by adjustment of the dipole lengths and spacing. The third is a measurement study by Viezbicke for the US Department of Commerce and National Bureau of Standards. Many independent investigations of multi-element Yagi antennas have shown that in general the gain of a Yagi is directly proportional to the array length provided the number, lengths and spacings of the elements are properly chosen.

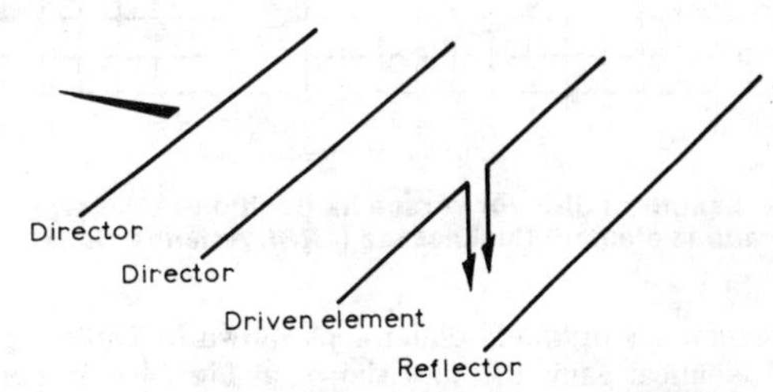

Fig 21. "Four-element" antenna system, using two directors and one reflector in conjunction with a driven element

It must be emphasized that, although there is a certain amount of latitude in the positioning of the elements along the length of the array (with Greenblum's dimensions in Table 1 the gain will not vary more than 1dB), the optimum resonance of each element will vary with the spacing chosen. The most critical are the reflector and first director as they decide the spacing for all other directors and most noticeably affect the matching.

The optimum director lengths are in general greater, the closer the particular director is to the driven element. However, the length does not decrease uniformly with increasing distance from the driven element. Fig 22 shows experimentally derived lengths of elements for various material diameters assuming they are mounted through a cylindrical metal boom which is two or three diameters larger than the elements. Some variation in element lengths will occur using different materials or sizes for the support booms. This will be increasingly critical as frequency increases. It should be noted that the water absorbency of insulating materials will also affect the element lengths, particularly when in use.

Fig 24 shows the expected gain for various numbers of elements if the array length complies with Fig 23.

The results obtained by Powers using the "centre spacings"

Table 1. Optimum element spacings for multielement Yagi arrays

No. elements	R–DE	DE–D_1	D_1–D_2	D_2–D_3	D_3–D_4	D_4–D_5	D_5–D_6
2	0·15λ–0·2λ						
2		0·07λ–0·11λ					
3	0·16 –0·23	0·16 –0·19					
4	0·18 –0·22	0·13 –0·17	0·14λ–0·18λ				
5	0·18 –0·22	0·14 –0·17	0·14 –0·20	0·17λ–0·23λ			
6	0·16 –0·20	0·14 –0·17	0·16 –0·25	0·22 –0·30	0·25λ–0·32λ		
8	0·16 –0·20	0·14 –0·16	0·18 –0·25	0·25 –0·35	0·27 –0·32	0·27λ–0·33λ	0·30λ–0·40λ
8 to *N*	0·16 –0·20	0·14 –0·16	0·18 –0·25	0·25 –0·35	0·27 –0·32	0·27 –0·33	0·35 –0·42

DE = driven element; R = reflector; D = director.
N = any number, director spacings beyond D_6 should be 0·35–0·42λ.

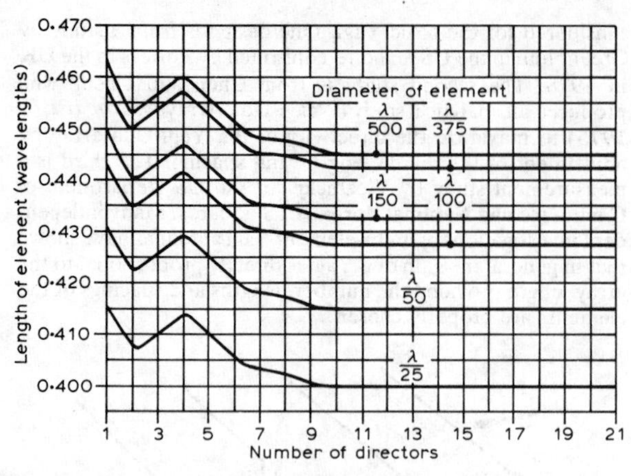

Fig 22. Length of director versus its position in the array, for various element thicknesses (*ARRL Antenna Book*)

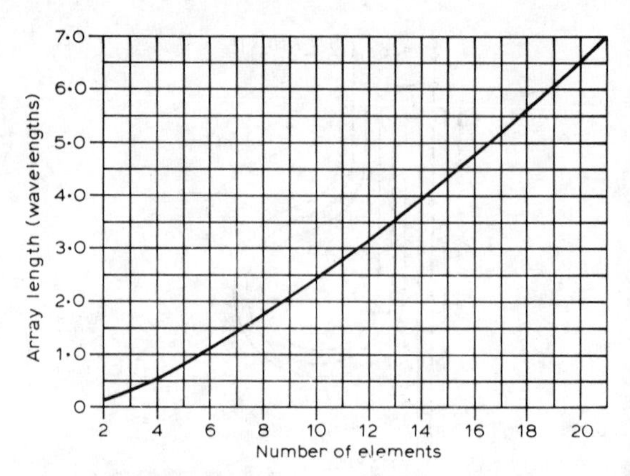

Fig 24. Gain (dB) over a λ/2 dipole versus the number of elements of the Yagi array (*ARRL Antenna Book*)

of Greenblum's optimum dimensions shown in Table 1 produced identical gains to those shown in Fig 24 with nearly identical radiation patterns in both the E and H planes (V or H polarization). Sidelobes were at a minimum and fair front-to-back ratios were obtained.

At frequencies below approximately 1,000MHz on most professional antenna measurement ranges and under normal working conditions, ground reflections and particularly their differences between H and V polarization give a false indication of antenna performance. However, new techniques, which include an optimum pattern shape of the measurement receiving antenna, have produced results down to almost 100MHz which are sufficiently close to the expected theoretical figures as to be acceptable for standards pattern measurement. Fig 25 shows radiation patterns for such an optimized vertically polarized antenna using Greenblum's dimensions. The antenna is mounted such that the null is in line with the supporting mast and the ground. The antenna supporting stub on the top of the mast was made of an insulating material such as glass fibre or resin-impregnated wood, and was approximately λ/2 in size.

Considerable work has been carried out by Chen and Cheng on the optimizing of Yagis. Tables 2 and 3 show their results obtained in 1974, by optimizing both spacing and reasonant lengths of the elements. Figs 26 and 27 show comparative radiation patterns for the various stages of optimization.

The example is for a six-element Yagi with conventional shortening of the elements. The gain figure produced wa[s] 8·77dB relative to a λ/2 dipole. Optimizing the element length produced a forward gain of 10dBD. Returning to the origina[l] element lengths and optimizing the element spacing produced [a] forward gain of 10·68dBD which is identical to the gain show[n] for a six-element Yagi in Fig 24. Using a combination of spacing and element length adjustment obtained a further 0·57dBD gain, giving 11·25dBD as the final forward gain.

Comparing the Greenblum results with those of Chen an[d] Cheng indicates from the comparison of number of elements that optimum element spacing has been achieved with different dimensions. It should be noted that a different reflector or firs[t] director spacing has been used to give good matching with [a] folded active element. An investigation of Greenblum's

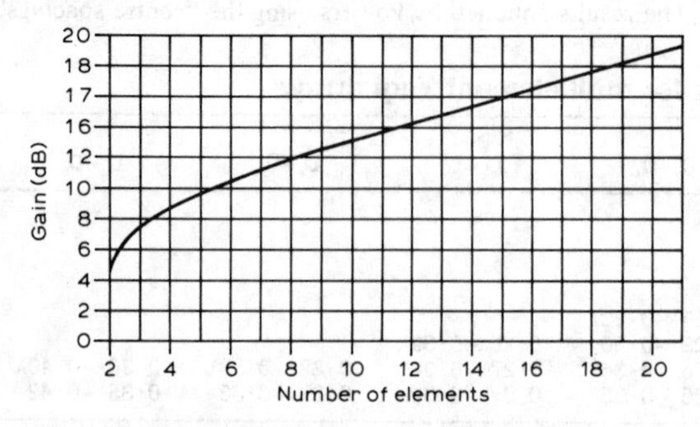

Fig 23. Optimum length of Yagi antenna as a function of number of elements (*ARRL Antenna Book*)

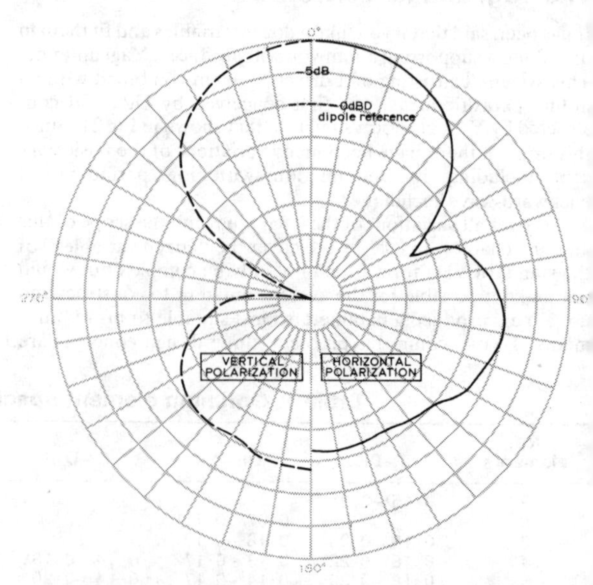

Fig 25. Decibel radiation patterns for a four-element Yagi optimized for minimum ground and mast distortion, and minimum sidelobes, configured for vertical polarization using Greenblum's dimensions. The use of a decibel scale emphasizes the lobe structure, giving more definition at the lower radiation levels

Table 2. Directivity optimization for six-element Yagi–Uda array (perturbation of element lengths)

	h_1/λ	h_2/λ	h_3/λ	h_4/λ	h_5/λ	h_6/λ	Directivity (referring to λ/2 dipole)	Gain (dBD)
Initial array	0·255	0·245	0·215	0·215	0·215	0·215	7·544	8·77
Length-perturbed array	0·236	0·228	0·219	0·222	0·216	0·202	10·012	10

$b_{i1} = 0\cdot250\lambda$, $b_{i2} = 0\cdot310\lambda$ ($i = 3,4,5,6$), $a = 0\cdot003369\lambda$.

Table 3. Directivity optimization for six-element Yagi-Uda array (perturbation of element spacings and element lengths).

	h_1/λ	h_2/λ	h_3/λ	h_4/λ	h_5/λ	h_6/λ	b_{21}/λ	b_{22}/λ	b_{43}/λ	b_{34}/λ	b_{35}/λ	Directivity (referring to λ/2 dipole)	Gain (dBD)
Initial array	0·255	0·245	0·215	0·215	0·215	0·215	0·250	0·310	0·310	0·310	0·310	7·544	8·77
Array after spacing perturbation	0·255	0·245	0·215	0·215	0·215	0·215	0·250	0·289	0·406	0·323	0·422	11·687	10·68
Optimum array after spacing and length perturbations	0·238	0·226	0·218	0·215	0·217	0·215	0·250	0·289	0·406	0·323	0·422	13·356	11·25

expected gain figures for optimum total array length is, however, in very close agreement with Chen and Cheng's results, being typically 11·9dBD for a six-element Yagi compared to 11·25dBD.

A recent publication of the US Dept of Commerce and National Bureau of Standards (*Yagi Antenna Design* by Peter P. Viezbicke) provides very detailed information in about 20 or so pages, based on experimental measurements made on 400MHz at a model antenna range while optimizing designs. The information, presented largely in graphical form, shows very vividly the effect of different antenna parameters on realizable gain. For example, it shows the extra gain that can be achieved by optimizing the lengths of the different directors, rather than making them all of uniform length; it also shows just what extra gain can be achieved by stacking two elements, or from a two-over-two array. In fact it shows: (a) the effect of reflector spacing on the gain of a dipole; (b) effect of different equal-length directors, their spacing and number on realizable gain; (c) effect of different diameters and lengths of directors on realizable gain; (d) effect of the size of a supporting boom on the optimum length of parasitic elements; (e) effect of spacing and stacking of antennas on gain; (f) measured radiation patterns of different Yagi configurations.

In very general terms, the highest gain reported for a single boom structure is 14·2dB for a 15-element array (4·2λ long reflector spaced at 0·2λ, 13 graduated directors): see Table 4.

In general it has been found that array length is of greater importance than the number of elements, within the limit of a maximum element spacing just over 0·4λ. Reflector spacing and, to a lesser degree, the first director affects the matching of

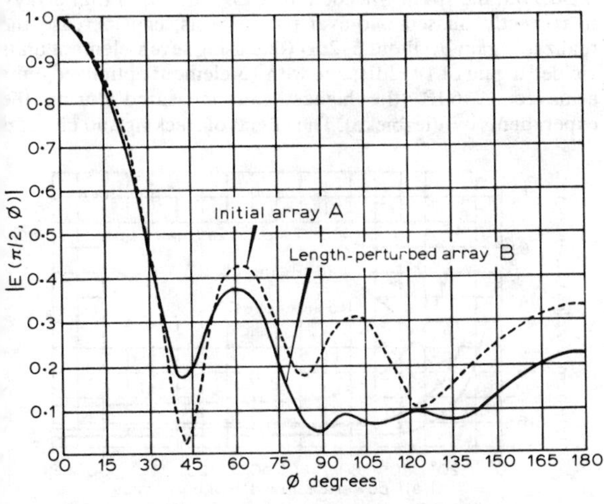

Fig 26. Normalized patterns of six-element Yagi-Uda arrays from Table 2. The gain improvement of B over A is +1·2dB (*Proc IEEE*)

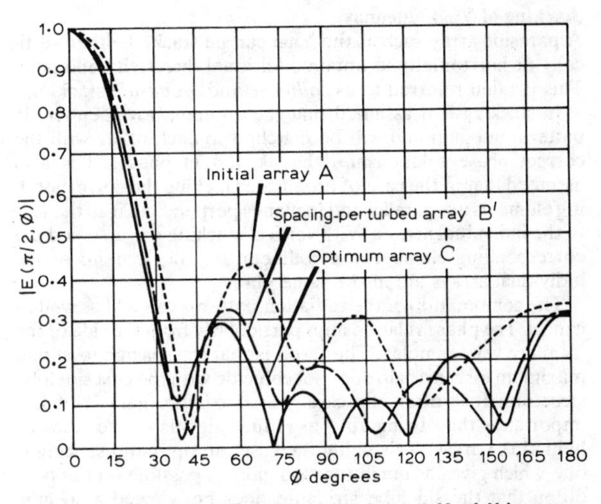

Fig 27. Normalized patterns of six-element Yagi-Uda arrays from Table 3. The gain improvement of B over A is +1·9dB, while that of C over A is +2·5dB (*Proc IEEE*)

Table 4. Optimized lengths of parasitic elements for Yagi antennas of six different lengths

Length of Yagi (λ)	0·4	0·8	1·20	2·2	3·2	4·2
Length of reflector (λ)	0·482	0·482	0·482	0·482	0·482	0·475
Length of directors (λ)						
1st	0·424	0·428	0·428	0·432	0·428	0·424
2nd	—	0·424	0·420	0·415	0·420	0·424
3rd	—	0·428	0·420	0·407	0·407	0·420
4th	—	—	0·428	0·398	0·398	0·407
5th	—	—	—	0·390	0·394	0·403
6th	—	—	—	0·390	0·390	0·398
7th	—	—	—	0·390	0·386	0·394
8th	—	—	—	0·390	0·386	0·390
9th	—	—	—	0·398	0·386	0·390
10th	—	—	—	0·407	0·386	0·390
11th	—	—	—	—	0·386	0·390
12th	—	—	—	—	0·386	0·390
13th	—	—	—	—	0·386	0·390
14th	—	—	—	—	0·386	—
15th	—	—	—	—	0·386	—
Spacing (directors) (λ)	0·20	0·20	0·25	0·20	0·20	0·308
Gain (ref dipole) (dB)	7·1	9·2	10·2	12·25	13·4	14·2

Element diameter 0·0085λ. Reflectors spaced 0·2λ behind driven element. Measurements at 400MHz. (*Due to P. P. Viezbicke*).

the Yagi. Optimum tuning of the elements, and therefore gain and pattern shape, varies with different element spacing.

Rationalizing, near optimum patterns and gain can be obtained using Greenblum's dimensions up to typically six elements. Good results for Yagis in excess of six elements can still be obtained where, as is the case with amateur vhf transmissions at vertical polarization and for measurement purposes at both polarizations, ground reflections need to be minimized.

Chen and Cheng have in fact employed what is commonly called *long Yagi techniques.* Yagis having in excess of six elements begin to show an improvement in gain with the bonus of fewer elements when this technique is employed.

Stacking of Yagi antennas

A parasitic array such as the Yagi can be stacked either vertically or horizontally to obtain additional directivity and gain. This is often referred to as *collinear* and *broadside* stacking.

In stacking it is assumed that the antennas are identical in pattern and gain and will be matched to each other with the correct phase relationship, that is, fed in phase. It is also assumed that in the case of broadside stacking the corresponding elements are parallel and in planes perpendicular to the axis of the individual arrays. With vertical stacking it is assumed the corresponding elements are collinear and all elements of the individual arrays are in the same plane.

The combination of the radiation patterns can add as well as cancel. The phase relationships particularly from the side of the Yagi are very complex. The result is that the spacing to obtain maximum forward gain does not coincide with the best sidelobe structure. It is often the case that maximum gain is of less importance than being able to reduce signals to the sides or behind the array. This being the case, an optimum spacing is one which gives as much forward gain as possible on the condition that the sidelobe structure does not exceed a specific amplitude in relation to the main lobe. Fig 28 gives typical optimum spacing for two arrays under three conditions:

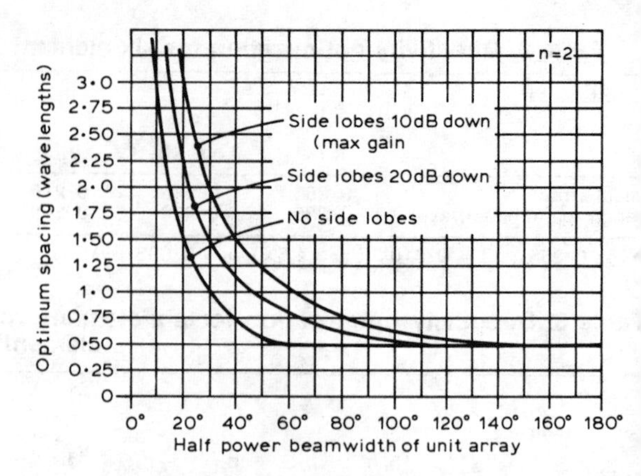

Fig 28. Optimum stacking spacing for two-unit arrays. The spacing for no sidelobes, especially for small beamwidths, may result in no gain improvement with stacking (*ARRL Antenna Book*)

optimum forward gain with sidelobes down 10dB, sidelobes 20dB down and for all intents and purposes no sidelobes. The no-sidelobe case can correspond to no additional forward gain over the single unit.

Fig 29 gives the corresponding spacing for four stacked units. The spacing in Figs 28 and 29 are taken as the distances between array centres. When units are stacked in a collinear arrangement λ/2 spacing would mean physical contact of the ends of the elements so that a spacing in excess of λ/4 will be needed to minimize the direct interaction of the elements.

The maximum forward gain of two stacked arrays is theoretically +3dB with +6dB for four stacked arrays. More complex arrays could produce higher gain but losses in the matching and phasing links between the individual arrays can outweigh this improvement. When stacking two arrays, the extra achievable gain is reduced at close spacing due to high mutual impedance effects: with two seven-element arrays a maximum of about 2·5dB can be achieved with 1·6λ spacing; with two 15-element arrays it was also possible to achieve the extra 2·5dB but the spacing needed to be 2λ. The use of four arrays, in correctly phased two-over-two systems, can increase the realizable gain by about 5·2dB (one using seven-element units yielded a gain of 14·2dB; one with 15-element optimized units achieved 19·6dB, the highest gain measured during the experiments by Viezbicke). The effects of stacking and physical

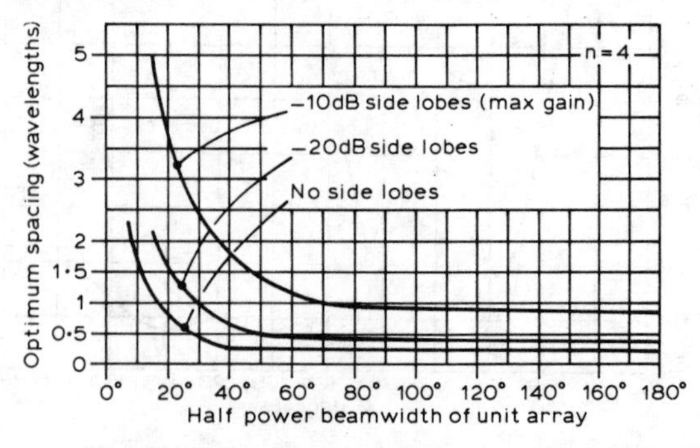

Fig 29. Optimum stacking spacing for four-unit arrays (*ARRL Antenna Book*)

Table 5. Spacing of Yagi antennas to obtain desired null angles as described in the text

ull angle	10°	15°	20°	25°	30°	35°	40°	45°	50°	55°	60°
pacing in wavelengths	2·5	1·75	1·5	1·25	1·0	·85	·75	2·25	1·9	1·7	1·65

s well as electrical phase relationship can be used in two ways o minimize directional interference.

An improvement in front-to-back ratio can be accomplished vertical stacking by placing the top Yagi λ/4 in front of the wer Yagi as shown in Fig 30. The top antenna is fed 90° later han the bottom antenna.

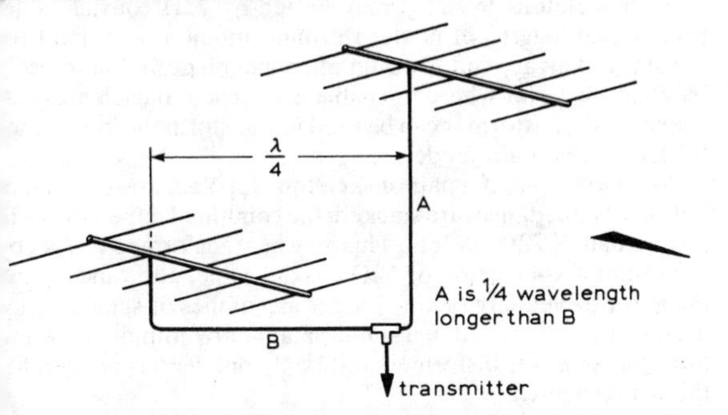

ig 30. Improving the front-to-back ratio of stacked Yagi antennas with offset vertical mounting

If the interference is largely from the forward direction, eeding the antennas in phase as shown in Fig 31 but varying the pacing between the arrays will give a primary null in the ombined patterns at specific angles. Results for five-element agis are shown in Table 5. This can be useful where beams are et in a fixed direction.

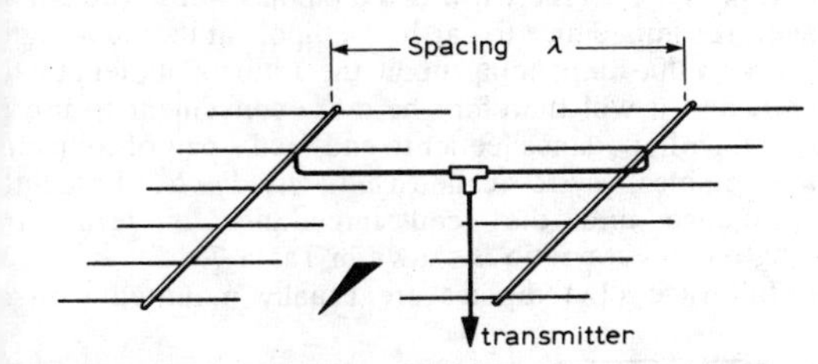

Fig 31. Desired null angle as shown in Table 5 is determined by the spacing between the two Yagi antennas

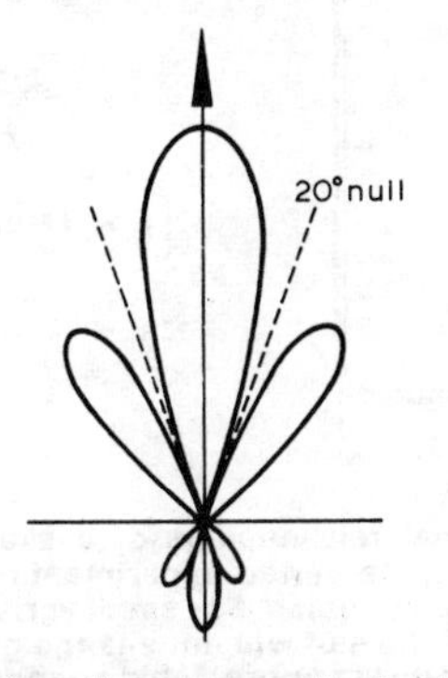

Fig 32. Response of two five-element Yagi antennas positioned for a 20° pattern null

Table 6. Typical dimensions of Yagi array components

	Length 70·3MHz		145MHz		433MHz	
Driven elements						
Dipole (for use with gamma match)	79	(200)	38	(96)	12¾■	(32)
Diameter range for length given	½–¾		¼–⅜		⅛–¼	
Folded dipole 70Ω feed						
l length centre/centre	77½	(197)	38½	(98)	12½	(31·8)
d spacing centre/centre	2½	(6·4)	⅞	(2·2)	½	(1·3)
Diameter of element	½		¼		⅛	
a centre/centre	32	(81)	15	(39)	5⅛	(13·2)
b centre/centre	96	(244)	46	(118)	15½	(39·5)
Delta feed sections (length 70Ω feed)	22½	(57)	12	(30)	4⅜	(11)
Diameter of slot and delta feed material	¼		⅜		⅜	
Parasitic elements						
Element						
Reflector	85½	(217)	40	(101)	13¼	(33·7)
Director D1	74	(188)	35½	(90·2)	11¼	(28·6)
Director D2	73	(185·4)	35¼	(89·5)	11⅛	(28·2)
Director D3	72	(183)	35	(88·9)	11	(27·9)
Succeeding directors	1in less	(2·5)	½in less		⅛in less	
Final director	2in less	(5)	1in less		¾in less	
One wavelength (for reference)	168¾	(428·6)	81½	(206·9)	27¼	(69·3)
Diameter range for length given	½–¾		¼–⅜		⅛–¾	
Spacing between elements						
Reflector to radiator	22½	(57·2)	17½	(44·5)	5½	(14)
Radiator to director 1	29	(73·7)	17½	(44·5)	5½	(14)
Director 1 to director 2	29	(73·7)	17½	(44·5)	7	(17·8)
Director 2 to director 3, etc	29	(73·7)	17½	(44·5)	7	(17·8)

Dimensions are in inches with centimetre equivalents in brackets.

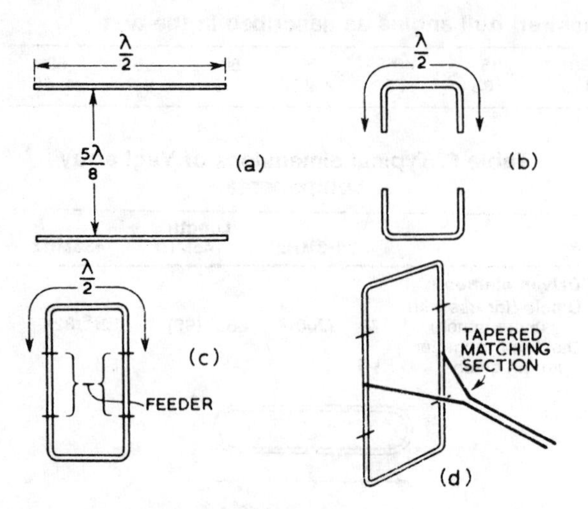

Fig 33. Development of a skeleton slot radiator

Disadvantage of conventional Yagi arrays

Perhaps the most important disadvantage of the Yagi array is that the variation of the element lengths and spacings causes inter-related changes in the feed impedance. To obtain the maximum possible forward gain experimentally is extremely difficult because for each change of element length it is necessary to re-adjust the matching either by moving the reflector or by re-setting a matching device. However, a method has been devised for overcoming these practical disadvantages. It involves the use of a radiating element in the form of a skeleton slot, which is far less susceptible to the changes in impedance caused by changes in the parasitic element lengths.

A true slot would be a slot cut in an infinite sheet of metal, and such a slot when approximately λ/2 long would behave in a similar way to a dipole radiator. In contrast with a dipole, however, the polarization produced by a vertical slot is horizontal (ie the electric field is horizontal).

The skeleton slot was developed in the course of experiments to determine to what extent the infinite sheet of metal could be reduced before the slot antenna lost its radiating property. The limit of the reduction for satisfactory performance was found to occur when there remained approximately λ/2 of metal beyond the slot edges. However, further experiments showed that a thin rod bent to form a "skeleton slot" of dimensions approximately 5λ/8 by 5λ/24 exhibited similar properties to those of a true slot.

The manner in which a skeleton slot functions can be understood by referring to Fig 33. Consider two λ/2 dipoles spaced vertically by 5λ/8. Since the greater part of the radiation from each dipole takes place at the current antinode, ie the centre, the ends of the dipoles may be bent without serious effect. These ends may now be joined together with a high-impedance feeder, so that end feeding can be applied to the bent dipoles. To radiate in phase, the power should be fed midway between the two dipoles. The high impedance at this point may be transformed down to one suitable for the type of feeder in use by means of a tapered matching section transmission line (ie a delta match). Practical dimensions of a skeleton-slot radiator are given in Fig 34.

It is important to note that two sets of parasitic elements are required with a skeleton-slot radiator and not one set as required with a true slot. One further property of the skeleton slot is that its bandwidth is somewhat greater than a pair of stacked dipoles.

Skeleton-slot Yagi arrays in stack

Skeleton-slot Yagi arrays may be stacked to increase the gain but the same considerations of optimum stacking distance as previously discussed apply. The centre-to-centre spacing of a pair of skeleton slot Yagi arrays should vary between 1λ and 3λ or more according to the number of elements in each Yagi array.

Each skeleton-slot Yagi may be fed by 72Ω coaxial cable using equal lengths of feeder to some common feed point for the stacked array, and it would of course be desirable to use a balun at the point where the cable is attached to each array. A coaxial λ/4 transformer can be used to transform the impedance to that of the main feeder.

As an example, if a pair of skeleton-slot Yagi arrays, each of 72Ω feed impedance, are stacked, the combined impedance will be one-half of 72Ω, ie 36Ω. This may be transformed to 72Ω by the use of a λ/4 section of 52Ω coaxial cable, allowance being made for its velocity factor. Larger assemblies of skeleton-slot Yagi arrays can be fed in a similar manner by joining pairs and introducing λ/4 transformers until only one feed is needed for the whole array.

Stacked dipole arrays

Both horizontal and vertical beamwidths can be reduced and gain increased by building up arrays of driven dipoles. This arrangement is usually referred to merely as a *stack*, or sometimes as a *bill-board* or *broadside* array. Since this type of array is made up from a number of radiating dipoles, the feed impedance would be extremely low if the dipoles were centre-fed. However, the impedance to earth of a dipole at its end is high, the precise value depending upon the ratio of its length to diameter, and it will therefore be more convenient to use a balanced high-impedance feeder to end-feed a pair of collinear half-wave dipoles, a system called a *full-wave dipole*. The length for resonance and the feed impedance in terms of wavelength/diameter ratio is shown in Table 7.

The full-wave (1λ) dipoles are usually mounted with a

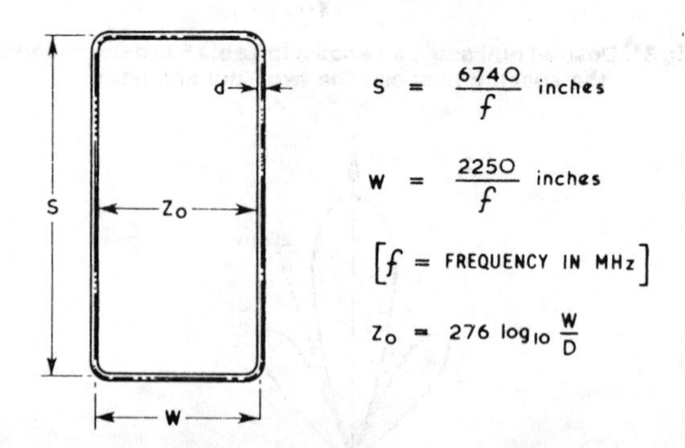

Fig 34. Dimensional relationships of a skeleton-slot radiator. Both S and W may be varied experimentally from the values indicated by these formulae. For small variations the radiation characteristics of the slot will not change greatly, but the feed impedance will undergo appreciable change and therefore the length of the delta matching section should always be adjusted to give a perfect match to the transmission line

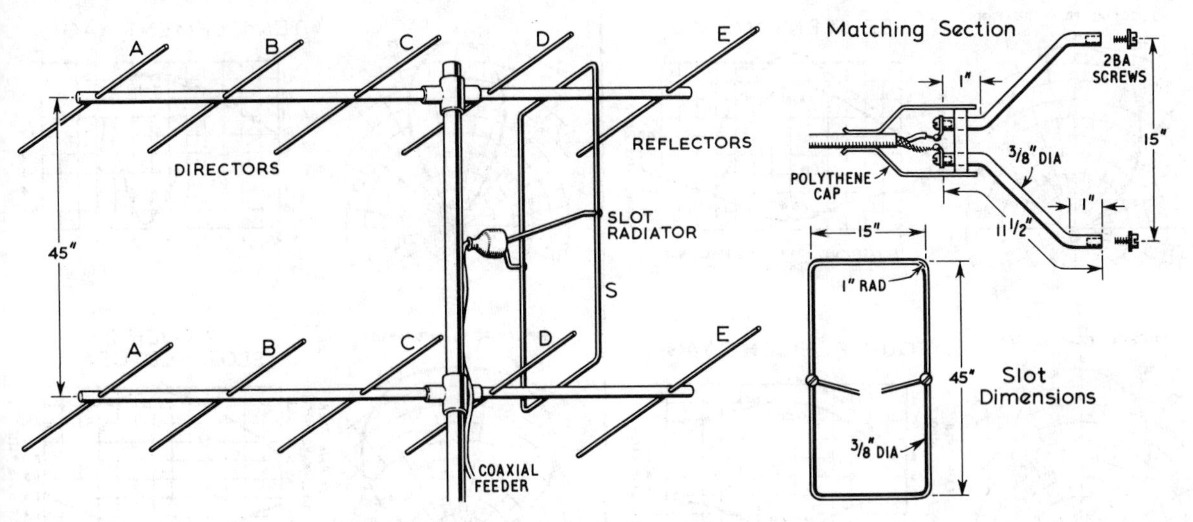

Fig 35. A six-over-six slot antenna

centre-to-centre spacing, horizontally and vertically, of $\lambda/2$, and are fed in phase. Typical arrangements for stacks of 1λ dipoles are shown in Fig 38. Note that the feed wires between dipoles are $\lambda/2$ long and are crossed so that all the dipoles in each bay are fed in phase. The impedance of these phasing sections is unimportant provided that the separators, if used, are made of low-loss dielectric material, and that there is sufficiently wide separation at the cross-over points to prevent unintentional contact.

To obtain the radiation pattern expected, all dipoles should be fed with equal amounts of power (as indeed would be desirable in any multi-radiator array), but this cannot be achieved in practice because the dipoles which are farthest from the feeder have a greater feeder loss than the nearest. However, by locating the main feed point as nearly symmetrically as possible these effects are minimized. Hence it would be preferable for the antenna shown in Fig 38(a) to be fed in the centre of each bay of dipoles; the feeder to each bay must be connected as shown to ensure that the two bays are fed in phase. If they were fed 180° out-of-phase the resultant beam pattern would have two major side lobes and there would be very little power radiated in the desired direction. Fig 38(b) shows two vertically stacked bays of 1λ dipoles fed symmetrically and in phase.

Fig 36. A high-gain 432MHz antenna consisting of four 8-over-8 fed Yagi units arranged in a square formation

Table 7. Resonant lengths of full-wave dipoles

Wavelength / Diameter	Value of Dipole length / Wavelength for resonance	Feed Impedance (Ω)
50	0·85	500
100	0·87	900
150	0·88	1,100
200	0·896	1,300
300	0·906	1,500
400	0·916	1,700
700	0·926	2,000
1,000	0·937	2,400
2,000	0·945	3,000
4,000	0·951	3,600
10,000	0·958	4,600

The dimensions used in calculating the ratios must be in similar units (eg both in metres or both in centimetres). From *Aerials for metre and decimetre wavelengths* by R. A. Smith.

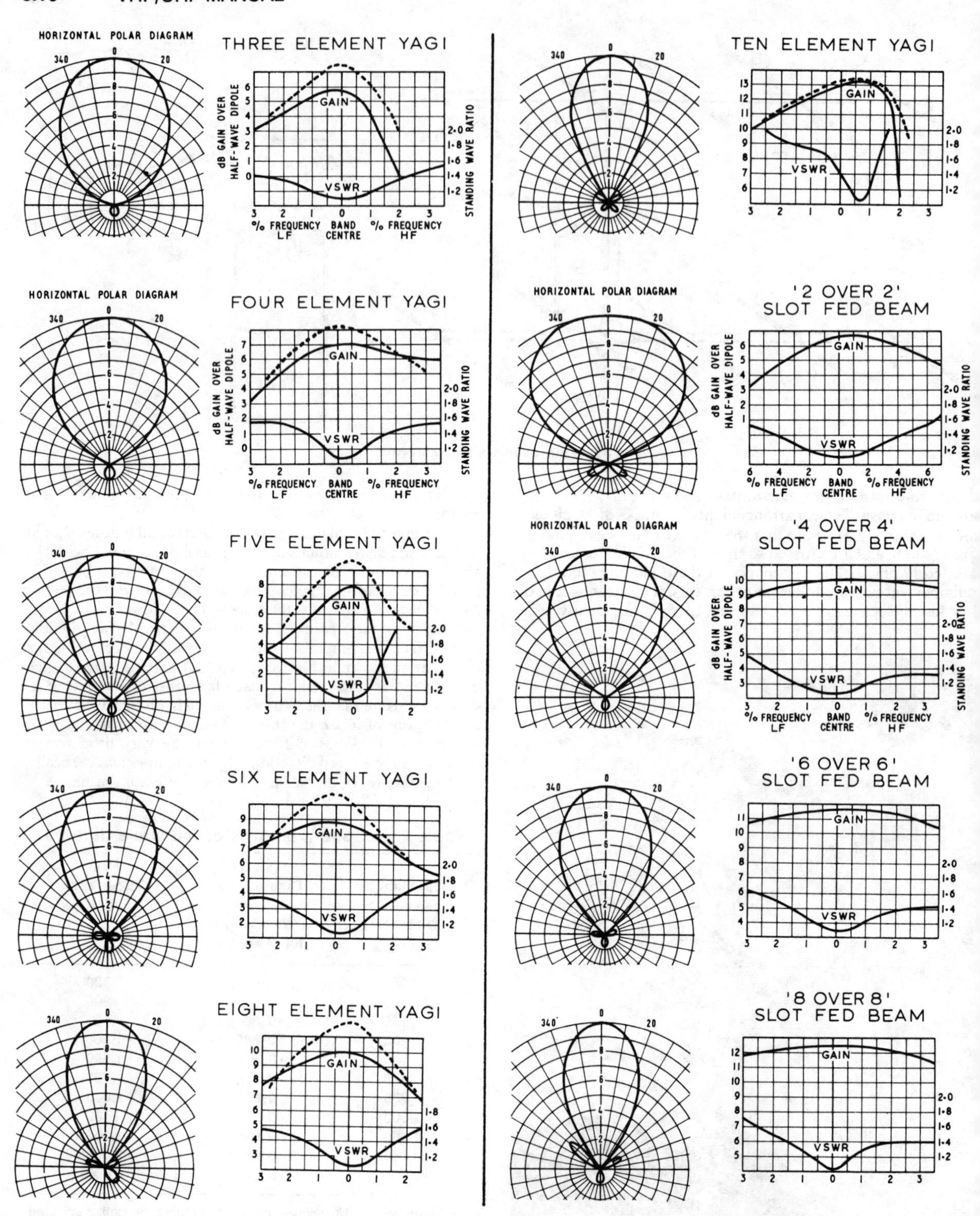

Fig 37. Charts showing voltage polar diagram and gain against vswr of Yagi and skeleton-slot antennas. In the case of the six Yagis the solid line is for conventional dimensions and the dotted lines for optimized results as discussed in the text

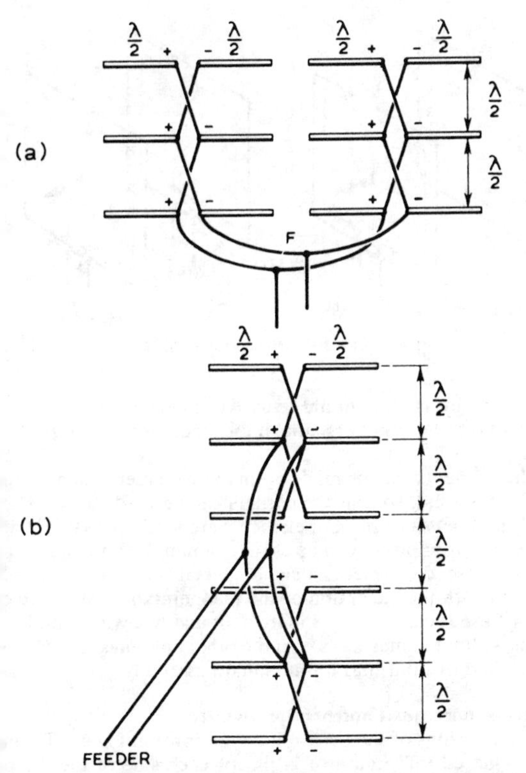

g 38. Two stacks of 1λ dipoles. Note that the feedpoint *F* is uidistant from each bay of dipoles. For example of element lengths, see Table 1

The spacing at the centre of each 1λ dipole should be suf-cient to prevent a reduction of the resonant frequency by the apacitance between the ends. In practice this spacing is usually bout 1in for the 144 and 432MHz bands.

Matching can be carried out with moveable short-circuited pen-wire stubs on the feed lines. The practical aspects of this peration are dealt with in a typical case later in this chapter.

As with the Yagi array, the gain can be increased by placing a flector behind the radiating elements at a spacing 0·1 to ·25λ, a figure of 0·25λ being frequently chosen. For the 32MHz band and for higher frequencies, a plane reflector ade up of 1in mesh wire netting stretched on a frame can be sed in place of the resonant reflector at a similar spacing. The esh of the wire should be so orientated that the interlocking vists are parallel to the dipole. The wire netting should extend least λ/2 beyond the extremities of the dipoles in order to nsure a high front-to-back ratio.

The λ/2 sections of the 1λ dipole should be supported at the urrent antinodes, ie at their centres, either on small insulators r in suitably drilled wooden vertical members. Supports ould not be mounted parallel to the elements because of ossible influence on the properties of the antenna.

The bandwidth of this type of antenna is exceptionally large nd its adjustments generally are far less critical than those of agi arrays.

For a stack having an adequate wire-net reflector, the hori-ontal beamwidth θ, vertical beamwidth Φ, and power gain G ompared with an isotropic radiator) can be calculated ap-roximately from the following formulae

$$\theta = \frac{51\lambda}{a} \qquad \Phi = \frac{51\lambda}{b} \qquad G = \frac{4\pi ab}{\lambda^2}$$

where a and b are the horizontal and vertical dimensions of the reflector respectively, both being expressed in the same units as the wavelength.

These formulae are true only for an array which is large compared with the wavelength, but are suitable as a criterion for judging antennas of any type provided the equivalent aper-ture or capture area is known.

Disadvantage of multi-element arrays

As the frequency becomes higher and the wavelength becomes shorter, it is possible to construct arrays of much higher gain although, as already described, the advantage is offset by the reduction in capture area. However, if the practice already described (namely that of using many driven or parasitic ele-ments, either in line or in stack) is adopted, the complications of feeding become increasingly greater. Also, as the frequency increases the radiation loss from open-wire lines and from phasing and matching sections likewise increases, and it is then difficult to ensure an equal power feed to a number of radiators.

Preferably, therefore, the antenna should have a minimum number of radiating or other critical elements, such as resonant reflectors or directors.

12-element stack for the 432MHz band

Fig 39 illustrates the assembly of a 12-element stack arranged in two horizontal bays of three 1λ dipoles having a gain of 13dB. With the dimensions indicated the centre fre-quency is 432MHz. The radiating elements are constructed from thin-walled ⅜in diameter brass tubing to which the feeder and phasing wires are soldered. The centres are supported on ½in polythene insulators mounted on vertical 1in by 1in wooden members. The reflecting screen is made from 1in mesh galvan-ized wire netting mounted on a framework of aluminium-alloy angle. Each bay of three 1λ dipoles is fed at the centre; the feed line taken straight through the reflector, and each of these feed lines is matched to the 300Ω open-wire feed line by a moveable short-circuited stub. The two 300Ω feeders, one from each bay, are joined together to the output of a totally enclosed coaxial balun and a two-stub tuner. The antenna is fed with 72Ω coaxial cable.

To match the antenna to the feeder, first one bay of the beam is disconnected, and a 300Ω 1W carbon resistor is substituted. The stub on this side should be set to exactly λ/4 long.

The remaining bay is then matched approximately to the open-wire feed line. This may be determined by using a very low wattage bulb (for example, 6V, 0·06A), the screwed body of which is held in the hand. The presence of standing waves is then examined by observing the glow in the bulb as it is slid along the feed line with its centre connection in contact with one of the feed-line conductors. The procedure is then reversed, the resistor being placed so as to represent the bay that has been matched. Both bays are then reconnected and the final match-ing carried out by means of the two-stub tuner using a slotted line or other matching device. If no special apparatus is avail-able the array should be tuned for maximum gain as already described.

The quad

The quad antenna is particularly useful for locations where neighbours may object to full-size Yagi types.

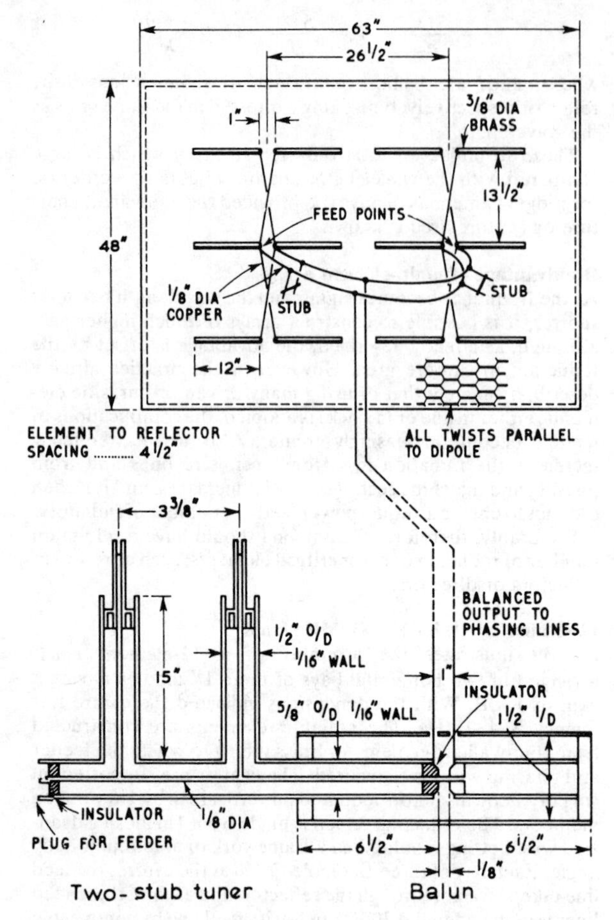

Fig 39. A 12-element stack for 432MHz, complete with two-stub tuner and enclosed coaxial balun

In spite of its small physical size a forward gain of 5½ to 6dB can be obtained and its front-to-back ratio is significant; there is no reason why directors should not be added to the basic two element array in the same manner as applied to the normal Yagi.

Typical dimensions for both 70MHz and 144MHz are given in Table 8. The actual spacing should initially be made adjustable and for a 144MHz antenna the spacing between the radiator and reflector will be between 7in and 9in for a 72Ω

Table 8. Design dimensions for 70 and 144MHz quad antennas

Band	Reflector 1 total length	Radiator 2 total length	Director (if used)	Approx. length of stubs if used Reflector s/c	Director s/c
70MHz (a)	173 (439)	165 (419)	157 (399)	—	—
70MHz (b)	165 (419)	165 (419)	165 (419)	8 (20·3)	8 (20·3)
144MHz (a)	84 (213)	80 (203)	76 (193)	—	—
144MHz (b)	80 (203)	80 (203)	80 (203)	4 (10·1)	4 (10·1)

Dimensions are in inches with centimetre equivalents in brackets.

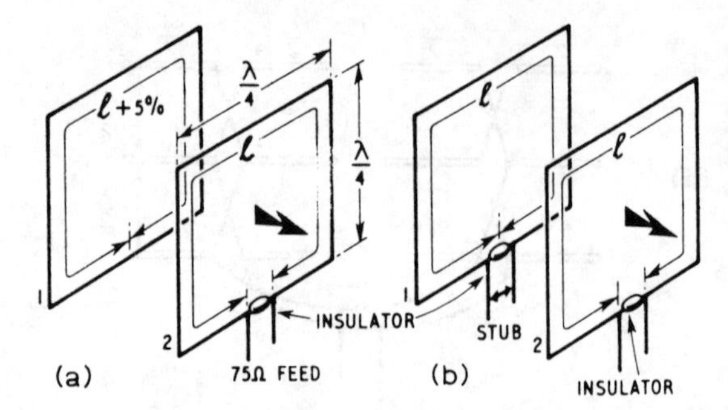

Fig 40. Quad antenna dimensions

cable. Ideally a balun should be used to connect the cable to the radiator but this is not essential if the feeder is short and of low loss.

The elements may be made of ⅛in to ¼in diameter aluminium, preferably solid, so that the corners can be bent easily. If the vertical dimensions of both elements are made the same, the two short cross-pieces can be used to mount the antenna to the mast. These cross-pieces may be metal so that the whole antenna with the exception of the feedpoint and the reflector stub (if used) can be very solidly built and will withstand high winds without damage. As with the other antennas, quads may be stacked or built into a four-square assembly.

A four-square quad antenna for 144MHz

The dimensions of the basic quad are shown in Fig 41. Taking the "squared up" figure of 20¾in for each side of the driven element it will be seen that this approximates to 0·255λ in free space at 144MHz. The spacing between the two elements on

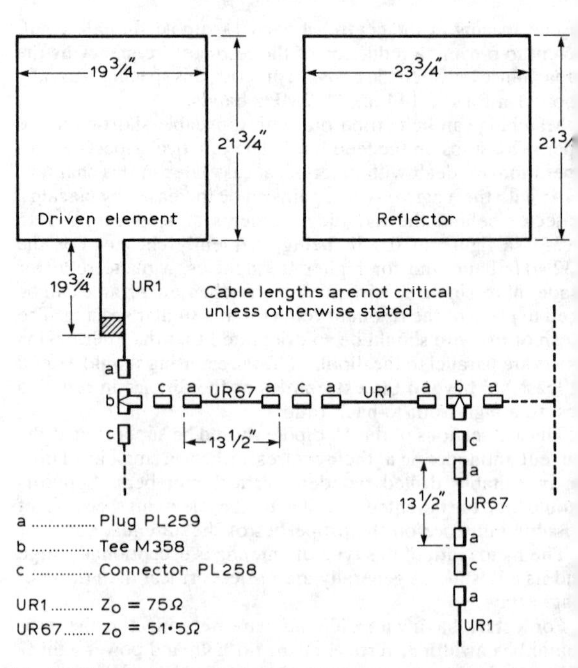

Fig 41. Physical arrangement of the antenna system shown in Fig 42 with details of matching sections of coaxial cable

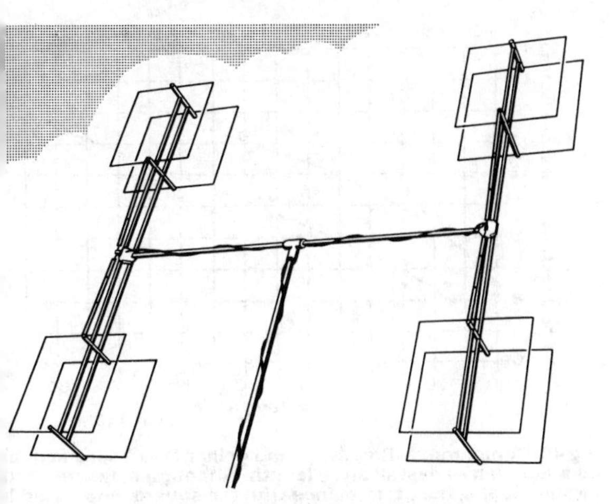

Fig 42. A 144MHz cubical quad array

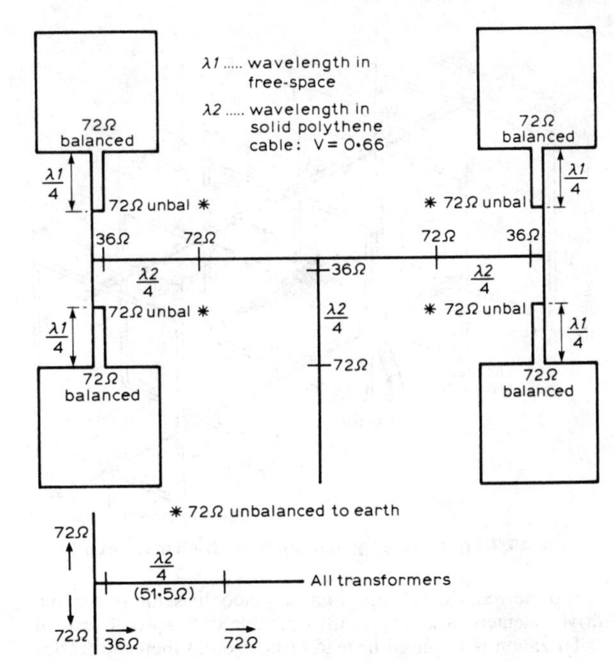

Fig 43. The complete electrical system of the cubical quad array described

single unit only (see below) to provide a correct match into the 72Ω feeder was found to be 7in which approximates to 0·08λ. The spacing between the elements has a markedly critical effect on the swr although the forward gain of the antenna is not affected in so drastic a manner.

The antenna has a forward gain of 5dB over a λ/2 dipole and a back-to-front ratio of better than 20dB.

Two quads. Two quad antennas mounted one above the other at a centre-to-centre spacing of 5λ/8 (=65in) and paralleled through a single λ/4 51·5Ω transformer. Performance figures for this type of antenna are typically a forward gain of 8·2dB over a λ/2 dipole with a back-to-front ratio of better than 10dB at 144MHz. To obtain the 72Ω input impedance for the double system it may be found necessary to open out the spacing of the reflectors from the driven element on both quads to 9in. This is necessitated by the fall in input impedance on a single quad due to the mutual coupling of the pair.

Four quads. The final form of the antenna is shown in Figs 42 and 43. The layout is determined by the ease with which the feeder cable can be run, and also to avoid a long length of unguyed mast. The spacing between the elements is 9in as in the case of the double quad while the vertical spacing between quads is 65in in the absence of the torsional loading problem, the horizontal spacing was set at 81½in centre-to-centre, ie a full wavelength in free space.

The gain of this arrangement is 13·5dB over a λ/2 dipole with a back-to-front ratio of 18dB. The polar diagram is shown in Fig 44.

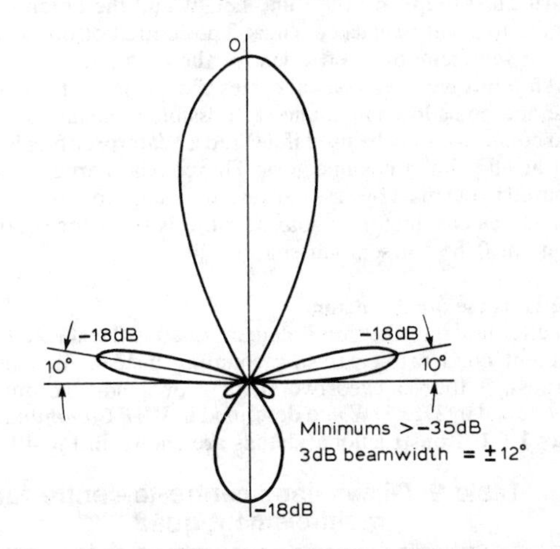

Fig 44. Horizontal polar diagram of the complete array

Multi-element quad antennas

Interest in multi-element quad antennas has increased recently, mainly because they offer a better performance with reduced side lobes compared with the simple Yagi.

Generally the maximum number of elements is five, and where more gain is needed a pair may be stacked either vertically or horizontally—for maximum mechanical strength the vertical arrangement is to be preferred.

The whole structure may be made up of aluminium tube (or rod for the elements), and the only insulator necessary is the feed point of the driven element.

In construction, it is an advantage to make each element from one piece of material. A ⅜in aluminium rod will bend round corners much more readily than tube, and does not need a filler to prevent distortion. The corner radius should be kept small but, if it has to be large, due allowance for the shortening of the total length of the element should be borne in mind.

For mechanical simplicity (and appearance) it is an advantage to arrange for all the element heights to be the same, and vary the width.

Fixing the elements to the boom and the boom to the mast is probably best done using standard tv antenna parts. Although suitable blocks or clamping arrangements can be made, they usually tend to be unnecessarily heavy.

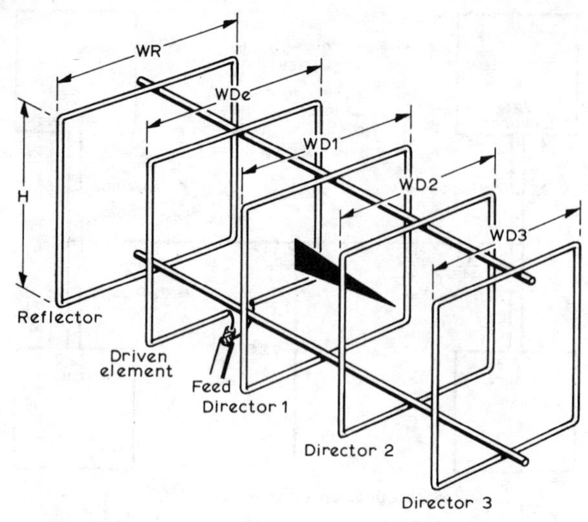

Fig 45. General arrangement of a multi-element quad

If preferred, the reflector may be made the same size as the driven element, and tuned with a suitable stub. Also, if vertical polarization is required instead of horizontal then the feeder should be attached to the centre of one of the vertical sides of the driven element.

All quad loops are the same height and the antenna looks similar to a pair of stacked Yagis. The centre bottom section of the driven element is left open for the feed line.

All joints between coaxial cables should be as short as possible and be as low impedance as possible (coaxial "T" pieces and connector may be used if desired). Waterproofing is essential at all joints or connectors. The coaxial harness must be secured to the mast by tape to prevent damage to joints in gales.

The velocity factor of coaxial cable is 0·66 for solid polythene or 0·86 for semi-air-spaced.

A quadruple quad antenna

An alternative to the multi-element quad is the stacked multi-element quad using parasitic coupling instead of a phasing harness. A four-stacked two-element or quadruple quad was developed by DL6DW and described in *VHF Communications* May 1971. Constructional details are shown in Fig 49.

Table 9. Dimensions centre-to-centre for multi-element quad

Height H		21 (53·3)	21	21	21
Width Reflector	WR	24½ (62·2)	24½	24½	24½
Driven	WD_e	20½ (52)	20½	20½	20½
Director 1	WD_1	—	18 (45·7)	18	18
Director 2	WD_2	—	—	16 (40·6)	16
Director 3	WD_3	—	—	—	14 (35·6)
Spacing					
Reflector to Driven		7 (17·8)	19 (48·3)	20 (50·8)	20
Driven to Director 1		—	12 (30·5)	14½ (36·8)	14½
Director 1 to Director 2		—	—	14½	14½
Director 2 to Director 3		—	—	—	14½
Approx gain (dB)		5	7·5	10·5	12·5

Element diameters all ⅜in; Feed impedance in all cases is 75Ω. Dimensions are in inches with centimetres equivalents in brackets.

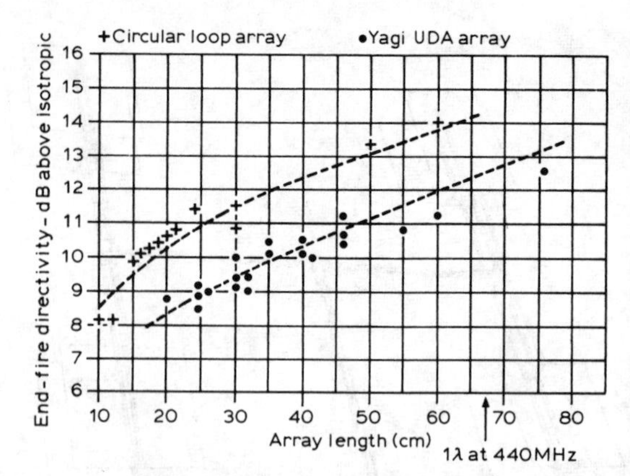

Fig 46. Comparative directivity (and gain) of the Yagi and quad as a function of overall array length. Although measured with circular loops, the performance with the square loops used in the quad is comparable. The measurements were made at 440MHz by W0HTH but also apply at lower frequencies (*ARRL Antenna Book*)

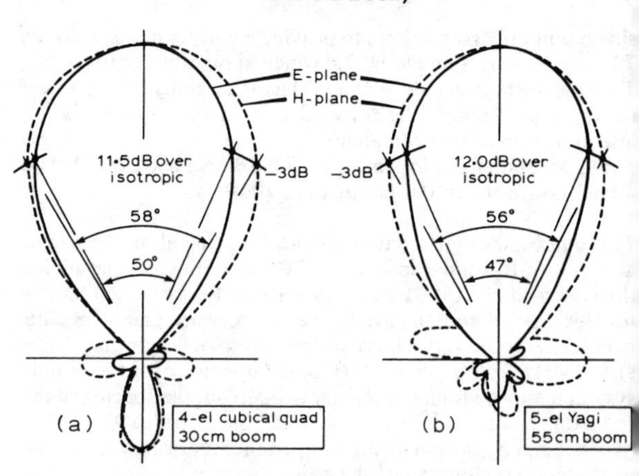

Fig 47. Measured voltage patterns of four-element quad and five-element Yagi showing approximately equivalent band-widths (*ARRL Antenna Book*)

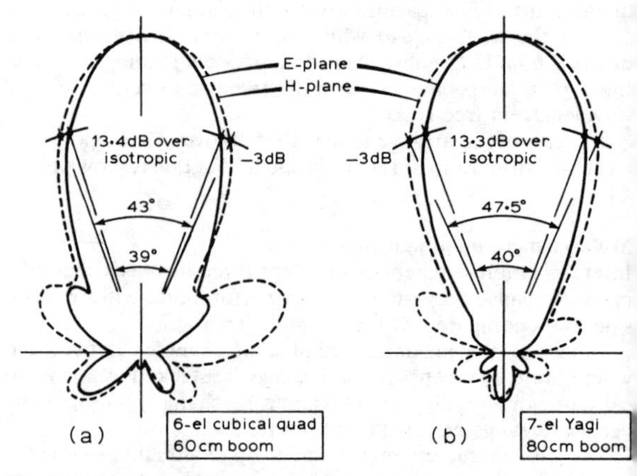

Fig 48. Measured voltage patterns of six-element quad and seven-element Yagi (*ARRL Antenna Book*)

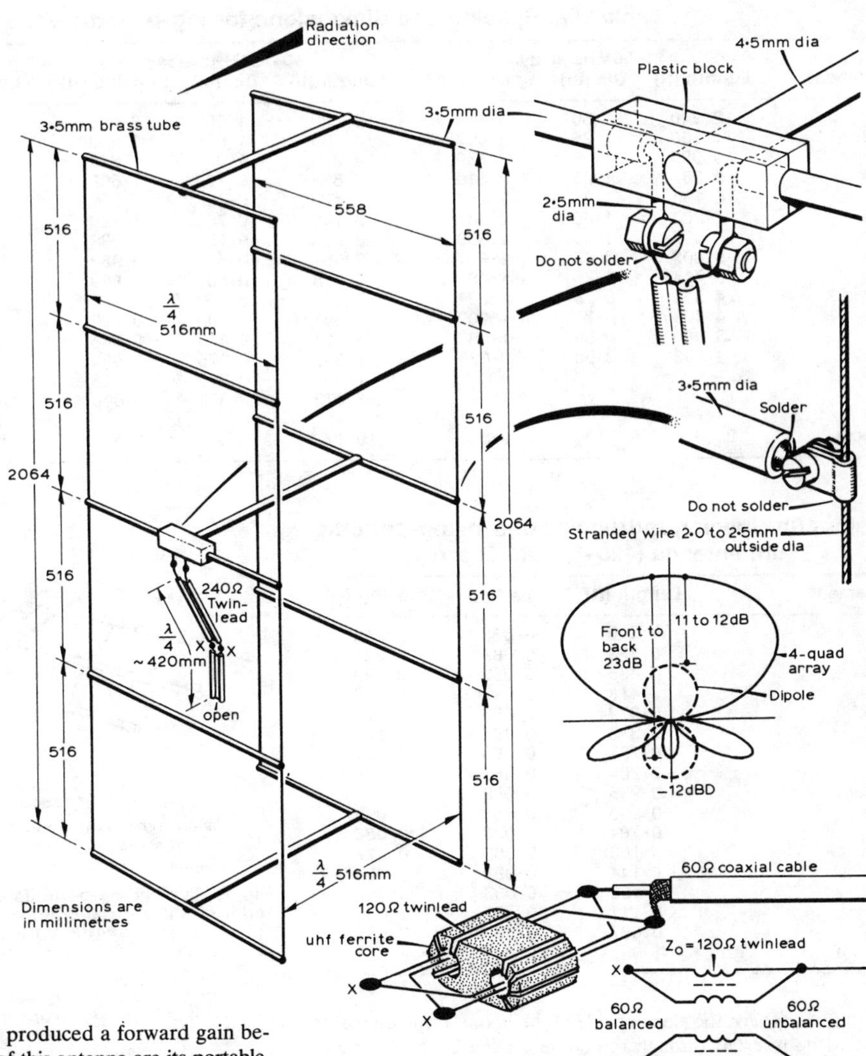

Fig 49. Quadruple quad. The match point XX should be found experimentally and will be approximately 200mm from the open end (*VHF Communications*)

Measurements of this antenna produced a forward gain between 10 and 11dBi. Advantages of this antenna are its portable nature and that nearby objects cause a minimum of detuning effects. With this multiquad construction the interaction of the resonant element lengths gives each quad section a resonant circumference of 1·04 which deviates from the dimensions of a conventional quad even when the length of diameter ratio of the conductor is accounted for. With the dimensions used and the spacing between the driven element and the reflector (0·25λ) the best front-to-back ratio and lowest environmental dependence was achieved.

Log periodic

The log-periodic antenna was originally designed and proved at the University of Illinois in the USA in 1955. Since then the military, in particular, have made considerable use of this antenna. Its particular properties are an almost infinite bandwidth, governed only by the number of elements used, and the directive qualities of a Yagi antenna.

Table 10a shows typical dimensions for element spacings and length for log-periodic arrays which are derived from a computer-aided design produced by W3DUQ in *Ham Radio*, August 1970. Other frequency bands can be produced by simple scaling of *all* dimensions.

The tabulated parameters have a five per cent overshoot in the working frequency range at the low end and a 45 per cent overshoot at the high-frequency end to maintain logarithmic response over the complete frequency range specified. In log-periodic operation approximately four elements are active at any one specific frequency, hence the need for the high- and low-frequency extension. The alpha or logarithmic element taper is 28° for all three antennas, which exhibit a forward gain of 6·55dBD with a front-to-back ratio of typically 15dB and a vswr better than 1·8:1 over the specified frequency range.

The construction can be straightforward but it should be noted that the element lengths for the highest-frequency antenna were calculated for the elements to be inserted completely through the boom, flush with the far wall. The two lower-frequency antennas have element lengths calculated to

Table 10a. Spacing and dimensions for log-periodic vhf antennas

Element	21–55MHz array Length (ft)	Dia (in)	Spacing (ft)	50–150MHz array Length (ft)	Dia (in)	Spacing (ft)	140–450MHz array Length (ft)	Dia (in)	Spacing (ft)
1	12·240	1·50	3·444	5·256	1·00	2·066	1·755	0·25	0·738
2	11·190	1·25	3·099	4·739	1·00	1·860	1·570	0·25	0·664
3	10·083	1·25	2·789	4·274	1·00	1·674	1·304	0·25	0·598
4	9·087	1·25	2·510	3·856	0·75	1·506	1·255	0·25	0·538
5	8·190	1·25	2·259	3·479	0·75	1·356	1·120	0·25	0·484
6	7·383	1·00	2·033	3·140	0·75	1·220	0·999	0·25	0·436
7	6·657	1·00	1·830	2·835	0·75	1·098	0·890	0·25	0·392
8	6·003	0·75	1·647	2·561	0·50	0·988	0·792	0·25	0·353
9	5·414	0·75	1·482	2·313	0·50	0·889	0·704	0·25	0·318
10	4·885	0·75	1·334	2·091	0·50	0·800	0·624	0·25	0·286
11	4·409	0·75	1·200	1·891	0·50	0·720	0·553	0·25	0·257
12	3·980	0·50	1·080	1·711	0·375	0·648	0·489	0·25	0·231
13	3·593	0·50	0·000	1·549	0·375	0·584	0·431	0·25	0·208
14				1·403	0·375	0·525	0·378	0·25	0·187
15				1·272	0·375	0·000	0·332	0·25	0·169
16							0·290	0·25	0·000
Boom	25·0	2·0	0·5	16·17	1·5	0·5	5·98	1·5	0·5

Table 10b. Spacing and dimensions for log-periodic uhf antenna (420–1,350MHz array)

Element	Length (ft)	Dia (in)	Spacing (ft)
1	0·585	0·083	0·246
2	0·523	0·083	0·221
3	0·435	0·083	0·199
4	0·418	0·083	0·179
5	0·373	0·083	0·161
6	0·333	0·083	0·145
7	0·297	0·083	0·131
8	0·264	0·083	0·118
9	0·235	0·083	0·106
10	0·208	0·083	0·095
11	0·184	0·083	0·086
12	0·163	0·083	0·077
13	0·144	0·083	0·069
14	0·126	0·083	0·062
15	0·111	0·083	0·056
16	0·097	0·083	0·000
Boom	1·99	0·5	

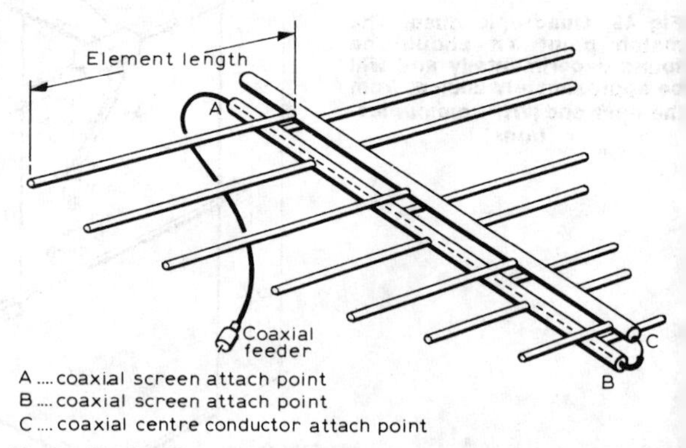

Fig 50. Typical log-periodic antenna. Note that the bottom is fed from the coaxial outer while the top boom is fed from the centre conductor (*Ham Radio*)

butt flush against the element side of the boom. If the elements are to be inserted through the boom on the 21–55MHz and 50–150MHz antennas, the boom diameter must be added to the length of each element.

As the supporting booms are also the transmission line between the elements for a log-periodic antenna they must be supported with a dielectric spacing from the mast of at least twice the boom-to-boom spacing; otherwise discontinuities will be introduced into the feed system. Feed line connection and the arrangement to produce an "infinite balun" is shown in Fig 51. Any change in the boom diameters will necessitate a change in the boom-to-boom spacing to maintain the feed impedance. The formula to achieve this is

$$Z_0 = 273 \log_{10} \frac{D}{d}$$

where D is the distance between boom centres, and d the diameter of the booms.

The antenna can be orientated either horizontally or vertically (if a non-metal mast section is used) to suit the polarization required. The horizontal half-power beamwidths will be typically 60° with a vertical half-power beamwidth of typically 100°.

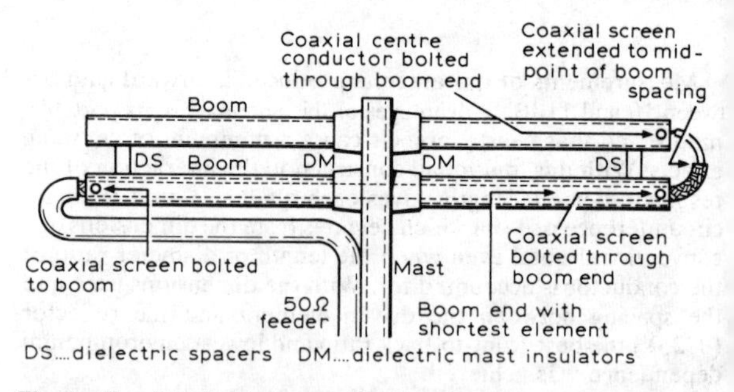

Fig 51. Feeding the log periodic is relatively simple. Remove the outer plastic jacket from the feedline for the entire length of the boom, so that the coaxial outer is permitted to short itself inside the boom as well as the solid electrical connections at each end of the boom (*Ham Radio*)

Log-periodic Yagi bandpass antenna

This is an antenna with an interesting and useful bandpass characteristic giving a flat response over a wide band, and significant attenuation outside.

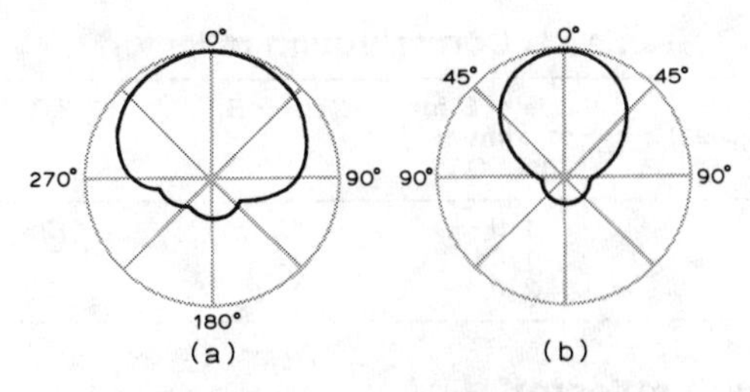

Fig 52. Typical log-periodic voltage radiation patterns (a) horizontal, (b) vertical (*Ham Radio*)

It is basically a combination of a log-periodic driven section with a parasitic Yagi section.

The prototype 50MHz design gave a gain of 12dBD and a bandwidth of 2MHz. The details given in Fig 53 are for 144MHz, where the bandwidth would be around 5MHz.

This type of characteristic offers obvious advantages in terms of reducing adjacent channel interference; and also giving a more constant performance over the whole 144 to 148MHz band. The simple Yagi, by comparison, is essentially a narrow-band antenna.

The corner reflector

The use of an aperiodic plane reflector spaced behind a radiating dipole has already been discussed. If this reflector is bent to form a V, as shown in Fig 55, a considerably higher gain is achieved. The critical factors in the design of such an antenna array are the corner angle α and the dipole/vertex spacing S. The curves in Fig 56 show that as α is reduced, the gain theoretically obtainable becomes progressively greater. However, at the same time the feed impedance of the dipole radiator falls to a very low value, as can be seen from Fig 57. This makes matching difficult and hence a compromise has to be reached. In practice the angle α is usually made 90° or 60°; adjustments in a 60° corner are a little more critical although the maximum

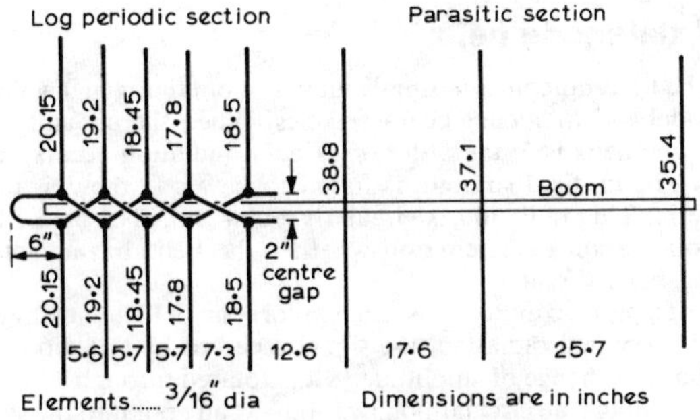

Fig 53. A log-periodic Yagi bandpass antenna

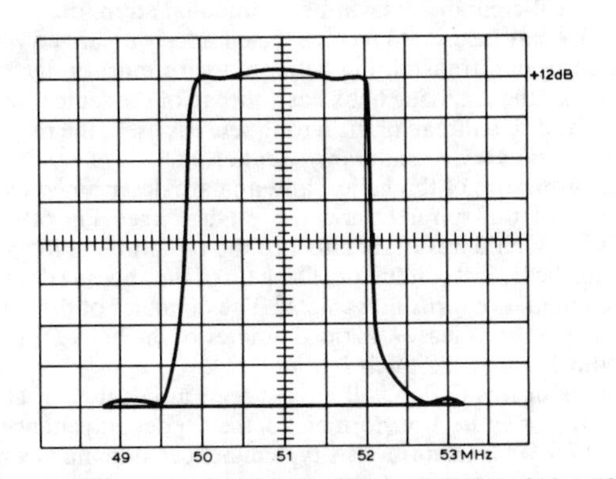

Fig 54. Gain versus frequency characteristic of the 50MHz log-periodic Yagi

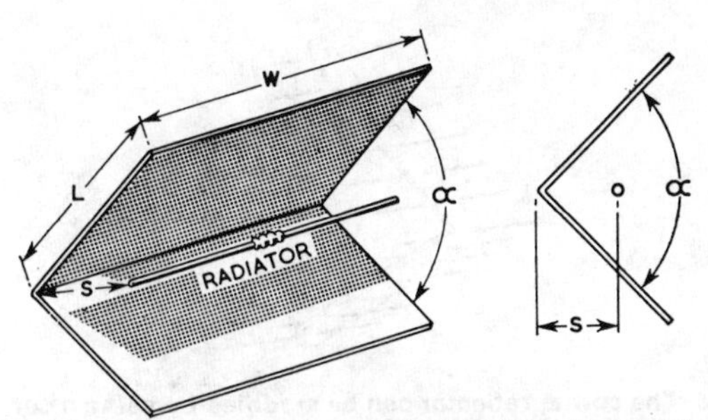

Fig 55. Corner reflector. The $\lambda/2$ dipole radiator is spaced parallel with the vertex of the reflector at distance S; its characteristics are shown in Figs 56 and 57

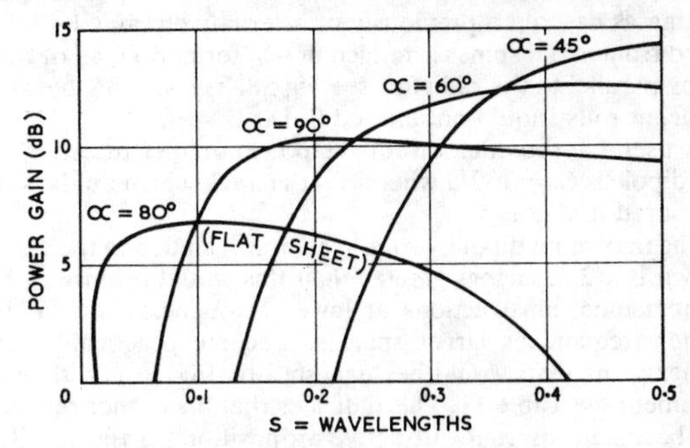

Fig 56. Theoretical power gain obtained by using a corner reflector with a $\lambda/2$ dipole radiator

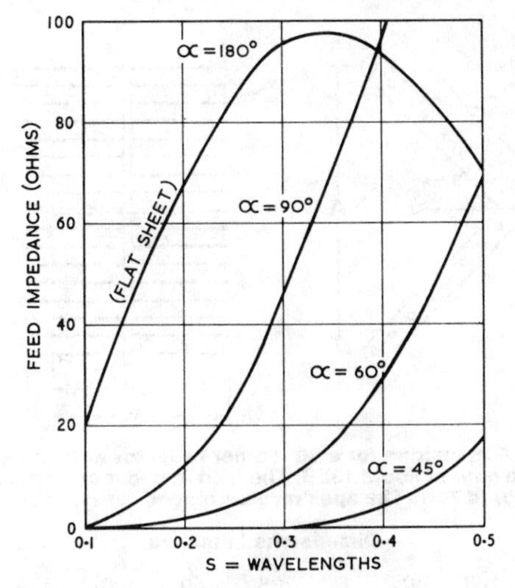

Fig 57. Feed impedance of a $\lambda/2$ dipole provided with a corner reflector: see Fig 55

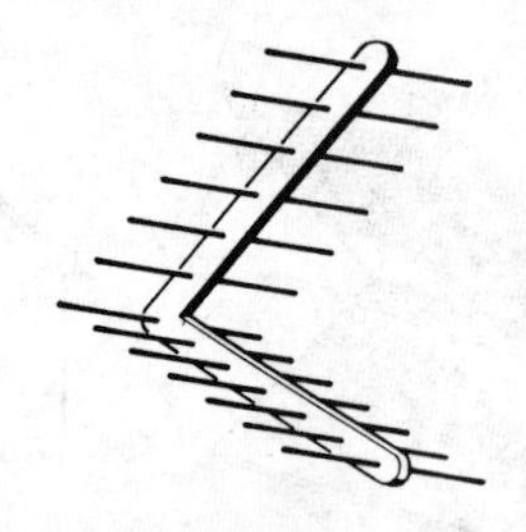

Fig 58. The corner reflector can be modified by using a set of metal spines arranged in V-formation to replace the sheet metal or wire-netting reflector

obtainable gain is higher. The final matching of the radiator to the line may be carried out by adjusting the distance S.

It does not greatly affect the gain over a useful range of variation but causes a considerable change in radiation resistance. A two-stub tuner may also prove helpful in making final adjustments.

The length L of the sides of the reflector should exceed 2λ to secure the characteristics indicated by Fig 56 and 57, and the reflector width W should be greater than 1λ for a $\lambda/2$ dipole radiator. The reflecting sheet may be constructed of wire-netting as described previously or alternatively may be fabricated from metal spines arranged in a V-formation, all of them being parallel to the radiator: see Fig 58. The spacing between adjacent rods should not exceed $0{\cdot}1\lambda$.

A useful approximation for the power gain G referred to a $\lambda/2$ dipole is $G = 300/\alpha$ where α is the angle between the sides measured in degrees.

The maximum dipole/vertex spacing S included in the curves shown is $\lambda/2$. Spacings greater than this would require rather cumbersome constructions at lower frequencies, but at the higher frequencies larger spacings become practicable, and higher gains than would be suggested by Fig 56 can then be obtained; see Table 11. This indicates that the corner reflector can become a specially attractive proposition for the 1·3GHz band, but the width across the opening should be in excess of 4λ to achieve the results shown.

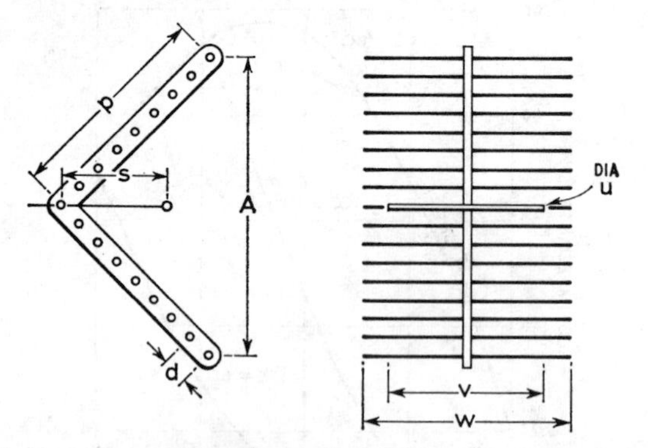

Fig 59. Dimensions for a 60° corner reflector antenna system giving a gain of about 13dB. The feed impedance of the dipole radiator is 75Ω. The apex may be hinged for portable work

Dimensions in inches

Band	p	s	d	v	w	A	u	λ
144	100	40	6	38	50	100	3/8	82
433	35	13¼	1½	12¾	20	35	¼	27¼
1,296	12	4½	½	4	8	12	⅛	9⅛

Table 11. Corner/trough reflector

Angle α (degrees)	Value of S for maximum gain (λ)	Gain (dBi)	T (λ)
90	1·5	13	1–1·25
60	1·25	15	1·0
45	2·0	17	1·9

Trough reflector

To reduce the overall dimensions of a large corner reflector the vertex can be cut off and replaced with a plane reflector, an arrangement known as a *trough reflector*. Similar performance to that of the large corner reflector can thereby be achieved provided that the dimensions of the trough do not exceed the limits indicated in Table 11, which shows the gain obtainable for greater values of S than those covered by Fig 56, assuming that the reflector is of adequate size. T is the distance between the plane reflector and the theoretical apex of the vertex.

The resulting antenna has a performance very little different from the corner reflector type and presents fewer mechanical problems since the plane centre portion is relatively easy to mount on the mast and the sides are considerably shorter.

The gain of both corner reflectors and trough reflectors may be increased still further by stacking two or more and arranging them to radiate in phase, or alternatively by adding further collinear dipoles within a wider reflector similarly fed in phase. Not more than two or three radiating units should be used since the great virtue of the simple feeder arrangement would then be lost.

Axial-mode helix

The helix antenna is a simple means of obtaining high gain and wideband frequency charactersitics. When the circumference of the helix is of the order of 1λ axial radiation occurs; ie the maximum field strength is found to lie along the axis of the helix. This radiation is circularly polarized, the sense of the polarization depending on whether the helix has a right- or left-hand thread.

If a pick-up dipole is used to explore the field in the direction of maximum radiation, the signal received by this dipole will show no change of amplitude as it is rotated through 360°, thus indicating true circular polarization. At any point to the side of the helix the wave will be elliptically polarized, ie the horizontal and vertical components will be of unequal strength.

A helix may be used to receive the circularly polarized waves radiated from a transmitting helix, but care must be taken to ensure that the receiving helix has a thread of the same sense as the radiator; if a thread of the wrong sense is used, the received signal will be very considerably weaker.

The properties of the helical antenna are determined by the diameter of the spiral D and the pitch P (see Fig 60) and depends upon the resultant effect of the radiation taking place all along the helical conductor. The gain of the antenna depends on the number of turns in the helix. The diameter of the reflector R should be at least $\lambda/2$, the diameter of the helix D should be about $\lambda/3$ and the pitch P about $\lambda/4$.

A helix of this design will have a feed impedance of about 140Ω; this may be transformed to the feeder impedance by means of a $\lambda/4$ transformer. A typical helical antenna having a seven-turn helix has a gain of approximately 12dBi over a 2:1 frequency range. However, to achieve this gain fully it is

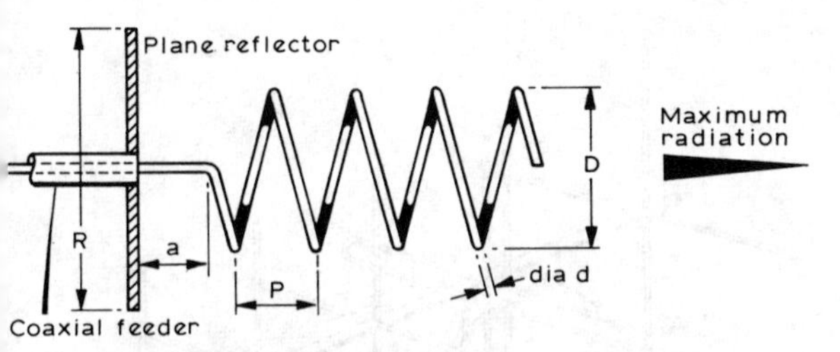

Fig 60. The helix antenna. The plane reflector may take the form of a dartboard type of wire grid. The dimensions given in the table are based on a pitch angle of 12°. The helix, which may be wound of copper tube or wire, the actual diameter of which is not critical, must be supported by low-loss insulators

necessary to use a circularly polarized antenna (eg a helix of the same sense) for reception. If a plane-polarized antenna, such as a dipole, is used there will be a loss of 3dB.

A practical helix antenna for 144MHz

The greatest problem to be overcome in this type of antenna for 144MHz, with its relatively large helix diameter of 24½in, is the provision of a suitable support structure.

Fig 61 shows a general arrangement, in which three supports per turn (120° spacing) are shown, and details of suitable drilling of the central boom are given in Fig 62.

The helix may be made of copper, brass, or aluminium tube or rod, or coaxial cable. This latter alternative is an attractive material to use, being covered and substantially weatherproofed. If coaxial cable is used the inner conductor should connect to the outer at each end, or be removed completely.

The reflector is located at a distance *a* behind the start of the first turn, and is supported by crossed supports from the central boom. The material for the reflector can be any kind of metal mesh—such as chicken netting or plastic-coated garden mesh.

The central boom should be sufficiently rigid to adequately support the whole structure, and should at the same time be of a non-metallic material such as wood, thick-wall plastic tube or thick-wall glass fibre. Although glass fibre is more expensive it would undoubtedly be worthwhile for a permanent installation.

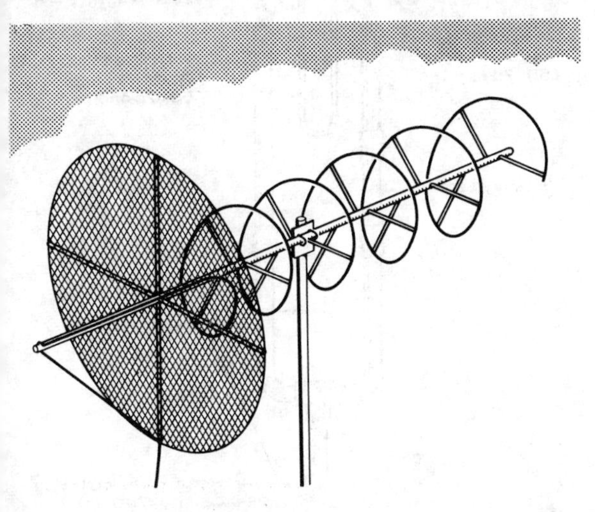

Fig 61. General arrangement of support structure for a five-turn helical antenna for 144MHz

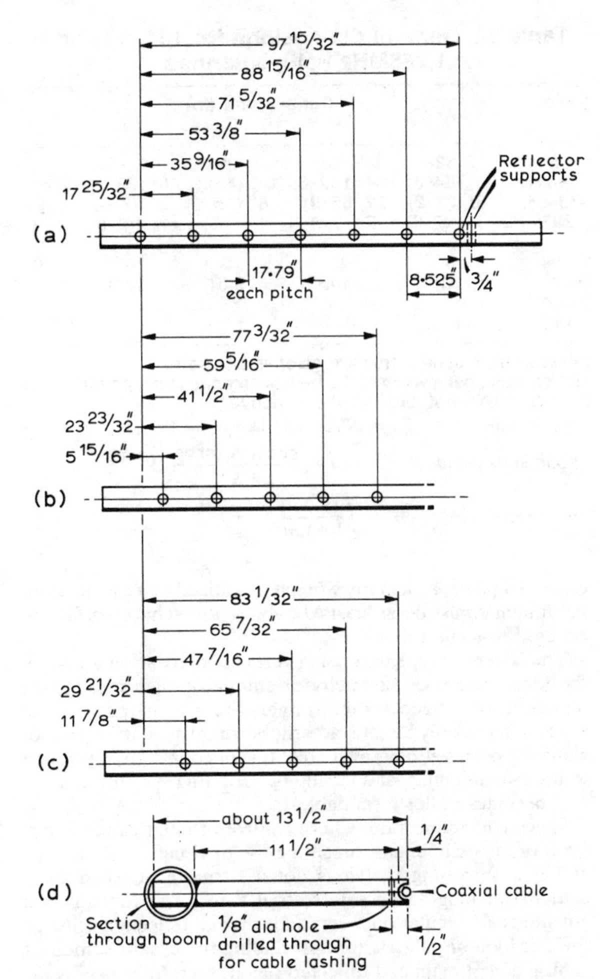

Fig 62(a) First side drilling dimensions, reflector support holes are drilled at right-angles; (b) and (c) are drilled at intervals of 120° and 240° respectively from (a). (d) Gives cutting and filing dimensions for the element stand-offs, fractions of 1 in to be to nearest $\frac{1}{32}$in

The length of the final turn of the helix can be adjusted to obtain optimum circularity. This would entail rotating a dipole set up in line with the helix at a distance of, say, 10m, to be outside the near field and clear of all objects. The signal obtained from the dipole will be constant for all points of rotation when the helix is optimized for circular polarization. Any variation of the signal is known as the *polarization axial ratio* or *boresight ellipticity*, and is usually expressed as a ratio or decibel figure.

Control of antenna polarization

During recent years, vertical polarization has become popular for mobile operation in the UK, due to the basic fact that it is far easier to obtain omni-directional radiation with a vertical antenna than it is with horizontal one. This is particularly important on a vehicle, where the mechanical simplicity of a short vertical rod considerably outweighs the complexity of a halo or

Table 12. General dimensions for 144, 433 and 1,296MHz helix antennas

Band	Dimensions (in)				
	D	R	P	a	d
General	0·32λ	0·8λ	0·22λ	0·12λ	
144MHz	25½ (64·8)	64 (162·6)	17¾ (45)	8¾ (22·2)	3/16–½
433MHz	8¾ (22·2)	22 (55·9)	6 (15·2)	3 (7·6)	½
1,296MHz	3 (7·6)	7 (17·8)	2 (5)	1⅛ (2·8)	¼–⅛
Turns	6	8	10	12	20
Gain	12dB	14dB	15dB	16dB	17dB
Beam-width	47°	41°	36°	31°	24°

Dimensions in centimetres are given in brackets.
The gain and beamwidth of the helical antenna is dependent upon the total number of turns as shown above

Bandwidth $= 0{\cdot}75$ to $1{\cdot}3\lambda$

Feed impedance $= 140 \times \dfrac{\text{circumference}}{\lambda}\ \Omega$

Beamwidth (degrees) $= \sqrt{\dfrac{12{,}300}{\text{No turns}}}$

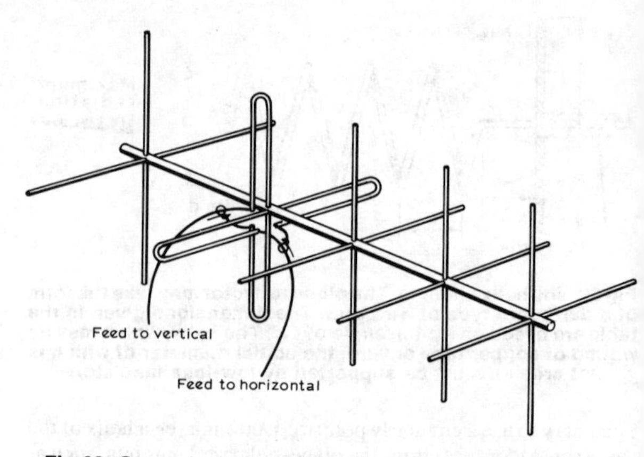

Fig 63. General arrangement of a crossed Yagi antenna

crossed dipole, particularly when it is realized that the horizontal antenna must be at least λ/2 above the vehicle surface to ensure low-angle radiation.

The advent of repeaters using vertical polarization for much the same reason of simplicity of antenna design means that operation of a fixed station, either direct to mobiles or via repeaters, can only be satisfactorily accomplished if a means of changing polarization is available. It is of course quite possible to use two antennas, and ideally two rotating systems, but the cost becomes rather formidable.

Space communication, where control of polarization is difficult or impossible, has forced the use of circular polarization and it is surprising that it is not used more between fixed stations for long-distance terrestrial work. The fundamental advantage of circular polarization is that all reflections change the direction of polarization, precluding the usual addition or subtraction of main and reflected signal; therefore there is far less fading and aircraft flutter when circular polarization is used at each end of the link. The use of circular polarization at one end only, with normal horizontal or vertical at the other end of the link, naturally results in a 3dB loss, and therefore to achieve the full advantages of circular polarization it is necessary for all stations to use it.

The usual practice when using circular polarization is to standardize on clockwise in the northern hemisphere, and this may well become standard for the amateur by its regular adoption. The direction of polarization is referred to as viewed from the *rear* of the antenna.

Changing all vhf operations to circular polarization is obviously not practical, but if a system of switching polarizations were in use at all stations it would soon become evident that circular was the best, and there would of course be the added bonus that vertical would be available for operation with mobiles. Having used a system of polarization switching, big variations are found in polarization from stations, in particular mobiles. Quite often a mobile using a vertical antenna has been found to be of equal strength on all polarizations and in some cases a definite advantage for circular has been shown.

Circular polarization normally brings to mind the helix antenna, which can only produce modes of circularity, depending upon whether the thread of the antenna element is wound clockwise or anti-clockwise. Horizontal or vertical polarization is possible from helix antennas, but only by the use of two helices and suitable phasing, with no real means of control. The simple means of changing polarization is to mount a horizontal Yagi and a vertical Yagi on the same boom, giving the well-known crossed Yagi. Separate feed to each section of the Yagi brought down to the operating position will enable the user to switch to either horizontal or vertical, but it is perhaps not generally realized that it is a relatively simple matter to alter the phasing of the two Yagis in the shack and obtain four more

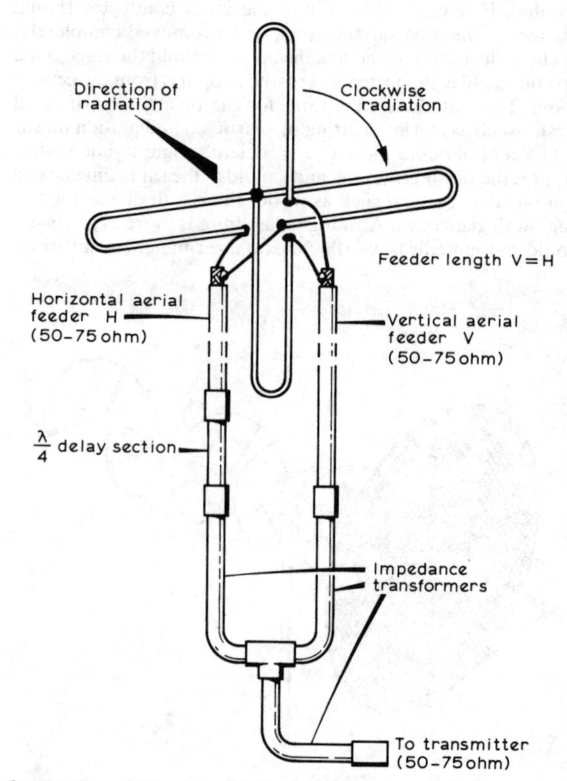

Fig 64. General arrangement of feeders with delay line (phasing) for clockwise radiation

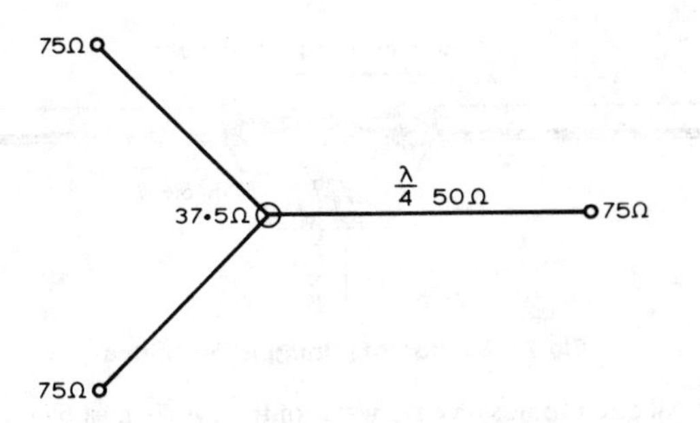

Fig 65. Matching two 75Ω antennas by paralleling to 37·5Ω and increasing impedance to 75Ω again

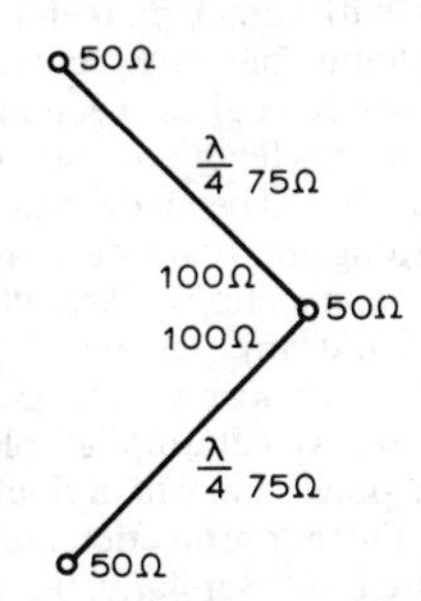

Fig 66. Matching two 50Ω antennas by increasing impedance to 100Ω and paralleling to 50Ω again

polarization options, namely two slant positions—45° and 135°, together with two circular positions—clockwise and anti-clockwise, which with horizontal and vertical gives six positions altogether.

Although vertical polarization is mechanically and electrically advantageous when using a simple dipole type of antenna, the presence of the mast in the same plane as the vertical elements on a Yagi considerably detracts from performance. This can be very simply overcome with a crossed Yagi with polarization switching, mounting the antenna with elements at 45°. The mast then has little effect on the vertical performance, and vertical and horizontal only can still be produced by feeding both antennas in the correct phase relationship.

Assuming therefore that a crossed Yagi is mounted at 45° with individual feeders to the operating position, the polarization available and the phasing required is as follows:

Slant position 45° and 135°	Antennas fed individually
Circular positions clockwise and anti-clockwise	Both antennas fed with 90°+ or 90°− phase relationship
Horizontal and vertical	Both antennas fed with 0° or 180° phase relationship

This all sounds very complicated, but in actual fact the desired result may be accomplished relatively simply with a three-gang six-position Yaxley-type wafer switch. A coaxial switch is the "pure" way to do the job, but considering the cost of a three-gang six-way coaxial switch together with the necessary plugs and sockets, the difference in performance is just not worthwhile on 144 MHz.

The first problem to overcome is simply that of providing the correct matching for feeding two antennas in parallel. Briefly, with 75Ω antennas the two feeders are simply paralleled, giving 37·5Ω and λ/4 of 50Ω feeder used to transform back to 75Ω, as illustrated in Fig 65. 50Ω antennas are treated in a slightly different way in that λ/4 of 75Ω feeder is used in each feeder to transform up to 100Ω and the two are placed in parallel to produce 50Ω again, as shown in Fig 66.

Phasing is simply a question of altering the length of the feeders to each half of the crossed Yagi as the polarization is changed. Where a 90° phase shift is required, λ/4 of feeder is inserted and where a 180° phase shift is required, λ/2 feeder is inserted. The polarization switch must therefore arrange for correct matching by switching in the appropriate λ/4 impedance transformer and correct phasing by switching in the appropriate length of feeder.

There is an added complication in that by no means all antenna systems are 50Ω, and a considerable number of 75Ω users still remain on vhf. 50Ω has become an international standard and is of course completely standard on low frequency; it can therefore only be a matter of time before all vhf installations are 50Ω.

Figs 67 and 68 show the necessary switching arrangements for 75Ω and 50Ω antennas respectively. The normal drawing of

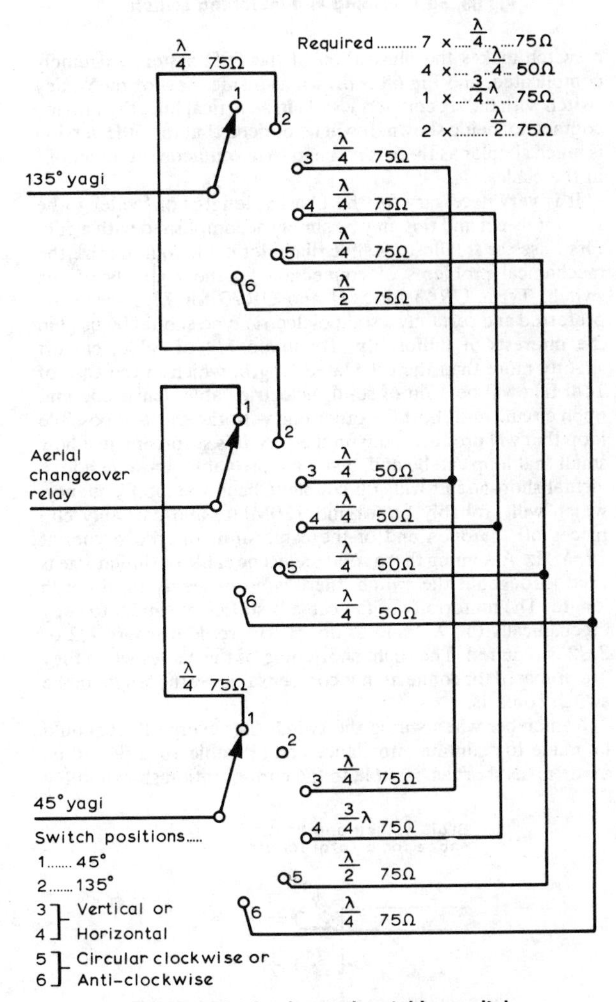

Fig 67. 75Ω phasing and matching switch

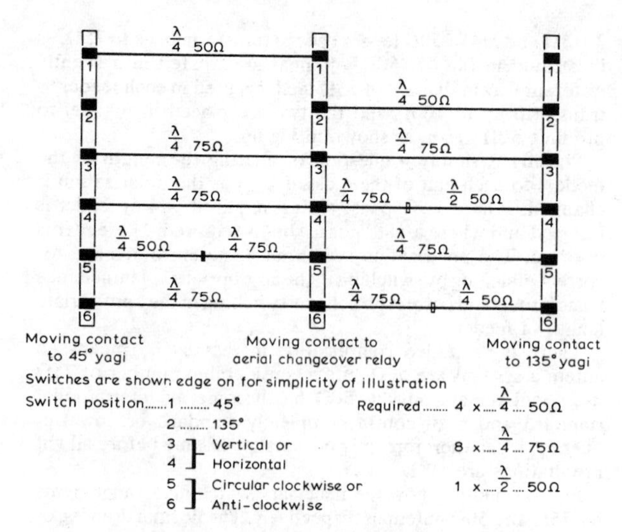

Fig 68. 50Ω phasing and matching switch

a switch makes the illustration of the 50Ω system extremely complicated, and Fig 68 is drawn as a side view of the Yaxley switch with the six contacts visible in a vertical line, the moving contact not being shown. It will be noticed that the 50Ω version is much simpler as there is no need to manufacture T-junctions in the cables.

It is very necessary for the phasing lengths of feeder to be accurately cut and this may be simply accomplished with a gdo. First, use the smallest possible diameter cable to minimize the mechanical problems of connection to the contacts of the switch. Types UR43 for 50Ω and UR70 for 75Ω are to be preferred and certainly a solid dielectric type should be used in the interests of uniformity. To obtain λ/4 of cable, cut off slightly more than the calculated length, which in the case of 144MHz will be 15in of solid dielectric cable, leave one end open circuit, and short the other end with the shortest possible loop that will produce a dip on the gdo. It is surprising just how small that loop can be and, given a reasonably sensitive gdo, a virtual short-circuit will still couple. Check the dip frequency, which will probably be around 120MHz, and carefully clip pieces off the open end of the cable until the dip occurs at 145MHz. Assuming that a solid dielectric cable of similar size is used throughout the switch, there is no necessity to dip each length. The uniformity of the cable is sufficient simply to copy mechanically this λ/4 and to double or treble it where λ/2 or 3λ/2 is required. The slight shortening of the cables when they are prepared for connection is compensated by the length in the switch contacts.

Remember when wiring the switch that every effort should be made to maintain impedance and all cable ends should be made up as short as possible to the configuration shown in Fig

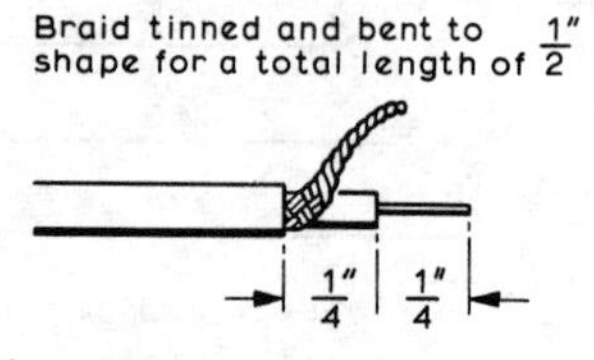

Fig 69. Method of "tailing" coaxial cable

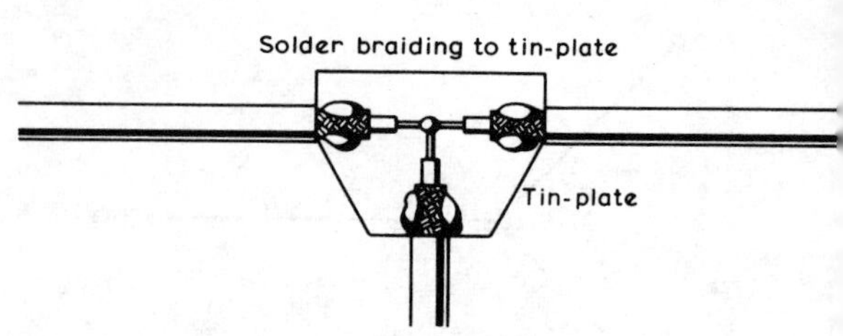

Fig 70. Method of joining three cables

69. All outer braids on each wafer of the switch must be joined together by the shortest possible route and not connected to the frame of the switch. The use of the Radiospares Maka-switch miniature switches with small diameter cable makes for a beautifully neat assembly, but very great care indeed is needed to deal with the many coaxial connections in a switch of this small size. The joining of a length of 50Ω and 75Ω is important, and here every effort should be made to maintain the coaxiality of the cable by pushing the braid back away from the inner, making the inner connections carefully, taping up with polythene tape to avoid any possible short-circuit, and then bringing the braids back again over the tape and binding securely with fine wire. Any attempt at soldering will probably be disastrous, as the polythene will undoubtedly melt with the risk of short-circuit. Further protection may be given by a layer of tape over the entire joint. Similarly, the T-junctions required

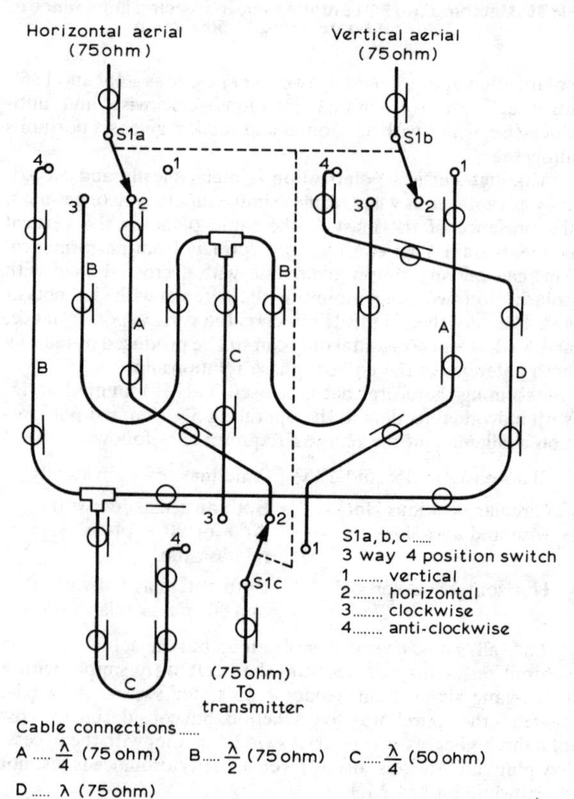

Fig 71. An alternative arrangement for feeding crossed Yagi antennas which provides various polarizations at the click of a switch

Table 13. Received signals expected with various switch connections

Switch position	Polarization of signal (dB down)					
	Horiz.	Vert.	45°	135°	Clock-wise	Anti-clock-wise
Horizontal	Max	20/30	3	3	3	3
Vertical	20/30	Max	3	3	3	3
45°	3	3	Max	20/30	3	3
135°	3	3	20/30	Max	3	3
Clockwise	3	3	3	3	Max	20/30
Anti-clockwise	3	3	3	3	20/30	Max

on the 75Ω switch may be made up by cutting small triangular sections of tinplate and quickly soldering the outers of each cable to the tin; in this case short-circuits may be seen and avoided. Fig 70 illustrates the method.

Assuming that the switch has been satisfactorily built, there is now the problem of whether the feeders to the halves of the crossed Yagi are of the correct individual length. Ideally, these feeders should be cut mechanically and electrically to equal length before installation, and the two halves of the crossed Yagi should be in exactly the same place on the boom. While the feeders may be cut accurately, it is mechanically difficult and almost impossible to mount the two halves of the Yagi in the same place. They inevitably have to be spaced by a few inches. It is therefore necessary to correct this mechanical displacement of phase by an equal displacement of length of the feeders, and in practice it is far easier to simply connect everything up with unknown lengths of feeders and adjust the length of one or both feeders until the switch operates correctly.

A convenient method of adjustment is to receive a horizontally-polarized signal of constant amplitude from a local station, ensuring that the transmitting and receiving antennas are beamed directly at each other. This point is vitally important—a beam antenna only radiates its intended polarization from the main lobe—a fact which will become very evident in subsequent use of the switch. The feeder lengths should now be adjusted so that all slant and circular positions are equal, together with maximum rejection in the vertical position of the switch. The choice of which shall be the horizontal and vertical positions can now be taken. Accurate S-meter readings logged for each position of the switch after every feeder adjustment are essential. Typically, the slant or circular positions will be about one S-point down on the horizontal, while the vertical position will be some six S-points or 20 to 30dB down. To avoid the problem of the man trying to level the legs of a four-legged table and finishing up with a 3in-high table, when cutting feeder lengths cut only 1in at a time from one feeder. When the recorded readings indicate that the last cut as one too many, cut that last piece from the other feeder and the optimum situation will be restored.

With the Yagis mounted at 45°, it may appear surprising that a horizontal signal can produce differing signal strength on each antenna, but this will happen until the respective feeders are of equal length. The reason is the inevitable mis-match (sometimes deliberate to improve noise factor) which occurs at the input to the converter or receiver. Remember the object is *equal* signals, not maximum signals—converter mis-match can be compensated for and *maximum* signal strength achieved by altering the length of the main feeder after the switch, which will not affect the phase relationships between the antennas.

The question now arises as to which of the circular polarization positions are clockwise or anti-clockwise. This subject merits an entire article; it will be remembered that even the world's top telecommunication engineers got this one wrong on the first transatlantic tv broadcast via Telstar. Should the operator wish to define the circular positions, then with accurately cut equal feeders and an accurately made switch, position 5 will be clockwise and 6 anti-clockwise, providing the antenna connections are as shown in Fig 68. If the antenna connections are not known, then the only way to calibrate the switch is to receive a known circularly-polarized signal, when the respective positions will be immediately evident.

A correctly wired and phased switch should perform as in Table 13.

Hand-held portable antennas

Normal-mode helix

Much has been said for and against what is termed the *normal-mode helix* as used on hand-held transceivers. Unfortunately the method of operation and the results obtainable for this type of antenna have been much misunderstood by amateurs and professionals alike. Most theoretical papers only consider the helical equivalent of the $\lambda/4$ whip while most users of this antenna are in fact using the equivalent of a physically reduced $3\lambda/4$ whip.

A helix will work in the normal mode when the diameter and pitch of the helix is less than $0 \cdot 1\lambda$. When working in this mode the radiation is from the side of the helix, and when the diameter is considerably less than $0 \cdot 1\lambda$ the resultant "spring" has a radiation pattern similar to a short vertical monopole or whip.

A $3\lambda/4$ whip over a moderate ground plane has a resistive match very close to 50Ω. If this whip is coiled into a helical spring as previously described it will resonate to approximately 50Ω but at a somewhat lower frequency. If the spring is trimmed to the original frequency the result will be an antenna of about $0 \cdot 1\lambda$ long matching to approximately 50Ω. The actual wire length tends to be around $\lambda/2$ to $5\lambda/8$ long at the working frequency. The capacitance formed between the turns of the

Fig 72. A typical commercial helical antenna with screw mounting facility

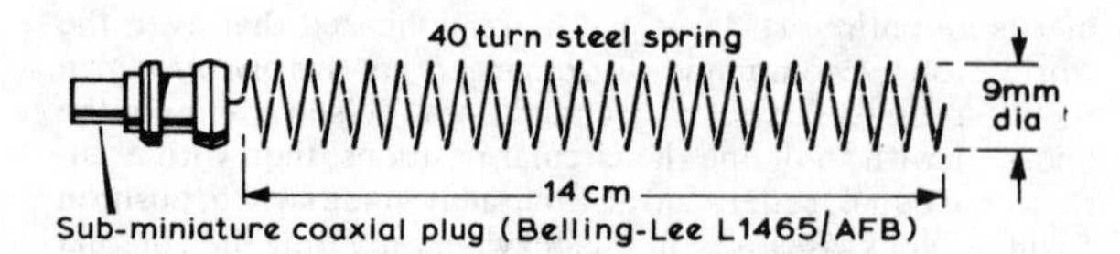

Fig 73. Details of a home-made helical whip for 145MHz. A BNC plug could also be used

spring has "loaded" the antenna such that it still resonates as a 3λ/4 antenna. This capacitance also tends to modify the matching under various conditions.

Because of its construction, the spring is very reactive off-resonance and this makes it very important that it be resonated for the specific conditions that prevail in its working environment.

Fortunately it is only necessary to change the number of turns to resonate the spring over such diverse conditions as a large ground plane and no ground plane at all. However, the match referred to 50Ω can vary between about 30 and 150Ω at the extremities. Under typical hand-held conditions, however, and depending on the frequency of operation, the spring tends to be fairly close to a 50Ω impedance match. This is shown in Fig 73 which also gives an indication of the number of turns required for a typical 9mm diameter helix for 3λ/4 resonance.

An important consideration is that since the helix is a reduced size and aperture antenna two factors arise. First, the radiation resistance is lower than the equivalent linear whip so the choice of a good conducting material is important to remove resistive losses. A steel spring compared with a brass or copper-plated helical can waste 3dB of power in heating up the spring. The aperture of the helical is a third the physical size of the λ/4 whip and would moreover indicate a loss of 4·77dB. However results obtainable with copper-plated, Neoprene-sheathed helical antennas, correctly matched to a hand-held transmitter at 145MHz, are at worst −3dB and at best are +1dB compared to the equivalent λ/4 whip (which is −6dB compared to a λ/2 dipole). One thing that will be seen however is that the top of the spring on a hand-held transceiver will often need to be raised to a position corresponding to the top of the equivalent λ/4 whip to receive or transmit the maximum signal strength.

A similar device resonated on to a λ/2 square ground plane

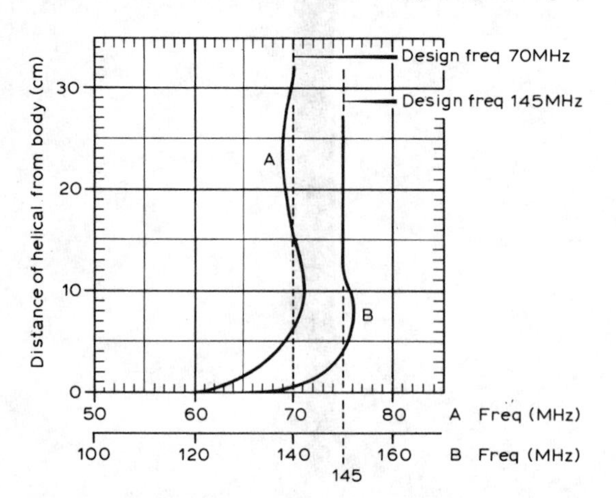

Fig 74. Frequency shift of a helical antenna on a typical hand-held transceiver for various distances from the body

could give results 2–3dB below a λ/2 dipole. An alternative arrangement using a bifilar wound helix gives identical results (within 0·2dB) to a λ/2 dipole.

The helical or spring has an interesting and difficult operating characteristic when supported close to the body, particularly at the higher frequencies. Fig 74 shows the typical results of a 145MHz or high-band spring and a 70MHz or low-band spring as it is brought closer to the body. The interesting effect which occurs at several centimetres from the body can be seen, where the resonance of the spring, instead of continuing to decrease due to body capacitance, suddenly increases the frequency of resonance. At 2cm and closer the operating frequency suddenly decreased due to body capacitance. Unfortunately this very changeable area occurs at the typical mounting distance of a body-worn transceiver. However, many transceivers are required to be raised to the mouth when transmitting and this puts the antenna back to its best operating conditions.

HB9CV mini-beam

An antenna that falls into the category of horizontally or vertically polarized, portable rather than mobile, or for base station

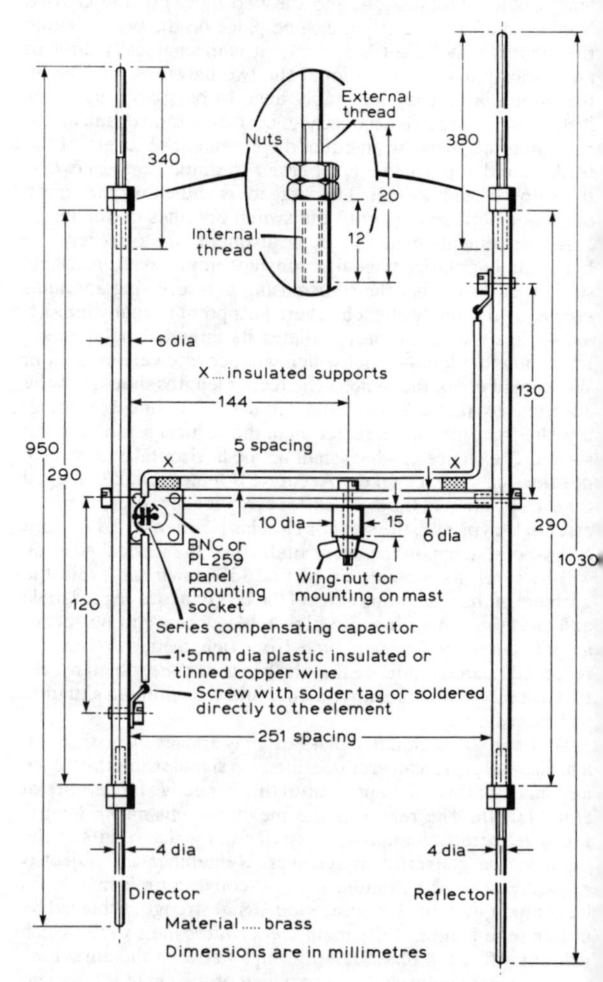

Fig 75(a). A collapsible HB9CV antenna for the 144MHz band (*VHF Communications*)

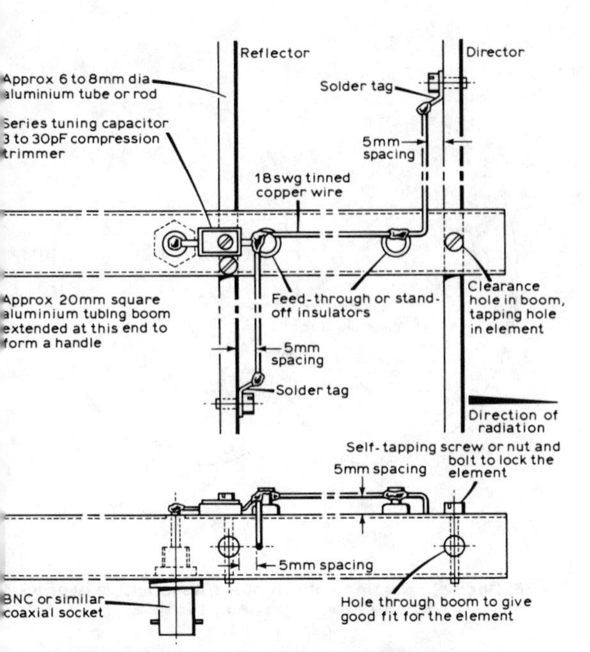

Fig 75(b). Alternative construction of the HB9CV Dimensions as per Fig 75(a)

use, is the HB9CV mini-beam. Similar units are the *lazy H*, and *ZL special* often used on the hf bands. The HB9CV version, however, has one or two mechanical advantages which makes it particularly suitable for vhf portable use.

Figs 75(a) (taken from "The HB9CV Antenna for VHF and UHF", H. J. Franke, DK1PN, *VHF Communications* February 1969) and 75(b) show two methods of construction for the HB9CV antenna. A point that should be stressed is that a *series* capacitor of 3–15pF is required to adjust finally the gamma match/phasing combination to a vswr of about 1·3:1 against 50Ω. The dimension of the element spacing and the transmission lines, particularly the spacing (5mm), is critical for optimum impedance matching and phasing, and hence gain and front-to-back ratio.

The principle of operation is as follows. If two dipoles at close spacing, typically 0·1–0·2λ, are fed out of phase, "end fire" radiation will occur in a direction at right-angles to the line of the dipole elements. If the dipoles are resonant at the same frequency a bidirectional pattern with a gain of typically 3dB referred to a single dipole will be realized. However, if correct phasing between the elements is used, a unidirectional or beam pattern is produced. The different lengths found on most HB9CV antennas assist with bandwidth. The end at which the beam is fed designates the direction of radiation. A theoretical gain in excess of 6dBD should be possible. However, depending on the construction techniques, gains between 4 and 5·5dBD with front-to-back ratios between 10 and 20dB tend to be realized in practice. The radiation patterns shown in Figs 76(a) and 76(b) are for the antenna of Fig 75(a), which has a gain of typically 5dBD. Note the differences obtained when mounted at 10m (30ft) above the ground, and hand-held between 1 and 2m above the ground, as would be the case if the antenna was being used for direction finding.

The HB9CV was mounted on a professional glass fibre radiation pattern measuring mast for the 10m test. This ensured a minimum disruption of the antenna radiation pattern when set up for vertical polarization.

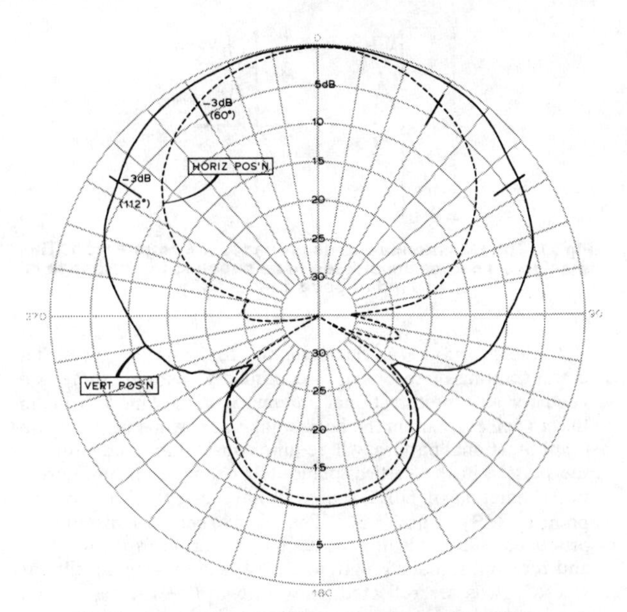

Fig 76(a). HB9CV antenna at 10m above ground

Mobile antennas

The choice of an antenna for mobile vhf and uhf use is dependent on several factors. As the frequency increases the aperture of the antenna decreases. This means that larger gains are required for uhf than vhf to overcome the loss of aperture as well as the radiation path loss due again to the increase of working frequency.

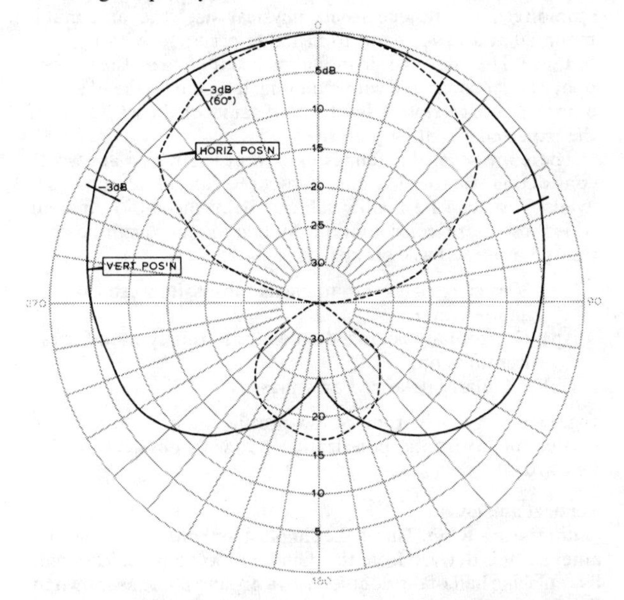

Fig 76(b). HB9CV antenna at 1–2m above ground, hand held

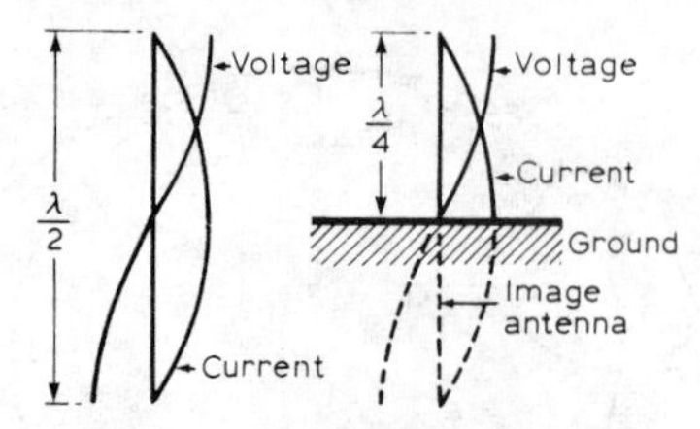

Fig 77. The λ/2 antenna and its grounded λ/4 counterpart. The missing λ/4 can be considered to be supplied by the image in ground of good conductivity

As the direction of a vehicle, relative to the station to which it is transmitting or receiving, is continually changing there is a need for an omnidirectional antenna system. This will mean that to achieve gain in the horizontal plane, while retaining an omnidirectional pattern, will require considerable reduction of the pattern in the vertical plane. For example an omnidirectional antenna of 6dBD gain will have a typical half-power point (−3dB) of under 30°. The narrow beam or disc that is produced will result in considerable variation in transmitted and received signal strength as the vehicle or antenna tilts or where signals are reflected, as will always be the case, from nearby objects. A compromise has therefore to be arrived at to obtain maximum gain in the best direction which gives minimum disruption of signals when mobile.

The choice of polarization is not only dependent on compatibility with stations being received and the optimum polarization for the propagation path concerned, but the aesthetics and mechanical complexity of the antenna used and its mounting position on the vehicle.

Antennas, particularly when vehicle-mounted, must always be considered as an integral part of the environment in which they are to be used. Radiation patterns quoted by manufacturers can be completely different when an antenna is in use. Increased gain normally means an increase in physical size. This improvement of gain can be lost, with a probable loss of omnidirectivity, if, due to its physical size, the antenna is mounted at a lower point to facilitate access to a garage, for instance. The difference in mounting an antenna on the wing or boot of a car compared with mounting it on the top dead centre of the car roof can lose at least 3dB of gain with the variations of the expected radiation patterns.

There are several antennas in current use which are worth considering. In addition one or two specialized antennas are available or can be readily fabricated by the radio amateur which also merit consideration. Mobile antennas can be considered in three basic groups:

(i) Vertically polarized antennas more often used for fm and repeaters.
(ii) Horizontally polarized antennas normally used for ssb transmission.
(iii) Circularly polarized antennas.

together with a sub-group of low-profile antennas to produce vertical or horizontal polarization but with physical heights below 0·1λ.

Vertical antennas

Quarter-wave whip. This is the simplest and most basic mobile antenna. It is derived from the doublet or λ/2 dipole. Marconi, by replacing half of the doublet with a ground plane as shown in Fig 77, found that the image of the vertical λ/4 section was

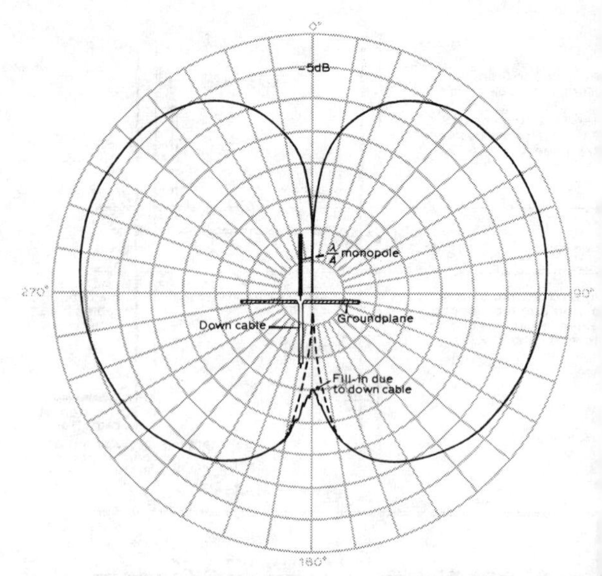

Fig 78. Decibel radiation pattern of a λ/4 monopole over a λ/2 square ground plane at 145MHz

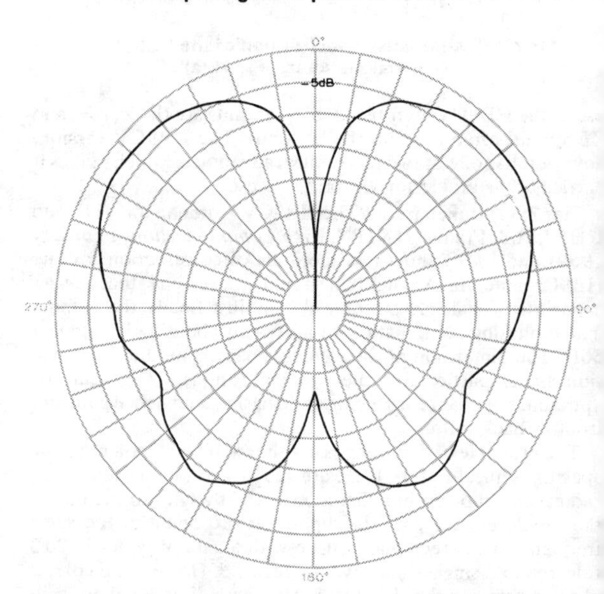

Fig 79. Decibel radiation pattern of a λ/4 monopole over a 1λ square ground plane at 145MHz

"reflected" in the ground plane, producing an antenna which was substantially the same as the original dipole. The theory of operation showed that if the ground plane was infinitely large and made of a perfectly conducting material, all of the radiation associated with the lower half of the dipole was radiated by the top half giving, in fact, a 3dB improvement over the dipole. In practice the size of the ground plane and its resistive losses modify the pattern and this 3dB is never realized. Figs 78 and 79 show optimum patterns of a λ/4 whip measured on a ground plane of λ/2 sides and λ sides. Although the pattern is raised from the horizontal, on a medium ground plane the loss of

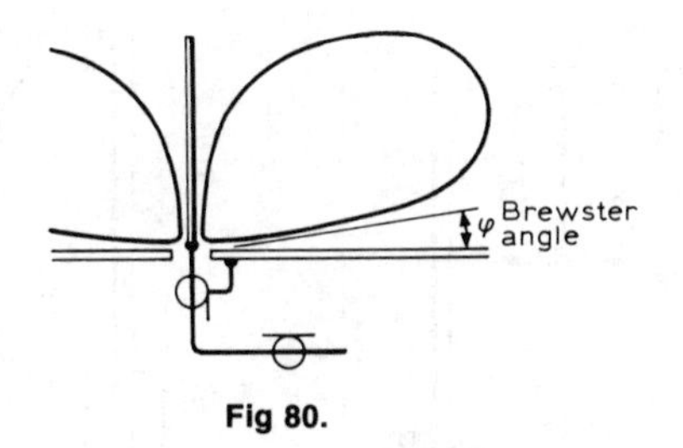

Fig 80.

orizontal gain is relatively small (20° and 1dB at 0° in Fig 78 ut 40° and 6dB at 0° in Fig 79).

However, as the ground-plane size increases the main lobe ontinues to rise until the situation of Fig 80 occurs. When a adiator is mounted over a ground plane as described, the input npedance is typically halved. So for the λ/4 whip or monopole ie input impedance is typically 36Ω + j, that is to say, approxi- ately half the resistance of the dipole but with an additional eactive component.

Considering 50Ω as being the standard cable impedance used t vhf and uhf, this would produce a standing wave at the ntenna base of about 1·5 to 1. The simplest way to overcome is mismatch is first to slightly increase the length of the whip produce an inductive reactance to cancel the capacitive reac- nce normally obtained. In practice this also raises the resistive alue of the whip and a close match can usually be obtained to 0Ω cable. Should a vswr bridge or similar (of 50Ω characteris- c impedance) be used to set up the whip, when a match has een achieved, the length of the cable should be changed and ie match re-checked. If there is no change in the meter read- g, then the antenna is matched to the cable. If a change does ccur then the antenna/cable combination has been matched to ie vswr meter and the whip should be re-adjusted until hanges in cable length have minimal or no effect. It is prefer- ble that the added cable length is not an exact multiple of a λ/2 r λ/4 as this, particularly with a multiple of λ/2, will confuse the esults.

The ground-plane effects and aperture size of the λ/4 whip nd to limit its use at vhf and uhf. At uhf the aperture is small nd the pattern tends to be raised in the vertical plane due to the rge ground-plane area. It is therefore not often used at those equencies. At vhf, ie 144MHz, the compromise of the λ/4 hip's simplicity and size (about 49cm or 19¼in) often balances ith its medium aperture and tendency on some vehicles to ave a raised vertical pattern. At 70MHz the physical dimen- ions are such (about 102cm/40in) that this is the normal limit- ng factor to the use of the λ/4 whip as opposed to gain devices. he aperture of the antenna at this frequency is compatible with ath-loss conditions, and the ground-plane size is such that the adiation angle when roof mounted is fairly low. However, the hape of the radiation pattern can have a loss of 3dB in the mnidirectivity each side of the vehicle.

he λ/2 and 5λ/8 gain antenna. Using the ground-planing tech- iques described for the λ/4 whip, gain antennas can be pro- uced. If the λ/2 dipole is extended in length, maximum for- ard gain (before the pattern divides into several lobes) is btained when the dipole is about 1·2λ. This becomes the aximum length of 5λ/8 for a ground-plane antenna. A natural xtension to the λ/4 whip is the λ/2 whip. However, such a adiator fed against a ground plane has a high input impedance.)n the other hand, a 3λ/4 radiator fed against a ground plane has a resistive input of almost exactly 50Ω but is above the optimum length for a reasonable pattern shape.

If the λ/2 whip could be made to look like a 3λ/4 radiator then it would be possible to obtain a 50Ω resistive input. A series coil at the ground-plane end of a λ/2 radiator can be used to resonate it to 3λ/4, but the input is still fairly high impedance and reactive. If, however, the coil is shorted to the ground plane a tapping point up the coil will provide the required impedance and the addition of a non-critical capacitor in series will compensate for the reactive components. Fig 81 shows details of such an antenna.

As the aperture of the antenna has been doubled compared with the λ/4 whip, twice the effective radiation is obtained, ie approaching 3dB gain. This assumes however, that there is minimum resistance in the radiating element, ie it must be copper-plated or similar.

The maximum radiator size of 5λ/8 for a single-lobe pattern can also make use of the impedance characteristics of the 3λ/4 radiator. Construction is in fact simpler than the λ/2 antenna. If the radiating element is made 5λ/8 with a series coil equivalent to λ/8 at the ground plane end, an input impedance very close to 50Ω can be obtained. With correct materials a gain close to 4dBD can be achieved by the increase in aperture over the λ/2 antenna. The radiation pattern is often raised more than that of a λ/2 antenna so the slightly improved gain of the 5λ/8 may not always be realized.

Fig 82 gives details of the series 5λ/8 whip. One other advantage of this antenna is that over a wide range of mounting and ground-plane conditions it will self-compensate for impedance and resonance changes. It is preferable for both the λ/2 and 5λ/8 antennas to be on a hinge mount, particularly if roof-mounted, to enable folding or "knock" down with obstructions like trees and garages.

Various gain figures have been given for the "five-eighth-wave". Unfortunately not all antennas use optimum materials.

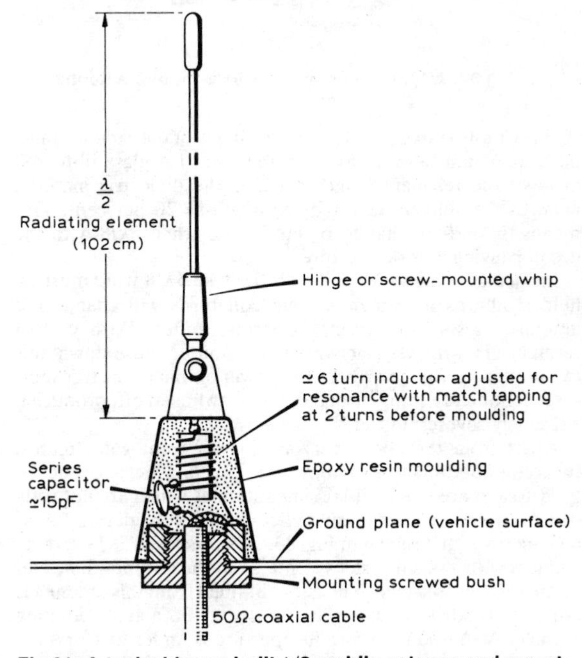

Fig 81. A typical home-built λ/2 mobile antenna and mount

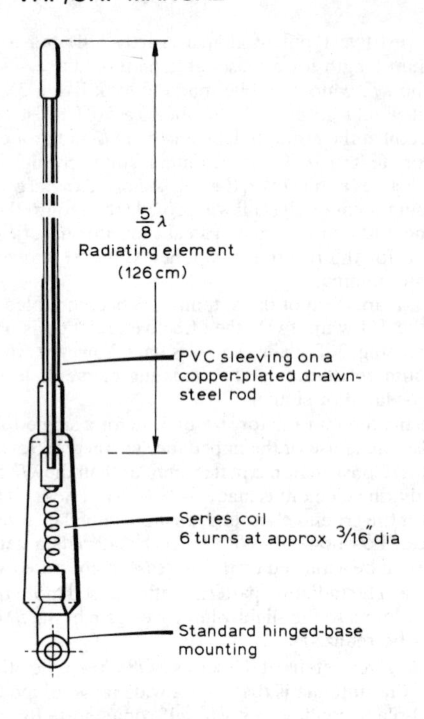

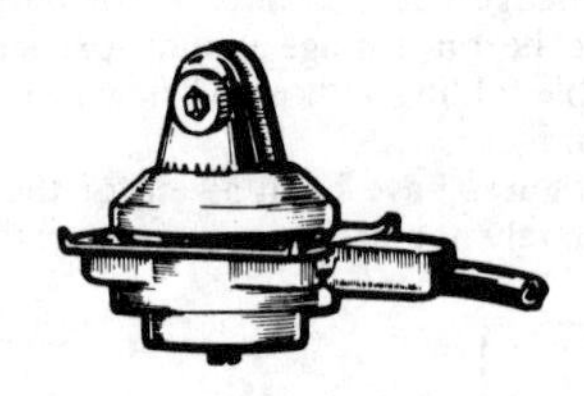

Fig 82. A typical commercial 5λ/8 mobile antenna

As previously stated, the dc resistive losses of the radiator must be a minimum, and in addition the use of a glass fibre rod changes the resonant length because the dielectric material changes the velocity factor by as much as 20 per cent. This means the radiator has to be cut shorter than 5λ/8 with the accompanying loss of aperture.

Incidentally, the series coil with the true 5λ/8 whip must be held rigidly as movement of the coil turns will change the antenna's resonance, giving apparent flutter. With certain transceivers with vswr-activated transmitter close-down this can produce a situation where the power output of the transmitter is continually being turned down or switched off, producing extremely severe "flutter".

Apart from the above reasons for different gain figures, several ground-plane antennas discussed in articles about the 5λ/8 system are in fact discussing antennas which are not truly of this nature. One of these devices worth considering for its own merits is that shown in Fig 83. It consists of a 5λ/8 vertical element with a reactive sleeve of 0·2λ at the ground-plane end of the vertical as shown. The gain obtained from this antenna is typically 1·8dBD and, as can be seen, the actual radiating element A–A and therefore its aperture is under that of a λ/2 antenna.

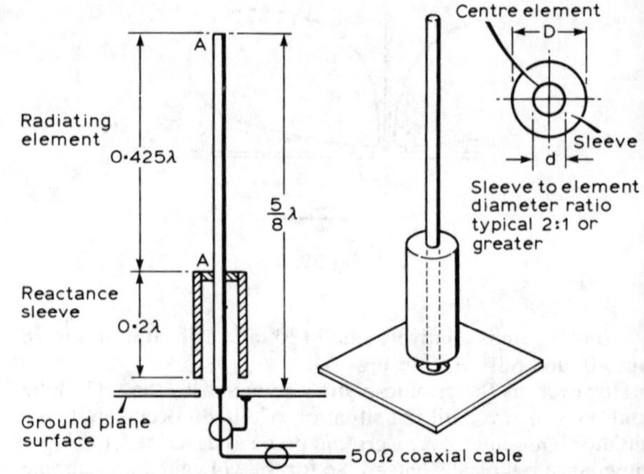

Fig 83. The reactance-fed 5λ/8 monopole. Typical gain is +1·8dBD (*Ham Radio*)

Another antenna with similar properties but different in construction is the "J" and "Slim Jim". This is described late on in this chapter.

Low-profile antennas

An alternative to vertical ground-plane antennas are devices to reduce the physical size of the system. The reduction of physical size normally implies loss of aperture and therefore gain. However, of the three antennas discussed in this section, one in fact produces a gain referred to a dipole of +1dB.

The λ/2 ring radiator. Although called a ring radiator, in fact radiation is produced by the slot formed between the horizontal λ/2 ring and the ground plane.

Consider a λ/2 slot in a metal sheet. If the sheet is rolled into a cylinder such that the two ends of the slot come together, an omnidirectional vertically polarized radiator is produced. As with the conventional λ/2 slot an impedance match can be obtained by tapping along from one end. Also, if the slot is just under λ/2 a capacitor across the centre will resonate it to λ/2 again. As with the skeleton slot developed by G2HCG, if the ground-plane sheet at the top of the slot is reduced to produce a ring and the lower ground-plane section is bent into the horizontal plane the low profile of Fig 84 is produced. Dimensions in terms of electrical degrees and specific sizes for optimum performances for 144MHz and 432MHz are shown in Table 14. Halving the dimension H or the loop diameter D (with the necessary increase of capacitance and match point to re-tune to frequency) will halve the radiation capability.

The λ/2 ring radiator is a fairly high-Q antenna and has therefore a reduced bandwidth compared to a dipole (typically 3 per cent compared to 10 per cent for a monopole). Gain is 1dBD. If the ground plane is completely reduced, as was the top section previously described, a double ring radiator is produced. Both ring radiators lend themselves to discreet fixed antennas.

The ground-planed normal helical. The normal-mode helical antenna, described previously, when vehicle mounted is approximately 2–3dB down on a dipole and the order of 0·1λ or less in height. Often an acceptable match to 50Ω can be obtained by simply adjusting its resonant length. Alternatively a small inductance or capacitor across the base or an input

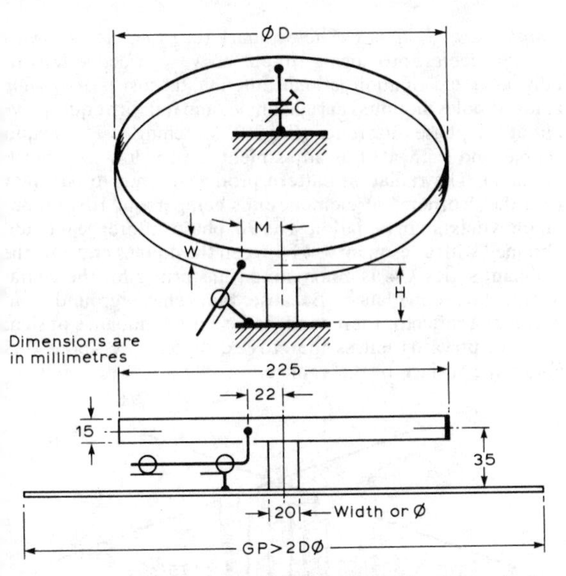

ig 84. A low-profile vehicular antenna with vertical polarization. Gain is 1dBD, termination 50Ω

apping on an earthed helical as shown in Fig 85 will provide the equired matching.

he blade antenna. If an earthed λ/4 vertical is "bent over" and n input is tapped along it to provide the required matching as hown in Fig 86, an antenna is produced which, being so close o the ground plane, produces vertical polarization with a patern typically that of Fig 87. This antenna, with a small apacitor across A–A′ to facilitate a range of tuning, is often eferred to as a *blade antenna*. This is due to its original use on ircraft where it was moulded into a blade shape to produce treamlining.

Iorizontal antennas

Iorizontally polarized antennas for a mobile station become omplex and bulky when gain is required. A simple antenna vhich produces an almost omnidirectional horizontal radiation attern is the *halo* in its various forms. Basically this is a λ/2 ipole, often gamma matched, which is bent round into a circle

Table 14. λ/2 ring radiator dimensions

	Theoretical	VHF measurement antenna	UHF measurement antenna
Frequency	*f* MHz	145MHz*	433MHz
Diameter *D*	52 degrees	298mm	100mm
Height *H*	8 degrees	39mm	15·5mm
Diameter *d*	nom. 1–2 degrees	15mm 20swg strip	10mm 20swg strip
Match *M*	5 degrees for 50Ω	28·7mm	9·7mm
Tuning capacitor *C*	To give capacitive reactance, nominally 250–500Ω	2–5pF	0·5–2pF

*Tunable 137–148MHz.

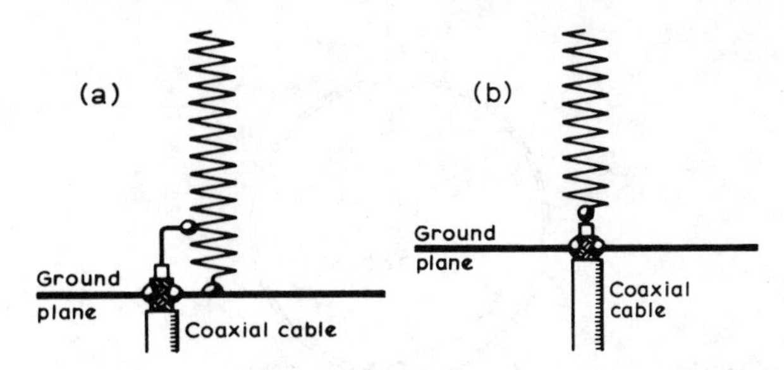

Fig 85. Two ways of feeding a helical antenna: (a) shunt feed, (b) series feed

or square. As can be seen in Fig 88(a), when correctly resonant the resultant radiation pattern is somewhat offset in favour of the direction of the gap. Best results are obtained when mounted at a minimum height of 70cm, 0·34λ at 144MHz, above the ground plane produced by the vehicle roof.

An extension of the λ/2 halo is the *full-wave* or *lambda loop*. A 1λ loop is drawn in at one point to the centre to produce both a support and a match transformer, to approximately 50Ω (see Fig 88(b)). The addition of a 1:1 Pawsey stub or similar balun (see earlier section on matching) produces a near-omnidirectional pattern with a unity gain relative to the maximum radiation of a dipole. A comparison of the halo and the lambda radiation patterns are shown in Fig 89.

Further extension to three loops can be produced to form the *super turnstile* but the complexity and sheer physical size tends to limit this sort of structure to only the most daring radio amateur.

Both the lambda loop and the super turnstile require to be at least 0·34λ above the ground plane surface to work satisfactorily.

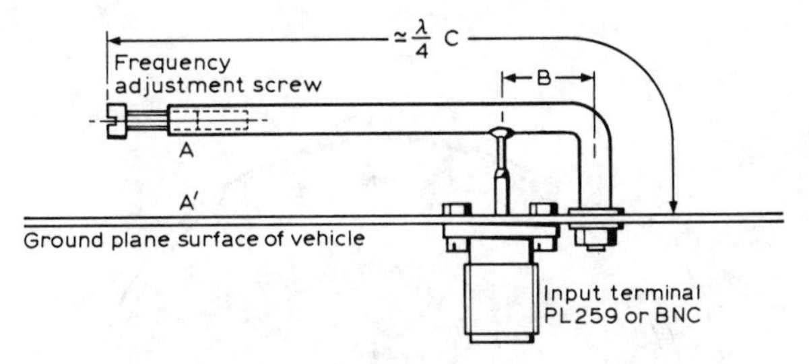

Fig 86. The basic form of the blade antenna

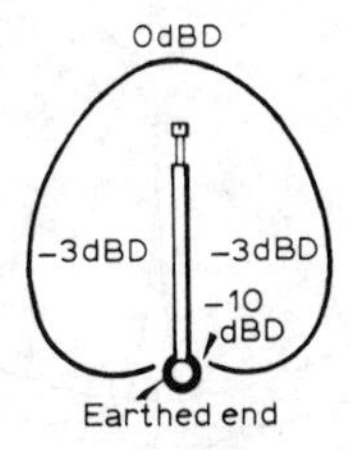

Fig 87. Typical radiation pattern of the blade antenna. Dimension C should be less than λ/4 such that an inductor formed by an extended screw at A will resonate the antenna. Dimension B is two-thirds of a wavelength at the operating frequency.

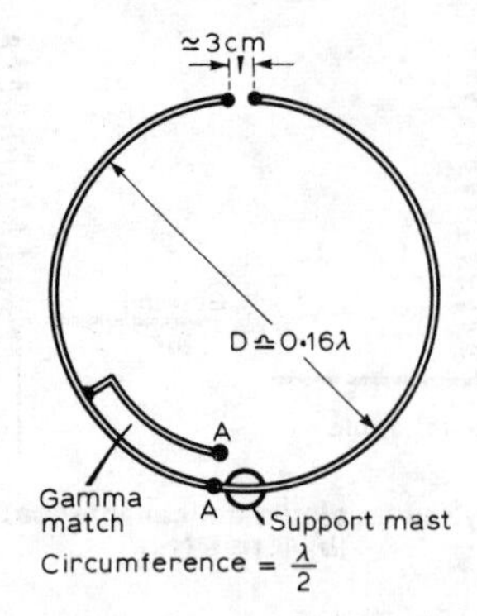

Fig 88(a). Dimensions of the λ/2 halo

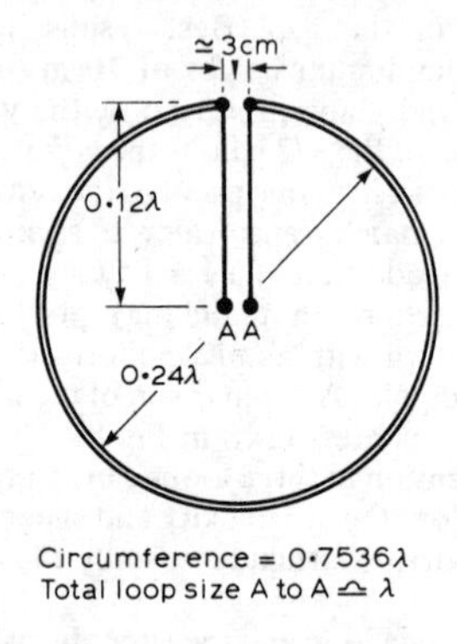

Fig 88(b). Dimensions of the lambda loop

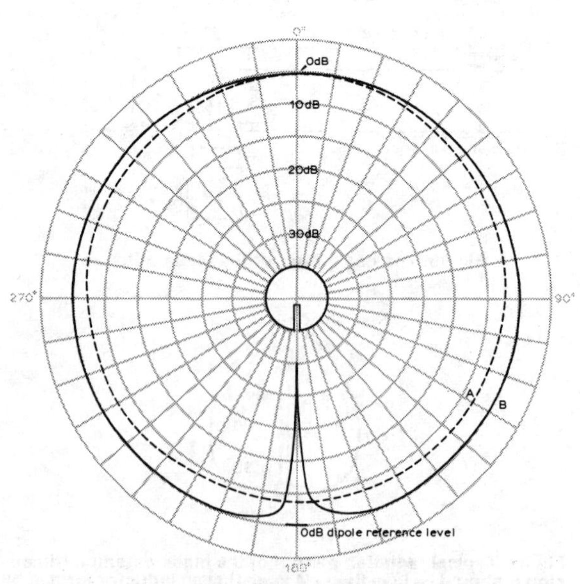

Fig 89. Decibel radiation pattern comparison of halo (A) and lambda loop (B) antennas

Simple crossed dipoles. The ordinary turnstile, also known as *crossed dipoles*, provides a simple yet very effective horizontally polarized, omnidirectional antenna. It consists of two horizontal dipoles mounted at right angles and fed with equal power but at 90° phase difference (Fig 90). Matching to 75Ω is quite simple and with a little adjustment a very low swr can be obtained. The radiation pattern produced tends to be square with the "corners" at element ends being about 1dB up on a dipole's maximum radiation. The 90° phase difference is readily obtained with a resonant λ/4 between the dipoles and a further resonant series λ/4 as a matching transformer for the characteristic line impedance. Because the vehicle ground plane becomes a reflector there tends to be a predominance of signal radiated upwards unless the crossed dipoles are about 0·5λ above the surface of the vehicle.

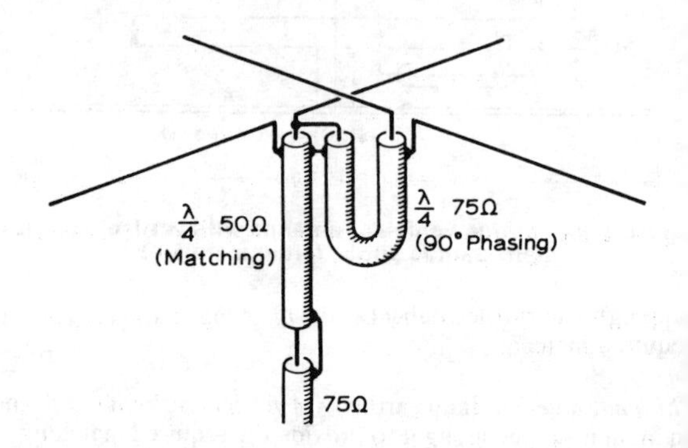

Fig 90(a). Phasing and matching arrangement of crossed dipoles

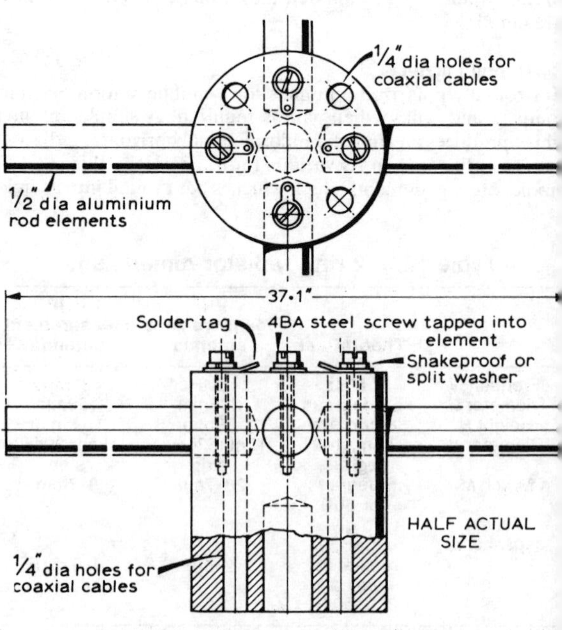

Fig 90(b). Details of central insulator

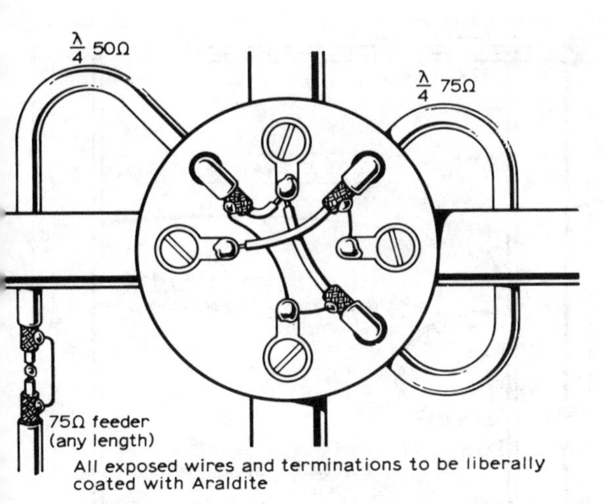

Fig 90(c). Connections of coaxial sections

Omnidirectional base station antennas

The horizontally polarized omni-V for 144MHz

This antenna consists of a pair of λ/2 dipoles. The centres of the dipoles are physically displaced to produce a quadrature radiation and the ends of each dipole are supported on a λ/4 shorted stub. A pair of Q bars are tapped down the stubs to a point where the impedance is 600Ω so that when the two units are fed in parallel they produce an impedance of 300Ω at the centre. A 4:1 balance-to-balance coaxial transformer is fitted to the centre point of the Q bars so that a standard 75Ω coaxial cable feeder may be used. The general arrangement is shown in Fig 91(a). Fig 91(b) shows how the antenna may be arranged to give a bi-directional radiation pattern.

The λ/4 ground plane

Since base-station monopole antennas are usually mounted on masts atop buildings, a perfect ground plane is not present. In most cases the ground plane is simulated by wires extending horizontally from the base of the monopole. Two popular forms of such are shown in Figs 95(a) and (b). The ground-plane wires are usually four in number and from 0·28λ to 0·30λ in length; the optimum length is often selected experimentally to produce a maximum of the vertical radiation pattern in the horizontal plane. When the ground-plane wires are properly adjusted, the entire antenna closely resembles a dipole with respect to its radiation pattern and gain (typically within 0·5dB of that a free-space dipole).

A refinement is obtained by adding a parallel grounded section to the monopole to form a folded monopole. The dc path formed to ground affords protection against lightning surges; also the folded configuration is inherently more broadbanded than the single wire. For equal diameters in the two parts of the fold, the radiation resistance would be quadrupled (nominally 4 × 37·5 = 150Ω. The grounded side is made smaller in diameter to lower the resistance to 50Ω and provide a better impedance match to the conventional line than is obtained from the simple monopole.

An alternative feed is shown in Fig 95(c). Its advantage is that the short-circuited λ/4 line formed in the upper end of the mast supports the monopole rigidly without loading the feed point since it presents a high impedance. A λ/4 matching section is sometimes placed in the transmission line at the feed point to improve the impedance match between the antenna and the line.

The skirted antenna

Although the λ/4 monopole over a ground plane behaves electrically as a λ/2 dipole in free space, the radial projections of the ground rods are sometimes objectionable physically. Furthermore, the ground rods shield the mast and prevent the excitation of parasitic elements needed to form high-gain arrays. The coaxial skirted antenna shown in Fig 96 behaves as a λ/2 dipole in free space by using a skirt to form the bottom half of the dipole and a choke to isolate the antenna from the mast.

The gain sleeve dipole (vertically polarized)

The gain sleeve dipole is derived from the 1·8dBD shunt-feed 5λ/8 previously mentioned in the mobile antenna section.

The radiating element B–B is in principle a centre-fed 1λ element but is fed coaxially to make it an end-fed one. Having effectively twice the aperture of the λ/2 dipole, a gain of typically 2·5–3dB is achieved.

Mechanical construction is open to interpretation but a beer can or plastic water-pipe format are two solutions. It should be noted that the mounting point should be at A–A and not on the 0·25λ sleeve.

The discone

This antenna has not found too much favour with amateurs in the past, though frequently used for commercial and military purposes. Unlike many other types this antenna is not only omnidirectional but also has wideband characteristics. It is capable of covering, say, the 70, 144 and 432MHz bands or 144, 432 and 1,296MHz, although there will of course be some variation of the swr over such a wide range.

Also, since the antenna can operate over roughly a 10-to-one frequency range, it will more readily radiate any harmonics present in the transmitter output. It is therefore important to use a suitable filter to adequately attenuate the harmonic outputs. The radiation angle tends to rise after the first frequency octave.

The discone consists of a disc mounted above a cone, and ideally should be constructed from sheet material. Many amateurs would find this impossible to realize, but with little loss the components may be made of rods or tubes as illustrated in Fig 98, with a minimum number of rods of eight or preferably

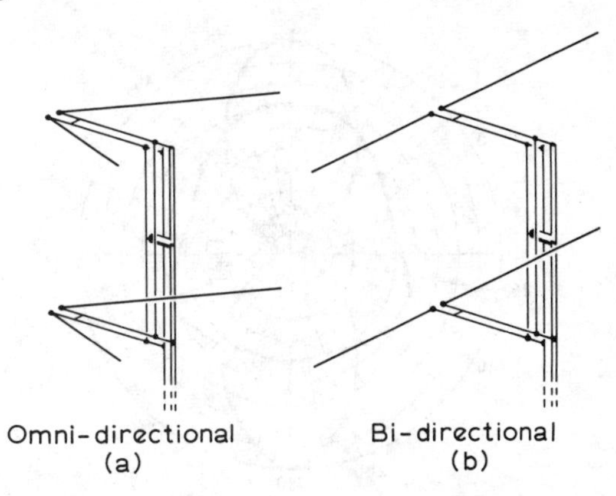

Fig 91. Formation of the omni-V antenna

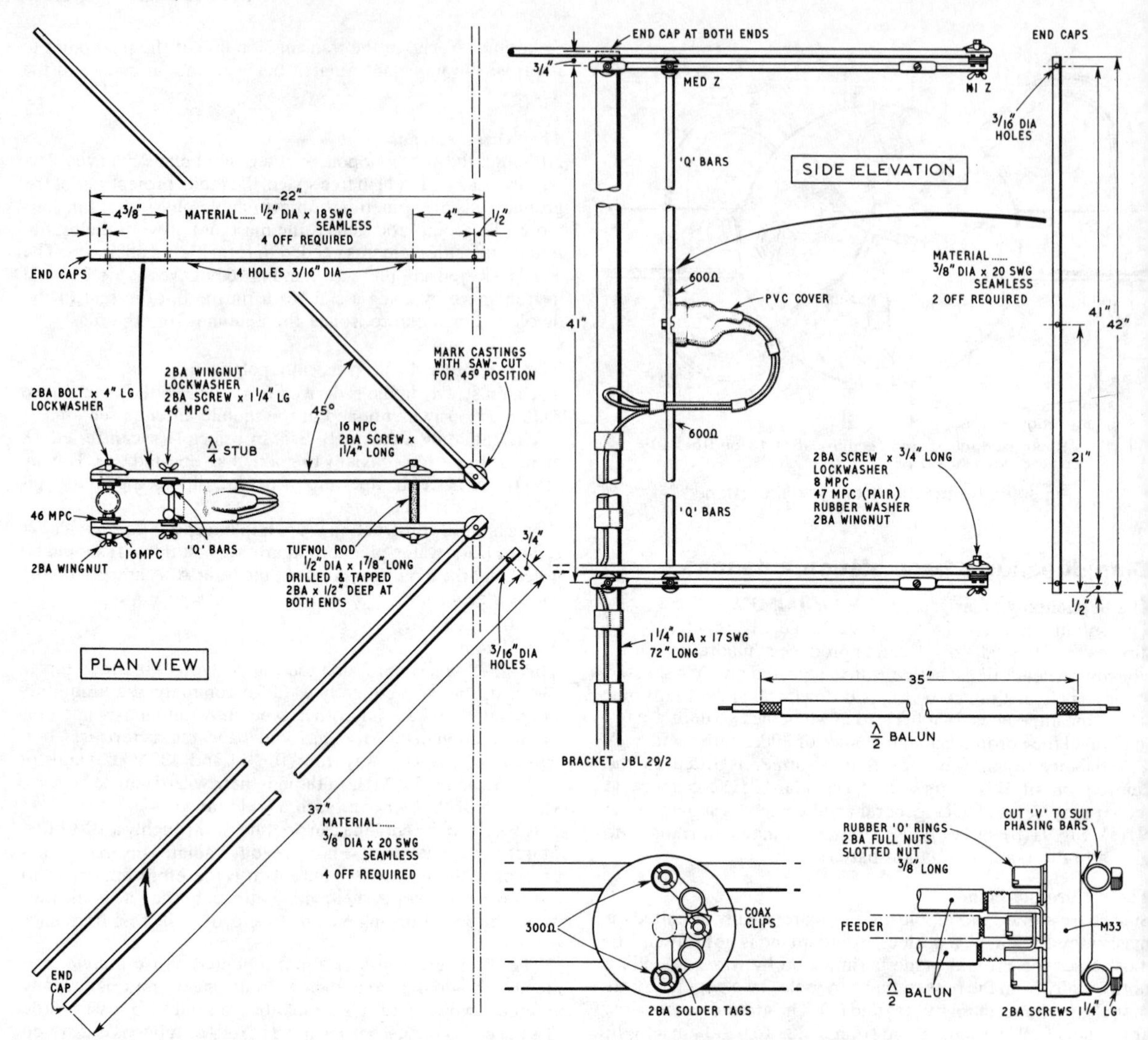

Fig 92. The mechanical details of the construction of the omni-V

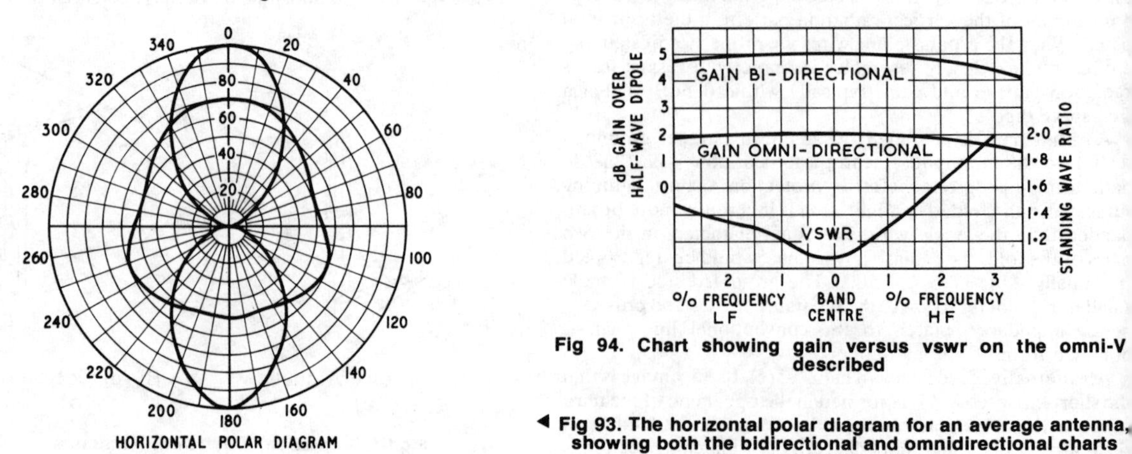

Fig 94. Chart showing gain versus vswr on the omni-V described

◀ Fig 93. The horizontal polar diagram for an average antenna, showing both the bidirectional and omnidirectional charts

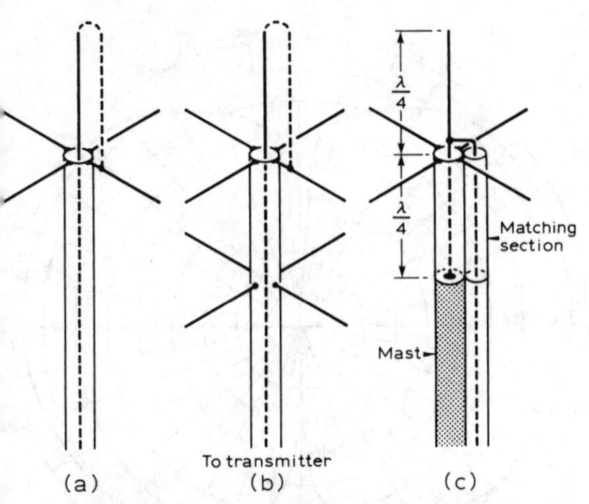

Fig 95. Ground-plane simulation for the mast-mounted vertical antenna. The folded section is shown in dotted lines, and a modified feed is shown in (c) (from *Antenna Engineering Handbook* by Jasic. © 1961 McGraw-Hill. Used with the permission of McGraw-Hill Book Co)

16. Of course, open mesh may be used as an alternative, bearing in mind the windage increase.

The important dimensions are the end diameter of the cone and the spacing of this from the centre of the disc, so that the terminating impedance is correct, eg 50Ω.

The primary parameters are shown in Fig 99 with dimensions as follows:

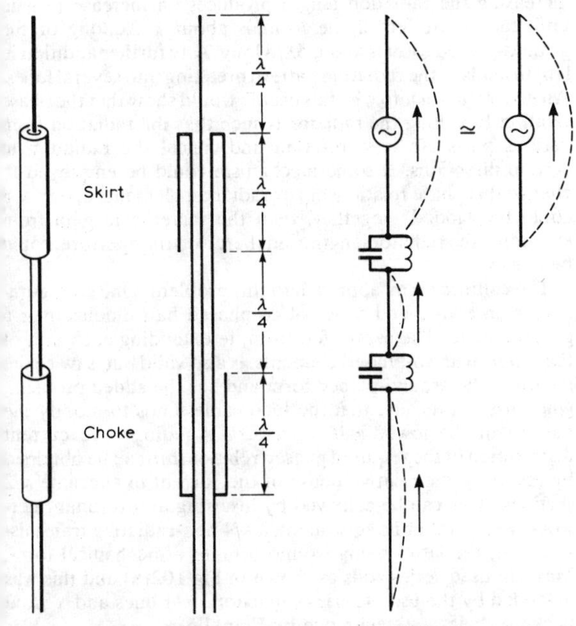

Fig 96. Coaxial centre-fed λ/2 dipole with choke (from *Antenna Engineering Handbook* by Jasic. © 1961 McGraw-Hill. Used with the permission of McGraw-Hill Book Co)

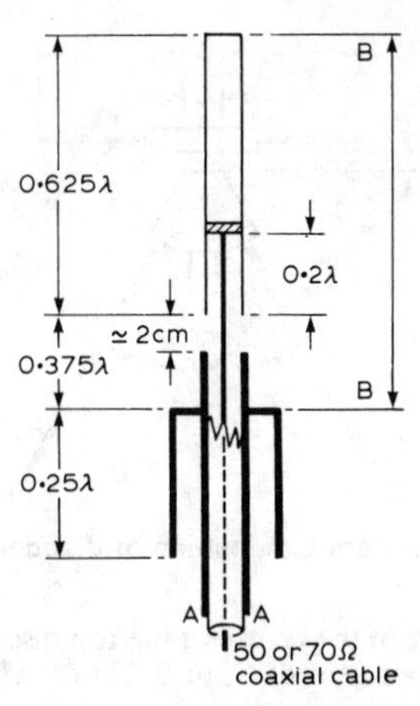

Fig 97. Gain sleeve dipole

A the length of the cone elements, these are λ/4 at the lowest operating frequency, or 2,952/*f*(MHz) in.

B the overall disc diameter, this should be 70 per cent of λ/4.

C the diameter of the top of the cone, this will be decided to some extent by the diameter of the coaxial cable, but for most purposes 0·5in will be suitable.

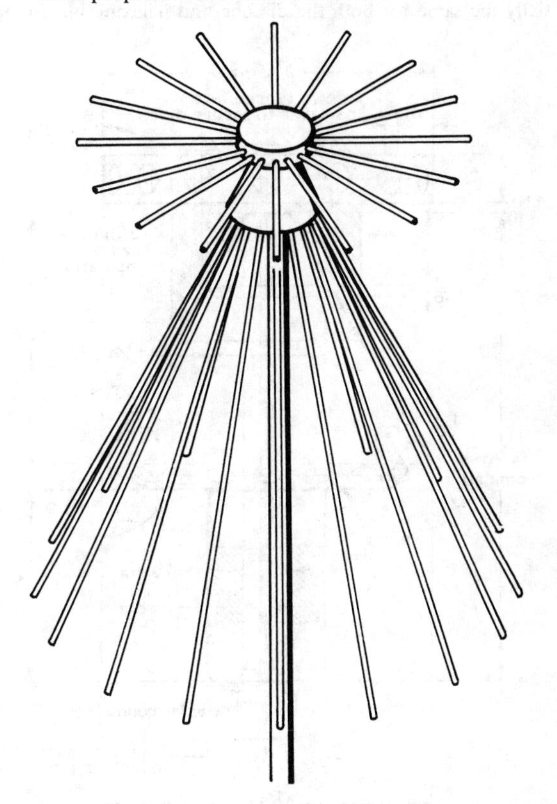

Fig 98. General arrangement of skeleton form of discone antenna

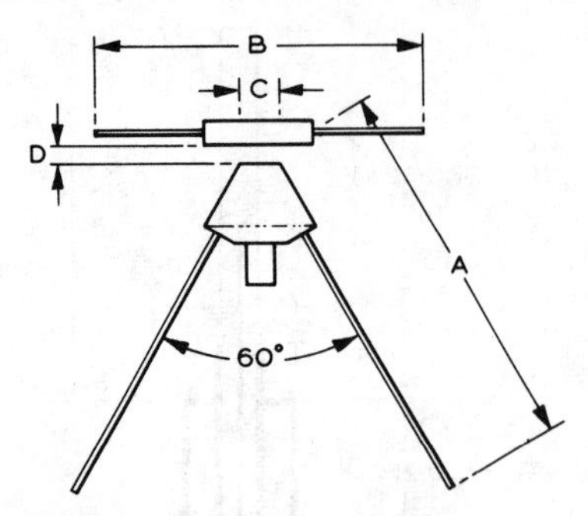

Fig 99. Primary dimensions of discone antenna

D the spacing of the centre of the top disc to the cone top, this is 20 per cent of C, or 0·1in for 50Ω.

The detail given in Fig 100 of the hub construction will be suitable for any design using a 50Ω cable feed and may be taken as an example. There is likely to be some problem in producing a suitable insulator which may be made of a potting resin or turned from ptfe or other stable low-loss material.

An extension of the discone is the *helicone*. The elements of the conventional discone can be replaced with helical elements working in the normal mode as previously discussed.

In its simplest form only eight elements are required for the disc and for the cone. Gain and the radiation pattern is essentially the same for both the discone and helicone but for the helicone the usable bandwidth is reduced to approximately one-third.

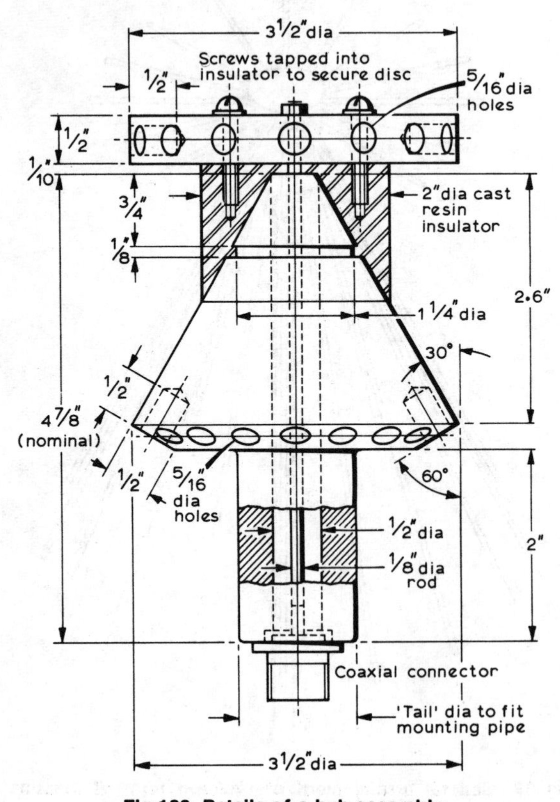

Fig 100. Details of a hub assembly

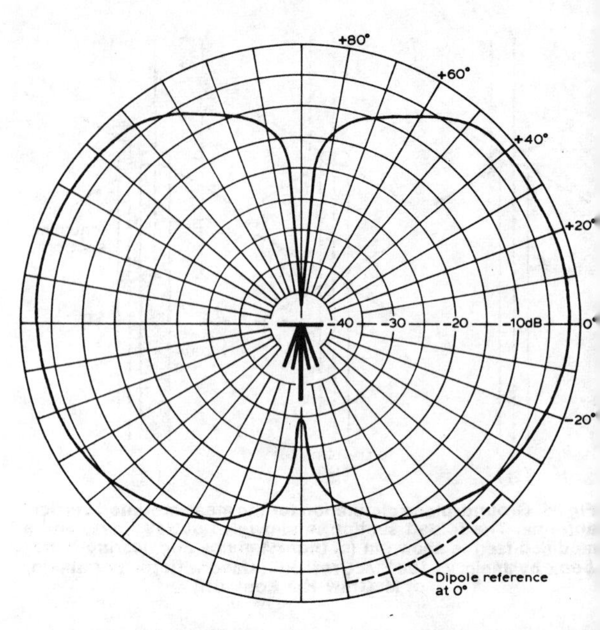

Fig 101. Typical discone and helicone decibel radiation pattern over the first 2:1 frequency range. As the frequency increases above 2:1 the pattern tends to rise above the horizontal level until at about 5:1 in frequency the main direction of radiation is above 45° from the horizontal

Collinears (vertical polarization)

As previously mentioned with vertical mobile antennas, increasing the radiation length produces an increase in gain until the centre-fed dipole form is about 1·2λ long or the ground-planed form is about 5λ/8 long. Any further addition in length leads to the radiation pattern breaking into several lobes. An investigation into why this occurs would show that the phase relationship along the radiator is such that the radiation from various parts are in opposition and cancel the radiation in certain directions. If some mechanism could be employed to change this phase relationship or radiating elements up to 5λ/8 could be "added" together, then the increase in gain from extending the radiator length, and therefore the aperture, could be achieved.

The collinear is an approach to this problem. One configuration is an end-to-end series of co-phased half dipoles over a ground plane. The centre-fed form, ie extending each arm of the dipole with co-phased elements, is also valid but is twice the length of the ground-planed form and has the added problem, when used vertically, that the feed cable tends to modify the pattern of the lower half. A natural standing-wave current distribution of the required phased relationship can be obtained by reversing the relative phase of the current in alternate λ/2 sections. This can be achieved by inserting anti-resonant networks every λ/2 or its equivalent, a λ/4 non-radiating transmission line, the latter being wound up into a mechanical form. Marconi used series coils as shown in Fig 102(a) and this was extended by the use of series capacitors, λ/4 lines and a "fold back" or "zig-zag" technique by Franklin.

Fig 102(b) places the successive current maxima less than λ/2 apart by using a series capacitor for power factor correction

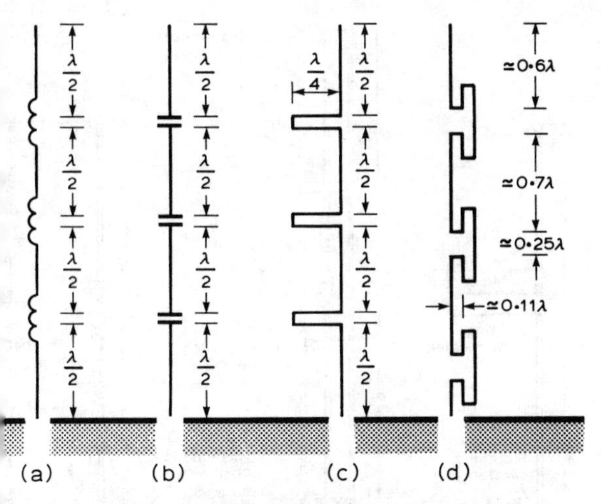

'ig 102. The collinear as developed by Marconi and Franklin from *Antenna Engineering Handbook* by Jasic. © 1961 McGraw-Hill. Used with the permission of McGraw-Hill Book Co)

at midway between successive maxima. Unfortunately the current is not the ideal zero at the insertion point for the capacitors. The zig-zag of Fig 102(d) is somewhat frequency dependent due to insulator capacitance and effects of rigging.

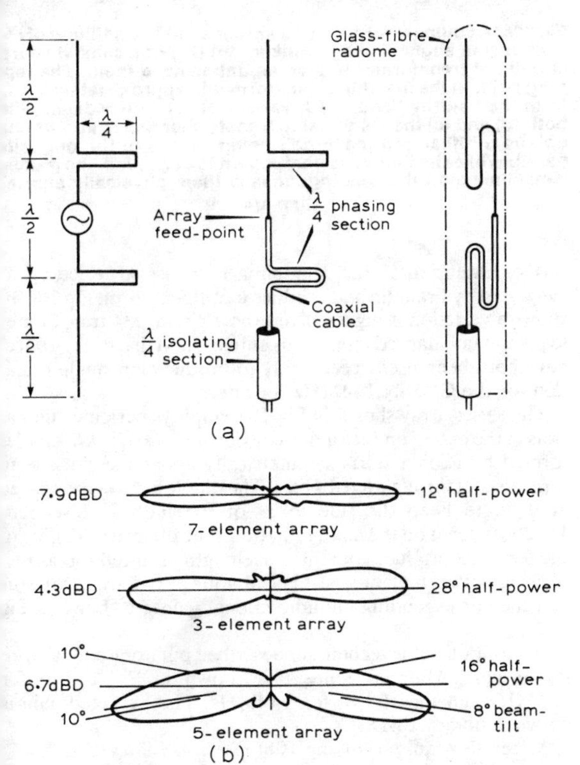

Fig 103. (a) Development of modified Franklin array. (b) Vertical radiation patterns (from *Antenna Engineering Handbook* by Jasic. © 1961 McGraw-Hill. Used with the permission of McGraw-Hill Book Co)

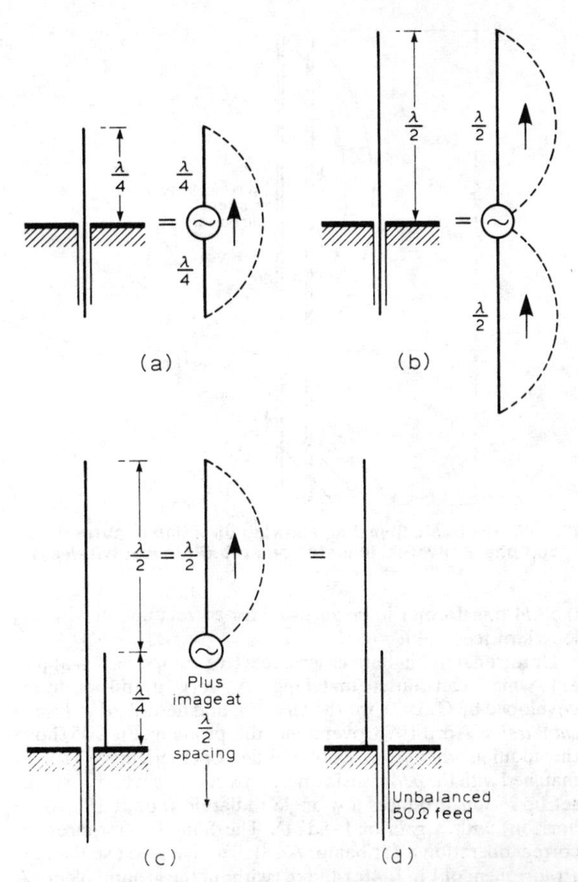

Fig 104. The derivation of the grounded J antenna (from *Antenna Engineering Handbook* by Jasic. © 1961 McGraw-Hill. Used with the permission of McGraw-Hill Book Co)

Practical collinears in radio amateur use tend to be variations of Fig 102(a) and (c). The radiating elements are not limited to λ/2 sections; λ/4, λ/2 and up to 5λ/8 radiators can be combined with various degrees of success. In addition, various collinears have omitted the ground plane and replaced it with variations of the λ/4 matching transformer. This leads to a reduction in gain as the antenna no longer has an image reflected in the ground plane. However, when mounted under its normal working conditions an "image" can be reflected in the mast supporting the antenna and almost the maximum gain is obtained. Variations of the ground-plane structure can also modify the input impedance and radiation angle of an antenna.

Referring to the section earlier on stub matching, it can be seen that a centre-fed 1λ or a λ/2 end-fed dipole can be matched by connecting them to the "open" end of a short-circuited λ/4 line. Similarly a λ/2 dipole can be end fed with an open-circuit λ/4 transformer where it is used as a series impedance transformer. This produces the antenna shown in Fig 104(c) and (d), usually known as the *J antenna* due to the shape, particularly when not used with a ground plane.

Fig 104(c) and (d) has an unbalanced feed and can be connected directly to coaxial cable without a balun. With the radiating λ/2 section set to resonance after compensating for the length-to-diameter ratio, Fig 104(c) and (d) then require

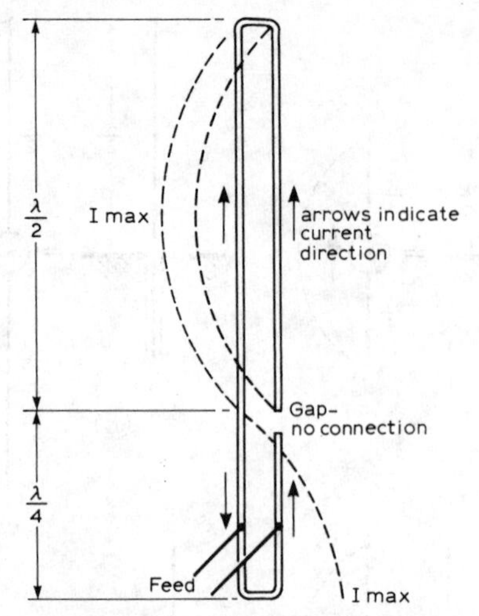

Fig 105. The basic Slim Jim, showing direction of current flow and phase reversal in matching stub (*Practical Wireless*)

the λ/4 transformer to be adjusted for correct match with any length of feed cable.

Unfortunately, in both cases a reactive component is apparent which can upset matching. A very useful addition, developed by G2BCX for the *Slim Jim* and described in *Practical Wireless* April 1978, overcomes this problem. Fig 105 shows the addition which consists of a folded open-circuit λ/2 dipole matched with the λ/4 transformer. This antenna when correctly set up *in situ* produces low-angle radiation (about 10° above horizon) with a gain of 1·8dBD. The Slim Jim requires for correct operation a 1:1 balun. An alternative is to use the feed arrangement of Fig 104(c) and (d) without the ground plane. A

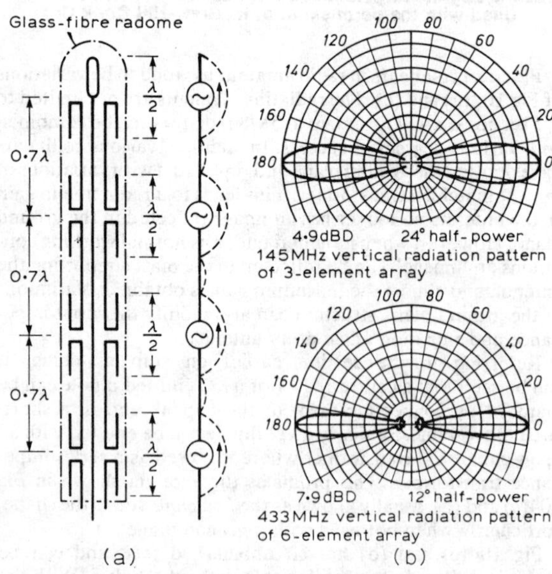

Fig 107. A series-fed collinear array of λ/2 diples (from *Antenna Engineering Handbook* by Jasic. © 1961 McGraw-Hill. Used with the permission of McGraw-Hill Book Co)

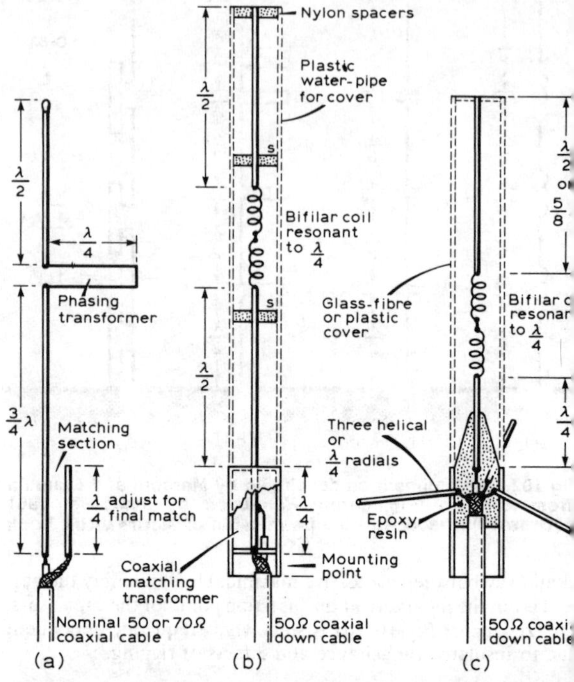

Fig 106. A collinear form of the J antenna. (a) The addition of λ/ sections as suggested by Franklin. (b) Use of a coaxial short circuit λ/4 transformer to give an unbalanced input. The tapping point in the matching transformer is approximately 0·15 from the "earthy" end. (c) A variant of (b) with radials. With both (b) and (c) the λ/4 phasing transformer has been "wound up" as a bifilar coil (each coil being wound in the opposite hand). While the inductive component is cancelled, the mutual capacitance on the windings makes them physically shorter than λ/4

further extension to the J antenna is to use λ/4 sections as suggested by Franklin and produce a collinear form. Fig 106(b) shows a variation using a coaxial short-circuit λ/4 transformer to give an unbalanced input. This antenna and that of Fig 106(c) have both been used successfully to produce low-angle radiation for the GB3SN 144MHz repeater.

The series array shown in Fig 107 employs periodic annular slots in the outer conductor of a coaxial line to excite λ/2 dipoles formed by adding skirts symmetrically about the slots, ie to form coaxial through-fed dipoles. The dipole centres are spaced at 0·7λ to keep the side lobes of the individual sections 15–20dB down on the main radiation. The dielectric loading of the feed line produces the full wavelength required for correct phasing between elements. Typical voltage radiation pattern and the corresponding omnidirectional gain are shown in Fig 107(b).

A variation of the techniques described but using coils as with the original Marconi concept is shown in Fig 108(a) for 432MHz and Fig 108(b) for 144MHz. The expected gain is between 6 and 7dBD.

Materials required for Fig 108(a) are as follows:

One 2·5cm dia 10cm long glass fibre tube
One 4·0mm dia 1·2m long glass fibre rod
Four 2·0mm dia 20cm long glass fibre rods
Length of braiding from junk multicore cable

Length of 18swg wire for matching coils
Approx 5cm square of singled-sided pcb

First, adjust the bottom 5λ/8 element to give minimum swr; this is done by adjusting the tapping point on the bottom coil (approx 4¼ turns). A fine adjustment can be made by altering the length of the first 5λ/8 element.

Next fix on the centre matching coil and the top element. Please note that to obtain the best results both elements should be approximately 5λ/8 and within reason the same length. A good swr is obtained by adjusting the centre matching coil (the coil is spread over λ/4).

The matching coil provides the phase change necessary to feed the top element and so adjustment is quite critical. It has been found that if the matching coil has to be "squeezed up" to obtain a good swr, then the coil has too many turns. The opposite is true if the coil has to be greater than λ/2 for a good swr.

To prevent the collinear going off tune once set up, the elements were secured to the centre glass fibre rod and the matching coil taped with self-amalgamating tape. Provided care is taken in setting up, an swr of close to 1·1 to 1 can be obtained.

Materials required for Fig 108(b) are as follows:

Two ½in dia by 47½in ± ½in, 5λ/8 elements (adjustable)
Four 19¼in rods for ground plane
One ¼in dia by 30in insulated rod
One 1in dia insulated tube (a cotton reel can be used instead)
18swg wire for matching and phasing coils.

The diagram shows extra insulated tubing over the matching and phasing coils to give more mechanical strength and weather-proofing.

Setting up is carried out as follows. First, the length of the bottom 5λ/8 element must be adjusted to give the minimum swr possible.

Next fix on the phasing coil and the top element which must be the same length as the bottom element. Then obtain the best swr possible by adjusting the phasing coil.

This coil provides the phase change necessary to feed the top element; it is a length of 18swg wire, about 1λ long, coiled up to give 70–72 turns on a ¼in former. It was found that the λ/4 spacing between the two elements is more critical than the number of turns. 68 turns gave satisfactory swr on one version.

Some difficulty may occur in setting up the phasing coil. Before taking too many turns off, go back to the first stage to ensure that the bottom 5λ/8 element is correctly matched. If the bottom element is not correctly matched the collinear will not tune up. Careful adjustments in setting up should produce a swr of 1·1 to 1.

A technique that has not been discussed but is widely used involves feeding conventional λ/2 dipoles in phase from a single source or adjusting the phase relationship of cable lengths between dipoles. There is a degree of interaction between cables and radiating elements but individual dipoles can be positioned to modify the pattern shape. The example given in Figs 109, 110, 111 is probably the simplest to implement and was devised for the GB3ER 432MHz band repeater.

Satellite antennas

For the average radio amateur satellite antennas fall into two groups, both of which are *ground-station antennas*, that is, those on the ground rather than on the satellite itself. The two groups

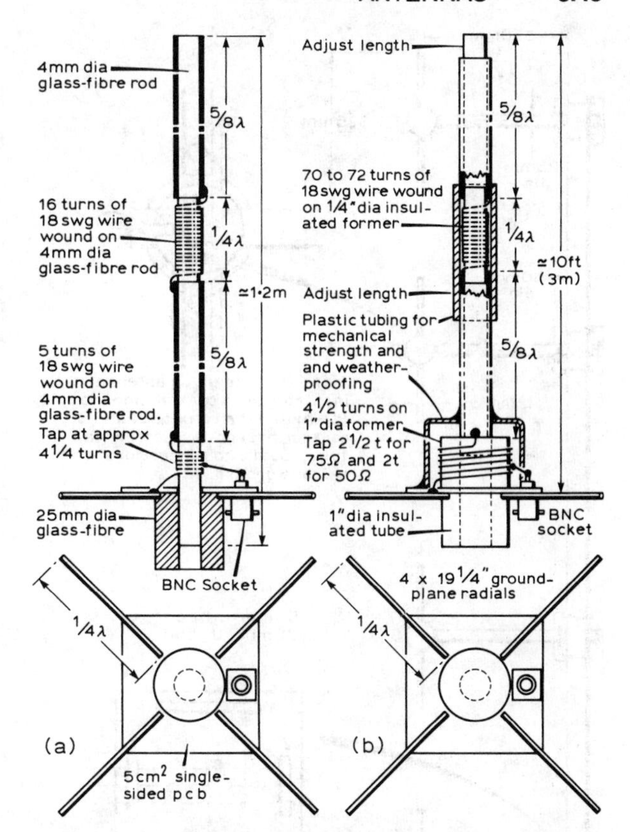

Fig 108. (a) A 432MHz collinear. (b) A 144MHz collinear (*UK FM Southern Journal*)

are *steerable*, which enable the passage of the satellite to be tracked across the sky, and *fixed* which, as they in the ideal case have a hemispherical radiation pattern, receive the satellite signals equally in any direction and do not require to track the satellite's passage. The tracking antennas are usually of high gain while the fixed antennas are usually relatively low gain due to the hemispherical coverage required. Fortunately, as signal losses between ground and satellite are low, being mostly line-of-sight path with no obstructions, relatively low-gain antennas of the fixed variety are often acceptable for reception of amateur or weather satellites.

However, as the satellite tends to rotate, both groups of antennas are normally circularly polarized, right-hand by convention, to compensate for variations in polarization.

Of the higher-gain tracking antennas, crossed Yagis and the helix are used in the main, with the crossed Yagis probably the easiest to construct and most readily available commercially. The section on pp 8.24 and 8.26 gives details of crossed Yagis and the helix.

For fixed or low-gain steerable antennas, several variations of crossed dipoles can be used and also the *volute*, which is a fractional turn four-element helix that can be made to give either directional gain or hemispherical circular polarized coverage. It is worth noting that a conventional single element helix requires two or more complete "turns" to obtain circular polarization.

Fig 112 shows a simple arrangement of crossed dipoles above a ground plane. This type of antenna can be scaled for use

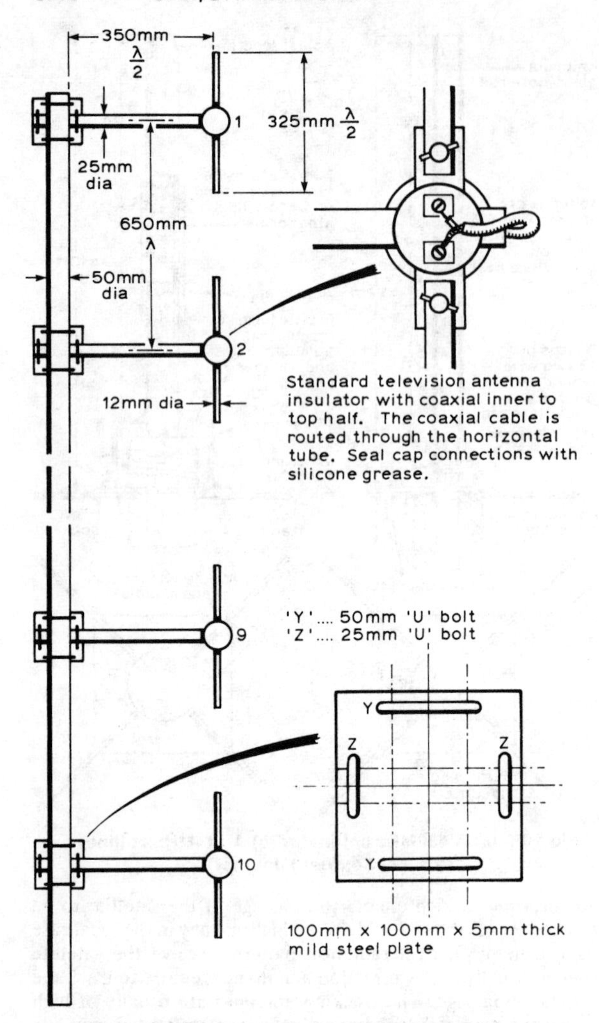

Fig 109. Mechanical details of GB3ER collinear

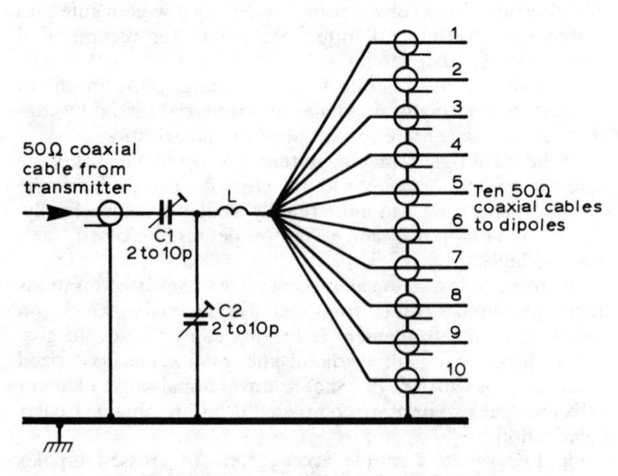

Fig 110. Matching unit of GB3ER collinear

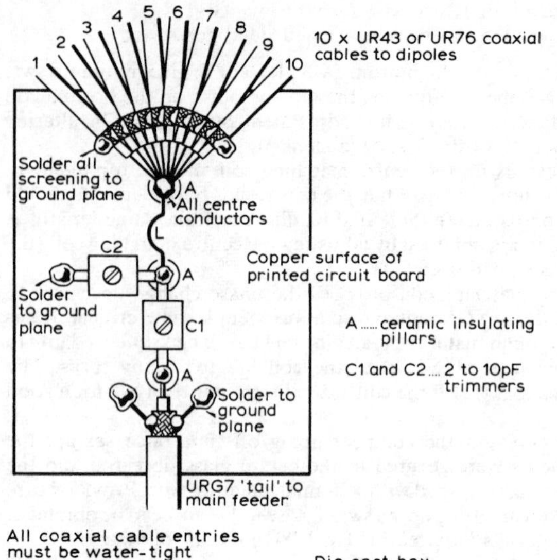

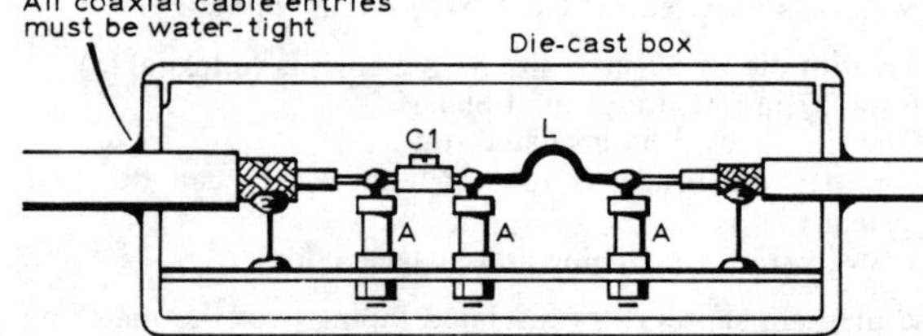

Fig 111. Matching unit layout of GB3ER collinear

at 29, 145 or 432MHz. A suggested version for 145MHz is shown in the figure. Mechanical problems may make the reflectors inadvisable in a 29MHz version. The height above ground can be about 2m for 145MHz and 3m for 29MHz.

Typical dimensions are:

29MHz	driven elements	(λ/2)	188in	477·5cm

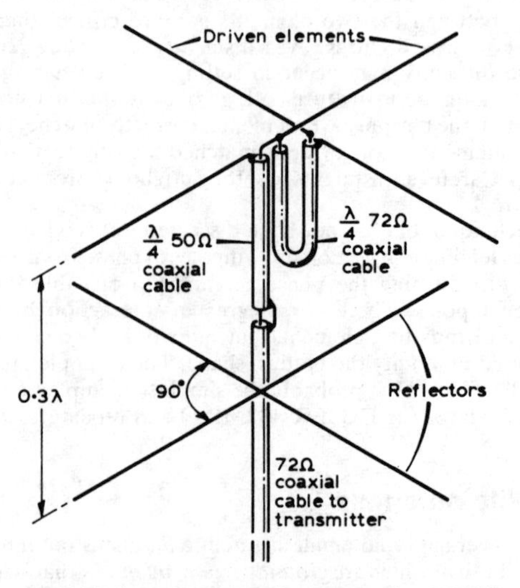

Fig 112. A crossed-dipole antenna for 145MHz

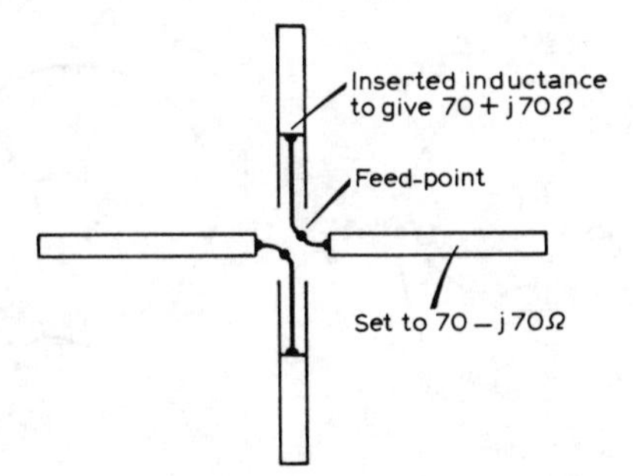

113. Achieving phase quadrature by introducing a reactance in one arm

5MHz	driven elements	(λ/2)	38in	96·5cm
	reflectors		40·5in	103cm
	spacing	(0·3λ)	24·5in	62·2cm

The phasing line comprises λ/4 of 72Ω coaxial cable, and the tching section λ/4 of 50Ω cable. When calculating the gth of the λ/4 sections, the velocity factor of the cable must taken into account. Typically this is 0·8 for cellular and ni-airspaced types, and 0·66 for solid dielectric cables, but ification of the correct figure for the cable used should be tained. As an example, a matching section of RG59/U would 13in (33cm) in length.

It is preferable to have a 1:1 balun included at each dipole tre to ensure a consistent pattern through 360° of muth. Dependent on the spacing between the dipoles and ound plane the radiation pattern can be made to be predomntly to the side for satellites low on the horizon or up for erhead passes. By drooping the dipole elements at 45° and h a spacing of approximately 0·4λ of the dipole mounting ss about the ground plane, a compromise radiation pattern n be achieved that tends to be hemispherical. As horizontal d vertical polarization is affected differently by ground lections, low-to-horizon flight paths will not produce circular

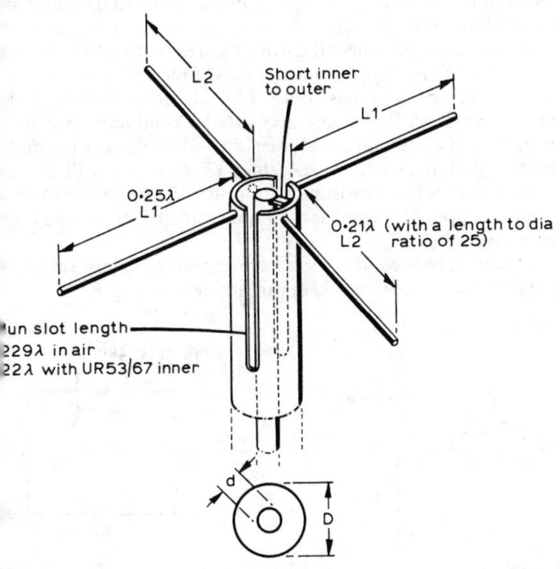

114. A starpole turnstile. $D/d = 1\cdot86$ for 75Ω and $1\cdot5$ for 50Ω

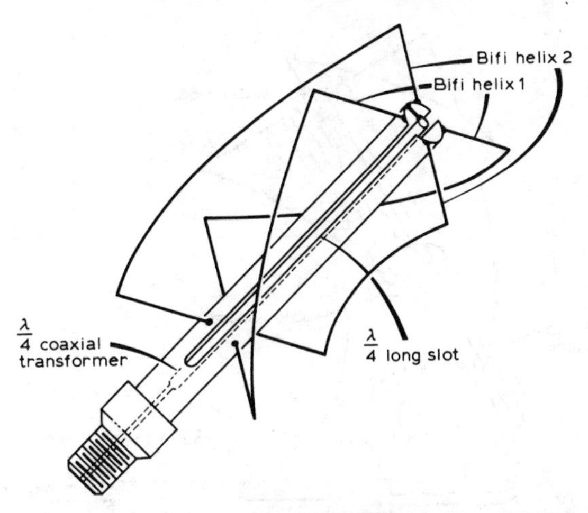

Fig 115. A quarter-turn volute with split sheath or slot balun (*Microwave Journal*)

polarization. This is due both to ground scatter from the satellite and ground reflections at low levels of incidence at the receiving antenna and its ground plane.

Circular polarization is normally produced by feeding one dipole 90° out of phase to the second dipole by means of a phasing harness containing an extra λ/4 on one side.

An alternative approach to this method of phasing is to utilize the phase properties of a capacitive or inductive reactance.

Suppose, for example, that the length and diameter of the dipoles are made to give a terminal impedance of 70 −j70Ω (capacitive). By introducing a series reactance (inductive) of +j70Ω at each terminal of one of the dipoles (Fig 113) the terminal impedance of this dipole becomes 70 +j70Ω. With the two dipoles connected in parallel the current in each dipole is equal in magnitude but, due to the opposite phase differences of 45° in each dipole, a total phase difference of 90° (phase quadrature) is achieved which produces circular polarization.

The two impedances in parallel become 70 +j0Ω so the addition of a 1:1 balun provides a direct match to a 70Ω coaxial line. If the impedance of the balun is correctly proportioned this match can be to the standard 50Ω coaxial line. Radiating elements can be drooped as previously described to improve the hemispherical coverage. An easier way of introducing the series inductance is simply to make one dipole long, therefore inductive, at the working frequency, and one dipole short, therefore capacitive at the working frequency.

Fig 114 shows a working example of the *starpole* turnstile arrangement. The reactive components were chosen as ±25Ω and dimensions were based on the reactive information for dipoles as shown in Fig 8 in this chapter.

The volute can also make use of both phasing line or the reactance method to produce circular polarization. The number of "turns" or part turns of the radiating elements combined with their length can be used to produce various radiation patterns. Radiation patterns produced for several combination of turns and resonant lengths are shown in Figs 117(a) through to (d) with general details of the volute in Figs 115 and 116 (C.C. Kilgus, "Resonant Quadrifilar Helix Design", *Microwave Journal* December 1970). It must be noted that elements that are multiples of λ/4 have open-circuit ends, while the elements that are multiples of λ/2 can be short-circuited to the mounting structure.

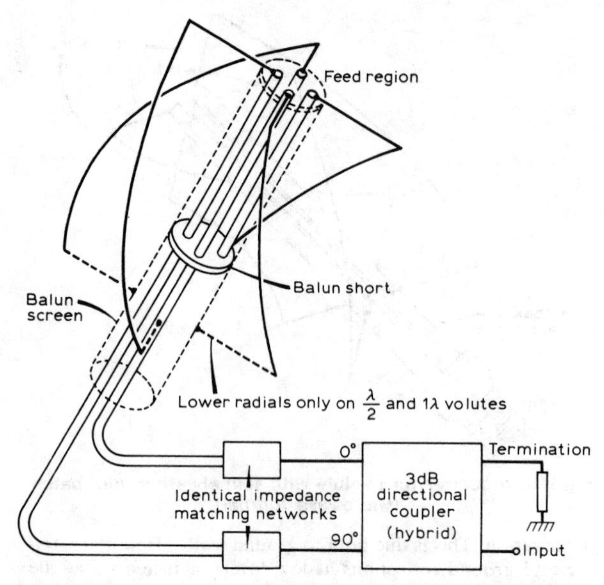

Fig 116. The general arrangement using Pawsey stub baluns. A half-hybrid or λ/4 phasing harness as used for the crossed dipoles can be used in place of the directional coupler (*Microwave Journal*)

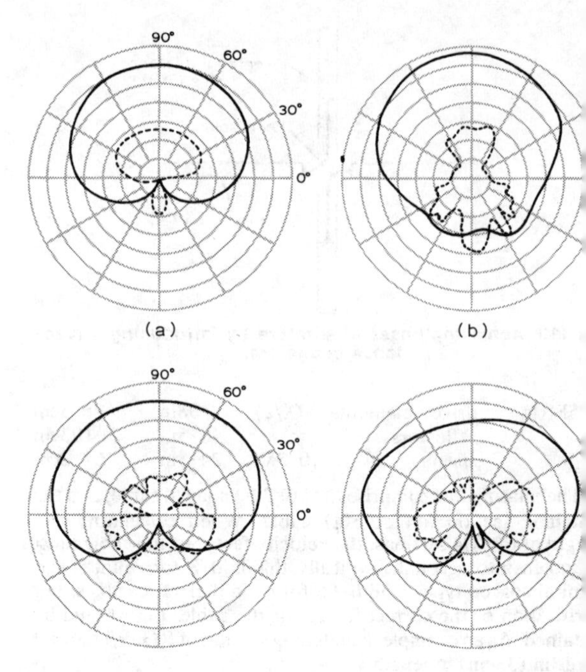

Fig 117. (a) Three-quarter turn λ/4 volute radiation pattern. (b) Three-quarter turn λ/2 volute radiation pattern. (c) Three-quarter turn 3λ/4 volute radiation pattern. (d) Three-quarter turn 1λ volute radiation pattern (*Microwave Journal*)

Materials for elements

The radiating efficiency of an antenna may be defined as the ratio of the power radiated to the power input to the antenna. The difference between the radiated power P_r and the input power P_{in} is the power lost in dissipation by the antenna itself, P_d.

An antenna can be represented by the equivalent circuit shown in Fig 118. Power in such a circuit can only be lost in a resistive element, so that both the power dissipating elements are shown as R_r and R_d. R_r is proportional to the power radiated (effective radiation resistance) and R_d is proportional to the power dissipated in the antenna itself (effective loss resistance). When considering the relative efficiencies of the various materials for antenna elements it is the value of the effective loss resistance R_d which is important. Since most vhf and uhf antennas are made up of various elements of more or less uniform cross-sectional area, the dc resistance may be calculated from

$$R_{dc} = \frac{L}{A} \times \text{resistivity}$$

where L is the strength, A is the area, and "resistivity" is the resistance per unit length or unit area of the material involved, and this is usually given in ohms per cubic centimetre.

For example, taking L as λ/4 at 144MHz, and A as the area of ⅛in diameter rod, then typical values of R_{dc} are:

Metal	Resistivity (Ω/cm³)	Resistance (R_{dc})
Copper	$1 \cdot 72 \times 10^{-6}$	0·0023Ω
Aluminium	$2 \cdot 83 \times 10^{-6}$	0·0037Ω
Zinc	$5 \cdot 9 \times 10^{-6}$	0·0077Ω
Brass	$7 \cdot 5 \times 10^{-6}$	0·0098Ω

All these are negligible with respect to the radiation resistance R_r of a λ/2 dipole, which for the chosen element diameter is about 65Ω. This however is only part of the effective loss resistance.

As the frequency of the current flowing in the material is increased from zero frequency (or dc) another factor, *skin effect*, modifies the current distribution in the cross-section of the conductor, concentrating it more and more in the outer skin as the frequency is raised.

This therefore reduces the working area of the conductor and increases its effective resistance. At vhf the skin carrying most of the current becomes quite thin, about 0·0005in, and is proportional to the square root of the conductor resistivity. From this, it is obvious that the skin will be thicker for metals with higher resistivities, and their rf resistance will be less, relative to their dc resistance, than for the better conductors such as copper. This makes their use more attractive than might be expected.

The rf resistance, R'_{rf} for a current which is constant on the length of a λ/2 element is approximately as follows.

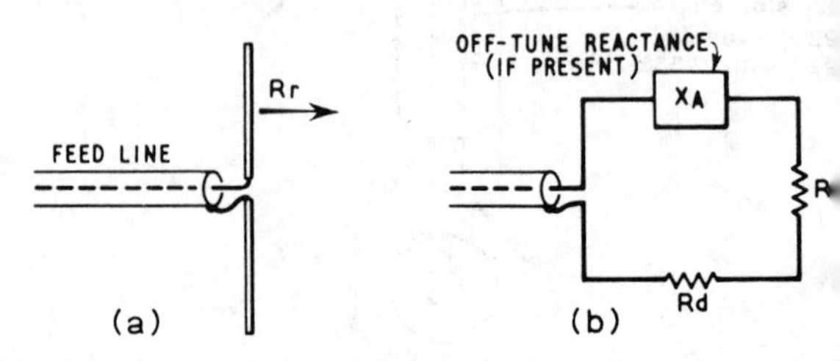

Fig 118. An antenna and its equivalent circuit

Metal	Skin depth	RF resistance (R'_{rf})	Ratio R'_{rf} to R_{dc}
opper	0·00022in	0·34Ω	148
luminium	0·00028in	0·41Ω	110
inc	0·00040in	0·60Ω	78
rass	0·00045in	0·68Ω	69

The radiation efficiency and antenna loss in decibels for the etals considered are as shown below:

Metal	R_L	Radiation efficiency	Loss due to antenna elements
opper	0·17Ω	99·75%	0·011dB
luminium	0·20Ω	99·7%	0·013dB
inc	0·30Ω	99·5%	0·022dB
rass	0·34Ω	99·4%	0·026dB

These figures are for elements of $\frac{1}{8}$in diameter; for elements f the more popular diameters $\frac{1}{4}$in to $\frac{1}{2}$in the rf resistance will be wer, although for very thin-walled tubes the dc resistance may e greater.

The following simple formulae can be used to calculate the kin depth of R'_{rf} resistance.

For solid rod elements

$$R'_{rf} = R_{dc} \times \frac{\text{Diameter (in)}}{4 \times \text{skin depth (in)}}$$

'or thin-walled tubes

$$R'_{rf} = R_{dc} \times \frac{\text{Wall thickness (in)}}{\text{skin depth (in)}}$$

$$\text{kin depth at vhf (in)} = 2\sqrt{\frac{\sigma}{\mu F}}$$

here σ is resistivity in ohms per cubic centimetre, μ is pre- neability (taken as 1 for non-ferrous metals) and F is frequency n hertz.

lectrolytic corrosion

he use of dissimilar metals in an antenna system is likely to ause considerable trouble due to electrolytic corrosion. Each metal has its own electro-potential, and unless metals of similar potential are used the difference will cause corrosion at the point of contact even when dry. When moisture is present this effect will be even more severe.

If, for any reason, dissimilar metals must be used then considerable care should be taken to exclude moisture, the corrosive effects of which will vary with the atmospheric pollution.

The various metals can be arranged in groups as follows:

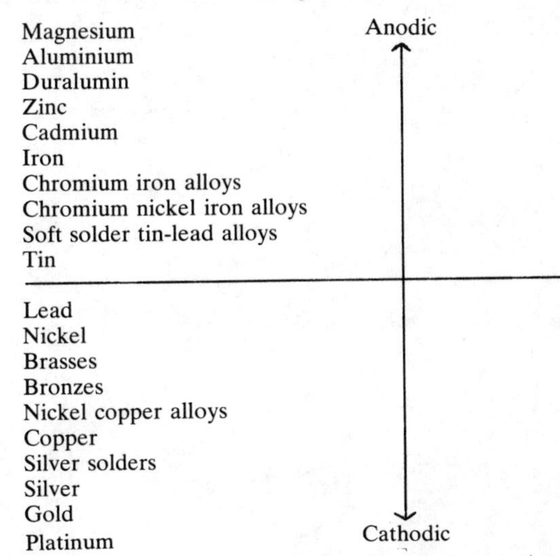

Metals in each of the above groups may be used together with little corrosive action, but metals from different groups will suffer from this effect. Also, since the above is arranged in order, the greater the spacing in the list, the greater will be the effect.

The lower of the metals in this list will corrode those in the upper portion. For example, brass or copper screws in aluminium will corrode the aluminium very considerably, whereas with cadmium-plated brass or copper screws there will be very much less corrosion of the aluminium.

'HAPTER 9

ʌicrowaves

Microwaves" is a useful and widely used term to describe equencies of 1GHz and above in both a professional and mateur context. In the amateur field, the distinction is most ppropriate for two reasons: first, above this frequency much of e design, construction and operation of equipment is highly xperimental in nature and, second, the relatively wide amateur locations, which range from 60MHz to many gigahertz, nable many techniques to be used in the microwave part of the ectrum which cannot be accommodated within the relatively arrow allocations at lower frequencies. Microwaves therefore present a unique opportunity for exploring new techniques nd operation methods, with the 1·3GHz allocation to be garded as the critical "link" band common to both "vhf" and) microwaves.

In this chapter, emphasis will be given to the 1·3, 2·3, 10 and 4GHz bands, although much material will be of a general ature. A basic difference from the 3rd edition format is that an tempt has been made to bring together all the practical infor- ation for each of the bands into individual sections so that it is ow less necessary to seek out relevant information spread roughout various parts of the book. The exceptions are ntennas, which are considered together at the end of the apter, and propagation which is dealt with in Chapter 2. More ecifically, narrow-band equipment for 1·3 and 2·3GHz is rst discussed, and this is followed by a review of some tech- iques special to microwaves. This in turn is followed by specific formation on both wide-band and narrow-band 10GHz quipment, and then on wide-band 24GHz equipment. As oted earlier, the final part considers antennas for the mic- owave bands.

3and-planning on microwaves

he microwave bands allocated at present in the UK, together ith those that will become available to amateurs as a result of WARC '79, are summarized in Table 1, with those allocated to the amateur-satellite service given in Table 2.

The width of the allocations makes it necessary to have preferred sub-bands of operation because it may be impractical to produce equipment that covers the whole allocation. For wide-band equipment, the choice of operating frequencies can be made on a band-by-band basis since the equipment is usually made to cover one particular band. So far, it has been necessary only to plan the 10GHz band. Due to the difficulty of pulling certain common klystrons, the sub-band for wide-band operation originally adopted was 10,000 to 10,100MHz. However, in order to make this equipment more compatible with narrow-band equipment, the current IARU Region 1 band plan specifies the use of the 10,400 to 10,500MHz part of the band for wide-band equipment. A preferred operating frequency of 24,125MHz has been proposed for 24GHz wide-band equipment.

The sub-band specified for narrow-band operation follows the well-established practice at lower frequencies of being in simple harmonic relationship with one another. This allows existing equipment to be used as drivers to multipliers to higher frequencies, and greatly facilitates the monitoring of transmissions. The relationship between the frequencies of the sub-bands and 144MHz is shown in Fig 1. The two main features are that virtually all the bands above 2,300MHz can in principle be covered by multiplying from a single driver operating at 1,152MHz, and that the 10,368MHz sub-band is a special case in that it can be generated by multiplying from both 1,152MHz and 1,296MHz. The significance of the 1,296MHz band is that it is typical of lower microwave frequencies, and yet it can be generated in a straightforward way from existing vhf equipment either by tripling from 432MHz or by mixing 144MHz with the standard microwave driver frequency of 1,152MHz.

As shown by Fig 1, usable harmonics of 1,152MHz also fall into the 76, 142 and 241GHz bands, which will be allocated for amateur usage, but not into the 47 and 120GHz bands.

The sub-bands for narrow-band operation are defined

Table 1. UK amateur service allocations

llocation	Status of amateur allocation
,240–1,325MHz	Secondary
,310–2,450MHz	Secondary
,400–3,475MHz	Secondary
,650–5,680MHz	Secondary
,755–5,765MHz	Secondary
,820–5,850MHz	Secondary
0,000–10,500MHz	Secondary
4,000–24,050MHz	Primary
4,050–24,250MHz	Secondary
7·0–47·2GHz	Primary
5·5–76·0GHz	Primary
42–144GHz	Primary
48–250GHz	Secondary

Table 2. UK amateur satellite service allocations

Allocation	Status of amateur allocation	Comments
1,260–1,270MHz	Secondary	Earth-to-space only
2,400–2,450MHz	Secondary	
5,650–5,670MHz	Secondary	Earth-to-space only
5,830–5,850MHz	Secondary	Space-to-earth only
10,450–10,500MHz	Secondary	
24,000–24,050MHz	Primary	
47·0–47·2GHz	Primary	
75·5–76·0GHz	Primary	
142–144GHz	Primary	
248–250GHz	Primary	

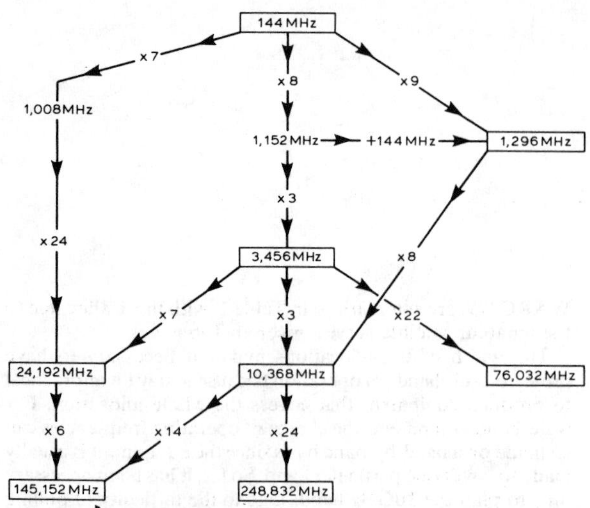

Fig 1. The relationship between the frequencies for narrow-band working for bands above 144MHz

as 1,152*n* to 1,152*n* + 2MHz, eg 3,456–3,458MHz; 24,192–24,194MHz. However, recent changes in the licensing conditions in some countries (including the UK) may mean that this simple system may no longer apply to 2,304–2,306MHz, and that a new sub-band will need to be designated.

1·3GHz EQUIPMENT

A large proportion of the equipment in use on this band is still home-constructed, although commercially-built equipment is becoming more common. The following section describes a number of practical designs which cover the range of techniques used at this frequency.

Interdigital converters for 1·3 and 2·3GHz

The converters for 1·3GHz and 2·3GHz described below are based on an original design by W2CQH [1]. Since much of their circuitry is common they will be described together. The main advantage of these designs is that all the necessary functions, ie final local oscillator multiplication, filtering, mixing and signal filtering, are all performed by one assembly which is based on an interdigital filter. This means that a separate final local-oscillator multiplier does not have to be constructed, nor is any additional signal filtering necessary to suppress the image response. The design is capable of a much lower noise figure than the "trough-line" designs previously published, which is the only type of mixer also combining all microwave functions in one assembly. The interdigital design has been found very easy to duplicate and get working, and is in use by a large number of stations.

The heart of the unit is the interdigital network. Referring to Fig 2, this consists of five rod elements L1–L5. L1, L3 and L5 are low-*Q* coupling elements, while L2 and L4 are resonant at the signal and local oscillator frequencies respectively, and perform the filtering functions. D2 acts as a ×4 or ×6 multiplier, producing a few milliwatts output at the local oscillator frequency of 1,152 or 2,160MHz for 50–150mW drive at 384 or 360MHz. A suitable local oscillator design to provide t drive power is described below. D1 is the mixer diode, and t 144MHz i.f. output is fed to a low-noise amplifier stage usin BFR34A transistor.

Construction

The unit is built on a 7½ by 4½ by 1/16in piece of double-sid copper laminate board, which is also used as the lid for t die-cast box which houses the converter. Constructional poi should be clear from Figs 3, 4 and 5. The sidewalls of the mix assembly may be bent up from sheet brass or copper, and t rod elements are soldered to this. A cover made from doub sided copper laminate is fitted to the mixer assembly as the fin stage of assembly. Note that no screening is required at the en of the interdigital unit.

Tuning-up

Apply 50–100mW of drive to the lo drive input socket, a connect a voltmeter between TP1 and earth. Carefully adj the 10pF trimmers repetitively, using an insulated trimmi tool, until a maximum reading of at least 1·5V is observe Next, monitor mixer current on the meter fitted for the pu pose; this meter should be shunted by a suitable resistor so as give an fsd of 5mA. Insert screw C12 and screw in until maximu mixer current of at least 1mA is obtained. With the specifie dimensions the first peak observed should correspond to t correct tuning point. However, it may be possible to tune-up c the wrong frequency, being evidenced by very poor perfo mance later on. The procedure is to either listen to a loc station to check that the correct tuning point has been found, to measure the local oscillator frequency formally. This may b achieved with sufficient accuracy by the well-known Lecher li method in no more than about 10min—including making t Lecher line. A suitable Lecher line is shown in Fig 6. Conne

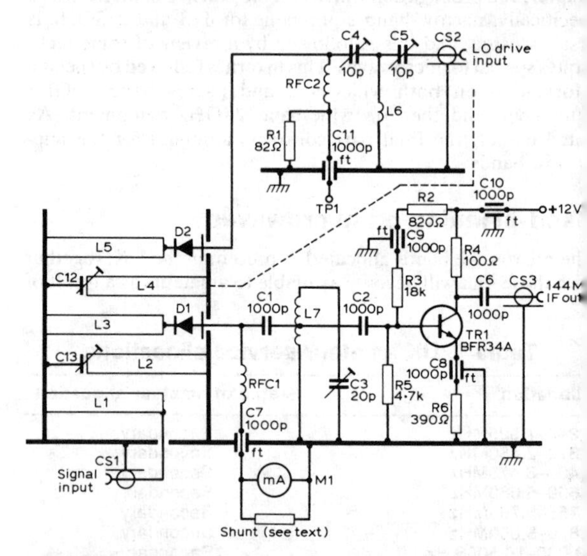

Fig 2. Schematic diagram of the interdigital mixer unit. L1 – L interdigital rods. L6: 4·5cm 20swg copper wire bent to form on turn loop. L7: 5t 20swg ¼in i.d. ¾in long, tapped 1½ turns from eart end. RFC1, RFC2: 3½t 30swg on two FX1115 ferrite beads end-t end. FT: 1,000pF feedthrough capacitors. All trimmers: plastic f types. All 1,000pF capacitors other than feedthrough capacito are miniature ceramic plate. D1, D2: Motorola MBD102 or simil uhf Schottky barrier mixer diodes

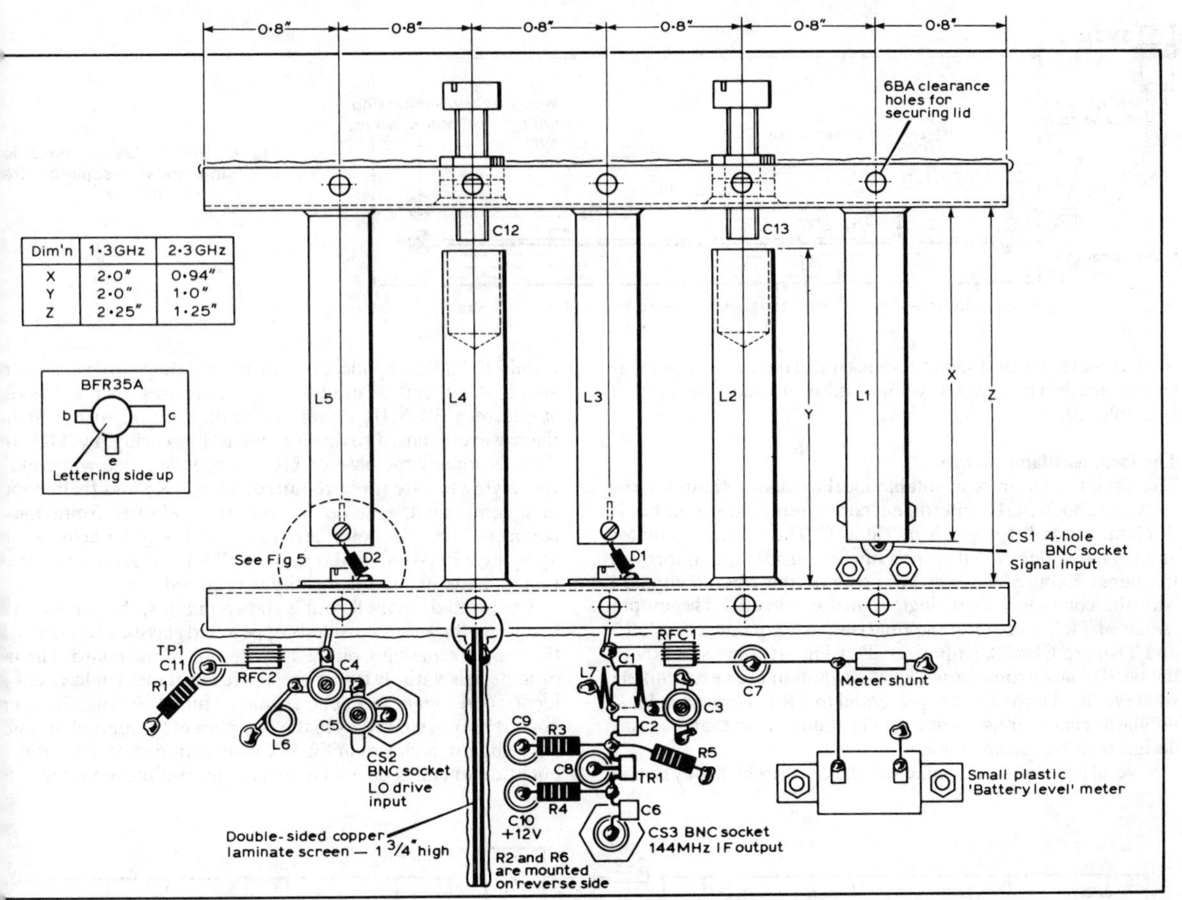

g 3. Layout of mixer assembly. The interdigital assembly is covered by a lid. If pcb is used, both sides must be earthed to the screen

ıe BNC plug to the antenna socket and tune C13 until the mixer urrent dips. To obtain greater sensitivity, the meter shunt may e temporarily removed. Next, short the two Lecher lines ›gether using a suitable metal object, such as a screwdriver, nd slide this up and down the line until a small peak in the ıixer current is observed. Note the position of the short, and ide it away from this point until the next peak is found. The ·equency in megahertz being measured is then equal to 5,000/d where d is the distance between the two points in ·entimetres.

Next, connect a 144MHz receiver to the i.f. output socket and adjust the 20pF trimmer for maximum noise. If no peak is found, it will be necessary to experiment with the tapping points of the 1,000pF capacitors on L7. Connect a preamplifier or noise source to the antenna socket and unscrew C13 until a noise peak is heard. Alternatively, an antenna can be connected, and C13 unscrewed until maximum signal strength is obtained from a local station. Final adjustments may be made to C12, 13 and the

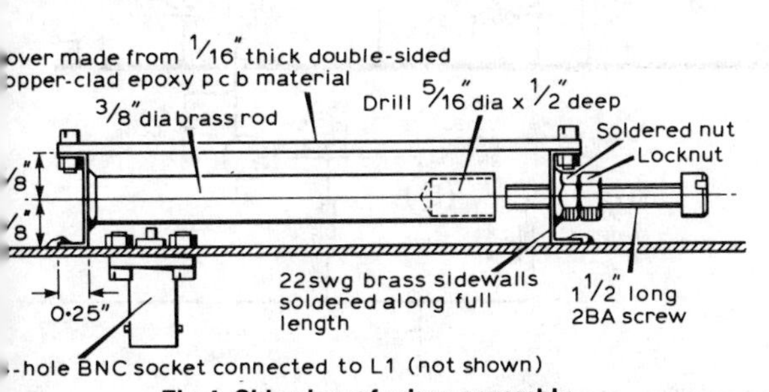

Fig 4. Side view of mixer assembly

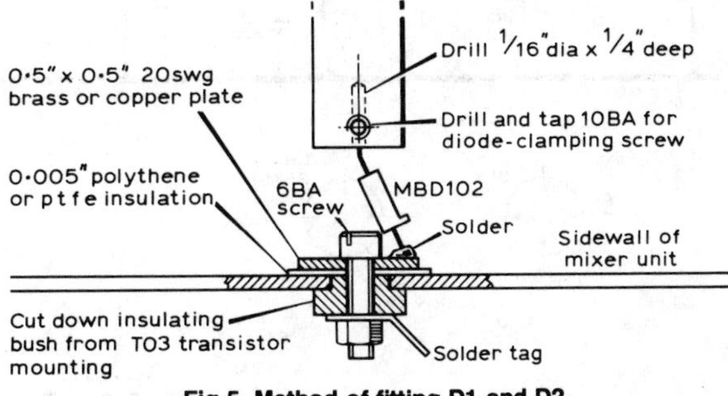

Fig 5. Method of fitting D1 and D2

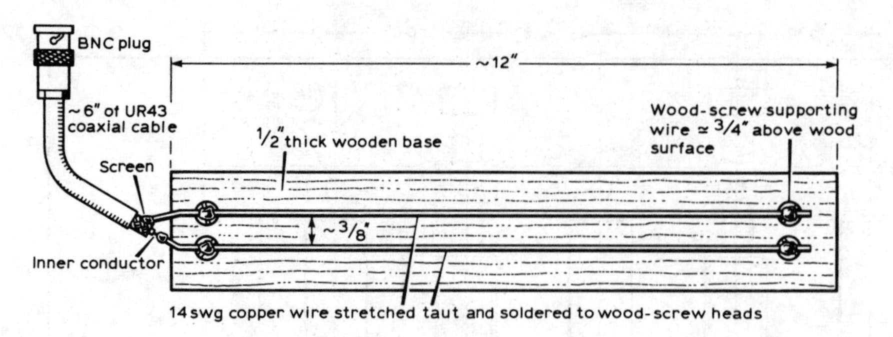

Fig 6. Simple Lecher lines fo checking local oscillator fre quency

20pF trimmer for best signal-to-noise ratio on a weak signal, or an automatic noise figure optimization aid may be used if available [2].

The local oscillator source

The circuit diagram of a suitable local oscillator chain for the 1·3GHz and 2·3GHz interdigital converters is shown in Fig 7. A components list is given in Table 3. The crystal oscillator employs a Butler circuit, which offers considerably improved frequency stability and very low noise output when compared with the commonly used single-transistor circuits. The output circuit of TR2 is tuned to the final output frequency, and TR3 and TR4 are Class A amplifiers. This imparts high stability to the design, and problems with self-oscillation are very unlikely whatever load impedance is presented to TR4. Very often local oscillator chains are only marginally stable at best, and so this design is to be recommended.

Several functions are available in the circuit which may not be required in this application, although they are very usef should the circuit be used for other purposes, such as the fir stages of a 384MHz driver for multiplication to the high microwave bands. Provision is made for keying, by TR5 ar TR6. Normally the base of TR6 is grounded by a wire link. the keying facility is not required, TR5, TR6 and their assoc ated components may be omitted, the end of R15 previous connected to TR5 being grounded. FM may be achieved b applying a low-level audio signal to TR1: no external conne tion is made unless this facility is required.

The printed circuit layout is shown in Fig 8, the pcb materi being $\frac{1}{16}$in thick double-sided copper-clad glassfibre epoxy, wi the copper remaining on the reverse side of the board. The us of materials with different dielectric constants could result i incorrect resonant frequencies for the tuned circuits. The com ponent layout, viewed from the component (ground-plane) sid of the board, is shown in Fig 9. Construction is straightforwa but attention must be paid to achieving absolute minimum lea

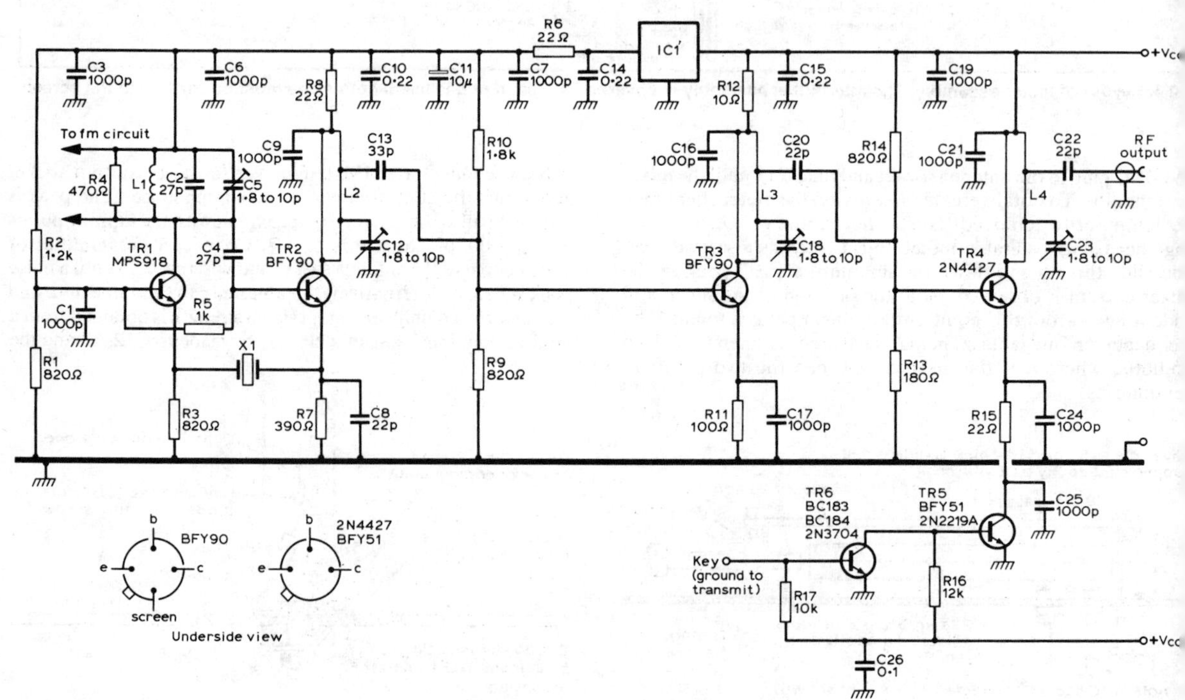

Fig 7. Circuit of local oscillator chain

11 rows of white dots, 9 holes + and 10 holes ⊕ are drilled 3/64" dia

Drill all holes 1/32" dia

TOP

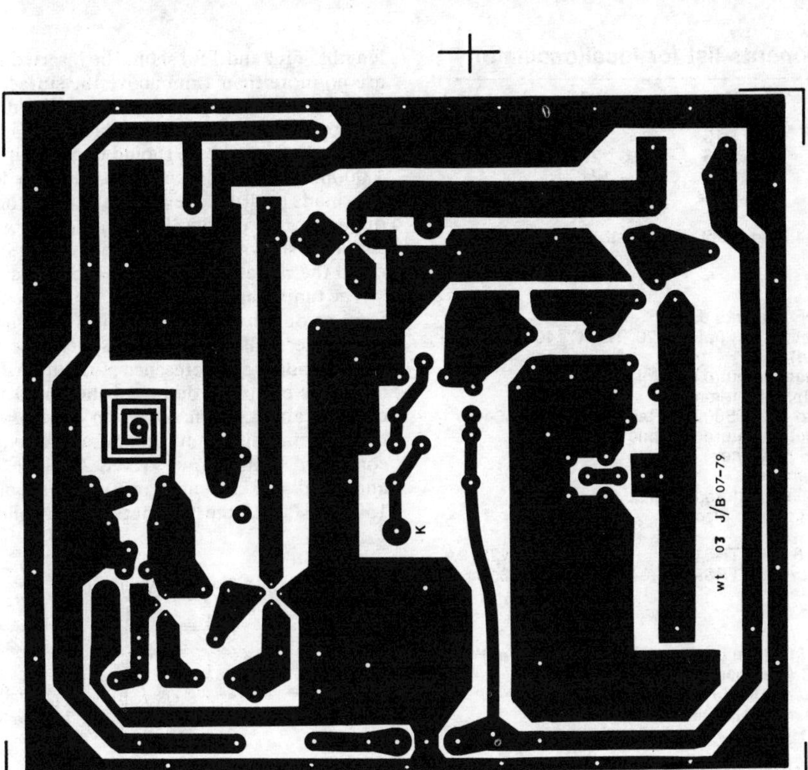

Fig 8. Details of pcb. The board is double-sided glassfibre epoxy board having a dielectric constant of 5

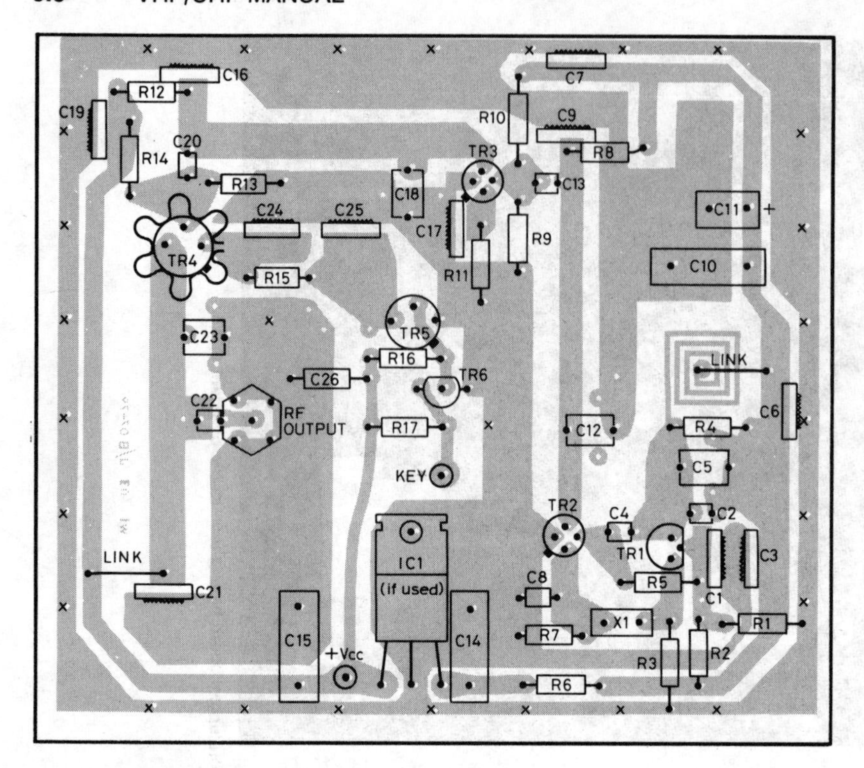

Fig 9. Component layout. X indicates where wires join top and bottom earth planes

Table 3. Components list for local oscillator

R1, 3, 9, 14	820Ω	**R11**	100Ω
R2	1·2kΩ	**R12**	10Ω
R4	470Ω	**R13**	180Ω
R5	1kΩ	**R15**	22Ω
R6, 8	22Ω	**R16**	12kΩ
R7	390Ω	**R17**	10kΩ
R10	1·8kΩ		

All resistors 0·25W TR4 2 per cent (Electrosil, metal oxide)

C1, 3, 6, 7, 9 16, 17, 19, 21, 24, 25	1,000pF leadless disc (Steatite 1,000pF/80/20 TEFK7 400V recommended)
C2, 4	27pF subminiature ceramic disc
C5, 12, 18, 23	1·8–10pF film trimmer (Mullard 809–05002 or Radiospares 125–648)
C8, 20, 22	22pF subminiature ceramic disc
C10, 14, 15	0·22μF polyester
C11	10μF tantalum
C13	33pF subminiature ceramic disc
C26	0·1μF ceramic disc

TR1	MPS918	**TR5**	BFY51 or 2N2219A
TR2, 3	BFY90	**TR6**	BC183 or BC184 or 2N3704
TR4	2N4427		

IC1 (if used)	LM340T12 (National) or 7812 (Radiospares) 12V or 7808 (Radiospares) 8V
X1	HC18/U or HC25/U fifth overtone crystal
L1 to L4	Printed microstrip lines
Heat sink	TO5 (TR4)
PCB mounting socket	SMA, SMB or SMC

lengths. TR1 and TR4 should be inserted such that their bodies are no more than 1mm above the surface of the board, while TR2 and TR3 should be pushed fully home, with their cans being soldered to the ground plane. TR4 is fitted with a push-on heat sink. Special care should be taken in the mounting of the 1,000pF leadless disc ceramics. They are located in slots in the pcb, made by drilling several holes close together and then filing out using a needle file. They should by positioned and soldered *exactly* as shown in Fig 10. Ensure that the solder flows properly on to the metallization of the capacitors.

The tuning-up procedure for the unit requires the use of some form of output indicator, such as that shown in Fig 11(a). A multimeter, initially on its most sensitive range (eg 50μA), is used to indicate the presence of rf output. The output indicator is connected to the output of the board via a short length of coaxial cable. Alternatively, an hf/vhf swr indicator may be used, set initially to maximum sensitivity, with a 50Ω resistor connected to its output socket. Apply +13·5V to the board, and check the current drawn which should be approximately 150mA. Preset the trimmers to the following positions: C5

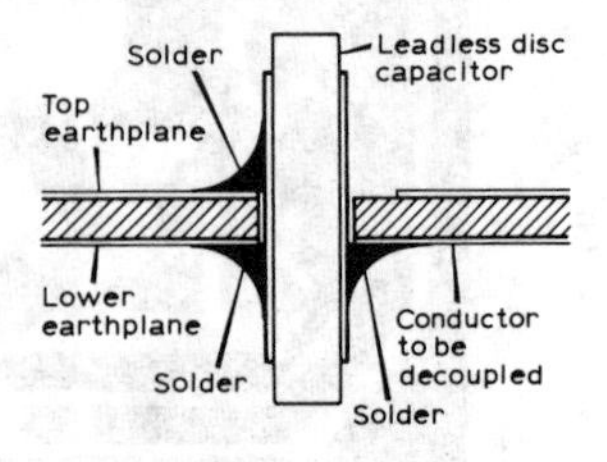

Fig 10. Soldering of leadless disc capacitors

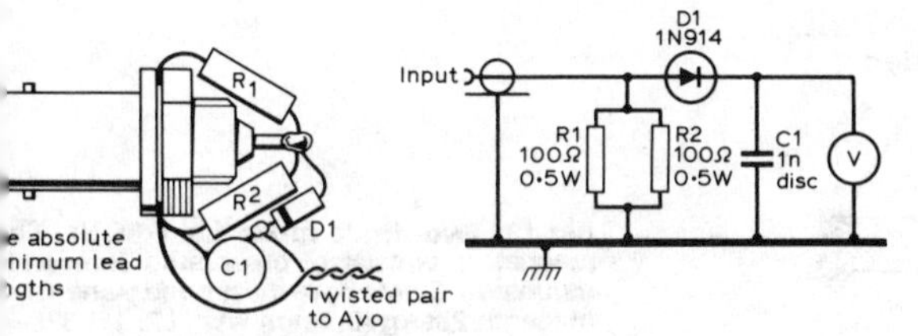

Fig 11(a). Construction of power meter on a bnc socket

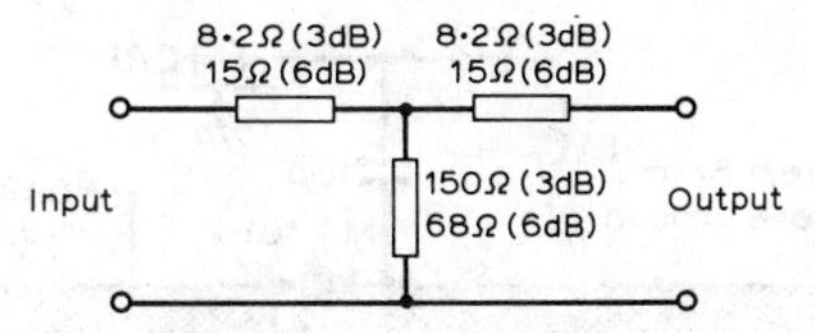

Fig 12. 3 or 6dB attenuator for fitting between local oscillator chain and final multiplier, if required

bout 50 per cent meshed, C12 about 40 per cent meshed, C18 bout 80 per cent meshed and C23 about 50 per cent meshed. ome output should then be detected, and this is maximized by ning the trimmers. It should not be possible to tune up on the rong frequency using the component values specified but, if in oubt, check with an absorption wavemeter. The position of C5 nould not be too critical as regards output power, and may be sed to trim the frequency.

When the board is tuned up, it should produce at least 100mW output. It may be the case that the board produces too much ower to drive the multiplier diode, and an attenuator may be ecessary between the board and the multiplier diode. Too uch drive can result in less-than-optimum harmonic output om the diode. Designs for suitable 3 and 6dB attenuators are iven in Fig 12. These should be located between the lo input ocket on the mixer unit and the matching network feeding the ultiplier diode.

'win-diode harmonic mixer for 1·3GHz

'his is an efficient mixer using $\lambda/2$ linear circuits connected ogether by a pair of diodes in parallel but with reversed polar-y and pumped at half the usual frequency, eg 634MHz instead f 1,268MHz. It offers several advantages:

- a very low oscillator power (−3dBm)
- no dc return necessary
- no tuning needed with $\lambda/2$ strip lines
- high isolation between all ports

In operation each diode is "turned-on" once during the local oscillator cycle, the diodes being 180° apart. Both are off when the oscillator voltage is zero. Since the local oscillator frequency is approximately half that of the rf input, the grounded $\lambda/2$ line looks like an open circuit to the local oscillator port and like a low impedance to the rf port. A noise factor of about 6·5dB may be expected.

Details of the construction are given in Fig 13. This consists simply of two $\lambda/2$ strip lines, 5mm ($\frac{3}{16}$in) wide copper or brass, mounted 1·5mm ($\frac{1}{16}$in) above a ground plane. One (right-hand in diagram) is grounded at the end, the other (left-hand line) is left open. Hot-carrier diodes are needed to achieve the noise figure mentioned above. The $\lambda/2$ line circuits may be scaled for higher frequencies.

A strip-line diode multiplier for 1·3GHz

A strip-line multiplier circuit fabricated on 1·5mm glassfibre pcb is illustrated by Fig 14. This multiplier triples from 400MHz and produces 0·5mW output from a drive of 500mW. A dc return for the diode is required. If this is not provided by the

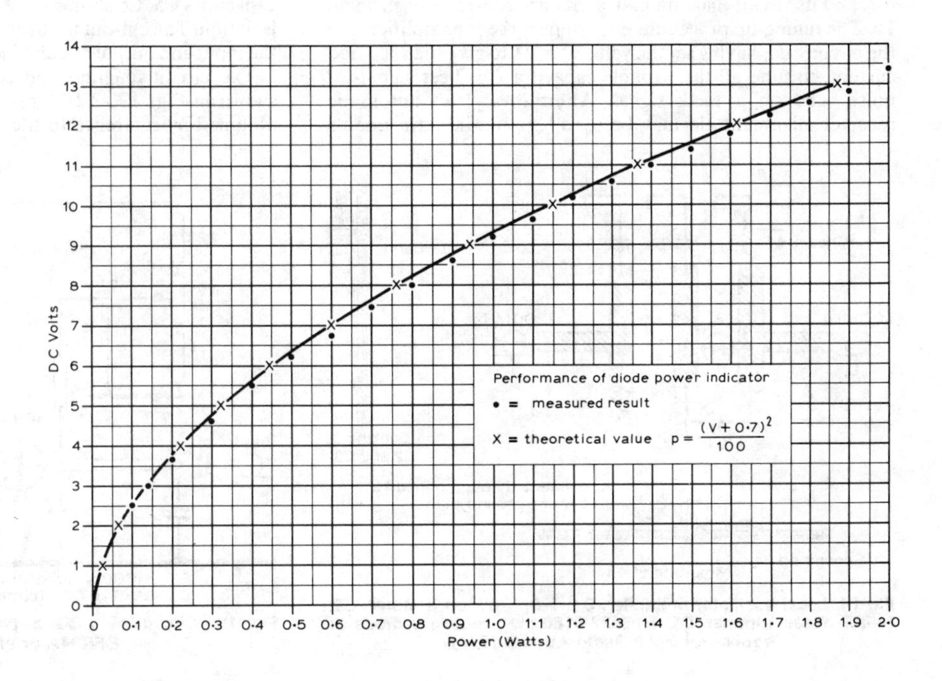

'ig 11(b). Calibration of power meter

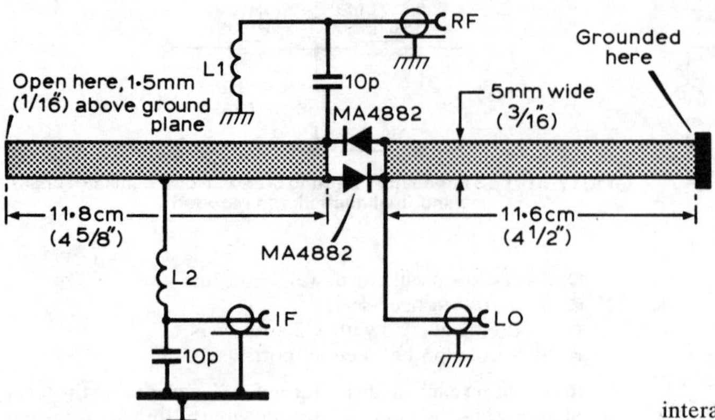

Fig 13. Two-diode mixer for 1·3GHz. Th resonators consist of brass strip 5mm wid mounted 1·5mm above the ground plane. L1: 1 in length 28swg (0·3mm) wire. L2: 15t 32sw (0·22mm) wire, 1·5mm diameter. (*Ham Radi* August 1978)

driver, a 0·33μH choke should be fitted as shown. It is essential that the trimmers be adequately earthed using the method given in Fig 14.

An rf preamplifier for 1·3GHz

Most modern converter designs for 1·3GHz, including the interdigital design described earlier, have overall noise figures in the region of 10dB. While acceptable results may be obtained using such converters, there is usually a considerable advantage to be gained by using one or more preamplifiers. The preamplifier described has a gain of approximately 8dB and a noise figure of about 4dB. One such preamplifier with a converter having a 10dB noise figure will reduce the overall noise figure to 6dB, while two such preamplifiers in cascade will give an overall 4·6dB noise figure. There is little advantage in using more than two preamplifiers.

The preamplifier uses a BFR90, BFR91 or BFR34A transistor, and its circuit diagram and layout are shown in Fig 15 and 16. The tuning-up procedure is to connect the preamplifier into the circuit and, having set the value of RV1 to give the specified current, to tune all the variable capacitors for best signal-to-noise ratio on a weak signal. Alternatively, an automatic receiver alignment aid may be used [2]. As the adjustments interact to some extent, it will be necessary to go several time around the "loop" until the optimum settings have been deter mined. If the converter has a tuned input, this should b adjusted also.

Since the tuning may be affected if any of the interconnectin cables are changed, the preamplifier should be connected up a it would be used in the final system.

Strip-line preamplifier for 1·3GHz

A high-gain preamplifier for the 1·3GHz band can be made b using strip-line tuning inductors, but the most important facto in achieving high gain and low noise figure is to use the bes transistor that can be obtained for the purpose.

The type required is one which has strip connections such a those in the SOT100 package. It should also be of a type tha operates satisfactorily up to at least 2GHz. Such devices may b expected to have a gain in the region of 15 or 16dB with a nois figure of about 4dB.

With this level of gain at this frequency, isolation of the inpu and the output must be as good as possible. The rf bypas capacitors C5, C6 should be leadless type to preserve the circui isolation. The cut-out for the transistor on the screen separatin the input and output circuits should be kept as small as possible.

The circuit diagram and component layout of the unit i shown in Figs 17 and 18 respectively. Further details can b obtained by reference to the original article [4].

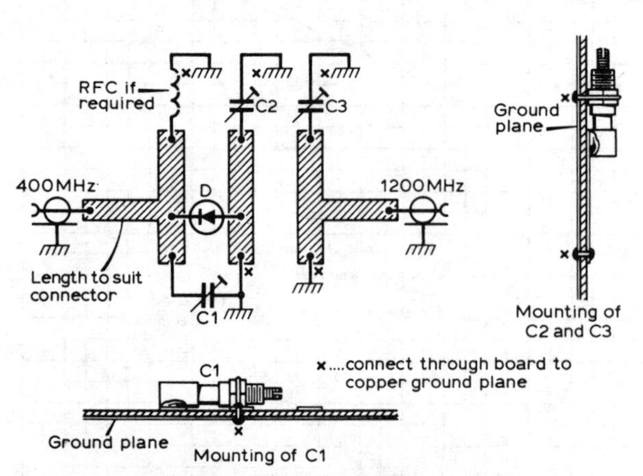

Fig 14. Local oscillator multiplier. C1: 1–9pF piston trimmer. C2: 1–5pF piston trimmer. D1: HP5082-0180 step recovery diode or equivalent (*Ham Radio* August 1978)

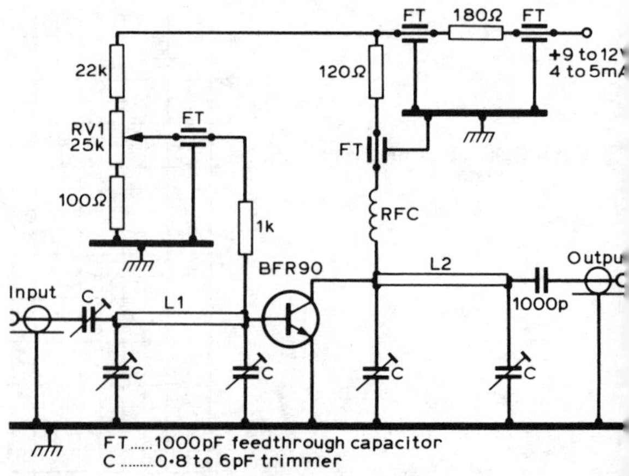

Fig 15. Circuit of 1·3GHz preamplifier using BFR90, BFR91 BFR34A or similar transistor

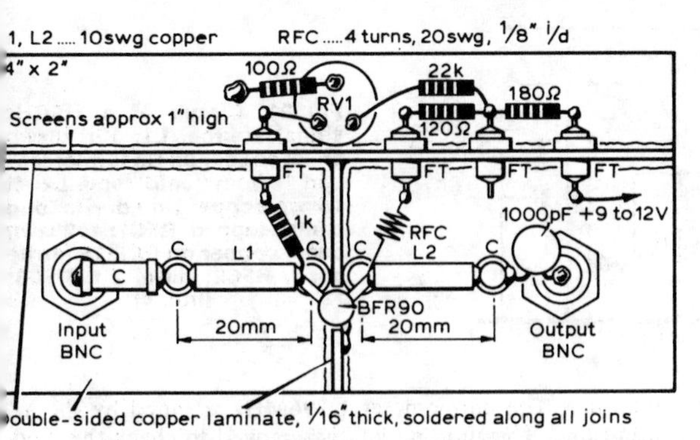

Fig 16. Layout of preamplifier. The $\frac{1}{16}$in double-sided copper laminate base and screens should be soldered along all joins

Using rf preamplifiers on 1·3GHz

Unlike the interdigital converter design described above, many converters possess little or no front-end selectivity. When preamplifiers are used which are relatively broadband, such as the design shown in Fig 15, the overall noise figure may be improved to a lesser extent than expected. This is because the preamplifier generates noise at the image frequency, which is mixed down to the i.f. by the converter, thus degrading the signal-to-noise ratio. In the worst case, when image and signal frequency response are equal, the sensitivity of the receiver can be reduced by 3dB. The problem can be cured by placing a suitable filter between the preamplifiers and the converter. The filter needs to be of low loss, otherwise the resulting reduction in pre-mixer gain may increase the mixer's contribution to the overall noise figure by an unacceptable degree.

A simple filter suitable for the purpose is shown in Fig 19. It consists of a shortened λ/4 line, tuned by a 2BA screw, with capacitive input/output coupling via two BNC sockets. The square outer conductor can be fabricated from copper sheet. In use, the filter is connected between the converter and the preceding preamplifier using the cables to be used in practice. The BNC sockets are screwed in and out, while keeping the filter on frequency by adjusting the 2BA screw, for best signal-to-noise ratio on a received signal. Final adjustment is best done using an automatic noise figure optimization unit aid [2]. When used with a 144MHz i.f., the filter will provide up to 35dB rejection of image signals. The insertion loss is less than 1dB. The filter may also be used in the output of a transmitter.

A pcb bandpass filter for 1·3GHz is shown by the design given in Fig 20 [3]. It consists of three elements, each of which is tuned by a piston-type trimmer. It is essential that these trimmers have a low-impedance connection to earth. The coupling between the elements is provided by the stray capacitance of the trimmer stators. With 1–5pF trimmers, the tuning range is

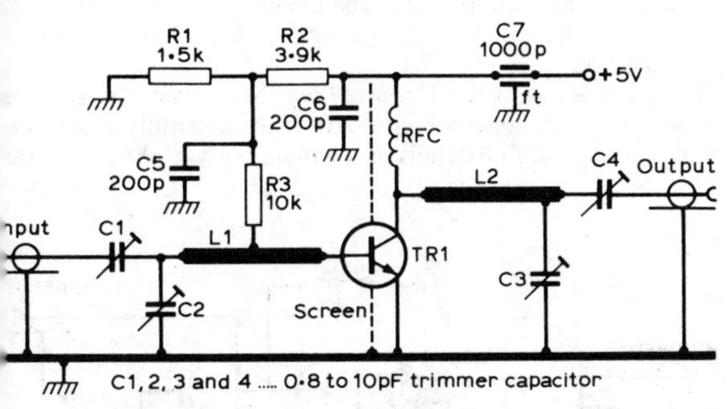

Fig 17. Circuit of a stripline preamplifier for 1·3GHz

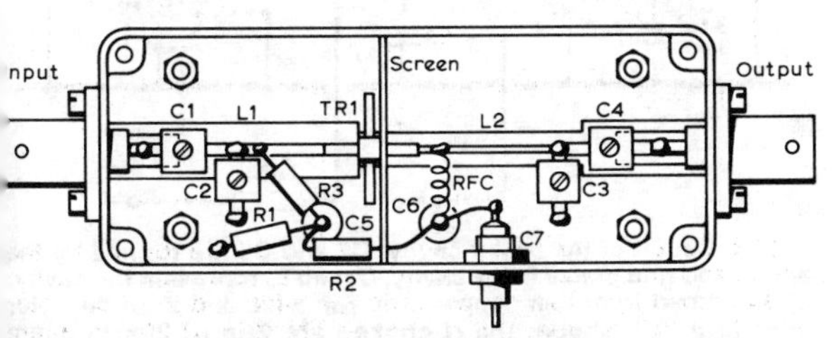

Fig 18. Layout of preamplifier

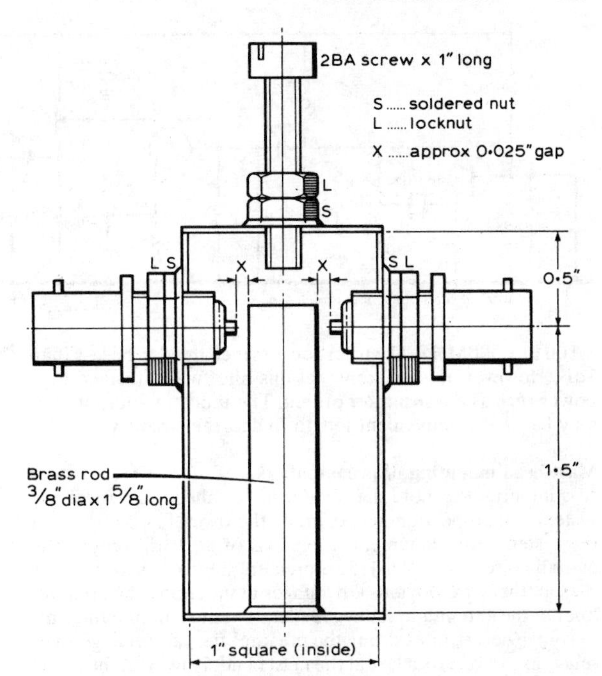

Fig 19. A simple filter for 1·3GHz

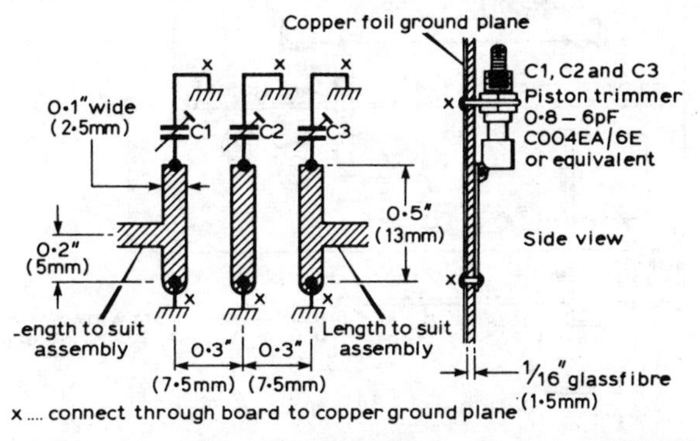

Fig 20. A microstrip filter. Suitable capacitors are type C004EA/6E or equivalent (*Ham Radio* August 1978)

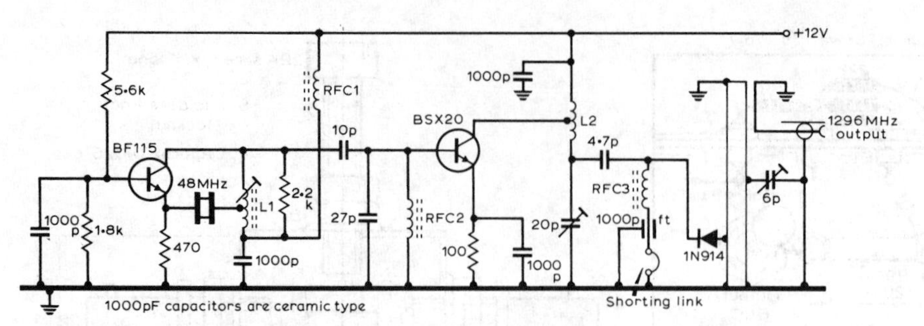

Fig 21. Circuit of a 1·3GHz signal source. L1: 12t 28swg enam copper on ½in former tapped 1t from "cold" end. L2: 4t 18swg copper ¼in i.d. 7/16in long centre-tapped. RFC1: 4t 28swg enam copper on FX1115 ferrite bead. RFC2: ditto. 2½t. RFC3: ditto, 4t

1,100 to 1,500MHz. The insertion loss is claimed to be less than 1dB. However, it is unlikely that this filter will withstand high power such as a transmitter output. The input and output lines may be of any convenient length to suit the circuitry.

Mast-head mounting of preamplifiers

It is important to note that feeder losses ahead of a receiving system will proportionately degrade the overall noise figure of the system. For example, a cable loss of 3dB will reduce the overall noise figure of a 4·5dB preamplifier to 7·5dB. For this reason, there are obvious advantages in mounting the preamplifier at the antenna to reduce feeder losses to a minimum. This of course necessitates fitting the preamplifiers and change-over relays in a waterproof box at the mast head. However, the effort involved is well rewarded by the significant improvement in performance achieved.

A 1·3GHz signal source

The unit shown in Figs 21 and 22 is intended to act as a portable "mini-beacon" for testing receivers and for aligning and comparing antennas. Even though the output power is probably only at the microwatt level, it is more than adequate for most purposes. Indeed, when connected to an antenna of 20dB gain, it has been received at good strength over a distance of 20km.

The unit is built on a piece of double-clad printed circuit board which forms the lid of a standard die-cast box. The crystal oscillator at 48MHz is followed by a BSX20 tripler to 144MHz, the output of which is fed to a 1N914 diode used as a ×9 multiplier. The harmonic at 1,296MHz is tuned by the λ/4 output line. The shorting link is removed to check the diode current, which should be about 10mA.

With shortened output lines, it is probable that similar units could be used for 2·3GHz and higher frequencies.

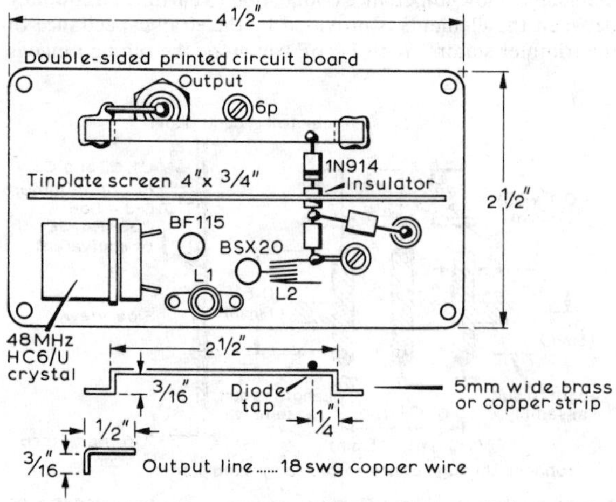

4 1/2"
Double-sided printed circuit board
Output
6p
1N914
Insulator
Tinplate screen 4"x 3/4"
2 1/2"
BF115
BSX20
L1
L2
48MHz HC6/U crystal
2 1/2"
3/16"
Diode tap
1/4"
5mm wide brass or copper strip
1/2"
3/16"
Output line......18swg copper wire

Fig 22. Layout of major components

Triplers for 1·3GHz

The simplest method for generating power on 1,296MHz is to triple from 432MHz. These triplers can be modulated satisfactorily using cw or fm, and less satisfactorily using a.m. Two designs are given, both of which employ the 2C39A valve. Although these triplers require more constructional effort than varactor triplers, they have the advantages that they are more easily aligned and more stable, and may later be readily modified for ssb operation. Varactor multipliers tend to be unstable and in general require the use of a spectrum analyser to ensure satisfactory operation.

A cavity tripler for 1·3GHz

As is indicated by the circuit diagram shown in Fig 23, the 2C39A valve operates in the grounded-grid mode with the drive being applied directly to the cathode. The output is taken via a loop which couples into the cavity.

Construction

The cavity is constructed from 20swg sheet brass, the general details of which, together with part of the assembly order, are shown in Fig 24. Full details of the main body of the cavity are

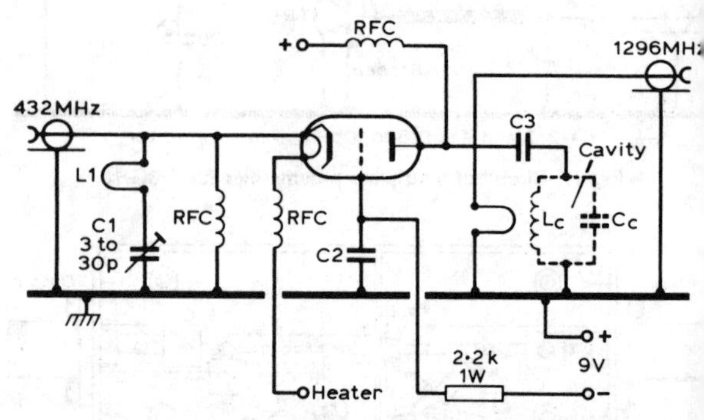

Fig 23. Circuit of the tripler cavity. C2 and C3 are formed by the anode and grid plates in the cavity; C_c and L_c represent the cavity; L1 is formed from thin copper strip 3/16in wide and 2 11/16in diameter bent to a "U" shape; the rf chokes are 2½in of 20swg enam copper wire on a 3/16in diameter former

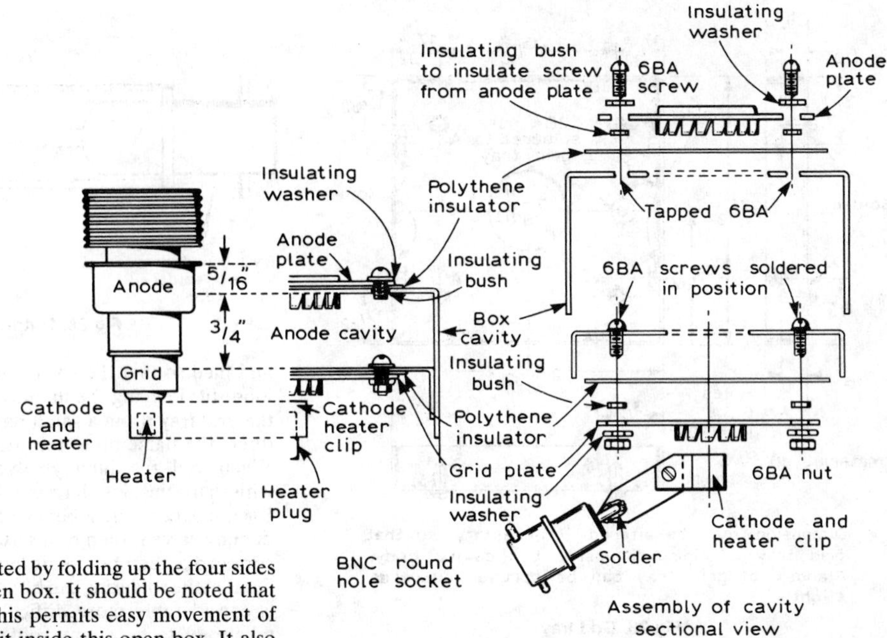

Fig 24. Assembly of cavity

shown in Fig 25. This is constructed by folding up the four sides of a flat sheet to produce an open box. It should be noted that the corners are not soldered. This permits easy movement of the grid tray which is a sliding fit inside this open box. It also allows a good contact to be made between the grid tray and the box when the side fixing screws are tightened.

The position of the grid tray in the box is the coarse adjustment for the anode circuit. Fine tuning is achieved by means of a tuning paddle which is also illustrated in Fig 25. This consists of a $\frac{5}{8}$ by $\frac{3}{4}$in metal plate which is soldered into a slot cut into the end of a $\frac{1}{4}$in operating spindle. A wider fine tuning range is provided by an alternative method which uses the coaxial tuning capacitor shown in Fig 26. Output from the cavity is taken via the $\frac{1}{2}$in outside diameter tube mounted directly opposite the fine tuning control. Into this tube slides the output coupling probe illustrated in Fig 28. It is important to ensure that the

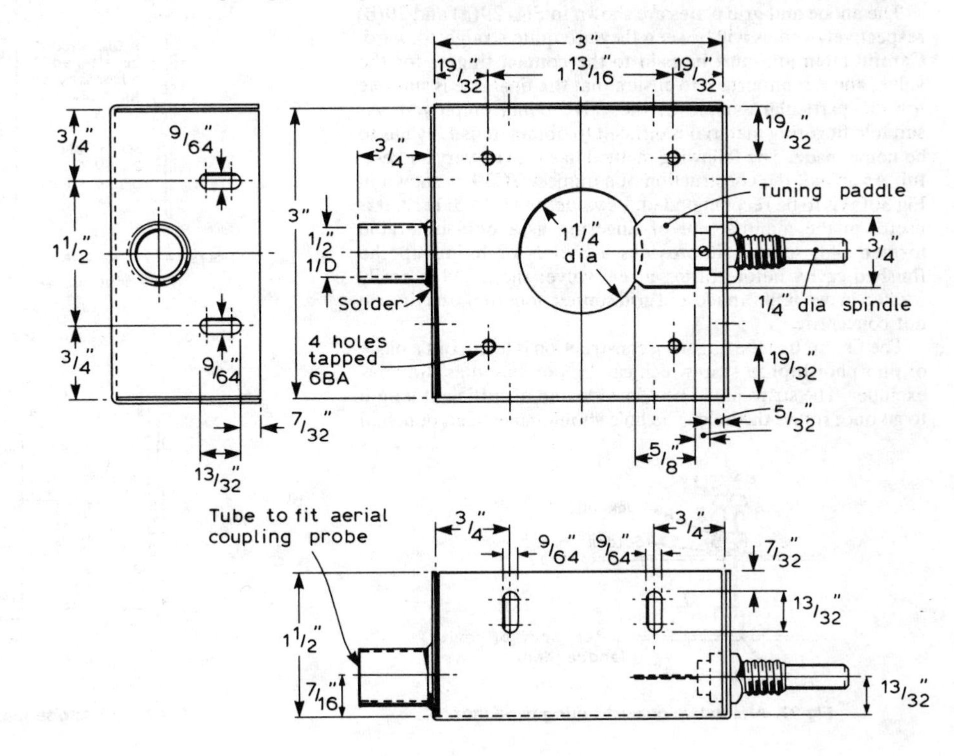

Fig 25. Box cavity body

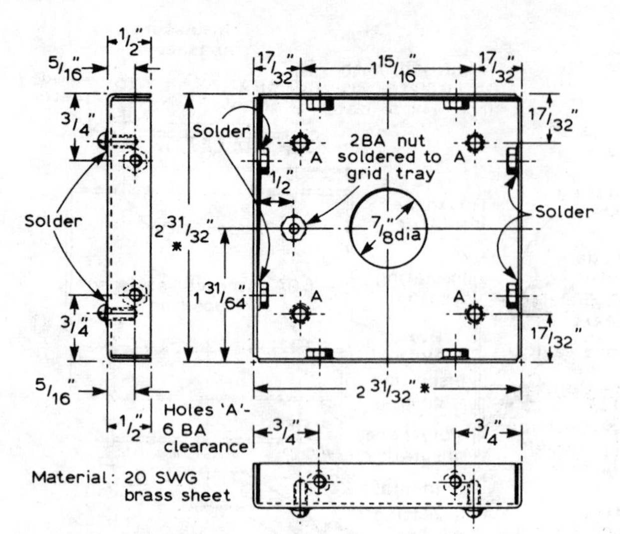

Fig 26. Grid tray

probe unit is a reasonably tight fit into the tube on the side of the cavity, and to this end the two parts should if possible be constructed from telescopic tubing. Since the diameter of the outer tube is not critical to within $\frac{1}{32}$in it is permissible to cut a lengthwise slot in it to allow it to be closed up slightly and thus ensure a tight fit round the probe.

The anode and grid plates are shown in Figs 29(a) and 29(b) respectively and as will be seen they are quite straightforward. Careful attention must be paid to the contact fingers for the valve, and it is important to ensure that the final size is suitable for the particular sample of the valve being employed. As suitable fingering material is difficult to obtain, it usually has to be home-made. The following method has proved very successful. As an aid, the construction of a dummy 2C39 as shown in Fig 30(a) is to be recommended. Its value is two-fold. First, it is useful in the manufacture of fingering as a non-solderable former and, second, it provides a means of lining up the finished cavity before fitting a real valve: the 2C39 is easily broken in two if the anode and grid connections of the cavity are not concentric.

The first step in the fingering construction is to cut out a piece of phosphor-bronze strip which can be purchased as draught-excluder. The strip should be $\frac{3}{16}$in wide and of sufficient length to go once round the hole. The hole should have been punched

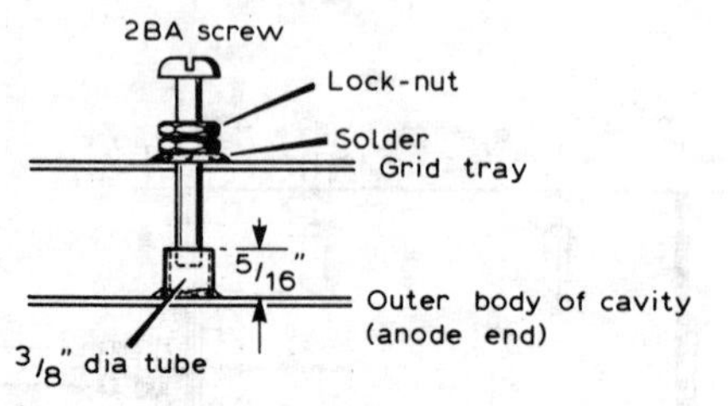

Fig 27. Alternative coaxial tuning capacitor

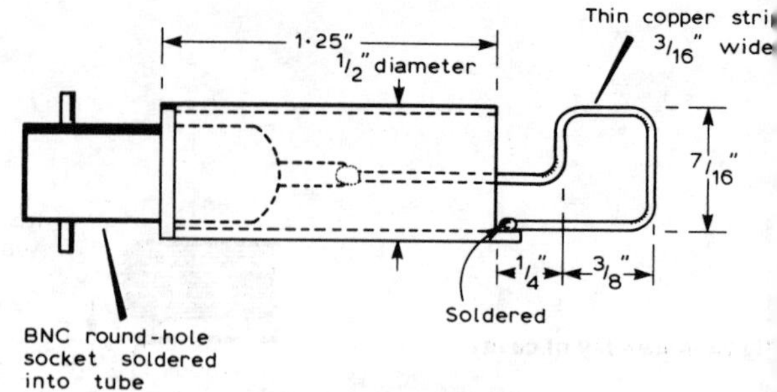

Fig 28. Output coupling probe

and filed so that the valve with the strip wrapped around is a loose fit. Leaving the dummy in place, the strip is soldered to the grid tray using a small flame. Care should be taken not to direct the flame on to the strip, or its springiness may be lost. When cool, the dummy valve is withdrawn and V-cuts made with sharp tinsnips all round the strip as indicated in Fig 30(b). Each separate strip is bent with long-nosed pliers as shown. The dummy valve is then re-inserted to preform the fingering to its correct diameter before fitting a real valve. It should be pointed out that the soldering can be done without a dummy valve, but it is considerably more difficult. If attempted, care should be taken not to leave any solder on the inside of the fingering before the valve is fitted.

Polythene, or preferably ptfe, sheet 0·005–0·010in thick and cut to shape is used as insulation between the anode plate and the cavity body. Polythene is unsuitable at anode voltages

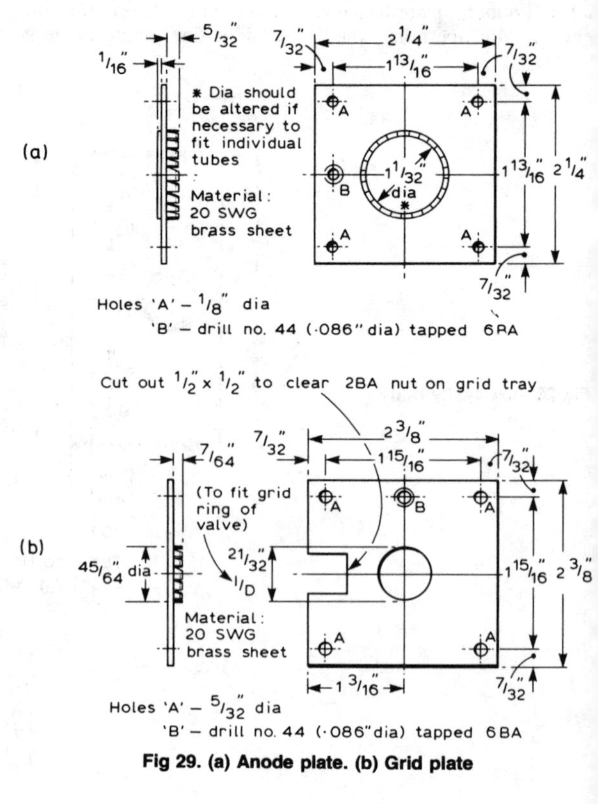

Fig 29. (a) Anode plate. (b) Grid plate

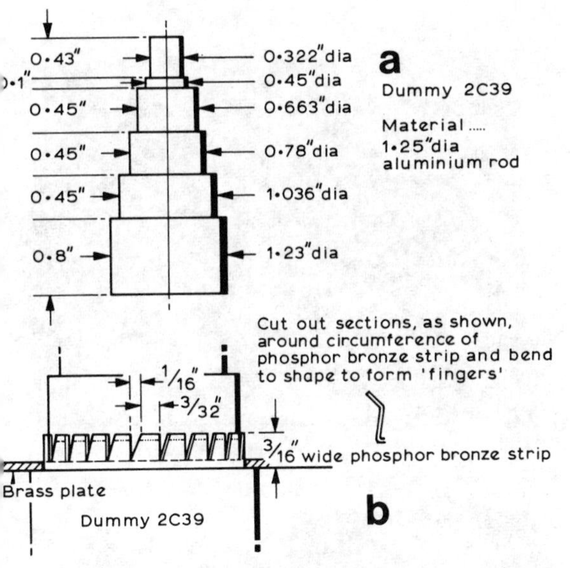

g 30. (a) Details of dummy 2C39. (b) Construction of fingering

bove 600V. Between the grid plate and the grid tray, a similar heet of polythene or ptfe is used.

The coaxial input socket is mounted on the bracket shown in ig 31 and this is held on to the side wall of the cavity by means f two of the screws which hold the grid tray in position. The ead from the coaxial socket to the cathode of the valve is made rom thin copper strip $\frac{3}{8}$in wide. If copper strip is not available, rass may be used so long as it is thin. It is important that the ead be not too rigid as otherwise there may be a danger of amaging the valve.

The input inductance (see L1 in Fig 23) consists of a length of rass or copper strip, $2\frac{11}{16}$in long by $\frac{3}{16}$in wide, formed into a U vith arms of equal length. With the base of the cavity upper- nost, this U-shaped inductance is inverted and soldered at one nd to the coaxial socket, and at the other end to the 3–30pF hilips trimmer. The earthy end of this trimmer is soldered to a ag located under one of the two 6BA screws in the corner of the rid tray farthest away from the coaxial input socket.

The 2·2kΩ grid resistor is soldered to a tag secured by a short BA screw to the centre of one side of the grid plate. It is articularly important that this screw, and its counterpart on he anode plate, are filed off flush with the underside of the late, otherwise the insulation will be damaged, and a short- ircuit may occur.

Adjustments and operating conditions

Connect the 9V bias supply to the valve with a 0–50mA meter n series with the negative lead. Apply a 6V source, capable of upplying 1A, to the heater of the valve. Do not attempt to pply ht at this stage, but connect the anode of the valve from he solder tag on the anode plate via a 100mA meter to the avity body.

If 432MHz drive is applied to the cathode, grid current will low, and some anode current will show on the 100mA meter. The trimmer C1 and the inductance L1 should be adjusted to ive maximum grid current. This should be in the region of 25mA. The earthing point of the trimmer may need changing to a different point on the grid tray if insufficient grid current is noted. There are a number of combinations of the capacitance of C1 and the inductance of L1 which will give resonance at 432MHz; the correct ratio of these two is quite critical in order to achieve maximum drive to the tripler. Once the grid current is of the correct order, then the meter in the anode circuit should read between 30 and 60mA.

When a suitable level of grid current has been achieved, attention can be turned to resonating the anode cavity. For this it is necessary to have some means of indicating 1·3GHz output. A suitable "in line" power indicator is described below in Fig 47.

First, set the tuning paddle to an angle of 45° to the axis of the valve. Preset the 2BA tuning screw to about half penetration. Slightly loosen the grid tray fixing screws and then carefully move the grid tray in and out until resonance is found. At resonance, a small dip in anode current should occur and some rf output should be observed on the power indicator. Lock the grid tray in position and check that resonance can still be obtained using the 2BA tuning screws and/or the paddle. The anode may now be disconnected from the chassis and taken to a supply of about 350V positive via an rf choke. The anode current may lie anywhere between 50 and 100mA, depending on the valve. The angle and penetration of the output probe may then be adjusted for maximum output. After such adjustment the anode cavity will need retuning. The position of the valve in the cavity may also be optimized for best signal power output.

Acceptable levels of amplitude modulation may be achieved by modulating only the 432MHz drive to the 1·3GHz tripler. For cw operation, the 432MHz stage can be keyed: under key-up conditions the anode current in the tripler should fall to zero.

A strip-line tripler for 1·3GHz

The schematic circuit diagram for this form of tripler is given in Fig 32. As can be seen from the general arrangement shown in Fig 33, and the two photographs, the amount of engineering required is rather less than for the cavity described in the previous section.

Construction

The anode circuit is enclosed in a standard die-cast box $4\frac{5}{8}$ by $3\frac{3}{8}$ by $2\frac{1}{4}$in. The lid is replaced by a copper or brass plate, $\frac{1}{16}$in thick, with a U-shaped screen of the same material soldered to the new plate as shown in the photographs. Dimensions of the plate and of the anode and grid circuits are given in Fig 34.

The plate forming the anode strip-line is mounted $\frac{13}{16}$in above the chassis plate by two insulated pillars, and the ht supply to this is connected to a tag under one of the fixings, through the rf

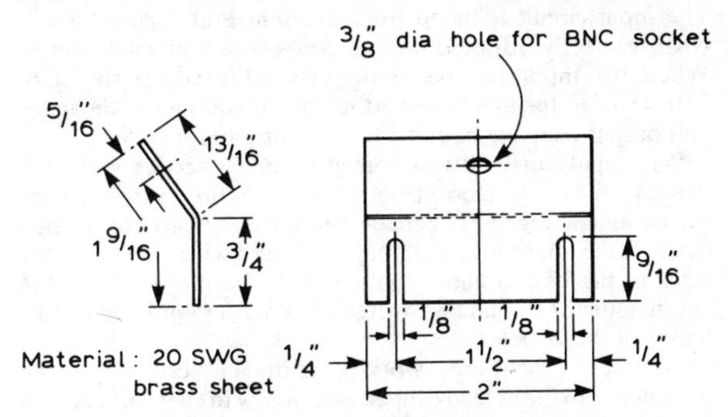

Fig 31. Bracket for input connector

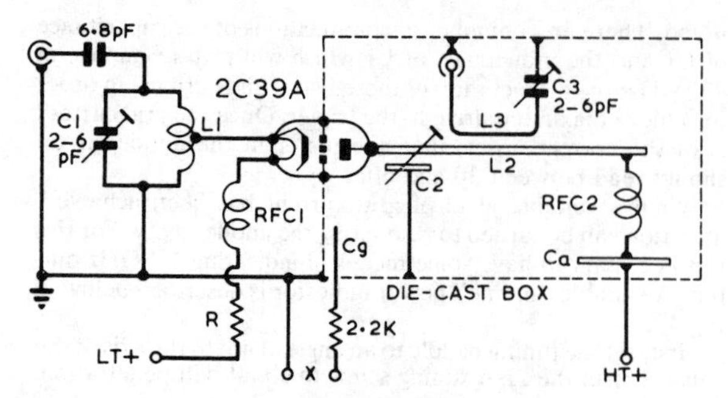

Fig 32. 2C39A stripline tripler to 1·3GHz

choke (RFC2) to the ht bypass capacitor centre fixing screw insulated under the plate, through the plate to the supply socket.

The grid, which is at rf earth potential, is connected to a 2in square plate insulated from chassis and fixed by three nylon and one metal screws. Note that the insulation is on the underside.

The screw is connected to the 2·2kΩ resistor, which is in turn connected to the chassis plate. When it is required to read grid current, this connection is lifted off and a meter connected between it and the chassis plate. The insulation of both the ht and grid bypass capacitors is 0·004/6in thick ptfe or other similar material.

As can be seen from the top view photograph, the input circuit L1, C1 is fitted into the top left-hand corner close to the valve and the input socket. Contact to the valve anode and grid is made by use of a phosphor-bronze fingering $\frac{7}{32}$in long soldered to the anode and grid plates. The fingering should face the same direction.

It is necessary to get a good rf seal between the chassis plate and the die-cast box if good efficiency is to be obtained. Copper foil (0·1mm thick) folded into four layers and used as a gasket has been found to be very effective in doing this.

An alternative output coupling arrangement which has been found to give a higher output in some cases is shown in Fig 35. A single-hole fixing BNC socket is mounted in the position previously specified for C3, and the original hole for the output socket is blanked off. The output probe is a strip of copper, the coupling of which is adjusted by rotating the socket. Optimum coupling is with the probe approximately half-meshed.

Adjustment

For full-power operation, a drive power of 10W is required. The input circuit is tuned for maximum grid current, which when correctly adjusted should be between 30 and 40mA. When the input has been properly adjusted, apply ht of 250–450V to the anode and adjust the anode tuning capacitor and output coupling circuit for maximum output.

With inputs up to 50W no forced cooling is needed, but if the valve is to be operated at its full input rating, provision for forced-air cooling must be made. Since the die-cast box forms a cavity at the operating frequency, any holes which are cut in the sides of the box to allow cooling air to be blown across the anode radiator should be covered with mesh to prevent disturbance of the rf field.

For local short-range working, sufficient output can be obtained with the ht lead connected directly to chassis, ie at zero anode voltage.

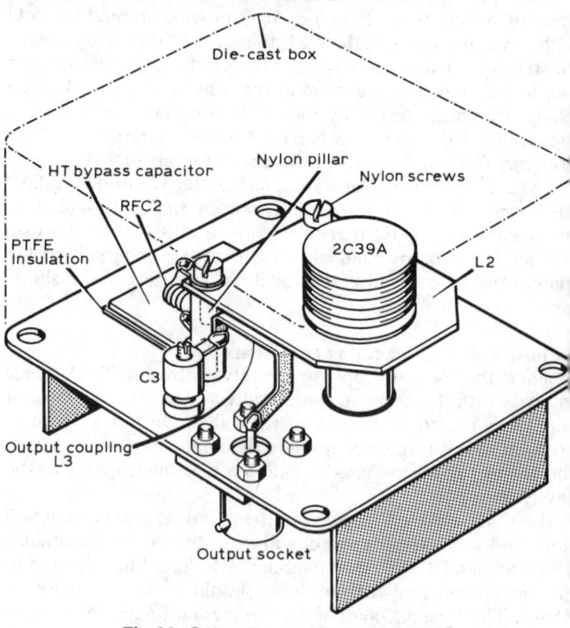

Fig 33. General arrangement of tripler

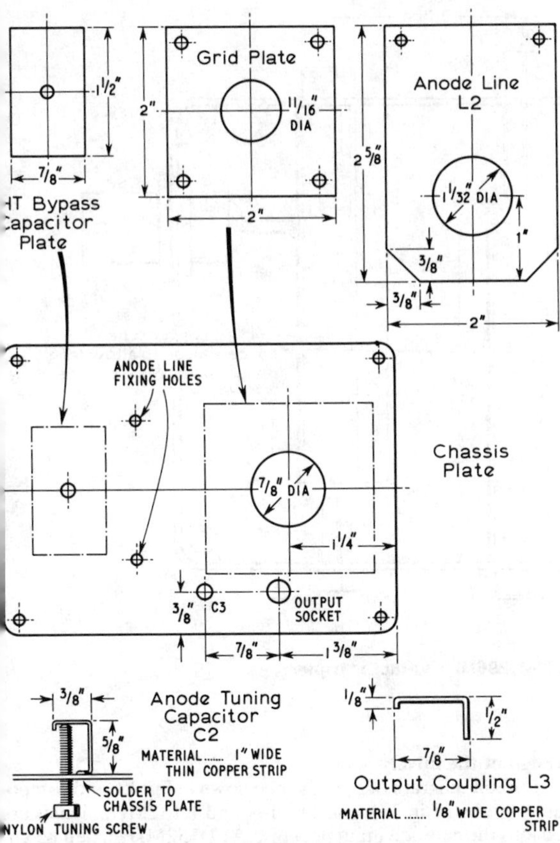

Fig 34. Construction details of anode and grid circuit

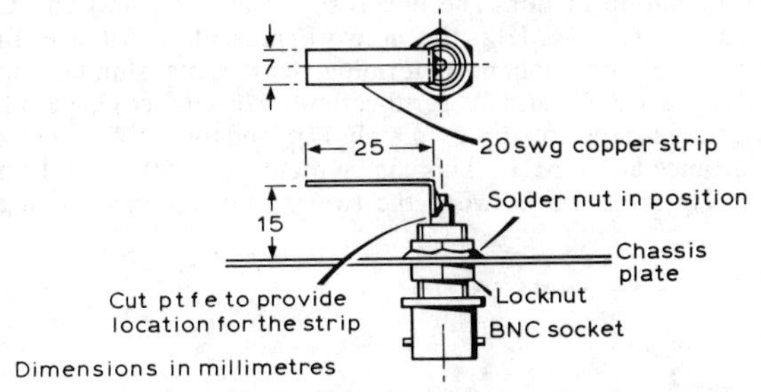

Fig 35. An alternative output probe

A low-power varactor tripler for 1·3GHz

The unit is built into a 4½ by 2½in die-cast box with a thick dividing screen separating the input circuit from the double-tuned output filter.

Details of the circuit and component layout are shown in Figs 36 and 37 respectively. L1, C1 and C2 form the input matching circuit while C3 and L2 form a series-resonant circuit to provide a low-impedance input to the varactor diode. C4 and its connection form a second-harmonic shunt circuit to provide an idler circuit.

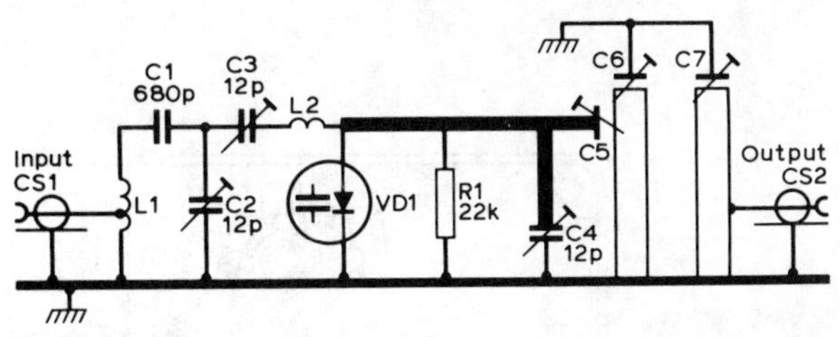

Fig 36. Circuit of a low-power varactor tripler. L1: 2t 18swg, tap ¾t from ground, 0·8in diam. L2: 1t 18swg $\frac{3}{16}$in diam. VD1: BXY37D equivalent

Construction

The input matching components are bolted through the base of the die-cast box together with the earthing tag under C4. Another earthing tag is screwed in a convenient position for L1.

The varactor diode is mounted in a bar of aluminium which forms a screen across the box. The diode is held between a copper screw in the screen and the brass block holding the 6BA filter coupling screw. Several different case styles exist for suitable varactors, and some slight modification of the diode mounting assembly may be necessary if a different diode is used to that shown in the prototype.

Using a BXY37D an output of 900mW for an input of 2·5W should be obtained.

Adjustment

This is best carried out with the aid of a spectrum analyser. For those with access to this equipment no details need be given, but a rough alignment can be achieved using the following procedure.

Equipment needed:

- 3W source of 432MHz
- Diode detector
- 10dB attenuator capable of taking the full output
- High-Q break or good 1·3GHz filter
- DC amplifier for diode detector

A good attenuator of about 10dB is 20yd of UR43 coaxial cable. Connect the tripler to the attenuator through a filter and monitor the output on the diode detector and dc amplifier. Ideally, a 50Ω 10dB pad feeding a coaxial diode mount is required to minimize mismatch effects.

Apply about 0·5W of 432MHz and tune the output filter screws on the 1·3GHz tripler until some output is detected. Increase the output to maximum by tuning the input matching capacitors and the second-harmonic rejection trimmer. When these adjustments have produced the best output, increase the coupling into the filter by screwing in the filter coupling screw through the access hole in the side of the box. Repeat the output filter tuning and input match tuning until maximum output power is obtained. Always retune all the trimmers and output filter after making a coupling adjustment as any alteration in coupling will detune the output filter and give an apparent loss of power before retuning.

Once the unit has been adjusted for its maximum output with 0·5W input, the power may be increased to 3W, but re-adjustment will be needed at the higher power input.

Generation of single-sideband on 1·3GHz

As on lower frequencies, the single-sideband mode is now used quite extensively for phone communication on 1·3GHz. The most practical way (for home construction) of generating

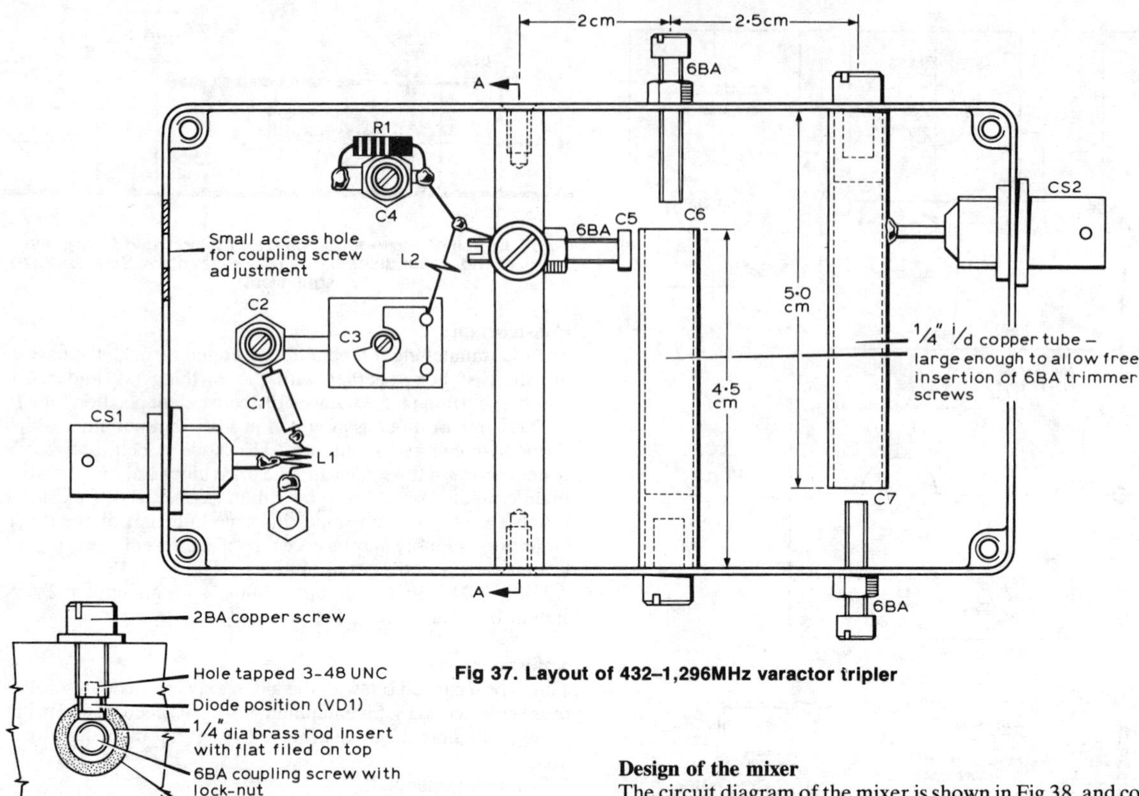

Fig 37. Layout of 432–1,296MHz varactor tripler

single-sideband at this frequency is to use the high-level mixing technique. The equipment described consists of a mixer and a linear amplifier, both using 2C39A valves, the combination being capable of at least 50W p.e.p. output.

The inputs to the mixer are 1,152MHz (local oscillator) and 144MHz. This combination is preferable to mixing 1,268MHz with 28MHz, due to the greater separation between the wanted signal and the spurious products, making filtering much easier.

Design of the mixer

The circuit diagram of the mixer is shown in Fig 38, and components are listed in Table 4. The 144 and 1,152MHz signals are fed into the cathode input network. At 1,152MHz it behaves as a $\lambda/2$ line, with one end held at zero rf potential by C2, and the other end connected to the cathode of the 2C39. This brings the cathode itself to a low rf potential and minimizes any tendency to oscillation at uhf. The line is tuned by C3 (fine) and C4 (coarse). At 144MHz, the network presents resistance and capacitance components determined by the total shunt capacitance C2, C3, C4 and C_{gk} (grid-cathode capacitance) in parallel with a resistance of approximately $1/g_m$ and the 1·3GHz choke reactance at 144MHz. This can be matched to 50Ω by C1 and L1. The isolation between the two input frequencies is high

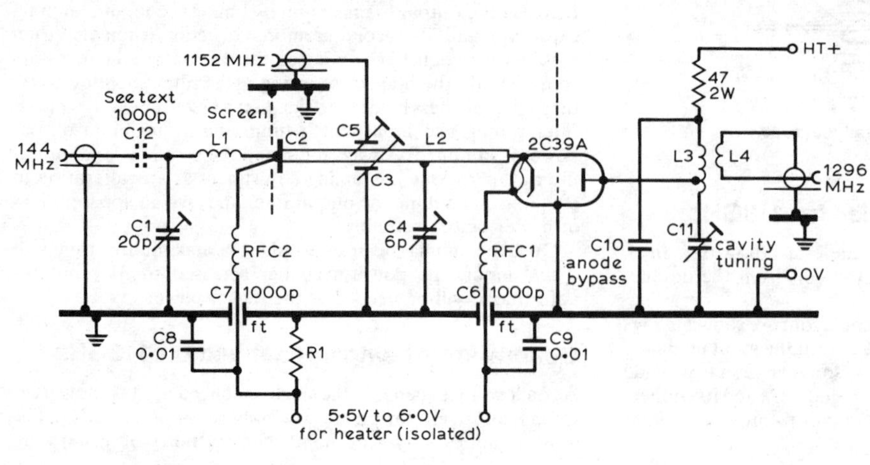

Fig 38. Circuit of 2C39A ssb mixer for 1·3GHz

Table 4. Components list for ssb mixer

1	20pF Mullard ceramic tubular trimmer
2	20pF homemade capacitor
3	$\frac{3}{8}$in dia disc carried by 2BA screw
4	6pF Mullard ceramic tubular trimmer
5	Brass tab (see Fig 40(c))
6, C7	1,000pF feed-through
8, C9	0·01μF ceramic discs with very short leads (144MHz bypass to reduce radiation)
10	Anode bypass
11	Cavity tuning see (Fig 27)
12	1,000pF disc ceramic (see text)
1	3t 18swg copper wire $\frac{5}{16}$in i.d.
2	1,152MHz input line
3	Anode cavity
4	Output loop
FC1, RFC2	8t 22swg enam copper close wound on $\frac{1}{8}$in mandrel
1	Chosen to give 20–30mA standing current (typically 100–270Ω with 400V ht)

since the variables C3 and C4 are small compared to the total shunt capacitance.

Since the valve is operated in a grounded-grid configuration, bias voltage is developed between cathode and earth across R1. This voltage is present on both the heater supply and the 144MHz input socket, and care must be taken not to short it out. An isolated heater supply must therefore be used, and there must not be a dc short to earth in the output network of the 144MHz exciter. If the latter is not the case, a 1,000pF disc ceramic capacitor with short leads should be connected in series with the 144MHz input.

Construction of the mixer

The cathode circuitry is shown in Fig 39. It is built into a trough section box, the bending and drilling details of which are shown in Fig 40(a). A tight-fitting lid is recommended to reduce 144MHz radiation. A screen, shown in Fig 40(b), is soldered into the trough and serves as one part of C2. Fig 40(d) shows the 1,152MHz line with the brass disc serving as the other half of C2.

The spring-clip cathode connection is made from thin springy brass sheet. A convenient heater connection can be fabricated from an old wander plug insert, cut short and bent outwards to form a good fit. It is important not to leave too large a blob of solder on the plug when soldering on the heater choke, as the solder may melt under fault conditions (particularly if the cathode is not forced-air cooled) and short out the heater supply.

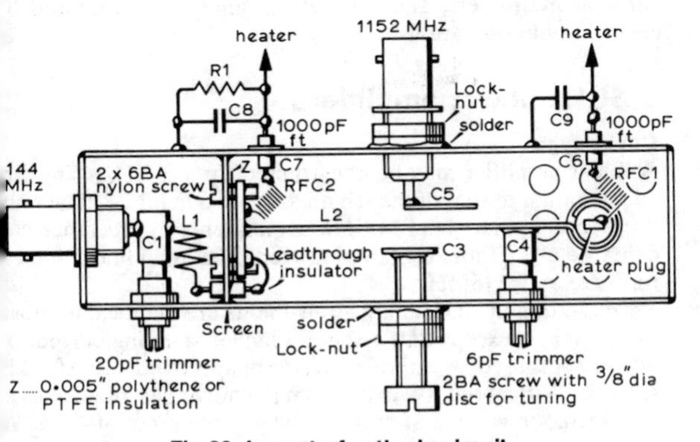

Fig 39. Layout of cathode circuit

X..... Bend up at 90° and solder four corners

Hole 'A'.....clearance for trimmer 'B'.....2BA clearance
'C'.....3/8"dia 'D'.....3/16"dia 'E'.....6BA clearance
'F'.....clearance for leadthrough insulator
'G'.....clearance for 1000pF feedthrough capacitor
Material...... 18 or 20swg brass or copper unless otherwise stated

Fig 40. Details of the construction of (a) the trough, (b) the screen, (c) the input tab, and (d) the input line

The anode cavity is the same as that used in the cavity-type tripler described above in Fig 24. Since the grid bypass capacitor is not required, the grid fingering is soldered directly into the grid tray. A $\frac{21}{32}$in hole should therefore be punched in the grid tray instead of the $\frac{7}{8}$in hole shown above.

The mounting of the trough assembly above the grid tray of the anode cavity is shown in Fig 41. The bracket is necessary both electrically and mechanically and should not be omitted.

Tuning and adjustment

Apply 5·5 to 6·0V to the heater and +400V to the anode, and ensure that there is adequate forced-air cooling to the latter. The anode current should be set to approximately 20mA by varying R1. A value of 270Ω should be found suitable for initial tests. Some 2–3W of 1,152MHz drive should then be applied, and the 6pF trimmer adjusted for maximum anode current. Fine tuning may be accomplished by adjusting the 2BA screw. The input matching can be optimized by bending the input tab to vary its spacing from the line and then retuning. When the anode current has been maximized it should be around 50-60mA. Leaving the 1,152MHz drive connected, apply 5–8W of 144MHz cw drive and adjust the 20pF trimmer for lowest input vswr. The anode current should then be around 80–100mA.

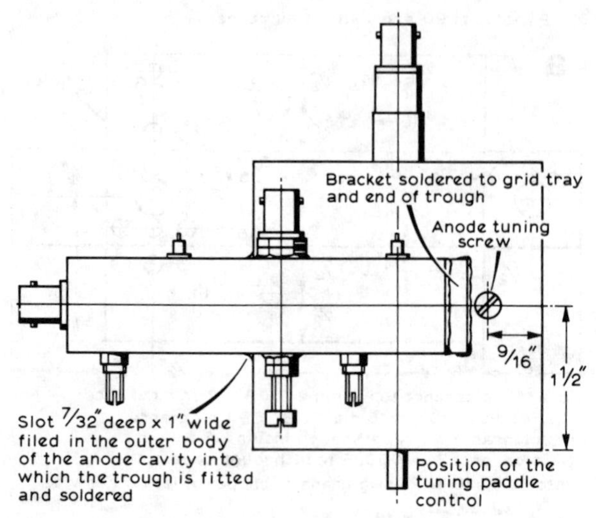

Fig 41. Location of the input circuitry on the anode cavity

Some form of power-indicating device terminated by a dummy load is then connected to the output socket. A suitable dummy load may be made from 50ft or more of thin (½in or less) 50Ω coaxial cable, terminated by a resistor which may be conveniently mounted inside a BNC plug or in-line socket. Bulbs are not generally suitable for dummy loads at 1·3GHz.

The output probe and tuning paddle are rotated so that they are at an angle of 45° to the axis of the valve, and the anode tuning screw adjusted for maximum output. If the cavity does not resonate, the grid tray can be moved as described above. Once resonance is achieved, the output matching may be optimized by altering both the penetration and angle of the output probe. The tuning paddle can then be used for fine tuning, eg to correct for warm-up drift. As a final check, ensure that virtually all output indication disappears when the 1,152MHz drive is removed. If this does not happen it is possible that the anode cavity has been resonated to 1,152MHz by mistake. This should not be possible, however, if the cavity dimensions have been adhered to.

When the unit is operating correctly, the ht voltage may be increased up to about 800V for a used valve, or 1,000V if a new ceramic valve is employed. Since the efficiency of the mixer is only about 10 per cent, adequate cooling is vital to prolong valve life. A cw output of 3–4W should be obtained with 400V ht and, with 1,000V, 10W has been achieved.

SSB operation with the mixer is quite straightforward, and the maximum 144MHz drive is about 5–10W p.e.p. Signal-quality reports have been very favourable: there is apparently no audible difference in the quality of the 1·3GHz ssb compared to the 144MHz drive.

If it is intended to use the mixer itself as a transmitter, a filter should be used between the mixer and the antenna. A suitable design is given in Fig 46 which will give adequate rejection at 1,152MHz, and also at the image frequency of 1,008MHz.

1,152MHz drivers

The ssb mixer described in the previous section requires a few watts of drive at 1,152MHz. A valve tripler and a varactor tripler are described below.

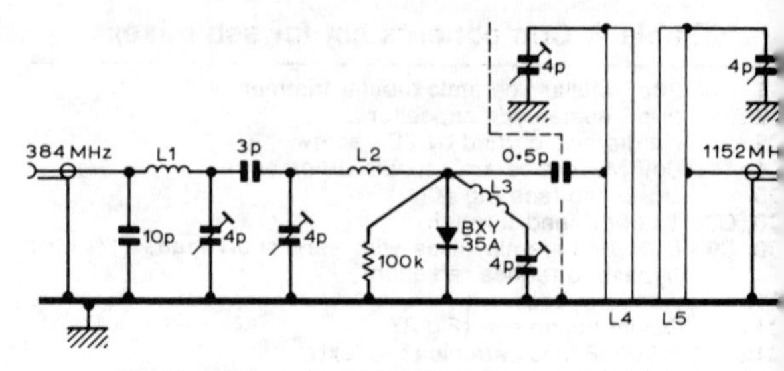

Fig 42. Circuit of a 384/1,152 MHz varactor tripler

A 384/1,152MHz valve tripler

A suitable 1,152MHz exciter can consist of a driver delivering 6–7W at 384MHz to a 2C39A tripler. Suitable starting frequencies for the oscillator are 42·6667, 48 or 96MHz, with output stages using transistors, varactors, or valves such as the QQV03–20A. There are a number of 432MHz designs which can be modified for 384MHz. A suitable starting point would be the local oscillator shown in Fig 7 followed by one or two stages of amplification.

A successful 2C39A tripler was based on the cavity design given in Fig 24 but with the following changes in dimensions to reduce the operating frequency to 1,152MHz.

Anode cavity: 3$\frac{3}{8}$in square
Grid tray: 3$\frac{11}{16}$in square
Anode bypass plate: 2½in square
Grid bypass plate: 2$\frac{5}{8}$in square

The remainder of the circuitry was the same as described earlier, except that the input inductance was increased in length to 3in.

A 384/1,152MHz varactor tripler

A design for a varactor tripler is shown in Figs 42 and 43. The BXY35A varactor employed, which is available on the surplus market, has a maximum input rating of 30W and as a tripler should generate 5 to 10W: for an input of 4W at 384MHz, just over 1W at 1,152MHz should be obtained.

The original unit was built in an RS Components die-cast box, type 993. The corresponding Eddystone box is about ⅛in smaller all round, and if this type is used the dimensions of lines L4 and L5 can be shortened. If this is done it is possible that the unit may also be tuned up as a 432/1,296MHz tripler. The 4pF tuning capacitors used were type 82025–4E.

As noted earlier, great care is required in the aligning of varactor multipliers, and a spectrum analyser is required to ensure stable operation.

1·3GHz power amplifiers

Cavity type

A linear amplifier may be constructed for 1·3GHz using circuitry similar to that of the ssb mixer shown in Fig 38. The only difference is that the 144MHz components in the input circuitry, ie C1, L1 and C4, are removed. The input line will then resonate at 1,296MHz.

The setting up and tuning adjustments are identical to those of the mixer, except that a slightly higher standing current of 40–50mA is used. A cathode resistor of approximately 100Ω is suitable. With about 8W drive from the mixer described above, and an anode voltage of 800V, a cw power output of 45–50W has been achieved with nearly 50 per cent efficiency.

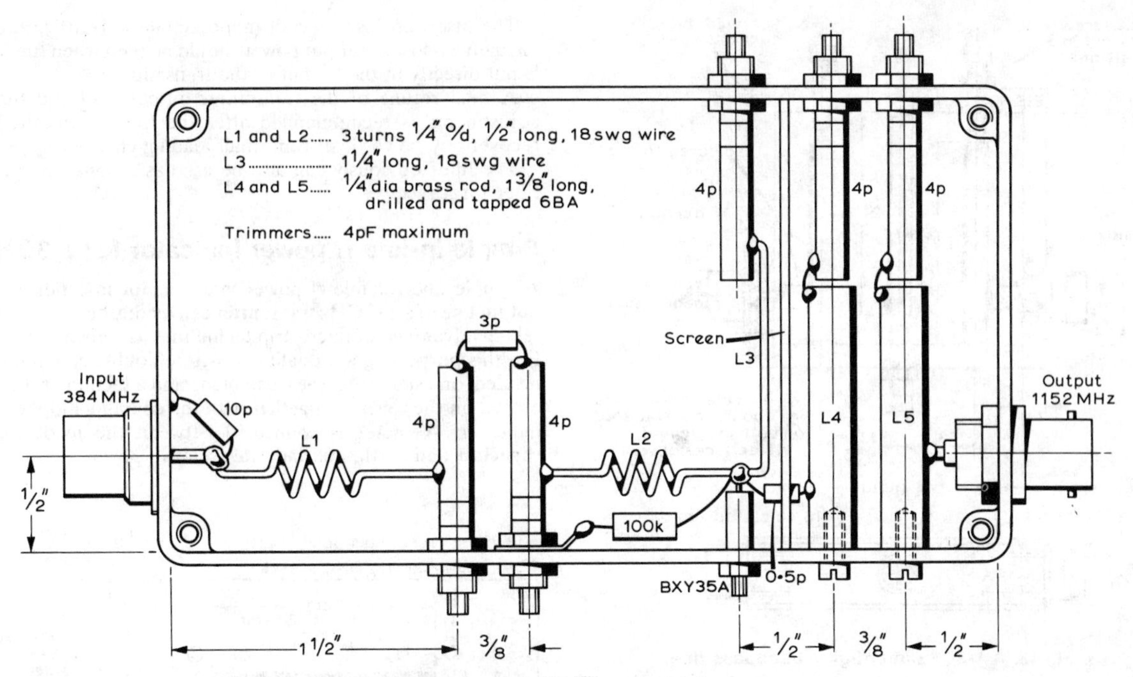

Fig 43. Layout of the varactor tripler

Strip-line type

The schematic circuit diagram and the layout of the amplifier are shown in Figs 44 and 45. These involve only changes to the input circuitry of the tripler shown in Fig 32.

The modifications involved are as follows:

(a) The anode circuitry remains essentially unchanged except that the thickness of the insulation of the decoupling capacitor C_a should be increased to 0·008 to 0·012in if the higher ht voltages are used.

(b) The grid is connected directly to the chassis via fingering soldered to the inside of an $\frac{11}{16}$in hole drilled in the chassis plate. This arrangement results in much increased gain compared with when the grid is decoupled by a capacitor.

(c) The input circuitry consists of a pi-network, the inductance L_A of which is optimized by changing the thickness of wire used to produce the maximum anode current for a given level of drive. L_K is a $\lambda/4$ choke, one end of which is joined both to the heater/cathode connection of the

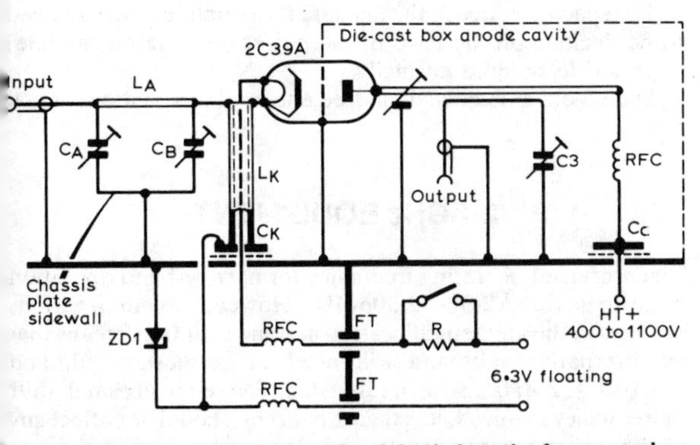

Fig 44. Circuit of a 1·3GHz amplifier. LA: 1in length of copper wire, diameter $\frac{1}{8}$in. LK: $\lambda/4$ cathode line 1$\frac{3}{4}$in long $\frac{1}{8}$in diameter brass or copper tube. CA, CB: approximately 20pF, $\frac{1}{2}$in square plate with 0·002in insulation clamped to chassis with a nylon screw or a 22pF ceramic chip capacitor. ZD1: high-power zener diode, voltage 5–14V, selected to give anode current of 5–10mA with ht applied but no drive. RFC: 7t $\frac{1}{8}$in diameter 22swg enamelled copper wire

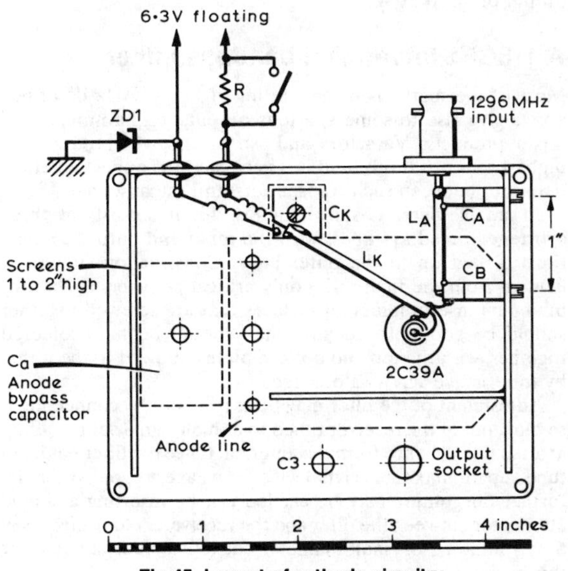

Fig 45. Layout of cathode circuitry

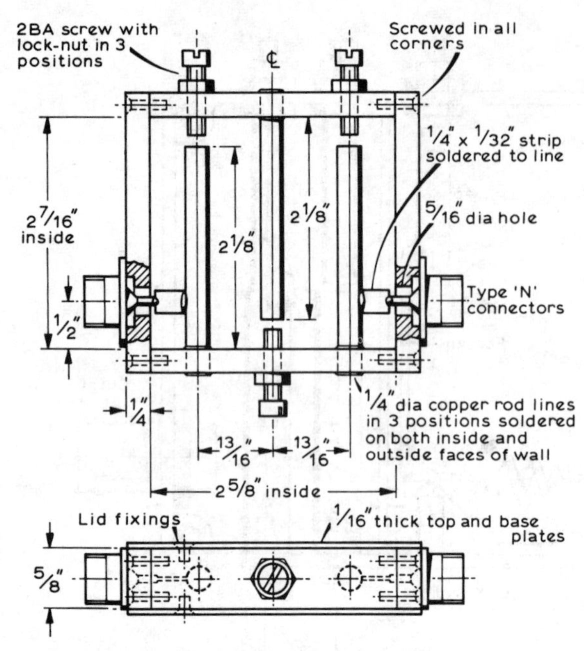

Fig 46. A 1·3GHz interdigital bandpass filter

valve and to C_B/L_A, and the other end is decoupled by C_K. The wire to the heater connection runs through the tube comprising L_K. A consequence of earthing the grid is that a "floating" heater supply is necessary. Note that the inner of the input coaxial connector is "live" at the bias voltage of the cathode, and a suitable isolating capacitor may be necessary with some drivers. The resistor in the heater line should reduce the voltage to 5·5 when the ht is applied.

The amplifier should have a gain of about 10dB and an output of up to 50W.

A 1·3GHz interdigital bandpass filter

Most of the methods of generating rf at 1·3GHz described above give rise to some spurious outputs, eg harmonics and mixer products. Varactors and ssb mixers will produce the highest spurious levels, and it is necessary to connect an effective filter between such transmitters and the antenna.

A suitable filter is shown in Fig 46. It consists of three shortened tuned λ/4 lines, with the input and output connections tapped on to the outer lines. Construction should be evident from the figure, the only critical point being that for minimum insertion loss all surfaces that are screwed together should be good fits. Ideally, they should be hard-soldered together, with the top and bottom plates screwed to the frame by four or five screws along each side.

Adjustment of the filter may be carried out by connecting it to the input of the receiver tuned to a small signal source set up at a suitable distance from the antenna. Once the filter has been tuned up for maximum signal with the weakest signal available, further fine tuning may be carried out by inserting a simple attenuator between the filter and the receiver. A long piece, say 5 or 10m long, of small-diameter coaxial cable is suitable for this purpose.

The insertion loss is small (approximately 0·5dB), and so virtually no loss of output power should be seen when the filter is put directly in the output of the transmitter.

A final retune of the transmitter output load and tuning adjustments is recommended after the filter is installed to recover any power lost from small loading changes.

The filter obviously can also be used as a signal-frequency filter for a receiver.

Simple in-line rf power indicator for 1·3GHz

A simple and reliable rf power indicator for insertion in the output line of a 1·3GHz transmitter can readily be constructed, taking advantage of microstrip techniques as shown in Fig 47. For this purpose, good-quality glassfibre double-clad board is needed, one side being the earth plane and a section of the line etched on the reverse, together with the coupling loop for the indicator. A meter is connected between the feedthrough capacitor and earth, and indicates relative power.

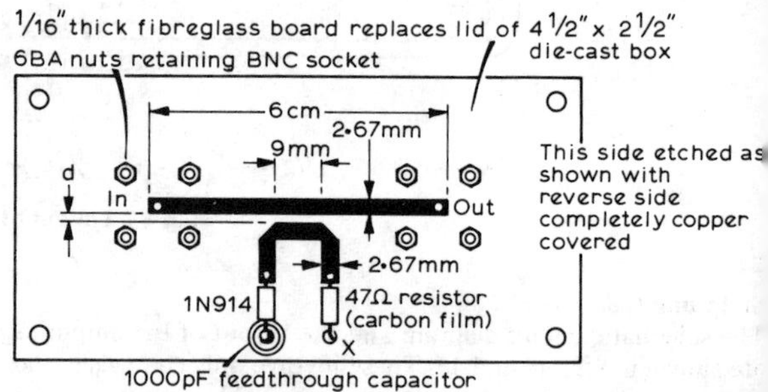

Fig 47. A simple forward power indicator. A germanium diode can be used if better sensitivity is desired

The insertion loss of this type of indicator is of the order of 0·5dB, and it may therefore be left permanently in circuit.

The spacing between the line and the coupling loop will need to be decided on the basis of the power (voltage on the line) expected to be used normally.

The whole assembly should be enclosed in a suitable metal box.

2·3GHz EQUIPMENT

The preferred operating frequency for narrow-band operation hitherto has been 2,304–2,306MHz. However, as noted earlier, changes in the amateur allocation in some countries means that an alternative sub-band will need to be designated, and 2,320–2,322MHz has been suggested. The relatively small shift in frequency involved, less than 1 per cent, should not affect any of the design information given below.

2·3GHz interdigital converter

A successful interdigital converter for 2·3GHz is described with the 1·3GHz version, to which reference should be made.

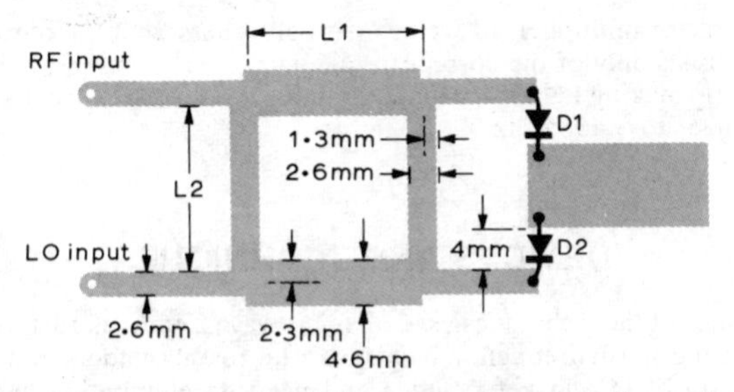

Fig 48. Branched-arm 3dB hybrid balanced mixer dimensions for $\frac{1}{16}$ in glassfibre pcb, ϵ = 5·5. For 1·3GHz, L1 = 29mm and L2 = 28mm; for 2·3GHz, L1 = 17mm and L2 16mm; for 3·4GHz, L1 = 11·5mm and L2 = 11mm

Balanced mixers for 1·3, 2·3 and 3·4GHz

A simple microstrip branched-arm 30dB hybrid balanced mixer for operation on 1·3, 2·3 or 3·4GHz may be made from standard glassfibre double-clad copper pc board. The latter should have a thickness of $\frac{1}{16}$in and a dielectric constant $\epsilon = 5\cdot5$. The dimensions of the mixer are given in Fig 48. The circuit of a suitable RC coupled i.f. preamplifier is shown in Fig 49. This has a bandwidth of 10MHz at 70MHz and a gain of approximately 24dB, with a noise figure of about 2dB.

This type of mixer is broadband. It is therefore necessary to fit a suitable filter between it and any preamplifier if the overall signal-to-noise ratio is not to be degraded.

A 2·3GHz signal source

The unit shown in Fig 50 is a ×16 multiplier which generates 2,304MHz from 300–500mW drive at 144MHz. The multiplier is built on a double-sided pcb which forms the lid of a standard 3·6 by 1·5 by 1·2in Eddystone die-cast box. The unit is aligned by applying the 144MHz drive and tuning C1 and C2 to peak the diode current at approximately 30mA. The output line is tuned using the 4BA screw which constitutes C3.

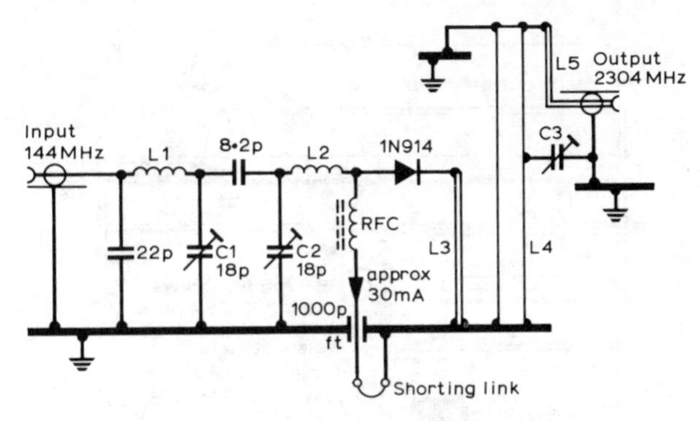

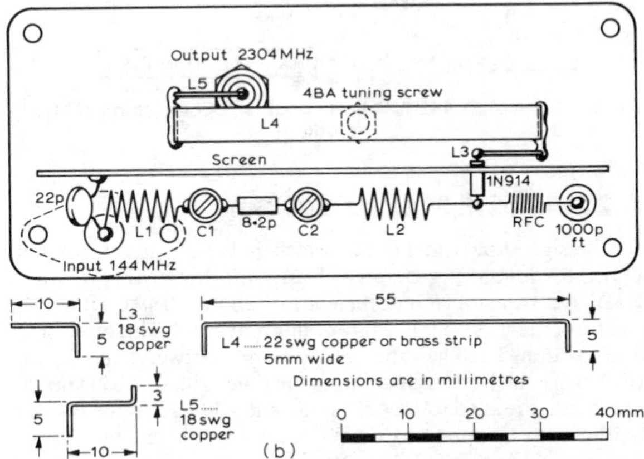

Fig 50. Signal source for 2,304MHz. L1: 4t 20swg enam copper wire ¼in i.d. L2: 5t ditto. C1, C2: 18pF tubular trimmer. RFC: 3t 22swg enam copper wire on ferrite bead. C3: 4BA screw in nut soldered to pcb

A simple 1,152/2,304MHz doubler

The doubler shown in Fig 51 consists of two troughs 1in wide and 1in deep bolted together, one being tuned to 1,152MHz and the second to 2,304MHz. The $\lambda/2$ lines are set centrally in the troughs and are tuned by 0BA screws running through nuts soldered to the bottom of the troughs. The multiplier diode is a single 1N914 (1S44) which passes through a small hole drilled through the common wall of the troughs. The doubler is driven by a QQV02–6 amplifier at 384MHz followed by a BXY35C tripler to 1,152MHz. Using a 4ft dish fed via 40ft of UR67 cable, which will have a loss of several decibels, signals have been received five miles away at S9 plus.

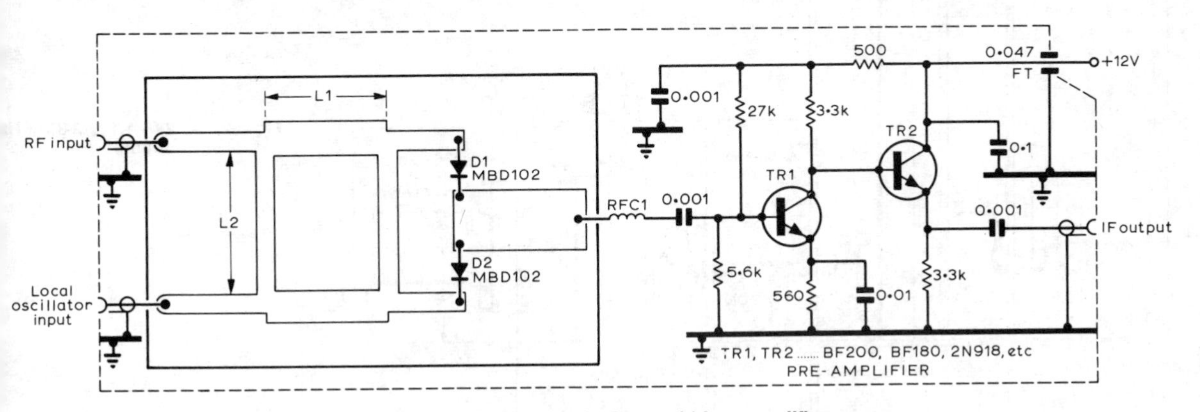

Fig 49. Hybrid balanced mixer and i.f. preamplifier

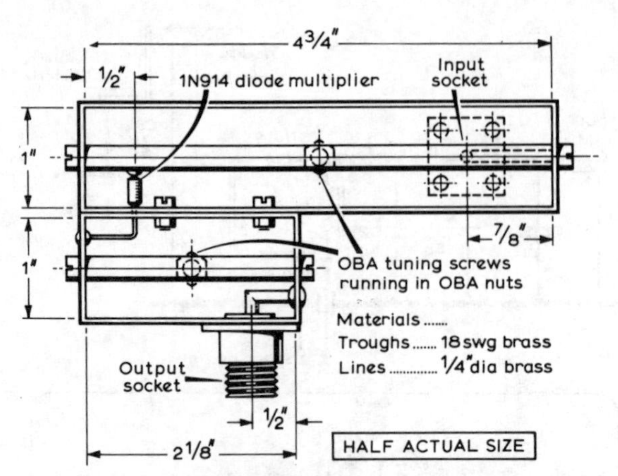

Fig 51. A simple 1,152/2,304MHz doubler circuit using a 1N914 diode

A 2W 1,152/2,304MHz doubler

The design shown in Fig 52, which is based on the original G3LQR doubler, generates 1–2W at 2,304MHz from a BXY36C varactor at an efficiency of about 60 per cent.

The doubler is built in a box of internal depth 1in, fitted with a close-fitting lid. The varactor is mounted between line L2 and the base of the box: one end fits in the hole drilled in L2, and the other in a threaded rod set in a large nut soldered to the bottom of the box. Coupling to the varactor is adjusted by a 10pF trimmer, while that to L3 is taken by an adjustable tab soldered to the end of L2. The output is taken via a capacitor fabricated on the end of the BNC connector: both these tabs should be carefully adjusted for maximum output.

Tuning of the input and output lines can be done with 2BA screws as shown but, if screws with a finer thread are available, then they are to be preferred. Great care must be taken with this varactor multiplier, as well as with all others, that the output consists only of the correct frequency.

By making L3 0·51in long, the same design can be used as a tripler to 3,456MHz.

DEVICES AND TECHNIQUES

Many of the techniques used on microwaves, particularly those on the lower frequency bands, can be readily understood in terms of hf and vhf practice and need no elaboration here. However, there are many other techniques used which are peculiar to microwaves, and it is the exploration and exploitation of these which provides part of the fascination and challenge of these frequencies.

Some of the techniques employed professionally are most sophisticated and would be out of place in a handbook such as this, so that the techniques to be described here will be restricted to those which are part of current amateur practice.

Waveguide

The principal function of waveguide is to carry rf signals from one part of a system to another in a relatively loss-free way. In this respect it performs a similar function to coaxial cable at lower frequencies. It differs from coaxial cable in the following ways:

- Waveguide has a comparatively low loss, usually one or two orders of magnitude lower than coaxial cables when used at the same frequency.
- The minimum cross-section of a waveguide is related to the frequency of use, and is of the order of a wavelength. A particular size of guide cannot therefore be used below a critical frequency, and usually is not operated above twice this frequency. The frequency of use of coaxial cable, on the other hand, is virtually unlimited from dc upwards.

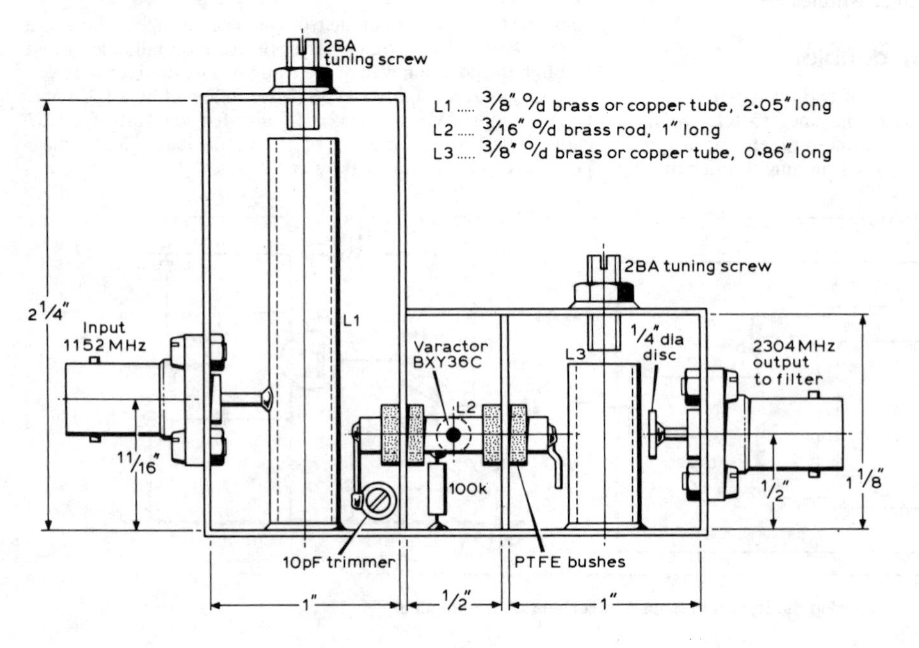

Fig 52. A 2W 1,152/2,304MHz doubler

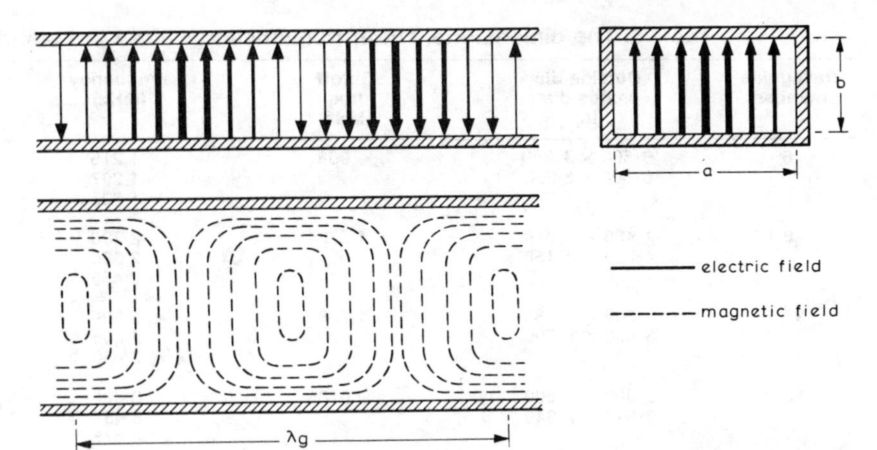

Fig 53. Electric and magnetic field configuration for the TE_{10} waveguide mode

- The physical size of waveguide is such that many components can be built inside it, or immediately around it, so that a complete rf system frequently consists of a number of individual waveguide components bolted together. This technique can of course be used in coaxial systems, but is much less common in amateur equipment.

Rectangular waveguide

The most common form of waveguide consists of a hollow pipe with a rectangular internal cross-section. It is usually made from brass because of the good mechanical properties and machinability of this material. However, copper or even silver is used when electrical losses must be kept to a minimum, or where the high thermal conductivity of these materials is necessary to dissipate heat. Aluminium and magnesium alloys are sometimes used where weight is an important factor.

Any waveguide can theoretically propagate an infinite number of electromagnetic patterns. Each type, usually called a mode, has its own electrical and magnetic field configuration, some of which can be very complicated. Fortunately, the most commonly employed mode is also one of the simplest. Because it corresponds to the lowest frequency at which the waveguide can readily propagate rf energy, it is called the *dominant mode*. In more practical terms, this mode requires a smaller waveguide for propagation than any other mode at the same frequency. Under a widely used system for describing mode configurations, it is known as the TE_{10} mode.

The electric and magnetic fields of the TE_{10} mode are shown by Fig 53. The electric field is transverse to the guide and extends between the two walls closest together. The intensity of the electric field is maximum at the centre of the guide, and drops off sinusoidally to zero intensity at the edges. The magnetic field is in the form of loops which lie in planes parallel to the broad faces of the guide. The plane of polarization is parallel to the electric field: for horizontal polarization, the broad faces of the waveguide should be vertical.

The permissible range of internal dimensions of a waveguide is related directly to the wavelength at the frequency of operation. For the dominant TE_{10} mode, the absolute minimum value of the broad internal width (a as in Fig 53) is $0 \cdot 5\lambda$, ie there must be sufficient room to fit in at least one half-wavelength. If a is made even slightly less than $0 \cdot 5\lambda$, then the attenuation is very high. The frequency at which $0 \cdot 5\lambda$ equals a is known as the *cut-off frequency* of the waveguide. The *cut-off wavelength* λ_c is obviously equal to $2a$.

The broad width of the waveguide preferably should not exceed one wavelength. If a is greater than λ, then it becomes possible to fit in more than two half-waves, with the risk of generating a basically different electromagnetic pattern, ie the waveguide can *overmode*. It is important to avoid this condition as the pattern of the electromagnetic radiation will differ between input and output ports, and devices which necessarily have to be designed to suit a particular mode may no longer work effectively.

The practical minimum size of the broad width is somewhat greater than the value $0 \cdot 5\lambda$ for the following reason. Unless the waveguide is filled with a dielectric, the wavelength within the guide at a particular frequency, λ_g, is always greater than the wavelength in free space, λ. The relationship between the two for the dominant TE_{10} mode is:

$$\lambda_g = \frac{\lambda}{\sqrt{1 - \left(\frac{\lambda}{\lambda_c}\right)^2}} = \frac{\lambda}{\sqrt{1 - \left(\frac{\lambda}{2a}\right)^2}}$$

where λ_c is the cut-off wavelength for the waveguide. It will be seen that as the value of a tends to $\lambda/2$ so λ_g tends to infinity. To avoid very large values of λ_g, which would increase both the length of components and also electrical losses, the minimum value of a is usually made about $0 \cdot 6\lambda$.

The practical maximum broad width is usually made somewhat less than a wavelength to reduce the risk of overmoding due to discontinuities within the waveguide, such as components fitted to the inside, or joints between sections. A typical maximum is $0 \cdot 95\lambda$.

The narrow internal width of the waveguide, dimension b in Fig 53, must be less than $0 \cdot 5\lambda$ since it must not be possible to fit in a half-wave in the undesired direction, otherwise the input and output signals may become cross-polarized. A typical maximum value is $0 \cdot 45\lambda$.

Waveguide is available in a range of standard sizes to cover all microwave frequencies with some overlap. Table 5 given below summarizes types suitable for the frequencies of amateur bands together with values for the cut-off frequency, and λ and λ_g at the band edges and the centre of the sub-bands adopted for narrow-band working. The maximum frequency of operation for each of the waveguides is usually made just less than twice the cut-off frequency.

A flexible form of wavelength is also available. This is used in connecting systems together where there are difficulties in

Table 5. The dimensions, cutoff frequencies, λ and λg of standard waveguides

Waveguide number	Outside dia inside dia (in)	Cutoff freq (MHz)	Frequency (MHz)	λ (mm)	λg (mm)
6	6·500 × 3·250	908	1,215	246·733	371·294
	6·500 × 3·250		1,297	231·133	323·654
			1,325	226·249	310·637
8	4·460 × 2·310	1,372	2,300	130·337	162·417
	4·300 × 2·150		2,305	130·056	161·878
			2,450	122·359	147·710
9A	3·560 × 1·860	1,736	2,300	130·337	198·635
	3·400 × 1·700		2,305	130·056	197·663
			2,450	122·359	173·361
10	3·000 × 1·500	2,078	3,400	88·169	111·391
	2·840 × 1·340		3,457	86·717	108·505
			3,475	86·266	107·626
12	2·000 × 1·000	3,152	5,650	53·058	63·933
	1·872 × 0·872		5,761	52·036	62·169
			5,850	51·244	60·831
14	1·500 × 0·750	4,301	5,650	53·058	81·821
	1·372 × 0·622		5,761	52·036	78·221
			5,850	51·244	75·601
15	1·250 × 0·625	5,259	10,000	29·978	35·246
	1·122 × 0·497		10,050	29·828	35·004
			10,369	28·911	33·547
			10,500	28·550	32·987
Old English	1·100 × 0·600 *	5,901	10,000	29·978	37·133
	1·000 × 0·500		10,050	29·828	36·849
			10,369	29·911	35·161
			10,500	28·550	34·517
16	1·000 × 0·500	6,557	10,000	29·978	39·703
	0·900 × 0·400		10,050	29·828	39·383
			10,369	28·911	37·322
			10,500	28·550	36·553
20	0·500 × 0·250	14,047	24,000	12·491	15·407
	0·420 × 0·170		24,193	12·391	15·221
			24,250	12·362	15·167
22	0·360 × 0·220	21,075	24,000	12·491	26·109
	0·280 × 0·140		24,193	12·391	25·246
			24,250	12·362	24·991

* Approximate

aligning, and is particularly useful for connecting waveguide equipment to antennas. The waveguide is constructed from thin-walled corrugated tube and is normally protected by a rubber sheath. Although it will withstand gentle flexing, rough handling can permanently increase its lossiness.

Practical aspects of waveguide

Waveguide is a precision product: its dimensions and those of associated components such as flanges are controlled within the order of 0·001in. The reason for this is that many commercial applications such as radar involve the transmission of very high powers, and even small discontinuities along the waveguide run greatly reduce its power handling capacity. This is not yet a problem in the amateur context, but the precision does greatly facilitate the construction of equipment, particularly when using hand tools.

The rule of thumb that discontinuities of less than λ/10 or λ/20 have relatively little effect may be applied to waveguide. It is therefore perfectly practical for the amateur to fabricate waveguide and flanges, and indeed this is frequently done in the construction of antennas and feeds for antennas. Care should be taken to avoid lumps or even films of solder within the guide as this material is quite lossy. Great care should also be taken to remove materials such as wire wool (which may be used for cleaning), carbonaceous matter such as flux, and also water, as these can be very lossy at microwave frequencies.

Flanges may be fitted by slipping them on to the waveguide so that a small amount protrudes, and then soldering or brazing in place. Jigging is usually not necessary. The excess waveguide may be trimmed by turning in a lathe or by milling. Alternatively, the end may be cut back by filing, and finished by rubbing on wet carbide paper on a sheet glass working surface: if care is taken not to rock the component, then an excellent flat surface will be obtained.

Waveguide flanges are usually available with either a plain face or one with a deep groove. The latter type is known as a

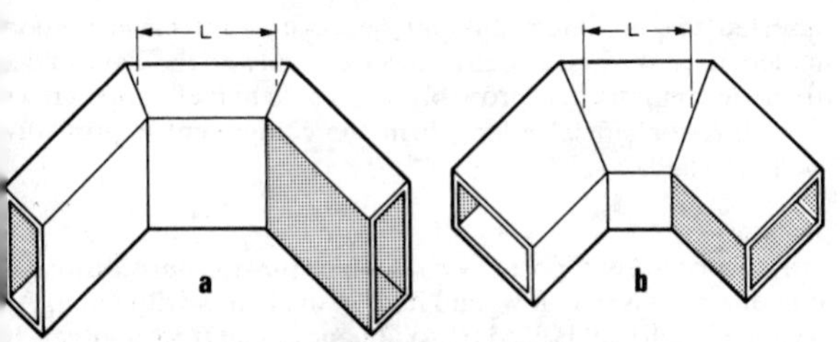

Fig 54. Fabrication of (a) E-plane and (b) H-plane bends. The length *L* should be an odd number of quarter guide-wavelengths

choked flange and is intended to produce rf electrical continuity across the waveguide junction without physical continuity. They are used in conjunction with plain flanges in high-power applications, and are therefore unnecessary in current amateur equipment. They may be used if available without disadvantage. Flanges may also be fitted with rubber sealing rings if the joints are to be exposed to the weather.

Waveguide bends and twists

Bends are sometimes required to facilitate the assembly of equipment. The simplest form is one in which a piece of waveguide is simply bent with a radius of curvature of several wavelengths. The change in impedance of the guide in the bent section compared with a straight section tends to cancel at the ends, and the wideband nature of the waveguide is scarcely affected by the bend. This approach is an example of the general rule which is applicable to waveguide—you can get away with many things provided you do it slowly over a number of wavelengths.

Commercially, bends are made by filling a straight waveguide with a low-melting point alloy or with sand to prevent the sides buckling, and bending around a former. Alternatively, they may be produced by electro-depositing metal on to a shaped mandrel (electroforming). Satisfactory bends (by amateur standards, anyway) can be made by clamping one end of a length of guide, applying a *light* load to the other, and heating with a brush flame until the correct local deformation has occurred before moving to the next section.

The bends made in this way necessarily are large. Bends having a small radius of curvature can be made by fitting straight lengths of guide into specially shaped corner pieces which are available commercially. They also may be fabricated as shown in Fig 54. The midpoint length L should be an odd number of quarter guide-wavelengths so that reflections at the two discontinuities will tend to cancel.

Twists are pieces of waveguide which, as their name implies, are twisted through an angle so that equipment using one plane of polarization may be connected directly to another of differing polarization. Commonly the angle of rotation is made 90°. Twists may be made using the same techniques as for large bends, and their length should again be several wavelengths.

Directional couplers

Directional couplers are widely used at lower frequencies, mainly to measure the forward and reflected power to an antenna system. They are also used in this way at microwave frequencies, but a more important use is as the "heart" of transmitters and receivers.

In general terms, a directional coupler consists of two transmission lines which can interact electrically so that a proportion of the power flowing in one line is fed to the second in one direction only. Fig 55 shows two transmission lines AB and CD which are coupled. If power is supplied to port A, then a fraction appears at port D, and the difference at port B. In a perfect device, no power will appear at port C. The coupling factor is defined as the ratio of the power supplied to port A to that appearing at port D, ie:

$$\text{Coupling factor} = 10 \log \left(\frac{P_A}{P_D}\right) \text{dB}$$

Typical values for this factor are between 3 and 60dB.

In real devices, some power appears at port C, and a measure of the quality of the coupler is its *directivity*, which is defined as:

$$\text{Directivity} = 10 \log \left(\frac{P_D}{P_C}\right) \text{dB}$$

In well-designed couplers, this ratio is in the region of 30dB. The actual power appearing at port C compared with the input at port A is, of course, smaller by the sum of the coupling factor and the directivity.

The input and output ports on this type of coupler can be interchanged. Thus, if power is applied to port D, the coupled output will appear at port A, or if applied to port C, the coupled output will appear at port B. Because of this interchangeability, couplers are classed as *reciprocal devices*.

Directional couplers come in many forms, the choice of design for a particular application being made in terms of suiting the layout required and the coupling coefficient necessary. However, most waveguide types consist of two lengths of guide sharing a common wall in which a hole or pattern of holes is made. An example is the side-wall coupler shown in Fig 55.

Two holes spaced $\lambda_g/4$ apart connect the two guides, the size of which controls the degree of coupling. Waves moving from port A pass through both holes and arrive at port D in phase, regardless of the distance between the holes since they both travel the same distance. The two sets of waves therefore reinforce each other. However, the two sets of waves arriving at port C travel lengths which differ by twice the distance between

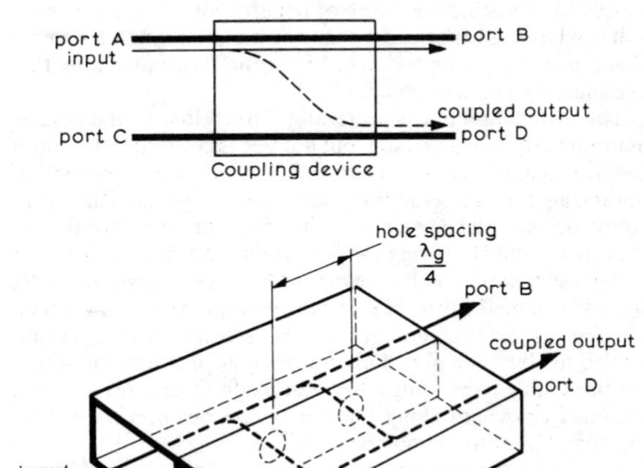

Fig 55. (a) Schematic form of directional coupler. (b) Practical side-wall directional coupler

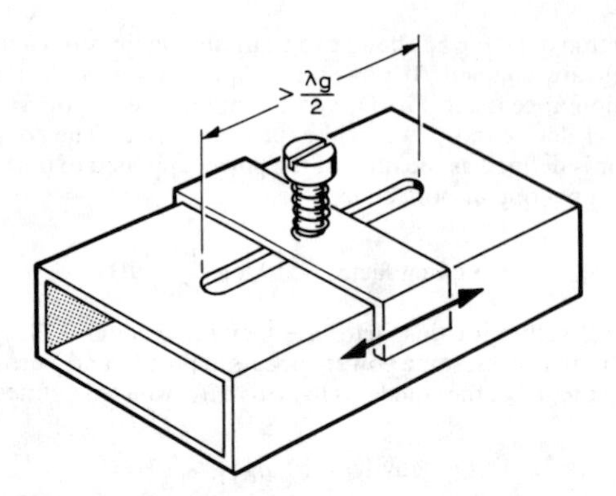

Fig 56. A sliding screw tuner used to eliminate mismatch

the coupling holes. If the spacing is made $\lambda_g/4$, then the path difference will be $\lambda_g/2$, and consequently the waves will be out of phase and will cancel. Since this distance depends directly on λ_g, the degree of cancellation is a given design (ie the directivity) will change somewhat if the coupler is used at another frequency. In most applications this is not an important factor—port C will often be terminated in matched load.

In general, the degree of coupling of a particular configuration of holes is also somewhat dependent on frequency, so directional couplers are usually designed for a particular frequency of use.

Practical designs of three forms of directional couplers are shown in Figs 68 to 71.

Sliding screw tuner and matching screws

One of the attractions of working in waveguide is the ease with which certain operations can be done compared with lower frequencies. An example is the sliding screw tuner, which is illustrated in Fig 56. A single screw, if fitted in the correct position along the centre line of the broad face of a waveguide, can be made to tune out almost any mismatch in the system simply by adjusting the depth of penetration. This adjustment will hold over a range of frequency which, although narrow in absolute terms (in the region of 1 per cent), is usually more than adequate by amateur standards.

The matching screw is preferably fitted close to the component that requires matching, but not necessarily so. Its position is fairly critical within the range $\pm$ $\lambda_g/4$, and a method of optimizing this is to mount the screw on a carriage which rides along the waveguide as shown in Fig 56. Both the carriage and the screw should be spring-loaded to eliminate mechanical play.

An electrically similar device uses three screws mounted centrally along the broad face of the waveguide as shown in Fig 57. During experimental work, the screws may be spring-loaded to eliminate play, but after final adjustment the screws are preferably fixed using a lock nut. Again, the screws may be mounted anywhere along the waveguide but preferably near the component to be matched.

The setting of either the single screw or the three-screw tuner can of course be done using a vswr bridge if available. Alternatively, they can be set during final testing of the equipment. For example, if fitted to a reactive antenna, they are tuned to maximize signals received or transmitted, and if fitted to a mixer, to optimize the signal/noise ratio on a received signal.

In the case of the three-screw tuner, usually only one or two screws will have a significant effect. The screws should be inserted the minimum amount necessary to achieve a good match. If the screws have to be inserted well into the waveguide, then the component is probably a bad match; if all three screws have little beneficial effect, then the component is probably well matched.

Isolators

An isolator is a two-port device in which the transmission loss in one direction is very low, and high in the reverse direction. As its name implies, it is used to isolate one circuit from another. It is frequently used to protect oscillators, so that power generated by the oscillator can pass unimpeded to the external circuitry, but any power reflected by the circuit is heavily absorbed and therefore does not influence the oscillator. In one sense, an isolator appears as a perfect matched load to the oscillator.

The operation of an isolator depends on the special magnetic property of ferrites. These are magnetic oxides of iron with controlled additions which, because of their high resistivity, are relatively loss-free even at microwave frequencies. When they are saturated by an external magnetic field, their magnetic properties vary in different directions perpendicular to the applied magnetic field.

A common form of waveguide isolator consists of a length of waveguide to the inside of which is fitted a ferrite component. This is magnetically biased by an external magnetic field generated usually by a permanent magnet. The waveguide field corresponding to both forward and reverse waves passing through the waveguide are distorted by the ferrite, but to a differing degree. A lossy material is placed within the waveguide at a point where the field due to the forward wave is zero, and where that due to the reverse wave is at a maximum. The forward wave therefore passes through with little attenuation, usually much less than 1dB, while the reverse wave is heavily attenuated, generally by more than 20dB.

Although isolators can greatly simplify the construction and operation of equipment, there are a number of precautions which should be taken in their use. Clearly they must be connected the right way around. Their operation can be permanently degraded by a change in the magnetic properties of the biassing magnet caused by mechanical knocks, or allowing the isolator near steel components or external magnetic fields. They provide isolation over a restricted range of frequencies, in some cases as low as 5 per cent in width. Harmonics, for example, may be only poorly attenuated.

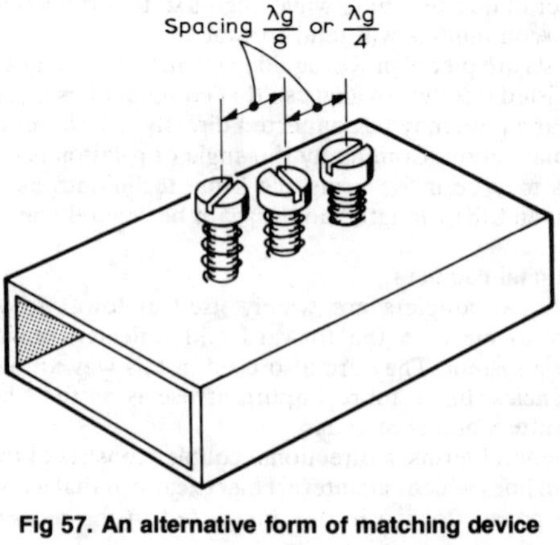

Spacing $\frac{\lambda g}{8}$ or $\frac{\lambda g}{4}$

Fig 57. An alternative form of matching device

Circulators

A circulator in its most common form is a three-port device in which adjacent ports are effectively connected in one direction but not in the reverse direction. Thus, using the notation of Fig 58, signals pass readily in the direction of the arrows, that is from port A to B, from B to C, and from C to A, but there is negligible transmission in the opposite sense, from A to C, C to B and from B to A.

As an example of the use of a circulator, a transmitter connected to port C would effectively connect to an antenna attached to port A, but not to a receiver connected to port B. Signals picked up by the antenna would pass to the receiver on port B with little loss, but not to the transmitter on port A. Any *output* from the receiver, eg local oscillator leakage, would be dissipated in the transmitter. A circulator clearly makes an ideal transmit/receive switch.

A wavelength form of circulator consists of three arms at 120° joined to a central boss, at the centre of which is placed a slab of ferrite which is magnetically biassed by a permanent magnet. The ferrite effectively rotates the standing wave pattern so that coupling can only occur in one direction.

The precautions in handling circulators are similar to those described for isolators. The direction of rotation should be most carefully checked otherwise damage to equipment may result. Thus, in using a circulator as a transmit/receive switch, the transmitter would be connected directly to the receiver input if the wrong direction of rotation were assumed.

Circulators, like isolators, operate efficiently over only a narrow bandwidth. The technique for retuning commercial circulators to amateur frequencies which has proved successful in some cases is described below.

Modifying surplus circulators

Surplus circulators set for about 9·3GHz have been successfully modified for use at 10GHz, but the operation requires the appropriate test equipment. The existing tuning screws, which are usually firmly fixed in position, are carefully drilled out and the holes retapped, if necessary with a slightly larger thread. New screws are fitted and the circulator is retuned to the new operating frequency. The degree of isolation between ports, which is probably poor at this stage, is adjusted by altering the degree of magnetization of the permanent magnet. A few turns of heavy insulated wire are wrapped around the magnet and energized by repeatedly discharging a large capacitor (say 10,000μF) charged to 2–20V until the degree of isolation is maximized. The polarity of the discharge current is determined by experiment.

Circular waveguide

Circular waveguide can be used to transmit rf energy. Its principal disadvantage is that, unlike rectangular waveguide, it possesses no characteristic that positively prevents the plane of polarization rotating about the axis of the guide as the wave travels along it. RF corresponding to one plane of polarization injected at one end of a guide may not necessarily have the same polarization at the other end. For short lengths of waveguide this is not a severe problem, and circular guide is commonly used in constructing feeds for paraboloidal dishes.

Limits in dimensions, similar to those which apply to rectangular waveguide, also restrict the size of circular wavelength that may be used at a given frequency without the risk of overmoding. The dominant mode for circular waveguide is the TE_{11} mode, the cut-off wavelength for which is given by:

$$\lambda_c = 3 \cdot 412a$$

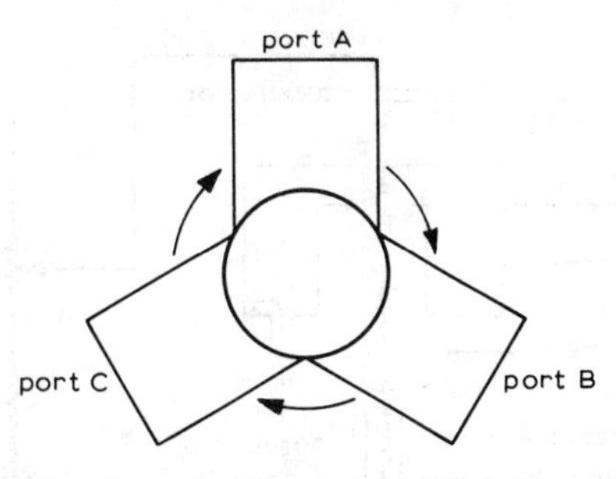

Fig 58. Coupling characteristics of a circulator. Power is coupled only from port A to B, port B to C and port C to A

where a is the internal radius of the waveguide. The value for λ_g is given by:

$$\lambda_g = \frac{\lambda}{\sqrt{1 - \left(\frac{\lambda}{\lambda_c}\right)^2}} = \frac{\lambda}{\sqrt{1 - \left(\frac{\lambda}{3 \cdot 412a}\right)^2}}.$$

The next higher mode is the TM_{01} mode for which $\lambda_c = 2 \cdot 613a$. Since this represents a frequency only about 30 per cent higher than that of the dominant mode, it is clear that circular waveguide can be used over a much narrower frequency range than rectangular waveguide if all risk of overmoding is to be avoided.

Any cylindrical tubing of reasonable uniformity of bore can be used as circular waveguide. Typical are copper tubing as used in central heating installations, and empty tin cans with any internal lacquer removed.

Klystron oscillators

Using a klystron is probably the simplest way of generating power at microwave frequencies. A klystron is a valve-like device which usually has the necessary frequency-determining components built in, so that merely applying the appropriate working voltages is all that is required to produce rf power. The output may be via a coaxial connector, a coaxial line terminating in a radiator, or via waveguide. The overall efficiency of a klystron is typically a few per cent.

The construction of a simple form of reflex klystron is shown schematically in Fig 59. A fairly conventional heater/cathode assembly is used to produce a focused electron beam which is directed at a second electrode called a *resonator*. This consists of a cavity which is resonant at the design frequency of the klystron and is operated at normal valve anode voltages and currents. Built into many klystrons is a mechanism by which the dimensions of the cavity can be altered so that its resonant frequency can be changed. The resonator has two central holes through which part of the electron stream can pass. Beyond the resonator is a third electrode which is biased a few hundred volts negative with respect to the cathode. Electrons approaching this electrode are repulsed and return either to the resonator body or back through the holes in the resonator. For obvious reasons, this third electrode is called a *reflector* or a *repeller*.

The mode of operation of a klystron is as follows. Electrons emitted by the cathode have a wide range of velocities. If the klystron is assumed to be oscillating, then the rf field existing in the holes in the resonator will affect the velocity of the electrons

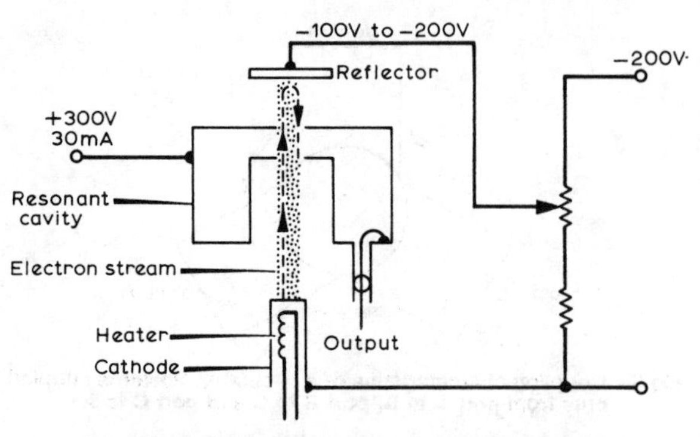

Fig 59. Configuration of a simple form of klystron

passing through, slower moving electrons being retarded and faster electrons being accelerated. In other words, the electron stream is velocity modulated at the frequency of oscillation of the klystron. Because of their higher velocity, the faster electrons travel further into the resonator/reflector space and therefore cover a relatively long path before returning into the vicinity of the resonator. Slower electrons, however, travel a shorter path albeit at low velocity. The overall effect therefore is that the time-of-flight of electrons tends to be the same irrespective of initial velocity, so that electrons which enter the resonator/reflector space in a random manner return together in bunches.

If these bunches pass back through the holes in the resonator at a point in the oscillation cycle such that the electrons are slowed by the rf field, then they will deliver power to the resonator and the klystron will oscillate. This oscillation will be strongest when the time-of-flight of the electrons in the resonator/repeller space corresponds to $n + 3/4$ cycles of the resonator frequency, where n is an integer. If the bunches pass through the resonator when the field is trying to accelerate them, then energy will be removed from the resonator and oscillation will be suppressed.

The time-of-flight of the electrons is dependent on the reflector voltage, and therefore oscillation will occur only when the voltage is set to a number of particular voltages. This is illustrated by Fig 60(a). The reflector voltage which produces the highest peak is normally selected. Note that if the resonator

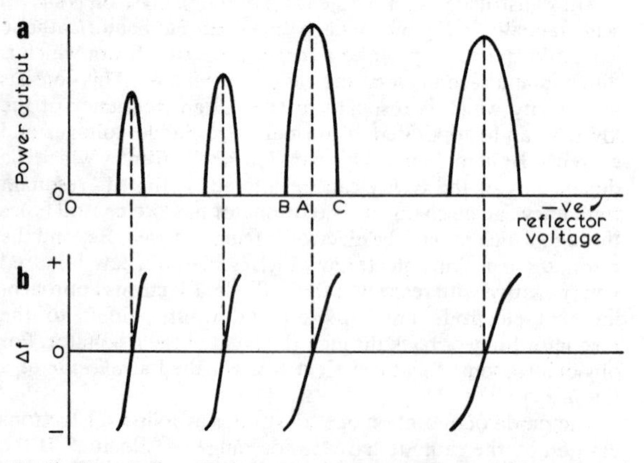

Fig 60. The relationship between reflector voltage of a klystron and (a) power output, (b) frequency of oscillation

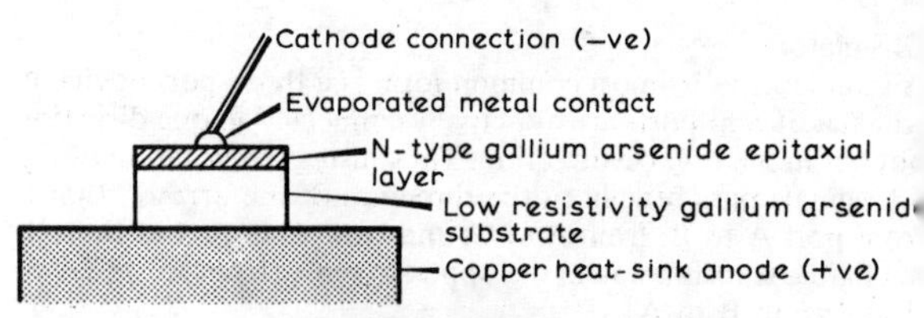

Fig 61. Construction of a Gunn diode

cavity is tuned to a different frequency, then the reflector voltage will also have to be altered to maintain output.

Changes of the order of a few volts to the reflector voltage when the klystron is oscillating have two main effects: the output power varies from zero to maximum, and the frequency of oscillation varies in a fairly linear manner as shown by Fig 60(b). The frequency range of this electronic tuning is of the order of 10MHz before the output power falls to half its maximum value. These characteristics can be used in modulating the device by the appropriate choice of reflector voltage and modulating voltage as the following examples show.

- If the reflector voltage is set for maximum power output, that is operating point A in Fig 60(a), then a small modulating voltage will generate fm with little a.m. This is the operating condition usually used in current amateur practice.
- If the reflector voltage is set midway between A and B, or A and C then an additional modulating voltage will produce a mixed a.m./fm output.
- If the reflector voltage is set at or just below B, and pulse modulation is applied with a peak voltage sufficient to reach point A, then a pulse/fm output will be obtained. Alternatively the reflector may be set at or just above point C.

Adjustment of the reflector voltage can also be used as a fine tuning control of limited range. This may be done either manually, or by an afc voltage. The latter technique may be used to lock the oscillator on to an incoming signal or on to a local frequency standard.

Because of the dependence of frequency on reflector voltage, and to a lesser extent resonator voltage, the dc supplies should be stable and hum-free.

Gunn diodes

So far, Gunn diodes seem to have been used by amateurs only in the 10GHz and 24GHz bands, although they are available for other microwave frequencies. Their form of construction is illustrated by Fig 61. The active part of the device is a thin layer of gallium arsenide grown epitaxially on a slice of similar material of about 0·02in diameter. This substrate has a low resistivity and acts as a connection to one side of the epitaxial layer and in turn is bonded to the metallic base which is a heat sink. A lead bonded on to a metallic film evaporated on to the other face of the epitaxial layer forms the second connection.

When a voltage exceeding 350V/mm thickness is applied to the epitaxial layer, a high field domain is generated at the cathode which drifts slowly towards the anode. When it reaches the anode, it produces a current pulse and a new domain forms at the cathode. The transit of the domains through the epitaxial layer therefore determines the natural pulse rate, which primarily depends on the thickness of the layer. For a 10GHz diode the thickness is in the region of 10μm (0·0004in).

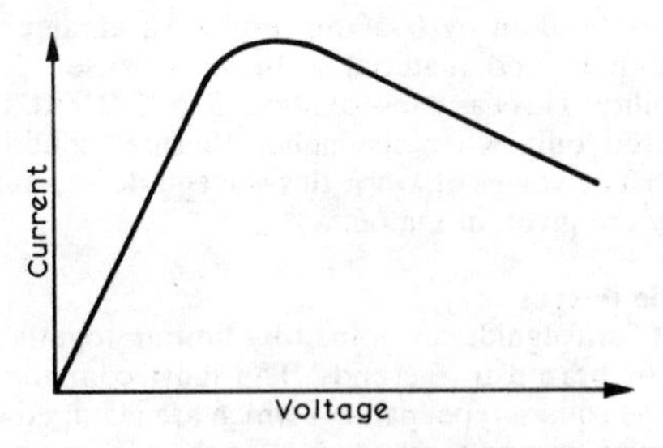

Fig 62. Voltage/current characteristics of a Gunn diode

When the Gunn diode is operated in a resonant cavity, the pulses are converted into normal sinusoidal oscillations. The Gunn diode is then subjected to an external alternating field, and this can control the rate of production of new domains and therefore of current pulses. By adjusting the resonant frequency of the cavity, the effective frequency of oscillation of the diode can be significantly changed both above and below its natural frequency set by the transit time effect.

The relationship between applied voltage and current is shown in Fig 62. The maximum current taken by a typical small 10GHz device is at about 4V, and increasing the voltage results in a fall in the current taken. The usual operating voltage is about 7V, which is well into the negative resistance region. The form of the rf output/applied volts curve is shown in Fig 63. Maximum power is obtained at 8 to 9V.

The *Q* of the cavity strongly affects the amount the frequency of oscillation can be pulled. Low-*Q* cavities, such as the coaxial type shown in Fig 64, have a *Q* in the range 50–150. These can be tuned mechanically over a wide range, typically an octave, or up to 700MHz by a varactor. High-*Q* cavities, such as the waveguide cavity shown in Fig 99, have a *Q* of about 1,000, and can be tuned mechanically over a frequency range of about 30 per cent, or a few tens of megahertz with a varactor. However, coaxial cavities are much more sensitive to temperature changes, about 1MHz/°C compared with 180kHz/°C, and to the match of the load, compared with waveguide cavities. The latter type are therefore usually preferred by amateurs: coaxial types would appear to be of value mainly where varactor tuning over a wide range is required.

The effect of operating volts on frequency for the two types of cavity is shown in Fig 65. The rate of change of frequency with voltage clearly depends on the *Q* of the cavity and the operating point. If the oscillator is to be tuned or modulated by varying

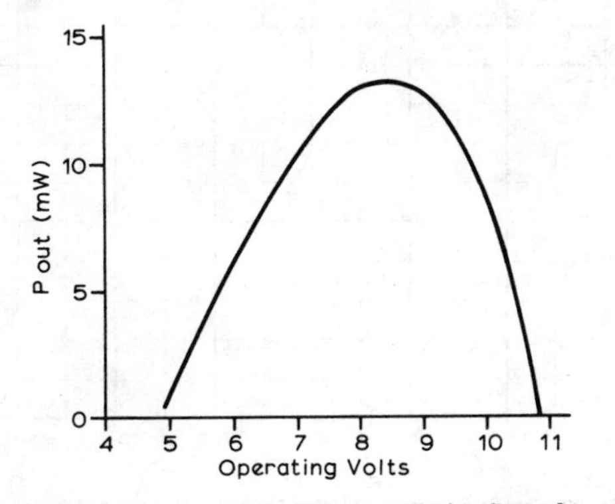

Fig 63. Typical form of output against applied voltage for a Gunn diode

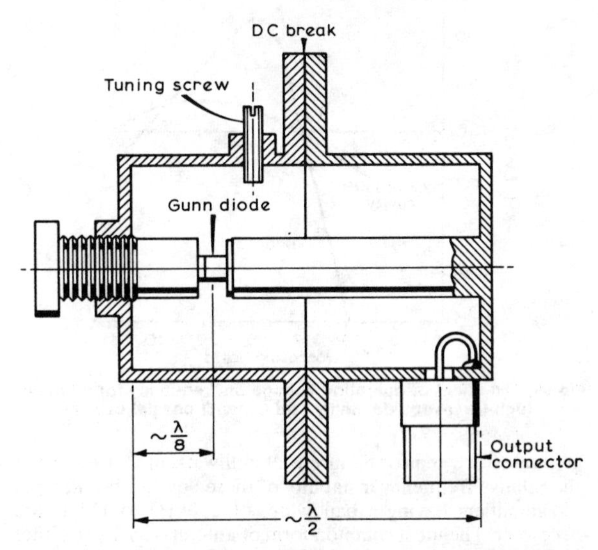

Fig 64. A typical coaxial-cavity Gunn oscillator (Mullard)

the applied voltage, then the operating point should be well down from the peak of the curve, say at 7V. Note that this value does not coincide with maximum output. Ideally, the frequency/voltage relationship should be determined for each oscillator, but an approximate operating point can be set by reducing the operating voltage so that the output power is 20 to 30 per cent lower than the maximum obtainable.

Although the manufacturers recommend a working voltage not exceeding 7V, it is possible with most devices to obtain a peak power 2 to 10 times the cw value by driving the oscillator with pulse voltages up to 30V. Some devices will not stand such a high driving voltage, and will tend to break down above about 15V.

High-power Gunn diodes which generate up to 500mW at 10GHz are available, but do not yet seem to have percolated through to the surplus market.

EQUIPMENT FOR 10GHz

There are several reasons which account for the relatively high popularity of this band with UK amateurs. The main attraction is the challenge of the quite different constructional and operating techniques that are required at high microwave frequencies, and it is gratifying that so many amateurs, many of whom are quite inexperienced even at vhf, have responded to this challenge.

The advantages of the 10GHz band compared with those at 5·7GHz or 24GHz are that the waveguide used is of a particularly convenient size, which results in compact equipment without placing too high a demand on accuracy in construction, that some components are available on the surplus market, and that there are no special propagation problems. With narrow-band equipment, there is the extra advantage that the preferred frequency of operation, 10,368MHz, may be generated in two convenient ways: either via 1,296MHz (×8) or from the common microwave driver frequency of 1,152MHz (×9).

Most of the equipment used so far consists of transceivers which employ a single small klystron or Gunn oscillator to

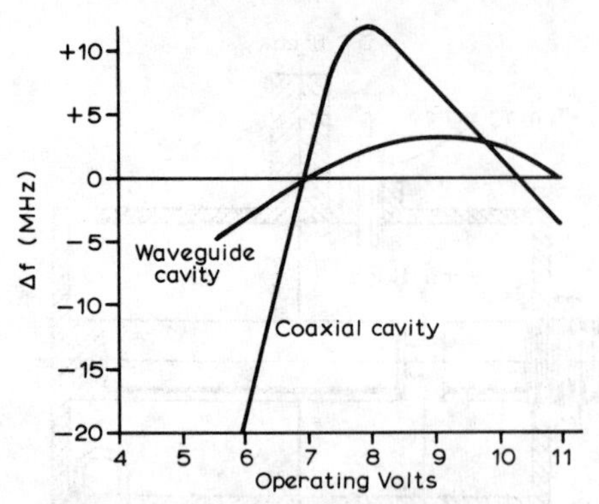

Fig 65. The effect of operating voltage on frequency for a typical high-Q waveguide cavity and a low-Q coaxial cavity

generate a few tens or hundreds of milliwatts of rf. Because of the relative frequency instability of these devices, broad-band i.f. amplifiers having a bandwidth of 250kHz to 1MHz are necessary. The most common form of antennas used are either horns with a gain up to 25dB, or dishes from 1 to 3ft in diameter.

It is most important to realize that this type of equipment, despite its simplicity, will have a free-space range usually of several hundred miles, and consequently is capable of working under normal propagation conditions all the line-of-sight paths available in the world. Over shorter paths, say 100km in length, most equipment has sufficient reserve so that initial contacts can be made even if the equipment is grossly inefficient.

More recently this simple equipment has been used with much success over long non-optical paths, taking advantage of the low losses associated with super-refraction within the humidity duct formed over water, and of knife-edge diffraction obtained by pointing transmitter and receiver antennas at peaks of intervening hills and mountains. Clearly, in operating at these frequencies, much more thought and planning is required than is usual in amateur practice.

Relatively high power (1W) narrow-band (10kHz) crystal-controlled equipment is currently being built which should make possible reliable communication over obstructed paths 100 miles in length or more via tropospheric scatter.

As was noted earlier, most waveguide equipment is assembled by bolting together a limited number of components to produce the required configuration. Generally speaking, there is much latitude in the physical design of the individual components, so that in making a receiver, for example, any one of a number of designs of mixers can be combined with one of a variety of rf sources used as a local oscillator, and so on. It is therefore appropriate to first describe the construction of practical components and then to discuss various ways in which they can be fitted together.

Much of the design data, although applied to 10GHz equipment, is given in general terms so that it can be applied to other sizes of waveguide for use at other frequencies. Where the dimensions are not given in terms of wavelengths, for example $\lambda_g/4$ or $\lambda/2$, the actual lengths given can be scaled by the ratio of the wavelengths or of guide-wavelengths as appropriate.

Waveguide

The waveguide recommended for use at 10GHz is WG16, which has internal dimensions 0·900in by 0·400in and external dimensions 1·000in by 0·500in. For most amateur applications, the preferred material is brass because of its good machinability. This has a loss of about 5·5dB/100ft. Copper is usually used only when its higher thermal conductivity is necessary. The values of λ_g for this waveguide as a function of frequency are given in Fig 66.

Waveguide flanges

Sections of waveguide are joined by bolting together flanges soldered or brazed to the ends. The most common form of flange is the square type, pairs of which are clamped with four bolts. Round flanges are also used in the UK, and these are clamped together by an external locating ring and nut. Although bulkier than the square flanges, they can be assembled without tools, and therefore are sometimes preferred for antenna connections to facilitate manual changeover. The dimensions of the flanges are given in Fig 67. Plain flanges are usually used, those incorporating a choke being not really necessary at amateur power levels. A waveguide joint may be made weatherproof by using a plain flange in conjunction with one fitted with a rubber sealing ring.

In most cases, flanges can be soldered in place, but where the joint is under considerable mechanical stress, it should be brazed. Because waveguide components are made with high precision, jigging during soldering is usually unnecessary. For most practical purposes, it is sufficient to slip the flange on to the waveguide so that the guide projects just beyond the face

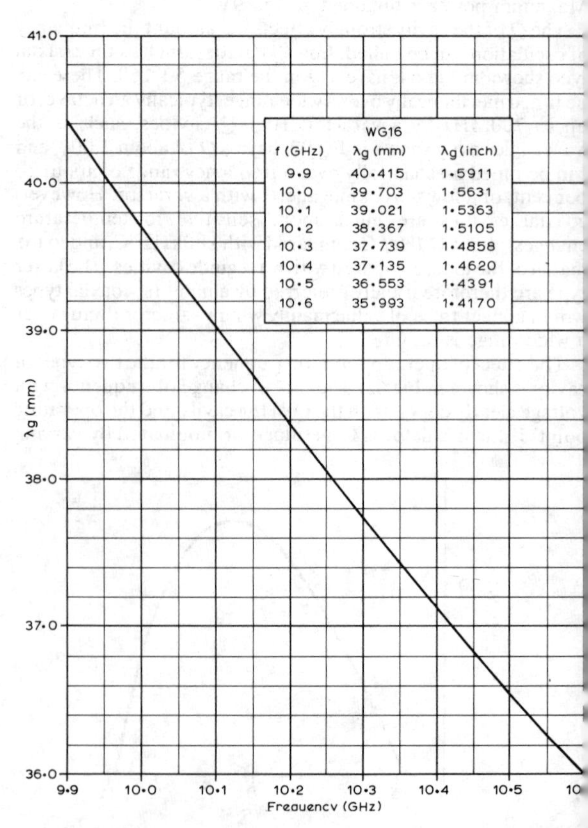

WG16

f (GHz)	λg (mm)	λg (inch)
9·9	40·415	1·5911
10·0	39·703	1·5631
10·1	39·021	1·5363
10·2	38·367	1·5105
10·3	37·739	1·4858
10·4	37·135	1·4620
10·5	36·553	1·4391
10·6	35·993	1·4170

Fig 66. The relationship between frequency and guide-wavelength λ_g for waveguide 16

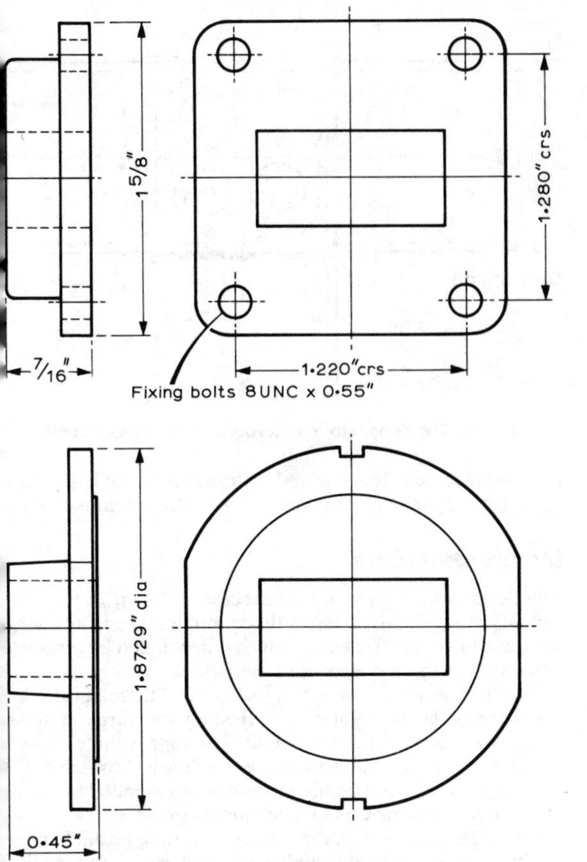

Fig 67. Dimensions of standard waveguide 16 flanges

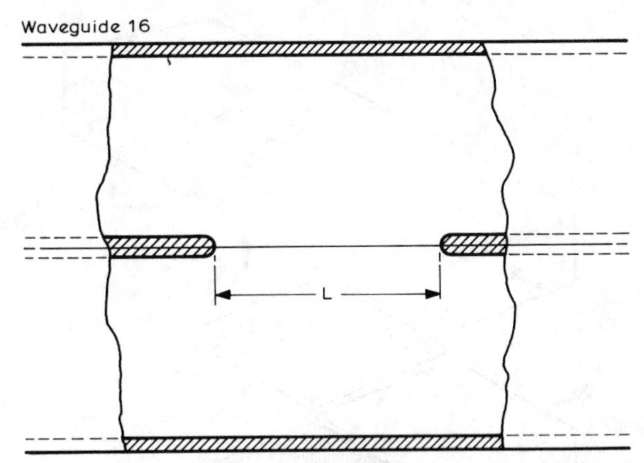

Fig 68. A short slot hybrid 3dB directional coupler. The length of the iris L is $0 \cdot 66\lambda_g$ and the height is equal to the narrow width of the waveguide

nd then to solder with a small gas flame. The excess guide can e removed by filing, and finished by carefully rubbing the face f the flange over silicon carbide paper backed by a sheet of lass. If care is taken not to rock the assembly, then a very flat urface can be obtained. Finally, any burrs or solder within the vaveguide should be carefully removed.

)irectional couplers

Many different designs of directional coupler exist. The three shown below are commonly used and all are relatively simple to nake.

A 3dB coupler

The construction of a short slot hybrid coupler is shown in Fig 58. Windows $0 \cdot 66\lambda_g$ long and 0·4in high are cut in a narrow ace of two pieces of waveguide which then are mounted so the windows coincide. For waveguide 16, the length L is 26·0mm 1·023in) for 10,050MHz, and 24·6mm (0·970in) for 10,369MHz.

A 9–30dB cross-directional coupler

A feature of this design is that up to 9dB coupling can be obtained, which is sufficiently large for use in the type of simple equipment to be described later. The coupling can be made as small as required, and data is given in Table 6 for down to 30dB. However, for a coupling of less than 20dB or so, other types which are simpler to make are usually preferred.

The form of the coupler is shown in Figs 69 and 70. The coupling slots may be machined in the wall of one waveguide, but a separate plate as shown is recommended for kitchen table constructors. Note that because the thickness of the plate recommended (0·036in) is slightly smaller than the wall thickness of the waveguide (0·050in), then the assembly becomes self-jigging. The coupling slots can be cut by clamping an oversize piece of brass sheet in a vice, and using the edge of the vice as a reference for drilling and filing. The 1in square outline is then marked as a "best fit" to the slots actually cut. This procedure is much more effective than trying to cut slots accurately in a 1in square plate.

The walls of the waveguide can be removed by drilling and filing. A piece of wood fitted inside the guide prevents damage to the opposite face. By continually monitoring with a micrometer or vernier gauge, an accuracy of 0·001in can easily be achieved even with simple hand tools. For soldering this type of work where the assembly can be thoroughly washed, solder paint spread thinly over the joints to be soldered is recommended as this avoids the problem in feeding solder to the less accessible parts. A gentle gas flame or a hot plate is used for heating. Alternatively, merely clamping the components mechanically together is sometimes satisfactory.

The round-hole cross coupler

When a directional coupler with a coupling coefficient greater than 20dB is required, a convenient design is the round-hole coupler illustrated by Fig 71. Coupling is via three circular holes drilled at corners of a square of side equal to $\lambda_g/4$. The degree of coupling varies with the ratio of the diameter of the larger holes to that of the broad internal width of the waveguide. The smaller hole has a diameter two-thirds that of the larger holes.

For waveguide 16, $a = 0 \cdot 9$in and λ_g is 1·550in at 10,050MHz, or 1·474in at 10,369MHz. A 25dB coupler for the lower frequency, for example, would require two holes 0·311in in diameter and one 0·208in diameter, spaced 0·194in from the centre lines of the waveguide.

The holes may be drilled in the wall of one of the waveguides, preferably the input arm, the corresponding broad face wall of

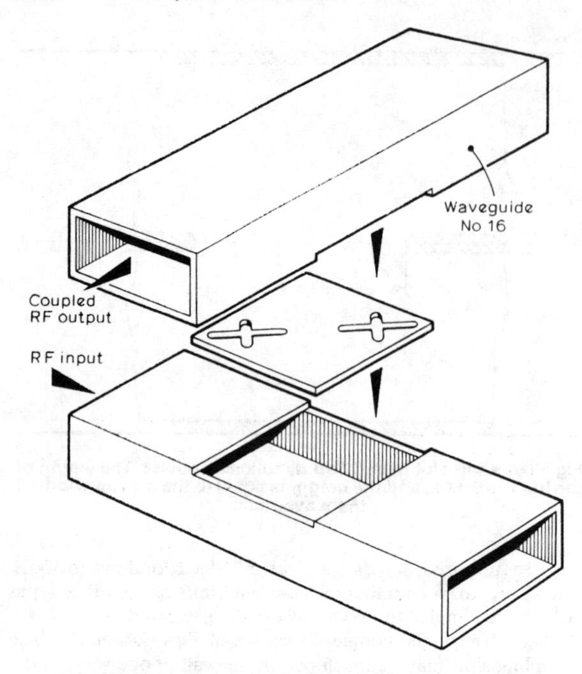

Fig 69. Exploded view of a 9 to 30dB cross-coupler

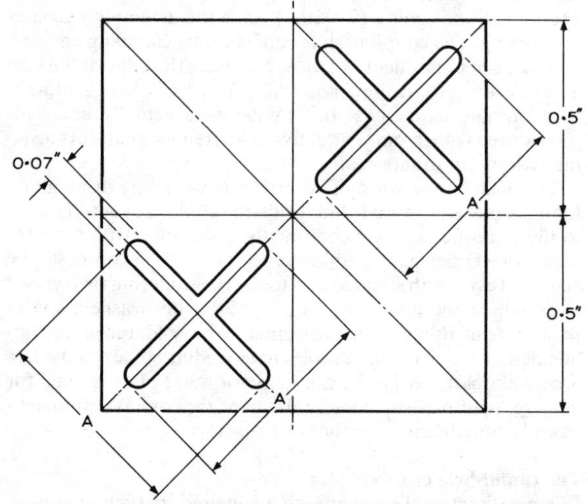

Fig 70. Dimensions of septum plate. Material 0·036in (20swg) brass or copper

Table 6. Dimensions of cross-coupler slots

Coupling (dB)	Dimension A (in)	Slot width (in)
9	0·510	0·072
12	0·504	0·065
15	0·462	0·065
20	0·410	0·065
25	0·367	0·065
30	0·328	0·065

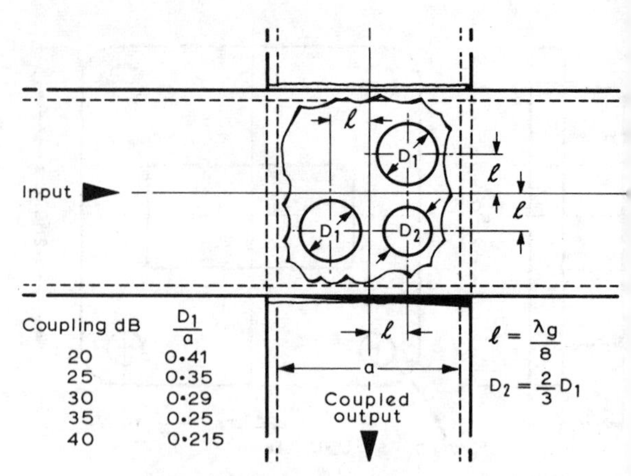

Fig 71. The dimensions of a round-hole cross-coupler

the second piece being removed. Alternatively, the holes can b drilled in a separate plate as described for the previous coupler

Mixers/detectors

The design of a simple mixer/detector is shown in Fig 72. It consists of a 1N23-type mixer diode mounted centrally across the waveguide, the live end of which is decoupled by capacitor fabricated in the way shown in the figure.

Its use as a detector is given in Fig 72. The mixer diode is matched to the waveguide by adjusting the three matching screws for maximum current output. The approximate relationship between power input and meter reading is shown in Fig 74. The range of the detector obviously can be extended by the use of calibrated attenuators or directional couplers.

When used as a mixer, the i.f. output is taken from between the live end of the mixer diode and the decoupling capacitor, the meter now being used to measure and set the mixer diode current at its optimum value. The matching screws should be adjusted for best noise figure rather than for maximum diode current: these adjustments do not necessarily coincide.

A mixer using the CV2154, CV2155, SIM2 or SIM3 type of diode is shown in Fig 73. It is tuned by an adjustable rf short and

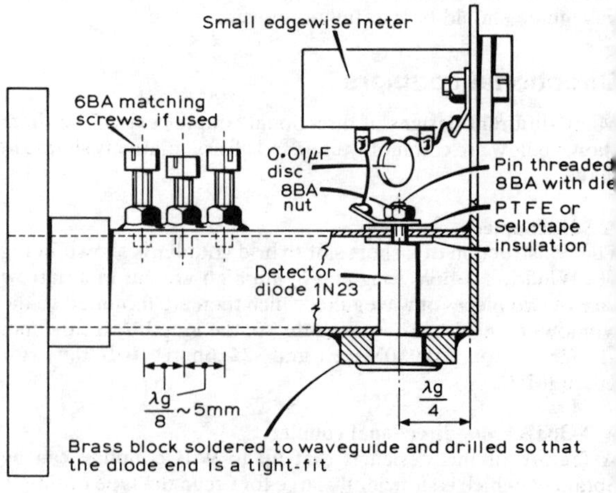

Fig 72. A simple mixer/detector for 10GHz

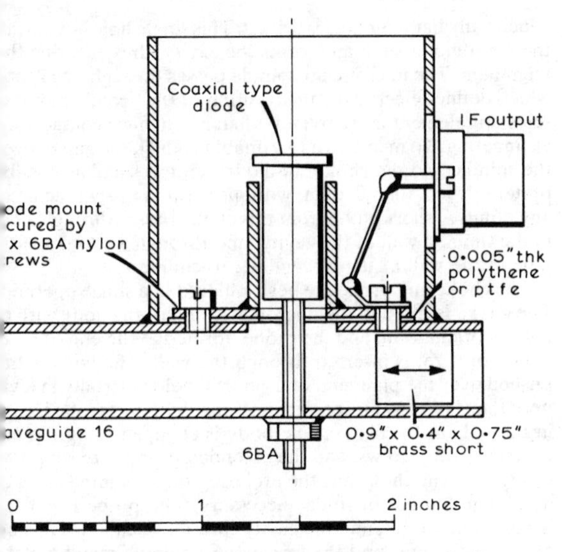

Fig 73. A 10GHz mixer using a CV2154-type diode

raising the diode within its mount. The optimum mixer rrent for this diode is 0·5 to 1mA.

ough measurement of power

onventional mixer diodes can be used to provide an indication rf power with an accuracy sufficient to prevent gross mistakes the construction of microwave equipment. The relationship tween rf input and dc output for a typical diode is shown in g 74. Although these data apply specifically to X band, the sults obtained at other microwave frequencies would be pected to be similar. Each curve corresponds to a particular tal series resistance. The resistance of meters, which is typilly 100Ω for 1mA fsd, 1,000Ω for 100μA fsd and so on, in me cases is significant and must be allowed for.

As an example of the use of these data, suppose a mixer is fed a a 20dB (×100) directional coupler from a klystron, and a rrent of 0·9mA is observed on a meter having a resistance of 0Ω. The power indicated by the diode corresponds to 4mW of rf, which implies that the klystron is delivering in the gion of 140mW. Comparing this value with manufacturer's ta will give a guide to the efficiency of the system.

The corresponding data for Schottky barrier diodes is given Fig 75.

Vavemeters

uch current equipment on 10GHz employs free-running oscil-tors, the frequency stability of which, although surprisingly od (typically one part in 10^4), nevertheless is poor by crystal-ntrolled standards. Building a wavemeter actually into the stem is not only desirable to ensure operation within the and, but will also considerably improve the chances of making ntacts.

The wavemeters to be described are all absorption types mply because a proven design for a transmission wavemeter is ot available. This is less of a problem than would be imagined nce in most equipment some means of power indication is cessarily built in, so that an absorption wavemeter associated

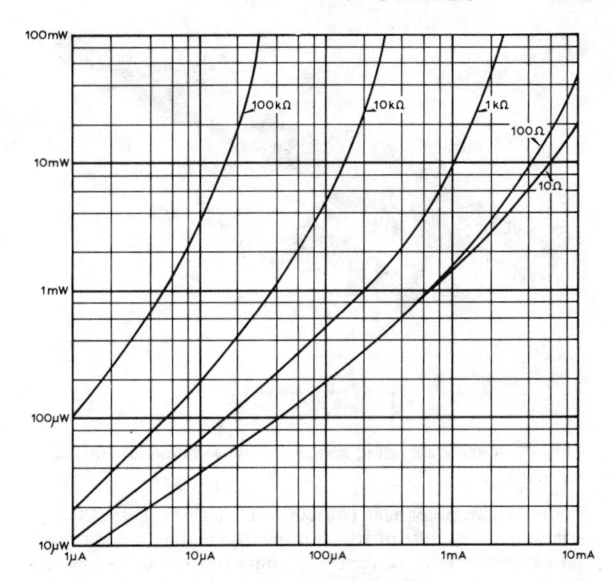

Fig 74. The approximate relationship between rf power input and dc output for a standard point-contact mixer diode for specified total series resistance

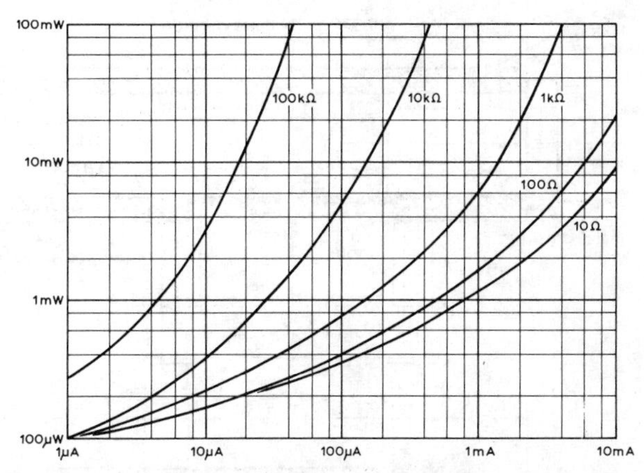

Fig 75. The approximate relationship between rf power input and dc output for a typical Schottky barrier mixer diode

with a mixer/detector is virtually equivalent to a transmission wavemeter.

The wavemeter shown in Figs 76 and 77 enables frequencies to be measured between at least 9·5 and 11GHz with an accuracy of ±10MHz. An important feature is that it is self-calibrating, which avoids the need to refer to a precision frequency standard. It consists of a rod of adjustable length set coaxially in a cavity, which is loosely coupled to waveguide forming part of the rf system. Absorption of power occurs when the rod resonates, that is, when the rod is electrically (but not necessarily physically) either λ/4 or 3λ/4 long.

Because the wavelength is short at these frequencies, the tuning rates of this type of wavemeter tend to be high; in the region of 1,300MHz/mm for the λ/4 mode, and 440MHz/mm for the 3λ/4 mode. The constructional problems that could be associated with these rates have been avoided by the use of a

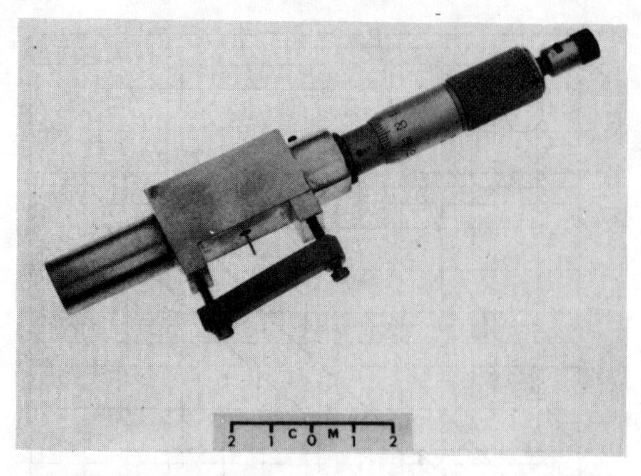

Fig 76. A self-calibrating absorption wavemeter for 10GHz

standard micrometer head (Moore and Wright type 952M or its variants), the spindle of which forms the resonating element. The wavemeter body is fabricated from a block of brass through which a ½in diameter hole is drilled. This single hole both locat the micrometer stem and forms the cavity, thus ensuring th alignment. The micrometer spindle passes through a λ/4 cho which defines electrically the position of the "cold" end of t resonant element more reliably than mechanical contacts su as fingering. To maintain a reasonably high Q, the gap betwe the spindle and the choke should be kept as small as possib preferably less than 0·01in, without them actually touching any point. A short probe from this choke passes through a hc in the thinned wall of the cavity, and through a correspondi hole in the wall of the waveguide, to couple rf.

The choke and probe are best soldered in a single operatic The choke is fitted in the micrometer end of the body with t correct orientation, and the probe, formed at the end of a 12 length of wire, is inserted through the wall. The body is th pushed over the plain end of a ½in drill held vertically in a vi until the choke is in its correct position, with the probe locat in the hole in the choke. The body is clamped using the mi rometer fixing screws, and the extended probe wire support externally. The choke and the probe are then soldered using t minimum amount of solder necessary. The probe is cut to length of about ⅜in, and the cavity carefully cleaned. The bo of the wavemeter and the micrometer spindle may be plat

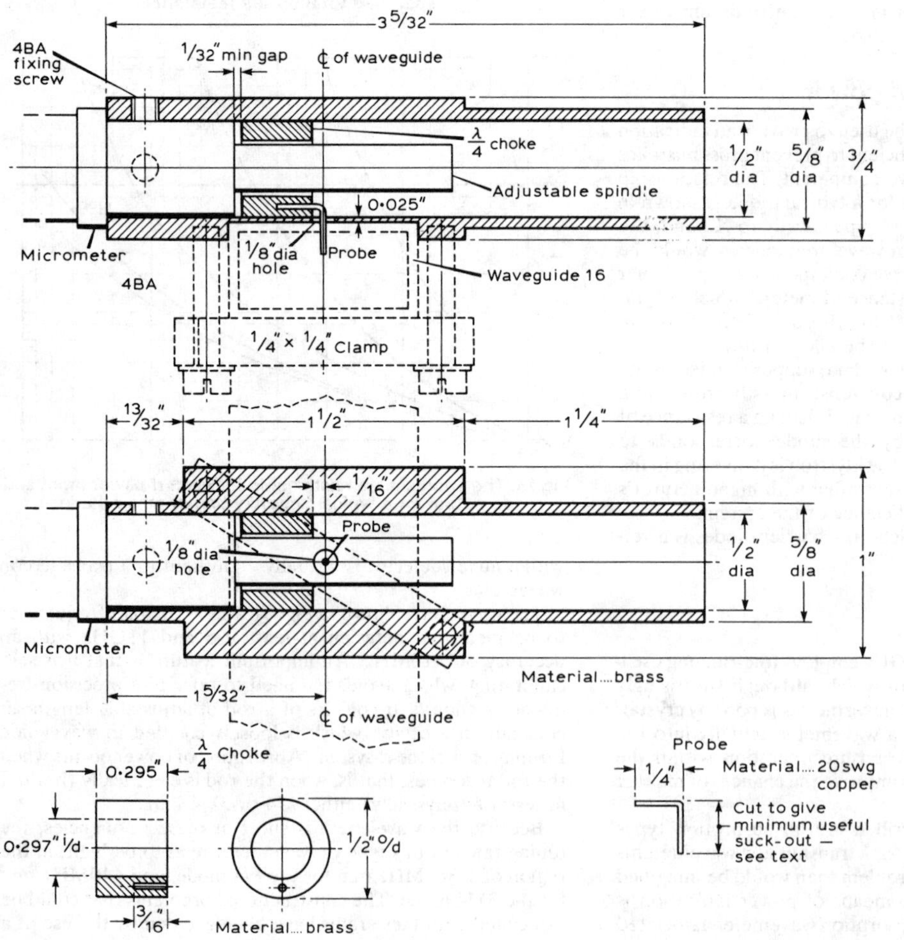

Fig 77. Construction of t self-calibrating wavemeter

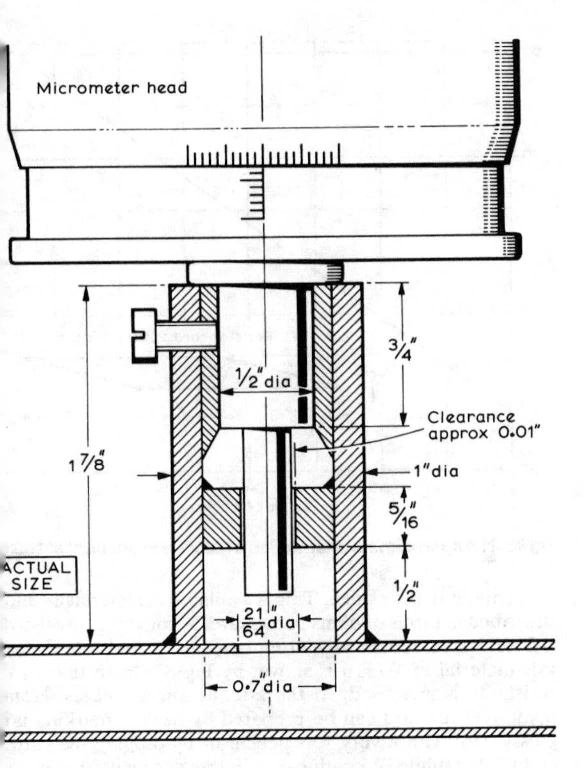

Fig 78. A high-Q wavemeter for 8–12GHz

ith gold, copper or silver, although this is not really necess-y—the plating on the spindle should not exceed 0·0002in or fficulty may be found in re-assembling the micrometer.

To calibrate the wavemeter, a source of rf and a means for tecting relative power levels are required. These will nor-ally be part of the receiver or transmitter with which the avemeter is to be used. The probe should first be trimmed to duce the "suck-out" to the minimum convenient, for ample, a 10 per cent reduction in mixer current. For each of a mber of (unknown) frequencies the micrometer readings R_1 d R_2, corresponding to the $\lambda/4$ and $3\lambda/4$ suck-outs, should be oted. The difference between these readings is accurately $\lambda/2$ the frequency measured. Hence

$$f(\text{MHz}) = \frac{C}{2(R_1 - R_2)}$$

here R_1 and R_2 are in millimetres and $C = 299{,}600$ for air at 5°C and 30 per cent humidity. A conventional calibration rve can be built up in this way for both modes: normally lvantage should be taken of the slower tuning rate of the $3\lambda/4$ ode.

The wavemeter shown in Fig 78 has a Q in the region of 000, and therefore a resolution of about 2MHz. It can be librated to measure frequencies from 8 to 12GHz. The avemeter consists of a resonant cavity 0·7in diameter and ·5in long, end-coupled to waveguide. It is tuned by the spindle f a standard micrometer head, the electrical position of the cold" end of which is defined by a $\lambda/4$ choke. Fortunately the libration is linear with frequency in the range 10 to 10·5GHz ithin about 1 per cent, the tuning rate measured being almost

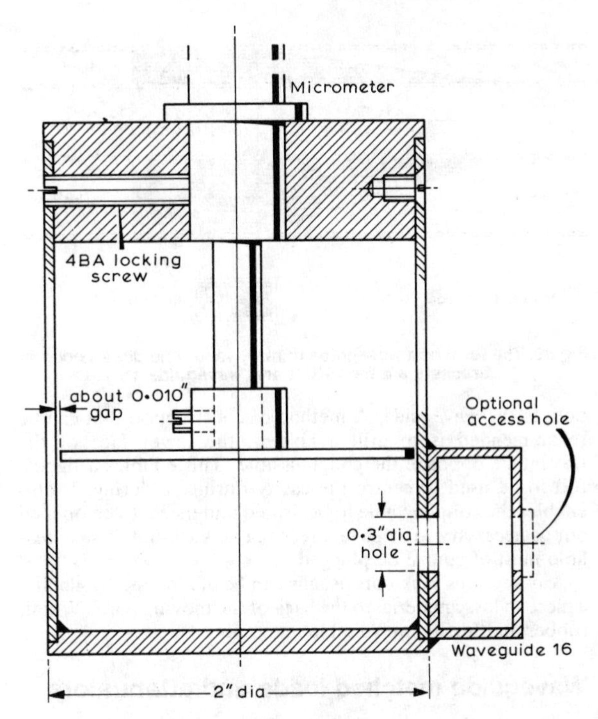

Fig 79. A simple 10GHz wavemeter

exactly 10MHz/0·01mm. If one accurate calibration point can be determined within this range, then a calibration for the remainder can be calculated without undue error. To take full advantage of the resolution of this wavemeter, a drum-type micrometer (such as Moore and Wright type 480M) can be used. Alternatively, a smaller micrometer such as type 952M may be employed, perhaps with a reduction drive and a directly calibrated scale.

The original wavemeters were made from 1in diameter brass bar which was drilled and reamed to produce a tube. The choke was made as a separate part. To assemble, a 0·7in drill was clamped vertically in a vice, and the wavemeter body was positioned on this to locate the choke correctly and held in place by the micrometer clamping screws. The choke was soldered into place, the joint checked visually, and then the waveguide was soldered. An accurately turned sleeve served to locate the micrometer head. Other methods of fabrication may be used, for example machining the body, choke and sleeve from a solid bar, provided that the internal dimensions quoted are adhered to. Alternatively, a flange may be fabricated on the body of the wavemeter so that it can be bolted rather than soldered to the waveguide. In the original versions, only the micrometer spindle was plated (0·0002in copper or gold), although even this is not really necessary.

Another type of wavemeter is shown in Fig 79. To achieve a high Q, the rotating end plate should be a close fit with the wall of the cavity but must not touch it at any point. One method for ensuring this is to clamp the plate on the micrometer actually to be used but with the spindle projecting. The spindle can then be mounted in a lathe for turning the plate to the required diameter.

The suck-out is strongly dependent on the size of the coupling

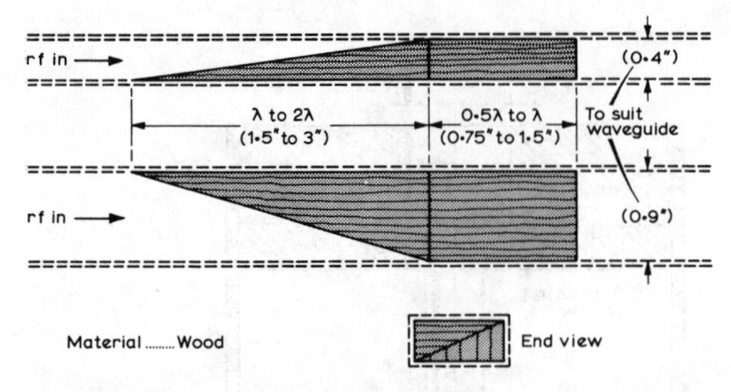

Fig 80. The form of a waveguide dummy load. The dimensions in brackets are for 10GHz and waveguide 16

hole to the waveguide. A method of construction that can be recommended is to drill a hole in the lower face of the waveguide opposite the coupling hole. This enables a jigging rod to be used to centre the cavity during soldering. It also enables the coupling hole to be drilled undersize, to be opened out as necessary to achieve a reasonable suck-out. The access hole must of course be plugged.

Any spurious suck-outs usually can be eliminated by glueing a piece of lossy material to the back of the moving plate. Wood, rubber and ferrite are suitable materials.

Waveguide matched loads and attenuators

A robust load can be made from wood. In the design shown in Fig 80, a good match is ensured by the long taper at the "hot" end. Its efficiency as a load may be checked by fitting it to a system. If a sliding short-circuit placed behind the load can be moved over half a wavelength without affecting the system, then the load is absorbing all the power.

A compact low-power dummy load is shown in Fig 81. A piece of resistor card, typically 200Ω per square, is passed through slots cut in the narrow wall of the waveguide and is glued in position. Any rf passing through the resistor is reflected from the short and attenuated a second time. For 10,050MHz, $\lambda_g/4$ = 9·84mm (0·388in); for 10,369MHz, $\lambda_g/4$ = 9·33mm (0·367in).

Attenuators are also made by fitting lossy material into the waveguide: in this case both ends are tapered to provide a good match in both directions. A convenient form of resistive material consists of graphite powder bonded on to paxolin-type

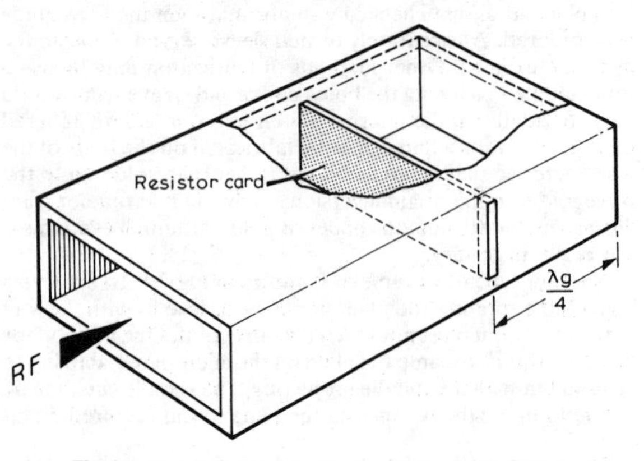

Fig 81. Construction of a low-power matched load

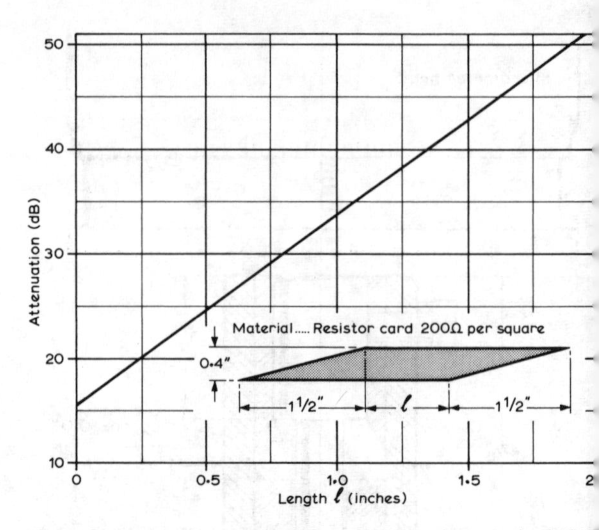

Fig 82. The approximate attenuation of 200Ω resistor card at 10GH

sheet about 0·02in thick. This is available commercially and i described in terms of ohms per square. A convenient resistivit is 200Ω per square, and the attenuation measured at 10GHz fc this material in WG16 is shown by Fig 82. Note that as th resistivity is increased, so the attenuation decreases. Home made resistor card can be prepared by heavily marking non glossy card with a very soft pencil, or by dipping the card i colloidal graphite. A coating of cellulose can be used as protec tion.

For maximum attenuation, the resistive sheet should be fitte half-way across the broad dimension of the guide, and go fron wall to wall in the other direction. A convenient method c supporting it is to prepare a length of expanded polystyren (which is transparent to microwaves) to fit inside the guide, slic this into two and then sandwich the attenuator between the tw halves. Dummy loads can obviously be made in the same way Even quite low value attenuators make good loads: a 10d attenuator should have a vswr of less than 1·3:1, and a 15d attenuator less than 1·05:1, due to power passing back throug the attenuator.

Waveguide variable attenuators

A variable attenuator is a particularly valuable piece of tes equipment, even if it is not calibrated. In an fm receiver th audio signal-to-noise ratio varies strongly with the input signa strength only over a narrow range of inputs. In practice on therefore tends to hear signals with a high signal-to-noise ratic or nothing at all. It is only by chance that signal strengths are i the narrow range of a few decibels when noisy signals ar produced, so that the audio quality may be used as a guide fo adjusting the equipment for optimum performance.

The effective signal strength can of course be changed b altering the antenna and/or pointing it away from the optimun direction. However, a more satisfactory method is to insert variable attenuator in the connection to the antenna. This ca be adjusted so that alignment can be done under the mos sensitive conditions, and with a more direct measure c improvements in performance.

A widely used method of construction is to mount a shee resistive element as shown in Fig 83(a) so that it can be move across the guide. The attenuation is at a maximum when th

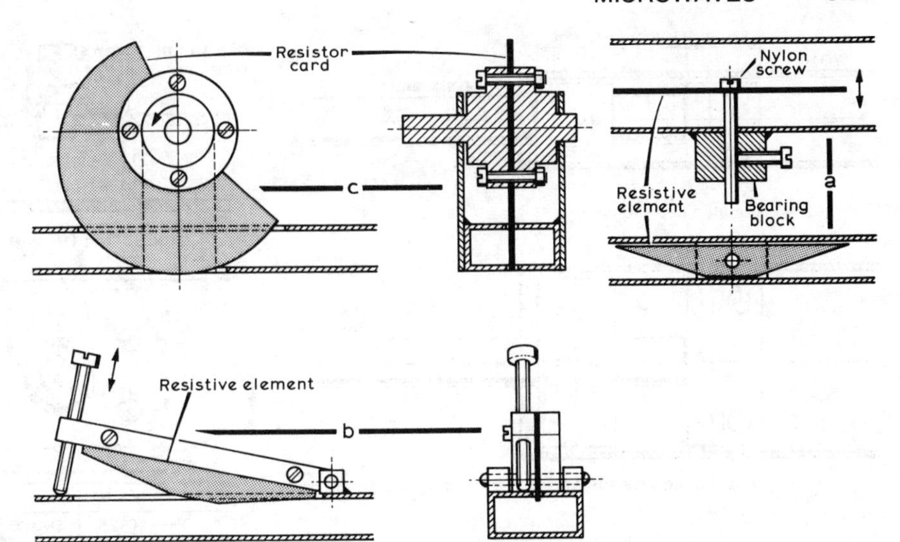

g 83. Construction ethods for variable attenuators

ement is half-way across the guide, and reduces as it pproaches a side wall. If the element can be made a close fit gainst the side wall, then the attenuation becomes insignific-nt, and the attenuator can be permanently installed. For etails of a suitable resistance card, and dimensions of the lement, see Fig 82. The push rod can be metallic if its diameter small compared with the height of the guide (say ⅛in diameter ompared with 0·4in for WG16), and if fitted at the centre of e element so that any reflections from it are also attenuated.

Alternative designs are shown in Figs 83(b) and (c). In both f these, the resistive element is inserted progressively through slot in the centre of the broad face of the guide: in Fig 83(b) e element is clamped to an adjustable hinged arm and in Fig 3(c) the element is mounted eccentrically on a rotatable shaft. hese types of attenuator are in some ways easier to make, but ere is a slight risk of the slots resonating and producing purious effects. The maximum attenuation available can be creased if a second slot is cut in the lower face so that the esistive element can pass completely through the guide. A itable tool for cutting the slot is a small hacksaw blade with e sides of the teeth ground away to a width of about $\frac{1}{32}$in.

If the variable attenuator is calibrated, then it becomes a ost useful device indeed. For example, the efficiency of an ntenna can be measured by comparison with a horn of calcu-ated gain, and the overall performance of a system can be hecked against calculations so that the potential range of the ystem can be estimated. Some sort of scale for indexing the osition of the attenuator must, of course, be fitted. For the pe shown in Fig 83(a) a small micrometer is frequently used. knob and a scale is all that is required for that shown in Fig 3(c). Calibration is obviously straightforward if one has access o suitable calibrated attenuators, but difficult if not. One poss-ble method would be to make use of directional couplers.

ractical adjustable waveguide rf shorts

he simplest form of rf short consists of a block which is a firm ress fit in the waveguide and which can be clamped in place fter adjustment. The rear face of the block can be tapped to ake a screw which can be fitted to adjust the position of the hoke and then removed. If the block is a good fit in the aveguide, then its length is uncritical. However, it should be about $\lambda_g/4$ in length if not. A slightly smaller block insulated with Sellotape also works well.

An alternative form of choke which uses fingering to ensure contact is shown in Fig 84. The ends of the fingers should be carefully radiused using fine emery paper so that adequate contact pressure can be used without scoring the walls of the waveguide. The length of each of the sections is made $\lambda_g/4$, ie approximately 10mm at 10GHz.

For larger sizes of waveguide, it becomes practical to use a plate rather than a block, and a method for doing this is shown in Fig 160.

Another form of short is shown in Fig 85. It is important that the choke is a good fit in the waveguide so that it cannot wobble. The choke is floated on pips of an insulator which protrude about 0·01in. A method for making these inserts is to drill ⅛in holes about ⅛in deep in the appropriate positions on the choke and press in each a suitable piece of dielectric. The ptfe body of a standard feed-through insulator is ideal. The ptfe is cut off flush with the surface of the choke and the inserts are removed with a needle. The bottom of the hole is then packed with material of thickness equal to half the difference between the size of the choke and the dimension of the waveguide to be fitted, and the insert is replaced.

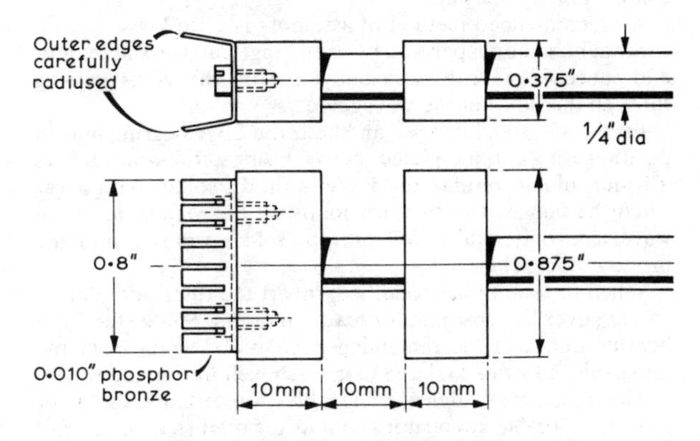

Fig 84. An adjustable rf short using fingering

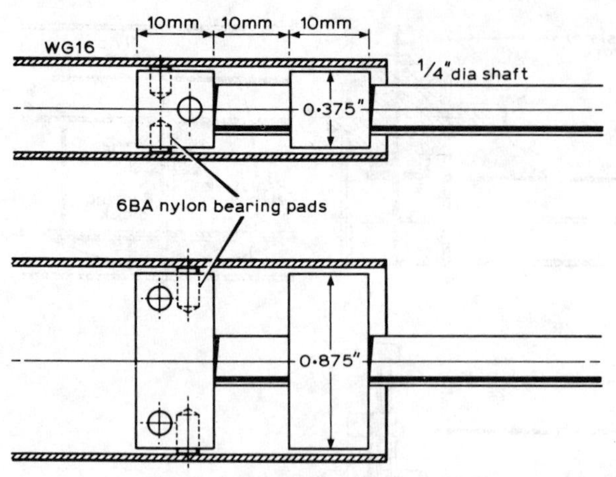

Fig 85. An alternative form of short

A second method is to tap a hole in the choke of just sufficient length to take a screw and then to fit a nylon screw. Using a micrometer to monitor the process, the nylon screw is cut back so that the height of the pip is equal to half the difference between the width of the choke and the inside dimension of the waveguide.

The insert on the opposite face is fitted in the same way, and trimmed so that the total width over the inserts is equal to the dimension of the waveguide. With a little care, it is easy to work within thousandths of an inch and effectively eliminate play.

Filters for 10GHz

The design for two filters which between them cover the whole of the 10GHz allocation is shown in Fig 86. Eight posts are fitted across the guide in precise positions and two tuning screws are used to set the frequency. The filters have an 80MHz equal ripple bandwidth, a 3dB bandwidth of 120MHz and an insertion loss of 0·3dB. Frequencies 1GHz away are attenuated by about 40dB.

Compared with other filter designs, this type is fairly tolerant in terms of constructional errors. Perfectly satisfactory filters have been made by marking out using a magnifying glass and an accurate rule and drilling, instead of the usual technique of using a milling machine.

A recommended method of assembly is as follows:

Straighten the copper wire by stretching. Cut oversize lengths and squeeze one end sufficiently to stop the wires passing through the holes in the waveguide.

Fit the wires and flanges, and hold the 2BA bearing nuts in position using chrome-plated screws. Using a flux which leaves a water-soluble residue (eg Baker's fluid), solder with a gas torch the flanges and the post joints on the *underside* of the waveguide only, which will prevent solder running into the inside of the guide.

When the solder has solidified, invert the filter and place a wet rag over the post joints already soldered. Solder the 2BA bearing nuts and the remaining post joints, again from the underside, allow to cool and then wash well in running water.

The filter can be aligned using a klystron or Gunn oscillator source, a variable attenuator and a mixer used as a detector, if more sophisticated equipment is not available.

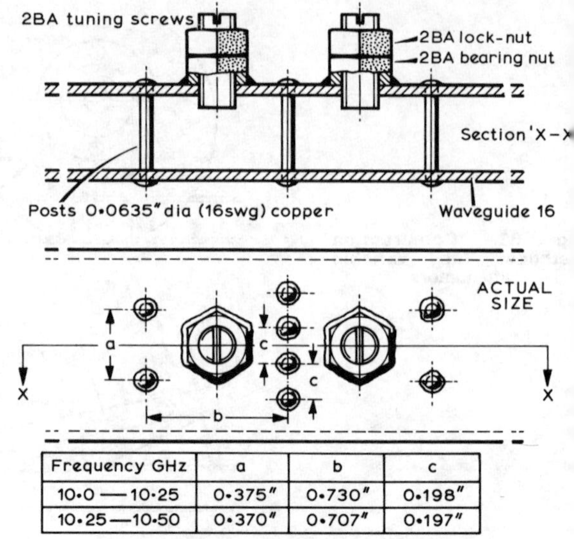

Frequency GHz	a	b	c
10·0 — 10·25	0·375"	0·730"	0·198"
10·25 — 10·50	0·370"	0·707"	0·197"

Fig 86. Waveguide 16 filters for 10–10·5GHz

The performance of bandpass filters having a slightly diffe ent method of construction is given in Fig 87. The filters hav 3dB bandwidths of either 20 or 60MHz depending on the dimensions as indicated in Table 7. They are particularly sui able for use in the local oscillator chain of a receiver to reduc the noise generated at signal frequency which would otherwis degrade the receiver performance. Even if a relatively low i.f. used, significant rejection of noise can be obtained; fc example, at 30MHz the rejection is 27dB. The 60MH

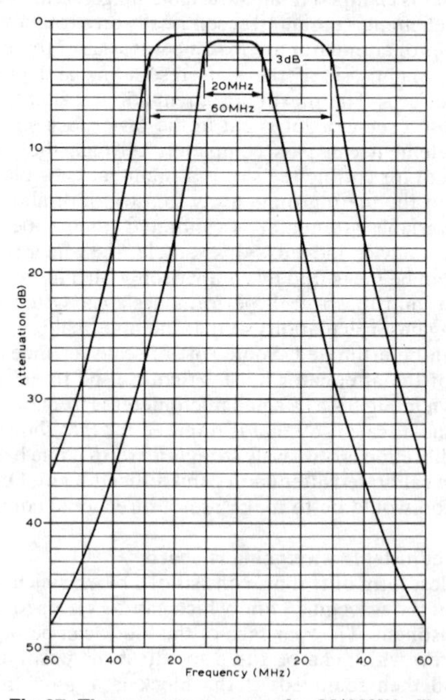

Fig 87. The response curves for 20/60MHz filters

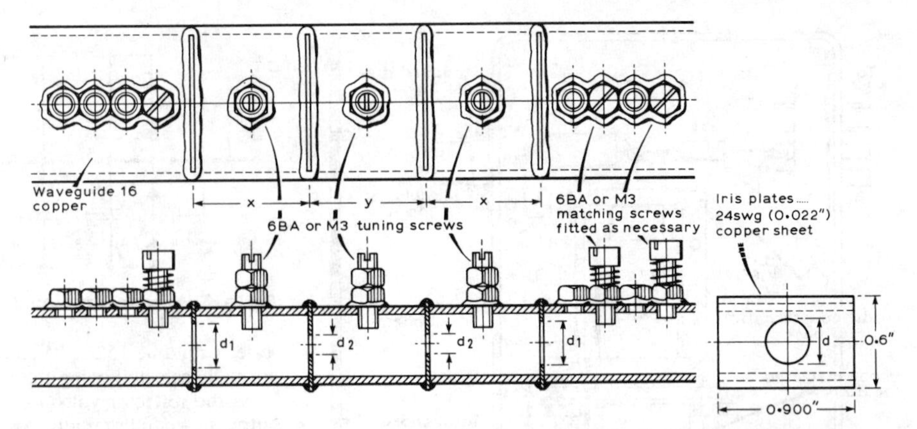

g 88. The construction of the ters. The dimensions are given in Table 7

andwidth filter is used to eliminate effectively the second hannel response of the receiver.

As is shown in Fig 88, the filter consists of a length of aveguide 16 in which iris plates are used to define three esonant cavities which are coupled by centrally placed holes of pecified dimensions. The basic design frequency is 10·5GHz, ut the tuning screws fitted may be used to tune the filters down o 9·5GHz at least. Matching screws are fitted at each end of he filter as necessary to tune out any mismatch with the external circuitry.

In order to maintain the Q of the filter, it should preferably be made entirely from copper. Brass should only be used if it can e copper- or silver-plated after assembly. The tuning screws an be of brass only if little of each projects into the cavities, therwise threaded copper rods should be used. The matching crews can be of brass, or even cadmium-plated steel if little rojects into the guide.

The filter can be constructed as follows:

(a) Scribe deeply into the top and bottom broad faces of the guide grooves corresponding to the position of the irises.
(b) Using a fine saw such as a junior hack-saw blade, first cut slots at each corner and then use these as a guide to extend the cuts across the full width of the top and bottom walls of the waveguide.
(c) Fit the iris plates in their correct positions, and fix them in place by bending the corners of the iris plates. Jig the tuning and matching screw bearing nuts (if fitted) using chromium-plated screws. Fit any flanges required and solder all joints in a single operation using a small gas flame. Alternatively, solder only the joints on the underside of the filter, invert it and solder the second set while the first is cooled by small pieces of tissue soaked in water. This technique prevents any solder entering the cavities, which would reduce their Q. It is safer to use plain solder with a flux that can be washed away (eg Baker's fluid) rather than to risk organic residues being left behind. Note that it is not necessary for the iris plates to make good contact with the side walls.

Table 7. Dimensions of the 10GHz bandpass filter

Filter 3dB bandwidth (MHz)	Dimensions (mm) X	Y	d_1	d_2
60	17·8	18·2	9·0	4·3
20	18·2	18·7	6·2	2·95

It is most unlikely that the filter can be aligned simply by connecting an rf source at one end and a detector at the other. A simple technique is to poke the inner of a short length of coaxial cable down through one of the matching screw holes between the filter and the rf source, and to measure the rf output using a diode connected to the other end. Adjusting the tuning screws will produce peaks or dips at resonance, after which the filter can be aligned in transmission. A more formal technique is to connect one end of the filter to a matched load, and the other end to an rf source via a directional coupler. With the filter off-tune, the amount of reflected power will be high, but this will decrease as the filter is tuned. When the reflected power approaches zero, the filter can be finally adjusted in transmission.

If required, the frequency of the filter can be raised by fitting large (0BA or M6) screws centrally through the side walls of each cavity.

Klystron rf source for 10GHz

Although small klystrons have to a large extent been superseded in professional applications by semiconductor devices such as Gunn diodes and impatts, nevertheless they are still attractive to amateurs because they usually work first time.

A practical waveguide 16 mount for the 723A/B klystron, and its near equivalents the KS9–20 and the 2K25, is shown in Fig 89. This klystron is similar to a metal octal valve, the main difference being that pin 4 is a coaxial line which terminates in a $\lambda/4$ radiator. The klystron is coupled to waveguide simply by passing this probe through a hole in the broad face of the guide, the hole being offset from the centre line by 0·18in to improve the match. To reduce the escape of rf through this hole, the probe is best passed through a $\lambda/4$ choke. One end of the guide is closed by an adjustable brass block which is positioned approximately $\lambda_g/4$ from the probe.

The klystron is mounted in a standard international octal base, pin 4 of which is removed and the hole enlarged to pass the probe. The base is mounted on bolts so that its height, and therefore the depth of penetration of the probe, can be adjusted to maximize output. It is strongly recommended that the klystron be contained in a sealed metal box to eliminate draughts (the temperature coefficient of frequency is 0·25MHz / °C), to provide electrical screening, and as a safety precaution necessary with some methods of operation.

A basic power supply to drive the klystron is shown schematically in Fig 90. The klystron may be operated with either the

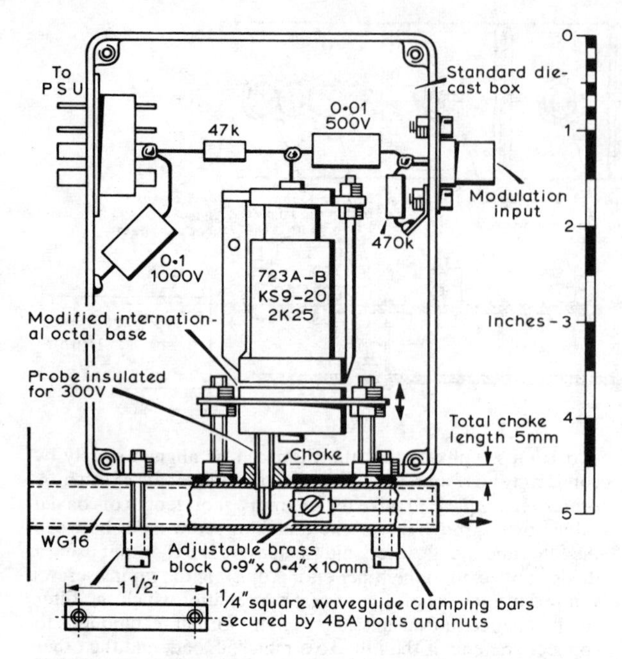

Fig 89. A waveguide mount for the 723A/B type klystron

reflector, the resonator or the cathode at earth potential, but two points must be borne in mind: the heater/cathode voltage must not exceed 50V, and the resonator is connected to the metal body. If the body is operated at earth potential then the heater supply must be floated. If the cathode and heater are at earth potential, then the body including the mechanical tuning screw and the output probe will be at +300V and due attention must be paid to insulation and protection. It is important that the reflector is not allowed to run at positive potential when the other supplies are connected as its valve grid-like structure is easily burnt out. RF power is generated by the klystron only when the reflector voltage is set at one of a number of quite critical voltages. These depend on the position of the mechanical tuning screw and vary from klystron to klystron. A typical

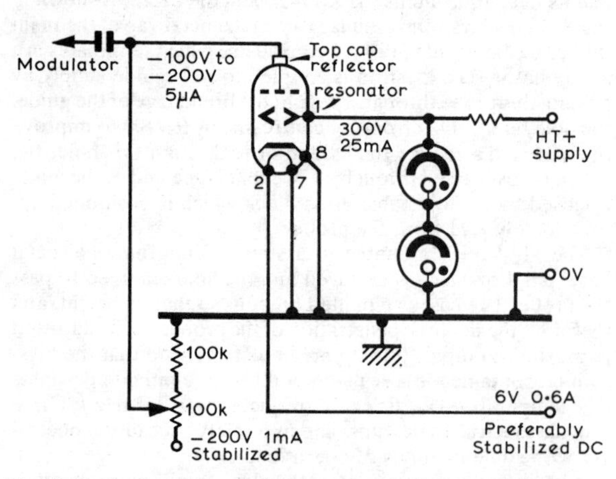

Fig 90. Basic power supply for operating a klystron of the 723A/B type

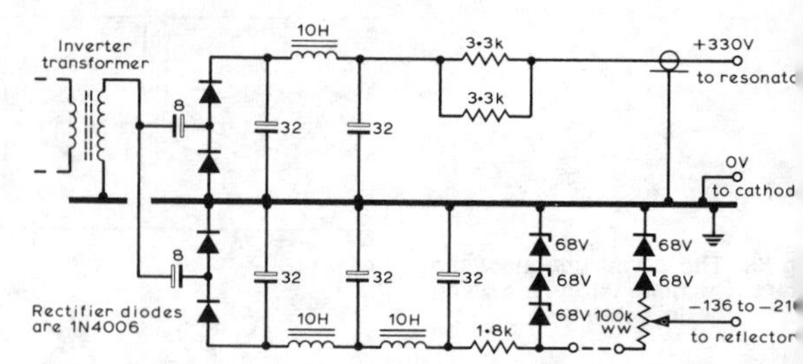

Fig 91. The secondary circuit of a simple inverter klystron ps

series would be 152 ± 3V, 172 ± 3V and 192 ± 3V, the or normally selected being the one producing maximum powe

As the reflector volts are changed from the optimum, th output power falls rapidly. A second effect is that the frequenc of oscillation changes—for the 723A/B klystron, a ±2V chang results in a frequency change of about ±20MHz. This charac teristic is valuable in providing a fine tuning mechanism, whic may be operated manually or by an afc system, and also allow the output to be frequency modulated by applying in the regio of 100mV rms of modulation to the reflector. It also implie that the reflector supply must be stable and hum-free to within few millivolts if unintended modulation is not to occur. Var ations in the resonator supply also affect frequency, although t only about one-fifth of that to the reflector. It is easier to reduc hum levels if the heater supply is dc rather than ac, and fre quency stability is improved if this supply also is stabilized, fo example using a simple transistor series stabilizer.

When in an unmodified state, the 723A/B klystron can b tuned over the range 8·5 to 9·6GHz by three turns of th tuning screw on the side of the klystron. This operates b mechanically changing the dimensions of the resonator cavity Most klystrons can be pulled into the amateur band by care fully filing away all of the weld locking the adjusting nuts on th side arm, and unscrewing these nuts progressively whil monitoring the maximum frequency that can be tuned. Mos klystrons can be made to work at 10·1GHz, some even to 10·5GHz. Recalcitrant klystrons can be encouraged by increas ing the resonator volts up to 350V.

The secondary circuitry of a simple inverter psu is shown in Fig 91. The variable voltage supply for the reflector may be obtained as shown, or via the afc circuitry shown in Fig 92. A simple heater circuit is shown in Fig 93, and that of a speech modulator in Fig 94.

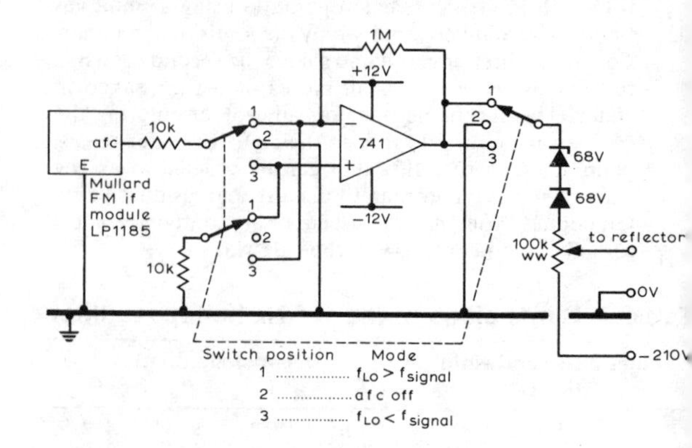

Fig 92. AFC circuitry

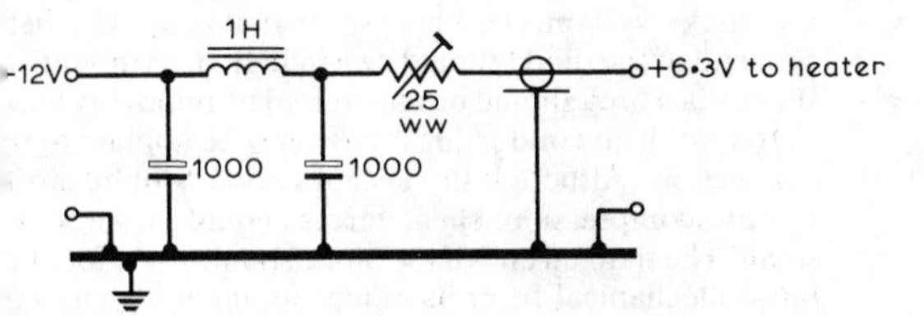

Fig 93. Simple heater circuitry

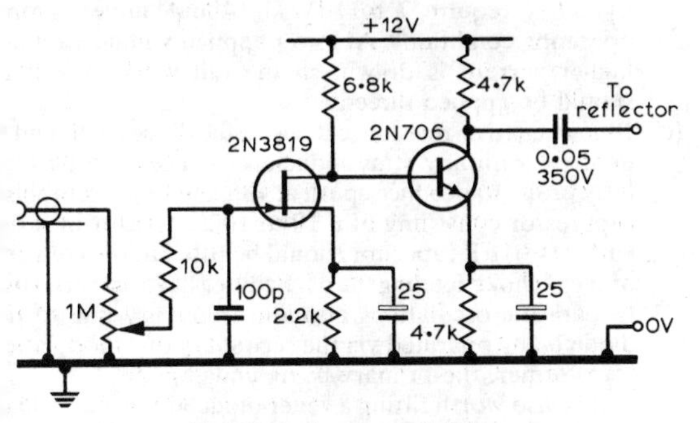

Fig 94. A simple modulator

32A/B klystron transceiver

he simplest form of equipment based on rectangular aveguide using this klystron appears to be that shown hematically in Fig 95. An actual transceiver to this design is own in Fig 96. The klystron is mounted on a length of aveguide, one end of which is connected to an antenna and to e other end a mixer. An absorption wavemeter is fitted be- veen the klystron and mixer.

In the original version, the klystron mount was identical to at shown in Fig 89, except that both ends of the waveguide ere extended and terminated in flanges. The wavemeter and ixer were those illustrated by Figs 79 and 73 respectively, though any similar units can be used.

The mode of operation is as follows. RF generated by the ystron passes both to the antenna to form the transmitted gnal, and also to the mixer to act as the local oscillator. The ode current resulting acts as the power indicator essential for oth setting the klystron reflector voltage and in observing the ick-out of the absorption wavemeter. In acting as a receiver, coming signals pass to the mixer, mix with the local oscillator gnal, and appear at the i.f. output.

Fig 96. A practical version of the transceiver shown with cover removed

It can be shown that optimum performance as a transceiver is achieved when half the power generated is transmitted and half is absorbed by the mixer—in this case only half the received signal is coupled into the klystron and lost. A consequence of this is that the mixer diode current, typically 10mA, is much higher than necessary for best performance, which not only is somewhat wasteful but results in some degradation of the noise figure of the mixer. However, if the unit is to be used only as a receiver, then the klystron output probe may be partially with- drawn from the waveguide until the mixer current falls to 0·25–1mA.

Assuming the klystron output to be 30mW, antennas to be dishes 2ft in diameter, an i.f. bandwidth of 1MHz and a receiver noise factor of 15dB, then this equipment will have a path loss capability of about 163dB: over line-of-sight paths, its range will be about 300km.

Gunn oscillators

Gunn oscillators are an attractive means of generating useful amounts of power at 10GHz. Compared with klystrons, a widely used alternative rf source, they have the advantages of requiring a relatively simple power supply (typically up to 10V at 150mA for low-power devices), they drift little on switching on, and can be tuned perhaps up to 500MHz by a single knob control. Like klystrons, they are easily modulated to produce

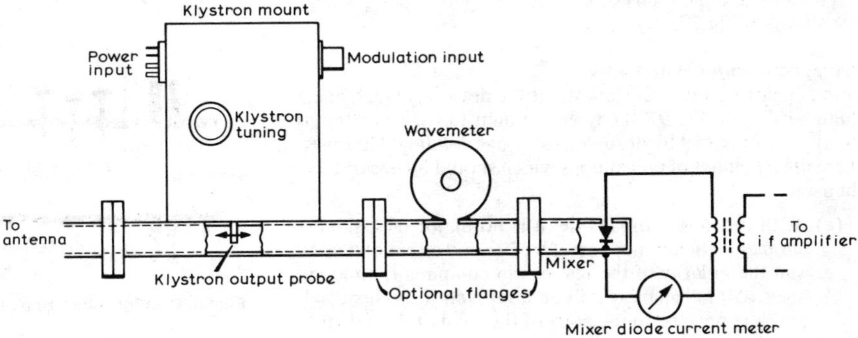

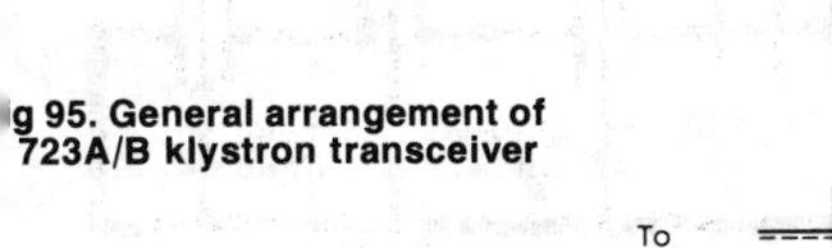
g 95. General arrangement of 723A/B klystron transceiver

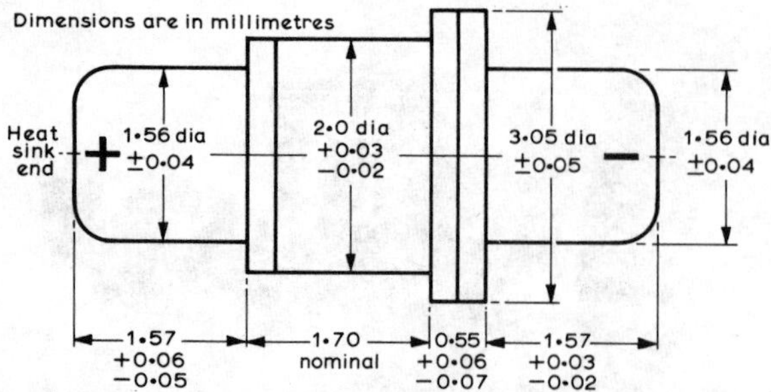

Fig 97. The outline dimensions of a typical low-power Gunn diode encapsulation

wide-band fm of highly acceptable quality, and can be readily fitted with an automatic frequency control. Most important, Gunn diodes, the low-power types only, are available on the surplus market at a moderate price. At present, high-power versions which generate typically 500mW do not yet seem to have percolated through to the surplus market.

The output power of the low-power types, of which the Mullard CXY11 series are examples, is in the range 5 to 15mW. This makes them ideal as local oscillators for receivers where the reserve power available, 10 to 15dB, makes possible a simple yet efficient method of oscillator injection. These levels of power also are adequate for transmitters: the potential range over line-of-sight paths to be expected varies from a minimum of about 50 miles when using dishes 1ft in diameter to a maximum of about 1,000 miles when using dishes 3ft in diameter.

Early attempts to use Gunn oscillators were not always successful. Many of the problems appeared when an attempt was made to tune them over a usefully wide range when erratic tuning was observed. In some cases this was due simply to poor mechanical design or construction and therefore could be identified easily. However, in other cases the oscillator would jump in frequency perhaps by hundreds of megahertz, stop oscillating, remain at a fixed frequency or even tune backwards. The same diode would often behave perfectly in an apparently identical cavity. The temperamental nature of high-frequency semiconductor devices seems at its worst in these negative-resistance types.

More recently, there seem to have been fewer problems, which presumably is due to better Gunn diodes, and to improved cavity design and construction.

Gunn oscillators can be tuned electrically by varactors, but this has been little used by amateurs to date, presumably because suitable devices have not yet reached the surplus market.

The outline dimensions of a common Gunn diode package are shown in Fig 97.

Precautions with Gunn diodes

Gunn diodes are relatively indestructible devices, in fact, being quite small (see Fig 97 for typical dimensions), probably as many have been lost by dropping as by overloading. However, there are a number of precautions which should be observed in their use:

(a) With low-power diodes there is no major heat-sinking problem. Diodes may therefore be used either end up to suit the polarity of the rest of the equipment, although their thermal stability will be improved if the heat sink end is connected to the body of the cavity rather than to the choke system. To improve heat-sinking, the hea sink end of the diode should be a tight fit in its mount an the contact area should be maximized by removing burr A trace of heat conducting grease may be applied to th connection. Although the encapsulation is quite stron in pure compression, shear forces should be kept ve small. The flanged end of the diode should therefore be loose mechanical fit in its mount to allow for any mi alignment.

(b) The diode must never be operated with reversed pola ity. They require 7 to 10V at 140mA under norm operating conditions. At lower applied voltages a muc higher current is drawn, so the full working voltag should be applied directly.

(c) Being negative-resistance devices, the diodes will tend t oscillate with any stray inductances. They are partic larly prone to produce spurii at vhf, and to prevent this suppressor consisting of a 10 to 100Ω resistor in serie with a 0·01μF capacitor should be fitted at the cold en of the rf choke feeding the dc. Failures have occurred du to parasitic oscillations at audio frequency due to th diode being operated via the secondary of a modulatio transformer, the primary being undamped.

It is also worth fitting a zener diode at the cold end c the choke to eliminate voltage spikes. It should be rated a about 0·5V above the maximum working voltage, inclu ing modulation and afc voltages.

(d) With more powerful diodes there is the risk that th power density at the end of the waveguide may excee the maximum safe level of 10mW/cm². The density fall to a much lower level even at a few inches away from th end of the guide, but nevertheless care should be taken a all times.

A simple 10GHz receiver with transmitte option

Design and construction

The receiver is shown schematically in Fig 98. It consists of simple mixer assembly which is connected directly to a Gun oscillator of the type which defines its cavity by an iris. Th mixer uses a length of waveguide into which is fitted the mixe diode, the hot end of which is decoupled and feeds the i. amplifier in the conventional way. Diodes of the 1N23 type ar recommended; those with later prefixes (E, F, G) are preferre for their lower noise figures. The signal-input end of the guid can be of any convenient length, and it is fitted with a matchin screw or screws to match the mixer diode to the waveguide. Th length of the waveguide at the local oscillator end is critical: i needs to be made electrically an odd number of quarter guid

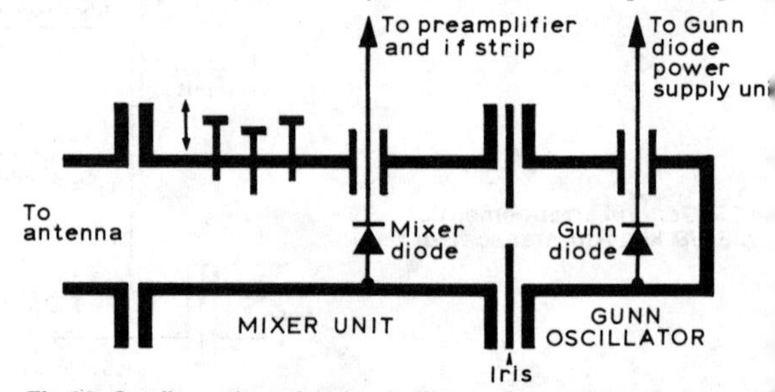

Fig 98. Configuration of a simple transceiver using a Gunn osci lator

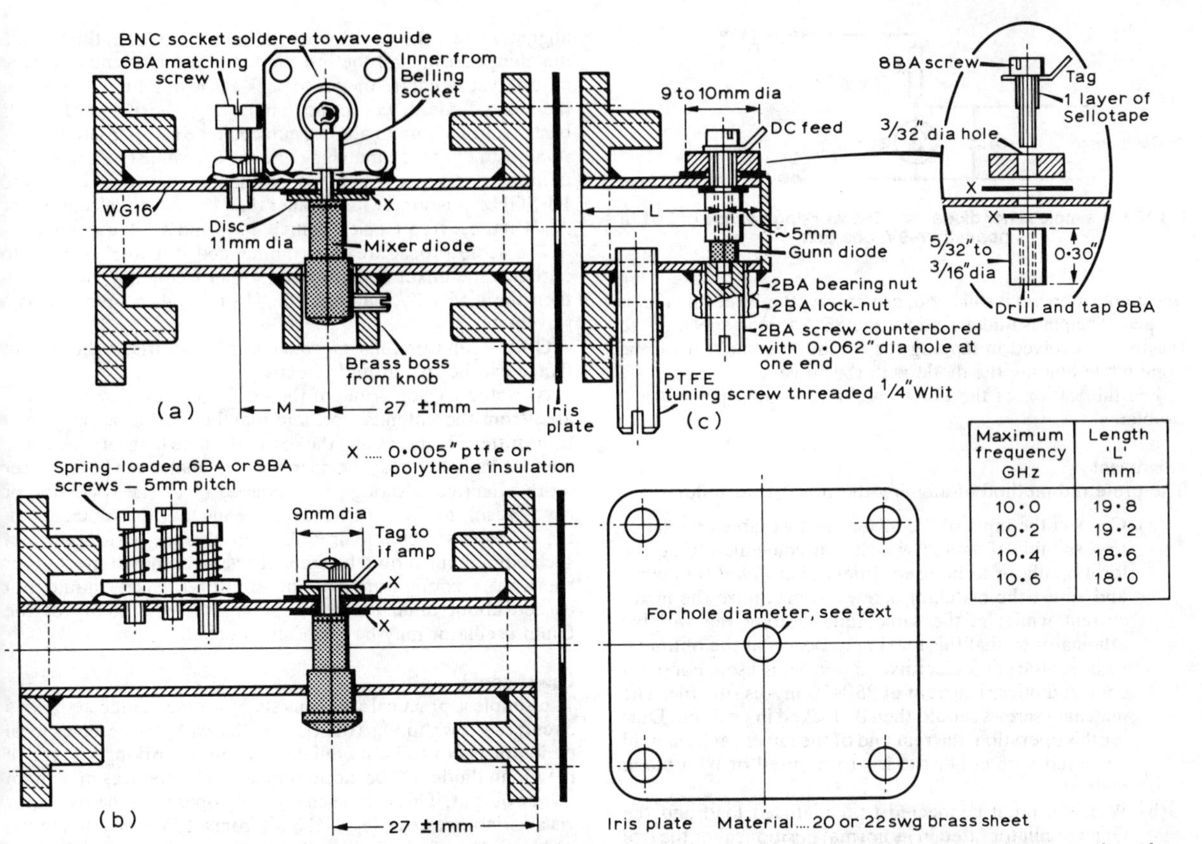

Maximum frequency GHz	Length 'L' mm
10·0	19·8
10·2	19·2
10·4	18·6
10·6	18·0

Fig 99. (a) One form of mixer assembly. The length *L* is 11mm for 10–10·1GHz and 10mm for 10·3–10·4GHz. (b) An alternative mixer. The matching screws can be placed where convenient. (c) A reliable Gunn oscillator

wavelengths, ie $n\lambda_g/4$, where n is 1, 3, 5, 7 etc as is convenient. This rear cavity is closed by the same iris as is used to define the Gunn oscillator cavity.

A basic problem in the design of receivers is how to couple the local oscillator drive into the mixer while keeping to a minimum the amount of signal lost by its coupling with the local oscillator circuitry. A feature of the present design is that this isolation is provided simply by using the iris to undercouple the Gunn oscillator. Apart from simplifying construction compared with other methods of achieving isolation, for example by using a directional coupler, the present method has the important advantage of enabling the loaded Q of the Gunn oscillator to be significantly increased. This means that the stability of the Gunn oscillator is improved, which in turn raises the overall efficiency of the receiver.

Practical details

Two forms of the mixer assembly (which were developed quite independently) are shown in Figs 99(a) and 99(b). Also shown as Fig 99(c) is a recommended design of Gunn oscillator. A feature of the design given in Fig 99 is that it requires the minimum amount of tools in its fabrication. Points that can be made with respect to its construction are:

(a) First drill a hole about $\frac{3}{32}$in diameter centrally through the broad faces of a suitable length of waveguide 16 and open one of the holes to 0·25in diameter.

(b) Remove the brass centre boss from a knob intended to be used with a 0·25in diameter shaft by breaking away the surrounding bakelite. Fit the two flanges in their positions and solder these and the boss in a single operation. The latter may be jigged using a 0·25in drill. Note that the position of the input flange is not critical in any way, but that at the oscillator end it should be within about 1mm of that specified.

(c) Drill and tap the holes for the matching screw. Remove the excess waveguide projecting from the flanges by sawing, filing and finally by grinding on wet silicon carbide paper backed by a sheet of glass. Carefully remove burrs from the inside of the guide, especially where the insulation is to be fitted.

(d) Carefully file away the lip from the mixer diode large connection (or from the adaptor if the diode is of the reversible type) so that the connection is uniformly 0·25in diameter.

(e) Drill the hole in the capacitor plate so that it is a tight fit on the diode pin. When assembling, press the diode against the wall of the guide before tightening the grub screw.

The construction of the design given in Fig 99(b) is similar, but in this case the diode is bolted to the bypass capacitor at one end, while the other end is made a tight fit in the wall of the guide. In mixer diodes that are reversible it will be found that

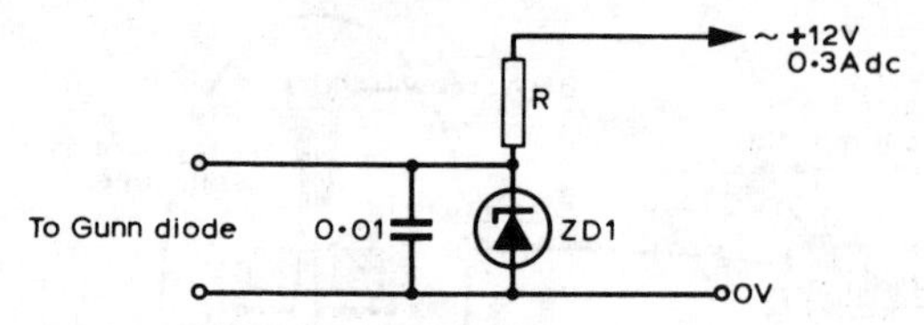

Fig 100. A simple zener diode psu. The working voltage of ZD1 is normally 7–9V. See text

one connection pin is solid and, preferably, this is the one that is tapped. The pin is undersized for the 8BA thread specified, so the forces involved in tapping the thread are small: it can be done while holding the diode with the fingers.

The fabrication of the Gunn oscillator should present few problems.

Alignment

The preferred method of aligning the mixer is as follows:

(a) Connect the input of the mixer via a variable attenuator to a suitable rf source, which can conveniently be the local oscillator to be used. Inject rf at *signal* frequency and adjust the matching screws to maximize the mixer current while, at the same time, setting the variable attenuator so that this maximum occurs at the optimum value for the particular mixer diode being used. For point contact diodes, a current of 250–500μA is suitable. The matching screws should then be locked in position. During this operation, the rear end of the mixer cavity should be closed with either the iris to be used or by a blank plate.

(b) With the input connected to a matched load and the Gunn oscillator fitted in its normal position, alter the size of the hole in the iris plate until the diode current is the same as that during (a). Obviously the size of the hole will depend on the output power of the oscillator but will normally be in the range 3–5mm diameter.

In an alternative method, the receiver is assembled with the antenna and waveguide run which is to be used. For initial tests an iris about 4mm ($\frac{3}{16}$in) in diameter is suggested. The matching screw is then adjusted to set the mixer current at about 250μA. If the current is greater than this, even when the screw does not penetrate into the guide, then the iris should be reduced in diameter. Conversely, if the mixer current obtained with up to the maximum recommended penetration of 3–4mm is still less than the optimum value, then the size of the iris should be increased. If the size exceeds 6mm, then there is a risk that the stability of the Gunn oscillator might be adversely affected. If the mixer current is still too low, then a fault in construction, a poor mixer diode or a badly-matched antenna should be suspected. The latter can be checked by substituting a large horn (or any other well-matched load) for the antenna in question. If correct operation is obtained, then the matching of the original antenna should be improved using, for example, another set of matching screws fitted to the antenna.

Alternative configurations

The critical dimension of the mixer assembly is the length of the guide between the diode and the iris. This was determined experimentally by fabricating an adjustable iris from 0·02in thick sheet 0·9in wide which was bent into the form of a square "U" with the base 0·4in wide. Using the set-up described under alignment (a), the position of the iris, the penetration of the matching screws and the insertion loss of the attenuator were adjusted at signal frequency to peak at the optimum current for the mixer diode. It was found that moving the iris away from its best position by up to about 1mm could be compensated for by re-adjustment of the matching screws. The value given in Fig 99, 27mm, represents a compromise length between 10·0 and 10·5GHz. It is somewhat smaller than the values calculated for $3\lambda_g/4$ at these frequencies, namely 29·8 and 27·4 respectively.

The same procedure is recommended if it were desired to optimize the mixer assembly at another frequency, or to lengthen the cavity by making it $5\lambda_g/4$ or $7\lambda_g/4$ in order to fit a wavemeter.

Other Gunn oscillators which employ an iris at the output flange can be substituted directly.

As noted earlier, some of the local oscillator power is radiated from the antenna port and may be used as a low-power transmitter. By increasing the size of the hole in the iris plate the amount radiated may be increased to make the transmitter more effective, although the reduced Q of the oscillator or cavity resulting from this change means that the efficiency of the receiver will be impaired. Despite this the performance of such equipment should be competitive with that of most other transceiver configurations. The size of the iris should not exceed about 6mm diameter, otherwise the stability of the Gunn oscillator may be seriously affected.

Power supply unit

The simplest practical psu consists of a zener diode stabilized circuit as shown in Fig 100. If, as in this case, the receiver local oscillator is not to be modulated, then the working voltage of the Gunn diode will be close to that which produces maximum power output. This can be checked by operating the oscillator via a variable resistor (eg 47Ω 3W) from a 12V 0·3A dc supply, and using the mixer diode current as a power indicator. A zener diode of the optimum working voltage and 1W rating can then be fitted, and the value of resistor R set so that the zener diode passes 50–100mA with the Gunn diode connected.

It is of advantage to be able to frequency modulate the receiver local oscillator with tone since this enables cw signals to be detected. If there is a chance that the unit will be used as a transceiver, if only as a low-power spare equipment, then it is worthwhile also to build in speech modulating facilities.

A modulated power supply for the Gunn diode is given in Fig 101, using the 7805 voltage regulator ic to provide a stable voltage for the Gunn diode. The voltage is varied by altering the resistor in its common lead. Better performance may be obtained from the LM317 ic which is designed for use as a variable-voltage regulator. Both are short-circuit protected.

Setting the operating voltage

The Gunn voltage should be set to about 0·5 to 1V above the point where oscillation starts. At this point the oscillator can be tuned smoothly over a wide range using the dielectric tuning screw, and its noise sidebands will be quietest. This will be important if a low i.f. such as 10·7MHz is used. Slightly more output can be obtained at higher voltages, but the oscillator will then be less well behaved. The front panel control used for fine tuning of the Gunn by varying the voltage should have a very restricted range, less than 1V, corresponding perhaps to 5MHz.

Because the voltage/frequency relation for the Gunn diode is not linear, the deviation obtained will vary as the supply voltage is increased. The operating point should be set with a preset resistor.

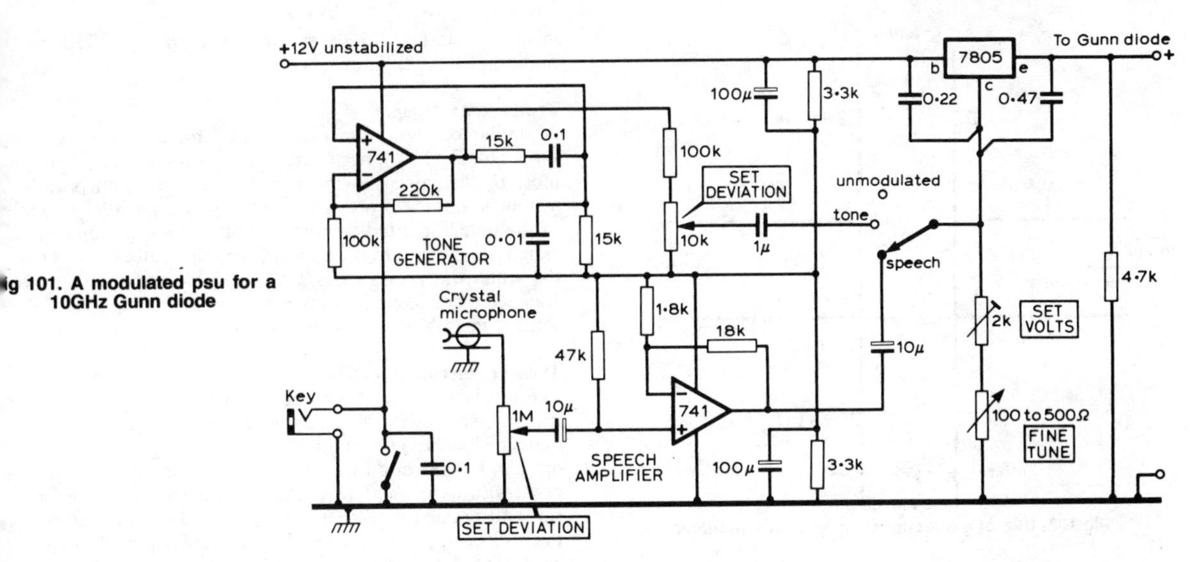

Fig 101. A modulated psu for a 10GHz Gunn diode

Equipment design

The design philosophy described below has been widely used with much success. It results in efficient equipment which can employ a variety of forms of local oscillator, and which can be modified step-by-step to produce more sophisticated equipment.

Receiver design

Two factors strongly influence the design of receivers for use at these frequencies.

(a) RF amplifiers are usually not practical, so the performance of the receiver is dominated by that of the mixer.

(b) It is not easy to make tuned circuits in waveguide systems, so there is the risk of a significant loss of signal via the mixer into the local oscillator circuitry, and vice versa. This effect is made worse by the necessity to operate the local oscillator close in frequency to the signal, typically within 1 per cent, in order that the noise factor of the i.f. amplifier can be kept low. At lower frequencies there is usually no problem because sharply tuned circuits can be used at both signal and oscillator frequencies, which are also usually spaced by several per cent, so that the coupling between the two is limited. In any case, rf stages can be fitted which greatly increases their isolation.

A simple method of reducing these losses is obviously to have loose coupling between the local oscillator circuitry and that at signal frequency. Because the signal must be coupled tightly to the mixer, this implies that there must be loose coupling between the mixer and the local oscillator. However, there is a price to be paid for this simplicity: as the degree of coupling is reduced, so the amount of local oscillator power must be proportionately increased to maintain efficient operating conditions for the mixer.

This approach is used in the Polaplexer configuration, the isolation between signal and local oscillator circuits being achieved by cross-polarizing the circuits. A second method is to use a directional coupler in the following way.

A basic characteristic of a coupler is that it is a reciprocal device. Consider as an example the 10dB cross-coupler described on p 9.31 and illustrated schematically in Fig 102. If a power P is applied to port A, then $0 \cdot 9P$ will appear at port C, and $0 \cdot 1P$ will appear at port B. If the coupler is well made, negligible power will be coupled to port D. If the same power is applied to port D, then $0 \cdot 9P$ will appear at port B, $0 \cdot 1P$ at port C and none at port A, and so on. Thus, by the appropriate choice of ports, two signals can be combined with a controlled degree of coupling.

In applying these characteristics to the design of a receiver, suppose that a local oscillator is connected to port D as shown in Fig 103. Then 9mW will appear at port B, 1mW at port C, and perhaps a few microwatts at port A. If a mixer is now connected to port C, and an antenna to port A, then the mixer will receive an injection of 1mW from the local oscillator and also 90 per cent of the signal applied to port A. Only 10 per cent of the signal will be coupled to port B and lost. Clearly, if the local oscillator power is increased to 100mW, and the mixer injection is maintained at 1mW, then the coupling coefficient of the directional coupler can be reduced to 20dB. In this case, only 1 per cent of the signal applied to port A would be coupled to port B and lost, a trivial proportion.

The only design work involved is the specification of the coupling coefficient of the directional coupler, and this is simply

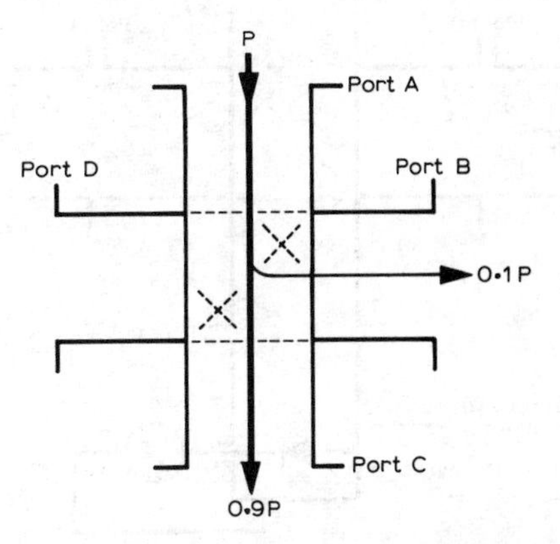

Fig 102. Power relationships in a directional coupler

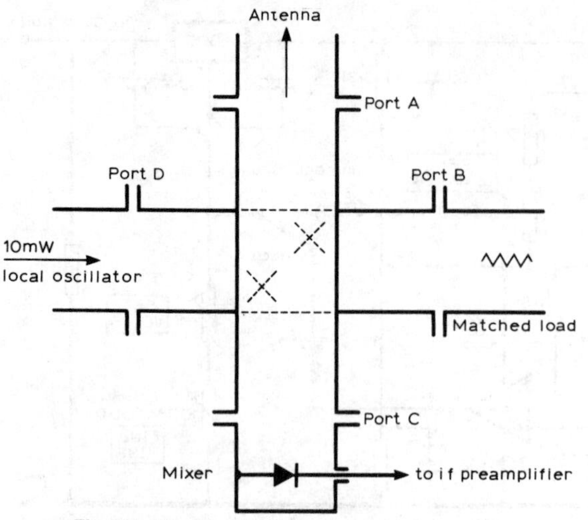

Fig 103. Use of a directional coupler in a receiver

the ratio of the power of the local oscillator to that required to operate the mixer efficiently. The latter power for point contact diodes is typically 0·25 to 1mW. Therefore, if a 723A/B klystron for example is used as the local oscillator, and is assumed to generate 30mW, then the coupling coefficient will be 30 to 120:1, ie 15 to 22dB. If the maximum coupling to be used is 10dB, a reasonable value, then the minimum local oscillator power will be 2·5 to 10mW.

The receiver is completed by fitting a load to port B to absorb the excess local oscillator power. This is desirable in stabilizing the local oscillator, and may also be important from a safety point of view. A wavemeter, which can be either an absorption or transmission type, can be fitted between the directional coupler and the local oscillator, or between the coupler and the mixer. The latter position is usually preferred as it reduces the pulling of the oscillator.

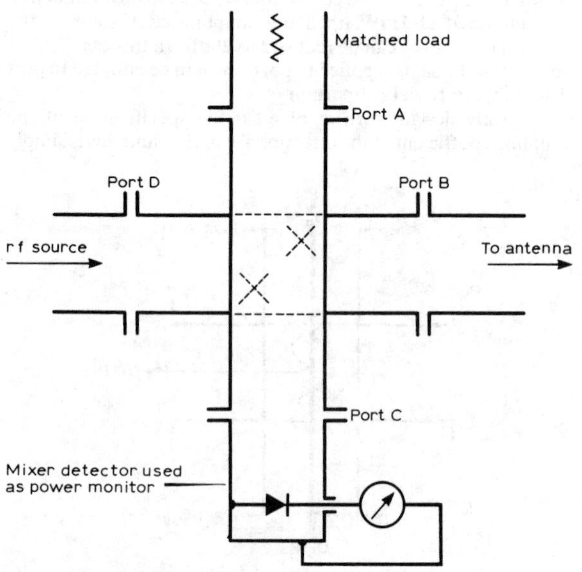

Fig 104. Use of a directional coupler in a transmitter

Transmitter design

A similar configuration can be used for a transmitter, as i shown by Fig 104. The rf source connected to port D supplie most of the power to the antenna connected to port B. A proportion of the power generated, typically 1mW, is couple to the detector fitted to port C. This gives a continuous indication of power output which is desirable in all cases but essential when the rf source is a klystron. A wavemeter may be connected between the coupler and either the detector or the r source. Port A is terminated in a load.

Transceiver configuration

The receiver shown schematically in Fig 103 differs from the transmitter shown in Fig 104 only in that the positions of the matched load and the antenna are interchanged, and therefore one can be converted to the other quite simply. An attractive procedure is to build two similar units with one set up as a transmitter and the second as a receiver. Both units can be used to check each other, and if one breaks down, then the other can be operated as a transceiver.

Various methods used to change from transmit to receive modes are summarized in Fig 105:

(a) Manual change-over of a single antenna. This is facilitated by using a bend to bring the ports into the same plane, and by terminating the antenna feed with a length of flexible waveguide. If square waveguide flanges are used, then pins may be fitted into the fixing holes of one flange and the flanges held together by bulldog clips. A wooden dummy load (Fig 80) can be slipped easily from port to port.
(b) Using separate receive/transmit antennas carefully aligned along the same axis. This technique allows full duplex operation.
(c) Using a circulator. This also allows full duplex operation. Note that the circulator must be connected with the correct rotation or the transmitter will be connected directly to the receiver.
(d) Changeover switches. A simple changeover switch can only be used with a separate transmitter and then only if the transmitter is switched off during receive. With transceivers, a more complex switch is required since the transmit port should be connected to a load if not to the antenna.
(e) A 3dB coupler. Allows full duplex operation, but there is a loss of 3dB on both transmit and receive.

Broadband i.f. amplifiers

In receivers in which it is not possible to use an rf stage, the overall noise factor is set by the sum of the noise factor of the mixer, that of the preamplifier (or head amplifier), together with any coupling losses between the two. For this reason considerable attention must be paid to the performance of the preamplifier, and to minimize losses it is often mounted as close as possible to the mixer. If a preamplifier has a reasonable gain then its output lead usually can be of any convenient length, and the noise factor of the following stages also becomes less critical.

The choice of first i.f. depends on the equipment with which the i.f. amplifier is to be used. If the receiver is an independent

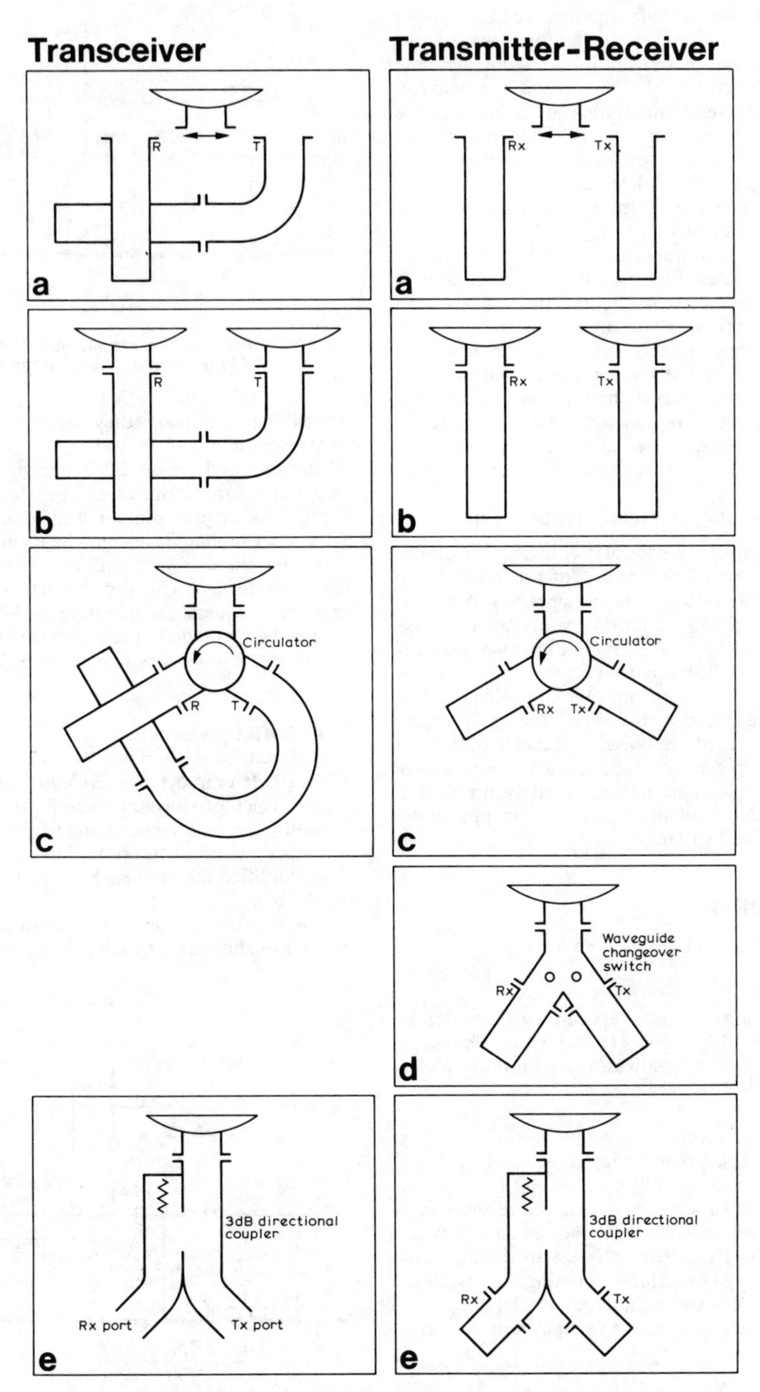

Fig 105. Various methods for connecting antennas

unit, then any suitable i.f. can be used. However, all transceivers must use the same i.f. if continual retuning is to be avoided.

As noted above, a separate receiver allows freedom in the choice of the i.f., which is of particular significance at the higher microwave frequencies with equipment based on waveguide. This is because all oscillators and mutiplier chains generate noise sidebands, which extend either side of the nominal frequency, and which decrease in amplitude the further they are removed from the centre frequency. Noise sidebands that are spaced at the i.f. away from the local oscillator frequency and which pass to the mixer will be detected as signal and will appear as noise at the output of the mixer. The signal-to-noise ratio of the output therefore will suffer.

This effect occurs at all frequencies, but is exaggerated at high microwave frequencies, because the local oscillator is necessarily operated relatively close to the frequency of the signal, usually within 1 per cent, to produce a low i.f. so that the noise factor of the following preamplifier can be kept low. This means that both receiver input channels are vulnerable to higher-amplitude noise sidebands than would be the case if a higher i.f. could be used. A second factor is that tuned circuits which are used at lower frequencies to reject local oscillator noise are difficult to make in waveguide, as has been noted earlier.

Two methods are used to get around this problem:

(a) To use as high an i.f. as possible without significantly degrading the overall noise factor of the receiver by increasing the noise factor of the preamplifier. A practical upper limit for the i.f. at this time would appear to be in the region of 200MHz. A high i.f. also has the advantage of reducing confusion between the response of the receiver to the main channel and the image channel.

(b) To use a balanced mixer. In this device, the a.m. (but not the fm) components of the noise are cancelled. A relatively low i.f. then can be used, and a value of about 30MHz appears to be typical. Unfortunately, no 10GHz designs intended for amateur construction appear to have been produced so far.

Practical i.f. amplifiers

Examples of i.f. amplifiers in use are as follows:

Narrow-band receivers

Conventional narrow-band a.m. receivers can be used to detect tone-modulated wide-band fm signals (F2A) with little loss in efficiency, provided that the i.f. bandwidth exceeds the modulation frequency (normally 1kHz).

Standard broadcast fm receivers

When preceded by a suitable preamplifier, these receivers have proved quite adequate as i.f. amplifiers.

A recommended modification is to encase the receiver in a complete metallic box: this will eliminate their main disadvantage—i.f. breakthrough. The receiver is set to a quiet frequency, the receiver tuning being done by tuning the first local oscillator. This approach has the advantages of a high first i.f., and the possibility of using the fm set for fine tuning over a ±10MHz range.

Practical preamplifiers

Tuned preamplifiers using 40673 dual-gate mosfets are shown in Figs 106 and 107. Although designed specifically for 28 and

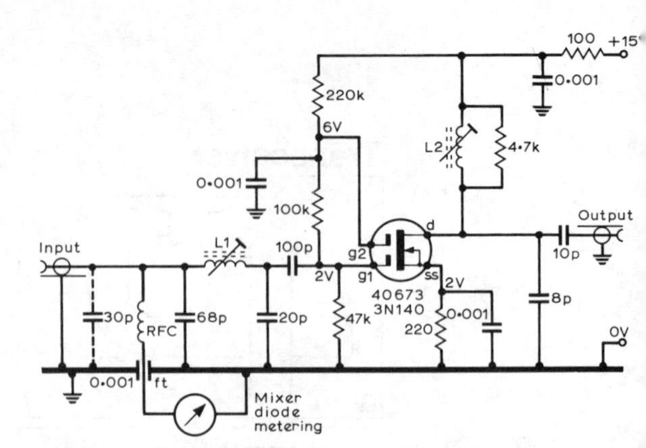

Fig 106. A preamplifier for use at 30MHz. RFC: 33μH: L1, L2: 18t 24swg enam copper wire on ¼in diam former

144MHz respectively, they can easily be modified for use at nearby frequencies.

The untuned preamplifiers shown in Figs 108 and 109 are best suited for systems using a tunable i.f. The circuit shown in Fig 108 has a gain of about 10dB and a noise factor of about 2dB. Two similar stages may be connected in cascade, the rfc providing the dc return path for the mixer being omitted from the second stage. This preamplifier has been used with intermediate frequencies operating at 30 to 200MHz, the only change being made to use an rfc having an inductance of from 30μH at the lower frequencies to 3μH at the higher frequencies.

A 10·7MHz preamplifier

The circuit for a low-noise 10·7MHz preamplifier is shown in Fig 110. It employs two BFY90 transistors in a dc-coupled circuit which produces an overall gain of approximately 35dB. The output is via a tuned circuit which provides some selectivity and also facilitates the provision of a low-impedance output. The amplified mixer noise level at this output will be typically 10–100μV.

The dc path for the mixer current is provided by the rfc and the optional meter. The latter is used to set the optimum mixer

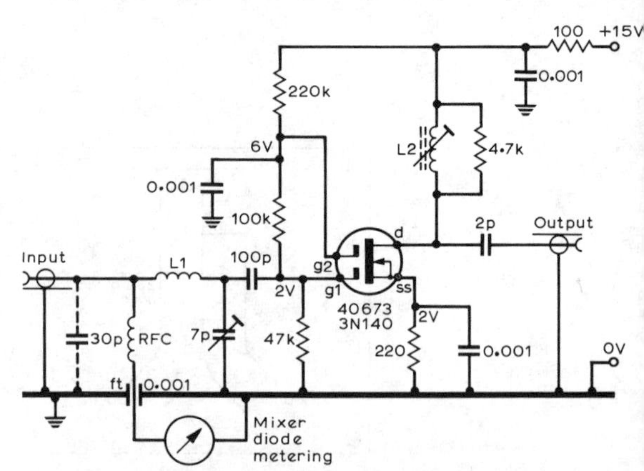

Fig 107. A preamplifier for use at about 150MHz. RFC: 3μH. L1: 5t 20swg enam copper wire ¼in i.d. ½in long. L2: ditto 6t on ¼in diam former

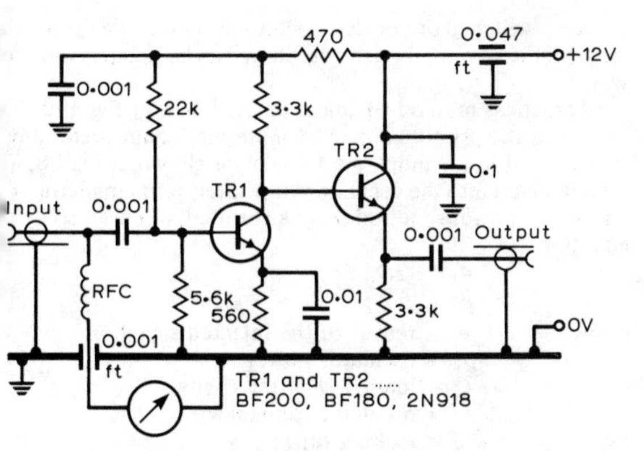

g 108. An untuned preamplifier for use at 10–150MHz. Its gain approximately 25dB. The rfc should have a value ranging from 100μH at 10MHz to 3μH at 150MHz

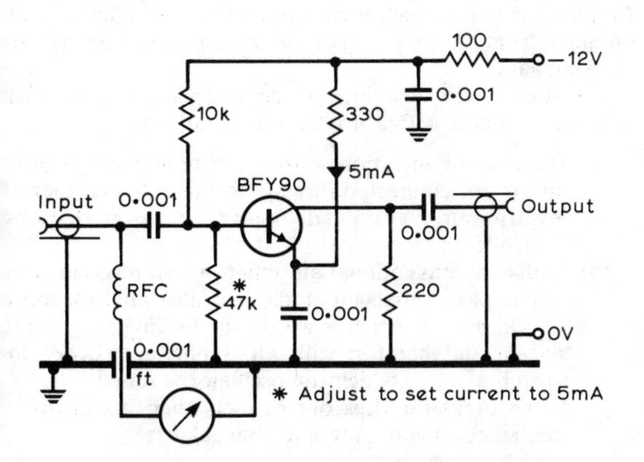

g 109. An untuned preamplifier for use at 30–200MHz. RFC as in Fig 108

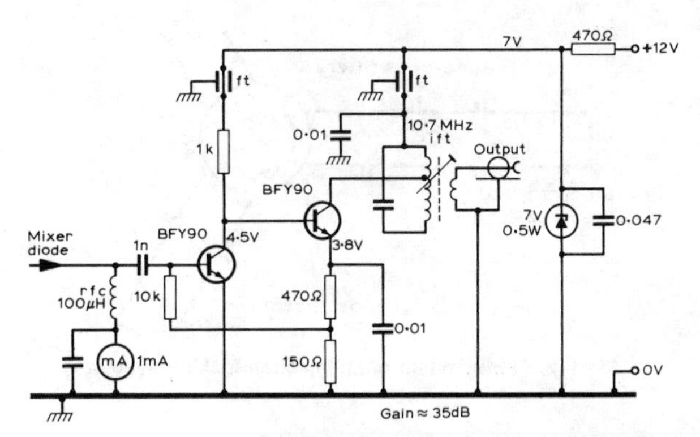

Fig 110. A low-noise 10·7MHz preamplifier with a gain of approximately 35dB

diode current and also can be the indicator for an absorption wavemeter for frequency measurement. As with all preamplifiers, the connection to the mixer diode should be as short as possible.

A 10·7MHz receiver

The circuit shown in Fig 111 is based on the CA3089E fm ic and the LM380 audio ic. The signal from the preamplifier shown in Fig 110 is fed to the CA3089E via a standard fm broadcast i.f. filter, the noise output of the preamplifier being well in excess of the 12μV required to achieve full limiting. The fm signal is demodulated in a quadrature detector using the tuned circuit LC which is also resonant at 10·7MHz. The Q of this circuit can be adjusted for best linearity by altering the parallel resistor. The demodulated audio output is taken from pin 6 and amplified by the LM380 ic, which will produce up to 1W audio in a 8Ω load.

A voltage logarithmically proportional to signal level is produced at pin 13. This is used to drive the S-meter which is an invaluable aid in aligning the high-gain antennas normally employed on microwaves. Pin 7 produces an afc output which will

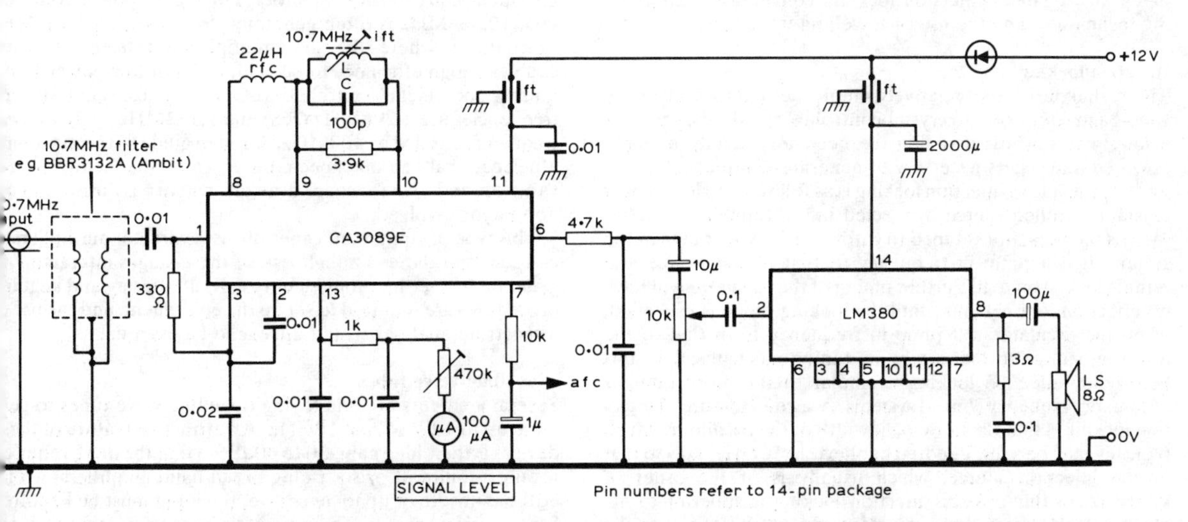

g 111. A 10·7MHz wide-band fm receiver. A suitable 10·7MHz filter would be the BBR3132A (Ambit). LM380 pin numbers refer to the 14-pin package

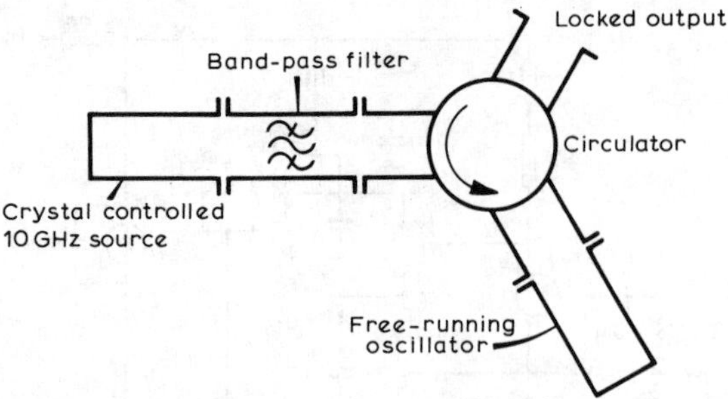

Fig 112. Configuration of an injection locking system

either source or sink a current of up to 100μA when feeding into a voltage of about 6V. This can be used, for example, to alter the supply voltage to a Gunn oscillator over a range of a few tenths of a volt, which will provide a useful afc capability.

Narrow-band 10GHz equipment

Narrow-band equipment is inevitably much more complicated than the wide-band equipment described earlier, in terms of both its construction and also the techniques required in its alignment. The main justification for changing to a narrow-band system is to increase the potential of a given size of equipment for working non-optical paths. As has been noted earlier, most wide-band equipment will cope with all line-of-sight paths available, and the extra complexity of narrow-band equipment can hardly be justified for this latter type of working.

The potential gain from reducing bandwidth is significant. If the i.f. bandwidth of the receiver can be reduced from 1MHz even only to 10kHz, then the system gain will be 20dB. If a.m. is used rather than fm then there will be a further gain of 10dB. A similar improvement in system gain can of course be achieved by pulse-modulating wide-band equipment, a technique sadly neglected by amateurs.

Interest in narrow-band equipment is comparatively recent in the UK, but already there are three approaches currently being investigated—injection locking, conventional multiplying techniques, and the use of travelling-wave tubes.

Injection locking

This technique offers a relatively simple method for converting wide-band equipment to crystal-controlled standards, and goes a long way towards avoiding the need for a chain of high-powered multipliers necessary to generate rf directly.

The principle of injection locking is as follows. If a low-power crystal-controlled source is injected into a tunable oscillator, then as the oscillator is tuned to within the locking range of the system, it will jump in frequency to that of the source and remain locked on to it. Further tuning of the oscillator will have no effect on its frequency until the locking range is exceeded, when the oscillator will jump in frequency from that of the injection source to that set by its tuning mechanism. In this behaviour, injection locking is similar to the more familiar automatic frequency control systems. A second feature of injection locking is that the noise bandwidth of the oscillator, which typically may be a few hundred kilohertz at 10GHz, falls to that of the injection source, which usually is of the order of kilohertz. In this respect, injection locking is superior to afc systems. If the injected signal is frequency modulated, then the oscillator will follow the modulation. Of course, if the injection source is switched off, or the oscillator is set outside the locki range of the system, then the oscillator can be tuned in the usu way.

A practical method of injection is shown in Fig 112. Th output of the crystal-controlled multiplier chain preferably first filtered in a bandpass filter such as shown in Fig 88, an then injected into the oscillator via a three-port circulator. Th amount of power required to lock the oscillator is given by th equation:

$$\frac{p_i}{p_o} = \left(\frac{2Q\Delta f}{f}\right)^2$$

where
p_i = power of the injected signal
p_o = oscillator power
Q = loaded Q of the cavity
f = oscillator frequency
Δf = locking range

As an example, if a klystron is assumed to have a loaded Q 100, then the relative power required to lock over a 5MH range at 10GHz is 0·01, or −20dB. If the klystron outp power is 30mW, then the injection power required is 300μV In the sense that a much-increased crystal-controlled output obtained from the source, then the system can be described showing gain.

A feature of this technique which makes it particularly sui able for amateurs is that it is relatively fail-safe.

(a) Because the injection source is of relatively low pow and is not connected directly to the antenna, then th level of spurious output does not need to be so rigorous controlled.
(b) Unlike a conventional amplifier, which responds to a signals passed to its input, the oscillator will lock only c to a harmonic which is within the locking range of th system, and therefore will only amplify inputs very clos in frequency to which the oscillator is tuned.
(c) If the oscillator slips out of lock, then it will drift i frequency usually only a few megahertz.

Direct multiplication

The equipment currently being developed employs standar multiplier stages using varactors. For higher-power transmi ters, 10,368MHz is often generated from existing 3,456MH transmitters where the low multiplication factor involve enables a high efficiency to be achieved. For low-power tran mitters and crystal-controlled 10GHz sources, other startin frequencies are 1,296MHz (×8) and 1,152MHz (×9), or eve frequencies as low as 400MHz. A rough guide to the maximu efficiency that can be expected is given by the factor $1/n^2$ fo varactors and $1/2n$ for snap varactors, where n is the multiplic tion factor involved.

This type of equipment generally uses varactor multipliers i cascade, and there is a high risk of these stages interacting t generate further harmonics. Very careful filtering and alignin procedures are required to set up the equipment, and the use o a spectrum analyser would appear to be essential.

Travelling-wave tubes

Several amateurs are employing travelling-wave tubes to ge erate up to 10W of rf at 10GHz. An attractive feature of thes devices is their high gain, 30 to 40dB, so that the drive require is only a milliwatt or so. Being broad-band amplifiers, with 3dB bandwidth of up to an octave, the input must be kept fre from spurious signals. Their main disadvantage is that they ar elaborate devices which require a fairly complicated psu.

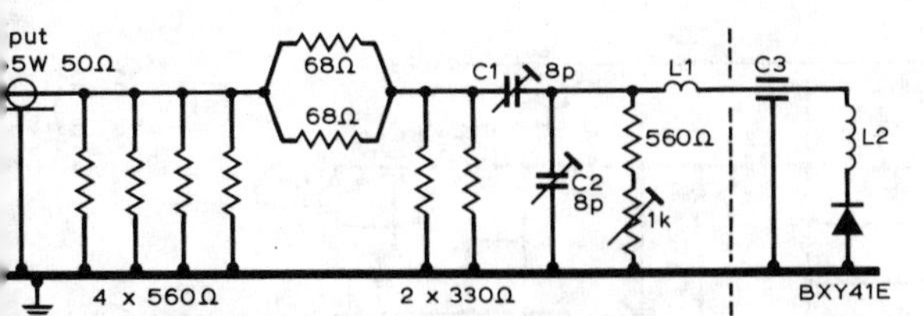

ig 113. Circuit of a varactor multiplier to 10GHz. All resistors W carbon, leads to be as short as practical. L1: 1¼t 4mm i.d. C1, :2: film dielectric capacitors. C3: capacitor formed between diode post and wall of guide. L2: inductance of diode post

A 10GHz varactor multiplier

A single varactor multiplier driven by a crystal-controlled ource at a much lower frequency, a 432MHz transmitter for xample, would appear to be an attractive way of getting on .0GHz. However, there are two problems with this type of nultiplier system. The first is the vulnerability to changes in perating conditions: minor variations in drive level or in their oad, for instance, can cause the output to break up into a large umber of spurii. This effect may be difficult to detect, let alone ure, without the use of a spectrum analyser, an instrument to vhich not many amateurs are likely to have ready access. The econd problem is that the output, even though crystal controlled, may have a perhaps-surprisingly large bandwidth, and herefore may be far from "narrow-band" by the standards of ower frequencies.

The circuit of a multiplier which has been proved to be most eliable is shown in Fig 113. An important feature of the design is the carefully-tuned impulse generator represented by L2/C3. This has been optimized for the BXY41E snap varactor although the MA44150 and MD4901 varactors can be used. It may not work with other diodes.

A second feature is the 6dB attenuator which is fitted between the varactor circuit proper and the driver in order to reduce the amount of interaction between the two. It appears that many of the problems with this type of multiplier are due to instability in the preceding driver stage caused by the widely-varying load represented by the varactor. The attenuator of course contributes to the low overall efficiency of the circuit (a characteristic which amateurs as a group appear unduly reluctant to accept), but this seems to be a small price to pay for reliability of operation. For a drive of about 2·5W at 350–550MHz, about 2–4mW of rf at 10GHz can be obtained, which is sufficient for the local oscillator of a receiver, for a small transmitter or as the driver to a travelling-wave tube.

The layout of the multiplier is shown in Fig 114. Note that it is essential to use a filter to remove harmonics from the output. Those shown in Figs 87 and 88 are suitable.

The second major problem with this approach to getting on 10GHz is the noise bandwidth of the 10GHz output. This noise originates in the oscillator and early multiplier circuits and is always present. However, it becomes much more apparent at 10GHz because the bandwidth is proportional to the square of the overall multiplication factor. Even with the least noisy driver available, which used a 101MHz neutralized glass crystal in a carefully-designed Butler circuit, the noise measured from a single-ended mixer was about 10dB worse than a Gunn oscillator when using a 10·7MHz i.f., and about 7dB when using a 30MHz i.f..

Fig 114. Layout of main components of the multiplier

A crystal-controlled frequency marker for 10GHz

A characteristic of operating wide-band equipment on 10GHz is that by the time one multiplies the uncertainties in frequencies of both transmitter and receiver and in the pointing of the highly directional antennas normally employed, the number of permutations that need to be covered before contact is established can be very considerable. The more-skilled operators tend to be more successful mainly because they can set their frequencies more precisely and can direct their antennas more accurately, and this can reduce very considerably the number of permutations that need to be covered before contact is made.

The simple unit to be described generates a large number of signals at precisely known frequencies which can be used to calibrate wide-band receivers and transmitters accurately, thus effectively eliminating uncertainties from this source. Although the output power of individual harmonics is very low, signals are detectable with efficient receivers even with up to 45dB attenuation between the unit and the receiver. This means that the unit can provide a rough check on the sensitivity of a receiver; signals should be detected by even the most inefficient of receivers. The output power is more than adequate for use as a frequency reference for an afc system, but is insufficient for the unit to be employed as a signal source for tuning up antennas. The range of the unit as a transmitter is only about 10m when antennas of 15dB gain are used.

Constructional details

The circuit diagram and layout of the marker unit are shown in Figs 115, 116 and 117. A components list is given in Table 8. TR1 is a crystal oscillator on 48MHz, and this is followed by a

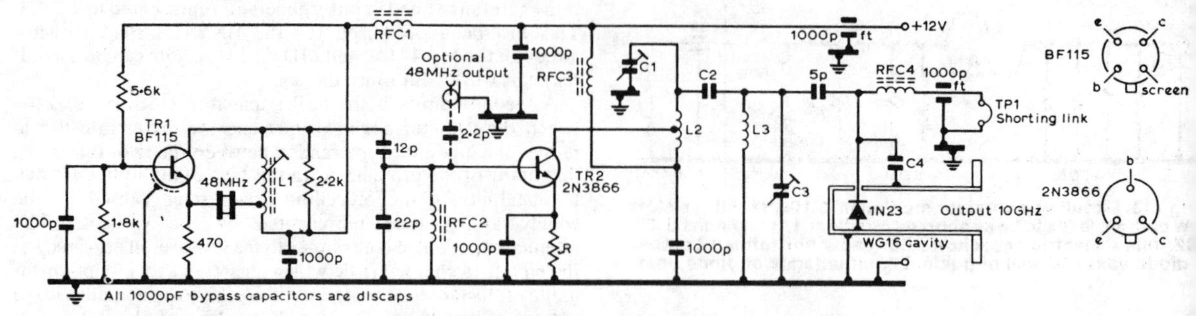

Fig 115. Circuit of the 10GHz frequency marker

doubler to 96MHz and by a mixer diode used as the final multiplier. TR2 should be fitted with a small heat sink and its emitter lead kept as short as possible, typically about $\frac{1}{8}$in. Its output is via a bandpass filter to reduce 48MHz feedthrough. This vhf circuitry is mounted on a piece of single-sided pc board which is bolted to the inside of the lid of a $4\frac{3}{8}$ by $2\frac{3}{8}$ by 1in die-cast box. The final multiplier consists of a length of WG16, at least $2\frac{3}{8}$in long, which is closed at one end, with a 1N23 mixer diode mounted centrally 0·29in (7·5mm) from the closed end. The waveguide is clamped to the outside of the lid, connection to the diode being made using the inner of a Belling-Lee socket which passes through holes drilled in the pc board and the lid, as shown in Fig 118.

In setting up the unit, L1 is adjusted to produce the maximum voltage across R; C1 and C3 are adjusted and re-adjusted to maximize the diode current measured at TP1. The value of R is then changed as necessary to set this current to 20–25mA. Finally, the frequency of the crystal oscillator can be checked on a counter via the optional output connector or using, for example, a 144MHz receiver. Some useful performance parameters are given in Table 9.

The choice of 48MHz and 96MHz as stage frequencies represents a compromise between generating a reasonable number of signals within the tuning range of most receivers, while minimizing the risk of confusion due to difficulty in identifying each of the harmonics. Other crystals may of course be

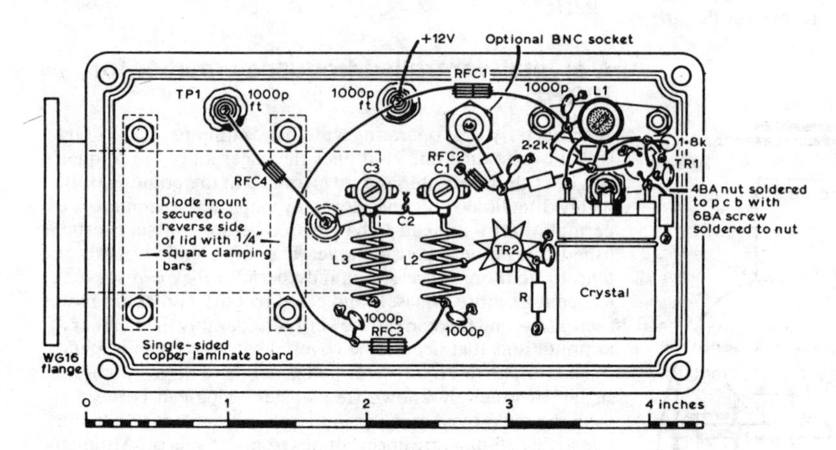

Fig 116. Layout of frequency marker

Fig 117. The 10GHz frequency marker

Table 8. Components list for frequency marker

1	10t 28g enam copper on 0·3in former tapped 1t from cold end
2, L3	5t 18g ¼in i.d. ½in long, L2 centre tapped
FC1, 3	2½t 28g enam copper on two FX1115 ferrite beads
FC2	2½t 28g enam copper on one FX1115 ferrite bead
FC4	10t 28g enam copper on one FX1115 ferrite bead
	68–100Ω, adjust during alignment to set 1N23 current to 20–25mA
1, C3	30pF trimmer: can be 20pF trimmer + 10pF fixed capacitor
2	Two lengths thin single-strand insulated wire twisted together for ½in
4	formed by a 0·005in ptfe or polythene sheet between the end of the 1N23 diode and the waveguide wall, as shown in Fig 118.

ısed, but there is an obvious advantage in using "round ıumber" frequencies, and especially those at such frequencies ıs 36, 54 and 72MHz which also produce harmonics at other ımateur frequencies and are therefore more easily measured.

Jsing the frequency marker

The unit as described produces relatively strong signals at)6MHz spacings, with signals about 20dB weaker spaced every ł8MHz. Note that no provision is made for modulating the ›utput. This is unnecessary if the local oscillator of the receiver ;an be frequency modulated with a tone, which greatly assists inding signals. In calibrating a receiver it is essential that its ocal oscillator is already calibrated to within about 20MHz ısing a wavemeter. The self-calibrating wavemeter shown in Fig 76 is more than adequate for this purpose. The marker is ›referably connected directly to the receiver via a variable ıttenuator, but alternatively it can be spaced from the receiver nput by a few feet. With 20–30dB attenuation, the receiver hould detect weak signals which are harmonics of 96MHz ›nly. If the attenuation is reduced to around 10dB, the 48MHz ntermediate harmonics should be as weak signals, together with the now-strong signals corresponding to 96MHz harmon-cs.

The number of signals heard will be more than perhaps expected because the receiver will almost certainly have no ›rotection against second-channel signals. Thus a receiver which is fitted with a 30MHz i.f. will respond to the relatively strong marker signals at 9,984MHz (104 × 96MHz) when its

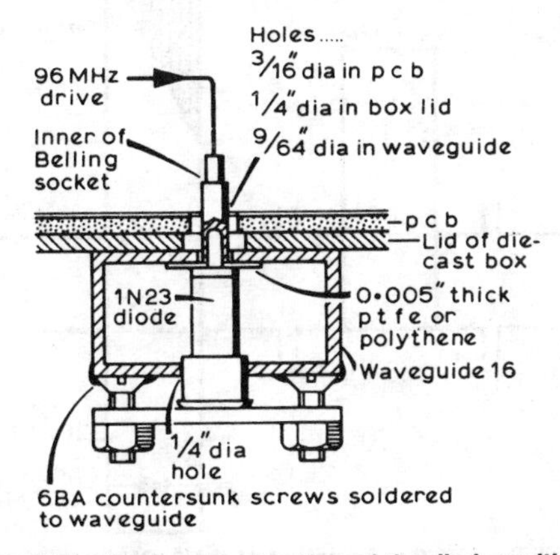

Fig 118. Section showing construction of the diode multiplier

Table 9. Performance figures for the 10GHz frequency marker

V supply	12V
I supply	25–40mA
$\frac{\Delta f}{\Delta V}$ (at 10GHz)	8kHz/V (change in final frequency as supply voltage is varied)
RF level of 96MHz harmonics in range 10·0–10·2GHz	−75dBm (approx)
RF level of intermediate 48MHz harmonics in range 10·0–10·2GHz	−95dBm (approx)

local oscillator is tuned to either 9,954 or 10,014MHz, and to signals at 10,080MHz (105 × 96MHz) when tuned to either 10,050 or 10,110MHz. The receiver will also respond to the relatively weak marker signals at 10,032MHz (209 × 48MHz) when the local oscillator is tuned to either 10,002 or 10,062MHz, and so on. The receiver local oscillator may therefore be calibrated precisely at several points, from which the (two) corresponding signal channels may be determined (provided that the i.f. is known accurately). If a larger number of calibration points is required, then either the i.f. may temporarily be changed, or a different crystal may be used in the marker.

The unit is small enough to be used "in the field" on a regular basis by simply waving it in front of the antenna. Alternatively, it could easily be built into the receiver, coupled by a 10dB directional coupler, to provide an instant check on its calibration, and in turn that of the transmitter.

24GHz EQUIPMENT

The basic techniques used for 24GHz (or for other waveguide bands) are of course the same as those used at 10GHz. The equipment can therefore be of similar form to that used on the latter frequency, although physically only about half its size. However, a feature of 24GHz operation which distinguishes it from that at lower frequencies is the strong dependence of propagation on the weather. The 24GHz allocation is near in frequency to the peak of a water absorption band, which means that water present in the atmosphere tends to absorb the radiation, thereby significantly increasing propagation losses. For this reason, the 24GHz part of the spectrum has been little used professionally and consequently there is little surplus equipment available; some test equipment omits this part of the spectrum. In particular, there appear to be available few klystrons which can be made to cover the amateur band at 24·0 to 24·25GHz. However, Gunn oscillators have recently become available at prices amateurs can afford. There seems to be no real reason why anyone with 10GHz experience should not now be successful at this higher frequency and, because of its special propagation characteristics, to contribute significantly to the art.

Equipment parameters

In order to estimate the size of equipment required for working long optical paths on 24GHz, some measure of the total path losses is required. The extra attenuation due to the presence of water molecules in the atmosphere of course covers an infinite range of values because it depends on the level of humidity, the size and shape of raindrops and the number intercepted. However, the following values are probably not untypical:

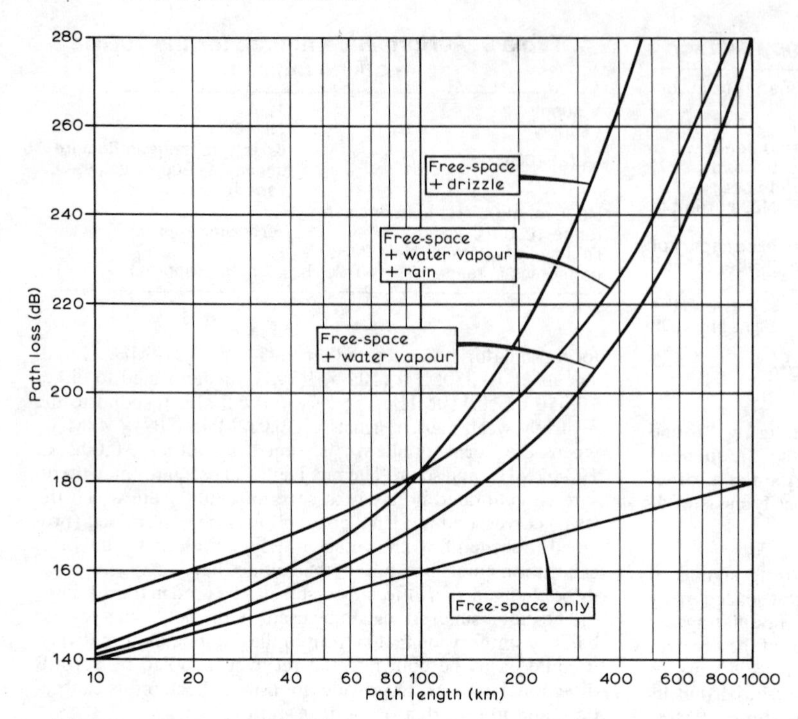

Fig 119. Influence of weather on path loss at 24GHz

(a) Water vapour at 0·1dB/km;
(b) light drizzle at 0·23dB/km assumed to cover all the path; and
(c) moderate rain, 5mm/h, at 1·2dB/km, one rain cell 10km diameter assumed per path.

These values, added to the normal free-space attenuation, are used to provide the various estimates of total line-of-sight path loss shown in Fig 119.

The potential range of various sizes of equipment are given in Table 10. This assumes an i.f. bandwidth of 10kHz or 1MHz, a receiver noise factor of 10dB, an i.f. signal/noise ratio of 10dB and antennas 1ft in diameter. The latter will have a gain of approximately 35dB and a 3dB-beamwidth of about 3°. Clearly the equipment required is significantly larger than at lower frequencies, and there is a greater incentive to use narrow-band techniques.

A simple 24GHz wide-band transceiver

The following design for a 24GHz transceiver uses basically the same techniques as those described earlier for 10GHz. The ready availability of commercial Gunn oscillators such as the Plessey GD033 for 24GHz means that the rather greater problems of constructing oscillators for this frequency compared with 10GHz can be avoided at modest cost without the need for access to machine tools.

The general configuration of the transceiver is shown in Fig 120. It is based on the use of a directional coupler in the manner described on p 9.46. In the receive mode, the Gunn oscillator is connected to port 1, and matched load to port 2, the mixer and wavemeter to port 3 and the antenna to port 4. By this means, the Gunn oscillator operates into a matched load, thus generating the best conditions for its stable operation.

In the transmit mode, the connections to ports 1 and 3 are

Table 10. Potential ranges for sizes of equipment

Transmitter power		
Wide-band	**Narrow-band**	**Range (km)**
1mW	10μW	28– 70
10mW	100μW	60–120
100mW	1mW	100–180
1W	10mW	130–160
10W	100mW	170–340

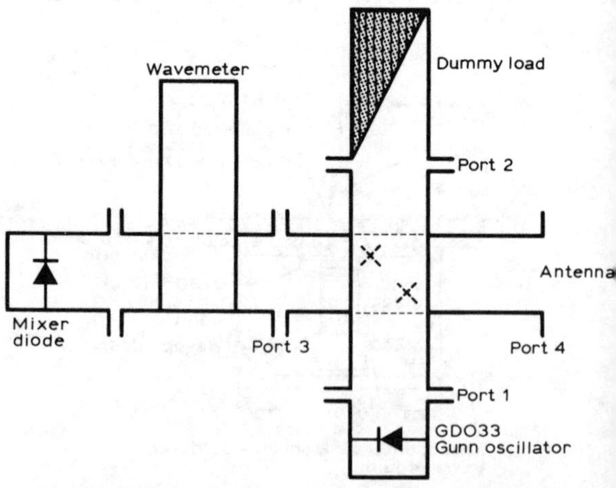

Fig 120. Configuration of the 24GHz transceiver

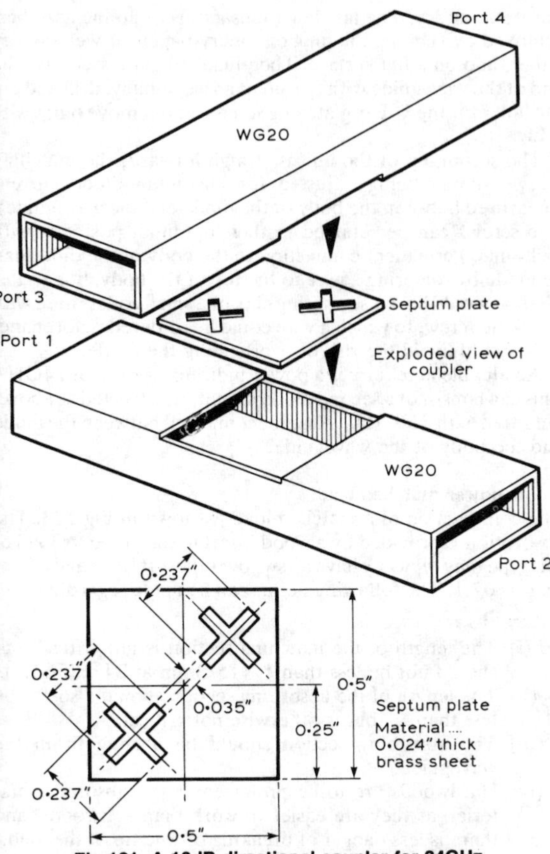

Fig 121. A 10dB directional coupler for 24GHz

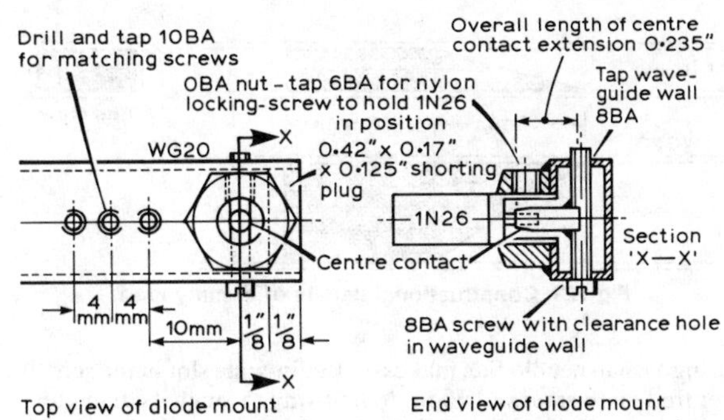

Fig 122. A 1N26 mixer for 24GHz

reversed, when the mixer can now be used as a power indicator and for checking frequency using the wavemeter.

In following sections, the construction of the individual components are described.

A 10dB directional coupler

To provide the correct level of local oscillator injection to the mixer diode, normally approximately 1mW, a directional coupler having a coupling coefficient of about 10dB is required with an oscillator generating 10mW of rf. A suitable coupler is the Moreno cross-coupler, the construction of which is shown in Fig 121. It can be made using hand tools using the following procedure.

Take two pieces of WG20 and file away the broad faces of both to leave 0·5in-long gaps. The two pieces should then fit snugly together—if this is not the case further filing will be necessary. The most difficult part of the coupler to make is the septum plate, but if the following procedure is used a minimum of trouble should be encountered.

First mark out the outside edges of the septum plate on a larger piece of brass, but do not cut out at this stage. Next, mark out the centre lines of the crosses, and drill holes approximately 0·030in in diameter adjacent to each other along these lines so that their edges are just touching. Take a small pointed rectangular-section needle file and reduce its thickness with a grinding wheel to about 0·030in over the last 0·25in of its length. The thin edge of the file is then used to remove the metal between the holes, and the larger edge to file the edges of the slots to the correct size. The dimensions of the slots should be monitored using vernier calipers. Once the slots are correct, the septum plate can be sawn out from the sheet, filed to size and deburred.

The septum plate is then placed in the cut-out of one of the pieces of waveguide, and the other piece placed over it so that the pieces are jigged together. The waveguides should then be firmly clamped together, heated with a small gas flame, and soldered along all the joining edges. After cooling, the coupler should be inspected for signs of solder in the coupling slots or inside the waveguides. If this has happened the soldering will have to be done again.

The directivity can be checked by first measuring the power coupled to the mixer diode using the configuration shown in Fig 120, that is, the power coupled in the correct direction. The oscillator and load are then interchanged. The power now indicated by the mixer is that due to imperfect directivity and should be lower by at least 10dB than indicated previously. If the relative powers can be measured by a power meter, then the directivity can obviously be measured in absolute terms.

A 1N26 mixer

The mixer shown in Fig 122 can be made using a vertical bench drill and hand tools only, no lathe work being necessary. The method of construction is given below.

First, square off the end of the waveguide, by marking out with a right angle, and filing to the marks. A 0BA hole is then drilled and tapped 0·25in from the squared-off end. The tapping should be commenced using a tapered tap, changing over to a plug tap when the tapered tap comes up against the opposite wall. Assemble a 0BA nut on a 0BA screw, the latter preferably cadmium plated or sufficiently dirty so as not to take solder readily. Screw this a short distance into the waveguide and tighten up the nut against the waveguide wall. Using a hot-plate or small flame to provide heat, solder the nut in place. When cool, remove the screw and drill out the nut and waveguide wall underneath the nut using a 5·7mm drill. Drill and tap the nut 6BA through one of its faces, and remove the burr on the inside using the 5·7mm drill.

Drill with an 8BA tapping drill through the centre of the narrow wall of the waveguide, 0·25in from the end, continuing through the opposite wall. Open up one of the holes to 8BA clearance, and tap the other 8BA. Assemble a 0·5in 8BA brass screw through the clearance hole and screw tightly into the opposite wall. Using the 5·7mm drill inserted through the 0BA nut, make a mark on the 8BA screw. Remove the screw and,

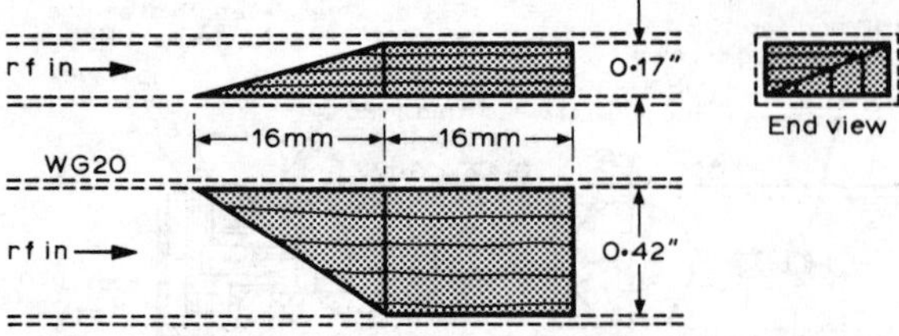

Fig 123. Constructional details of dummy load

using a small needle file, make a 0·090in-wide slot in the screw, centred on the marked point, to half-way through its diameter.

Next, prepare the centre conductor for the 1N26 in the following way. Remove the centre connecting piece from a cable-mounting bnc socket, saw off the end remote from the metal fingers, and file to length (0·235in). *Carefully* squeeze the fingers inwards at a point roughly half-way down their length, using the wire-cutting edges of a pair of pliers, so that an opposite pair of fingers are nearly touching. The connecting piece should then be a good push fit on the centre pin of the 1N26. An alternative connecting piece which does not require such modification can be one of the contacts from the high-quality ptfe type of transistor holder.

Wrap one layer of Sellotape around the bottom half of the 1N26, to insulate it when it is in operation, and push the modified centre connector on to the pin of the diode, making sure that it is fully home. Re-insert the 8BA screw into the waveguide, tightening until the filed slot is uppermost. Insert the 1N26 diode into the 0BA nut, pushing in until the centre connector engages into the filed slot in the 8BA screw. The end of the outer casing of the diode should then be approximately level with the inside wall of the waveguide. Using as large a soldering iron as will fit, quickly solder the centre contact to the 8BA screw, using a minimum of solder. Ensure that not too large a blob of solder remains on the joint. As soon as the solder solidifies, remove the diode to reduce the chance of damage, and check that the layer of Sellotape has not been damaged.

The shorting plug is then made by sawing out a piece of 0·125in brass sheet and carefully filing to size. Constant checking of the dimensions with a micrometer during filing will

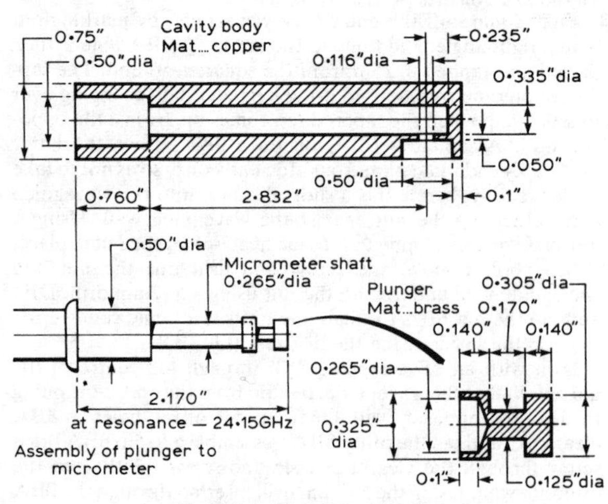

Fig 124. A high-*Q* wavemeter

ensure accuracy. The last few thousandths of an inch are best removed by rubbing the plug on emery-paper, or wet and dry paper, laid on a flat surface. The plug is then pressed into the end of the waveguide with the aid of a vice. Finally, drill and tap the holes for the 10BA matching screws, and remove burrs with a file.

The setting-up of the unit is straightforward; the matching screws simply being adjusted for maximum diode current (measured between the body of the diode and the waveguide). The screws can be retained in their optimum positions with lock-nuts. Permanent connection to the body of the diode can be made by soldering a wire to the top of the body, but a safer method would be to use a spring clip, or a small collar fitted with a locking screw, to which a wire could be soldered beforehand. This would avoid the risk of overheating the diode.

A valuable accessory is a power indicator for use at 24GHz. This can consist of a second diode mount, constructed as above but fitted with a 50–100μA meter connected between the diode and the body of the waveguide.

A low-power matched load

The construction of a matched load is shown in Fig 123. The absorption is provided by a wood insert in the guide. A load of this type may typically have a vswr over the 24GHz band of less than 1·07:1. The following points can be made regarding construction.

(i) The length of the matching section is not critical, but should not be less than λ_g (15·3mm at 24·125GHz).
(ii) The length of the absorbing section should also not be less than λ_g, but is otherwise not critical.
(iii) The absorbing section should be a snug fit in the waveguide.
(iv) Hardwoods are to be preferred as the absorbing material, as they are easier to work than softwoods, and there is less danger of breaking off the tip of the load.

The performance of the load is easily checked by moving a metal plate backwards and forwards just behind the load. No change in diode current in the receiver indicates that the load is absorbing all the power incident on it.

An alternative material for the load is the black conductive foam used for packing cmos integrated circuits. The power dissipation of the material is less than that of wood, although still adequate for low-power oscillators generating a few tens of milliwatts.

A high-*Q* wavemeter

The construction of a high-*Q* wavemeter for 24GHz is shown in Fig 124. The wavemeter consists of a resonant cavity which is tuned by a micrometer-driven plunger. This is coupled to the waveguide circuity via a small hole, the wall of the waveguide being removed so that the wavemeter body itself locally forms the wall of the waveguide.

The body of the wavemeter is preferably made of copper, although brass would probably be satisfactory. A standard 0–25mm micrometer head is employed. To ensure its precise alignment, the choke at the end of the plunger is first machined to near final dimensions and then bonded to the end of the micrometer shaft using an epoxy adhesive. The choke is then carefully machined to final size using very light cuts.

This type of wavemeter is not self-calibrating and it is therefore necessary to calibrate it against a standard wavemeter. When fitted to the transceiver, crystal-controlled marker signals can be used for final calibration. A simple design for the

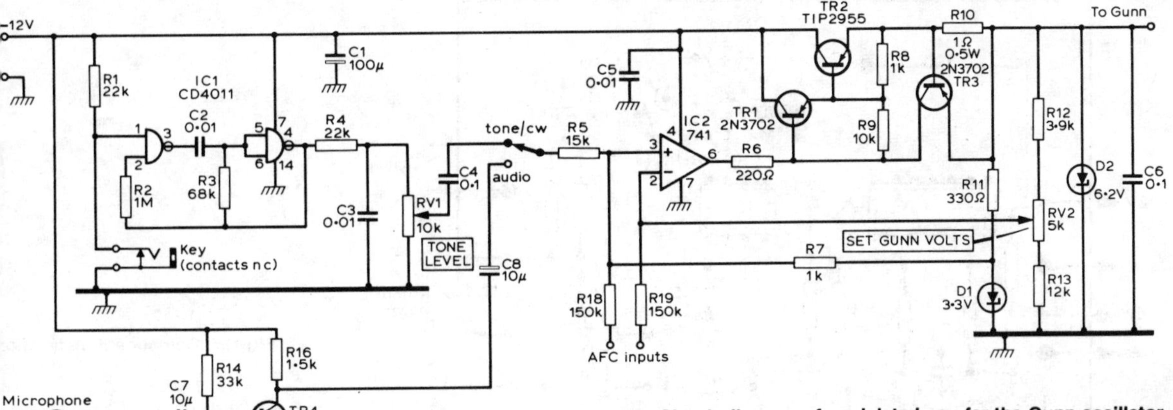

Fig 125. Circuit diagram of modulated psu for the Gunn oscillator

atter would be that shown in Fig 115 but with the WG16 eplaced by WG20, and the mixer diode changed to a diode uch as the 1N26.

A power supply/modulator unit

The circuit of a psu/modulator unit which supplies −5V at 250mA is shown in Fig 125. Note that it employs a positive-earth system in contrast to the more common practice of negative earth on 10GHz. One of its features is the inclusion of a current limiter, which makes the power supply short-circuit proof. Tone modulation is provided by a cmos oscillator followed by a simple RC filter. The microphone amplifier was designed for use with a crystal microphone, but should be suitable for most other types. In the unlikely event of more gain being required, the 330Ω resistor in the emitter of the microphone amplifier should be bypassed with a 10μF capacitor.

AFC inputs of either sense are provided, but if a negative earth i.f. strip is used, some form of level translator will be necessary. No connections are made to these inputs if the afc facility is not required.

A pcb layout for the power supply/modulator is shown in Fig 126 and the component layout in Fig 127. Double-sided copper-clad board should be used, the top surface being left copper covered to act as an earthing plane. A number of components are mounted externally, these being the tone/audio selector switch, the TIP2955 transistor (mounted on a heat sink, such as the die-cast box used to house the power supply), the microphone gain potentiometer and the output voltage

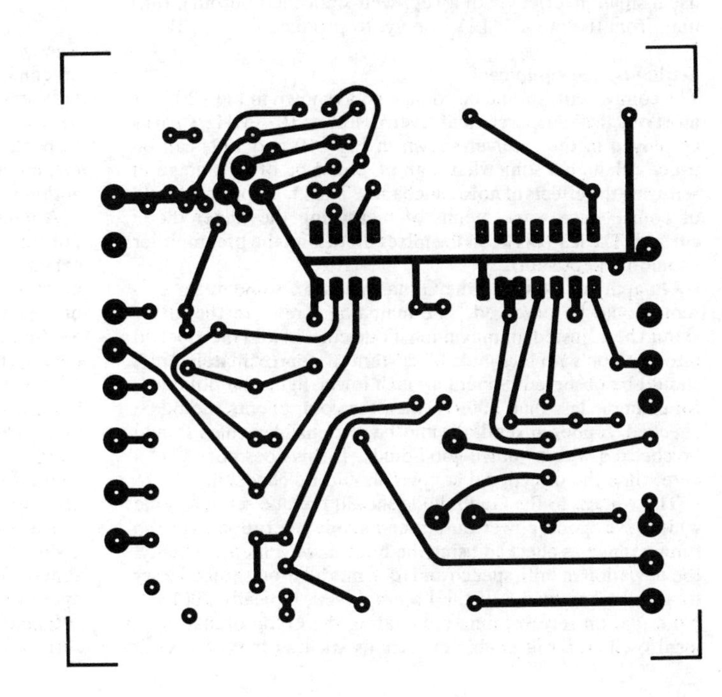

Fig 126. PCB layout for psu

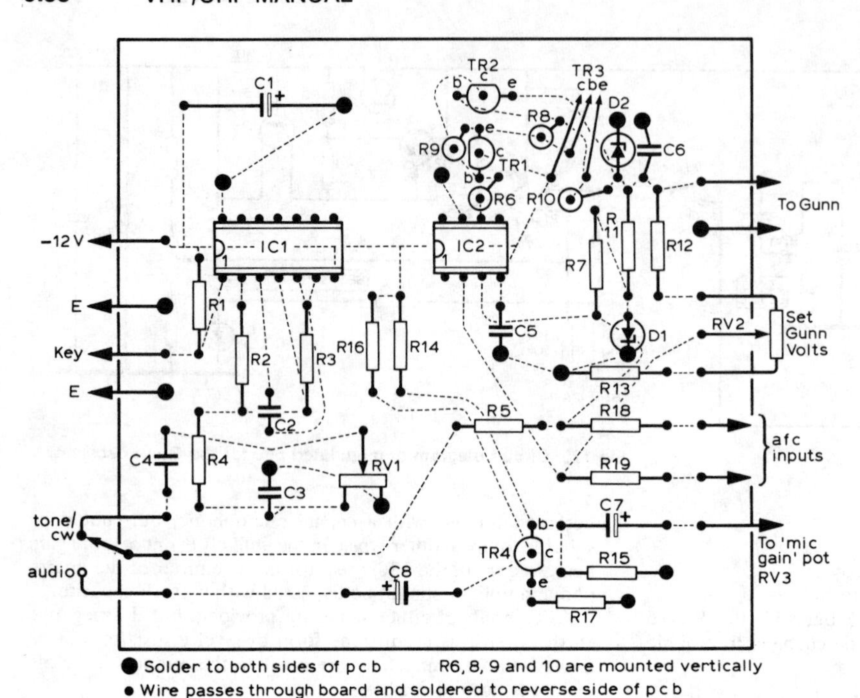

Fig 127. Component installation

setting potentiometer. The latter should be of the 10-turn variety for ease of tuning, since the available range of output voltage (3·5–5·5V) will tune the oscillator over almost 100MHz.

If the rest of the equipment has a negative earth, it will be necessary to run the power/modulator from a separate source such as another battery. A convenient alternative would be to use a small inverter (with a very well-smoothed output), running from the main + 12V supply, to produce the − 12V.

Setting up the equipment

The components should be connected as shown in Fig 120. For most practical purposes an i.f. even as low as 10·7MHz, such as employed in the receiver shown in Fig 110 and 111, can be used, although a somewhat high i.f. could be of advantage in reducing the effects of noise sidebands. The i.f. amplifier should of course have some means of measuring the mixer diode current. The lead between the mixer diode and the preamplifier should be kept short.

On applying power to the Gunn oscillator, some mixer current should be observed. The matching screws in the mixer should be adjusted for maximum diode current and then locked into position with lock-nuts. A current of approximately 1mA should be observed. Should a much lower figure be obtained, for example less than 200μA, then the components should be checked. A poor mixer diode may be responsible, which should be checked with a known good diode. If this does not effect a cure, then the directional coupler should be checked.

The voltage to the Gunn diode should then be set at a value which gives good power output and stable operation over the tuning range as checked using the built-in wavemeter. Finally, the deviation in both speech and tone modulation should be set to suit the bandwidth of the i.f. employed, typically 200kHz. Note that on receive, tone modulating the Gunn oscillator as local oscillator will enable cw signals such as from a crystal calibrator or from narrow-band equipment to be heard as an audio tone.

The mixer matching screws can be adjusted to produce the best signal-to-noise ratio using weak signals or a noise generator.

MICROWAVE ANTENNAS

The general form of the polar diagram of a typical high-gain antenna is shown in Fig 128. The 3dB and 10dB beamwidths indicated represent the angles through which the antenna may be rotated before the power transmitted or received falls respectively to a half (−3dB) or to a tenth (−10dB) of the maximum value. The 10dB level also represents the beamwidth within which most of the power is contained.

Antenna gain is of course achieved by increasing the proportion of energy transmitted in a particular direction at the expense of that in other directions. By increasing the gain of the antenna, the effective power of a transmitter or the sensitivity of a receiver may be increased, but the price to be paid is to need to align the antennas more precisely on the distant station. A special characteristic of microwave antennas is the relative ease with which high gains can be developed, values of 25 to 45dB being quite common. One is tempted to take advantage of this factor since it is a means of developing high radiated powers from small transmitters. However, the corresponding beamwidths become quite small, and much skill is required in handling the antennas effectively.

The approximate relationship between gain and beamwidth is shown in Fig 129, which assumes that the gain in both horizontal and vertical planes is the same, the usual case in amateur operation. This figure gives a guide to the accuracy with which antennas need to be pointed. For example, the 3dB beamwidth corresponding to an antenna of moderate gain, 35dB, is about

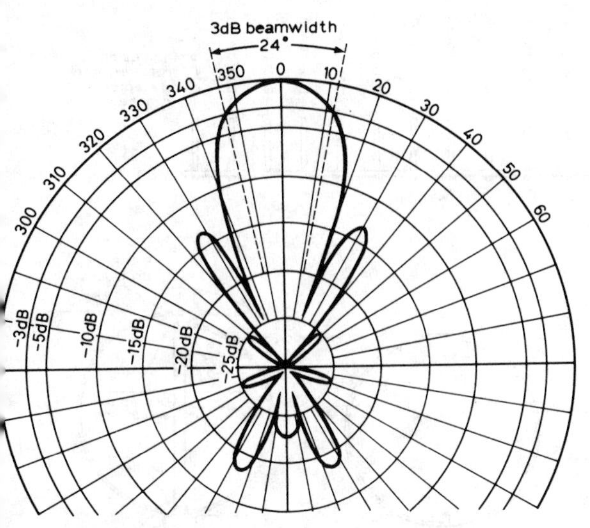

Fig 128. Typical polar diagram of a high-gain antenna. First sidelobe: −13dB; second sidelobe: −25dB

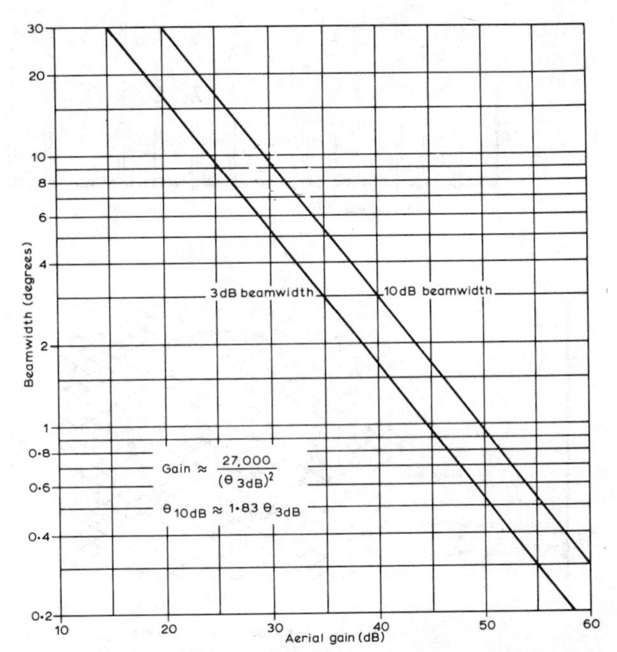

Fig 129. Approximate relationship between antenna gain and beamwidth

3°. To receive weak signals a few decibels above noise requires the antenna to be pointed within half this angle, ie within 1½°. For stronger signals, the 10dB beamwidth applies, but this is only about ± 3°. That this can be done regularly by amateurs, even under contest conditions, is a measure of the progress that has been made in this area.

Types of antenna

The three main types of antenna used on the microwave bands are Yagis, horns and parabolic reflectors. The latter are used at all frequencies while horns are restricted to the higher microwave bands. Antennas of the Yagi type are beginning to be popular on the 1·3GHz band where their compactness and low windage compared with dishes of the same gain repays the difficulty in their design and adjustment. Antennas such as corner reflectors and cylindrical paraboloids are now little used, mainly because of their low gain relative to parabolic dishes, or approximations thereto, of the same size.

Antennas for 1·3GHz

Yagi type antennas are used in most of the operations on 1·3GHz. The main reasons for this are that they offer relatively high gain with minimum weight and windage. Dishes less than about 3m in diameter are rather inefficient at 1·3GHz, and even these are inconvenient in many installations. Two well-tried designs for Yagi antennas are given below; the first has undergone considerable development since it was first described some years ago.

The loop-Yagi antenna

The design of the antenna is shown in Figs 130 and 131. Its construction is quite straightforward, but the dimensions given must be closely adhered to: after all, a 0·1in error represents about one per cent of a wavelength, or 13MHz. In drilling the boom, for example, measurements of the position of the elements should be made from a single point by adding the appropriate lengths; if the individual gaps are marked out, then errors may accumulate to an excessive degree. Elements other than the radiator are made from flat aluminium strip, the two holes in which are drilled before bending with a spacing equal to the circumference specified in the figure. The radiator is made from copper strip.

The radiator, and all screws and soldered joints, should be protected with polyurethane varnish after assembly, followed by a coat of paint on all surfaces. If inadequate attention is paid to this protection, then the gain of the antenna will decrease with time as a result of corrosion.

In the event of the specified materials not being available, some changes may be made to the thickness and width of the elements, and to the diameter of the boom, by altering the length of all elements to compensate, as detailed in Table 11. It may be found an advantage to use thicker, wider, elements to increase the strength of the antenna. As an example, an antenna could be made using a 0·75in diameter boom, and 0·25 by 0·063in loops. The correction factor would be 0·9 − 0·3 + 0·6 = 1·2 per cent. Thus all elements (ie reflector, driven element and directors) should be made 1·2 per cent longer, but the element spacing is not altered.

Provided that the antenna is constructed carefully, its feed impedance will be close to 50Ω. If an swr or impedance bridge is available, small final adjustments may be made by bending the reflector loop towards or away from the driven element.

A longer version has also been built, by adding 11 more directors at 3·56in spacing, producing an extra 1·7dB gain. The circumference of the new directors is 7·7in; D19–25 are also changed to this size.

Other versions of the antenna have been constructed for 432MHz, and 2·3, 3·4 and 10GHz. The dimensions of these have been derived by simply scaling linearly all the antenna dimensions, ie element thickness, width and circumference, height of driven element, spacing of driven element from the

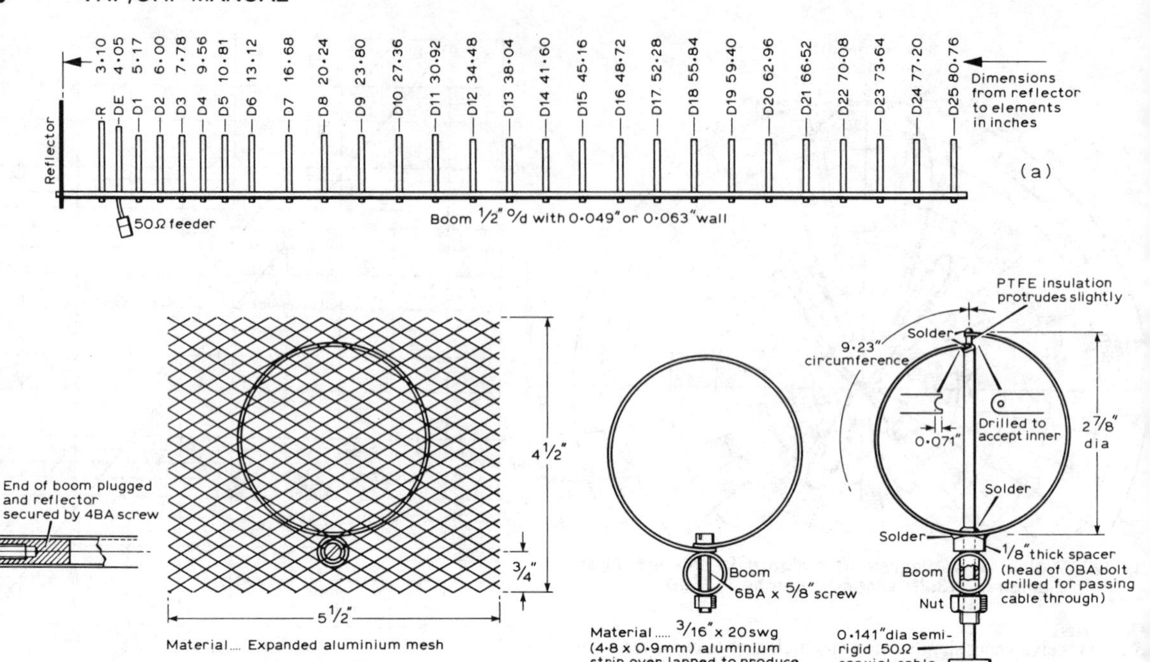

Fig 130. (a) Configuration of the loop-Yagi. The circumference of the driven element is 9·23in including the gap where the feeder is connected: the material is $\frac{3}{16}$in by 0·028in copper strip and is soldered directly to the feeder. The circumference of the aluminium strip reflector is 9·67in; directors D1–11 8·25in; directors D12–25 8·0in. The thickness and width are as for the driven element. (b) The mesh reflector and its mounting. (c) Mounting of the reflector and director elements. (d) Construction of the driven element

boom, element spacings, boom diameter and sheet reflector dimensions.

The antenna can be mounted using an element clamp from an old Yagi antenna. It is essential that the antenna be mounted on a vertical mast as horizontal supports in close proximity to the antenna can cause severe mistuning.

A long Yagi

The design of a 32-element Yagi is shown in Fig 132. Its polar diagram, and that of a shortened 27-element version of marginally lower gain, is shown in Fig 133. The element lengths are given in Table 12.

The method of construction is straightforward and evident from the figures. The critical dimensions marked should be observed, but other dimensions may be varied somewhat to suit the materials to hand. The ends of the boom should first be crimped and soldered to exclude moisture, and the mast extension and support arms then soldered into place. Starting with the smallest, the directors are soldered to the boom using a large (eg 250W) soldering iron. The elements are located in small grooves filed in the boom, and are initially cut slightly longer than required and filed to length after soldering in place. In this way the required accuracy of construction, within a few tenths of a millimetre, can be achieved. The director lengths are given in the table. The spacing between the reflector and radiator should be 73mm, and between the radiator and first director 42·2mm. The directors are all spaced 57·7mm apart.

The radiator and reflector may best be made by soldering together two L-shaped pieces of rod, one limb of each of which is accurately filed to length after bending. It may be found

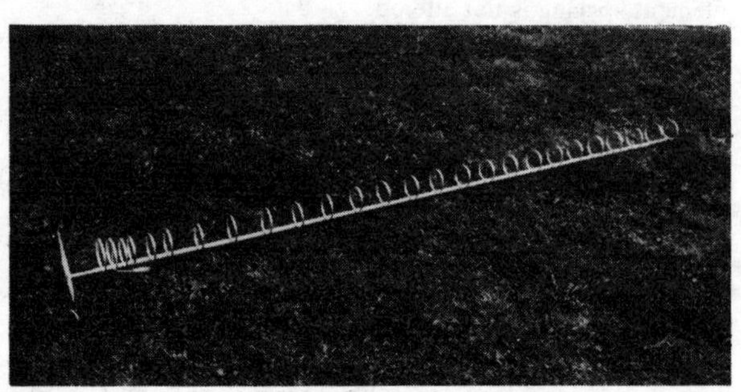

Fig 131. The completed loop-Yagi

Table 11. Correction factors to be applied to element lengths to compensate for changes in element thickness and width, and boom diameter, of 1·3GHz antenna

Thickness (in)	cf (%)	Width (in)	cf (%)	Boom dia (in)	cf (%)
0·028	0	0·1	+0·4	0	−0·7
0·063	0·6	0·1875	0	0·5	0
plot straight line		0·25	−0·3	0·75	+0·9
for other dimensions		0·375	−0·95	1·0	+2·1

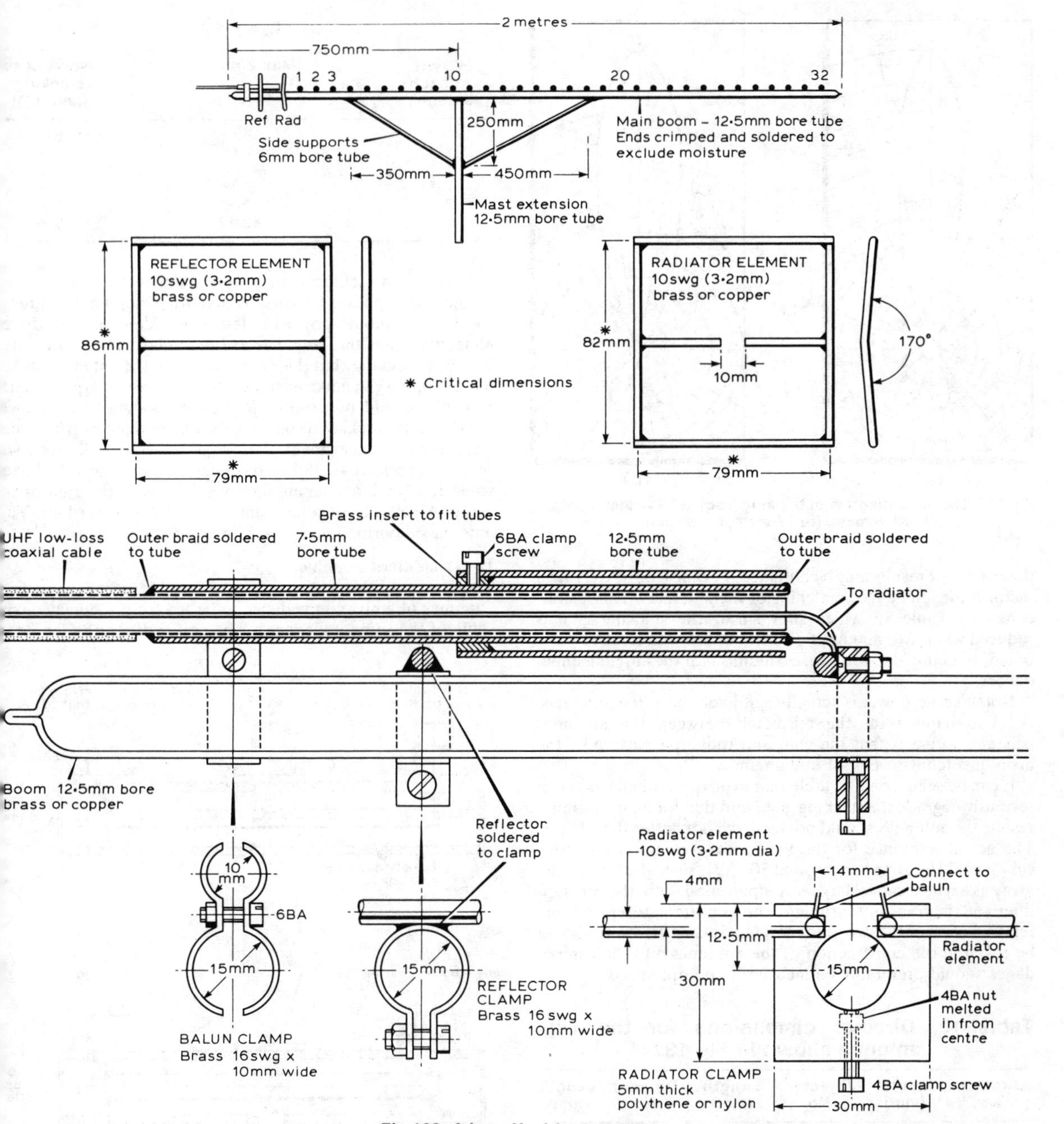

Fig 132. A long-Yagi for 1,296MHz

ecessary to use small clamps to hold joints in place while thers are soldered. The radiator clamp is fabricated from olythene or nylon. The hole to take the boom may be cut with heated piece of the boom material. The 4BA nut used to ecure this clamp is melted into place.

The balun assembly is constructed from a 7·5mm-bore tube 20mm long. Approximately 130mm of the outer protective overing is stripped from the full length of the uhf low-loss oaxial cable to be employed. The cable is pushed into the tube and the outer braid is soldered at both ends, taking extreme care not to melt the dielectric. The $\lambda/4$ coaxial sleeve is made from 12·5mm bore tube: the inside length is the critical dimension and should be 57·5mm. After final assembly, the antenna may be painted with aluminium paint to reduce corrosion.

Stacking Yagi antennas

More than one antenna may be stacked to achieve extra gain. However, several points should be borne in mind when this is

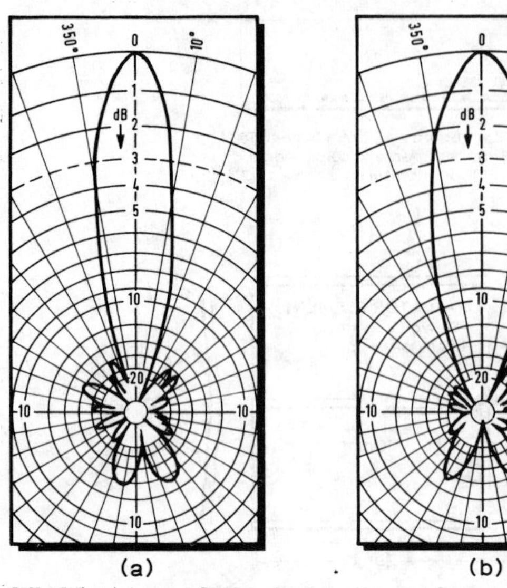

Fig 133. The polar diagram of the long Yagi. (a) 34-element standard version. (b) 27-element version

done, or poor results may be obtained. Perhaps the most critical factor is the impedance matching of the antennas. This is illustrated by Table 13 which shows how the stacking gain is reduced when two antennas of differing impedances are combined, assuming the worst-case condition for the antenna impedances.

Note that no power is actually lost in either of the antennas. All that happens as the mismatch between the antennas becomes worse is that the gain and radiation pattern of the array just tends to that of one antenna.

It can be seen from the table that even quite small vswrs can seriously degrade the stacking gain, and that for near-optimum results the antennas should possess vswrs of better than 1·1:1. The actual reference for the vswr measurement is less critical—it could be anywhere around 30–70Ω, since the vswr of the array as a whole can be largely compensated for in the preamplifier and the transmitter tuning. The important criterion is the relative vswrs of the two antennas. Great care therefore should be taken in the construction of the antennas and their impedance should preferably be measured and optimized.

Table 12. Director dimensions for the Yagi antenna shown in Fig 132

Director No	Length (mm)	Director No	Length (mm)	Director No	Length (mm)
1	101·7	12	88·9	23	76·2
2	100·5	13	87·7	24	75·1
3	99·4	14	86·6	25	74·0
4	98·2	15	85·5	26	72·8
5	97·1	16	84·3	27	71·6
6	95·9	17	83·2	28	70·5
7	94·8	18	82·0	29	69·4
8	93·5	19	80·9	30	68·2
9	92·4	20	79·7	31	66·9
10	91·2	21	78·5	32	64·8
11	90·1	22	77·4		

Material: 12 or 14swg brass rod

Table 13

VSWR of each antenna	Max Z/min Z	Worst case stacking gain (dB)
1	50	3
1·1	55/45	2·6
1·2	60/42	2·2
1·5	75/33	1·6
2	100/25	1·0
3	150/17	0·5

It is also most important to ensure that the antennas ar[e] connected in phase. This means that, for example, the outer o[f] the feeders should go to the left-hand side of all the drive[n] elements when the antennas are mounted in the array. It i[s] worth rechecking that this is the case with the antennas instal[l]led, as it is easy to make mistakes. Needless to say, equal length[s] of cable should be used to join each antenna to the powe[r] divider. The stacking distance is the one parameter which ma[y] require some experiment. Too large a stacking distance wi[ll] result in excessive sidelobes and a narrowing of the main beam while too small a stacking distance will lower the gain of th[e] array. A suitable starting point for the 27-element loop-Yag[i] antennas described above is 27in.

Power splitters/combiners

The power splitters shown in Fig 134 enable either two or fou[r] antennas of a given impedance to be fed from a single coaxia[l] cable of the same impedance. The unit consists of a length o[f]

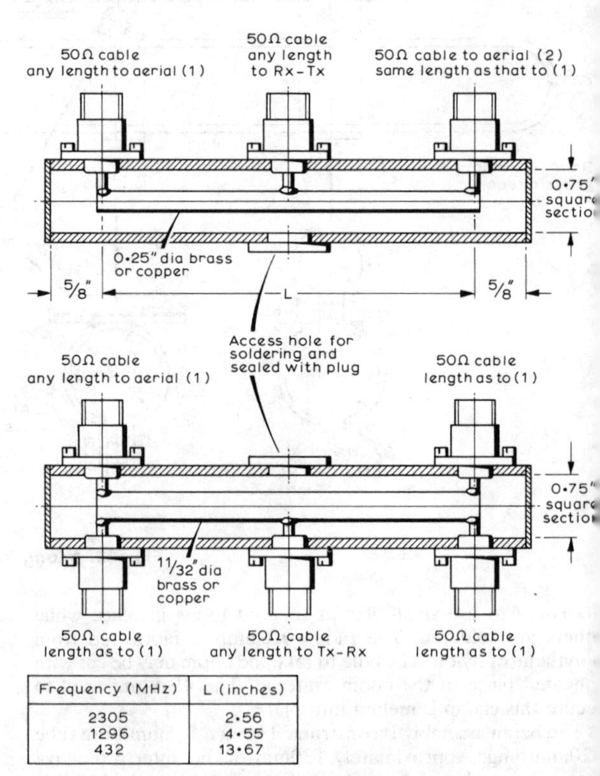

Frequency (MHz)	L (inches)
2305	2·56
1296	4·55
432	13·67

Fig 134. A 50Ω power splitter/combiner for connecting two or fou[r] antennas to a common feeder

Configuration	50Ω system: 2-way Zo = 72Ω	4-way Zo=50Ω
Square outer, round inner (d, D)	2·82	1·96
Round outer, round inner (d, D)	3·32	2·31
Square outer, flat strip inner (d, D)	1·54	—
Round outer, flat strip inner (d, D)	1·66	—

Fig 135. Ratios of *d/D* for other useful coaxial configurations

bricated coaxial line which performs the appropriate impeance transformations. The inner is made exactly λ/2 long (or ny odd multiples of λ/2) between the centres of the outer onnectors, and the outer is made approximately 1¼in longer. In e original design the outer was made from square-section uminium tubing, the ends of which and the access hole for oldering the centre connector being sealed with aluminium ates bonded with an adhesive. Alternatively copper or brass ubing may be used, and the plates soldered. Any other size of ner or outer within reason may be used provided that the ratio f the inside dimension of the outer to the diameter of the inner onductor is unchanged.

Other forms of coaxial line should work just as well. Fig 135 ives the design details for a number of configurations.

Parabolic dishes

Antennas based on paraboloidal reflectors are the most important type for the microwave bands. Their main advantages re that in principle they can be made to have as large a gain as is equired, they can operate at any frequency and they should equire little setting up. Disadvantages are that they are not the asiest things to make accurately, which limits the frequency at hich a given dish can be used, and large dishes are difficult to ount, and may have a high windage.

The basic property of a perfect paraboloidal reflector is that it onverts a spherical wave emanating from a point source placed t the focus into a plane wave, ie the image of the source is ocused at an infinite distance from the dish. Conversely, all the nergy received by the dish from a distant source is reflected to single point at the focus of the dish.

he geometry of the paraboloid

A paraboloid is generated by rotating a parabola about a line oining its origin and focus. Two methods for constructing a arabola are given below:

y calculation

Convenient forms of the equations of a parabola are, using the otation of Fig 136:

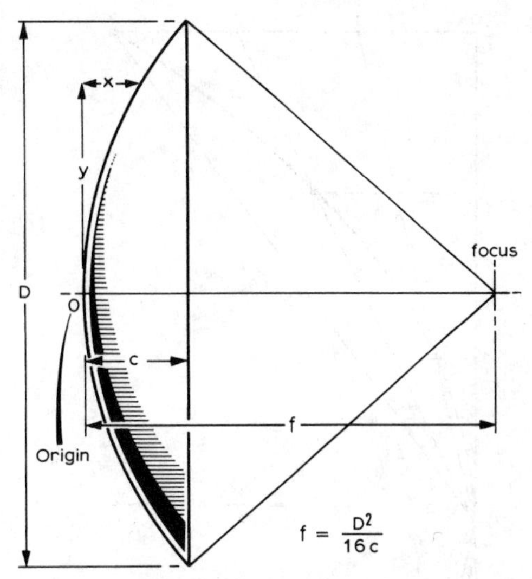

Fig 136. Basic geometry of a paraboloid

$$y^2 = 4fx \quad (1)$$

$$y^2 = 4Dx(f/D) \quad (2)$$

where $f = \dfrac{D^2}{16c}$

where y has both negative and positive values
D = diameter of corresponding dish
f = focal length
c = depth of parabola at its centre

Suppose we wish to construct the profile of a dish 36in in diameter having a f/D ratio of 0·6. The procedure is as follows:

(a) From equation (2), $x = \dfrac{y^2}{4D(f/D)} = \dfrac{y^2}{4 \times 36 \times 0{\cdot}6}$

$= 0{\cdot}01157y^2$.

(b) Tabulate the calculations for as many points as accuracy requires in the form:

±y (in)	y^2	$0{\cdot}01157y^2$ = x (in)
0	0	0
2	4	0·05
4	16	0·18
6	36	0·42
8	64	0·74
10	100	1·16
12	144	1·67
14	196	2·27
16	256	2·96
18	324	3·75

A plot of y from −18 to +18 versus the value of x calculated gives the required curve.

Graphical method

A simple graphical method for constructing a parabola is shown in Fig 137. The value of c is calculated from:

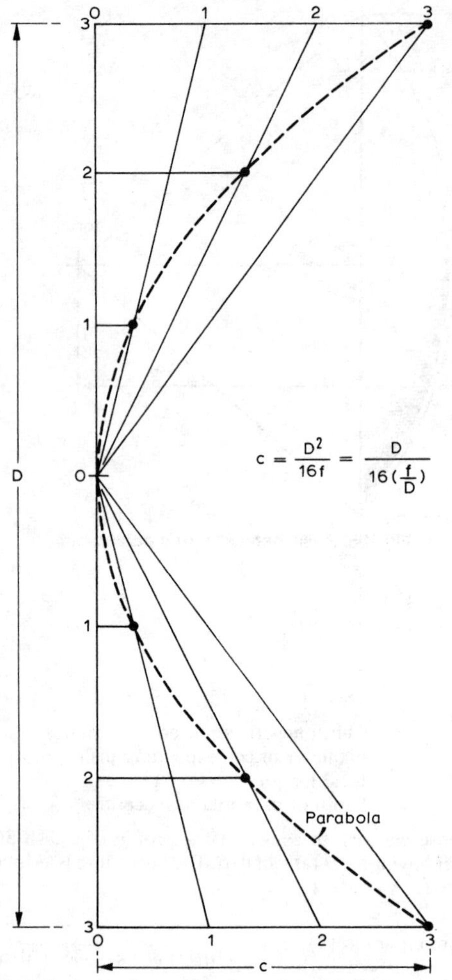

Fig 137. A simple graphical construction for a parabola

$$c = \frac{D^2}{16f} \text{ or } c = \frac{D}{16(f/D)}$$

Both axes are divided into the same number of equal parts in the way shown and numbered. Points where corresponding lines intercept describe the required parabola.

Factors affecting practical dish design and usage

Size

This is the most important factor since it determines the maximum gain that can be achieved at a given frequency, and the beamwidth resulting. The actual gain obtained is given by

$$G = \frac{4\pi A}{\lambda^2} \cdot \eta \text{ or } \left(\frac{\pi D}{\lambda}\right)^2 \cdot \eta$$

where A is the projected area of the dish and η is the efficiency, which is determined mainly by the effectiveness of illumination of the dish by the feed but also by other factors which will be discussed below. Each time the diameter of a dish is doubled, its gain is quadrupled, ie increased by 6dB. If both stations doub the size of their antennas, signal strengths can be increased b 12dB, a very substantial gain. A given dish used at twice th frequency also quadruples its gain if other factors do not inte vene.

The relationship between the diameter of a dish and its ga at frequencies of amateur interest is shown in Fig 138. A efficiency of 50 per cent is assumed, which seems to be typical o better amateur practice. Antennas with a diameter less than to 10λ generally will have a significantly lower efficiency tha this value. The corresponding beamwidths were taken from F 129.

Two factors tend to limit the maximum gain that can b achieved. On the lower microwave frequencies, the physic size of the antenna is the limiting factor. Thus a 30dB antenr on 1,296MHz will have a diameter of just over 10ft, whic could well cause problems in fabrication and mounting. At th higher microwave frequencies, the physical size of the antenr is less of a problem. Instead the narrowness of the beamwidt tends to be the limiting factor. For example, a dish 3ft i diameter used on 24GHz will have a gain of up to 44dB and beamwidth of 1°. Considerable skill is required in handlir effectively such a directive antenna.

The ratio of the focal length of the dish to its diameter

This ratio, f/D using the notation of Fig 136, is the fundament factor governing the design of the feed for a dish. The ratio is o course directly related to the angle subtended by the rim of th dish at its focus, and therefore also to the beamwidth of the fee necessary to illuminate the dish effectively. Two dishes of di ferent diameter but having the same f/D ratio can emplo identical feeds. Dishes having the same diameter but differe focal lengths require quite dissimilar feeds if both are to b illuminated efficiently.

Practical values for the f/D ratio range from about 0·2 to 1·0 The value of 0·25 corresponds to the common focal plane dis in which the focus is in the same plane as the rim of the dish However, values of the f/D ratio which produce a deeper dis are frequently used commercially where it may be important t minimize sidelobe response. With such dishes, the unwante interaction between antennas is reduced, albeit at the expens of antenna gain and extra difficulty in designing efficient feed Such considerations are unimportant in an amateur contex Indeed, the greater the sidelobe response the better, provide overall gain does not suffer.

As will be seen, there are a number of factors which influenc the choice of the f/D ratio. For most amateur applications th range 0·5 to 0·75 would appear to be optimum, althoug satisfactory feeds for dishes outside this range can be cor structed.

Changing the geometry of a dish

As a given dish is reduced in size, so its f/D ratio is reduce proportionately. Thus if a focal plane dish for which $f/D = 0{\cdot}2$ is trimmed to half its original diameter, then the smaller dis will have a f/D ratio of 0·5. This approach has been used t convert otherwise unused dishes into ones easier to illuminat efficiently. By trimming the dish appropriately, any f/D rati greater than the original can be realized. This effect, of cours can also be produced electrically by under-illuminating th dish.

The same effect happens in the opposite sense. If the origin curve of a dish is extended, then the f/D ratio of the resultin dish will decrease proportionately.

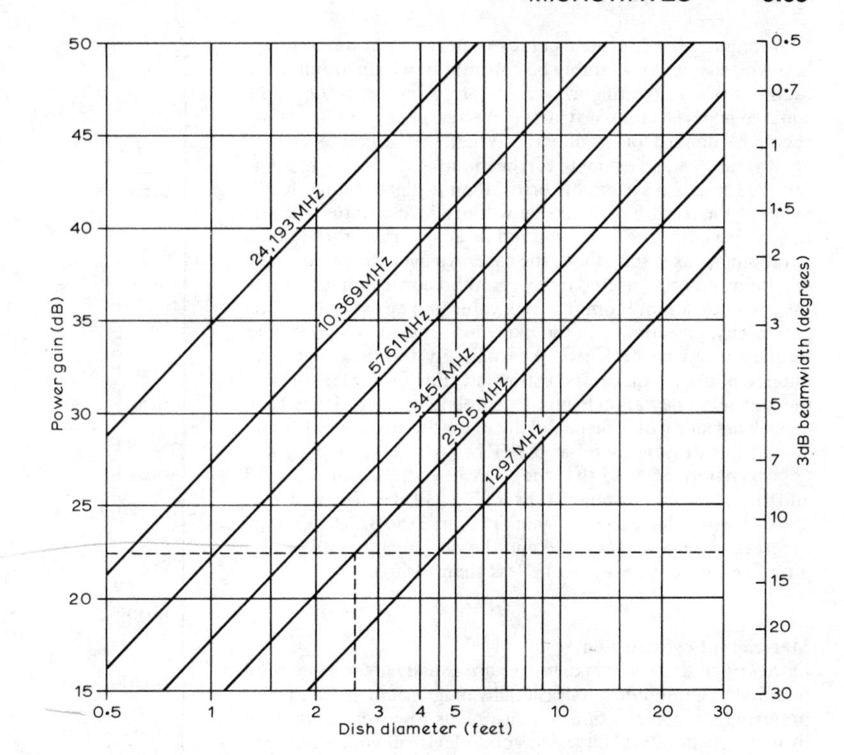

ig 138. Relationship between he size of a dish and its gain and eamwidth as a function of frequency. An overall efficiency of 0 per cent is assumed. As an xample, a dish 2·5ft in diameter t 2,305MHz will have a gain of 2dB and a beamwidth of about 12°

he effect of dish accuracy on performance

n understanding of the degree of accuracy required in a dish is nportant for two reasons. It enables the maximum frequency or efficient operation of a given dish to be determined, and it lso enables an estimate to be made of how much tolerances in onstruction can be relaxed, which may greatly influence the ase with which dishes can be constructed.

The reduction in gain due to surface irregularities depends on wo factors. First, the amount by which the actual surface eviates from a true paraboloid. This will be expressed as the ean value of the peak deviation in terms of a wavelength. The econd factor is the size of the regions of deviation relative to e wavelength at the frequency of operation. Thus a distinction made between short range irregularities which correspond to dish of accurate overall paraboloidal shape but with a bumpy urface, and long-range irregularities where the surface undulates about the mean shape of a paraboloid with a periodicity reater than a wavelength.

The relationship between loss in gain, the peak deviation and e periodicity is shown in Fig 139, which assumes that the eviations occur uniformly over the surface of the dish. If they re restricted to a limited area, then the loss will be proortionately lower. It can be seen that when the periodicity of e irregularities is a small fraction of a wavelength, for example /6, quite large irregularities of about $\lambda/8$ can be tolerated efore the gain is reduced by 1dB. Because of this, the effect of rojections such as rivet heads, or of depressions or small holes an usually be ignored.

However, where the periodicity exceeds a wavelength, the aximum deviation for a 1dB loss is reduced to about $\lambda/16$, and is to be noted that the loss increases rapidly as the deviation xceeds this value. For a peak error of about $\lambda/9$, for example, e loss resulting is about 6dB, in which case the dish could be replaced by an accurate dish of half the diameter without loss in gain.

Short-range irregularities are readily measured with a ruler.

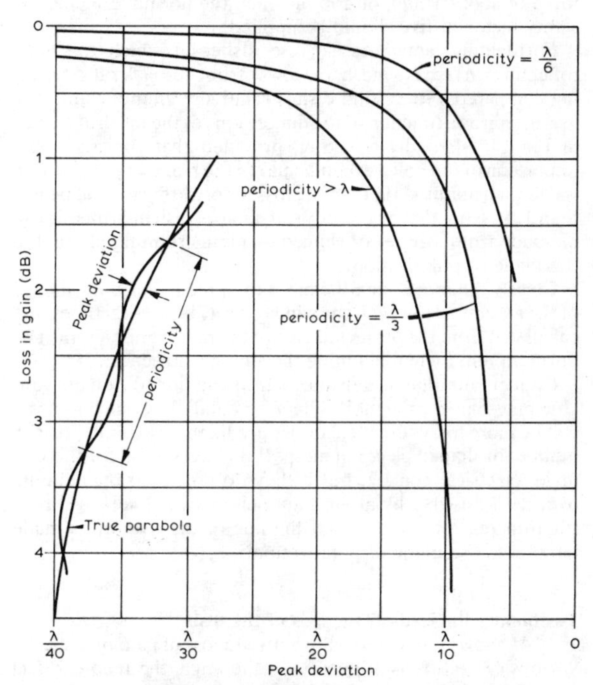

Fig 139. The effect of dish inaccuracy on performance

Checking the long-range accuracy requires a parabolic template which should preferably be accurate to within about $\lambda/20$. Methods of constructing a parabola are given on p 9.63, and suitable materials for constructing the template are aluminium sheet, hardboard or cardboard. When the template is held against the dish, an estimate can be made of the average deviation. If there is a systematic error, then a slight change in the value of the focal length chosen will produce a better fit, and this is specially true if the curvature is spherical rather than paraboloidal as is sometimes the case. An average value of the maximum error measured by this method corresponds to twice the peak deviation. From the peak value and an estimate of the periodicity, an estimate of the likely loss of gain at a particular frequency can be obtained. Alternatively the maximum frequency of operation can be estimated. For example, suppose the maximum deviation from the template measured was 1cm, ie peak deviation of 0·5cm, and this extended over about 10cm. Would this dish be useful at 5·6GHz? At this frequency λ is approximately 5cm, so that the peak deviation is about $\lambda/10$ and the periodicity is about 2λ. From Fig 139, it can be seen that this dish would have a loss in gain of about 3·5dB. At 2·3GHz, the peak error would be $\lambda/26$ and the periodicity about λ, the probable loss in gain would be less than 0·5dB.

Materials of construction

Dishes up to a few feet in diameter are usually made from solid material. Aluminium, or occasionally magnesium, is frequently preferred for construction because of its low weight, its high formability and durability, and good electrical characteristics. With increasing dish size, windage starts to become a severe problem. At a wind speed of 50mph for example, a not-uncommon value, the force on a flat object is about 9lb/ft². The structure supporting a dish 4ft in diameter would suffer a wind force of about 100lb, on top of which the normal engineering safety factor of five should be applied.

Fortunately, amateurs can use dishes in which the main reflecting surface is a mesh, the lower front-to-back ratio resulting compared with a solid dish is relatively unimportant. The loss in gain as a function of the dimensions of the mesh are given in Fig 140. Broadly speaking, provided that the maximum dimension of the hole perpendicular to the plane of polarization is less than about $\lambda/10$, then the loss in forward gain will be less than 1dB. Note that a perfectly satisfactory dish in principle can be made from a series of shaped elements running parallel to the plane of polarization.

Clearly the more open the mesh then the lower the windage of the antenna. However, the windage may be several times that calculated from the projected area of the mesh, and this must be borne in mind when planning the support structure.

Copper, aluminium, galvanized iron and tinned iron are suitable materials for the mesh. Plain iron and alloys such as brass will be more lossy. Practical dishes are likely to be made from a number of shaped pieces of mesh. It is not essential for these to make electrical contact, but if they do not, then they should overlap if possible by at least an inch or two. There will be a slight increase in efficiency if the line of the overlap is made parallel to the plane of polarization.

Positioning the feed off the axis of the dish

Fig 141 shows the relationship between loss of gain of dishes of various *f/D* ratios as a function of the angle the feed is offset from the axis in terms of 3dB beamwidths. This data shows two

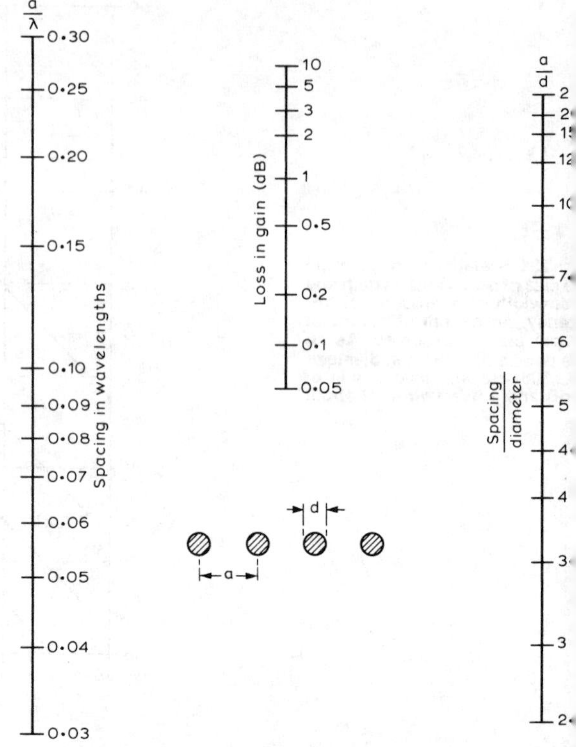

Fig 140. Loss in gain for a mesh reflector as a function of mesh si

important features. First, the effect of likely errors in constru tion on antenna gain is surprisingly low. For example, co sider a focal plane dish 5ft in diameter used on 2·3GHz. Th will have a focal length of 15in and a 3dB beamwidth of 7° (F 138). If the feed is offset by 2in (a large constructional erro then the offset angle is about 7°, ie one beamwidth. The resu ing loss in gain will be approximately 1dB. It would be even le with a dish of longer focal length.

However, it must be noted that if the feed is offset by a certa angle, then the beam reflected from the dish will be offset roughly the same extent. If the offset is in the horizontal pla then the error will usually be eliminated in "peaking" th antenna on the other station. However, if the feed is offset the vertical plane, then a proportion of the radiated power ma be directed up into the air or down towards the ground. Wi high-gain antenna systems, the loss this effect introduces can b most serious.

A second most important feature is that for dishes of hig *f/D* ratio, the feed may be offset by a number of beamwidt before a significant reduction in gain is introduced. For ma practical dishes it can be shown that this offset is sufficient enable two or three feeds to be sited horizontally alongside ea other, thus enabling one dish to be used at any time on mo than one band. This approach has the advantage over oth methods of multiband feeding in that each of the feeds can b independently fed and adjusted without affecting those fo other bands. It has a minor mechanical disadvantage that c changing frequency the dish will have to be re-aligned but, a this will be a fixed amount characteristic of the particul antenna system, this should not present any problems.

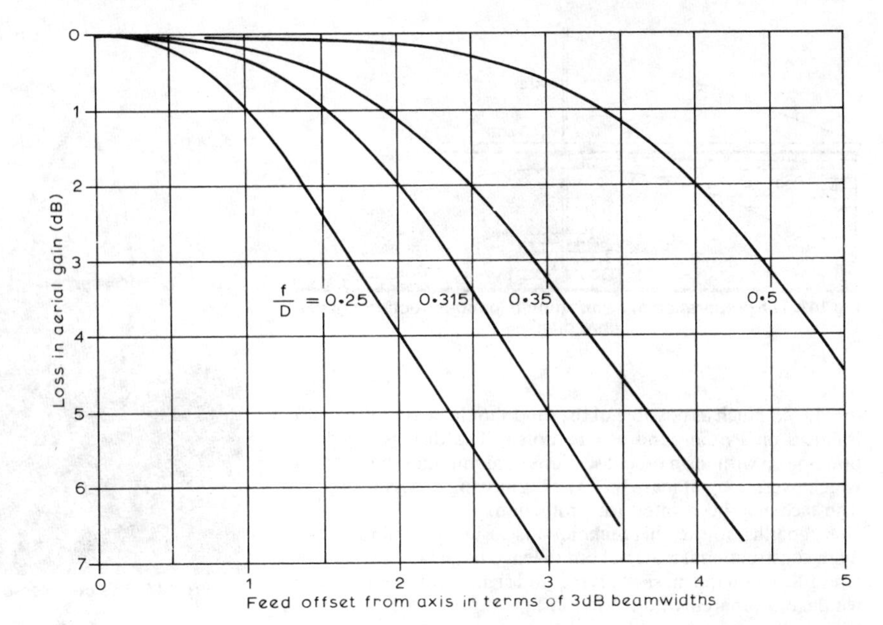

141. Loss in gain due to positioning a feed off the axis of a dish

he effect of obstructions in front of the dish

tting a feed in front of the dish inevitably obscures part of the sh and therefore causes some loss in gain. The effect is surprisgly small. Even when the diameter of the obstruction is 0·3 nes the diameter of the dish the loss is only 1dB. Most actical feeds (except perhaps those based on the Cassegrain stem) are usually much smaller, and therefore will have a gligible effect.

he optimum ratio of focal length to diameter of a dish

ne main parameters of interest of course are gain and efiency, but factors such as ease of construction, effects of rors in construction and the ease of the design and tuning of eds are also important. Sidelobe level and front-to-back ratio e of secondary importance in amateur operation.

The main factor favouring the use of a low *f*/*D* ratio is the mpactness of the antenna. Because the feed is placed at the cus or near to it, then the smaller the *f*/*D* ratio the shorter the cal length, and therefore the less bulky is the antenna.

An important factor favouring a high *f*/*D* ratio is ease of dish nstruction. It seems a fair assumption that the errors involved making a curved surface are related to the degree of curvare. The flatter the dish (ie the higher its *f*/*D* ratio), probably e more accurately it can be made. As has already been shown, e higher the *f*/*D* ratio the less critical also is the positioning of e feed. For dishes which are approximations to paraboloids, ere is a clear relationship favouring a high *f*/*D* ratio.

A second factor is ease of feeding. As is shown by Fig 151, the amwidth of the feed required to illuminate a dish efficiently creases rapidly as the *f*/*D* ratio of the dish is decreased, and ntrol of the beamwidth therefore becomes more critical. As it ppens the predictability of the beamwidth of a feed tends to crease as its beamwidth increases, which tends to compound e difficulties. As can be seen from Fig 151, most of the lvantages in this respect are achieved when the *f*/*D* ratio ceeds 0·5 to 0·6.

The use of a long focal length for the reflector minimizes sses due to differences in the position of the phase centres of a feed in the horizontal and vertical planes, and also those due to the large shift with frequency in the phase centre of multiband feeds such as log-periodic arrays. It also allows the siting of feeds alongside one another as an alternative to the latter form of multiband feeds. Finally, for a short focal length dish, there is a relatively large space loss. For a focal plane dish, for example, only the power contained within the 4dB beamwidth of the feed is reflected by the dish if an edge illumination of −10dB is specified. For a dish with an *f*/*D* ratio of 0·7, the power contained within a 9dB beamwidth is reflected by the dish, which is rather more efficient.

The above factors suggest that the larger the *f*/*D* ratio the better. Apart from mechanical problems in supporting a feed some distance in front of the dish, the main factor against very long focal length dishes is that a more directive and therefore bulkier feed is necessary. In practice, the obstruction of the aperture such feeds cause is only significant when small dishes are used at the lower frequencies. For most amateur purposes, the optimum *f*/*D* ratio therefore would appear to be in the range 0·5 to 0·75.

Practical dish construction

A glassfibre reflector

Glassfibre faced with aluminium kitchen foil or fine mesh offers a practical method, and perhaps the only method available to amateurs, for the construction of dishes sufficiently accurate for use at the higher microwave frequencies. Some form of mould is required, and this can be an existing solid dish or a plaster cast taken from one. A method of making a sand mould is illustrated by Fig 142. A template of the desired shape is rotated about a central pivot to cut the sand to shape which then is fixed by a coat of paint applied as a spray. Glassfibre impregnated with resin is laid on until the required thickness is built up, typically ¼in for a dish 4ft diameter. Plywood or metal stiffeners cut to shape are incorporated into the structure and any mounting fixtures required also are built up. The glassfibre should be allowed at least a week to harden before it is removed from the

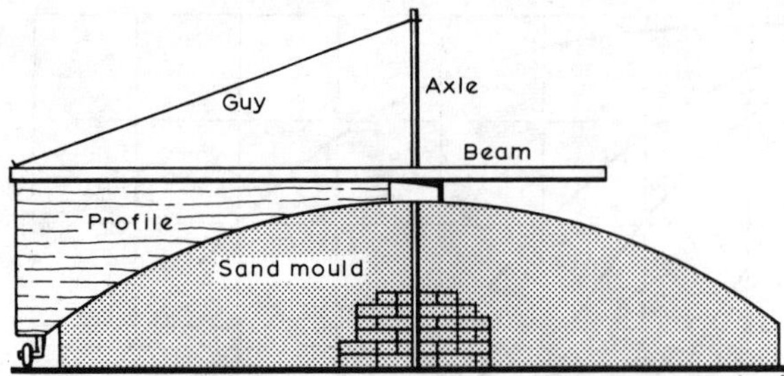

Fig 142. The preparation of a sand mould for constructing a glass-fibre dish

mould. As much as possible of the sand should be removed with thinners or acetone and a wire brush. The dish is faced by bonding on with resin precut sections of aluminium foil or mesh which overlap by at least ½in. After removing excess resin, the dish face may be painted for protection.

A modification to this technique is to use glassfibre as the main constructional material but to leave large holes which are later filled with the mesh. This method significantly reduces the windage compared with a solid dish.

Construction of a mesh dish

Figs 143 and 144 show a method of constructing dishes from shaped ribs covered with mesh. In the original version, which was 6ft in diameter, the dish was made in two halves to facilitate transportation. Eight ribs cut from waterproof (marine) plywood define the main shape of the dish, and inner circles of wire help in making the mesh conform to a near-paraboloidal shape. The perimeter is made from paper rope impregnated with resin—ordinary rope should suffice but the resin must be well worked in. Shaped sections of chicken wire are clipped to the spider with 22g tinned copper wire and the final structure is protected by paint.

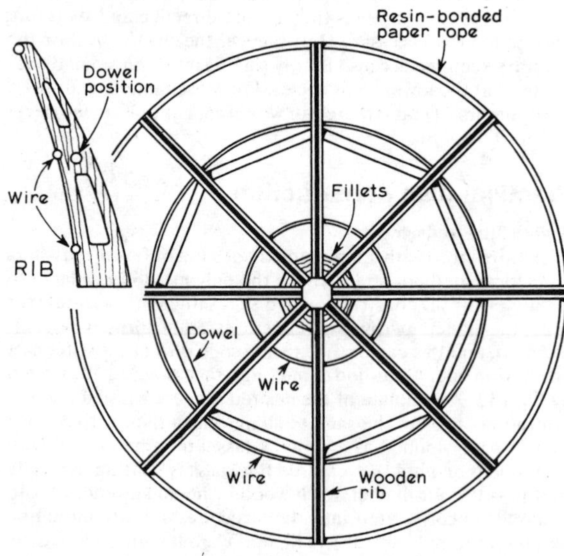

Fig 143. Framework for a mesh dish

Fig 144. The completed antenna with a circular horn feed

A dustbin lid antenna

Careful measurement of several ordinary galvanized iron dustbin lids of the smoothly rounded type has shown them to be sufficiently accurate paraboloids to be usable as dish reflectors up to 24GHz. Saucepan lids have also been successfully used in this application.

Checking the lid

Most of the lids that have been examined have had a relatively long focal length, typically 0·7 to 0·9 of the diameter. If a selection of lids is available, normally that with the shortest focal length is preferable since this will reduce the overall length of the antenna. A quick method of determining the *approximate* focal length f is from the equation:

$$f = D^2/16c$$

where D is the diameter of the lid and c is the depth of the curved part at its centre. Lids which have many dents or wrinkles greater in depth than about $\lambda/10$ at the design frequency should preferably be avoided.

It is well worthwhile spending some effort in measuring the profile of the lid accurately for two reasons: the "best-fit" paraboloid it will represent needs to be known with fair precision in designing the rest of the antenna, and the deviation of the lid from a true paraboloid will determine the maximum frequency at which the dish can be used. A successful procedure used was to cut a piece of hardboard (preferably coated with emulsion paint) to fit the profile of the lid within about ⅛in and then position it across a diameter. A short length of very hard pencil was held against the lid and moved across its surface to transfer the profile to the hardboard. This operation was repeated using a thin spacer, and a third profile taken at right angles. A comparison of the curves indicated both the reliability of the process and the uniformity of curvature: generally this was within the accuracy of measurement, about 0·01in.

A straight line was drawn to connect the ends of one curve and the difference between the two lines was measured a

Fig 145. A dust-bin lid antenna for 10GHz

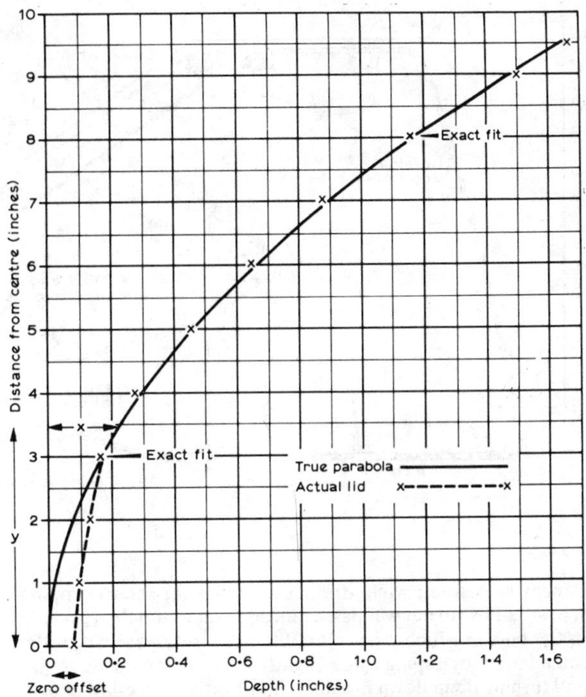

Fig 146. Comparison of the profile of a lid with a parabola

ıtervals of 1in on both sides of the centre. Comparing corres-ɔnding values gave a measure of the accuracy achieved which ȝain was generally within 0·01in. A systematic change in the ifferences would have indicated that the straight line had not een positioned properly. By subtracting the average value of ach pair of points from the value corresponding to the centre f the lid, the profile could then be tabulated in a more con-enient form.

In determining the "best-fit" parabola to the lid profile, the arabola was made to fit exactly at distances roughly 30 and 80 er cent from the centre, the area between these points corres-ɔnding to the part of the dish that does most of the work. The ɔcal length of this parabola is given by the equation:

$$f = \frac{y_2^2 - y_1^2}{4(x_2 - x_1)}$$

here x_1, y_1 and x_2, y_2 are the points on the lid profile to be tted.

For the 19in diameter lid used in the antenna shown in Fig 45 the fit was made at points y = 3in and y = 8in, the orresponding x values for the lid being 0·09in and 0·19in espectively. The focal length calculated from the equation bove was 13·75in and this value was used in the equation $x = {}^2/4f$ to calculate the required parabola. This curve is shown as ne full line in Fig 146. Also plotted as crosses are the measure-ıents taken from the lid, to all of which have been added a ero offset value of 0·07in to make the two curves coincide at he y = 3in and y = 8in points.

The fit between the two curves is remarkably good: the ırgest deviation of this lid from a true parabola is at the centre, ·07in, and elsewhere is less than 0·02in. These values corres-ond respectively to less than λ/17 and λ/50 at 10GHz and therefore would be expected to reduce the overall gain of the antenna by a fraction of a decibel only. Had the deviation exceeded λ/10 over much of the profile, then the lid would have been unsuitable for use at this high a frequency.

Constructional details

In the direct-feed method, the feed is mounted in a bearing which is supported from the rim of the dish by three or four struts. The bearing allows the distance between the feed and the dish to be adjusted to allow for uncertainty in the positions of the phase centre of the feed and the focus of the dish. A rigid structure is necessary: it must be remembered that the 3dB beamwidth of the antenna shown here is only ±2°, and that the total angular play of the feed relative to the dish must be a small fraction of this value, otherwise the antenna will be unreliable in operation.

The antenna layout was planned by plotting on squared paper the profile of the lid including its rim. Lines were drawn to connect the curved part of the lid to the focus and the horn feed positioned so as to just intercept these lines in the way shown in the detail drawing, Fig 147. A range of adjustment of 1in was considered adequate, and therefore this gap was left between the tapered part of the horn feed and the inside face of the feed mounting boss. Square waveguide flanges bolted to this boss acted as bearings for the feed. The size of the boss set the radius at which the struts could be fixed, and this in turn fixed the angle at which the boss skirt was set back. This angle is the same as that between the struts and the axis of the antenna. The size of the boss used, 3·5in diameter, causes less than 0·3dB loss in antenna gain although it might appear rather large.

The boss was turned on a single centre from dural. To jig the

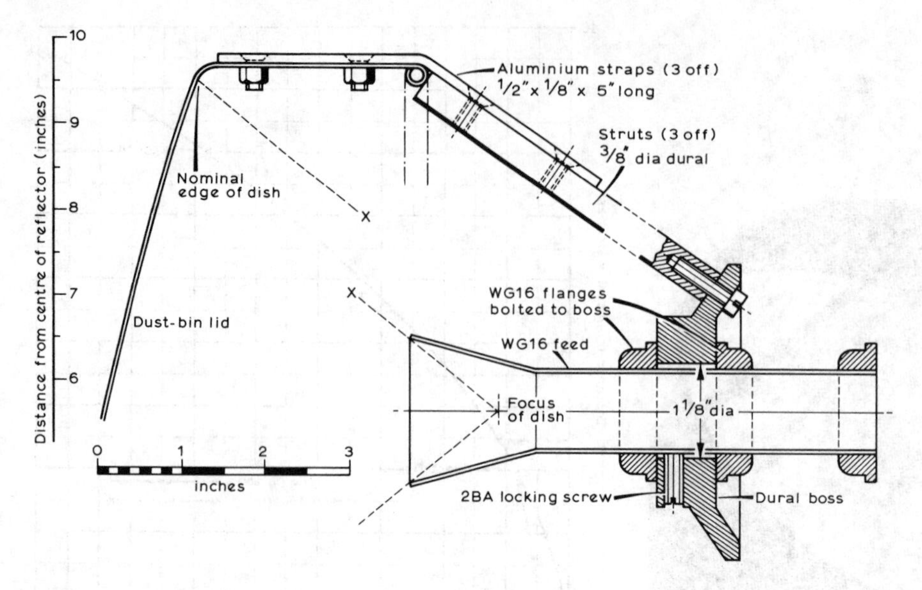

Fig 147. Detail drawing of fe support arrangement

flanges in position while drilling the holes for their clamping screws, a 1 by $\frac{1}{2}$in bar was passed through them and the 1$\frac{1}{8}$in hole in the boss in which it is a close fit. The struts were cut to the same length by taping three slightly oversize lengths together and turning them down in a lathe fitted with a three-jaw chuck. In drilling the fixing holes in these rods at the dish end, the antenna was assembled with two of the three struts taped in position to their straps. The third was clamped tight against the rim with a Mole wrench, the holes drilled and the bolts inserted, then the process was repeated for the other rods. By using techniques such as these, accurate alignment of the feed is virtually guaranteed.

To facilitate mounting the antenna on a mast, the handle on the lid was cut and the ends straightened and threaded $\frac{3}{8}$in BSF.

Alternative boss designs

Two other types of boss have been used on other antennas. In one, the waveguide part of the feed is built up by soldering 1 by $\frac{5}{16}$in or 1 by $\frac{3}{8}$in brass bars to the broad faces of the guide, the assembly then being turned down to 1$\frac{1}{8}$in diameter. This guide is made a sliding fit in the hole in a boss of similar design to that

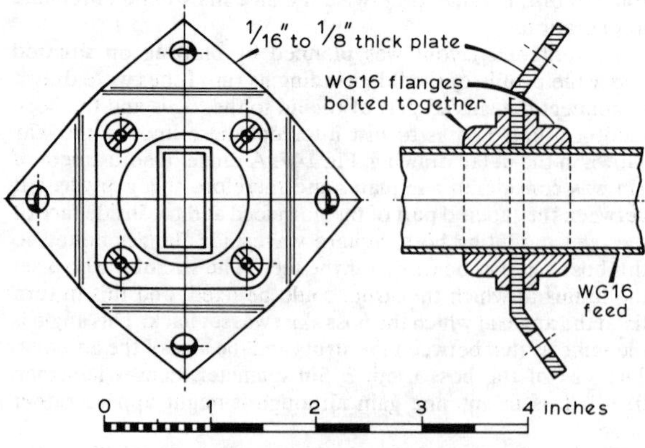

Fig 148. Alternative form of feed bearing

shown in Fig 147, the waveguide flanges of course being om ted.

For those without access to a lathe, the arrangement shown Fig 148 can be used. Construction is simplified if four struts a used. Care is required in bending the corner tabs to the corre angle, otherwise the mounting will be forced out of alignmen

The design of feeds for dishes

In a perfect feed system for a parabolic dish, all the ener would appear to emerge from a point source placed at the focu and would be contained within a cone which just intercepts t rim of the dish. All the energy then would be reflected by t dish in the form of a plane wave. This ideal picture is comp cated by several factors:

(a) Practical feeds have no sharp cut off. Generally t power density is at a maximum at the axis of the feed ar then falls off on either side. Clearly there is no absolu value of the beamwidth of the feed, and all that can specified is the beamwidth at which the power density for example, half or one-tenth of the maximum valu There is therefore a judgement to be made on t optimum beamwidth of a feed for a given dish. If too lov as is illustrated by Fig 149(a), most of the energy rad ated by the feed is reflected by the dish, but since t energy is concentrated at the centre of the dish, then t overall gain of the antenna suffers. If the beamwidth the feed is too high, as illustrated by Fig 149(b), much the energy radiated by the feed passes around the edge the dish and is lost. There is clearly an optimum bean width of feed which results in fairly uniform illuminatic of the dish, but with limited losses around the edge. Th is achieved when the illumination at the edge of the dis is approximately 10dB lower than at its centre, and th value will be assumed throughout this section.

(b) Because the rim of any parabolic dish is further from t feed than is the centre, there is already some loss built the system. This loss is called the *space loss*, and it vari according to the *f*/*D* ratio of the dish. For a focal pla

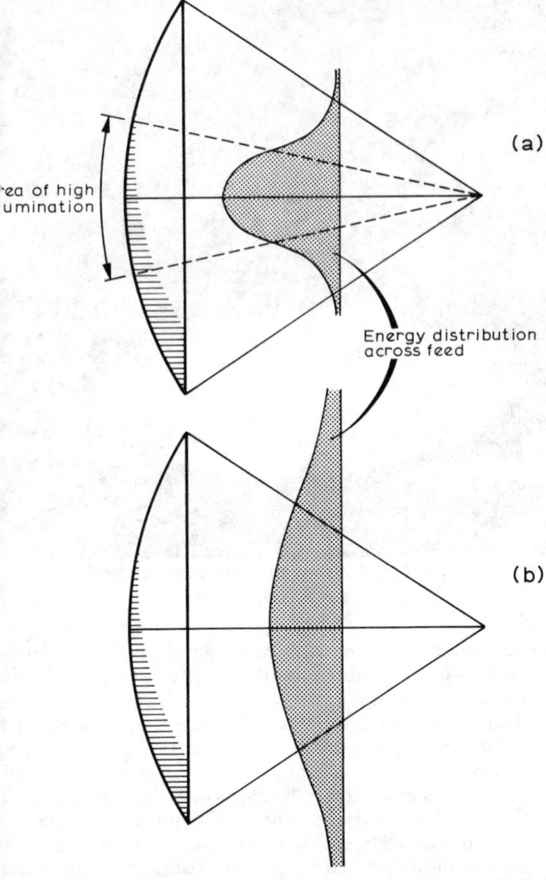

g 149. Non-optimum illumination of a dish. (a) Under-illuminated. (b) Over-illuminated

dish, it is equal to 6dB. Therefore, to produce an illumination at the edge of the dish 10dB down on that at the centre, the feed must have a beamwidth of 10dB less the space loss, ie a 4dB beamwidth, equal to the angle subtended by the rim of the dish at its focus, which is 180° in this example. For a dish of longer focal length, the space loss is smaller. For example, for a dish having a f/D ratio equal to 0·6, the space loss is 1·5dB. Thus a suitable feed would have a 10 − 1·5dB beamwidth equal to the feed angle of this dish, 88°.

(c) To achieve high efficiency, the dish must be illuminated evenly over its surface, and it is therefore desirable to control the beamwidth of the feed in both horizontal and vertical directions. Unfortunately the commonly used dipole/reflector and tin-can feeds are generally not very satisfactory in this respect. Pyramidal horns are much more satisfactory and their use will be described in a later section.

(d) The phase centre of a feed is defined as the point from which the energy appears to emanate. In practical feeds the phase centre is rarely a point since the size of the feed is always a significant fraction of a wavelength. The situation is further complicated by the fact that the phase centre in the horizontal (E–) plane may differ from that in the vertical (H–) plane. Multiband feeds such as log-periodic arrays suffer the additional disadvantage that the phase centres will move significantly as the frequency of operation is changed. The loss in antenna gain due to variations in the position of the phase centres clearly will be larger with dishes of short focal length since the effect will be *proportionally* greater. This is another factor favouring the use of dishes with a relatively high f/D ratio.

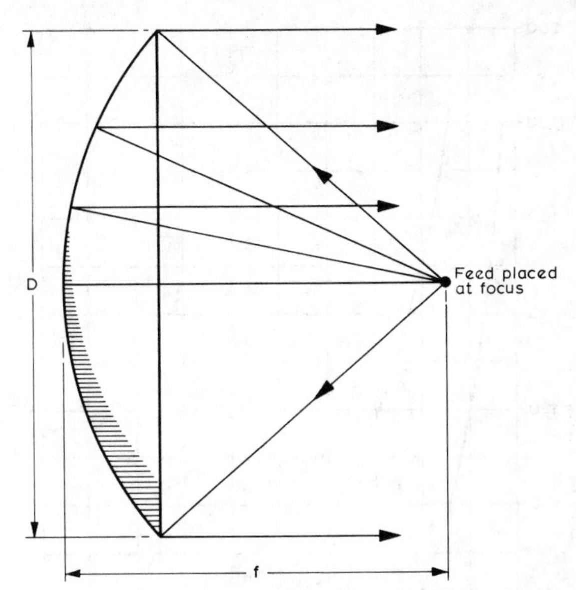

Fig 150. The geometry of a direct feed system

Practical feed systems

Direct feed

In this method, which is illustrated by Fig 150, the phase centre of the feed is placed at the focus of the dish. Power radiated by the feed as a spherical wave is converted by reflection at the paraboloidal reflector into a plane wave.

The characteristics of the feed required to illuminate the dish correctly are determined by measuring the f/D ratio by the methods described on p 9.68, and determining the beamwidth of the feed from Fig 151. Thus the feed for a focal plane dish for which $f/D = 0{\cdot}25$ should have a 3dB beamwidth of 155°. For a dish having a f/D ratio of 0·7, the 3dB beamwidth should be 46°. Alternatively, the 10dB beamwidth may be specified, and the corresponding value is 83°.

Fig 151 was derived assuming an edge illumination 10dB down on that at the centre of the dish. Due allowance was made for space loss. It will be noted that the beamwidth required changes very rapidly as the f/D ratio is reduced, which makes the design of suitable feeds for short focal length dishes rather more critical.

The main advantages of this method of mounting the feed are its simplicity in conception and construction. It has a high overall efficiency, and it leaves the back of the dish clear which can facilitate mounting the dish. Its main disadvantage is that with dishes of long local length, the feed support structure is quite bulky. Fig 152 shows a practical antenna system of this type.

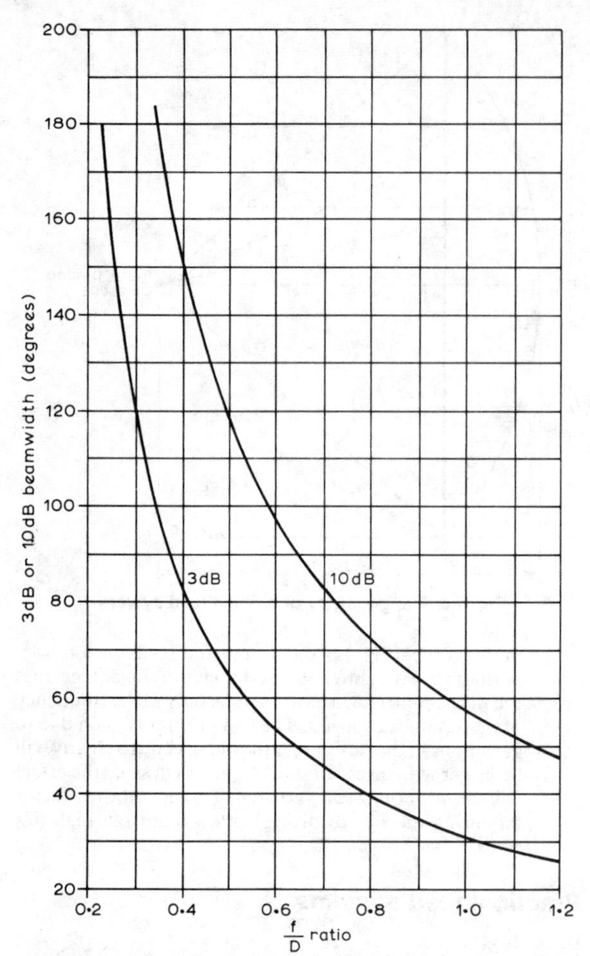

Fig 151. The 3dB or 10dB beamwidth of feeds for efficient illumination of dishes as a function of the ratio of their focal length to diameter (*f*/*D*). An edge illumination 10dB down compared with the centre is assumed

Indirect feed

Fig 153 illustrates the geometry of this method. Power radiated by the feed is reflected by a plane sub-reflector on to the main reflector. A spherical wave generated by the feed is converted by the sub-reflector into a spherical wave of the same radius of curvature but moving towards the dish. This, in turn, is converted by the dish into a plane wave.

The sub-reflector should preferably be a few wavelengths in diameter at least, but should not exceed 0·3 times the diameter of the main reflector if losses due to obstruction are not to exceed 1dB. Once the size of the sub-reflector is chosen, then its position is fixed—it must just intercept lines drawn from the real focus of the dish F_r to its rim. The position of the feed is also fixed. It is set at the virtual focus F_v which is as far in front of the sub-reflector as the real focus is behind, ie the lengths *m* are equal. Because the sub-reflector is planar, the virtual dish has the same diameter and focal length as the real dish, and therefore the design of the feed is the same as if the direct feed method were used.

The sub-reflector is usually made from solid material since it

Fig 152. A dish with a 10GHz direct feed

is so small, but mesh or wires running parallel to the plane of polarization and spaced by less than $\lambda/10$ offer a suitable alternative construction.

The main advantages of this method are that the feed can be supported from the centre of the dish (although this may complicate mounting the dish), and only a relatively light structure is needed to support the sub-reflector. Disadvantages of the method are that an extra component, the sub-reflector, needs to be aligned accurately, and that extra losses are involved compared with the direct feed method due to diffraction around the sub-reflector.

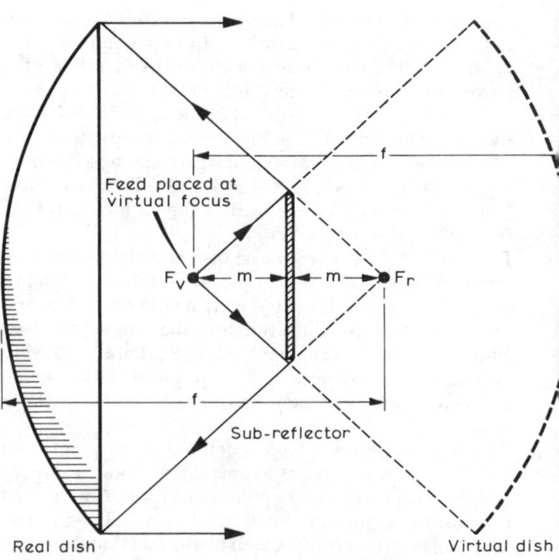

Fig 153. The geometry of an indirect feed arrangement

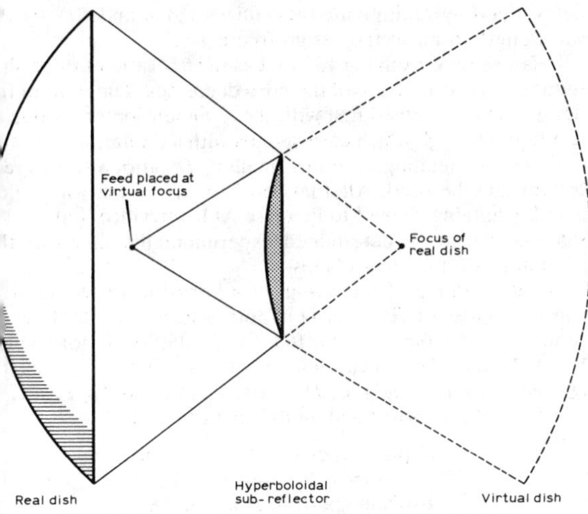

Fig 154. The geometry of the Cassegrain system

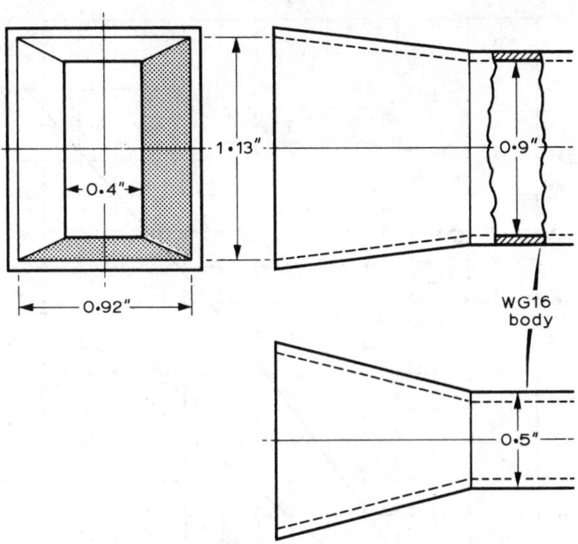

Fig 156. A typical pyramidal horn feed designed for a dish having an *f/D* ratio of 0·53 for use at 10GHz

Fig 155. A Cassegrain-fed dish using a hyperboloidal reflector

Cassegrain feed

The geometry of a Cassegrain system is shown in Fig 154. It is similar to the indirect feed method already described, the essential differences being that the planar sub-reflector is replaced by a shaped reflector having the form of a hyperboloid. The main result of this change is that the virtual dish seen by the feed has a longer focal length than the real dish. Thus a dish of short focal length which can be difficult to illuminate efficiently can be converted into one of longer apparent focal length. A second feature is that there is more flexibility in the positioning of the feed. There is no reason why, for example, the feed should not be mounted behind the dish firing through a suitable hole.

A completed antenna using this type of feed is shown in Fig 155.

Pyramidal horn feeds

Pyramidal horns have significant advantages over most other types of feeds which makes them especially suitable for use by amateurs. First, they offer a virtually perfect match over a wide range of frequencies and are therefore uncritical in their design and construction. Even quite large dimensional errors do not affect the quality of this match, but only the efficiency of illumination of the dish. A second advantage is that these horns can be designed to produce optimum illumination of the dish in *both* planes. With other types of feed, there may be little or no control of the beamwidth in one direction, and indeed, not much in the other.

The form of a horn is shown in Fig 156. It consists of a length of waveguide which is flared in one or two dimensions to produce the beamwidth required. For the higher microwave frequencies, the horn will probably be fed via waveguide, and the body of the horn feed will therefore usually consist of a length of waveguide which matches the rest of the system. At the lower microwave frequencies, the horn will probably be fed via coaxial cable, and some form of waveguide/coaxial cable transition will have to be employed, otherwise the design

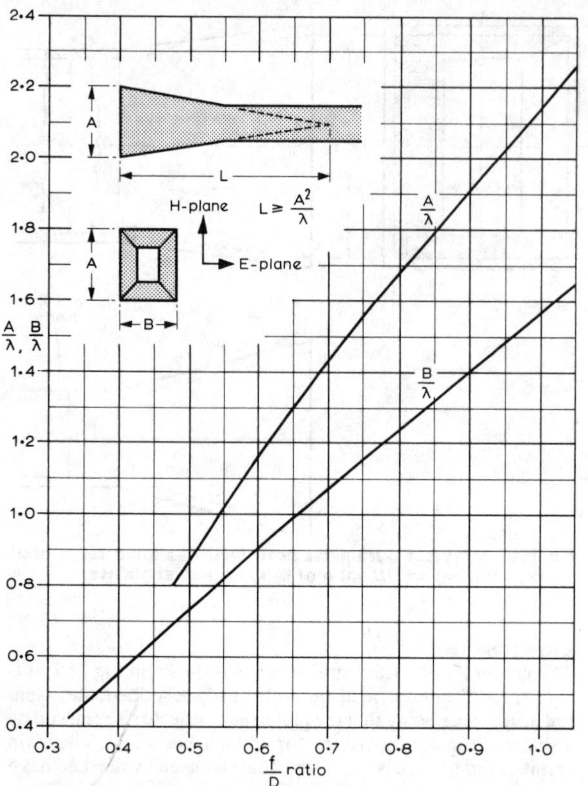

Fig 157. The dimensions of a pyramidal horn feed for a dish as a function of the ratio of focal length to diameter

method is the same. It is not necessary in this case to use a standard waveguide.

The dimensions of the pyramidal horn as a function of the *f*/*D* ratio of the dish to be illuminated are given in Fig 157. They are based on an edge illumination of 10dB down from that at the centre of the dish, and due allowance has been made for space loss. The dimensions are given in terms of wavelength at the frequency of operation, the actual dimensions of course being determined by multiplying the values of A/λ and B/λ by th wavelength in air at the design frequency.

It can be seen from Fig 157 that as the *f*/*D* ratio of the dish reduced so the aperture of the horn decreases. The limit of th design data is reached first with the A dimension at a value c A/λ equal to 0·8, which corresponds with a minimum *f*/*D* rati of 0·48. For feeding dishes of smaller *f*/*D* ratio, a Cassegrai system may be used. Alternatively the end of the waveguid may be suitably shaped to increase its beamwidth, but as th shaping has to be determined experimentally, much of th advantage of horn feeds is lost.

As an example of the design of a horn for a specific dish consider a dish of diameter D = 36in, which has a depth at it centre c = 4·26in, to be fed at 10,050MHz for whic λ = 1·174in. The focal length of the dish is given b $D^2/16c$ = 19·0in, and the *f*/*D* ratio therefore is 0·53. From Fi 157 the values corresponding to this ratio are:

$$\text{H-plane aperture } A/\lambda = 0{\cdot}96:$$
$$A \times 0{\cdot}96 \times 1{\cdot}174\text{in} = 1{\cdot}127\text{in}$$
$$\text{E-plane aperture } B/\lambda = 0{\cdot}78:$$
$$B = 0{\cdot}78\text{in} \times 1{\cdot}74\text{in} = 0{\cdot}916\text{in}$$
$$L \geqslant A^2/\lambda = 1{\cdot}127^2/1{\cdot}174 = 1{\cdot}081\text{in.}$$

At this frequency, a convenient waveguide is WG16, so practical horn would have an aperture of 1·127in by 0·916in tapering to 0·9in by 0·4in, and this design is shown in Fig 156.

By the same process of design, a horn feed for any dish with the same *f*/*D* ratio but for 1,296MHz would have an aperture o 8·74in by 7·10in, tapering to 6·5in by 3·25in, if WG6 were used, and one for 24GHz would have an aperture of 0·472in by 0·384in tapering to 0·420in by 0·170in for WG20.

Dipole reflector feeds for 1,296 and 2,304MHz

The basic arrangements of these feeds are given in Figs 158 and 159. Their radiation pattern makes them suitable for dishe with an *f*/*D* ratio of 0·25 to 0·35. The feeds are built around a length of fabricated rigid coaxial line, the inside dimensions o

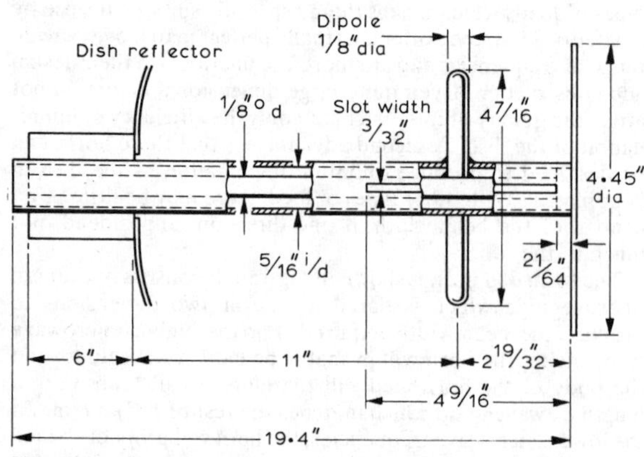

Fig 158. A dipole/reflector feed for 1,296MHz. The position of the feed is shown for a dish having a 12in focal length

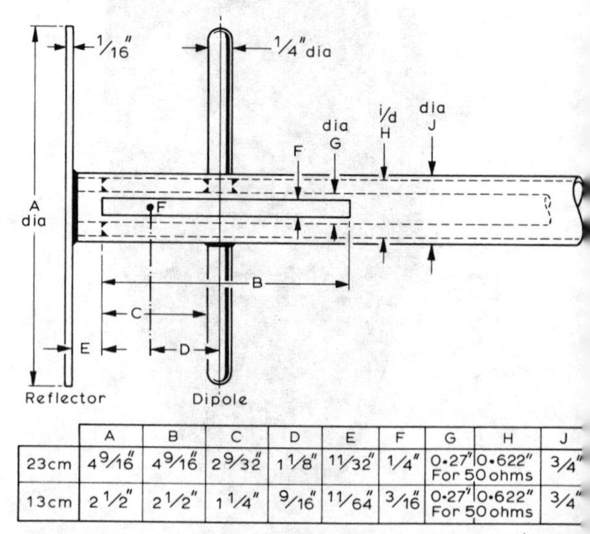

	A	B	C	D	E	F	G	H	J
23cm	4 9/16"	4 9/16"	2 9/32"	1 1/8"	11/32"	1/4"	0·27"	0·622" For 50 ohms	3/4"
13cm	2 1/2"	2 1/2"	1 1/4"	9/16"	11/64"	3/16"	0·27"	0·622" For 50 ohms	3/4"

Fig 159. Dipole/reflector feeds for 1,296 and 2,304MHz. The feed is mounted so that point F coincides with the focus of the dish

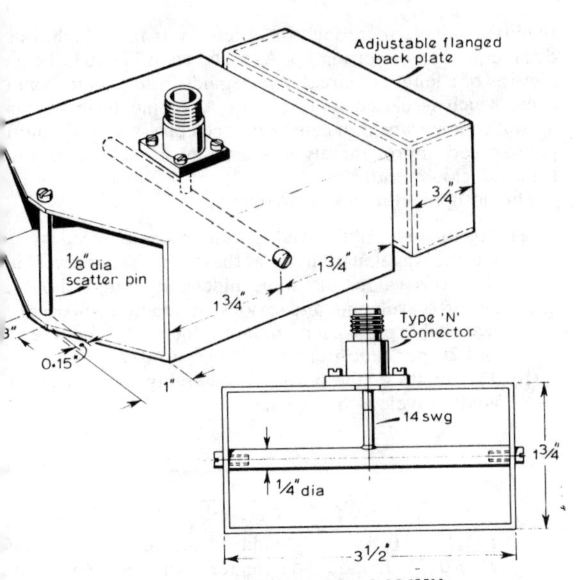

Fig 160. A waveguide feed for 2,304MHz

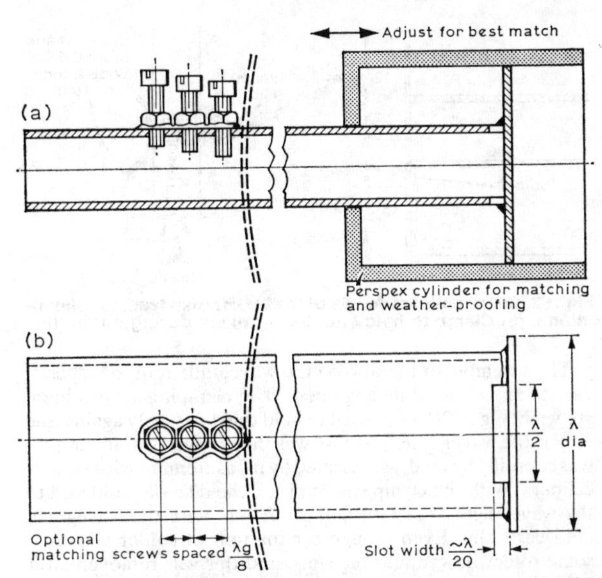

Fig 161. A simple feed for dishes having an *f/D* ratio of 0·25–3. Matching can be done either by matching screws as shown or as in (a) by using a Perspex matching (and weatherproofing) sleeve. (b) Side view of feed

he outer and the diameter of the inner being such as to produce n impedance of 50Ω. If required to operate with a 72Ω system, he ratio of these dimensions should be increased from 2·3:1 to ·3:1.

Waveguide feed for 2,304MHz

The design of a feed for dishes of short focal length is shown in Fig 160. By the use of a scatter pin, and by cutting the waveguide in the way shown, the angle of radiation can be increased significantly compared with a plain aperture. The feed is tuned by adjusting the position of the rf short which is then firmly bolted or soldered in place. The plane of polarization is parallel to the scatter pin.

Suitable materials for construction for the body are brass, copper or tinplate.

A simple waveguide feed for short focal length dishes

The dishes that amateurs inherit are often of the short focal length type; that is, the ratio of the focal length to the diameter of the dish typically is in the region 0·25–0·3.

The design of a suitable feed is shown in Fig 161. It is constructed by cutting two grooves in the end of a length of waveguide of appropriate size, and soldering on a circular end disc. The length of the slot formed, and also the diameter of the disc, are probably not critical within a few per cent, and the width of the slot even less so. Values for λ and λ_g for frequencies of amateur interest, together with details of suitable waveguides, are given in Table 14. Signals having the standard horizontal polarization are produced when the broad faces of the guide are vertical.

The feed can be used without any attempt to improve the match—the vswr is typically about 1·5:1. The match may be improved by conventional matching screws which preferably are fitted behind the dish as shown in order to reduce unwanted resonances. An elegant alternative method, which at the same time can be used in weatherproofing the system, is shown in the top figure. In this, a Perspex sleeve is made a sliding fit on both the end disc and the waveguide. By adjusting its position, the right proportion of power in the correct phase is fed back into the feed to cancel that reflected by the mismatch.

A dish feed for 24GHz

The dimensions of the 24GHz feed are shown in Fig 162(a). The method used to construct the feed was as follows. A piece of WG20 of sufficient length to reach the focus of the dish was taken, and its ends squared off by filing. The positions of the slots were marked out using vernier calipers and a right angle, and the slots filed out with a needle file. Repeated checking of the dimensions of the slots during filing ensured accuracy, most attention being paid to the length of the slots.

The end disc was made from 0·036in-thick brass sheet. A 0·5in square piece of this was cut out and soldered to a 0BA brass washer. Using the washer as a guide, the corners were filed off until the piece of brass was the same size as the 0BA washer. A small amount of further filing was then sufficient to reach the final size. The brass disc was then unsoldered from the washer, deburred, and the solder filed off.

Table 14

Centre frequency (MHz)	Suitable waveguide	λ (mm)	λg (mm)
1,297	WG6	231	324
2,305	WG8	130	162
3,457	WG10	86·7	109
5,761	WG14	52·0	78·2
10,050	WG16	29·8	39·4
10,369	WG16	28·9	37·3
24,193	WG20	12·4	15·2

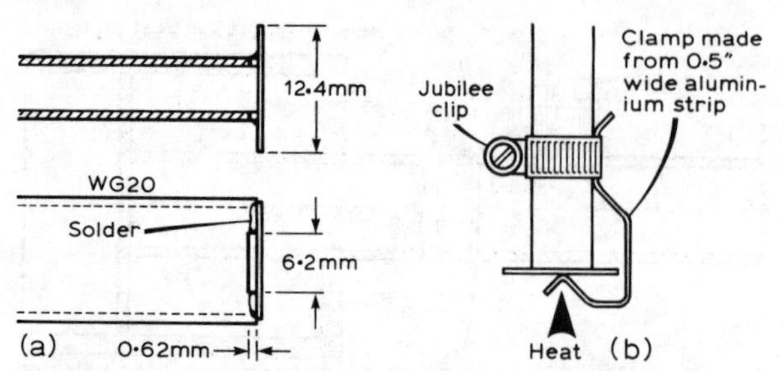

Fig 162. Constructional details of the 24GHz dish feed. (a) Dimensions. (b) Clamp to hold end disc in place during soldering

The assembly of the disc on the waveguide required special care to ensure accurate alignment. The clamping arrangement shown in Fig 162(b) was used to hold the disc firmly against the end of the waveguide. The disc was then moved around until it was centrally located, as indicated by measurement with vernier calipers. With the clamp still in place, the disc was soldered to the wavelength above a small gas flame, with the waveguide held vertically. Even though a minimum of solder was used some solder flowed into the slots, and this was removed after soldering by cutting it away with a scalpel blade, followed by the insertion of the end of a junior hacksaw blade into the slots (after removing one of the pins from the hacksaw blade).

The assembly was completed by sliding a $\frac{1}{8}$in-thick brass plate, with a 0·25 by 0·5in slot filed in its centre, on to the waveguide. This plate is for bolting to the dish to hold the feed in place. A home-made WG20 flange was then soldered on to the end of the waveguide. The assembly was held in the dish, and the feed slid backwards and forwards to find the point of maximum gain by listening to a remote signal source. The brass plate was then soldered in position, using a right angle to ensure that the plate was perpendicular to the waveguide in both planes.

Using this feed in a 0·35*f*/*D* 4ft dish, approximately 0·5dB of sun noise was seen, which is consistent with the calculated performance, based on a measured 18dB receiver noise figure, indicating very good performance of the antenna.

Circular horn feeds

This type of feed is quite common at the lower microwave frequencies, its main advantage being that it can be made from readily available materials. Its efficiency is fairly high, but does require some setting up. As is shown in Fig 163, the fee consists of a length of circular waveguide, often made from t cans, which is closed at one end. A simple form of coa ial/waveguide transition generally used consists of a $\lambda/4$ mon pole spaced approximately a quarter of a guide waveleng from the closed end.

The design factors are as follows:

(a) The diameter of the feed, D, must exceed $0{\cdot}586\lambda$, whe λ is the wavelength in air at the design frequency. If le than this value, the waveguide is operated above i cut-off wavelength and serious attenuation will occur. reasonable practical minimum value for D is between 1 and 20 per cent greater, ie $0{\cdot}65\lambda$ to $0{\cdot}7\lambda$.

(b) The length of the horn, L, preferably should exceed guide wavelength λ_g, where

$$\lambda_g = \frac{\lambda}{\sqrt{1 - \left(\frac{\lambda}{1{\cdot}706D}\right)^2}}$$

For $D = 0{\cdot}65\lambda$, L should be greater than $2{\cdot}4\lambda$: f $D = 0{\cdot}7\lambda$, L should be greater than $1{\cdot}8\lambda$. Note that the diameter of the feed approaches $0{\cdot}586\lambda$, the leng of the horn required increases very rapidly.

(c) The monopole should be about $\frac{1}{8}$in to $\frac{1}{4}$in in diameter an have an overall fixed length of about $0{\cdot}2\lambda$. A scre tapped into the end enables its resonant frequency to b adjusted. The distance between the monopole and th short-circuit must be determined by experiment. Th space required is in the region of $\lambda_g/4$, and the position c either the monopole or the short-circuit can be mad adjustable.

(d) The E-plane (horizontal) and H-plane (vertical) 3d beamwidth $\theta°$ is given by the values of $29{\cdot}4\lambda/D$ an $50\lambda/D$ respectively. That these differ significantly is on of the disadvantages of this type of feed since it results i uneven illumination of the dish. For the practica minimum value suggested for D, $0{\cdot}65\lambda$, the beamwidth respectively are 46° and 78°. Reference to Fig 151 show that these values correspond to an optimum *f*/*D* ratio fo the dish of 0·69 and 0·43 respectively, that is a mea value of 0·56, which represents approximately th minimum *f*/*D* ratio of the dish if it is to be illuminate reasonably efficiently.

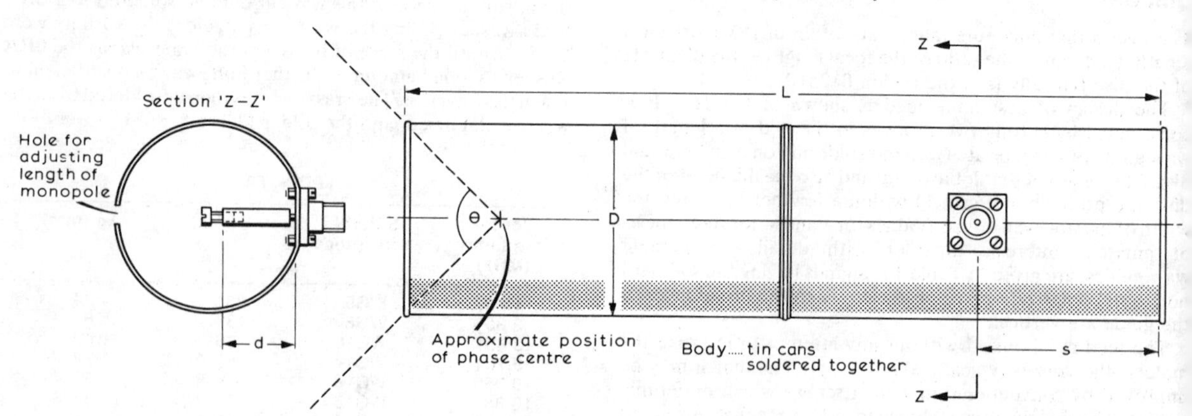

Fig 163. The design of circular horn feeds

Table 15

'requency (MHz)	D (in)	L (in)	d (in)	s (in)
1,297	5·9	>22	1·8	5·5
2,305	3·3	>12·3	1·0	3·0
3,457	2·2	> 8·2	0·7	2·0

There is a limited amount of flexibility of design. If the iameter of the horn is increased, then its length may be educed, but the beamwidth of the horn will also decrease. ypical dimensions of horns for the lower microwave frequen- es based on $D = 0{\cdot}65\lambda$ are given in Table 15. The equivalent hase centre of the feed will be in the region of an inch inside e mouth, and this point should be made to coincide with the ocus of the dish.

ligning and checking antennas

'he antenna is aligned by connecting some form of power etector and maximizing its output from signals received from a elatively distant transmitter. The only real problem is that of nsuring that the antenna responds only to the direct signal rom the transmitter, and not to any signals reflected from ntermediate objects. The risk of receiving reflections usually ncreases as the antennas are spaced further apart, but there is a ninimum desirable spacing: each antenna should be operated vell within the far field of the other. This means that the spacing hould exceed $2D^2/\lambda$ where D is the diameter of the larger ntenna and λ is the wavelength in the same units. For a dish 3ft n diameter used at 10GHz, for example, this distance is at least .00ft. A good test site is where the antenna is mounted on one ill and the transmitter at the same height on another a fraction f a mile away, with the valley between them broken up by rees, houses and rough ground. Again to minimize reflections, he transmitter antenna should have as high a gain as is avail- ble.

When large antennas and a powerful transmitter are used ver a comparatively short path, a convenient detector can be a onventional mixer. The meter measuring diode current should e the most sensitive available so that an attenuator can be itted between the antenna and the detector to minimize any nismatch. Over longer paths it may be necessary to use a eceiver as the detector. If this is an fm receiver, a variable ttenuator should be fitted so that the level of the signal applied o the receiver can be kept to the minimum possible and cer- ainly below that at which limiting occurs.

The operations that need to be done are as follows:

(a) Adjustment of the feed with respect to the dish. This is necessary because there is always some uncertainty in the precise position of the phase centre of the feed, and possibly that of the focus of the dish. The feed is slid in or out to maximize the received signal and then clamped in place.

(b) It is not safe to assume that the antenna is free from squint, however accurately it has been made. It must be remembered that the vertical beamwidth of even a small antenna such as that described above is only $\pm 2°$, and that a tilt in the vertical plane of only 3–4° will reduce its effective gain by about 10dB. Squint in the horizontal plane is unimportant as this will be eliminated in peaking the antenna on a transmitter. It is important to recognize that the axis of rotation of the antenna should be truly vertical, otherwise the antenna will be tilted when it is rotated into a different direction. This means that the pole supporting the antenna must be vertical, or the rotating platform of a tripod, for example, must be hori- zontal, within a fraction of the beamwidth of the antenna in use. When this has been arranged, the antenna is adjusted in the vertical plane for maximum signal. Repeat (a) and (b) while keeping the antenna in optimum position in azimuth as these adjustments will interact.

(c) Checking the gain of the antenna. If a calibrated attenuator is available, substituting a second antenna of known gain and adjusting the attenuator to produce the same detected signal will provide a direct measure of antenna gain. For an antenna of this type, an efficiency of 50–60 per cent of the theoretical value, which is given by $(\pi D/\lambda)^2$, is a practical limit. The gain of a conventional pyramidal horn, as shown in Fig 172, is sufficiently pre- dictable to be used as a standard.

(d) An invaluable facility is some sort of optical sighting device aligned precisely with the electrical axis of the antenna. One form of this consists of a tube 0·5–1in diameter fitted with a small hole at one end and with cross-wires at the other, which is clamped to the antenna mount. It is aligned by rotating the antenna for maxi- mum signal over a clear path. If the transmitter is visible the sighting tube is simply pointed at the transmitter and clamped in place. If the transmitter is not visible, the antenna is rotated precisely through the angle between it and a visible landmark as measured from a map, and the sighting tube set on the landmark. Subsequently, when operating from other sites, the antenna can usually be orientated accurately by reference to local landmarks. Such a sighting system can be specially useful when it is necessary to point the antenna in other than a horizontal direction—for example, when using a knife-edge diffrac- tion to cross hills.

It is well worthwhile checking the alignment of the antenna over a second path. If adjustments produce the same optimum alignment one can be reasonably sure that this is the correct one. A significantly different path is usually obtained by raising or lowering the antenna a few feet, or moving it sideways a short distance.

The flyswatter antenna

Operating microwave equipment for domestic locations immediately raises problems in mounting the antenna accu- rately, in weatherproofing it and feeding signals to it. New waveguide is expensive, and even good-quality coaxial cable is relatively lossy, typically up to 1dB/ft at 10GHz, and therefore cannot be used in long lengths.

One method for avoiding feeder problems is simply to mount *all* the equipment at the top of the mast and to feed the dc, af and i.f. supplies instead. This approach can still present prob- lems, of course.

If the equipment is to be mounted semi-permanently, then weatherproofing will need careful attention. On the other hand, if it is fitted to the mast only when it is to be used, then some ingenious engineering will be required to ensure that this can be done speedily and reliably as a matter of routine.

An alternative approach is the flyswatter or periscope antenna shown schematically in Fig 164. Although this form of

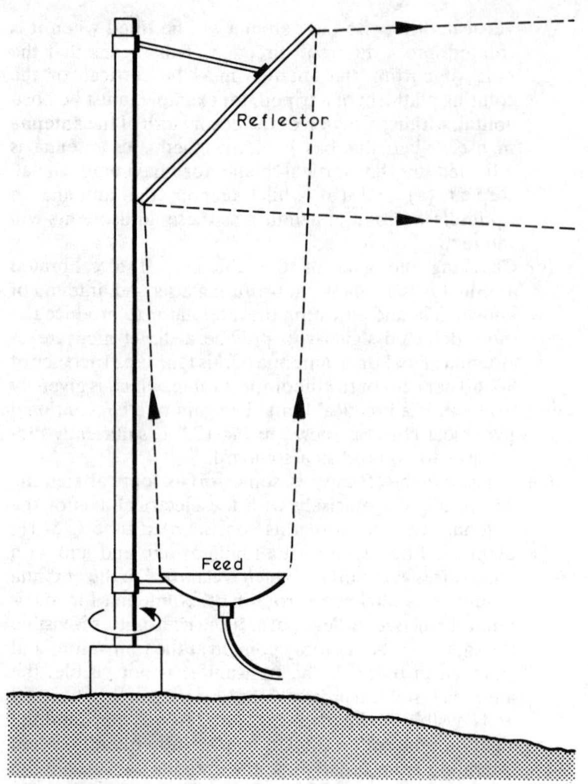

Fig 164. Configuration of the flyswatter or periscope antenna

antenna is widely used professionally, it seems to have receive little attention from amateurs.

In this system, the feed is usually a parabolic dish (althoug not necessarily so), and this directs signals upwards at a reflec tor mounted so as to reflect them horizontally. The area of th reflector illuminated normally is an ellipse which will have th ratio of major to minor dimension equal to 1·41 if the reflecto is set at 45°. An elliptical reflector obviously could be used, bu a rectangular one is usually preferred for ease of handling, an this actually produces extra gain. The reflector may be planar o curved parabolically, and the purpose of this article is to give a indication of the performance of both types in an amateu context. Although interest in this antenna originated fro operating at 10GHz, its potential at other frequencies will b briefly considered.

Design data

The generalized data from which the effective gain of variou configurations can be worked out are given in Fig 165 for plan reflectors and in Fig 166 for curved reflectors. The overall gai is a complicated interaction between some factors over whic one has a wide choice, such as the size of the feed and reflector other factors such as the feed/reflector spacing over which on has a restricted choice, and fixed items such as the wavelength

(a) Calculate the ratio a/R; ie the ratio of diameter of th dish feed and the minimum dimension of the reflector. I a feed other than a dish is used, then use the diameter of dish of equivalent gain.

(b) Calculate the value of function $\lambda d/4R^2$, rememberin that λ, d and R must be in the same units.

(c) Determine from Fig 165 or 166 the gain or loss corres ponding to these values.

(d) Add this gain or loss to the gain of the feed.

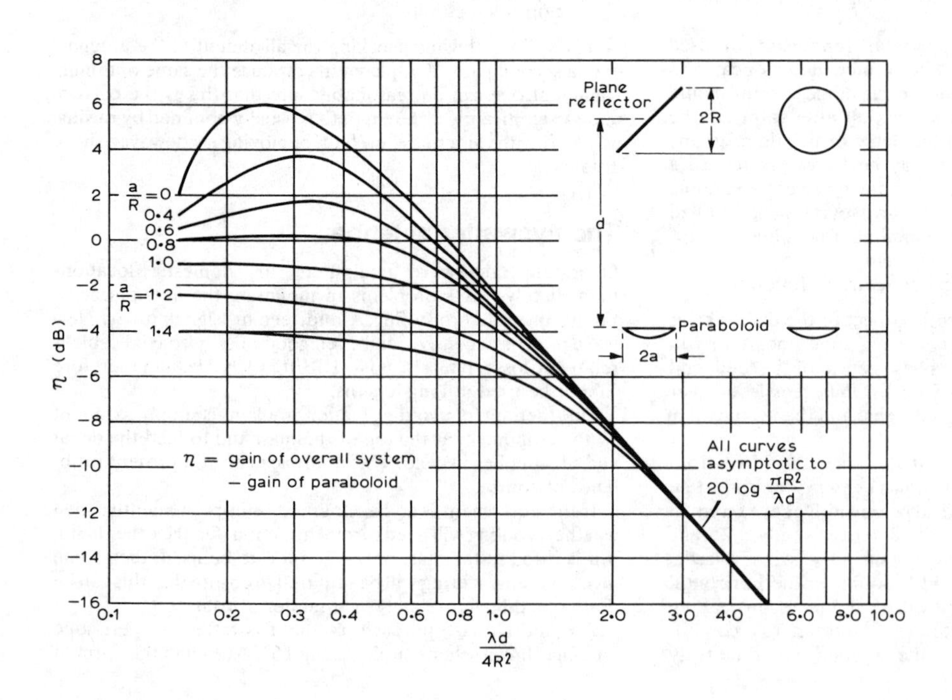

Fig 165. Relative gain with plane reflector

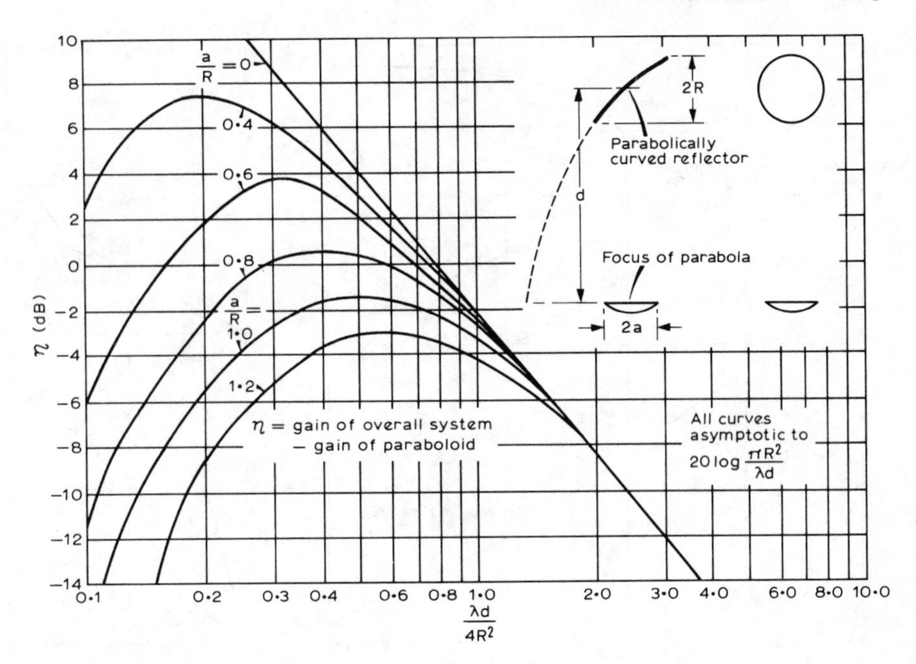

Fig 166. Relative gain with parabolically curved reflector

Systems using plane reflectors

Fig 167 illustrates the effect of dish and reflector size on overall gain in systems in which the minimum dimension of the reflector is made equal to the diameter of the dish feed. The reflector is assumed to be mounted at an angle of 45° to the horizontal so that the maximum dimension is made 1·41 times the minimum.

The important feature of these results is that they show that it is comparatively easy to achieve a reasonably high antenna gain in absolute terms despite the "transmission loss" being high in some cases. For example, a dish 1·5ft in diameter used with a reflector 1·5 by 2·1ft in size which is mounted 30ft up a mast will still have a gain of 25dB, despite a transmission loss of 5dB.

The effective "feeder" losses are interesting. With a dish 1ft in diameter, the loss is about 0·3dB/ft. Although rather high, it is still less than that characteristic of even good quality coaxial cable at this frequency. On the other hand, the loss with a dish 3ft in diameter is only about 0·05dB/ft, which is about the same as brass waveguide 16. As would be expected, the losses when using 1·5 and 2ft dishes are at intermediate values, 0·2 and 0·1dB/ft respectively.

Fig 168 illustrates for two sizes of feed the rather complicated way in which the overall gain is related to the size of reflector used. The lowest curve refers to a small feed used with a small reflector, and its performance can hardly be described as sparkling. However, by using a larger reflector the performance of the system improves dramatically, with the original 20dB gain still available at a feed/reflector spacing of 20ft. The upper four curves show the effect of reflector size with an "average" size of dish 1·5ft in diameter. Note that the peak gain is displaced to larger dish/reflector spacings which it may not be possible to use in a particular installation. At a spacing of 15ft, for example, the data suggest that the maximum overall gain is achieved with a reflector of *intermediate* size.

Systems using parabolically curved reflectors

The advantage of a curved reflector over a plane one is shown in Table 16, the values of gain being the maximum that can be

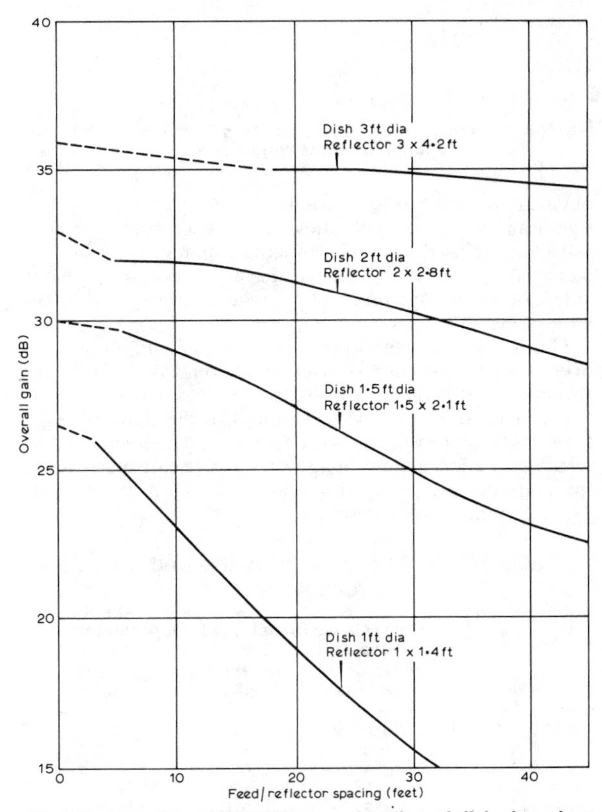

Fig 167. Overall gain at 10GHz as a function of dish size, plane reflector same size as dish

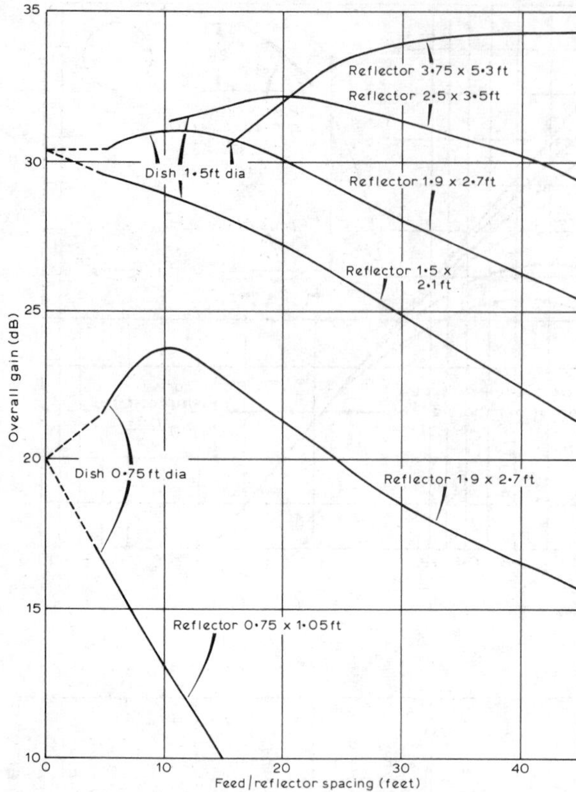

Fig 168. Overall gain at 10GHz for 0·75 and 1·5ft dishes as function of plane reflector size

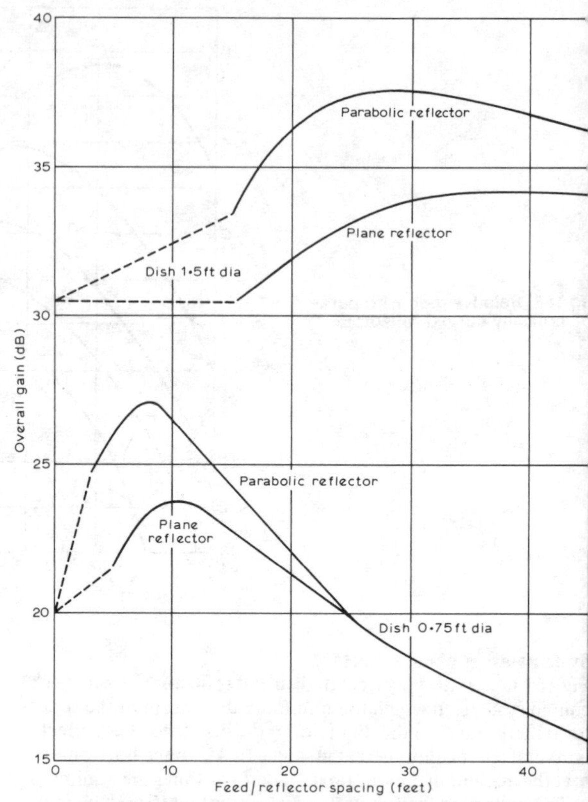

Fig 169. Comparison of plane and curved reflectors

obtained at each particular value of a/R. The advantage is significant only at low a/R ratios, that is when relatively large reflectors are used. Fig 169 shows the extent of the improvement for two sizes of dish feed, and again demonstrates that it may not always be practical to take advantage of these improvements.

This is simply because the enhancement of gain is observed over only a narrow range of values of the function $\lambda d/4R^2$, and that other considerations affecting the actual values of λ, d and R that have to be used may take it out of this narrow range. Even if the extra gain can be obtained, whether or not this justifies the effort of fabricating a curved reflector specially for the particular dish/reflector spacing to be used can only be decided in individual cases.

Table 16. Comparisons of plane and curved reflectors

a/R	Gain relative to dish feed Plane reflector (dB)	Curved reflector (dB)	Advantage of curved reflector (dB)
0·4	3·6	7·4	3·8
0·6	1·8	3·8	2·0
0·8	0·4	0·8	0·4
1·0	−1·0	−1·3	−0·3
1·2	−2·5	−3·0	−0·5
1·4	−4·0	—	—

Variation of performance with frequency

Fig 170 shows how the overall gain varies with height at a number of frequencies of amateur interest for a system consisting of a feed dish 1·5ft in diameter with a plane reflector 3·75 by 5·3ft in size. The curves show that at lower frequencies not only is the gain of the dish feed reduced, but the transmission loss also tends to increase and thereby reduces the gain even further. The latter effect is a reflection of the displacement of the value of the function $\lambda d/4R^2$ to higher values as λ increases.

If a "standard" for antenna gain is taken as 20–25dB, a value obtained from 1 to 4 long Yagi antennas, then this particular flyswatter system will certainly be competitive at frequencies of 5·7GHz and above, and probably at 3·4GHz if feeder losses are taken into account. At 2·3GHz and below, this antenna clearly is not competitive. Nevertheless it is worth noting that while it may not be justifiable to set up a reflector of *this* size specially for these lower frequencies, if one is already available then an antenna of moderate gain can be produced for the effort of just fitting a suitable feed.

Practical aspects of construction

Some of the factors affecting the construction of flyswatter antennas are as follows:

(a) With these and other high-gain antennas, the axis of rotation must be truly vertical, otherwise the beam will point successively above and below the horizon as it is rotated. If this deviation is larger than a small fraction of

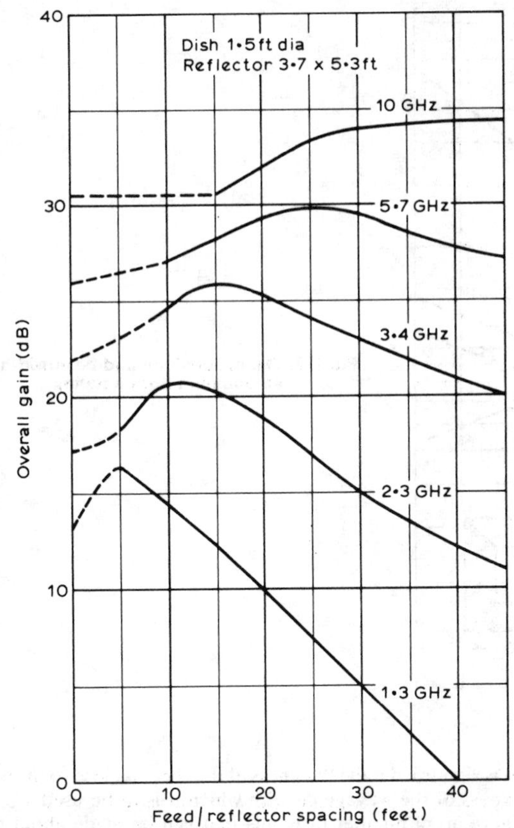

Fig 170. Gain of specified system as a function of frequency

the beamwidth of the antenna in the vertical direction, then the overall gain may be significantly reduced.

(b) It is not essential but it would appear simpler if the feed directs signals vertically upwards. A plane reflector in this case would be set at precisely 45° to the horizontal. Aligning the system would presumably only require the feed to be fitted with its centre immediately below that of the reflector, and the latter tilted to eliminate any squint while keeping the antenna peaked in azimuth. Curved reflectors will probably have to be set at the correct angle by trial and error.

(c) There is no reason why the feed should not be fitted some distance up the mast if this is more convenient for operating via, for example, a bedroom window.

(d) It is necessary that the reflector be flat, or curved parabolically, and not distort under wind pressure or other cause, within an overall error of $\pm$ $\lambda/10$. If a mesh reflector is used to reduce windage, then the spaces between the wires should not exceed $\lambda/10$ at the highest frequency of operation. For more details see Fig 140.

(e) As noted earlier, there is no reason why horn or Yagi antennas should not be used as the feed.

(f) One of the advantages of the flyswatter system is that a vulnerable part of any antenna, the feed itself, is readily accessible. It would seem to be worth spending much effort to make it possible to remove, replace and interchange feeds reliably so full advantage can be taken of this accessibility.

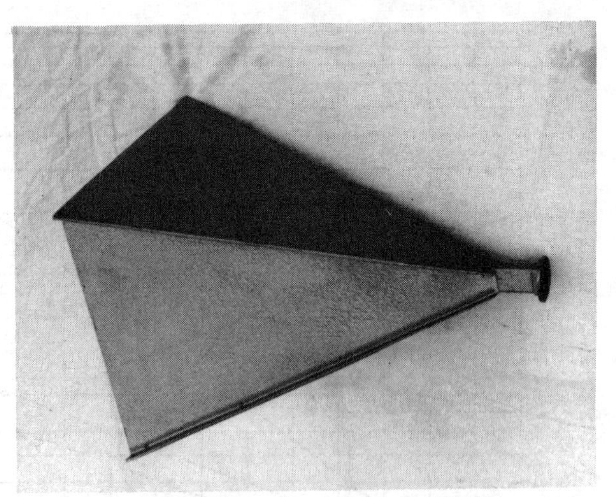

Fig 171. A large horn antenna for 10GHz

Large horn antennas

Large pyramidal horns are an attractive form of antenna, particularly for use at the highest microwave frequencies. They are fundamentally broadband devices which show a virtually perfect match over a wide range of frequencies. They are simple to design, tolerant of dimensional inaccuracies in construction and they need no adjustment. Horns are especially suitable for use with transmitters and receivers employing free-running oscillators, the frequency stability of which can be very dependent on the match of their load. Another advantage is that their gain can be predicted within a decibel or so, which makes them useful in both initially checking the performances of systems and also in acting as references against which the performance of other types of antennas can be judged. Their main disadvantage is that they are bulky compared with other types of antenna having the same gain.

An example of a horn antenna for 10GHz is shown in Fig 171. It consists of a length of waveguide appropriate for the frequency of use, which is smoothly flared in both planes so that a wave inside the guide can expand in an orderly manner. When the length of the horn is very large compared with the aperture, the wave emerging is nearly planar and the gain of the antenna is close to the theoretical value: $4\pi AB/\lambda^2$, where A and B are the dimensions of the aperture. For a horn of moderate length, the wave is spherical with its centre at the apex of the horn. Accordingly, the field near the rim lags in phase compared with that along the centre line of the horn and this causes a loss of gain. If the length of the horn is reduced further so that this phase lag exceeds $\lambda/2$, then large minor lobes will be produced. A practical horn is therefore a compromise between achieving the desired directional pattern and reducing the overall length of the horn.

The dimensions of an optimum horn and the approximate 3dB beamwidth are shown in Fig 172. The dimensions are given in terms of wavelengths, the actual measurements of course are obtained by multiplying the values by the wavelength in air at the design frequency. Fig 172 is based on the following relationships which assume an efficiency of 50 per cent:

$A/\lambda = 0{\cdot}443\sqrt{G}$ where G = gain in absolute value
$B = 0{\cdot}81A$
$L/\lambda = 0{\cdot}0654G$

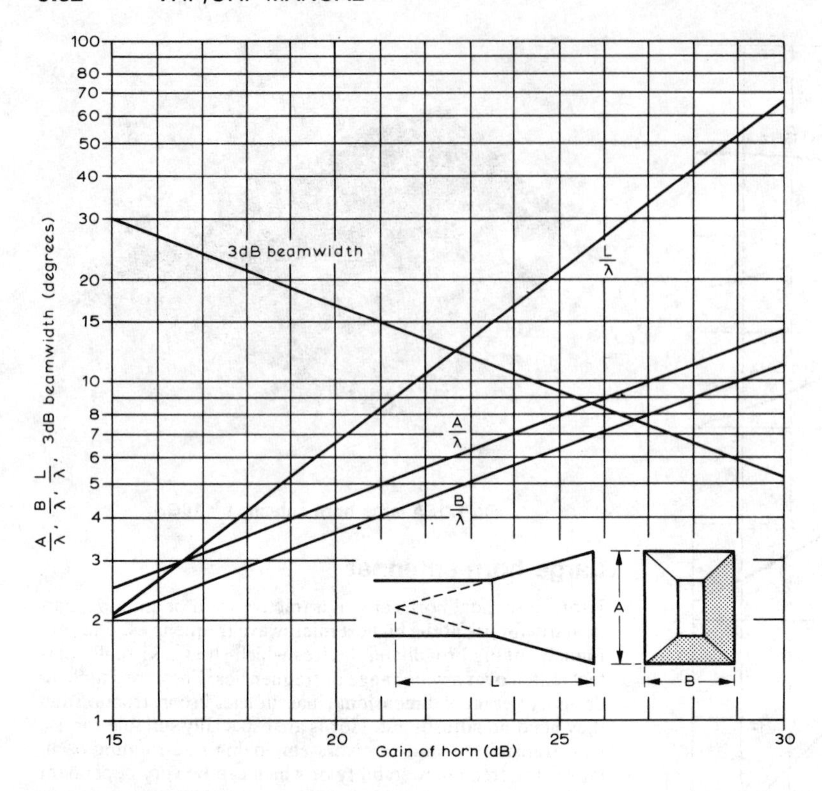

Fig 172. The dimensions and beamwidth of an optimum horn antenna

As an example of the use of this data, consider the design of a 20dB horn for use at 5,760MHz, for which $\lambda = 2{\cdot}05$in. From Fig 172:

$A/\lambda = 4{\cdot}4; A = 4{\cdot}4 \times 2{\cdot}05 = 9{\cdot}0$in
$B/\lambda = 3{\cdot}6; B = 3{\cdot}6 \times 2{\cdot}05 = 7{\cdot}4$in
$L/\lambda = 6{\cdot}5; L = 6{\cdot}5 \times 2{\cdot}05 = 13{\cdot}3$in

So the horn would have an aperture of 9 by 7·4in, tapering over a length of 13·3in to 1·372 by 0·622in if WG14 were used. The 3dB beamwidth of the horn would be approximately 16°.

As a second example, a 30dB horn for 24GHz would have an aperture of 6·7 by 5·1 in and a length of 30·7 in.

Note that for a given aperture, the optimum length L varies inversely with frequency. If a horn is used at a somewhat higher frequency than that for which it was designed, its gain will be marginally less than the predicted value. If used at a much higher frequency, then gross distortion of its radiation pattern may occur with consequent serious loss in gain.

At the lower microwave frequencies, the bulkiness of horns becomes a significant disadvantage, and therefore they are little used. For example, a 20dB horn for 1,296MHz would have an aperture 40 by 33in and a length of 5ft. The same gain could be achieved by a parabolic dish about 3½ft in diameter or a single long Yagi.

Construction of horns

Horns are usually fabricated from solid material, although there is no reason why mesh should not be used provided that the hole dimensions do not exceed $\lambda/10$. The most common materials are brass, copper or tin plate. Aluminium is rarely used because of difficulties in soldering. Construction of the horn is simplified if the thickness of the sheet is close to the wall thickness of the waveguide with which it is to be used.

There are a number of points that can be made about the construction of horns. The geometry of a horn is not quite as simple as it appears at first sight since it involves a taper from an aspect ratio of about 1:0·8 at the aperture to approximately 2:1 at the waveguide transition. For a superficially rectangular object, a horn contains few right-angles. It is therefore well worthwhile having a trial run using a cheap material such as tin plate or even cardboard before attempting to use a more expensive material.

The methods used in construction depend on the facilities available and the size of the horn. A difficult part is the junction between the horn and the waveguide extension. This must present a smooth transition and also be strong enough to withstand the large mechanical forces which tend to concentrate at this point. For all but the smallest horns, some form of strengthening is necessary. This can take the form of bent strips bolted using brass screws into holes tapped in the walls of the waveguide and the horn which are subsequently soldered in place. It is important that any of the screws projecting inside, together with any excess solder, are later carefully removed. The strips can also have a second function: that of jigging the components in place prior to soldering. This is usually necessary as up to six components may have to be joined together within a small region, and it may be difficult to solder one joint without affecting an adjacent joint.

For the waveguide 16 commonly used at 10GHz, advantage may be taken of old English waveguide which was common in wartime British radar. This waveguide has internal dimensions 1in by ½in which match the external dimensions of waveguide 16. An excellent support for the waveguide/horn transition can

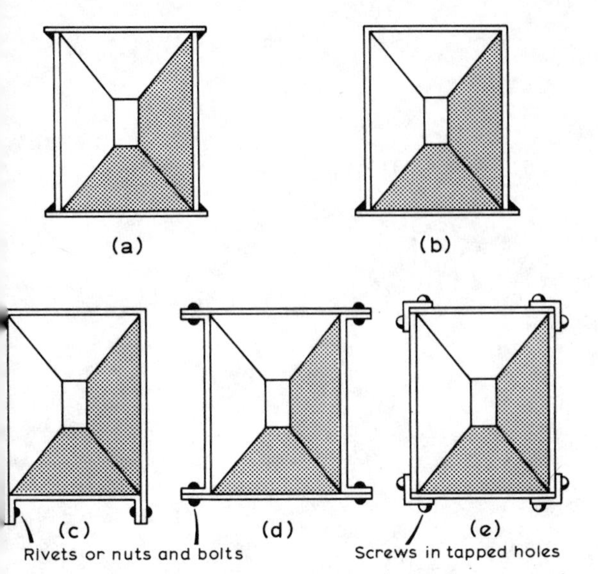

Fig 173. Various methods for constructing horns

e made by slitting the corners about half way down a short ength of the waveguide and flaring the sides to suit the angle of he horn.

An alternative approach is to omit the waveguide section of he horn. In this case the waveguide flange is tapered internally. t is necessary that the thickness of the sheet used to fabricate the horn be very similar to the wall thickness of the waveguide otherwise a step will be formed at the junction between the horn and the waveguide system.

Several methods have been used to fabricate the horn itself. Fig 173(a) illustrates what is probably the simplest method which is suitable for horns with apertures up to several inches. Four plates of the correct shape are soldered using a large soldering iron. Since in this technique the heating is localized, the joints can be made progressively and little jigging is required. If a sheet bending device is available, then other approaches may be used. As is shown by Fig 172(b), three sides of a horn can be bent from a single sheet. It is a convenient method of assembly if this component is brazed to the waveguide, the joint cleaned up through the open side, and the fourth side fitted by soldering.

With large horns it may be necessary to solder using a gas flame in order to get adequate heating. This introduces the problem of distortion of the sheet due to the inevitable uneven heating. By using the techniques shown in Fig 173(c), (d) and (e), the horns can be assembled to produce a stable mechanical structure prior to soldering. The spacing between the clamping screws or rivets should not be greater than about an inch.

It is important to have good electrical contact at the corners, but at the same time the amount of solder internally should be minimized as it is lossy.

References

[1] *QST* January 1974.
[2] *Radio Communication* January 1976, p36 (see Chapter 11).
[3] *Ham Radio* August 1978.
[4] *Radio Communication* July 1976, p506.

HAPTER 10

Space communications

ecent years have seen a considerable growth in the use of nateur artificial satellites for long-distance vhf communi-ition. Improvements in amateur equipment and the satellites emselves are bringing what was once a very specialized field to the mainstream of amateur activity. It is however possible at many amateurs are still suffering disappointment in their tempts to use this method of communication, due to an adequate knowledge of the fundamentals of satellite orbital ometry. This topic is therefore dealt with in some detail low before the aspects of station equipment are considered.

Unlike the moon, amateur satellites in orbit relatively close the earth's surface appear to move rather rapidly across the y from horizon to horizon. How long the satellite will be ithin the range of a station is dependent on two factors: (i) the titude of the satellite, and (ii) the distance it will be at the oint of closest approach to the station. The longest duration at y altitude will occur on orbits that pass directly over the ation location. The duration will decrease for orbits that pass rther away from the station. For instance, a satellite in a 000-mile orbit would be within "line of sight" range for about 5min on an overhead pass, about 20min when it comes only ithin 1,000 miles of a ground station and only about 10min ith a 2,000-mile distance of closest approach.

When using a satellite for two-way communication it is ecessary to take into consideration the length of time the tellite will be within the simultaneous range of all the stations volved. The higher a satellite is the greater the effective range ground station using it will have. Since higher satellites will be rther away from the ground station, signal strengths will be naller due to path losses unless either more powerful transmit-rs or higher-gain receiving systems are used. The greater the oint-to-point distance between the user and the satellite, the ore power or gain will be needed to maintain adequate signal vels. Therefore, although high-altitude satellites will allow ntacts with more distant stations, a more elaborate station ill be needed, or a satellite with larger transmitters and anten-as.

eometry of orbiting satellites

he laws governing the characteristics of one object rotating ound another were established long before communication tellites were thought of. The motion of the planets around the n has been a subject of study for a great many years, and the ws that have been derived from these observations are equally oplicable to man-made satellites placed in orbit around the rth. It is not intended to derive these laws here, but merely to ow how most of the information required for calculating bital parameters for a satellite can be obtained from a few mple equations.

The force of attraction between any two objects is defined in e basic laws of physics as being proportional to the masses of the two objects divided by the square of the distance between them. This may be written as

$$F \propto \frac{m_1 \times m_2}{d^2}$$

where m_1 and m_2 are the two masses and d is the distance separating them.

This concept is analogous to the property of magnetism where the force of attraction between two magnets (with opposite polarity) increases as the strength of either, or both, magnets is increased, and decreases as they are moved apart.

The other main factor to be considered is that under normal circumstances a body which has a certain velocity will continue to travel in a straight line unless an external force is applied to it. Thus, for the case where one object is rotating around another, a force must exist to cause the change in direction of motion from a straight line. This force is known as the *centripetal force* and may be written mathematically as:

$$P = \frac{mv^2}{d}$$

where m is the mass of the object, v its velocity and d the distance from the centre of the orbit.

Considering the case of a satellite moving in a circular orbit around the earth, it is apparent that the only mechanism that can provide this centripetal force is the gravitational attraction of the earth on the satellite. The gravitational force is in fact the weight of the satellite given by

$$W = \frac{GMm}{d^2}$$

where G is the universal gravitational constant, M is the mass of the earth, m the mass of the satellite and d the distance between the centres of mass.

Hence for a stable orbit $P = W$ and

$$\frac{mv^2}{d} = \frac{GMm}{d^2} \qquad \text{(i)}$$

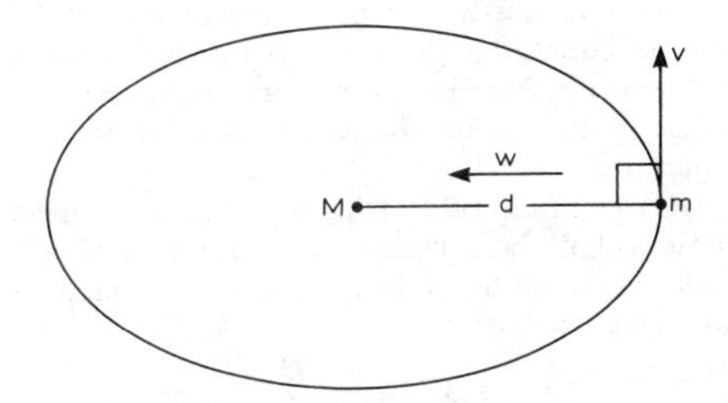

Fig 1. The gravitational attraction *W* provides the centripetal force required to cause the satellite to change from its straight-line motion

In the case of a satellite orbiting the earth, d is the sum of the radius of the earth, R (6,375km mean value) and h, the height of the satellite orbit. Equation (i) can then be re-arranged to give

$$v^2 = \frac{GM}{R + h} \qquad \text{(ii)}$$

The circumference of the orbit is given by $l = 2\pi(R + h)$ and, if the time required to complete one revolution (known as the *orbital period*) is τ, then from the general relationship, velocity = distance ÷ time, it can be seen that

$$v = \frac{2\pi (R + h)}{\tau} \text{ kilometres per second}$$

By substituting for v in equation (ii) we can arrive at the following expression for the period:

$$\tau = 2\pi (R + h)\sqrt{\frac{R + h}{GM}} \qquad \text{(iii)}$$

This shows that the orbital period of a satellite is completely independent of the mass of the satellite and depends only on the height of the orbit. The parameter GM is known as the *gravitational mass* of the earth and has a value of 398,600km³/s².

In the following calculations we shall take as an example the orbit of Oscar 8 which has a mean altitude of 900km. In fact the orbit was not completely circular (apogee 910km, perigee 898km) but the variations cause minor errors to the calculations. By substituting this value of h in equation (iii) the period is

$$\tau = 2\pi (6{,}375 + 900)\sqrt{\frac{6{,}375 + 900}{398{,}600}} \text{ seconds}$$

$$\approx 103\text{min}$$

Fig 6 shows how the satellite period varies for typical values of altitude. Another example that will be considered later is where the satellite altitude is 35,800km, which results in an orbital period of 23h 56·6min, ie the period of rotation of the earth. This is known as a *geosynchronous* orbit.

Many of the terms used in orbital geometry are self-explanatory but others may not be so obvious and the more important of these are described below.

Sub-satellite point: this is the point on the earth that lies directly below the satellite. At this point, corresponding to the time of closest approach, the distance to the satellite is a minimum.

Ascending node: this is the point where the satellite orbit crosses the equatorial plane when moving from south to north. It is also referred to as the *equator crossing point*, and expressed as degrees longitude measured from the Greenwich meridian.

Half angle of visibility: Referring to Fig 2, this is the angle ϕ. It represents half the coverage angle of the satellite which is subtended at the centre of the earth. It can be calculated from the following expression:

$$\cos\phi = \frac{R}{R + h}$$

Slant height: this is the distance from a point on the earth to the satellite. The maximum slant height occurs when the

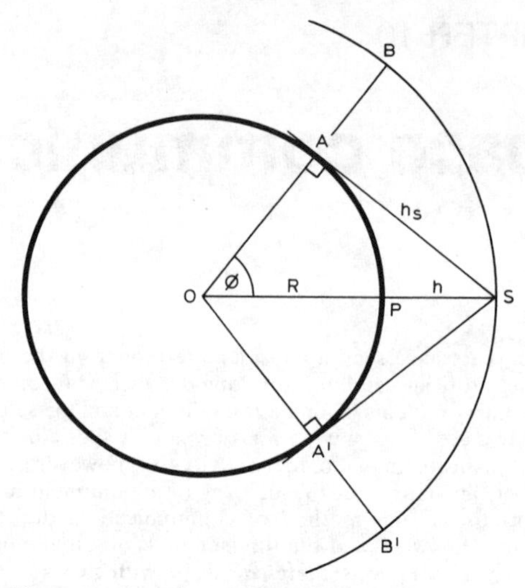

Fig 2. The geometry of a satellite orbit, showing the half ang of visibility (ϕ) and the slant height (h_s)

satellite is just at the horizon, ie from point A on Fig 2 and given by

$$h_s = R \tan\phi$$

Slant range: the sum of the slant heights between two poir on the earth within mutual visibility of the satellite. T maximum slant range will be twice the maximum slant heigh ie $2R \tan\phi$. It is necessary to know these distances wh calculating the path losses for the up-link and down-li paths.

Map range: the maximum great-circle distance between tw points on the earth that can simultaneously see the satellit In Fig 2 this is the length of the arc APA' and can be shown be equal to (220 × ϕ) km where ϕ is in degrees.

For Oscar 8 these parameters have the following values

Half angle of visibility	28·8°
Slant height (max)	3,500km
Slant range (max)	7,000km
Map range	6,336km

As pointed out earlier these values are all determined solely b the altitude of the satellite.

Doppler shift

A very important factor to be taken into account when consi ering the suitability of frequency bands for use in a satelli service is the amount of Doppler shift that will be imposed c the satellite emissions. This is determined by the relative velo ity of the satellite with respect to the particular point on th earth and increases in direct proportion to the frequency c transmission. From equation (ii) the satellite velocity may b calculated from

$$v = \sqrt{\frac{GM}{R + h}} \text{ kilometres per second}$$

Substituting the appropriate value for h for Oscar 8 gives velocity of 7·4km/s.

Fig 3 shows a satellite orbit which is inclined at an angle

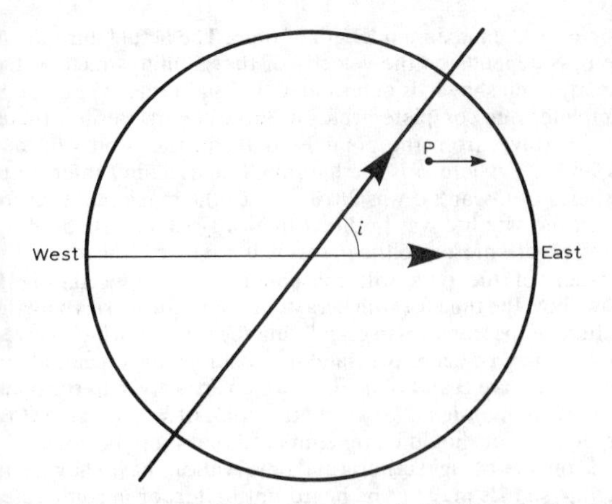

Fig 3. A satellite orbit inclined at an angle i to the equator. The point P is at a latitude of α°. The two arrows indicate the direction of rotation of the earth and the satellite orbit

o the plane of the equator, and a point P on the earth at a atitude α. The maximum relative velocity of the satellite with espect to the receiving point occurs as the satellite crosses the orizon and reduces to a minimum at the point of closest pproach. For an orbit which passes directly above the observer, the received frequency will be the same as that transmitted when the satellite is overhead, ie there will be no Doppler hift.

It can be shown that the relative velocity at any particular oint during an overhead orbit can be obtained from the following expression:

$$v_r = v \sin\left[\cos^{-1}\left(\frac{h_s^2 + (R+h)^2 - R^2}{2h_s \,.\, (R+h)}\right)\right] \quad \text{(iv)}$$

where h_s corresponds to the slant height at the particular point of the orbit. This expression does not take account of a number of factors; however, the only one of major concern is the effect of the rotation of the earth. In order to compensate for this effect it is necessary to replace the value v in equation (iv) with v' which may be calculated from

$$v' = \sqrt{(v \sin i)^2 + (v \cos i - 0{\cdot}46 \cos \alpha)^2}$$

where α is the latitude of an observer whose location lies on the satellite track. Hence for a location at a latitude of 50° and an orbit inclination of 98·99°, v' can be calculated as 7·45km/s (note that this value is greater than v because with a retrograde orbit (i>90°) the longitudinal component of the satellite velocity is in the opposite direction to the rotation of the earth).

If one considers a particular point during the overhead orbit at which the slant height is, say, 3,000km the relative velocity is 6·5km/s. The Doppler shift at this time may be calculated from

$$f_d = \pm \frac{v_r}{c} \times f$$

where f_d is the Doppler shift in hertz, c is the velocity of light in km/s and f is the transmitted frequency in hertz. For a beacon signal at 435·1MHz the Doppler shift under the conditions described above would be

$$f_d = \pm \frac{6{\cdot}5 \times 435{\cdot}1 \times 10^6}{3 \times 10^5} \text{ Hz} = \pm 9{\cdot}4\text{kHz}$$

This means that as the satellite approaches the observer the beacon frequency will be received 9·4kHz higher than its nominal value, falling to 435·1MHz when the satellite is directly overhead, then continuing to decrease by a further 9·4kHz. Thus the total change in the received frequency throughout the part of the orbit considered would be 18·8kHz as indicated in Fig 4. It should be remembered that when signals are relayed by a satellite transponder there will be a Doppler shift on the up-link and the down-link.

Longitude increment

It is useful to know by how much the longitude of the equator crossing point changes with each successive orbit, so as to enable long-term predictions to be made.

The accuracy achieved will depend on the number and degree of simplifications that are made to what is a highly complex problem. In the simplest case the earth is assumed to be a perfect sphere, rotating on its axis, and the motion of the earth and the satellite is assumed to be unaffected by the gravitational effects of other planetary objects. In this simple case the earth will have rotated by a certain amount after each orbit of the satellite. Since the earth completes one revolution in 24h (approximately), ie 1° every 4min, the amount by which it will have rotated in degrees during one satellite orbit will be equal to the satellite period in minutes divided by four. For example, for a satellite period of 115min the longitude at which the satellite would cross the equator increases by 28·75° per orbit.

In practice a number of additional factors have to be considered which give rise to perturbation of the orbital parameters.

(a) Rotation of earth around the sun. As well as the earth rotating around its own axis it also revolves around the sun with a period of 365·242days. This causes an apparent change to the orbital plane as seen from the earth. This effect is often referred to as *precession* of the orbit and results in a change of 0·985673° per day westerly in the equator crossing point.

(b) Oblateness of the earth. In the simple approach used above it was assumed that the earth is a perfect sphere, whereas the radius at the equator is approximately 20km greater than that at the poles. The effect of this equatorial bulge is to increase the gravitational attraction on the satellite at the ascending and descending nodes of the orbit. This produces

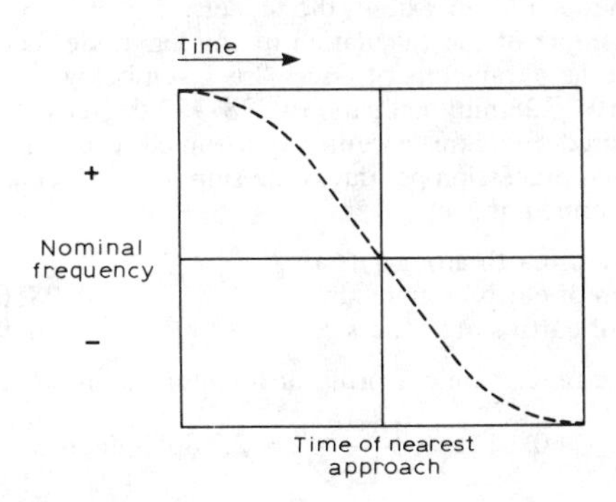

Fig 4. Variation of Doppler shift as the satellite passes a receiving station. The received frequency is at its nominal value when the satellite is at its nearest point, ie when its relative velocity is zero

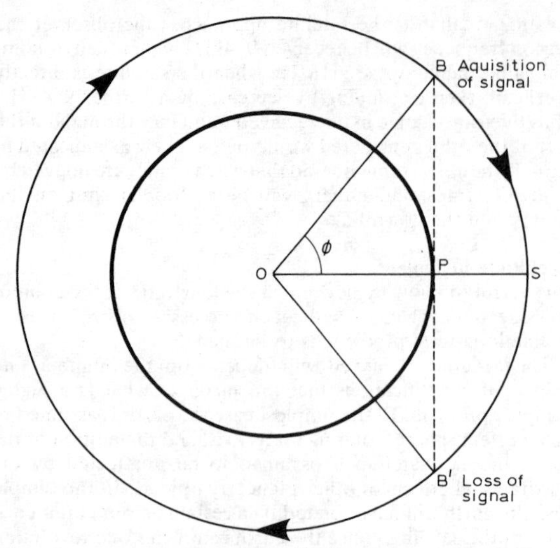

Fig 5. The satellite can be seen for its longest period when it passes directly overhead. Points B and B′ are the furthest at which the satellite can be seen

precession of the orbital plane without altering significantly the inclination or period of the orbit. The magnitude of the precession depends on the altitude, inclination and eccentricity of the orbit and may be obtained from the expression

$$P = 9{\cdot}964\left[\frac{R+h}{R}\right]^{-7/2}\left[1-e^2\right]^{-2}\cos i$$

where R, h and i are as previously defined, e is the eccentricity of the orbit and P is the precession to the west in degrees per day.

It can be seen from the above expression that if the inclination of the orbit is greater than 90° the precession is in fact in an easterly direction. It is possible by suitable choice of orbital parameters to make the precession due to the oblateness of the earth equal but in the opposite direction to that caused by the rotation of the earth around the sun. This is known as a *sun-synchronous orbit* and the longitude increment is simply the rotation of the earth in one satellite period. Orbit perturbations also result from the gravitational effects of the moon, the sun and, to a much lesser extent, the planets.

An example of the calculation of the longitude increment based on the parameters of Oscar 8 is given below:
Period: 103·228min; inclination = 98·989 degrees
Mean altitude: 905km (eccentricity assumed to be zero).

The total precession per day is the sum of the three components described above:

rotation of earth around its axis	360°
rotation of earth around sun	0·985673°
effect of earth's oblateness	−0·968°

Hence the precession per orbit, or longitude increment, is

$$360{\cdot}0176 \times \frac{103{\cdot}228}{24 \times 60} = 25{\cdot}8083 \text{ degrees}$$

Maximum satellite visibility time

Fig 5 shows a satellite whose orbit passes directly over the earth station at point P; under this situation the satellite is visible for the maximum length of time. The actual duration c the pass depends on the velocity of the satellite which, as ha already been shown, is determined by its altitude. The satellit completes one complete orbit, or 360°, in τ, its period: there fore to travel from the point B to B′ on the orbit will tak $2\phi/360 \times \tau$ where ϕ is the half angle of visibility referred t earlier. For Oscar 8 ϕ was 28·8°, hence the maximum time fo which the satellite was in direct line-of-sight was 16·5min.

In practice most satellite passes will not be overhead and th duration of the pass will consequently be reduced. Fig 6 shows how the time for which a satellite is visible varies with th altitude of the satellite. In calculating the time for which a give satellite may be seen, two satellite positions have been ident ified. These are B and B′ in Fig 5, which are known as the poin of *acquisition of signal* (aos) and the point of *loss of signal* (los respectively. It should be remembered that these positions ar based on line-of-sight criteria and observations have shown tha satellite signals may not be heard until after, or in some case before, the satellite rises above, or falls below, the horizon.

Free-space path loss

Assuming there are no obstructions between a transmitter an a receiver, ie line-of-sight conditions, the level of signal arrivin at the receiver depends on the transmitter power and the dis tance between the two stations. The amount of power radiate in the direction of the receiving station will be the product of th rf power fed into the antenna and the gain of the antenna in tha direction. For example, consider a transmitter with an outpu power of 10W, a feeder loss of 3dB and an antenna gain of si (expressed as a ratio). The power actually fed into the antenn would be −3dB relative to 10W, ie 5W; hence the radiate power would be 5 × 6 = 30W. The gain of the antenna wa taken as six which must, of course, be relative to some referenc value. For frequencies up to and in many cases including vhf the reference value is taken to be the gain of a λ/2 dipole However, at higher frequencies the reference taken is the iso tropic antenna, which is defined as one that radiates equally i all directions. In fact, the λ/2 dipole reference has a gain o about 2·1dB when compared with the isotropic. This poin often causes confusion and it is well worth checking what refer ence is being used by manufacturers when quoting the gain o their antenna.

Referring to an isotropic antenna and a transmitter power o P watts, the power flux density, E, at a distance d will be

$$E = \frac{P}{4\pi d^2} \text{ watts per square metre (W/m}^2\text{)}$$

Now the gain of the antenna may be obtained from th equation

$$G = \frac{4\pi A}{\lambda^2}$$

where A is the effective aperture, or capture area, of th antenna and λ is the wavelength.

Thus for an isotropic antenna, where $G = 1$, the aperture i given by

$$A = \frac{\lambda^2}{4\pi}$$

If an isotropic receiving antenna were placed at a distance d from the transmitter mentioned, the signal power received, P

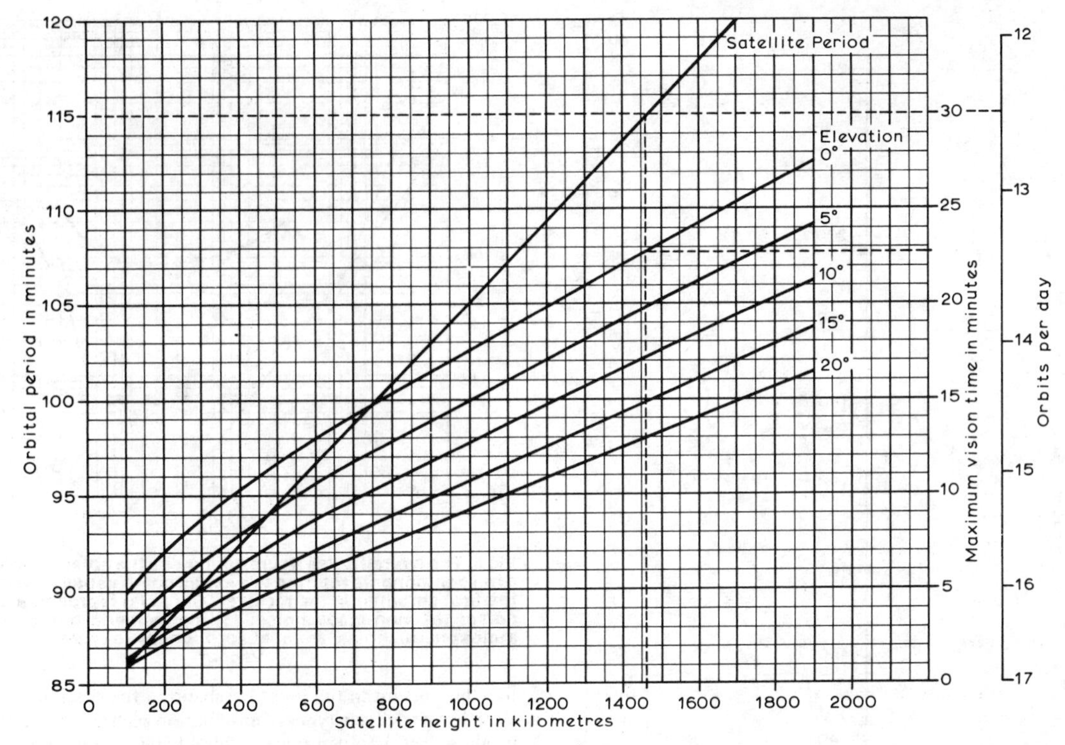

Fig 6. The time for which a satellite can be seen varies with the altitude of the satellite according to this chart

measured in watts), would be the product of the power flux ensity (W/m²) and the antenna aperture (m²) or

$$P_r = E \times A = \frac{P}{4\pi d^2} \times \frac{\lambda^2}{4\pi}$$

$$= P \times \left(\frac{\lambda}{4\pi d}\right)^2$$

t can therefore be seen that the transmitted signal has been educed by an amount $(4\pi d/\lambda)^2$ and this is known as the *ree-space path loss*. Since the value of this loss is often very arge it is convenient to express the value in decibel notation

$$P_L = 10 \log_{10}\left(\frac{4\pi d}{\lambda}\right)^2$$

$$= 20 \log_{10}\left(\frac{4\pi d}{\lambda}\right)$$

$$= 32 \cdot 4 + 20 \log d_{km} + 20 \log F_{MHz}$$

vhere P_L is the path loss in decibels, d_{km} is the distance in ilometres and F_{MHz} is the frequency in megahertz.

Example:

Consider a satellite with a transmitter power of 2W and an ntenna gain of 0dB relative to a λ/2 dipole (or 2·1dB with espect to an isotropic antenna). The effective radiated power is herefore

$$\text{erp} = 2 \cdot 1 + 10 \log_{10}(2\text{W}) = 5 \cdot 1\text{dBW}$$

f the distance to the satellite at a particular point is 2,000km nd the transmitted frequency is 145·98MHz, the free-space ath loss is

$$P_L = 32 \cdot 4 + 20 \log_{10}(2{,}000) + 20 \log_{10}(145 \cdot 98) = 141 \cdot 7\text{dB}$$

Now if the receiver antenna gain is 8dB the signal power at the input to the 144MHz receiver would be

$$P_r = 5 \cdot 1 - 141 \cdot 7 + 8 = -128 \cdot 6\text{dBW}$$

With the aid of Fig 7 the free-space path loss may be obtained for a wide range of frequencies and distances.

Typical link budget for an amateur satellite

All amateur satellites launched to date have been in sub-synchronous orbits and, at best, have had only single axis stabilization, ie one axis of the satellite had been kept constant in relation to the earth. Thus, it has only been possible to make use of simple non-directional antennas on board the satellite.

Transmitting station requirements

To calculate the amount of power required from an amateur station to access a satellite it is first necessary to know the signal level required at the input to the satellite receiver. The level at the input of Oscar 8 for full output was −100dBm, which should remain typical for future satellites. The required ground station power is calculated as follows:

Required signal level	−100dBm
Effective satellite antenna gain	0dB
Maximum slant range	4,550km
Free space path loss at maximum range	149dB
Required ground station erp	49dBm or 19dBW

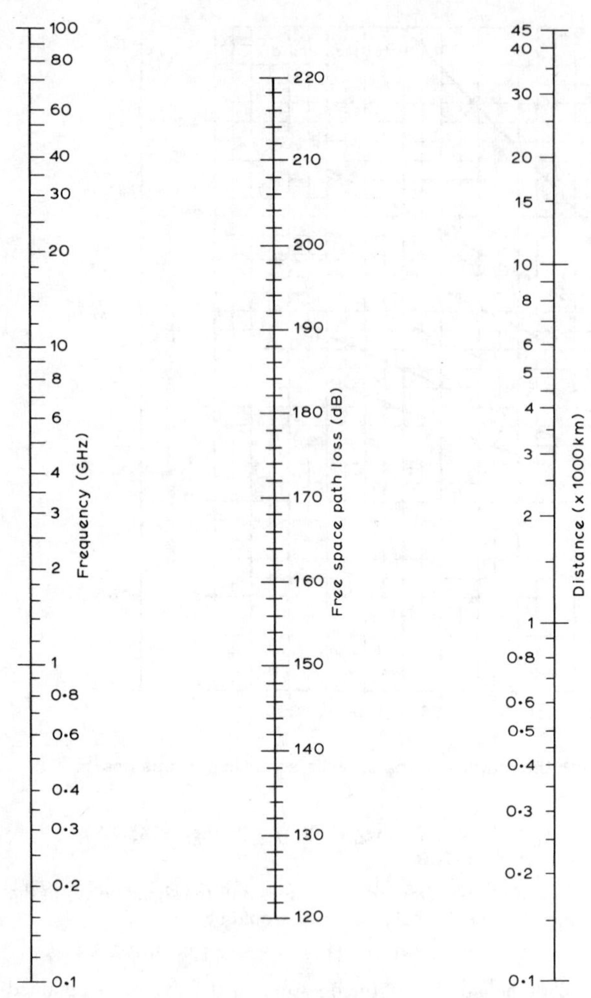

Fig 7. Nomogram for deriving the free-space loss for various distances and frequencies

This corresponds to an effective radiated power (erp) of about 80W. The erp is the product of the antenna gain and the amount of power actually fed to the antenna (not to the feeder). This figure can be achieved either by feeding 80W to an omnidirectional antenna, or a lower level of power to an antenna with some gain. From an operating point of view it is better to use an omnidirectional antenna since no tracking of the satellite is necessary. At higher frequencies where the signal losses are greater it may not be quite so easy to generate high levels of rf power, and it may become necessary to use high-gain antennas which require quite accurate methods of satellite tracking.

Receiving station requirements

For ssb operation a signal-to-noise ratio of 10dB is an acceptable working level, although for cw working much lower levels may be tolerated. A typical calculation is given below which derives the signal-to-noise ratio in a 3kHz bandwidth for a signal received from a satellite delivering a peak power of 1W at 29MHz. An allowance of 10dB is made for other signals that

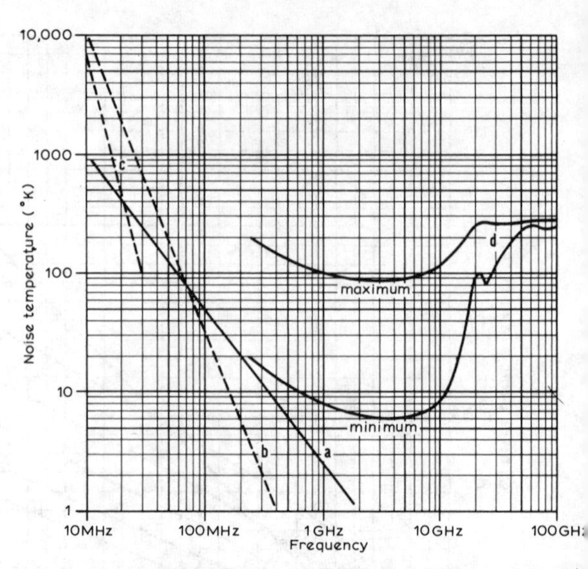

Fig 8. The overall noise figure comprises the noise temperatur of all components referred to a single point, usually the input t the first amplifier in the receiver. Curve (a) represents cosmi noise; (b) man-made noise; (c) atmospheric noise; and (d atmospheric noise from absorption by oxygen and wate vapour

may be present in the input passband of the satellite receiver With low duty cycle types of modulation such as ssb and cw suc an allowance would provide for about 50 transmissions throug the satellite provided there are no excessively strong signal present. The received signal-to-noise ratio is calculated as fol lows:

Satellite erp	0dBW (1W)
Multi-channel loading	−10dB
Maximum slant range	4,550km
Free-space loss	−135dB
Receiver antenna gain	0dB
Received signal level	−145dBW
Receiver noise bandwidth	3kHz
Receiver noise figure	15·0dB
Noise power in receiver bandwidth	−154·3dBW

hence signal-to-noise ratio = −145−(−154·3)
= 9·3dB

The receiver noise figure is mainly due to atmospheric noise If the receiving station were situated directly below the satellit the path loss would be reduced by about 10dB and the signal to-noise ratio correspondingly increased. A further improve ment could be obtained by employing an antenna with som gain.

Optimizing the receiving system

At hf the noise in a receiving system is generally swamped b the very high levels of atmospheric noise, sometimes known a sky noise (or temperature). The variation of this paramete with frequency is given in Fig 8, which clearly shows that in th microwave bands the sky noise reduces to a level where th noise generated within the receiver has a significant effect o the overall system performance. Thus it is very important, fo ystems working at the low levels involved in satellite and moonbounce working, to reduce the internal receiver noise to he lowest possible value. In general this means using the minimum of feeder, and selecting amplifiers with the lowest oise figure consistent with useful gain.

Fig 9 shows an outline diagram for a typical low-level eceiver. An input filter is not shown since the loss introduced is ighly undesirable, and the use of such a filter should be voided unless there is the likelihood of cross-modulation from djacent signals. (A filter will of course generally be required in he transmitter output.)

To find the overall noise figure of a receiver it is usual to find he noise contribution of each element and refer this to one oint in the receiver, normally the input to the first amplifier. 'his is done as follows: sky noise—a typical value might be 00K, which is the equivalent noise temperature at the output f the antenna. This noise signal will be attenuated by the eeder, which has a loss of 1dB, or 1·26 as a ratio; therefore the quivalent sky noise temperature referred to the input of the mplifier is:

$$\frac{100}{1 \cdot 26} = 79 \cdot 4\text{K}$$

'he feeder not only has a loss but also increases the noise emperature.

The noise temperature at the input end of the feeder is given y (1·26 − 1) × 290 = 75·3K.The general expression is (loss s a ratio −1) × ambient temperature in degrees Kelvin. Hence he noise temperature referred to the amplifier input is:

$$\frac{75 \cdot 3}{1 \cdot 26} = 59 \cdot 8\text{K}$$

The noise temperature of the amplifier is calculated from a imilar expression to that for the feeder loss, ie (noise figure as a atio −1) × ambient temperature in degrees Kelvin, which in his case is (2 − 1) × 290 = 290K. The coupling loss between he two amplifiers has a noise temperature of (antilog 0·2/10 −1) × 290 = 14·5K. This value is reduced by the amplifier gain vhen referred to the amplifier input, hence the equivalent noise emperature is 14·5/10 or 1·45K. The mixer stage of the econd amplifier usually has a much worse noise figure than the irst amplifier, but the higher the gain of the first stage the lower he effect of following stages. An 8dB noise figure is equivalent o a noise temperature of (antilog 8/10 −1) × 290 or 1,535K, vhich is reduced to 1,535/10 × 1·05 or 161K when referred to he input of the first amplifier. Thus the equivalent noise temerature at the input to the first has been calculated for each lement. The total noise temperature is simply the sum of each f the individual values:

Sky noise	79·4K
Feeder loss	59·8K
1st amplifier	290K
Coupling loss	1·45K
2nd amplifier/mixer	161K
	591·7K

'he noise figure is calculated from

$$N = 10 \log_{10}\left(\frac{T}{290} + 1\right) \text{ decibels}$$

vhere T is the total equivalent noise temperature. Hence for he receiver considered the noise figure is 4·8dB. By doing this ype of calculation it is possible to locate those areas in a eceiving system which have a significant effect on the overall performance. In particular it can be seen what the effect is if the second amplifier cannot be ignored.

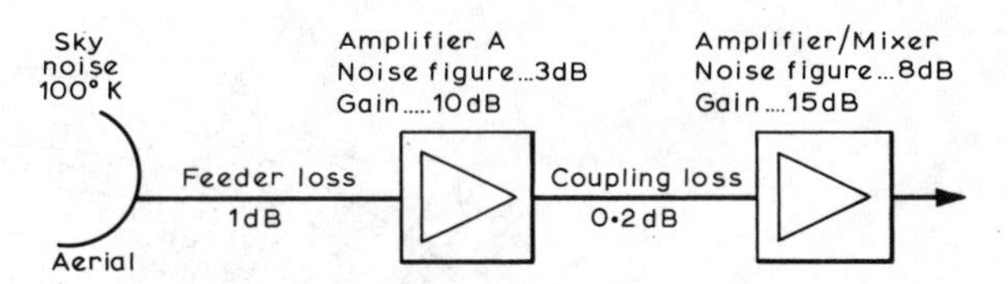

Fig 9. In the microwave bands the low signal levels used call for low-noise receivers. An outline of a suitable receiver is shown here

Tracking of satellites

In many cases it is possible to use omnidirectional antennas which avoid the need to ensure correct alignment with the continously changing position of the satellite. However, as higher frequencies are used the path losses increase and it is therefore necessary to employ antennas with adequate gain which in turn means more restricted beamwidth. In order to maximize the signal coupling between the satellite and ground station it is necessary to obtain the maximum useful gain from the antenna. To do this one needs to know the position of the satellite in terms of azimuth (bearing) and elevation as it progresses along its orbital path. Various methods have been proposed which rely on different types of map projection or look-up tables. The technique which appears to have gained the widest acceptance uses a polar projection and is often referred to as the "Oscalator". Fig 10 shows the map projection used, which is centred on the North pole and extends out to beyond the equator. Along with the map it is necessary to use two other projections—one giving the azimuth/elevation contours corresponding to the particular satellite and the other indicating the orbital track of the satellite. The map and various transparent overlays are available in the UK from AMSAT-UK [1]. The following details are given for those who may wish to generate their own overlay or possibly as the basis of a computer-based prediction/antenna-steering system.

Azimuth-elevation contour chart

It is possible to use a number of concentric circles centred on the QTH to determine the range and bearings to the satellite. However this method can produce significant errors which may be troublesome when high-gain antennas are used. There are three steps to produce the necessary data points to draw the contour:

1. The great-circle angle (ie the angle subtended at the centre of the earth) between the QTH and the sub-satellite point should be calculated. Fig 11 shows the great circle angle, D, and the other parameters required in the calculations. This angle can be calculated as follows:

$$D = \cos^{-1}\left[\frac{R}{R+h} \cdot \cos\gamma\right] - \gamma \text{ degrees}$$

where γ is the elevation angle of the satellite at the station, R is the radius of the earth (6,375km) and h is the altitude of the satellite.

2. Next it is necessary to calculate the latitude of the point on the first bearing (say 0°) which corresponds to the elevation angle

$$\sin B = \sin\alpha \cdot \cos D - \cos\alpha \cdot \sin D \cdot \cos C$$

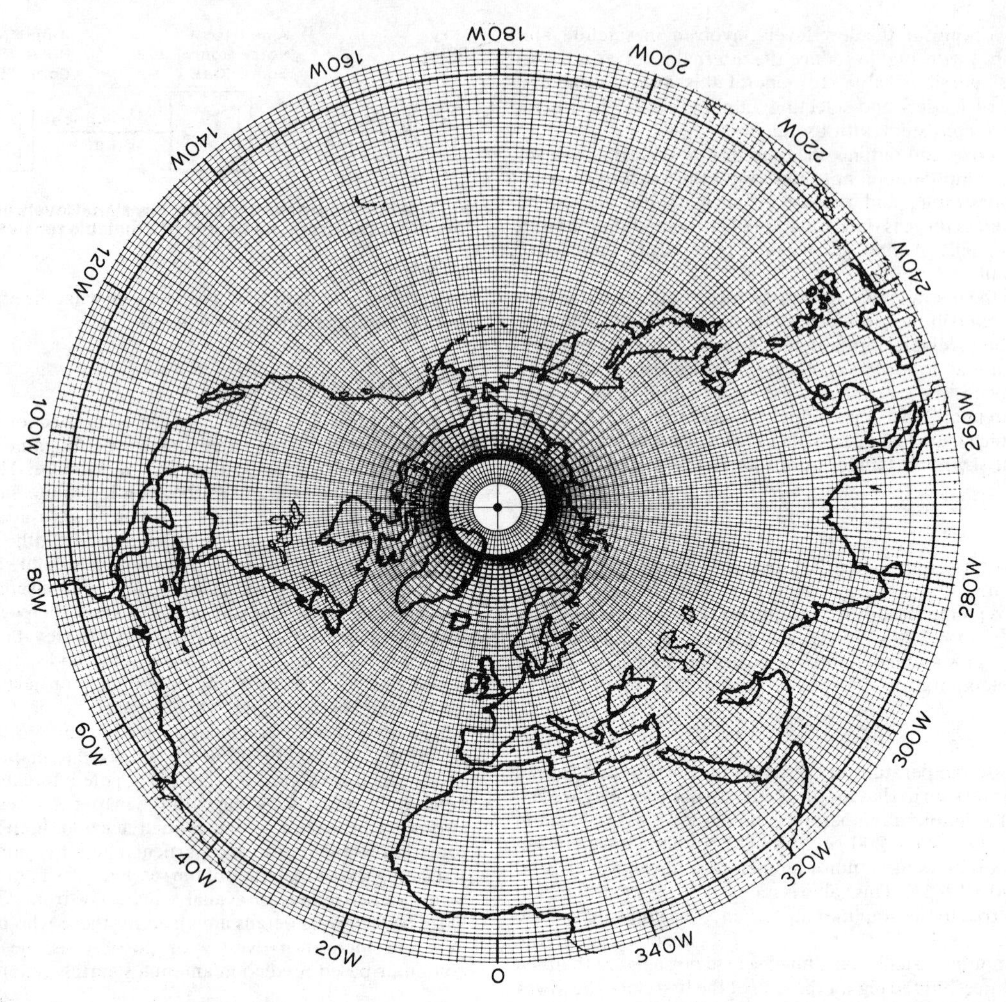

Fig 10. Polar projection map, used in conjunction with satellite orbital track and range circles to determine when satellite is within range

where B is the latitude of the sub-satellite point, α is the latitude of the station and C the bearing to the north (in this case 0°).

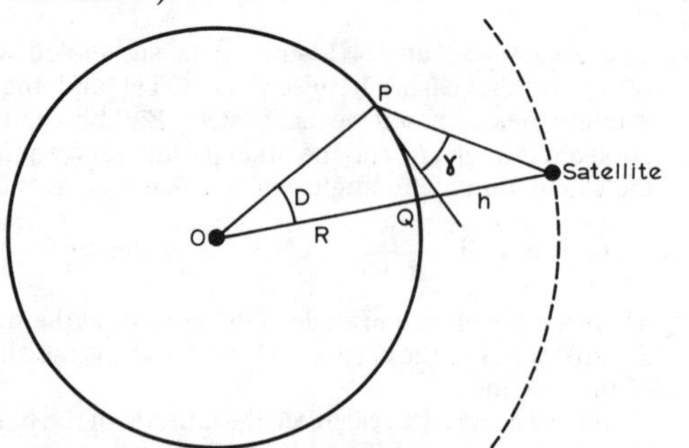

Fig 11. Q is the point on the surface of the earth which is directly beneath the satellite. The latitude is B° and longitude relative to the receiving station at P is L°

3. Finally the corresponding longitude of the sub-satellite point should be calculated.

$$\sin L = \frac{\sin C \times \sin D}{\cos B}$$

where L is the difference in longitude between the sub-satellite point and the station.

Thus the latitude and longitude of a point corresponding to a particular elevation angle have been calculated, on a heading of 0°. It is now necessary to calculate points for other headings at the same elevation angle. (Note it is only necessary to calculate points for headings between 0 and 180° as one side of the chart is the mirror image of the other). This procedure is then repeated for other values of elevation, say, 30° and 60°, and the data points plotted on the polar plot as shown on Fig 12.

Satellite orbital path

The only information required to determine the satellite track is the orbit period and the angle of inclination of the orbit to the

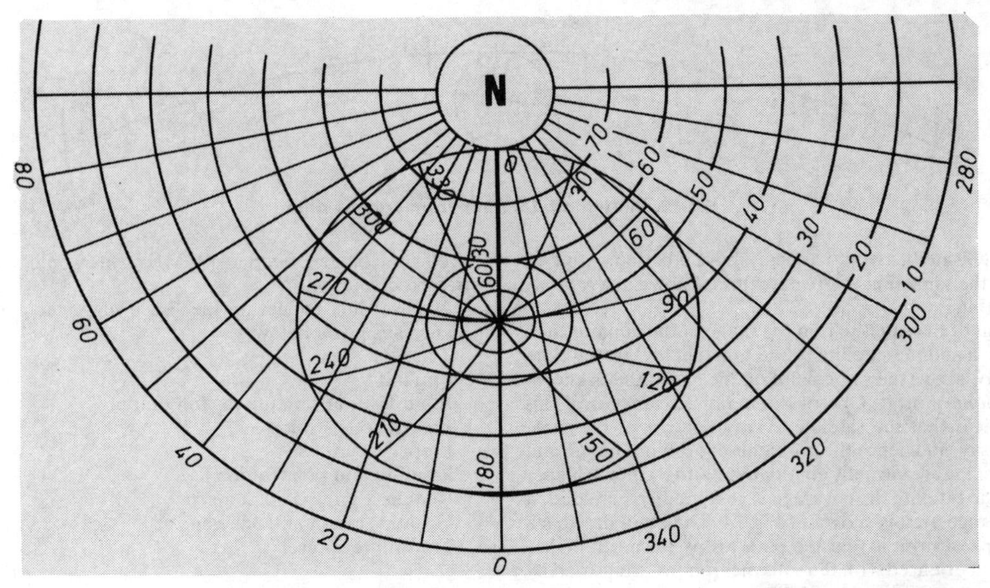

ig 12. Range circles for Oscar 8. The azimuth and elevation to the satellite are obtained from the intersection of the satellite track with the range circles

quatorial plane. The latitude of the sub-satellite point is given y:

$$\sin b = \sin (360 \, . \, t/\tau) \sin i$$

here t is the length of time, in minutes, from the time of the scending node, τ is the satellite period (min) and i is the angle f inclination.

The corresponding longitude of the sub-satellite point at time is given by

$$l = \cos^{-1} (\cos (360 \, . \, t/\tau) \div \cos b) \pm t/4$$

he factor $t/4$ is due to the rotation of the earth: the earth otates by approximately one degree every four minutes. When e orbit is retrograde, ie i is greater than 90°, $t/4$ is added, therwise it is subtracted.

As an example, the latitude and relative longitude of the)scar 8 orbit are given in Table 1. With the aid of the polar ıap, the orbital track (Fig 13) may be plotted on to a suitable ansparent material (eg sheet acetate). There are three points f reference which are particularly important to achieve accuate results.

1. The orbital track starts at latitude 0°, longitude 0°.
2. At a time equal to one quarter of the period, the satellite achieves its maximum latitude which is equal to i if $i < 90°$ or $(180-i)$ if $i > 90°$.
3. The point at which the satellite crosses the equator after passing the North Pole is at longitude [180° plus half the orbital increment]. This equator crossing occurs at a time equal to half the orbital period.

Jsing the orbit calculator

Vith the appropriate azimuth/elevation contour centred on the ser's location, the orbital track is placed with the North Poles ligned and the start of the track at the equator crossing point. It s now possible to read off the bearings to the satellite at any oint during the orbit as well as determining the period for which the satellite is within communication range, the aos and los.

Geosynchronous and geostationary satellite orbits

It was shown in the derivation of equation (iii) that the period of a satellite is determined by its altitude, and it has been noted that for a satellite altitude of 35,800km the orbital period is

Table 1. Orbital track for Oscar 8 based on inclination of 98·7987° and period of 103·276min

t (min)	Latitude	Longitude
0	0	0
2	6·9	1·6
4	13·8	3·2
6	20·7	4·8
8	27·5	6·6
10	34·4	8·6
12	41·2	10·8
14	48·0	13·4
16	54·8	16·7
18	61·5	21·0
20	68·0	27·5
22	74·1	38·4
24	79·2	60·0
26	81·2	100·6
28	78·4	138·1
30	73·0	157·0
32	66·8	166·8
34	60·3	172·8
36	53·6	176·9
38	46·8	180·8
40	40·0	182·5
42	33·1	184·7
44	26·3	186·6
46	19·4	188·4
48	12·5	190·0
50	5·6	191·6

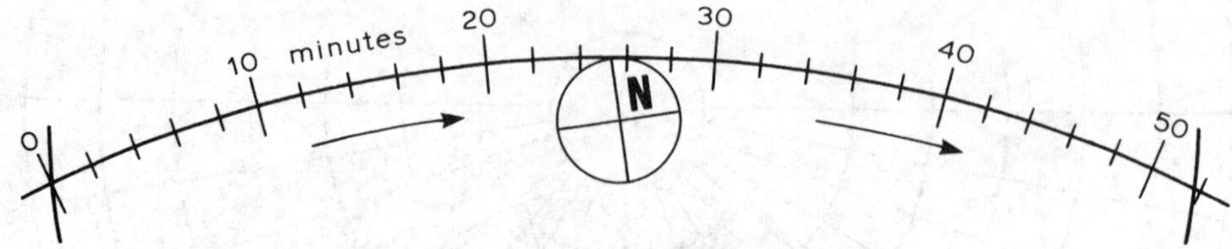

Fig 13. Plotted orbital track from Table 1 data

24h. Thus the satellite would appear above a certain point on the earth at the same time every day; this is known as a *geosynchronous* orbit.

If the orbit of the satellite is in the plane of the equator then both the earth and the satellite rotate together and the satellite will always be above the same point on the earth; this is known as a *geostationary* orbit. One of the major advantages of this type of orbit is that the satellite always appears at the same point in the sky, and hence the problems of orbit prediction and antenna tracking are virtually eliminated. With the much higher altitude of the satellite the coverage is very greatly increased; a typical coverage area is shown in Fig 14. The main drawback with this type of orbit is that the path losses are much higher than those experienced with the subsynchronous orbits used by present amateur satellites.

The most appropriate frequency band for the downlink, ie satellite-to-earth, is 435–438MHz, since at this frequency it is relatively easy to achieve low receiver noise figures (2–3dB) and high antenna gains (20–25dB). For the up-link the choice is perhaps less obvious but, due to the ease at which high power levels may be generated at 145MHz, this would seem to be preferred solution.

A power link budget for the above suggested choice of frequencies is given below.

2m uplink

Input level at satellite for full output	−130dBW
Free-space path loss	−168dB
Propagation loss	−1dB
Pointing and polarization loss	−2dB
Required ground station erp	41dBW
Ground station antenna gain	20dB
Transmitter power	21dBW
	or 126W

70cm downlink

Satellite erp	10dBW
Free-space path loss	178dB
Multichannel loading factor	−10dB
Propagation loss	−1dB

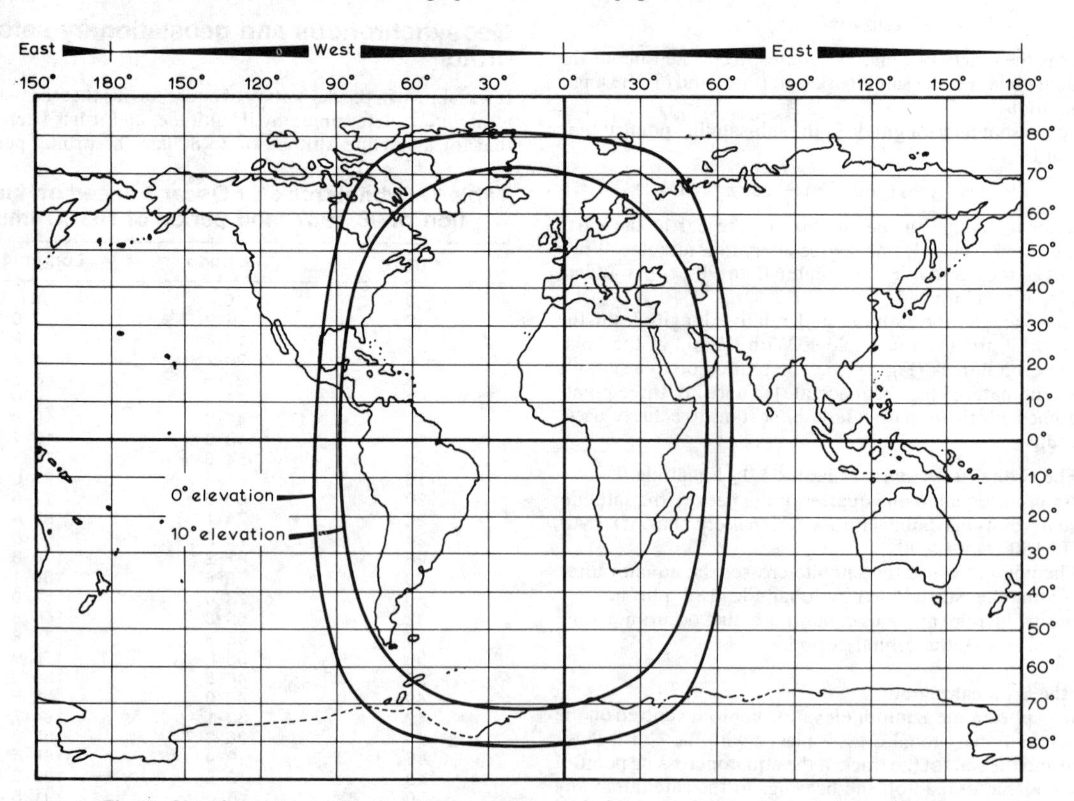

Fig 14. Showing the increased coverage area provided by a satellite in a geostationary orbit

Pointing and polarization loss	−2dB
Ground station antenna gain	20dB
Received signal level	−161dBW
Receiver noise figure	3dB
Signal bandwidth	3kHz
Noise power	−169dBW
Signal-to-noise ratio	8dB

ıus it can be seen that communication via a geostationary tellite is quite within the existing capabilities of many amateur ations.

atellite design

tellites such as the recent Oscar series can be regarded from e point of view of an amateur as similar to the repeaters rrently in use on 144 and 432MHz throughout the UK. The tellite communication equipment receives signals at one freency and simultaneously transmits them on another freency. However, once a satellite has been placed in orbit it is, present, not possible to carry out direct maintenance and pair. This situation may change in the future when the US ace Transportation System (the "space shuttle") becomes erational. In order to obtain the maximum operational etime from a satellite it is necessary to pay great attention to s design.

Most satellites can be considered as comprising two major b-systems—a service module and a payload. The service odule provides the basic structure of the satellite and includes e on-board "housekeeping" functions such as power supplies d regulators, satellite attitude control, thermal control, telemmand and telemetry functions. The payload of the satellite the part of the satellite which carries out the mission requireents, eg communications transponder.

pacecraft structure

'he main purpose of the structure is to provide a suitable latform for the service module sub-systems and the payload. It ıust provide adequate protection to all on-board equipment in espect of the adverse environmental conditions to which the pacecraft will be subjected throughout its lifetime. During the unch phase considerable vibration occurs, and when in orbit ıe structure may be required to provide electric and/or magnec screening according to the payload requirements.

One of the major problems in satellite design is to stay within ıe overall mass capability of the launch vehicle. It is therefore ery important to keep the mass of the structure, and all other arts of the service module, to a minimum. In this way it is ossible to maximize the size of the payload that can be carried.

nergy source and storage

n order to carry out many of its functions the satellite requires lectrical energy, eg power supplies for communication equipıent and in some cases energy for heaters. There are various ays in which this energy may be provided. Early satellites arried primary batteries which had a very limited life and could ot be recharged. Energy is generated on most current satellites y the use of chemical fuel cells, nuclear sources, and rather ıore commonly silicon solar cells. The chemical fuel cells re primary sources that have a finite life but it is not difficult to chieve lifetimes significantly longer than that required for ıost satellite missions. The silicon solar cell works by directly onverting solar energy into electrical energy. The solar cells are rranged to form panels or arrays and these are either attached o the main structure of the satellite or deployed on booms. At present silicon solar cells achieve an energy conversion efficiency of around 16 per cent, though it is hoped to improve this value by further development.

One of the main drawbacks with the solar cell energy sources is that energy is generated only when the cells are illuminated by the sun. Thus when the earth is between the satellite and the sun no energy can be generated. In order to allow the payload etc to operate under all conditions, including eclipse by the earth, it is necessary for some form of energy storage to be included in the service module. The most common method of achieving this is by means of nickel-cadmium batteries which, though not having a very good capacity-to-weight ratio (ie watt-hours per kilogram) are capable of withstanding a very large number of charge-discharge cycles.

Ideally the capacity of the storage batteries should be sufficient to allow full operation of the service module and payload during eclipse conditions. Also, it is desirable that the batteries should be completely charged before going into eclipse. This means that the solar cells must be capable of providing enough power to serve the normal requirements as well as charging the batteries. If this is the situation the satellite is said to have a *positive power budget*, otherwise it will be necessary to reduce, or completely switch off, power to the payload, in which case the satellite has a *negative* power budget.

Thermal control

During each orbit the satellite will be subjected to extremes of temperature by virtue of the presence, or otherwise, of the sun's illumination. Also, heat will be generated by the various electrical components onboard the satellite. In order to ensure correct operation of the various sub-systems it is essential that the temperatures at critical points in the satellite are maintained within acceptable limits. To achieve this it may be necessary to take precautions such as painting black those items that generate heat in order to improve heat dissipation.

Attitude control

It is important that the satellite transmitting and receiving antennas are always directed towards, or as a minimum not shielded from, the earth. With the very low gain antennas as used on amateur satellites to date it has been sufficient to stabilize the orientation of one axis of the satellite with respect to the earth. This has been achieved in some AMSAT satellites by incorporation of a bar magnet in the satellite, the idea being that the bar magnet should align itself with the earth's magnetic field. The satellite is still free to rotate about the axis of the magnet, but if the antennas are correctly sited this movement should not be too serious.

This method of stabilization is adequate for low orbiting satellites where the earth's magnetic field is quite strong. However for higher-altitude satellites or those using highly directive antennas it is necessary to use rather more sophisticated techniques. Many communication satellites use an attitude and orbit control system (aocs), in which the satellite is stabilized by spinning about one axis. This imposes limitations on the gain of the antennas that can be used except in the case of the later Intelsat series of satellites, where the antenna platform was de-spun. Future commercial communication satellites are likely to use three-axis stabilization in which the attitude of the satellite with respect to the earth is precisely controlled by means of onboard thrusters.

Telemetry and telecommand

In order to ensure that each part of the satellite is functioning as required it is desirable to be able to monitor certain parameters

Table 2. Parameters and equations for Oscar 7 morse code telemetry system

MC ch	Parameter	Red line lower limit Value	Count	Typical Value	Count	Red line upper limit Value	Count	Equation
1A	Total array current	N/A		0 to 2,300mA	0 to 78	N/A		$I_T = 29 \cdot 5N$ (mA)
1B	+X quad current	N/A		0 to 1,500mA	99 to 23	N/A		$I_{+x} = 1{,}970 + 20N$ (mA)
1C	−X quad current	N/A		0 to 1,500mA	99 to 23	N/A		$I_{-x} = 1{,}970 - 20N$ (mA)
1D	+Y quad current	N/A		0 to 1,500mA	99 to 23	N/A		$I_{+y} = 1{,}970 - 20N$ (mA)
2A	−Y quad current	N/A		0 to 1,500mA	99 to 23	N/A		$I_{-y} = 1{,}970 - 20N$ (mA)
2B	70/2 power out	0·5W	75	2·5W	44	8·0W	00	$P_{70/2} = 8(1 - 0 \cdot 01N)^2$ (W)
2C	24h clock time	0h	00	0 to 24h	0 to 95	24h	95	$t = 0 \cdot 253N$ (h)
2D	Batt ch-disch current	−1,200mA	20	−400 to +400mA	40 to 60	1,000mA	75	$I_B = 40(N - 50)$ (mA)
3A	Batt voltage	12·4V	60	13·6 to 15·1V	72 to 87	15·5V	91	$V_{BAT} = 0 \cdot 1N + 6 \cdot 4$ (V)
3B	½ Batt voltage	6·2V	62	6·8 to 7·6V	68 to 76	7·8V	78	$V_{\frac{1}{2}BAT} = 0 \cdot 1N$ (V)
3C	Batt ch reg 1 voltage	2·3V	15	6·4 to 7·5V	42 to 50	9·0V	60	$V_{CR1} = 0 \cdot 15N$ (V)
3D	Batt temp	5°C	61	20°C	51	35°C	41	$T_{BAT} = 95 \cdot 8 - 1 \cdot 48N$ (°C)
4A	Base plate temp	0°C	65	18°C	53	40°C	38	$T_{BP} = 95 \cdot 8 - 1 \cdot 48N$ (°C)
4B	PA temp 2/10 rptr	5°C	61	40°C	38	60°C	24	$T_{10} = 95 \cdot 8 - 1 \cdot 48N$ (°C)
4C	+X facet temp	−5°C	68	10 to 30°C	58 to 44	60°C	24	$T_{+x} = 95 \cdot 8 - 1 \cdot 48N$ (°C)
4D	+Z facet temp	0°C	65	10°C	58	40°C	38	$T_{+z} = 95 \cdot 8 - 1 \cdot 48N$ (°C)
5A	PA temp 70/2 rptr	5°C	61	28°C	46	60°C	24	$T_2 = 95 \cdot 8 - 1 \cdot 48N$ (°C)
5B	PA emit current 2/10 rptr	35mA	03	140mA	12	175mA	15	$T_{10} = 11 \cdot 67N$ (mA)
5C	Mod temp 70/2 rptr	5°C	61	28°C	46	60°C	24	$T_m = 95 \cdot 8 - 1 \cdot 48N$ (°C)
5D	Instr sw reg input current	23·3mA	15	27·4 to 53·6mA	20 to 52	60·2mA	60	$I_{ISR} = 11 - 0 \cdot 82N$ (mA)

within the satellite. This is achieved by means of a telemetry sub-system in which the appropriate data is transmitted to earth on the telemetry link. The system is based on the sequential scanning of sensors which monitor the appropriate parameters of the satellite. The outputs from the sensors are converted from an analogue value to a digital one by means of a suitable encoder.

For example, one of the sensors on Oscar 7 measured the total current from the solar array. The anticipated current range was from zero to 2·3A and the encoder had a linear law according to the equation

$$N = \frac{I_{ma} \times 78}{2{,}300}$$

where I_{ma} is the array current in milliamps and N is the digital output expressed as a two-digit number. Thus an encoder output of, say, 29 would correspond to an array current of 856mA.

Oscar 7 in fact carried two telemetry encoders—one a 24-channel morse code system and the other a 60-channel teletype system. The operation of the morse code system is described below.

The 24 channels were split into six blocks of four. Telemetry data corresponding to channels in block one are transmitted, in morse code, as "1A 1B 1C 1D" where the letters A, B, C and D represent two-digit numbers from 0 to 99. The data for block two are transmitted as "2A 2B 2C 2D" and so on up to "6B 6C 6D" followed by "HI HI" in morse code. The sequence then re-starts with block one. Table 2 shows the parameters and equations that enable the morse code telemetry to be decoded.

The following example explains how to use the information. Suppose part of the morse code telemetry data received was . . . 455 555 511 . . . By reference to Table 2 we can see that the data corresponds to channels 4D, 5A and 5B. 4D is the "+z facet temperature", and a count of 55 indicates a value of $[95 \cdot 8 - (1 \cdot 48 \times 55)] = 14 \cdot 4$°C. 5A is the "PA temperature 70/2 repeater" and again a count of 55 indicates a temperature of 14·4°C. 5B is the "PA emitter current, 2/10 repeater"; the count recorded was 11 which indicates a value of $(11 \cdot 67 \times 11) = 128 \cdot 4$mA.

By means of a suitable telemetry system it is possible to monitor the performance of the satellite; however, in the event of a component failure it may be necessary to alter the mode operation. This can be achieved by means of a telecomma facility whereby nominated control stations may send cod commands to the satellite as required. As indicated later, Osc 7 had various modes of operation, some of which were contr led by an internal clock and others by means of a telecommo link from suitably equipped ground stations.

Amateur satellites launched

Oscar 1

The first amateur satellite was designed and built by the Proje Oscar group (Oscar is an acronym for Orbiting Satellite Carr ing Amateur Radio). It was launched on 12 December 19 and consisted of a 100mW telemetry beacon operating 144·98MHz. More than 5,000 reports of the satellite we received from 600 amateur stations during its three-week lif

Oscar 2

This satellite was launched on 2 June 1962 and operated for days. Like Oscar 1 it carried a telemetry beacon in the 144MH band.

Oscar 3

This was the first "free access" satellite in the world, bei launched on 9 March 1965, only one month before Early Bir The transponder accepted signals within a 50kHz bandwid centred on 144·1MHz and re-radiated them arour 145·9MHz at a power level of 1W p.e.p. A 50mW telemet beacon also radiated on 145·85MHz. Operation lasted for on two weeks, during which time more than 100 stations com municated through the satellite, including two-way transatla tic contacts.

Oscar 4

This was launched on 21 December 1965 and carried a 144 432MHz transponder. Unfortunately the satellite failed achieve its correct orbit and only operated long enough fo about a dozen two-way contacts to be made. However, Oscar does have the distinction of providing the first direct satelli communication link between the USA and the USSR.

scar 5 (AO-5)
ıe fifth amateur satellite was designed and constructed in ıstralia. A newly formed group, the Radio Amateur Satellite ›rporation (AMSAT), checked the satellite for space operons before its launch on 23 January 1970. AO-5 carried emetry beacons on 144·05MHz and 29·45MHz and the ter could be switched by ground command. Although no mmunication facility was provided, AO-5 did provide valule experience in telecommand systems, which are now stanrd. Also, the two beacons allowed investigation of anomalous opagation.

MSAT Oscar 6
scar 6 was launched on 12 October 1972 as part of the yload of a Thor-Delta rocket carrying the NOAA-2 weather tellite. The orbital parameters were very similar to Oscar 5, owing access to the satellite several times each day. The mmunication equipment comprised a 144 to 28MHz transnder with a 100kHz bandwidth. The input frequency range as 145·90–146·000MHz and the output range ·45–29·55MHz.

Beacon signals were transmitted on 29·45MHz and 5·1MHz, although the latter failed after a short period of eration. A new feature on Oscar 6 was the Codestore unit ich is an 800-bit message storage unit capable of storing or aying back up to 18 words of morse code. The information om the Codestore unit was transmitted on the hf beacon signal suitably keying the oscillator. The type of message transmitd via the Codestore ranged from satellite orbital data to lemetry parameters such as battery voltage and current drain. scar 6 was still functioning well after nearly four years' operion, although times of operation were being restricted to nserve battery power.

MSAT Oscar 7
aunched from the Western Test Range (USA) on 15 ovember 1974, Oscar 7 provided excellent communication pabilities for many years beyond its planned life-time. The tellite, which weighed approximately 29kg, was placed in a 460km orbit with an inclination of 101·7°. The payload comised two communication repeaters, command and telemetry cilities, a store and forward message unit (Codestore) and ur beacons. Brief details of the transponders are given below.

45 to 29MHz repeater—100kHz transponder with a power ıtput of 2W p.e.p.

32 to 145MHz repeater—an effective radiated power of about)W was required to access this transponder when at maximum nge. The transponder had a useful bandwidth of 40–50kHz ıd an output power of 8W p.e.p.

MSAT Oscar 8
aunched on 5 March 1978 as probably the last of the low-orbit hase 2 satellites, this device contains two independent repeats and is designed for two modes of operation:

Mode A: 144 to 28MHz

Input frequency range	145·85–145·95MHz
Output frequency range	29·4–29·5MHz
Power output	1–2W
Morse code telemetry beacon	29·4MHz

he repeater was constructed by AMSAT and is intended for low-duty cycle signals such as cw and ssb. An erp of approximately 100W is necessary, using left-hand circular polarization in the northern hemisphere.

Mode J: 144 to 432MHz

Input frequency range	145·9–146·0MHz
Output frequency range	435·1–435·2MHz
Power output	1–2W
Morse code telemetry beacon	435·095MHz

The repeater was constructed by AMSAT Japan. As for the Mode A repeater, an erp of about 100W is necessary but in this case right-hand circular polarization should be used by stations in the northern hemisphere. The main orbital parameters of the Oscar 8 satellite are as follows:

Period	103·228min
Inclination	98·989°
Longitude increment	25·807° per orbit

As indicated earlier the satellite orbital path may be easily calculated from the above data. The lower orbit of Oscar 8 as compared to previous satellites means that the maximum visibility time is reduced to 16min and the map range to 6,300km.

RS1 and RS2
On 26 October 1978 the USSR launched Cosmos 1045 into a low polar orbit. Included with the launch were two amateur satellite packages RS1 and RS2 (also referred to as *Radio 1* and *Radio 2*). These satellites were very sensitive and suffered from problems arising from high-level signals accessing them, causing automatic shut-down of the transponders and rapid discharge of the on-board batteries. The main characteristics of the satellites were as follows:

Mean altitude	1,740km
Mean orbital period	120·4min
Inclination	82·5°
Up-link frequency band	145·870–145·915MHz
Down-link frequency band	29·350–29·395MHz
Beacon/telemetry frequency	29·400MHz (morse/rtty)

UOSAT Oscar 9
Designed and constructed at the University of Surrey, England, with considerable support from other amateur satellite groups, the satellite was launched on 6 October 1981, together with the Solar Mesophere Explorer (SME). Unlike the more recent of the Oscar series of satellites the main object of UOSAT was to encourage activity into the scientific and educational aspects of satellite technology. Thus, instead of one or two broadband communication transponders the spacecraft carried a wide range of individual packages, all controlled by an on-board microcomputer (Fig 15).

The orbital characteristics of the satellite as published shortly after launch were as follows:

Period	95·466min
Altitude	554·596km
Inclination	97·462°
Increment	23·8675°W per orbit

These values should be taken as rough indications only since after a few months' operation it became apparent that the low orbit of the satellite caused significant changes in these characteristics over quite small time intervals.

A detailed description of the spacecraft is contained in

Final test of UOSAT—Oscar 9

UOSAT—Oscar 9 Technical Handbook which is obtainable from [1].

Though the in-orbit tests on the spacecraft had not been completed at the time of writing, indications were that all on-board systems were functioning correctly, with the minor exception that the modulation on the 145MHz beacon was less than planned but quite adequate. A brief summary of the experiments is given below:

Telemetry

To cater for a wide range of user ground station facilities, 60 analogue telemetry channels and 45 digital status points are available for transmission via the vhf and uhf data beacons in the following formats:

1,200 baud ASCII	45·5 baud rtty (Baudot)
600 baud ASCII	
300 baud ASCII	10 or 20wpm morse code
110 baud ASCII	
75 baud ASCII	Synthesized voice

Data beacons

Two data beacons (145·825MHz and 435·025MHz) provide the engineering and experiment data links. Power output was 450mW and 400mW respectively using nbfm or cw accordi to the data input.

Propagation beacons

Phase-referenced beacons on 7·050, 14·002, 21·002 a 29·150MHz are intended to be used as part of a wide range ionospheric studies and beacons on 2,401MHz an 10·47GHz are included to encourage activity at these freque cies.

Education experiments

The satellite carries a ccd (charge coupled device) array whic provides two-dimensional images from a ground area of ap proximately 500km square. The image is transmitted on th 145MHz engineering beacon which can be received by a statio using relatively simple equipment.

A digitally synthesized speech module, controlled by th on-board computer, "speaks" telemetry and other data info mation. Transmission is on either of the data beacons and nbf is employed.

RS3–RS8

Several years elapsed after the relatively short life of RS1 an RS2 until the launch, on 17 December 1981, of a Soviet vehic carrying no less than six individual satellites. Numbered RS3 t RS8, the satellites were all given approximately the same initi orbital characteristics, though even with minor differences th cumulative effect over several hundred orbits can be quit substantial. The approximate values of the main paramete were as follows:

Period	119mi
Inclination	83
Orbital increment	30

Each of the satellites carried a "Mode A" type transponder i addition to sophisticated telemetry sub-systems feedin beacons at selectable frequencies at the edges of the transpor der pass-bands. Also, at least two of the satellites, RS5 an RS7, carried "Robot" transponders designed to allow automa tic cw contacts to be made with the satellites' on-board proce sor.

AMSAT-Oscar Phase 3

Amateur satellites launched to date have been designed operate in fairly low circular orbits, with altitudes up 1,500km. In spite of the low altitudes, communication ov distances of 7,000 to 8,000km has been possible, though on for short periods of time. The next generation of satellites - Phase 3 — will provide a capability to communicate over eve greater distances and, more significantly, for periods of up several hours. The first of the Phase 3 satellites was due to b placed into a highly elliptical orbit using one of the develo ment flights of ARIANE—the satellite launch vehicle of th European Space Agency, ESA. The launch took place on 2 May 1980 from Kourou in French Guiana; however after on 64s one of the four Viking engines developed a major fau This was followed by malfunctions on the other engines resu ing in destruction of the launcher at 108s after lift-off.

After the initial shock of the loss of the Phase 3A satellite ha diminished there was a considerable amount of discussion c what should be the future of amateur satellites. Fortunately th enthusiasm of the major participants of the programme co tinued and it was soon agreed to proceed with the constructic of a Phase 3B satellite.

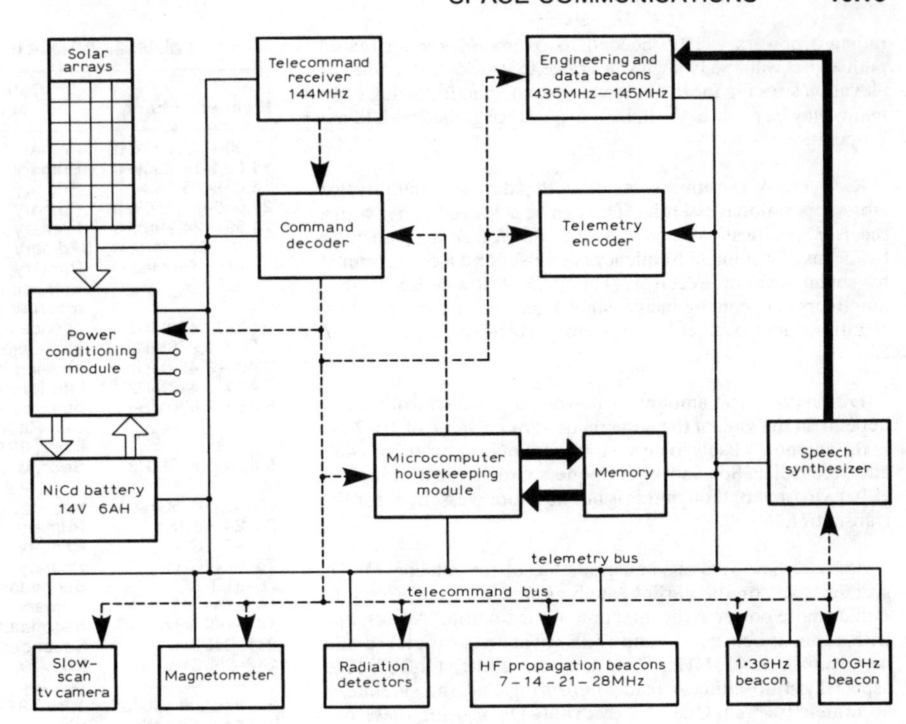

15. Block diagram of UOSAT-Oscar 9

At the time of writing the construction had been completed, ith a planned launch date of mid-1983. The satellite will carry vo communication transponders, one of which will operate in e new WARC allocation to the amateur-satellite service at 260 to 1,270MHz. The proposed frequency plan for the tellite is as follows:

Mode U

Up-link	435·175–435·025MHz
Down-link	145·825–145·975MHz
General beacon	145·8125MHz
Engineering beacon	145·990MHz

Mode L

Up-link	1,269·850–1,269·050MHz
Down-link	436·150–436·950MHz
General beacon	436·040MHz
Engineering beacon	436·020MHz

he orbital parameters will be determined by the initial transfer bit imparted by the launch vehicle, and the effectiveness of the on-board motor. The parameters that are likely to be aimed for are:

Apogee	39,000km
Perigee	1,500km

Due to the considerably increased altitude at apogee compared to earlier satellites the path loss to the satellite will be more than 30dB greater than for similar frequencies on Oscar 8. One obvious advantage that will be obtained with this type of orbit is the greatly increased area of visibility of the satellite, thereby permitting communication over much longer distances than have been achievable in the past. It should be appreciated that many more operators will be able to access the satellite at any one time, and therefore considerable self-discipline will be required to ensure that only the minimum power needed for a contact is in fact used.

Station requirements for the Phase 3 satellites. The main requirements for access to the Phase 3B satellite will be similar to those for the earlier low-orbit satellites except that greater

Table 3. Frequency plans for RS3 to RS8

	RS3	RS4	RS5	RS6	RS7	RS8
plink	–	145·86–145·90	145·91–145·95	145·91–145·95	145·96–146·00	145·96–146·00
ownlink	–	29·36–29·40	29·41–29·45	29·41–29·45	29·46–29·50	29·46–29·50
elemetry	29·41 29·321	29·360 29·403	29·331 29·452	29·441 29·453	29·341 29·501	29·461 29·502
Robot"						
uplink	–	–	145·826	–	145·835	–
downlink	–	–	29·331	–	29·341	–

radiated powers will be needed to overcome the increased path loss. It will also be highly desirable to provide some form of elevation steering for the antenna system. The following comments may be made in the light of experience gained with Phase 2 operations.

Receiver. A sensitive receiver with adequate stability for ssb/cw operation is essential. This can be achieved either with a receiver specifically designed for the down-link frequency, or by means of a suitable frequency converter and a conventional hf communication receiver. The use of low-noise rf pre-amplifiers is becoming increasingly accepted and can produce significant improvements in system performance if used with care.

Transmitter. The amount of power required will obviously depend on the gain of the antenna used but a value of 10–20W at the antenna is likely to be adequate for operation at both 435 and 1,269MHz. Some form of frequency variation is desirable, either vfo or vxo, though this is not absolutely essential for the transmitter.

Antenna. Since the maximum altitude of the satellite will be greater than for the earlier satellites it will be necessary to radiate more power in the direction of the satellite. An antenna with a gain of between 12 and 15dB (over an isotropic) should be adequate at 435MHz, rising to about 20dB at 1,269MHz, especially if attention is paid to ensuring that the satellite is accurately tracked. One of the advantages of using these frequency bands is that all antennas may conveniently be mounted on the same pointing system. Thus when the receiving antenna is adjusted to give the maximum signal the transmitting antenna is automatically adjusted. The prediction of individual satellite passes can be carried out using the techniques already described.

The prospect of the Phase 3 satellites opens up a new dimension to amateur satellite communication and indeed to amateur radio itself. Experience gained from the earlier and current Phase 2 satellites will enable amateurs to make the most effective use of the new facilities and thereby promote further advances.

Frequency allocations to the amateur satellite service

A World Administrative Radio Conference was convened by the International Telecommunications Union in 1979 with a view to consider the table of frequency allocations for all radio services. All existing amateur satellite allocations were maintained and a number of new allocations were made. In all cases, allocations to the amateur satellite service share all, or part, of an allocation to the amateur service. The revised regulations entered into force in January 1982 and a complete list of allocations is given in Table 4.

Moonbounce

One area of space communications that is attracting an increasing amount of interest in amateur circles is that of using the moon as a passive reflector of radio signals. In this way it is possible for two stations on opposite sides of the earth to communicate with each other when the moon is visible to both of them. Moreover, this can be achieved at vhf where the normal operating range is up to a few hundred miles. This

Table 4. Amateur satellite allocations

Frequency band	Category of services	Comments
7,000– 7,100kHz	Primary	E
14,000–14,250kHz	Primary	E
18,068–18,168kHz	Primary	N (note 1)
21,000–21,450kHz	Primary	E
24,890–24,990kHz	Primary	N (note 1)
28– 29·7MHz	Primary	E
144–146MHz	Primary	E
435–438MHz	In these bands the amateur satellite service may operate subject to not causing harmful interference to other services. See Radio Regulation 664	E
1,260–1,270MHz		N, earth-to-space on
2,400–2,450MHz		N
3,400–3,410MHz		N, Regions 2 and 3 on
5,650–5,670MHz		N, earth-to-space on
5,830–5,850MHz	Secondary	N, RR 808 space-to-earth only
10·45–10·5GHz	Secondary	N
24–24·05GHz	Primary	E
47–47·2GHz	Primary	N
75·5–76GHz	Primary	N
76–81GHz	Secondary	N
142–144GHz	Primary	N
144–149GHz	Secondary	N
241–248GHz	Secondary	N
248–250GHz	Primary	N

E—existing allocation (pre-1979 WARC).
N—new allocation.
Note 1: These bands will be available after transfer of existin services.

method of communication is often referred to as *eart moon–earth (eme)* working and the equipment requiremen are discussed later. It should be pointed out at this stage th eme does not rely on freak enhancements in propagation, ar the variation in signal levels for the bands considered should b no more than a few decibels.

At first sight it would appear that the very high signal loss involved would put this type of communication beyond th reach of radio amateurs. It is true to say that the type equipment required is somewhat more complex than the typic vhf equipment that is commercially available, but by caref choice of equipment in the important areas results should b attainable.

Most of the examples given in this section relate to eme 432MHz, which is not intended to imply that all eme activi occurs in this band, rather it has been chosen because it is th centre of the three bands most frequently used, ie 144, 432 an 1,296MHz.

Signal path loss

The moon rotates in a slightly elliptical orbit around the eart the distance between the two varying on a 28-day cycle. Th maximum and minimum distances (*apogee* and *perigee*) a approximately 407,000km and 356,000km respectively. To a observer on the earth the moon, which has a diameter 3,500km, subtends an angle of about half a degree (see Fig 16 so to achieve best results the transmitting (and receivin antenna beamwidth should ideally be no greater than this valu In practice this is not usually achievable but does provide a ultimate objective.

To decide what type of equipment is necessary the mo critical parameter that needs to be known is the effective pa

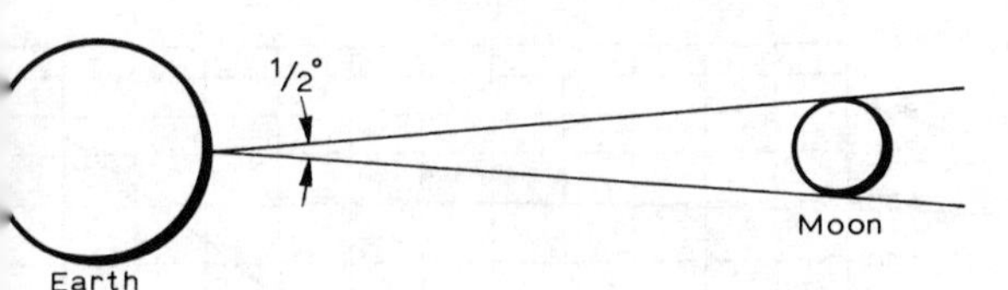

ig 16. To an observer on the earth, the moon subtends an angle of only half a degree

ɔss for a signal reflected by the moon. A convenient way of xpressing this is the *isotropic loss*, ie the loss between two ntennas that radiate equally in all directions.

Consider a transmitter on the earth radiating an effective ower of P_0 watts equally in all directions. At a distance d ıetres from the transmitter the power can be considered to be venly distributed over the surface of a sphere of the same adius. The surface area of the sphere is $4\pi d^2$ square metres so ne amount of power flux passing through any square metre of ne surface is $P_0/4\pi d^2$ watts per metre. This is known as the *ower flux density* and, when multiplied by the aperture or apture area of an antenna, gives the amount of power received y the antenna.

The total rf power collected by the moon depends on the urface area as seen from the earth. The aperture of the moon is pproximately equal to $\pi D^2/4$ square metres where D is the iameter of the moon. The power collected is thus the product of the incident power flux density and the moon's aperture, ie $P_0/4\pi d^2 \times \pi D^2/4$ or $P_0 D^2/16d^2$ watts. This power (or more ccurately a certain amount of it) is re-radiated in all directions, o produce a power flux density at the surface of the earth of

$$\frac{P_0 D^2}{16d^2} \cdot \frac{1}{4\pi d^2} \text{ watts per square metre}$$

The aperture, or effective capture area, of an isotropic ntenna is found from the equation $A = \lambda^2/4\pi$ square metres here λ is the wavelength. So the power level of the signal after eflection from the moon would be

$$P_0 \times \frac{D^2}{64\pi d^4} \times \frac{\lambda^2}{4\pi} \text{ or } P_o \times \left(\frac{D \times \lambda}{16\pi d^2}\right)^2 \text{ watts}$$

y substituting suitable values for D, λ and d the path loss for an me signal can be found. For 432MHz the mean path loss is 62dB with a maximum variation of ±1dB due to the variation f the distance between the earth and moon. Fig 17 shows the ariation of path loss with frequency. It should be remembered hat this is the ideal case and assumes that all the energy eceived by the moon is re-radiated.

ME link budget

s for a satellite system the received signal-to-noise ratio may e calculated from a power link budget as follows:

he overall signal-to-noise ratio is given by

$$\text{SNR} = P_0 - L_T + G_T - P_L + G_R - P_N$$

here P_0 = transmitter power (dBW)
L_T = transmitter feeder loss (dB)
G_T = transmitting antenna gain (relative to isotropic) (dB)
P_L = total path loss (dB)
G_R = receiving antenna gain (dB)
P_N = receiver noise power (dBW)

The last factor, P_N, is determined by the receiver bandwidth B and the total system noise temperature T_S.

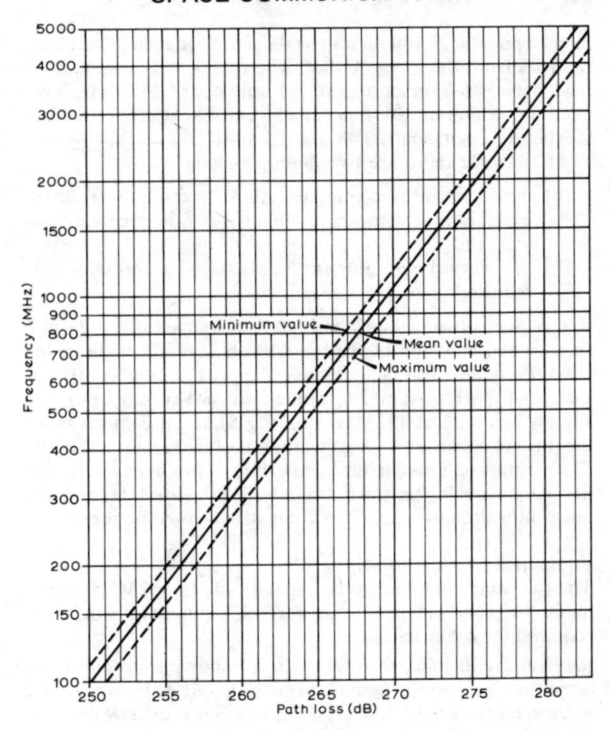

Fig 17. Variation of eme path loss with frequency

$P_N = 10 \log_{10} K \times B \times T_S$ where K is Boltzmann's constant: $1{\cdot}38 \times 10^{-23}$ W/Hz. T_S is the sum of the individual noise sources, referred to the output of the antenna

$T_S = T_A + (L_R - 1)\, T_L + L_R T_R$;
T_A = antenna temperature, K;
L_R = receiving feeder loss (expressed as a ratio);
T_L = physical temperature of feeder (normally 290K);
T_R = receiver noise temperature, K.

By substituting the relevant values into the above equations the snr can be calculated.

Example:

P_0 = 28·7dBW (750W)
L_T = 1dB
G_T = 25dB (16ft dish)
P_L = 262dB
G_R = 26·5dB
T_A = 100K
L_R = 0dB (ie preamp at antenna)
T_R = 93K (noise figure of 1·2dB)
B = 100Hz
$\therefore T_S$ = 100 + 93 = 193K
P_N = $10 \log_{10} K T_S B$
= −185·7dBW
∴ SNR = 28·7 − 1 + 25 − 262 + 26·5 − (− 185·7)
= 2·9dB.

From the above calculations it can be seen that even with fairly sophisticated equipment only marginal results are obtained. One factor of major significance to UK amateurs is that an output power of 750W has been assumed which is about 8dB more than is possible under licence conditions. However, it may be possible to obtain a special licence for such experimental work from the Home Office. The calculations given above have been based on an operating frequency of 432MHz, however eme communication is equally possible at other amateur frequencies, principally 144 and 1,296MHz.

At 144MHz there are two main problems:

(a) the increase in sky temperature, typically 200–300K, which limits the ultimate sensitivity of the receiving system, and
(b) the very large antennas necessary to produce the required gain.

The main advantages of the 144MHz band are that it is quite easy to generate the high power levels (subject to licensing conditions), and also the path loss is approximately 9·5dB less than for 432MHz. At higher frequencies the sky temperature is slightly less than at 432MHz (see Fig 8) and it is much more practical to construct high-gain antennas that are not too large. The major problems encountered at higher frequencies are that the path loss is higher (an extra 9·5dB at 1,296MHz) and it is more difficult (and expensive) to construct low-noise receivers.

Equipment considerations

The following comments relate specifically to 432MHz equipment but also indicate what sort of equipment would be required for other bands.

Receiver. With modern transistors it is possible to construct amplifiers with noise figures down to about 1dB, which is a noise temperature of 75K (see Fig 18). Since the sky noise at 432MHz is of the order of 50 to 100K there can be very great advantage obtained by keeping the receiver noise temperature down to this value. For example consider a system where the sky temperature is 100K; if the receiver noise figure were reduced from 4dB to 1dB the receiver sensitivity would be increased by almost 5dB. To obtain a similar increase in sensitivity from the antenna it would be necessary to increase its aperture by a factor of three.

The effect of feeder loss on the overall system noise temperature is equally as important as the amplifier noise figure. The degradation caused by even 1dB loss before the amplifier can be very much greater with an otherwise low-noise system. Whenever possible the preamplifier should be as close as possible to the antenna and ideally mounted at the feed point, thus reducing cable losses.

With most amateur terrestrial communications the effect of the second and subsequent stages can generally be ignored. This is not the case with eme and care should be taken to ensure that the stages after the preamplifier, and the interconnecting cable, do not significantly degrade the overall system.

It is standard practice to use conventional 432MHz down-converters with an i.f. output in the range of a good-quality hf receiver. It is important that the receiver should be very stable and that its calibration accuracy, including the error from the down-converter, should be within 1kHz or better.

The receiver bandwidth assumed in the link budget calculation was 100Hz, which means that communication is generally limited to cw only. While the use of narrow-band i.f. filters would seem desirable, this is not essential because of the inherent selectivity of the ear.

As a check on the receiving system a measurement of sun noise can be used as a good guide. This can be achieved by connecting a suitable voltmeter (preferably one with a decibel scale) across the af output of the receiver. Measurements of the noise level are then taken with the antenna pointed both towards and away from the sun. This should be done when th[e] sun is at a high elevation, and with the receiver operating wit[h] its agc switched off. The difference between the two readings [i]s taken to be the effective noise from the sun. Under norma[l] conditions (ie when the sun is not disturbed) the solar nois[e] would need to be at least 8dB if the equipment is to be used fo[r] eme.

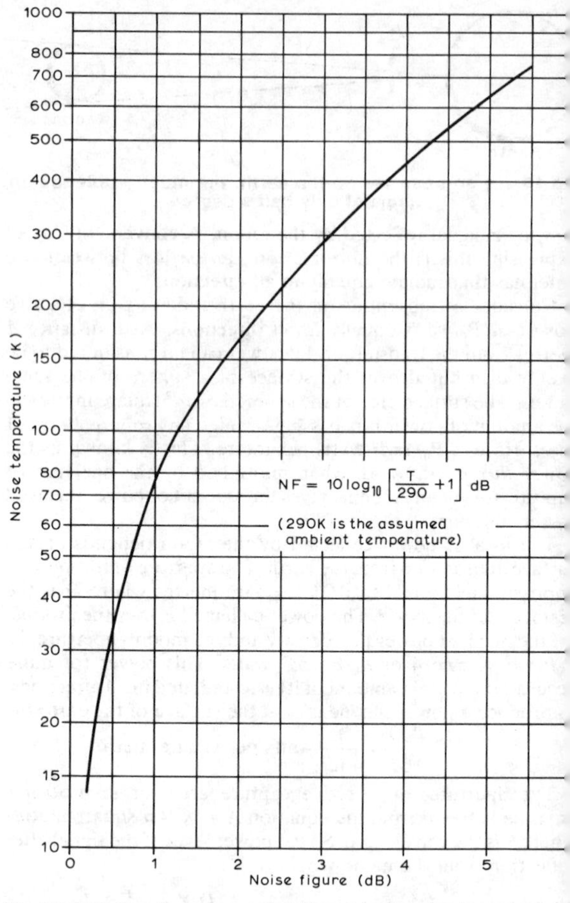

Fig 18. Relation between noise figure and noise temperatur[e]

Transmitter. Many transmitter designs capable of providin[g] high rf powers have been published, including elsewhere in thi[s] book. These frequently use readily available high-power te[t]rodes such as the 4CX250B. As with the receiving system, th[e] short-term stability of the transmitter must be as high as possible and the transmitter should be able to be set to within 1kH[z] of the chosen working frequency.

Antenna. The main requirement of the antenna is that its gai[n] should be as high as possible, the limitations being the physica[l] size that can be accommodated. Another very important con[]sideration is that the side lobe responses should be as low a[s] possible. If this is not so, it is possible for noisy sources whic[h] are nowhere near the main beam to seriously degrade th[e] antenna noise temperature.

Various types of antenna are possible for the three band[s] considered, eg parabolic dish, collinear array, and Yagi arrays

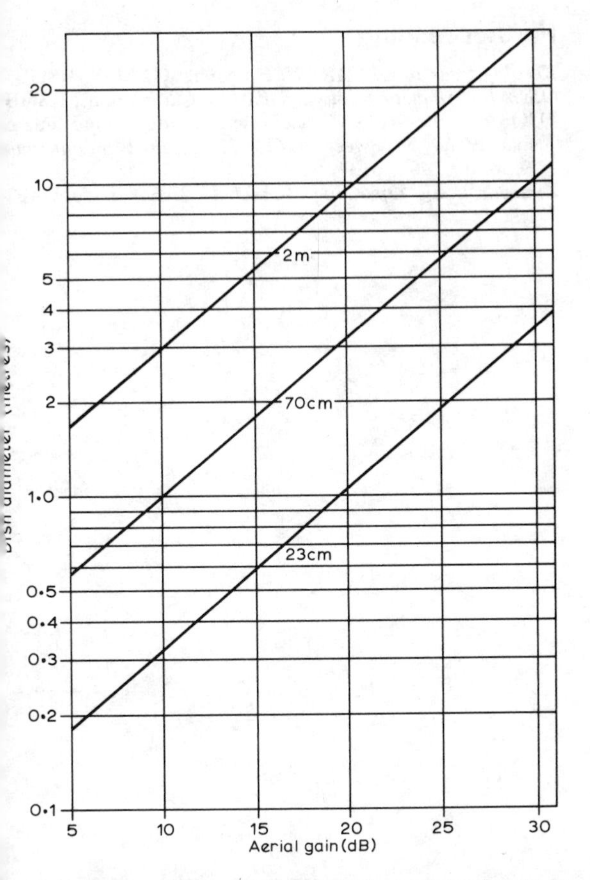

ig 19. **Diameter of a parabolic dish antenna for gains up to 30dB, assumed efficiency 50 per cent**

)ne of the most convenient types is the dish which, although aving the disadvantage of having a lower gain-to-size ratio ıan its competitors, does possess some other desirable fea-ıres. It is quite easy to construct and due to its non-frequency elective properties (except for the feed) it may also be used on ther bands. In order to overcome problems due to polarization ıisalignment it is convenient to use circular polarization, which gain is most easily achieved with a dish antenna. However, at resent the majority of antennas used, including dishes, employ near polarization.

To maintain the highest possible signal levels it is necessary ır the antenna to be kept pointed in the direction of the moon, nd two methods are commonly used. These are the polar ıount, which requires rotation about one axis only, and the zimuth-elevation mount which requires rotation about two xes. In spite of being apparently more complex, the az-el ıount is the more popular of the two. Information regarding ıe actual track of the moon across the sky can be derived from ıe data contained in *The Nautical Almanac*.

perating practice

ince eme provides such a marginal method of communication is essential that each operator should adopt identical methods f carrying out tests. Most eme tests are prearranged so that equency, time of commencement of test and order of calling ıay be established. In general the frequencies used are 144·000, 432·000 and 1,296·000MHz, with a suitable allowance for Doppler shift and calibration error. The procedure is for the first operator to send a transmission sequence for a period of 2½min, then to listen for a reply for a similar period of time. The calling sequence consists of the two callsigns, eg *G3UHF de G3SHF* (assuming cw is being used). Instead of the usual RST method of reporting, another system, TMO, has been developed specifically for eme. The reason for this choice of letters is that the morse code for each letter consists of only dashes and these are more recognizable if the signal is at, or even below, the noise level. The meaning associated with each letters is as follows:

T—reception of signal but not positive identification
M—signifies copy of part or parts of the callsigns
O—signifies copy of whole callsigns or words.
The letter R is sent as confirmation of contact.

If signal levels are sufficiently high, then reversion back to the RST system is sometimes done. Several slight variations of the above interpretations have been found and it is advisable to check what meanings are to be taken when the tests are arranged.

Complete tests may take up to one hour to carry out, during which time it will obviously be necessary to rotate the antenna along the track of the moon. Another problem that arises is that the polarization of the received signal changes due to an effect called *Faraday rotation*. As has been mentioned already, one method of overcoming such a problem is to use circular polarization, but the fading is only really significant at 144MHz and the problem is usually overcome by actually rotating the antenna, or, where possible, the feed. It should be remembered, however, to return the angle of polarization to its original value at the beginning of each transmit sequence, and that adjustment during a transmission should only be made at the receiving station.

As was discussed earlier, the distance between the moon and earth is more than 350,000km and consequently there is a time delay of about 2¼s between transmission and reception of signals. Also, different path lengths can occur due to reflection from different parts of the moon, so that the received signal consists of many components arriving at slightly different times. This can cause distortion and is particularly noticeable on voice transmission (ie ssb). The long time delay can be of some benefit in that it enables a station to monitor its own reflected signals.

The relative movement between the earth and moon causes the signals to suffer a Doppler shift which, unlike that experienced with satellites, remains roughly constant. The value of the frequency shift varies according to the time in the lunar cycle, but is never greater than = $3f$ hertz, where f is the transmission frequency in megahertz. So at 432MHz the maximum Doppler shift would be approximately 1·26kHz, ie if the transmit frequency were exactly 432MHz, then the received frequency would be 432·00126MHz, or 431·99874MHz depending on whether the earth and moon were approaching each other, or moving further apart.

Finally, the choice has to be made when to carry out the tests. The variation of earth-moon separation means that the path loss can vary by about 2dB so it is advisable to choose a time when this figure is a minimum. It is also desirable to conduct the tests when the moon is in a quiet part of the sky, well above the horizon and away from sources of noise such as the sun and the milky way.

If all of these techniques are adopted, the equipment previously outlined should enable contacts to be made with other stations similarly equipped.

Reference

[1] AMSAT—UK, secretary R. Broadbent, G3AAJ, 94 Herongate Road, Wanstead Park, London E12 5EQ.

Further reading

Keeping track of OSCAR, W. Browning, G2AOX, RSGB.

OSCAR—Amateur Radio Satellites, S. Caramanolis, RSGB.

"UOSAT—the AMSAT scientific and educational amateu spacecraft", M. Sweeting, G3YJO, *Radio Communicatio* February 1981, p134.

Amateur Radio Operating Manual, R. J. Eckersley, G4FT RSGB.

HAPTER 11

est equipment and accessories

the vhf region and above there is a considerable amount of perimentation and home construction, as well as the use of mmercially built equipment, and as frequencies in use are creased there are problems that can only be satisfactorily ckled using suitable test equipment. For example, the losses a coaxial cable increase with frequency, and it is important erefore to reduce the vswr between the transmitter and the tenna to a minimum, which will require some form of reflecmeter.

In the case of a receiver, where low noise is of paramount portance, it is extremely difficult to adjust an input stage or eamplifier for the best signal-to-noise ratio unless a noise nerator is used.

Details of these and other useful devices are described in this apter. They are generally straightforward, and provided care d attention to detail is taken satisfactory and reliable perforance will be achieved. Readers are also referred to *Test uipment for the Radio Amateur*, published by the RSGB.

uning adjustments for antennas

tune up any antenna system it is essential to keep it away m large objects, such as buildings, sheds and trees, and the ray itself should be at least 2λ above the ground. It is useless attempt any tuning indoors since the change in the surroundgs will result in completely different performance when the ray is taken outside.

Undoubtedly the most effective apparatus for tuning up any tenna system is a *standing-wave indicator* or *reflectometer*. If ere is zero reflection from the load, the standing-wave ratio the antenna feeder is unity. Under this condition, known as a *t line*, the maximum power is being radiated. All antenna atching adjustments should therefore be carried out to aim at standing-wave ratio of unity.

If suitable apparatus is not available, the next best course of tion is to tune the antenna for maximum forward radiation. A nvenient device for this is a field-strength meter comprising a ode voltmeter connected to a λ/2 dipole placed at least 10λ om the antenna. When adjustments have resulted in a maxium reading on this voltmeter, the feed line may nevertheless t be "flat" and therefore some power will be wasted. Hower, if the best has been done with the resources available it is ghly likely that good results will be achieved.

eflectometer for vhf

hen power at radio frequency is fed into a transmission line hich is correctly terminated at its far end, this power is propated along the line in terms of voltage and current waves and is absorbed in the load at the far end of the line. This represents e ideal condition for the transfer of power from a transmitter an antenna system. Such a condition is rarely, if ever, hieved due to the impossibility of presenting the transmission line with an absolutely matched load. In practice, it is possible only to terminate the line with an antenna or load which *approaches* the perfect condition. Under these circumstances a certain amount of power is reflected at this mis-termination and is propagated back down the line again by means of further waves of voltage and current travelling in the opposite direction, to be either absorbed or re-reflected at the generator according to whether the generator impedance terminates or mis-terminates the line.

The amount of power reflected from the antenna or load mis-termination is directly proportional to the magnitude of the mismatch on the line. Therefore the mismatch on the line, or in more practical terms, the standing wave ratio, may be expressed in terms of the ratio of the forward or incident and the backward or reflected powers (Fig 1).

It the swr = S, then the voltage reflection coefficient K is given by

$$K = \frac{S-1}{S+1} \tag{1}$$

Clearly, if a device can be constructed which will differentially respond to power in terms of direction then such a device can be used directly to measure standing wave ratio, and the ratio M of incident to reflected power is given in decibels by

$$M = 20 \log_{10} 1/K \tag{2}$$

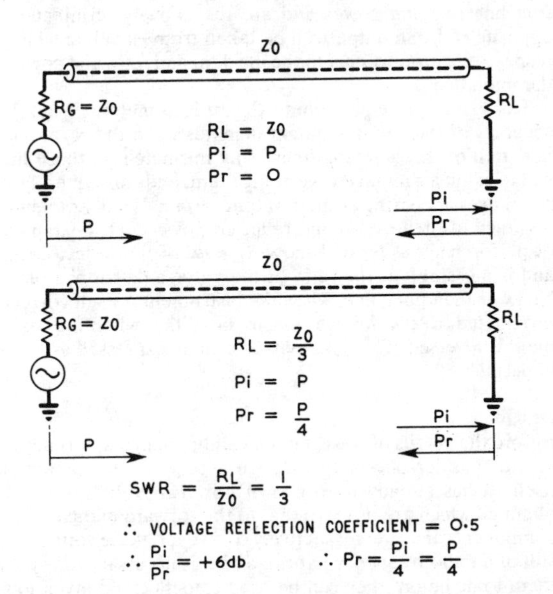

Fig 1. Effect of mis-termination on a transmission line in terms of the incident and reflected power at the load

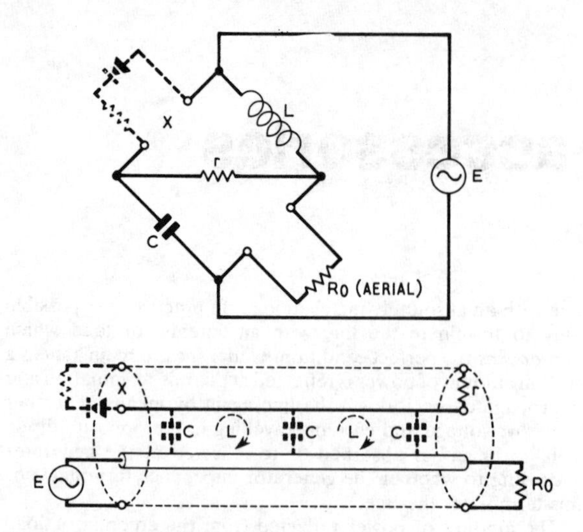

Fig 2. Maxwell bridge representation of transmission line couple

It can be shown that if a line whose length is short compared with a wavelength is introduced into the field of, and parallel to another line which is carrying power, then an amount of power is coupled into the secondary line which is directly proportional to the magnitude of the power travelling in either or both directions on the main line. The configuration of main and sampling lines may be regarded as a Maxwell bridge, the reactive arms of which are provided by the distributed capacitance C and mutual inductance L of the coupled lines, and the effective load on the bridge is r (Fig 2). Then if $r^2 = L/C$ the bridge is effectively balanced at all frequencies, and now power from the generator E appears in the load r, but a proportion appears in the detector load.

If two such subsidiary lines are coupled to a main transmission line carrying power and are respectively terminated at opposite ends, an output can be taken from each line which is respectively proportional to the incident and reflected power in the main line.

This is the principle behind the reflectometer, Fig 3. The accuracy of such an instrument depends upon the correct termination of the sampling lines. Any mismatch on those lines will result in a standing wave along them, and consequently the rf voltages appearing at their output terminals will not be proportional to the forward and reflected powers. This parameter of performance is termed the *directivity* of the reflectometer, and is measured as the ratio of the voltage developed on the backward sampling line, when the instrument is itself correctly terminated, to the voltage on this same line when the instrument is reversed. The directivity is usually expressed as a ratio in decibels.

Design

Before the details of construction can be finalized, it is necessary to consider one or two design aspects of the instrument itself. It has already been shown how two voltages may be obtained which are proportional to the forward and backward components of power respectively. However, these voltages are still of a radio frequency nature, and it is necessary to convert them to dc before they can be used to deflect a conventional meter.

If the forward voltage is arranged to produce fsd on the indicating meter, then clearly the meter can be calibrat directly in swr by observing the deflection produced by t backward voltage, and making due allowance for any diff ences in coupling between the two sampling lines and the ma line. This calibration will be valid independent of the actu transmitted power, since in each case the meter is adjusted t fsd.

In practice it is easier to arrange for identical sampling lin in which case the calibration of the meter becomes a simp question of the ratio of rms voltages applied at the rectifyi diodes. This places an inherent limit on the sensitivity of t instrument at low swr. However, provided that the relati couplings can be measured, it is possible to improve the over sensitivity for a given power and meter sensitivity by arrangi for an appreciably greater degree of coupling on the backwa sampling line than on the forward, and thus providing immediate improvement of x decibels in the lowest swr whi can be measured for a given deflection of the meter (Fig 4

Care must be exercised that the coupling from either line not increased to the point where the presence of the sampli line distorts the electromagnetic field around the inner of t main line sufficiently to cause an effective change of Z_0 of t main line and hence introduce an inherent swr in the instrume itself. As a general rule the coupling should not be greater tha 30dB to maintain an inherent reflection coefficient of less tha 3 to 4 per cent.

When the main line is carrying power which is subject amplitude modulation, then the sampling voltage from t forward (and the backward) line will also be subject to am litude modulation at the same modulation depth. Since th voltage has already been rectified and arranged to deflect t indicator meter to full scale, then if this rectified (or detecte signal is once more rectified, a dc voltage will be obtained whi is proportional to the audio frequency voltage modulating t

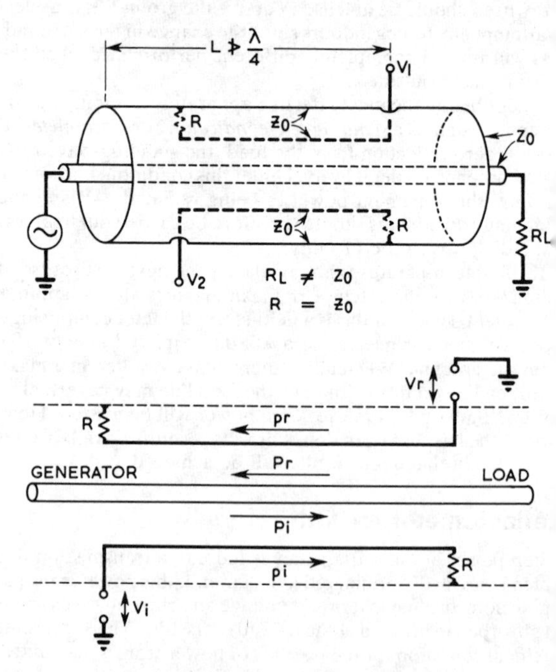

Fig 3. Arrangement of sampling lines to respond respectively incident and reflected powers

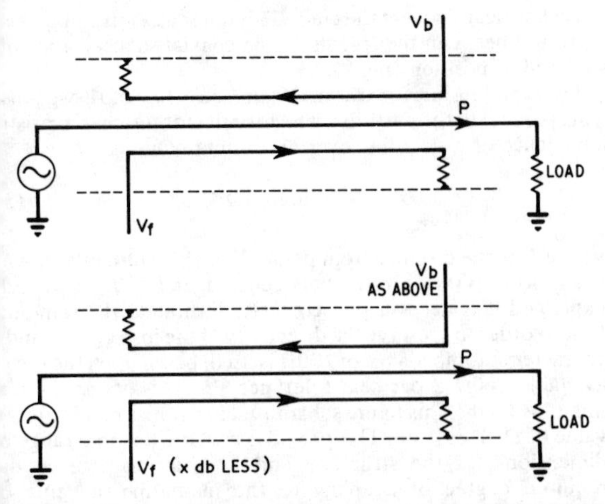

Fig 4. Instrument sensitivity and coupling ratios. (a) sampling couplings equal. V_f gives meter fsd, so swr V_b/V_f, say y dB, which corresponds to a given meter deflection. (b) sampling couplings different by x dB. V_f gives meter fsd less x dB for same power, swr V_b/meter fsd, so for same deflection as (a) swr = x + y dB

carrier. This voltage can then be used to deflect the meter and this can be calibrated directly in percentage modulation. This calibration will also, to a first order, be independent of the transmitted power, since the meter has been adjusted for fsd on the sampled detected carrier.

In practice it is necessary to resort to full-wave rectification of the detected carrier, although this does not really provide sufficient dc voltage to cause large excursions of the meter reading under full modulation conditions, ie it is not possible to advance the meter to fsd for 100 per cent modulation. It is recommended therefore that the "modulation meter" aspect of the instrument be regarded only as of an arbitrary quantitative nature.

The introduction of the instrument into a transmission line requires the use of plugs and sockets, and this in turn will lead to a discontinuity in the line at the ends of the reflectometer proper, due to the sudden transition from the relatively large inner of the instrument line to the inner of the coaxial fitting. The size of the inner conductor of the instrument must be large to maintain the line characteristic impedance while at the same time providing sufficient room to accommodate the sampling lines between the inner and outer conductors, ie this is a physical requirement. These discontinuities are of the right-angled step type, Fig 6, and there is an optimum arrangement of dimensions to provide minimum reflection at the step for any given characteristic impedance and inner conductors ratio. There is no simple arithmetical formula relating the step-length a to these parameters.

Construction

The design is based on a die-cast box 4½in by 3½in by 2in deep, with a partition running the length of the box and fitted to form a 2in square cross-section into which the trough line is assembled. Any other spacing may be used but this complicates the calculation of the Z_0 of the line.

The characteristic impedance of a coaxial line with a cylindrical inner conductor and a square outer is given by

$$Z_0 = 138 \log_{10} L/d$$

where L is the length of the side and d is diameter of the inner

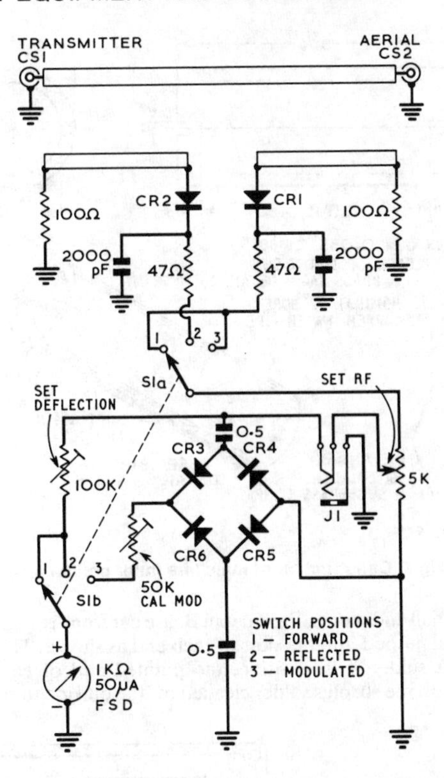

Fig 5. Circuit diagram of reflectometer, CR1, 2, OA91; CR3, 4, 5, 6 IN4148. CR3–6 should be bypassed by 1,000pF capacitors across each diode

conductor and L/d is $> 1{\cdot}5$. Substitution of 2in in this formula gives $d = 0{\cdot}6$in.

The rf connections to the box are made using Amphenol type SO239 coaxial sockets. It is important to use the variety having nylon-loaded bakelite insulation (yellow) to avoid distorting the inner of the socket when the line connection is being soldered.

These sockets are mounted centrally at each end of the 2in square section of the box, and their spigots are cut down so that the overall dimension from the inside face of the box to the end of the spigot is ¼in. The inner conductor, Fig 7 detail A, is slotted at each end for a depth of ⅛in and wide enough to accept 18swg brass sheet as a tight fit. It is important to ensure that the slots at each end lie in the same plane.

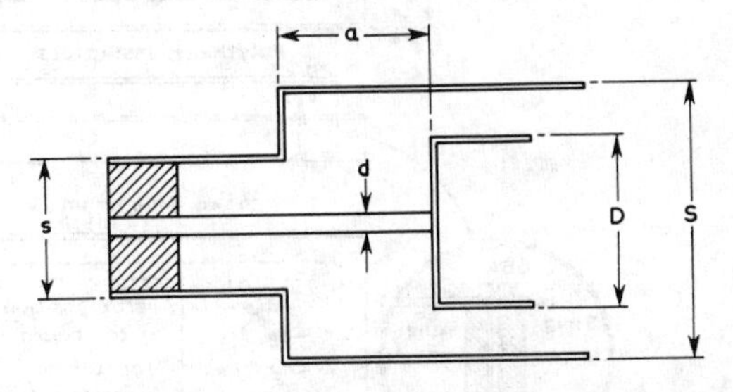

Fig 6. The characteristic impedance Z_0 is given by 138 $\log_{10}$ *s/d* which is also 138 $\log_{10}$*S/D*. The optimum step length *a* is a function of Z_0 *D/d*

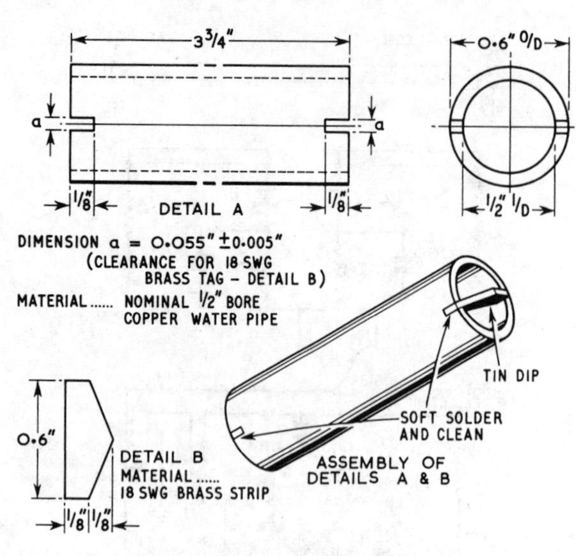

Fig 7. Construction of main line inner conductor

The small end pieces, Fig 7 detail B, are cut from 18swg brass sheet and pushed into the slots at each end as shown. They are then soft soldered in position, the pointed end of each tab tinned, and the surplus solder cleaned off the outside to restore the cylindrical shape at the ends. This inner assembly may then be rested between the spigots of the coaxial sockets, and soft soldered in position (Fig 9).

The sampling lines are formed from a strip line of 18swg brass lying parallel to the partition. The formula for the characteristic impedance of a strip line over an infinite plane is

$$Z_o = 230 \log_{10} 4D/W \quad (3)$$

where D is the distance from plane, W is the width of strip and the ratio D/W has a value between 0·1 and 1·0. As already explained it is necessary to correctly terminate the sampling lines in order to preserve the directivity of the instrument, and a characteristic impedance of 100Ω is used, based upon the use of available 100Ω 2 per cent tolerance ½W resistors as the terminating loads. This figure substituted in expression (3) gives a value of $D/W = 0{\cdot}68$. This provides a whole possible range of dimensions for the strip line and in order to achieve the required degree of coupling to the main line, a value of $D = 0{\cdot}25$in and hence $W = 0{\cdot}375$in was chosen by experiment. The sampling lines were made as long as conveniently possible, care being exercised to make them as near physically identical as possible.

The partition is made of 16swg aluminium sheet and the sampling lines mounted in the positions shown in Fig 8. The spacing of the sampling lines may be trimmed by adjustment at the terminated end when the instrument is being set up. The partition is assembled with sampling lines, tag board on rear,

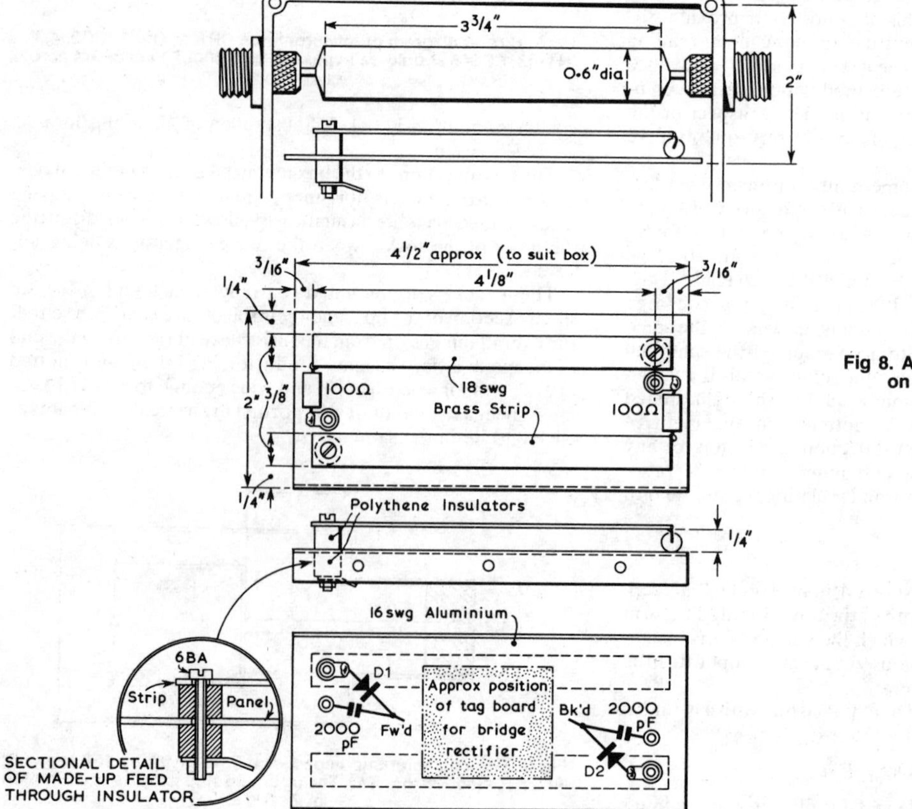

Fig 8. Arrangement of strip line on supporting portion

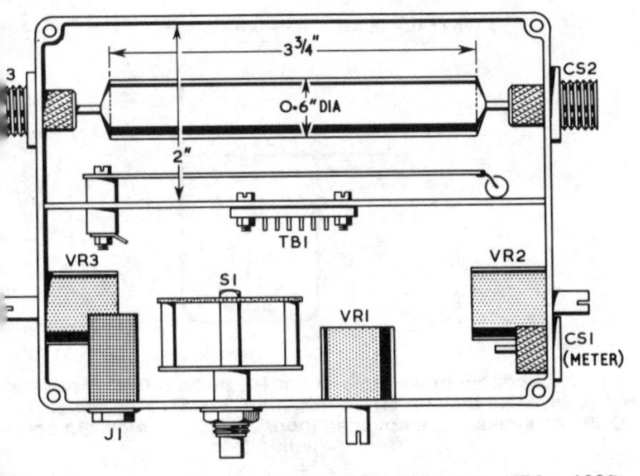

Fig 9. General assembly of reflectometer. VR1 = 50Ω, VR2 = 100Ω, VR3 = 5Ω

nd all components, before being fitted into the box. Connections from the other side of the partition to the various controls re made up as short flying leads to facilitate this assembly.

The position of the various potentiometers and switches is ot critical, and some alteration to the suggested layout may be ecessary if different-sized components are employed. Alternavely there is no objection to extending the dc outputs of the ampling line rectifiers to another chassis by means of a threeore cable. It is of course essential that the initial diode rectifiers re located immediately at the feedthrough bushes behind the artition, as shown in Fig 8.

Calibration

Accurate calibration of the reflectometer requires a signal enerator with calibrated output, a receiver with some form of arrier-level meter, and a load of known reflection coefficient uitable for direct connection to either end of the reflectometer st line (this load should be as near matched as possible). The rocedure is then as follows:

First terminate the antenna end of the instrument and measre the coupling of each sampling line in turn by the insertion ethod (Fig 10). Adjust the sampling line spacing for identical oupling. Then, using the signal generator injecting directly nto each sampling diode in turn (with sampling lines disconected), calibrate the indicating meter in terms of decibels elative to the injection voltage for fsd. This provides also a heck on the match of the diode characteristics of each sampling ircuit. These must be matched if the instrument is to read ccurately at all transmitted power levels. Two diodes at ranom from the box provided the results quoted for the proototype.

The instrument is then calibrated directly in terms of the ratio f backward to forward voltages, expressed in decibels, for all ransmitted powers, provided it is always adjusted to fsd on the orward position using the SET RF control. (The SET DEFLECTION ontrol should be set, for any particular meter, to such a value as o allow the SET RF control to function over the whole range of ransmitted powers expected.)

Many amateurs will, of course, not have the necessary test quipment outlined above available to them. However, this eed not detract greatly from the appeal of the instrument, ince, even without any calibration at all, the output from the ackward line will usually reduce as the swr on the main line is educed. Thus, the reflectometer may be used quantitatively to

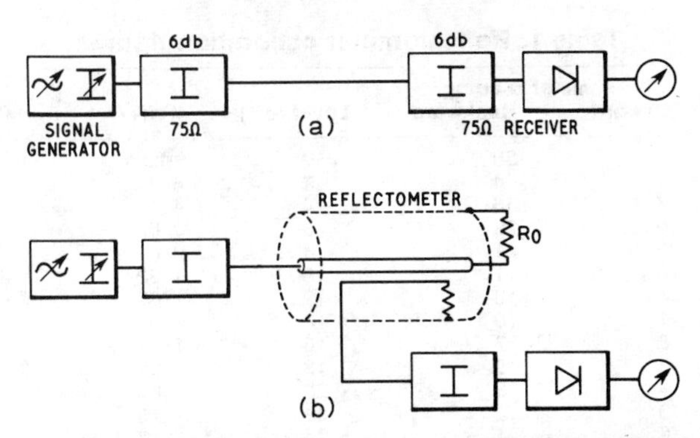

Fig 10. Insertion method for measuring coupling. (a) Set a signal generator attenuator to give an arbitrary deflection *K* on receiver meter. Note the signal generator attenuator setting, say, *x* dB. (b) Repeat the exercise with reflectometer in circuit and re-adjust the signal generator to give the same deflection *K* on the receiver meter. Read the attenuator setting, say, *y* dB. Then the coupling of the main line to the sampling line = x − y dB

indicate best swr when adjustments are being made to, say, an antenna system.

It is possible, without any test equipment other than a lowpower transmitter, to make some basic checks on the instrument as follows.

With an open circuit on the antenna end of the instrument, vary the power from the transmitter in steps, and take at each level the forward meter readings with the instrument connected normally, and then the backward meter readings with the instrument reversed. This will check the characteristic of the diodes, and also enable slight adjustments to be made to the sampling lines to equate the coupling. The latter adjustment should be carried out at the normal transmitter power only, for the best performance in practice.

Care must be exercised when carrying out such checks, to avoid damaging the pa valve of the transmitter through excessive dissipation on no load. Provided that the dimensions given have been followed closely, the errors introduced due to stray differences in the final instrument should not be more than 2 or 3dB. Inspection of the calibration table shows that for the lower values of swr such an error results in a very small error in swr, this becoming increasingly worse as the swr gets larger. Therefore, an uncalibrated but carefully built instrument can be expected to indicate swr to an accuracy of ±0·5 up to values of 2:1, becoming as poor as ±1·0 at 4 : 1. This should be quite adequate for most amateur uses.

The reflectometer described is designed for use in lines with a characteristic impedance of 72Ω. Errors ensue from its use in lines of any other impedance.

The swr column of Table 1 represents the conversion of backward meter readings for a forward reading of 50. For a given input level, the difference between lines was less than 1dB over the full range. Zero level is equivalent to 1V rms in 100Ω.

Power limitations

The sensitivity of the instrument is such as to provide fsd on a 50μA meter for a carrier power of 5W. The upper limit is set by the dissipation in the resistors terminating the sampling line. These are rated at ½W and, since the forward line is dissipating power 32dB down on the incident transmitted power, the maximum transmitted power should not exceed 500W carrier.

Table 1. Reflectometer calibration figures

Meter reading Forward	Backward	Level (dB)	SWR
50	50	0	infinite
43	44	− 2	8·8
37	36	− 4	4·4
30	29	− 6	3·0
23	21	− 8	2·3
18	17	− 10	1·92
14	13	− 12	1·67
11	10	− 14	1·5
8	7	− 16	1·37
6	5	− 18	1·29
4	3	− 20	1·22
3	2	− 22	1·16
2	1	− 24	1·13

Frequency range

The performance of the instrument is constant over the 144MHz band. The sensitivity will fall linearly with the decrease of frequency since the coupling lines are short. The impedance match of the instrument itself will deteriorate with increasing frequency due to the presence of the step discontinuities and also the variations in the terminating loads on the sampling lines, which will become increasingly reactive.

Alternative reflectometer

Another design of the unit just described is suitable for use at frequencies above 432MHz.

Fig 11 represents a section along coaxial line through which a current I is flowing in the direction indicated on the inner conductor. A loop is inserted through the outer wall into the field inside. One end of this loop is terminated by a resistor R and the other by an indicator M which may be any type of device, but usually a diode and microammeter. Current is induced into the loop, and the induced current I_m will be in the opposite direction to that flowing in the inner conductor. In addition, since there is capacitance between the loop and the inner conductor a current I_c flows in each leg of the loop. In the resistance arm I_m and I_c are additive whereas in the other arm they are in opposition.

By adjusting the capacitance C and the mutual inductance M, I_m and I_c can be made to cancel, and the indicator will then read zero. If the current I in the inner conductor is reversed, I_m reverses and the indicator will then read $I_m + I_c$.

With the aid of two loops it is then possible to read separately

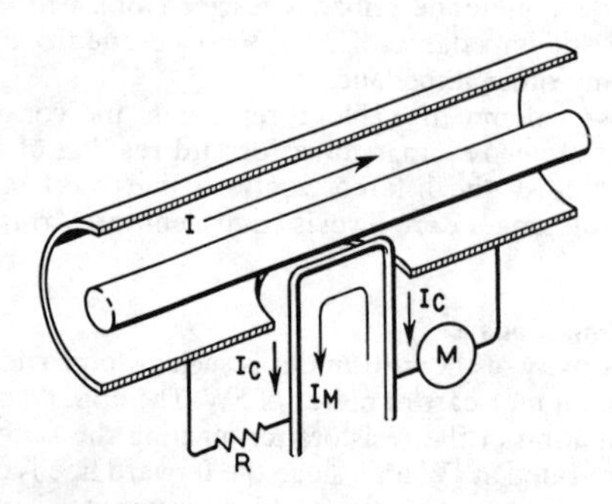

Fig 11. Illustration of the arrangement of the directional coupler into the sample section of the coaxial line

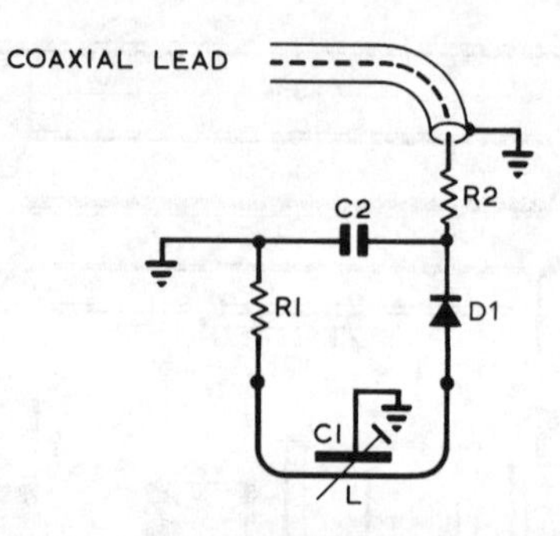

Fig 12. Circuit of coupler unit. R1 and R2 are both 70Ω ½W resistor C1 is ⅜in diam disc on 6BA studding; C2 is 47pF ceramic; D1 i OA91 or similar; L is coupling loop, 20swg, ½in wide, ⅜in space from mounting face

the two currents in the line, from which the reflection coeff cient K can be determined.

Line construction

In order to make the coupling to the inner conductor, it i necessary to have a section of the transmission line enlarged t enable the directional couplers to be inserted. The enlarge section may be either of round or square cross-section but th latter is easier mechanically unless access to a lathe is available The impedance of the new section of the line must, of course, b of the same impedance as the normal feeder line. (Fig 13 show

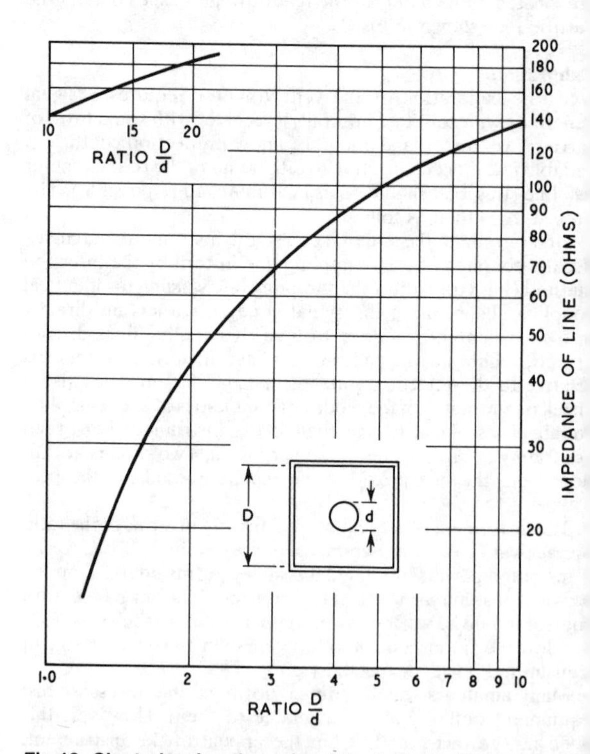

Fig 13. Chart showing the ratio of the internal dimensions of square unit to the external diameter of the centre conductor for us in calculating the dimensions of line sections of required impe dance

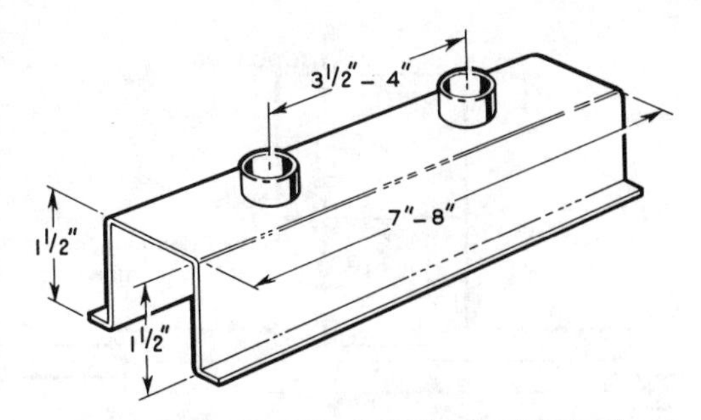

g 14. General arrangement of enlarged square section line showing position of coupler sockets

ıe relationship between the inner and outer dimensions for ny impedance between 20 and 200Ω.)

Fig 14 shows a suitable general assembly arrangement. ı this the bottom is closed by a suitable plate and the ends by lates fixed to all four sides of the square section. In order to reserve the impedance at each end of the enlarged line, tapers f constant D/d must be provided; this is shown in Fig 15.

etector head mounting

he detector heads and their sockets are made from telescope ıbes of about $\frac{15}{16}$in and 1in diameters, the sockets being $\frac{1}{4}$in long nd spaced approximately 4in apart on top of the square section nit as shown in the drawing. They are soldered into holes cut to t them and are slotted so that they may be clamped tightly to ıe detector heads. The clamps may be made from $\frac{1}{4}$in wide rass strip bent round and held together with a 6BA nut and olt.

he detector heads

wo views of one of the two detector heads—which are identcal—are shown in Fig 17. The heads are constructed on small rames made of $\frac{1}{4}$in wide thin brass strip bent into rectangles hich fit snugly into the tubes. It is upon these chassis that all ıe components are mounted. The upper end of each head is losed by a brass disc; the bottom end is made of resin board or imilar material. These end plates are held in position by 8BA crews, which are also used for fixing the chassis inside the tube. is important that the heads should be a good fit in their espective tubes so that the whole assembly can be easily ushed together.

The small trimmer capacitator (C1 in Fig 12) is made by crewing a piece of 6BA studding right through the rectangle nd end plates. A $\frac{3}{8}$in diameter disc is soldered to one end, the ther is slotted to take a screwdriver. The $\frac{3}{8}$in plate is then used

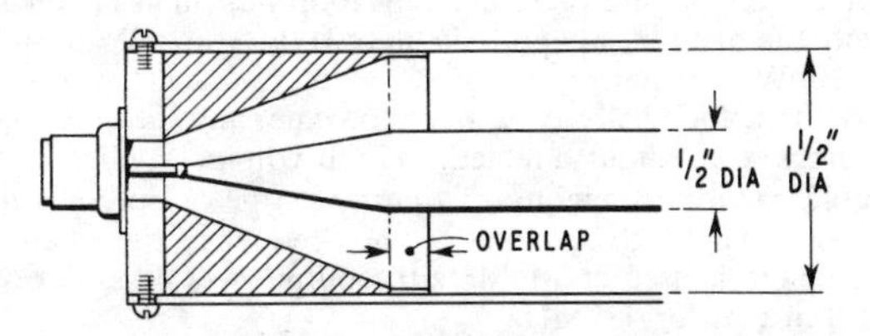

ig 15. End taper of both inner and outer of the section. The inner onductor may be shaped by turning or fitting a thin copper cone olled and soldered to inner conductor. The outer taper can be nade either by fitting blocks in the ends or folding thin sheets into he correct shape. If this latter method is used overlap should be allowed for adequate contact to the outer

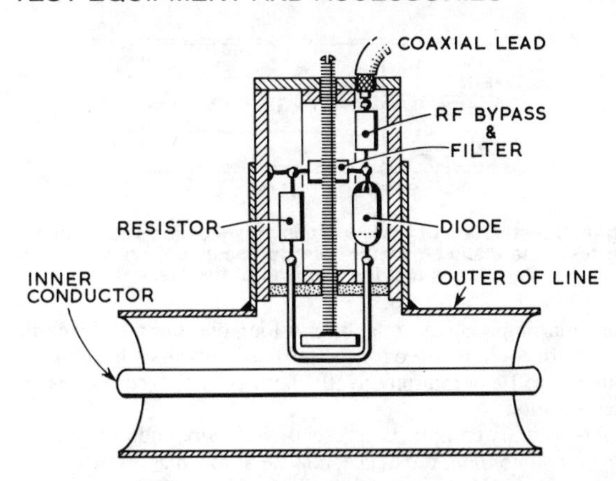

Fig 16. Practical design of a suitable directional coupler for the reflector of Fig 11

to adjust the capacitance between the loop and the earthy frame. The coupling loop is made from 20swg wire and is $\frac{1}{2}$in wide and $\frac{3}{8}$in above the resin board plate on which it is mounted. The loop is fixed through pairs of small holes $\frac{1}{2}$in apart. Each end of the loop is passed through one hole, folded back through its neighbour and pinched to make a firm anchorage for each leg.

It will be seen from the circuit of the detector head that one end of the loop terminates in a resistance R1, while the other feeds a germanium rectifier type OA91, the output of which is decoupled by C2 and R2. Television-type coaxial cable, terminated with coaxial connectors, can be used to feed off this dc output. The leads are passed through holes cut in the brass end discs, but care should be taken to anchor the braid securely inside the head by bending a long soldering tag round it and lightly soldering. The tag can then be bolted to the frame.

Terminating resistance

The initial setting-up process requires that a terminating resistance be used at one end of the unit. It must look like a resistance, even at 432MHz. This means that it must be coaxial and

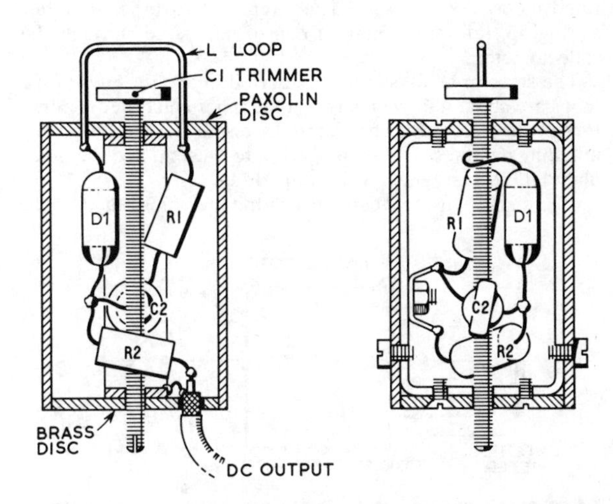

Fig 17. Two views at right-angles to one another, showing the construction of the detector heads

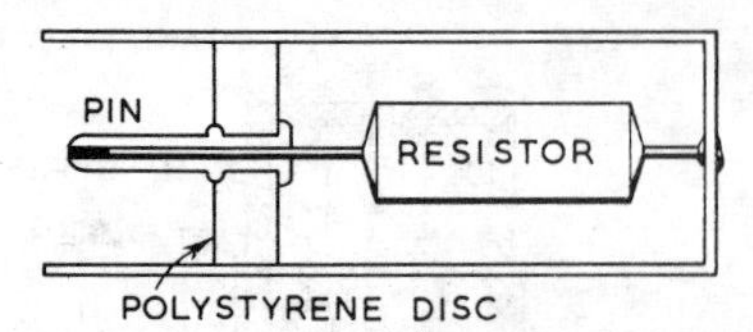

Fig 18. Construction of the terminating resistance as described in the text. The diameter of the tube is dependent upon the line impedance and the diameter of the resistor

of similar impedance to the line. A long piece of coaxial cable, say 100ft, could be used for the purpose but, as such a length is unlikely to be commonly available, a special accessory is the best solution.

An ordinary composition resistor with wire ends, even if it is the correct nominal resistance, may be as much as 50 per cent in error at 432MHz owing to the nature of the composition, and the high inductive reactance of the leads.

High-stability resistors of the cracked carbon type have, however, been found quite satisfactory. Welwyn type SA3623 or Painton type 74 are suitable. The resistor selected should have the same dc value as the required termination impedance. It is used as the inner conductor of a concentric line. The diameter ratio of the line must, however, be made for a 30 to 50 per cent lower impedance than the required value, because a line in which the inner conductor is all resistance has a somewhat inductive impedance. The smaller outer diameter, by providing greater capacitance, compensates for this effect. For 70Ω the ratio is 2 : 1. Using the types of resistor specified above, the 70Ω assembly ($\frac{3}{8}$in) diameter fits the Belling-Lee socket. The construction of these terminations is illustrated in Fig 18. When made as shown, the terminations are within 2 to 3 per cent of the correct value at 432MHz, although the wire leads to the resistors should still be as short as possible. In the 100Ω type, the pin should be mounted in a polystyrene disc made to fit tightly in the tube.

Setting-up procedure

Setting up the instrument is quite simple and requires only a low-power oscillator or transmitter that can be modulated, preferably with a continuous note. As the terminating resistor is rated at only 1W, care should be taken not to overheat it. After setting up, full power may of course be passed through the reflectometer.

The detector heads should be inserted so that the ends of the loops are about half-way between the inner and outer conductors of the line, using the clamps as depth controls. The terminating resistance is then plugged into one end and the modulated 432MHz signal fed into the other.

The signal will be heard in headphones plugged into the

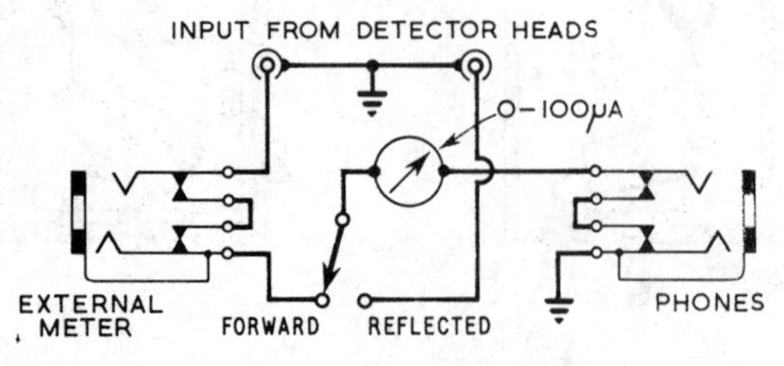

Fig 19. Circuit diagram of the meter switching for a mounted reflectometer

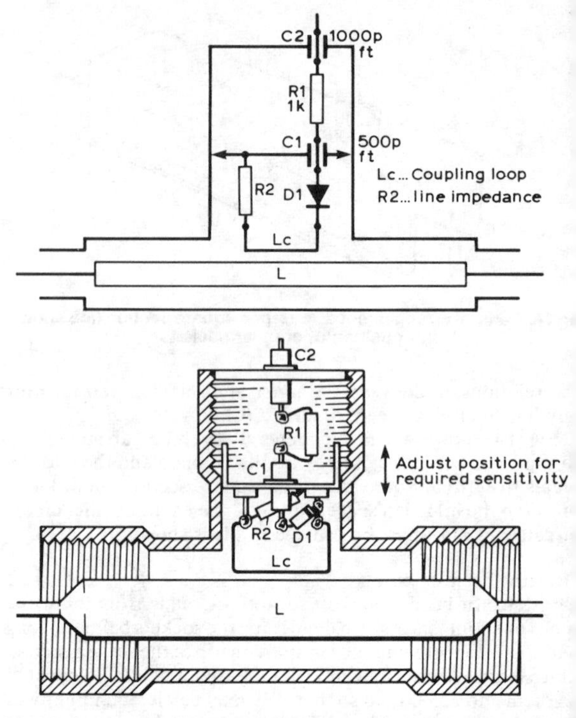

Fig 20. General arrangement of detector head using tee connector (copper water pipe)

phone jack and switched to the appropriate head. The head nearest the terminating resistor is next adjusted by simultaneously rotating it in its mounting and adjusting the trimmer until a sharp minimum is observed. This null point is quite well defined. The head should be securely fixed in position by its clamp. The input and output connections are then changed over, the phone switched to the other head and the procedure repeated.

This procedure can be carried out on 144MHz but the settings may need slight adjustment for 432MHz.

Use as a power meter

As the germanium detector has a reasonably good square-law response, the dc output from the heads is proportional to the power in the line. Accurate calibration as a power meter is, however, a difficult task; nevertheless, it is possible to give a rough idea of what meter readings meant in the prototype.

In the $1\frac{1}{2}$in square 70Ω line, if the loop was $\frac{1}{8}$in inside the line cavity the meter read approximately 100μA for 1W or 10mA for 100W of rf power.

With the loop halfway between the inner and the outer these readings were about doubled. As the voltage applied to the coupler is proportional to the frequency, the dc output will be proportional to the square of the frequency, ie when the instrument is used at 144MHz the output will be about one tenth of that for 432MHz.

Precision-type reflectometer

A precision-type reflectometer suitable for use up to about 2,300MHz can be built without too much difficulty, provided

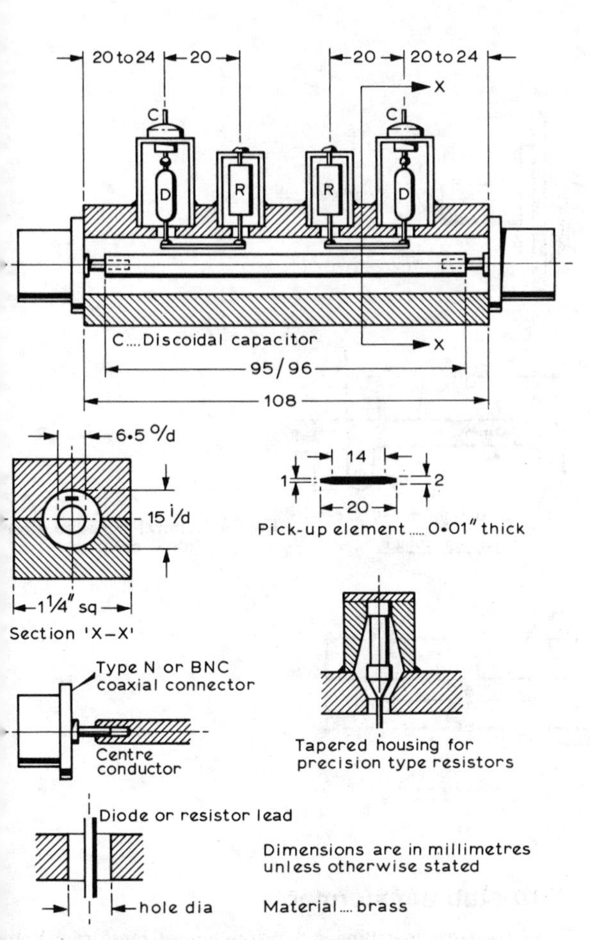

ig 21. Mechanical details of a precision-type reflectometer for use at frequencies up to 2·3GHz

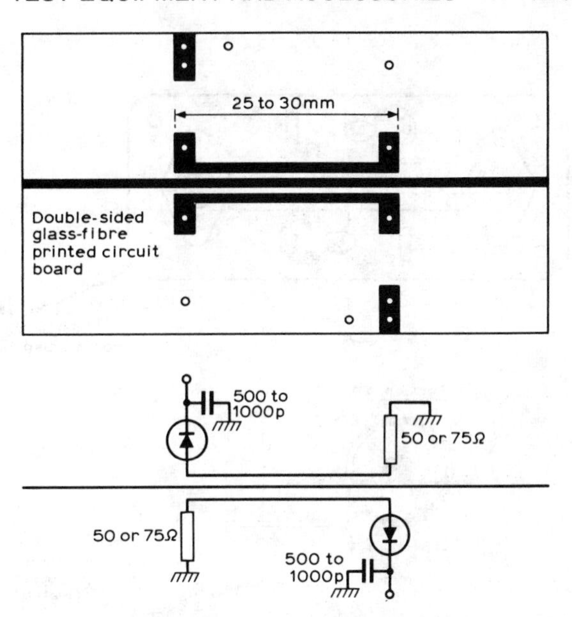

Fig 22. Printed circuit directional coupler

he parts can be adequately and accurately machined. Fig 21 hows the basic arrangement, which effectively contains two irectional couplers arranged back to back so that one indicates he forward power and the other the reflected power. The rawing does not give the final detail which can be varied ccording to the needs of individual constructors, although all alient dimensions are given.

It is important to bear in mind that impedance steps or iscontinuities must be avoided, both in the main line section nd the pick-up circuits. The details given are for 50Ω—if a 75Ω nit is needed suitable alterations to the dimensions must be nade.

The main body should be made of two pieces with a centre ole bored to 15mm diameter for a 6·5mm centre conductor any other sizes suitable for 50 or 75Ω may be used).

The ends of the centre conductor should be bored to take the entre connector of the coaxial connectors to be used. BNC- or N-type connectors are usually preferred, so that the fit is good, nd only one end need be soldered to keep it in position. This lso allows easy dismantling until finally adjusted.

The detector diodes and terminating resistance used will argely dictate the mechanical detail. The hole diameter hrough which their connections protrude to connect to the ick-up loops should be of an appropriate size to preserve the line impedance, and the spacing of the pick-up to the body should meet the same requirement.

If the terminating resistors are of the precision type with end caps instead of wire connections it will be an advantage to make the inner of the housing tapered to preserve a suitable impedance from zero at the shorted end to 50Ω at the open end.

It is desirable to keep the capacitance coupling down to a minimum between main centre conductor and the pick-up elements (loops). For this reason a thin sheet material such as 0·01in phosphor bronze is more suitable than wire.

Printed-circuit directional coupler

A simple method of constructing a directional coupler is by use of a printed circuit board, as illustrated in Fig 22. The line impedance can be made in accordance with the design information given in "Tuned circuits", Appendix 1. The coupling lines may be of any convenient length to suit the meter in use, but they should be short compared with λ/4.

The diodes should be signal type, such as point-contact germanium, and suitable for the frequency concerned. The terminating resistors should be as far as possible non-inductive type of good stability. The bypass capacitors may be disc, plate or feedthrough, and the latter has advantage in providing a terminal for connection to the meter. It is important that the actual value should be suitable for the frequencies to be used.

General-purpose directional coupler

A reliable directional coupler may be made employing readily available material as an alternative to the pcb type, without recourse to machine tools. A short section of air-spaced coaxial line is used, with the coupling loops inserted into the line through the slots in the outer tube.

The general arrangement is shown in Fig 23. The whole unit is assembled on a piece of single-sided copper-clad board made to fit on to a cast box (Eddystone 7969P). A piece of 8mm

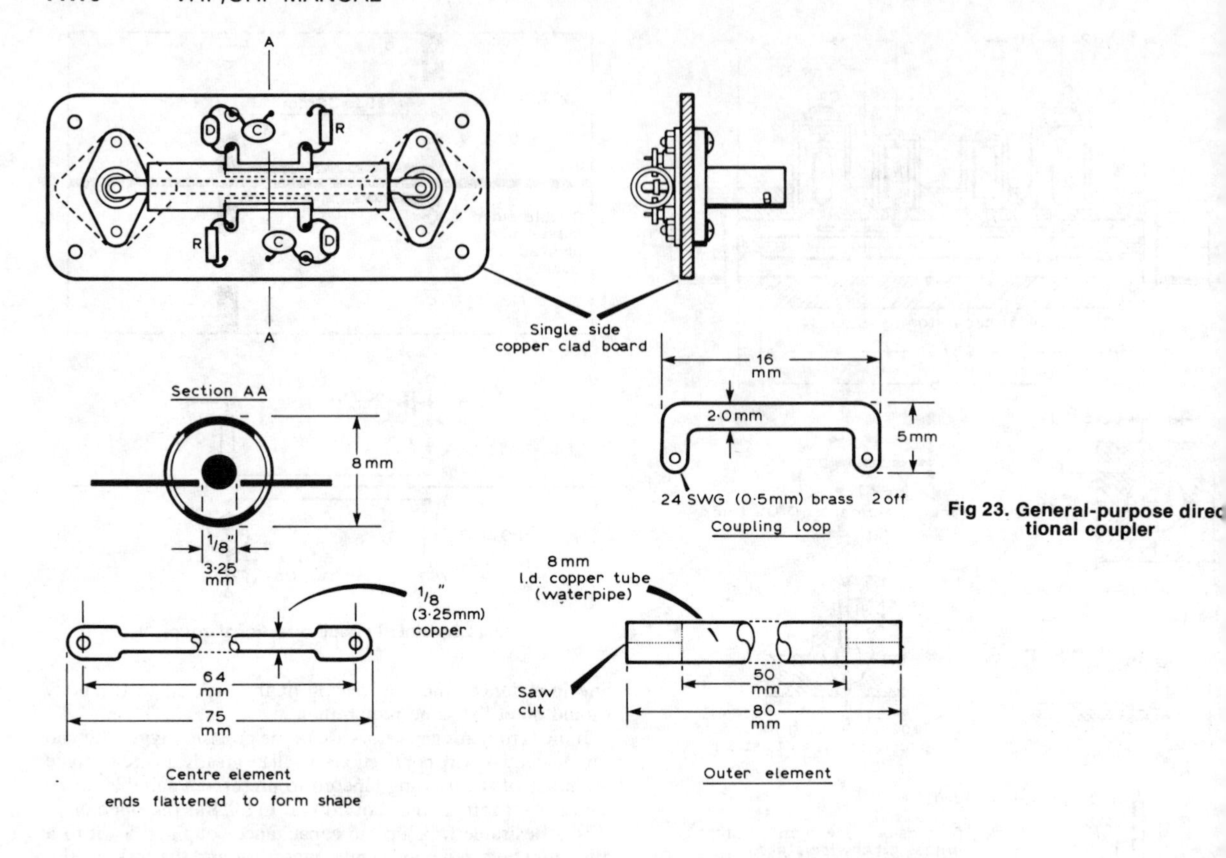

Fig 23. General-purpose directional coupler

copper tube (standard water pipe), with its ends opened out by cross sawing and slitting is attached to this, the inner line being chosen to suit either 50 or 75Ω. For 50Ω $\frac{1}{8}$in or 3·25mm is close enough and 14swg (2·3mm) copper is appropriate for 75Ω.

The coupling loops are made from 24swg brass or copper strip mounted on four small stand-off insulators. The spacing between them and the inner line should be equal and adjusted so that each provide the same readings when used either way it is connected. This should be done with the output socket connected to the appropriate terminating resistor, a 50 or 75Ω dummy load.

The inner conductor is best made from small-diameter copper tube, especially for the 50Ω case, so as to more easily be flattened at each end, in order that they can be drilled to fit over the socket centre connections.

General-purpose directional coupler

Two-stub transformer

For impedance matching, a two-stub tuner (transformer) provides a satisfactory method. It is effectively a coaxial or vhf pi-coupler.

The general arrangement is shown in Fig 24 and this is made using $\frac{1}{8}$in diameter centre conductor and $\frac{1}{2}$in diameter outer. The transformer will have a useful range of $Z_o/2$ to $2Z_o$.

If the section of line between the two stubs is made adjustabl

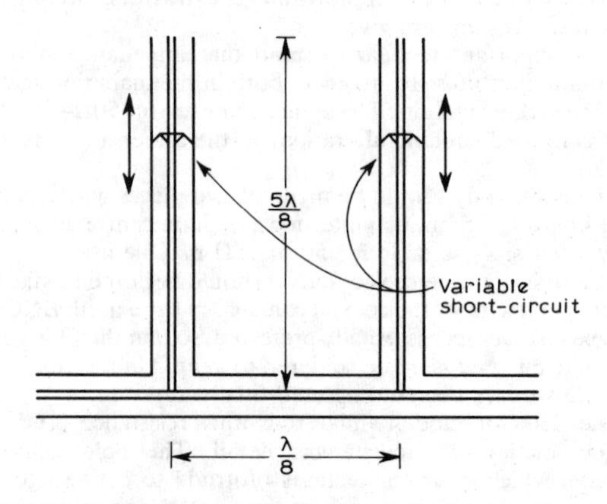

Fig 24. General arrangement of the two-stub transformer

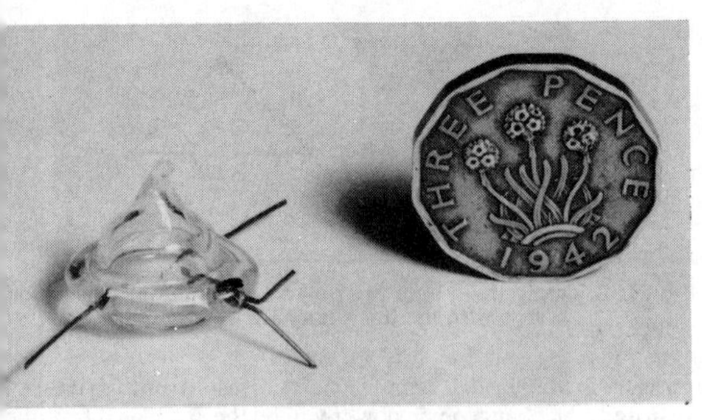

Typical thermal converter unit

nd the stubs themselves are long enough for the lowest fre-uency required, then a unit for use on more than one band can e made.

leasurement of rf power

here are a number of methods of power measurement capable f providing sufficient accuracy for all practical purposes up to GHz. Where power monitoring is sufficient (as distinct from ctual measurement) the methods outlined can be used at still igher frequencies but with rather less accuracy.

Whenever possible the measurements should be made at a elatively low impedance of, say, 50 or 75Ω. This is suitable for nost transmitter or exciter outputs but at higher impedances ome correction factors may become necessary.

In making power output measurements it should be remem-ered that all outputs, including harmonics and spurious emis-ions if any are present, will be included and, if it is required to neasure only the power of the wanted signal, then some form of iltering will be required. For most purposes this is not necess-ry, but some thought should be given to this aspect when lealing with varactor diodes or other semiconductors.

The thermocouple power meter

Basically this is an extension of the familiar thermocouple in rf mmeters used for reading antenna current in lf transmitters.

The main component is a thermal converter which consists of heating element, to the midpoint of which is attached a hermocouple. This is fixed by means of a suitable material to ive good heat conduction and electrical insulation. Suitable nits for use at vhf and uhf are normally enclosed in an evacu-ted envelope, the construction being such that stray reactive omponents are minimized. Their general form is similar to that f the old-type acorn valve (see photo).

In operation, when an rf current passes through the heater lement a thermal emf is produced in the thermocouple, the nagnitude of which will depend on the value of the rf current. For calibration, if the rf current is replaced by a dc or low-requency ac (mains frequency) current and its value adjusted o give the same thermal emf, it can be shown that the rf current as an rms value equal to that of the calibration current. There-ore, since the current can be measured accurately, this, ogether with the load resistance, will enable an accurate neasurement of the total rf power to be made.

Thermal converters are available in a wide range of heater atings and typical types are shown in Table 2.

The actual value of the heater resistance will, of course, vary

Table 2. Typical thermal converters

Current range (mA)	Heater resistance (Ω)	Thermocouple resistance (Ω)	Thermal emf (open circuit) (mV)
10	25	8	7
10	50	8	12
25	10	4	7
25	25	4	16–18
50	3	4	7
50	8	4	12–15
100	1·5	4	7
100	2	4	12–15
500	0·3	4	7
500	0·45	4	12–15
1,000	0·15	4	7
1,000	0·25	4	12–15

Available from Ormandy and Stollery Ltd, Osec House, Chapel Road, Brightlingsea, Essex, CO7 0HB.

with the temperature of the element and hence the current flowing. Therefore, in order to avoid a variation of the load resistance (and as a result a variation of the matching impedance seen by the source) it is desirable to provide a padding resistance to swamp these changes. As this type of instrument is very sensitive, for most amateur purposes some such arrangement will be needed to accommodate the power level to be measured. Suitable arrangements are shown diagrammatically in Fig 25.

In Fig 25(a) R1 is chosen so that the combination of the

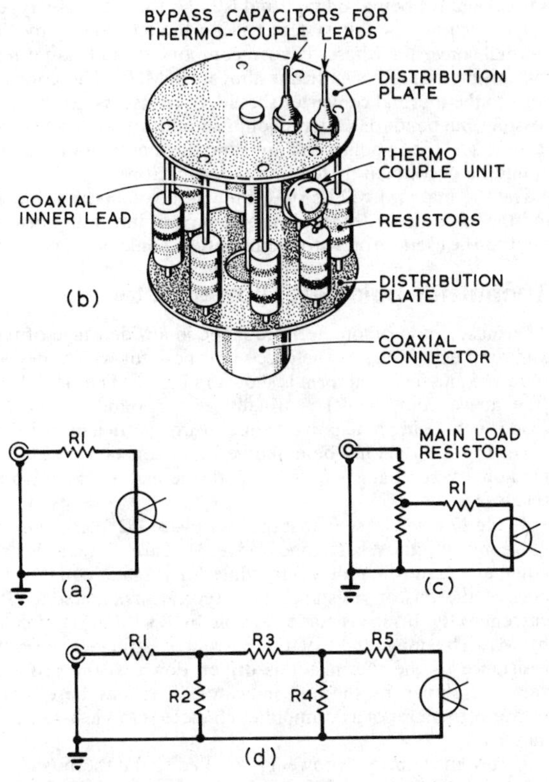

Fig 25. Method of use of thermal converter for higher powers

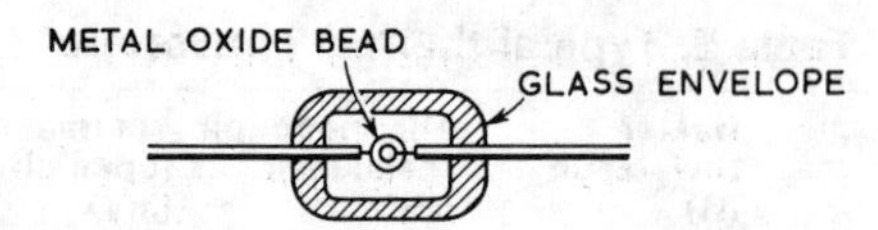

Fig 26. Construction of a microwave thermistor

heater element resistance and the external resistance (R1) is equal to the required load resistance.

When the higher powers are to be measured, or improved high-frequency performance is needed, the arrangement shown in Fig 25(b) should be adopted. In this the load resistance is made up of a number of small resistors arranged in parallel in a circular formation and connected to two plates, one fastened on to the outer of the coaxial connector and the other to the inner. The measuring thermocouple is connected in series with one of the resistors. In some circumstances the thermocouple can be connected in series with the centre connection for all the resistors.

Another alternative arrangement suitable for higher power is shown in Fig 25(c). In this case a single large resistor is mounted in a suitable housing and the thermocouple connected to a tapping near the earthy end, about 5 to 10 per cent of the total value. At higher frequencies still the use of a multi-section attenuator will generally provide a better match—this is shown in Fig 25(d). In this the components for the individual sections are chosen to provide constant dissipation as opposed to the usual requirement of constant attenuation. The construction of this type of attenuator should be such as to maintain a constant impedance, and the individual resistor units should be film type, R1, R3 and R5 being rod type and R2 and R4 of the disc type.

The accuracy of this system will be limited mainly by the thermal converter whose reactive components and skin effect will be increasingly significant above 500MHz. The connections to the thermal converter should, of course, be as short as possible, but bends or soldered joints should not be closer to the vacuum seal than about 4 to 5mm, and the thermocouple leads should be decoupled by feedthrough capacitors.

The thermal emf will be only a few millivolts (see Table 2) and therefore, in order that a robust type of indicating instrument can be used, a transistor dc amplifier should be employed.

Thermistor bolometer power meter

Thermistors and bolometers are made in a wide range of type and form depending on the precise purpose for which they are required, but a typical form is shown in Fig 26. The small bead (the active component) is usually a compound of metallic oxides possessing a negative temperature coefficient of resistance. In use, it should be embodied in a constant resistance, made to avoid changes in the impedance match which would result in errors.

In Fig 27 it will be seen that the thermistor R2 forms one arm of a conventional Wheatstone bridge. Resistors R3 and R4 are equal and form the ratio arms, while R1 is made equal to the desired thermistor resistance in a typical arrangement. The current to the bridge is made variable by RV1 and is indicated by M1. The magnitude of the current is adjusted until the resistance of the thermistor is driven down to the required value, as shown by the null indicator. This may be either a centre-zero meter or a dc amplifier connected to a less-sensitive meter.

If now an rf current (power) is applied to the thermistor, its temperature will rise and the bridge become unbalanced. If the

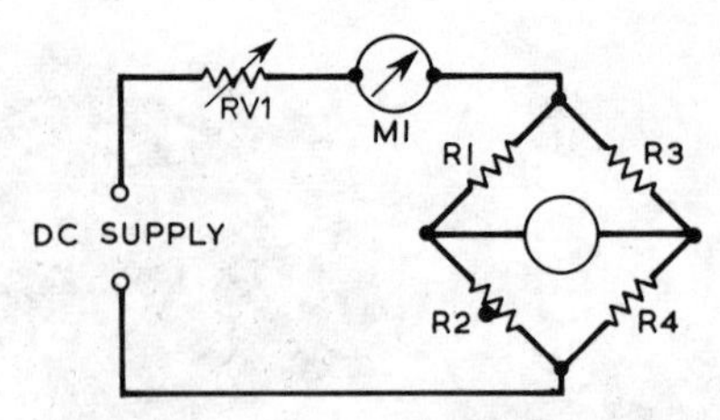

Fig 27. A simple thermistor bridge—a conventional Wheatstone bridge with the thermistor R2 as one arm

current in the bridge arms is now adjusted until balance is restored, the change in dc power will be the same as the applied rf power, assuming the conversion to heat is the same in both cases. The substituted power may be calculated from

$$P = (I_1^2 - I_2^2)R^2$$

where P is the substituted dc power, I_1 is the current through the thermistor at balance with no rf applied, and I_2 is the current through the thermistor at balance with rf applied.

The values of R3 and R4 should be made high compared with R1 and R2 and the current may be read directly from M1. Lower values of R3 and R4 should be of similar ratio to the values of R1 and R2 in order to simplify calculations.

Typical thermistors have an operating resistance of 50 to 500Ω, and for amateur purposes the mounting method shown in Fig 28 is preferred. In this case rf power is applied to the two thermistors R2 and R2′ via a capacitor C1 which provides dc isolation for the substitution power. For purposes of rf, R2 and R2′ are connected in parallel across the input by the capacitor C2, which together with C1 must have a low reactance compared with the impedance of the line carrying the rf power together with low loss at the operating frequency. The resistors R2 and R2′ are in series as far as the dc substitution current is concerned.

Most thermistors are of low power rating, usually in the region of 10mW, and should be used with the attenuator shown in Fig 25 when power in the 1W range is required.

Bolometers are similar in construction to thermistors, a fine wire replacing the metal oxide bead. However, they have a positive temperature coefficient of resistance and may be used in similar circuits to those used for thermistors. Their temperature coefficient is, however, lower than thermistors and they are therefore less sensitive.

For amateur purposes a bulb may be used in place of a proper bolometer and a festoon type is very suitable.

Lamps as rf loads

Probably the least expensive method of measuring rf power output is to use a two-lamp comparative method, where one

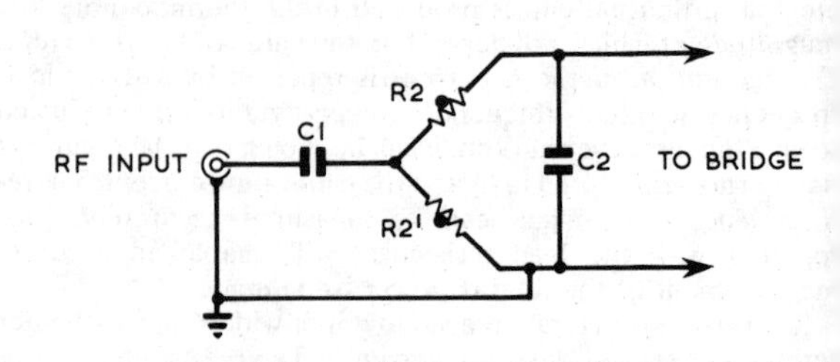

Fig 28. A coaxial thermistor mount

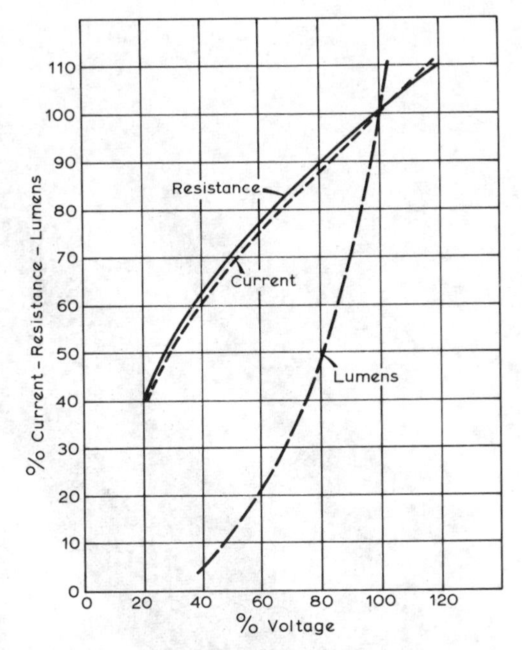

Fig 29. Characteristics of gas-filled lamps

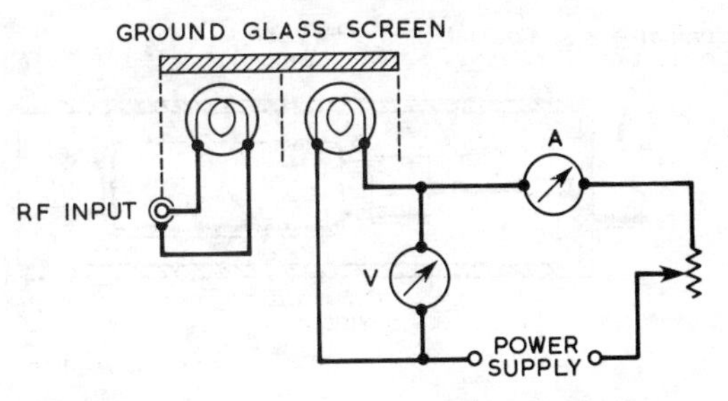

Fig 30. Diagram of a suitable two-lamp comparator, with a ground-glass screen making visual comparison easier

amp is connected to the equipment and the other to a variable ource of power. It is essential that both the lamps should be of he same type and power rating and it is desirable that before se the consumption data is recorded for both lamps so that llowances may be made for any differences.

The actual difference between two lamps of the same type nd rating is unlikely to be sufficient to make calibration essenial for practical purposes, but is necessary for those who wish to e as accurate as possible.

As may be seen from the typical curves shown in Fig 29 the ight output from a lamp varies rapidly with changes of voltage r current and it is important therefore that direct comparison f the output is made. This is best arranged by fitting the two amps side by side into a box having a ground-glass screen over he lamps and with a dividing panel between the two lamps. The wo lamps will then each illuminate the two separate halves of he ground-glass screen.

Matching is easier using a ground-glass screen instead of iewing the lamps directly and this is particularly true at the igher filament temperatures. When the lamps are enclosed in he box there is also much less interference by stray room ighting. A suitable arrangement is shown in Fig 30. A variable ower supply for the standard lamp is required and either a oltmeter and ammeter or a voltmeter and a calibration curve f the lamp is necessary for making measurements.

If a Variac or other iron-cored device is used to control the pplied ac voltage instead of a resistor it will be necessary to ake account of waveform error in moving-iron voltmeters and mmeters which read true rms values. This point may be a little cademic in view of the inherent inaccuracies of this form of ower measurement, but it may be of interest to those seeking he highest possible accuracy.

In this case the lamp is supplied with power either from the quipment or a measured source, the light output being bserved by means of a selenium photo cell and microammeter or a photographic exposure meter. The procedure is then as follows:

(i) First supply rf power to the lamp from the transmitter.
(ii) Take a reading of the light output using the indicator (selenium photo cell and micro-ammeter or exposure meter) at a suitable and measured distance.
(iii) Next, supply the lamp with a measured source of power, with the indicator at the same distance as before, increasing the light output until the indicator reads the same as in step (ii). The actual power output can then be computed from the calibration data of the lamp being used.

Lamps cannot, of course, be regarded as non-inductive and some care is necessary in making connections to keep the inductance as low as possible, particularly when using them at vhf and uhf. It is worth noting that the screw and single-contact type cap is more readily fitted to coaxial plugs or sockets than the double-contact bayonet type.

It is difficult to get a lamp which will be equal to the normal load resistance of 50 or 70/80Ω. It should also be remembered that its characteristic varies considerably with temperature. Nevertheless, the output indicated by this means is reliable, but retuning of the output is likely to be required when they are substituted.

Single-lamp method

The accurate measurement of output power at the low levels typical of transistor and portable equipment can be performed with relatively simple equipment.

The method consists of using a calibrated lamp as a load. The relationship between its resistance and the power is known, so that by measuring the resistance when rf power is being dissipated in it, the power can be readily determined.

First, calibrate the load lamp by taking readings of voltage and current. From this the resistance and power can be calculated, and these values can then be plotted to provide a chart of resistance against power using dc supply. The most suitable lamp for this application is the 12V 6W festoon type. Fig 31 shows the general arrangement of a coaxial unit.

This method is intended for use with a two-stub transformer for impedance matching, and this also provides the dc return for the lamp so that the resistance may be measured. A suitable resistance measuring circuit is given in Fig 32.

The construction of the load lamp is, as can be seen in Fig 31, straightforward. Care must be taken to ensure that there is adequate insulation between body and the end plate, and this resistance may be measured between points X and Y.

The measuring circuit should be arranged to pass a low

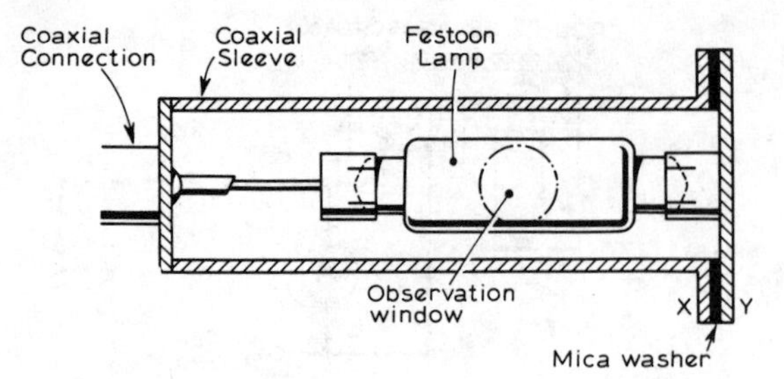

Fig 31. General arrangement of the lamp load

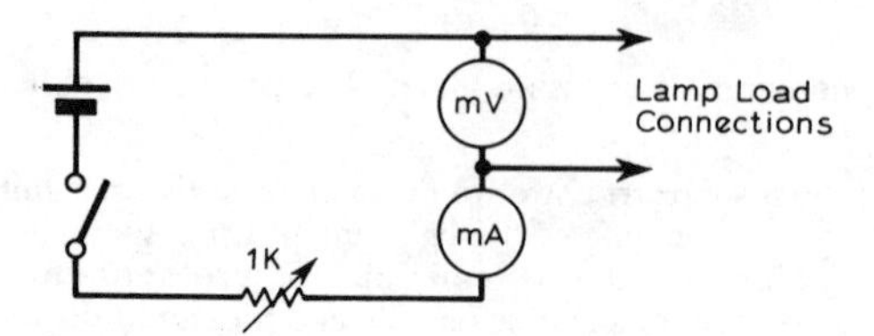

Fig 32. Resistance measuring unit

current such as 3 to 5mA, at which the voltage across the lamp will not exceed 100mV.

For some purposes it may be inconvenient to use the two-stub transformer, and if a reliable indicator without the impedance matching facility is suitable, then this can be achieved by inserting a capacitor in series with the centre conductor and making a dc connection to the lamp through an rf choke suitably bypassed.

Dummy loads

The production of a reliable dummy load does not present any real problem and it may be of two general forms:

(a) one large resistance
(b) a number of small 1 or 2W resistors arranged in a cylindrical form.

In the case of (a) the resistor element forms the outer of the coaxial line and to preserve its impedance the centre conductor from the free end to the coaxial socket should be of appropriate diameter. This may be calculated from:

$$Z_o = 138 \log_{10} \frac{D}{d}$$

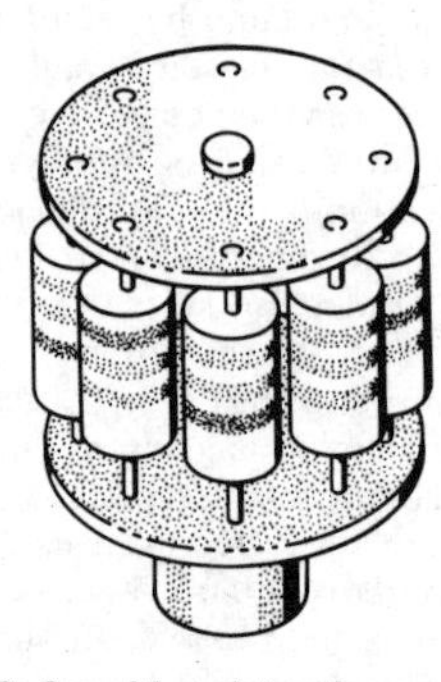

Fig 33. A multi-resistor dummy load

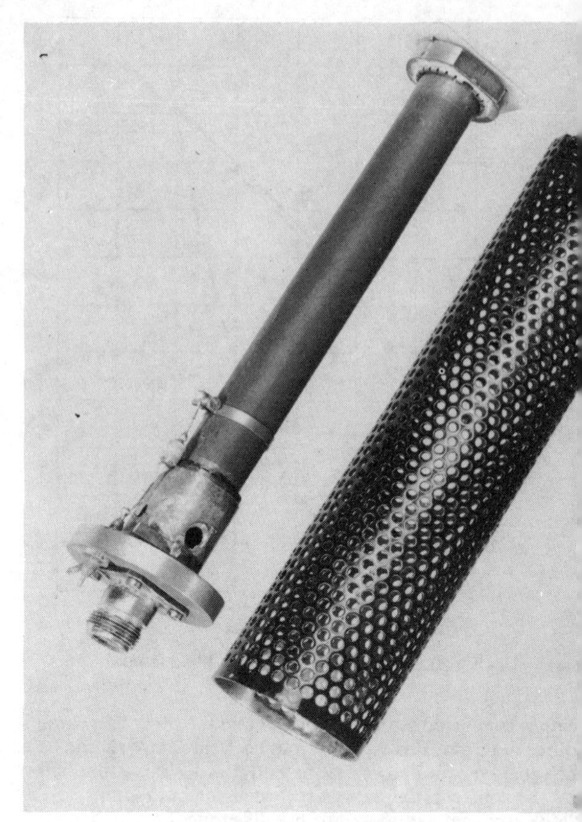

A dummy load incorporating a thermal converter for powe measurement

where D is the outside diameter of the resistor element and d i the diameter of the inner conductor. As an example, for a 75Ω 1in diameter resistor, the inner conductor should be 4·67mr or approximately 0·3in.

In the case of (b) a number of parallel-connected resistors t make up the wanted line impedance, which might be 50 or 70Ω can be assembled as shown in Fig 33. As described earlier unde

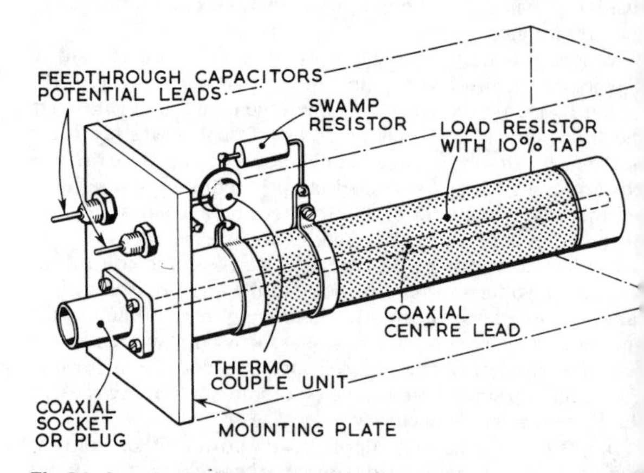

Fig 34. A suggested mechanical arrangement for a power mete using a thermal converter connected to a tap on the load resisto

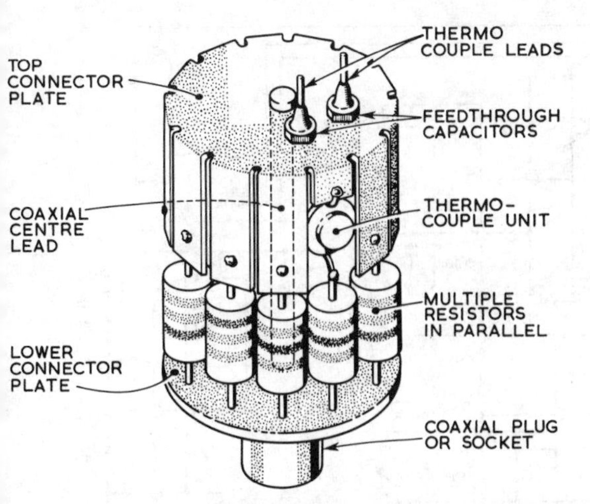

ig 35. An alternative arrangement for a power meter using a umber of resistors in parallel with the thermal converter unit connected to one of the resistors

Power measurement", a measuring device may be connected ı series with any one of the resistors to indicate power, but lternatively a bulb may be used as an indicator.

In either form, these dummy loads may be considerably ıcreased in power rating by immersion in a suitable liquid. 'ransformer oil is recommended, but ordinary oil may be used.

.ow-power output indicator

\ simple output indicator/power meter will be of considerable ssistance when setting up a low-power oscillator chain for a onverter or early stages of an exciter. Such an instrument may e readily constructed as shown in Fig 36. The circuit arrangeıent is simple, using a suitable load resistor of either 50 or 75Ω lepending on the impedance normally used. The power rating f this resistor may be 1W. A diode is connected to the live end f the resistor and also an rf bypass capacitor (eg 1,000pF) cross which the voltmeter is connected.

The voltmeter should preferably present no loading across he capacitor, ie be an fet voltmeter. If an ordinary moving-coil neter is used, it should be of reasonably high resistance such as !0,000Ω/V (a 0–50μA instrument with suitable series resistor vill be sufficiently accurate).

A typical voltage-power relationship is shown in Fig 37. This nay be calculated from the simple formula

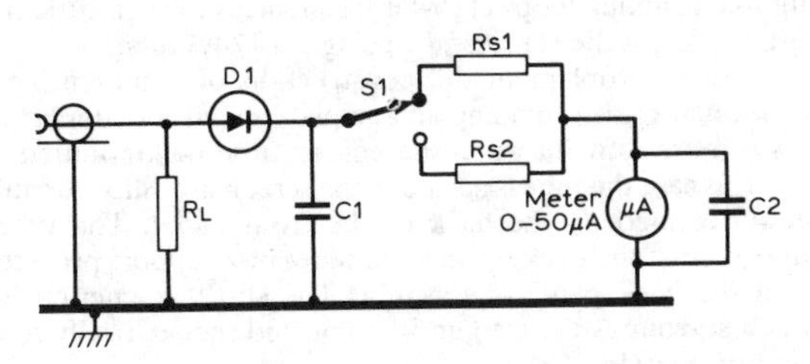

Fig 36. Circuit of the low-power meter/indicator. C1, C2, 1,000pF; Rs1, 10kΩ; Rs2, 100kΩ; D1, 1N914

Low-power output indicator (inside view)

$$\text{Power} = \frac{(\text{Voltage} + 0\cdot7)^2}{100}$$

0·7 is the correct factor for a silicon diode; for a germanium device use 0·2. In the example illustrated a two-range switch has been included, giving ranges 0·5 and 5·0V which should cover most low-power applications.

144MHz monitor crt display

The most satisfactory method of checking a transmission is to monitor the signal by use of a crt display. At some lower frequencies an ordinary oscilloscope may be modified for this purpose.

At vhf this is less easy and it is generally preferable to build a suitable unit for the purpose. The unit to be described is suitable for frequencies up to 144MHz.

It consists simply of a suitable timebase generator and the necessary power supply for this and the display tube. A linear timebase with a suitable frequency range is straightforward, but

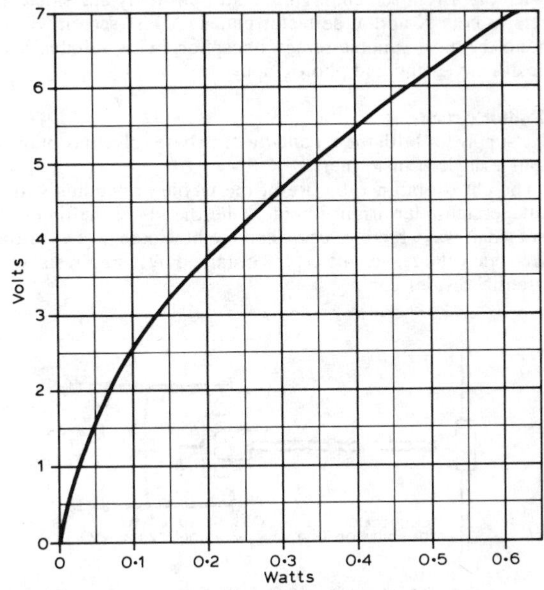

Fig 37. Typical voltage/power relationship for Fig 36

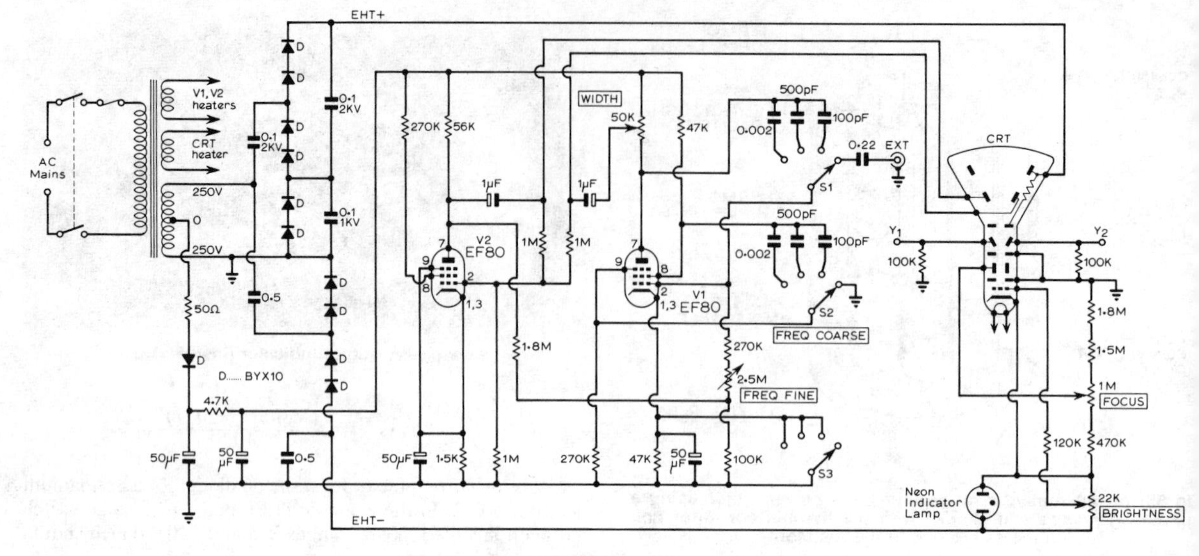

Fig 38. Circuit of the crt monitor

it is desirable that the output is such as to provide symmetrical input to the X-plates of the crt.

The signal should be applied directly to the Y-plates as the inclusion of amplifiers may introduce distortion. To do this satisfactorily the crt should have side contacts for plate connections. The deflection sensitivity should be as high as possible in order to give adequate display. A crt that meets these requirements will enable 144MHz signals to be viewed directly. The signal from the transmission line to the antenna may be sampled by a T connector feeding into a coupling coil which is coupled into a circuit tuned to the operating frequency, the Y-plates being connected across the tuned circuit.

A suitable crt for this purpose is the 900E or equivalent, which has a 9cm screen, high Y-plate sensitivity and side contacts to both X-and Y-deflector plates. A P31 screen will be found the most suitable screen phosphor, being suitable both for direct viewing and photography.

Monitor circuit

The supply for both the crt and the timebase valves is obtained from a single transformer.

The eht is obtained by use of the whole ht winding with a voltage-multiplier arrangement, while the ht for the timebase uses a half-wave rectifier using half the ht winding. The various electrode voltages for the crt are obtained by a high-resistance potential divider chain.

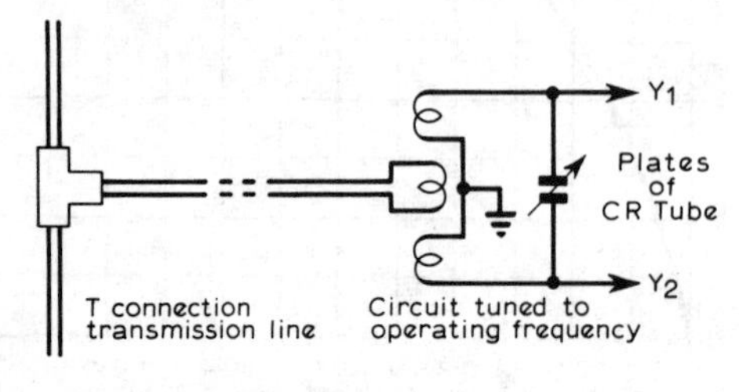

Fig 39. Method of connecting signal to crt

The timebase is a Miller-Transitron oscillator V1 (EF80 followed by a paraphase amplifier V2 (EF80) providing sym metrical X-plate scan.

A selector switch S1, S2 provides three basic frequenc ranges, and a fourth position allows the use of the valves a amplifiers with an external timebase if desired.

Other controls are FOCUS, BRIGHTNESS, FINE FREQUENCY an SCAN WIDTH. No control is provided for signal Y-plates.

The method of connecting the signal into the crt is shown i Fig 39. The actual position of the connections from the Y deflector plates on to the tuned circuit should be adjusted t obtain a suitable display height.

Construction

The form of the unit can be almost any convenient shape an size to fit into the station layout. Apart from the need for a suitable magnetic shield to fit the crt used, to prevent unwante beam deflection by stray magnetic fields, the layout is no critical.

Although valves were used in the prototype for the timebase transistors may of course be used with suitable modification to the power supply.

The linearity of the circuit given is good except at the extreme ends of the timebase frequency range. The sensitivity is sufficiently high to provide an adequate envelope pattern in the 2m band (about 5cm peak-to-peak) for modulated signals. By suitable coupling loops at lower frequencies there is little difficulty in filling the screen face using a 1474C tube.

A major problem in the construction of a unit using an instrument crt is providing an adequate means of support and this is more difficult when the unit is to be rackmounted.

In this case the tube is nested at the screen in a silicone rubber mould formed on the back of the front panel. The tube is supported at the back by an aluminium box support projecting from the back panel of the unit. The short magnetic shield which surrounds the crt gun is connected mechanically to the support box (Fig 40).

As indicated in Fig 40 the silicone rubber nest for the crt face

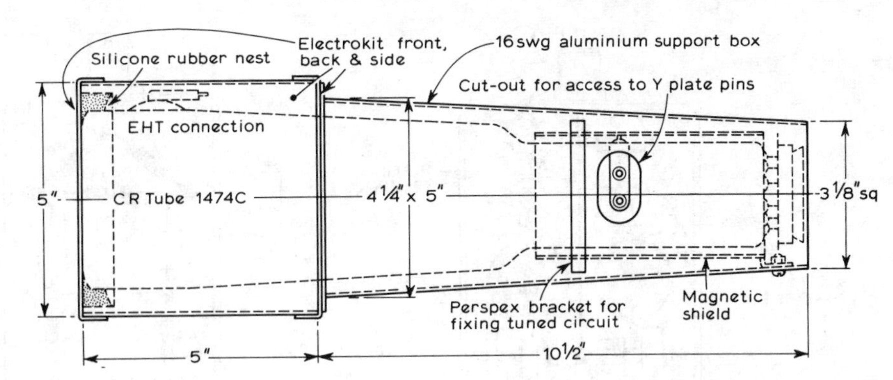

g 40. Side view of the crt mounting

ate is contained in a shallow metal frame approximately ¼in ider all round than the face plate.

After the window, the same size as the 10 by 8cm graticule, s been cut out and finished, the tube is stood vertically in sition and the silicone rubber poured into the space. When it s set the tube will be free to move, leaving the silicone rubber lhering to the metal frame.

A suitable cut-out in the back panel is made and around this e aluminium support box is fixed. Cut-outs are needed in the p and side faces to allow attachment of the leads to both the -plates (top face) and Y-plates (side face).

Alongside the Y-plate cut-out, an insulating bracket is fixed r the attachment of the tuned circuit across which the Y-plates e connected. Earth return resistors to the leads are also nnected at a convenient point to allow free access to the plate nnections.

The magnetic shield surrounding the crt gun has a cut-out at allows access to both X- and Y-plates, through the shield be. The shield is connected mechanically to the outer uminium support box, but the tube socket is left free for ease f fitting.

n rf bridge

his is a Wheatstone type bridge suitable for use on frequencies p to 432MHz. It requires care in construction to ensure absote symmetry of the component layout together with the use of iniature components and matched pairs where necessary. This will then give a bridge which has an accuracy of the order of 1 per cent of full-scale deflection which is good enough for practical purposes, and should fulfil most amateur needs.

The circuit of the bridge shown in Fig 42 is given in the same form as the component layout shown in the general drawing (Fig 43) and is self-explanatory.

The whole unit, which uses a separate meter, is built in the smallest-size standard die-cast box.

Operation

The method of operation with this bridge is to start with the value of impedance known and adjust the length of the stubs, or antenna matching device, until a balance is achieved.

This unit will be found ideal for cutting coaxial cable to quarter- and half-wavelengths, where known Z is either an open-circuit or a short-circuit. The accuracy that can be achieved will be better than 1 per cent of fsd of the meter.

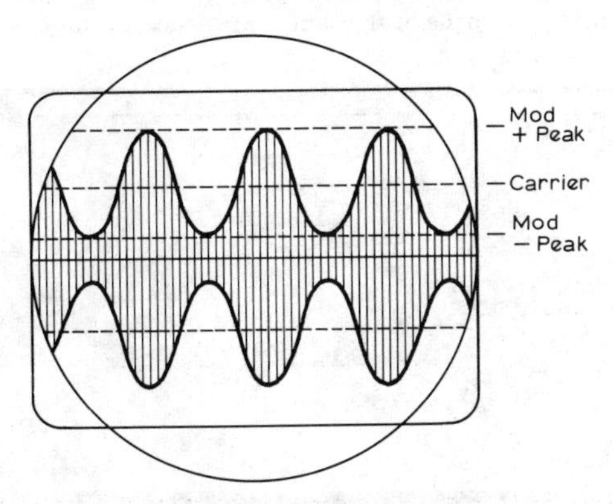

Fig 41. Signal envelope pattern

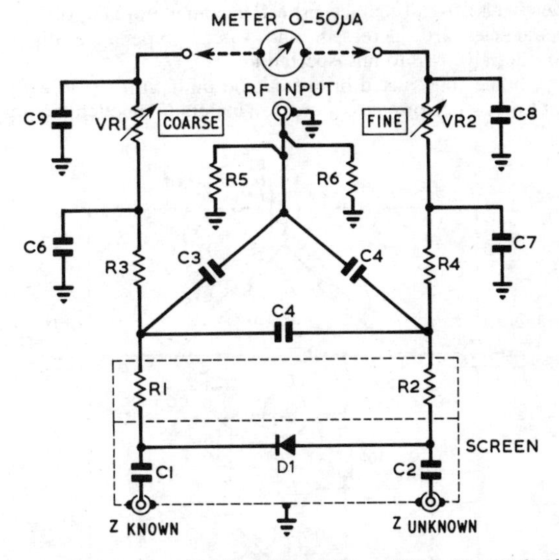

Fig 42. Circuit of an rf bridge. R1 and R2 are 100Ω ± 1% metal oxide type; R5 and R6 are terminating resistors consisting of two 150Ω in parallel for 75Ω; C1, C2 are 0·001μF ceramic disc; C3, 4, 6, 7, 8, 9 are 0·01μF ceramic disc; D1 is OA91 or CV2290; VR1 is 50kΩ miniature variable resistor; VR2 is 2·5kΩ miniature variable resistor; Z_{known} is 75Ω resistor fitted into a coaxial plug. If 50Ω is required then R5, R6 will be 2 × 100Ω − Z_{known} = 50Ω

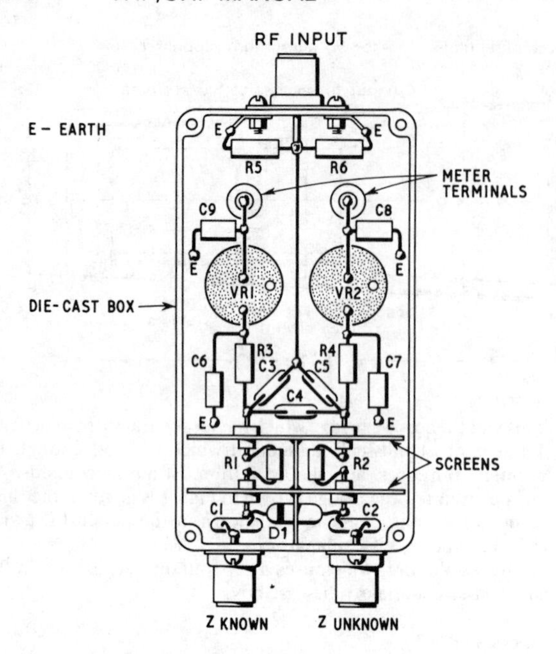

Fig 43. Component layout of the rf bridge

Resistive vswr bridge

Measurement of vswr below about 450MHz can be more conveniently done by use of a resistance bridge rather than a slotted line which is cumbersome at vhf.

VSWR measurements are most frequently associated with antenna and feed systems, yet there are many devices for which the vswr is a useful characteristic. It becomes more important as frequencies are increased, and where impedance discontinuities give rise to unsuspected losses.

A home-constructed bridge can be built without difficulty, but for best performance some care in detail is needed, notably

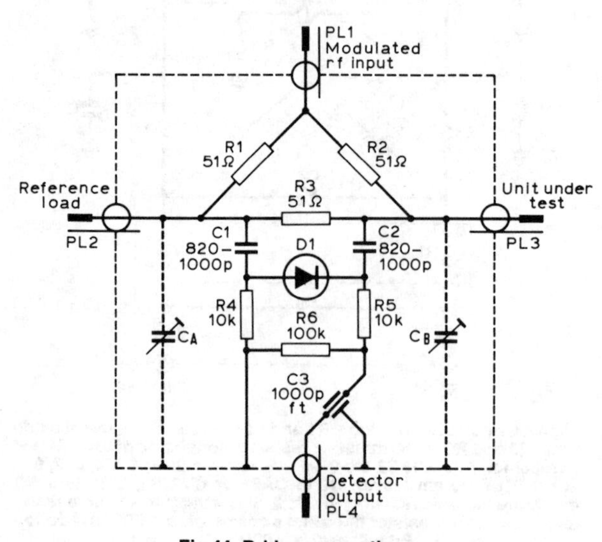

Fig 44. Bridge connections

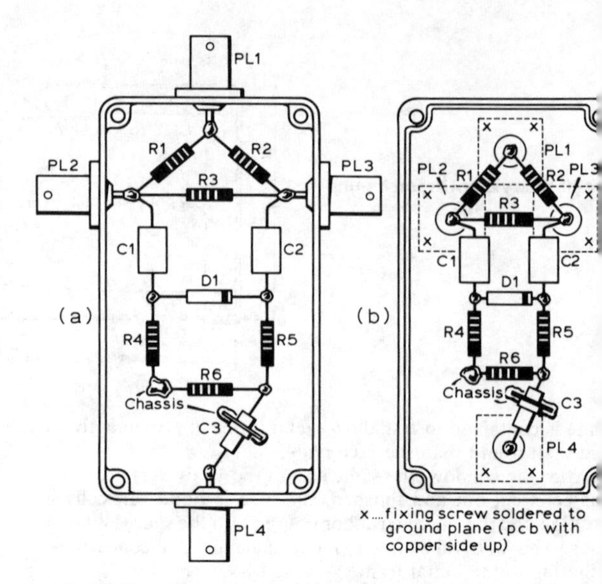

Fig 45. Two alternative methods of construction of the bridge

in the choice of matched resistors R1 and R2. Their installation is as far as possible identical both respect of their lead length which should be kept to a minimum, and location with respect to the ground plane and connections.

The connections of the bridge are shown in Fig 44, while in Fig 45 are shown two methods of construction, both based on a standard cast box. In method (a) the connections (BNC) are attached to the sides of the box and the circuit components fitted to single-sided copper glassfibre board. The board is positioned so that it is at the level of the insulation projecting from the BNC connectors, so that the important resistors R1, R2 and R3 rest on the copper ground plane when soldered in position.

In method (b) the whole of the assembly is fitted to the lid of the cast box with the copper-clad board fitted within the raised edge of the lid. In this form it is easier to make good connections between the board and the four connection sockets, using half nuts to two of the fixing screws of each of the sockets, which may be soldered in position.

In order to test the bridge, a modulated rf signal is connected to port P1 and an audio detector to P4. Then with two reference loads of the same impedance, in this case 50Ω

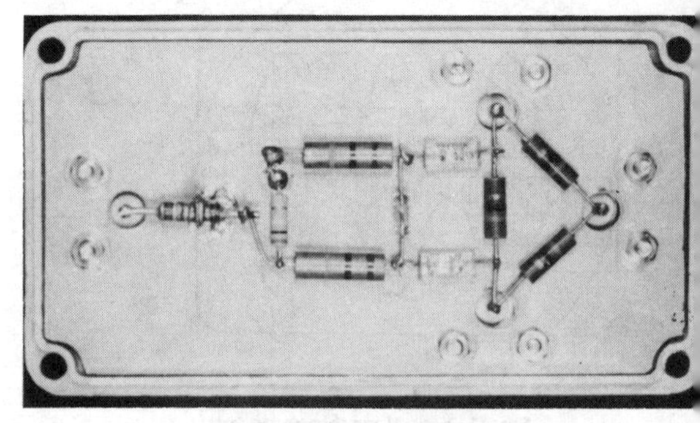

Resistive vswr bridge

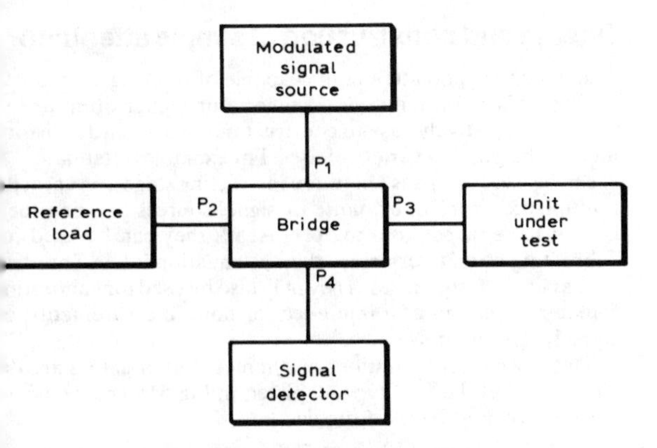

Fig 46. General set-up of the bridge

Plan view of the completed noise bridge

onnected to P2 and P3, the output detector should read a very ow value. If there is any significant output a small capacitance such as a small flag soldered close to either P2 or P3 as ndicated by C_A or C_B) should be added and adjusted to obtain alance and reduce any residual signal. Once substantial bal- nce has been obtained, the next step is to remove one of the wo reference load resistors from P2 or P3 when the detected utput will rise to 30dB or more. If the reference loads con- ected to P2 and P3 are interchanged no difference should be letected.

For a 50Ω bridge, it is useful to have one or two fixed value nismatch leads available such as a 75Ω one for 1·5:1 vswr, 25Ω or 2:1 and a short-circuit for an infinite vswr.

Operation of the bridge is readily appreciated from Fig 46. If dentical reference loads are connected to P2 and P3, signals vill be equal and in phase so that no output should be observed t P4. When the unit under test at P3 is different from that of the eference load at P2 a difference signal will be observed, which s proportional to this difference.

The bridge resistors R1, R2 may be any appropriate value uch as 50 or 75Ω; 50Ω is of more general application.

RF noise bridge

The rf noise bridge is basically a simple rf version of the Wheat- tone, which with reasonable care in construction will give reli- ble performance to over 200MHz and may still be useful up to 32MHz.

The basis of the unit is a noise source consisting of a zener liode operated under low-current conditions. The noise source s followed by a two-stage wide-band amplifier using resis- or/capacitor couplings. The noise output is fed into the bridge by a 1:1 balun toroidal transformer. In the noise bridge, a receiver is used as the indicator in place of a meter used in the ordinary Wheatstone bridge, as shown in Fig 47.

The noise generator, a zener diode or the base-emitter junc- tion of a standard transistor, is supplied from the battery via a resistor which can be either selected for the maximum noise output, or a variable. The wide-band amplifiers may use almost any transistor with good characteristics.

The toroidal transformer consists of a ferrite ring of material suitable for the maximum frequency needed with a core of approximately 15 to 20mm od, 7 or 7·5mm i.d. and 4 or 5mm thick. The transformer consists of two windings twisted together and wound on one half of the core. The third winding has the same number of turns and is wound in the same direc- tion as the twisted pair, on the other half of the core, making sure that the interconnections of the three windings comply with Fig 48.

The construction of this unit should preferably be based on a printed circuit, and the two coaxial sockets should be positioned so that they connect directly on to the printed circuit.

Alternatively, when the noise source and amplifier are built on a separate board from the bridge itself, then the bridge section can be tailored for vhf.

The variable element of the bridge should be a moulded- track type carbon film. Wirewound types are not suitable.

The value of the variable resistor R in Fig 47 depends on the resistance law used. If a linear law type is used the maximum value should be 100Ω to ensure a suitable spread scale in the region of 50 to 75Ω. However, as a greater range is likely to be useful, a log law 1kΩ type together with a parallel fixed resistor to make about 350Ω is recommended. This allows a wide range with suitable spread around 50 to 75Ω.

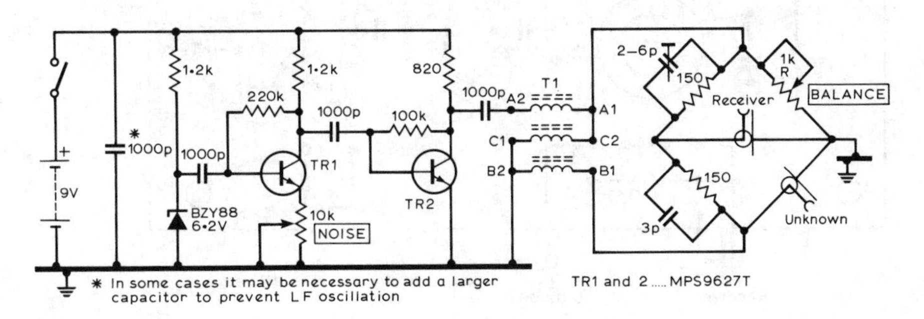

Fig 47. The circuit of the rf wide-band noise bridge. Suggested equivalent for the transistor is 2N708

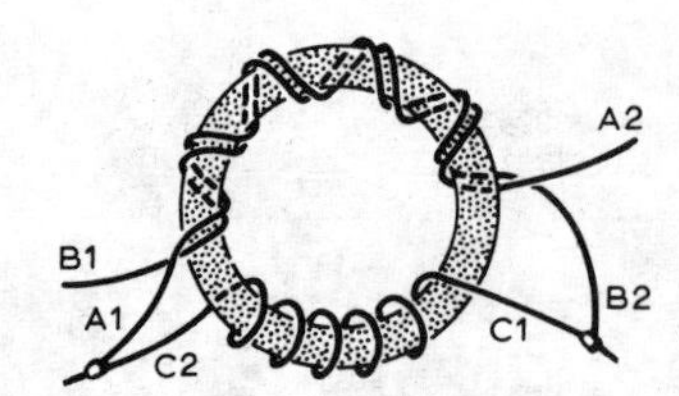

Fig 48. Toroidal coupling transformer

Toroid winding details

1. Cut three pieces of 36swg enamelled wire.
2. Twist two pieces together with turn pitch of about $\frac{1}{16}$in.
3. Wind 30 turns of twisted pair on one half of the core.
4. Wind 30 turns (third winding) on the other half of the core in the same direction as the twisted pair. It is important that the number of turns are the same but actual number of turns is not critical.
5. Interconnect windings as shown in Fig 48.

   A suitable core is Philips 4322.020.901020 or equivalent.

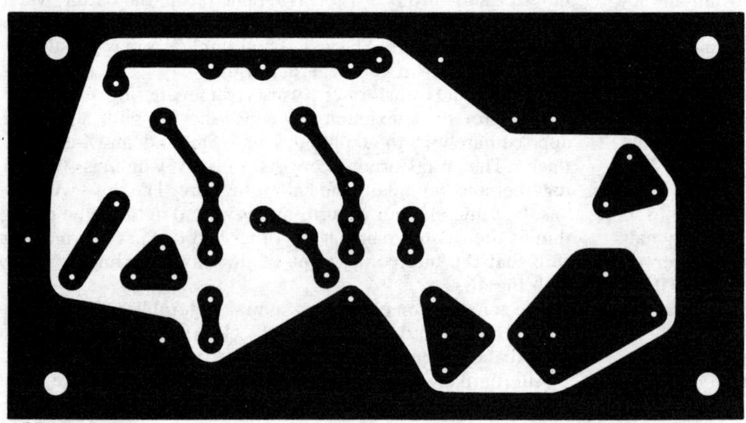

ACTUAL SIZE

Fig 49. Printed circuit track for the wide-band rf noise bridge

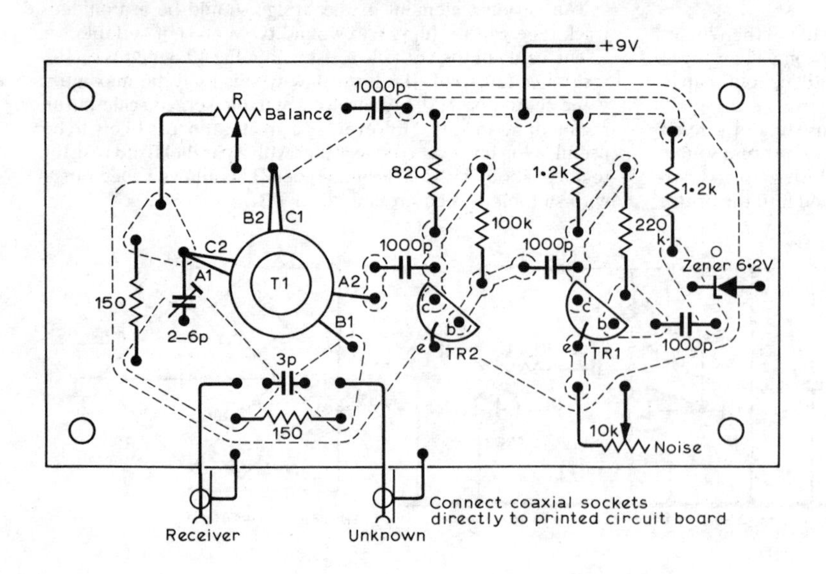

Fig 50. Component layout

Design and construction of simple attenuators

The need for good attenuators capable of working at frequencies up to several hundred megahertz or higher often arises. These are relatively easy to construct out of standard resistors and can be put to a variety of uses. For example, attenuators at rf can be used as "pads" between interacting stages, eg varactor multipliers, or to follow noise or signal sources to bring their output impedance close to 50Ω. At i.f. they can be used for calibrating attenuators, since their attenuation is fairly predictable at lower frequencies. They may also be used for calibrating S-meters, etc, and as a reference for noise measurements, eg sun and ground noise.

Two simple configurations of symmetric attenuators are the "T" type and the "π" type, depicted in Fig 51. The design of these is covered by the formulas:

"T" type:

$$\text{Attenuation (dB)} = 20 \log \left(\frac{50 + R1}{50 - R1}\right)$$

when

$$R2 = \frac{2{,}500 - R1^2}{2R1}$$

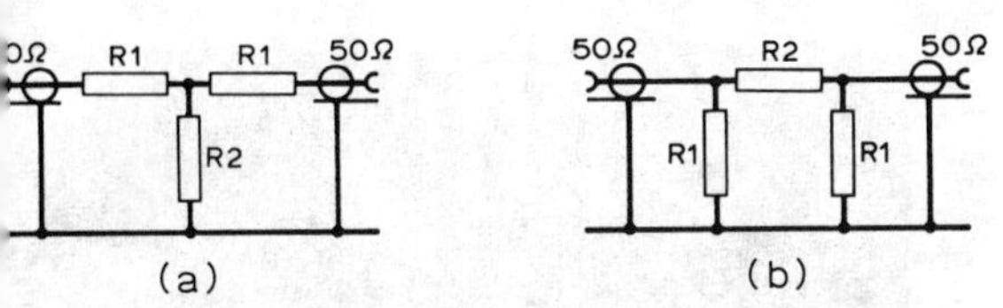

Fig 51. (a) "T"-type attenuator; (b) "π"-type attenuator

$$\text{Attenuation (dB)} = 20 \log \left(\frac{R1 + 50}{R1 - 50} \right)$$

hen

$$R2 = \frac{5{,}000R1}{R1^2 - 2{,}500}$$

"π" type

Design values for some useful attenuation levels are given in able 3. It will be seen that in most cases the values do not oincide with preferred resistor values. This restricts the levels f attenuation which can be obtained, and the best procedure ems to be to choose the nearest preferred values to R1 and 2. This usually results in an acceptably predictable perforance, but where the approximations are too great it may be etter to try the other configuration, or to use series or parallel ombinations of resistors for R1 and R2.

Two methods of construction are illustrated in Fig 52. A "π" pe is shown in (a) and "T" type in (b), but either version could e used in either design. The resistors should be of lowductance type, the common form of carbon film resistors eing particularly suitable. Lead lengths should be as short as ossible. For higher power attenuators at lower frequencies, arallel combinations of 0·5W carbon resistors can be used to crease dissipation. A 10dB attenuator, built in this way to andle 10W, measured 9·5dB attenuation at 432MHz with low wr.

Provided that care is taken, these attenuators can be used up 1–2GHz. The biggest error is likely to arise in the higher alue attenuators, where stray coupling may reduce the attenuation below the expected value. For this reason it is better to use everal low-value stages in cascade when a high value of attenuation is required.

Table 3. Design data for 50Ω "T" and "π" type attenuators

Attenuation (dB)	"T" type R1	"T" type R2	"π" type R1	"π" type R2
1	2·9	433	870	5·8
2	5·7	215	436	11·6
3	8·6	142	292	17·6
4	11·3	105	221	23·9
5	14·0	82	178	30·4
6	16·6	67	150	37·4
7	19·1	56	131	44·8
8	21·5	47·3	116	53
9	23·8	40·6	105	62
10	26·0	35·1	96	71
12	30·0	26·8	84	93
14	33·4	20·8	75	120
16	36·3	16·3	69	154
18	38·8	12·8	64	196
20	40·9	10·0	61	248
25	44·7	5·6	56	443
30	46·9	3·2	53	790

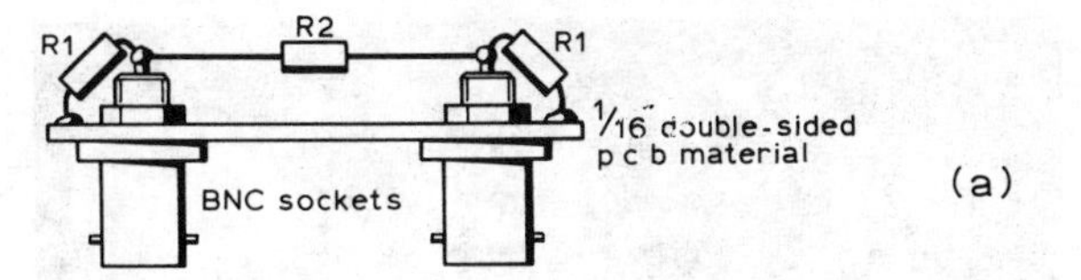

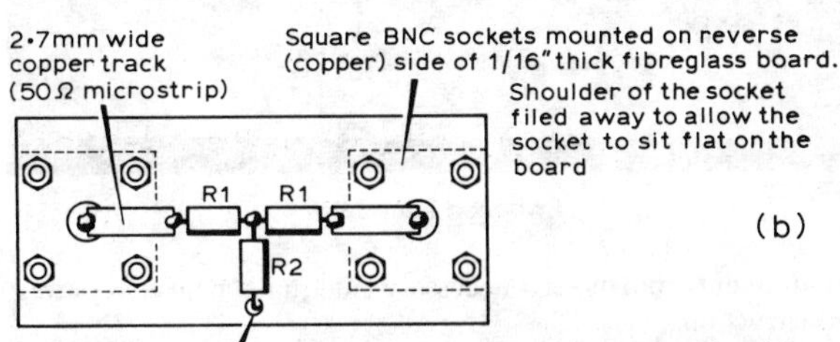

Fig 52. Methods of constructing attenuators: (a) below 500MHz, (b) above 500MHz

Switched attenuator

A switched attenuator has a number of applications in the amateur station; it may be made of either wide or limited range depending on the intended application.

The simple three-section unit illustrated (Fig 53) is intended for use between the output of a vhf transceiver having an output in the range of 10–20W p.e.p. and a following linear amplifier.

With the three stages of 2, 4 and 8dB, any level between 0 and 14dB may be selected.

In an attenuator which is to be used with a power source such as a transceiver, it should be remembered that a significant proportion of the input power will be dissipated in the resistors in the attenuator. The proportion is increased with the level of attenuation. In this case 2dB attenuation will dissipate 36 per cent of input power, 4dB 52 per cent, and 8dB 84 per cent.

Therefore adequately rated components are essential if the unit is to be used continuously. For an input of 10W: after a 2dB attenuation 6·4W are available for the next stage, after 4dB 4·8W, after 6dB (4+2) 3·45W, and after 8dB 1·6W.

Although the switched attenuator may be used, for normal general-purpose operation a single-stage fixed type is more likely to find favour once the degree of attenuation has been established. Such a unit can more readily be built using suitable

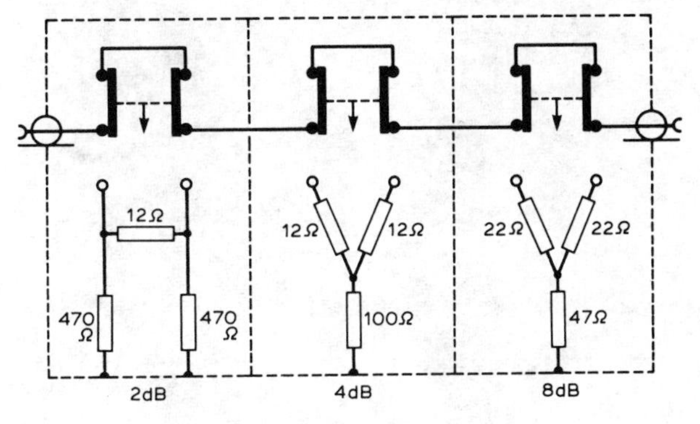

Fig 53. Circuit of switched attenuator

Switched attenuator

components and where necessary adequate heat-dissipating construction.

Noise generators

Most serious experimenters will need at some time or other to carry out tests to ensure that their receiving equipment is adjusted to the lowest possible noise factor.

It is worth noting at the outset that the best sensitivity does not usually occur at the same time as the lowest noise factor. No matter what devices are used in the receiver or converter, valve or semiconductor, some form of noise generator will be required.

Various forms of noise generator have been described from time to time. They all have their uses, though the only reliable and readily home-constructed type employs a thermionic diode.

Simple semiconductor noise sources are, however, useful for

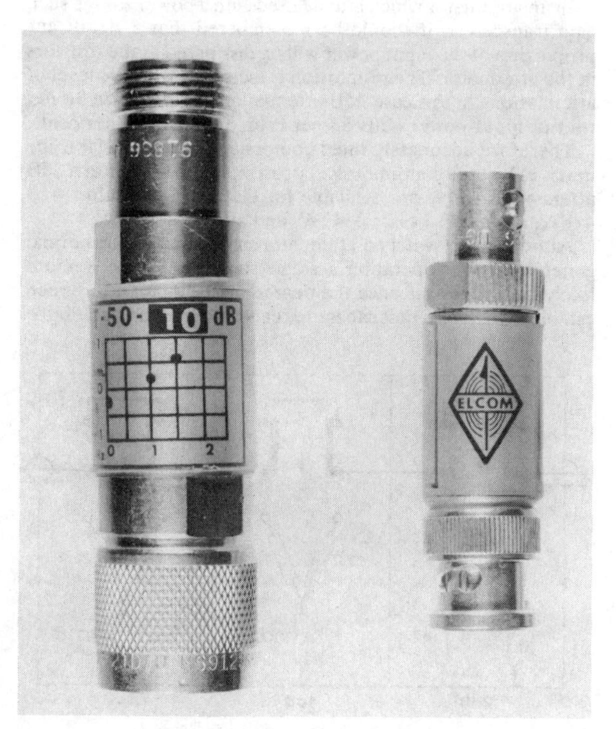

Typical low-power fixed attenuators (courtesy Aspen Electronics)

Typical high-power attenuator (courtesy Aspen Electronics)

comparative tests. Day-to-day repeatability is not reliabl although these devices can be very handy for portable equip ment checking. The hot-resistor type (the type has been called *Monode*) is very reliable but it is a fundamental type. To gene ate suitable noise output levels, the temperature needs to b high, and this can only conveniently be provided by suitab hot-filament lamps, such as the festoon type, and these will nc fit well into a coaxial circuit. There is a considerable difficult from the amateur's point of view, in that calibration of the lam in terms of current or voltage for the required temperatur range is impossible unless one has access to a suitable pyro meter.

The thermionic diode is both reliable and fundamental withi a frequency range not affected by transit time of the particula electrode system. For the normally available commercia diodes, 5722 Sylvania and A2087/CV 2171 M-O Valve Co, maximum frequency of 220MHz is possible without correction These are very suitable for most amateur purposes.

Accurate noise measurements above about 400MHz wil need a gas-discharge tube source. Coupling this device into th circuit is not too easy at low frequencies, but at shf wher waveguide is normally used, it is relatively straightforward, th discharge tube being inserted diagonally across the waveguid aperture.

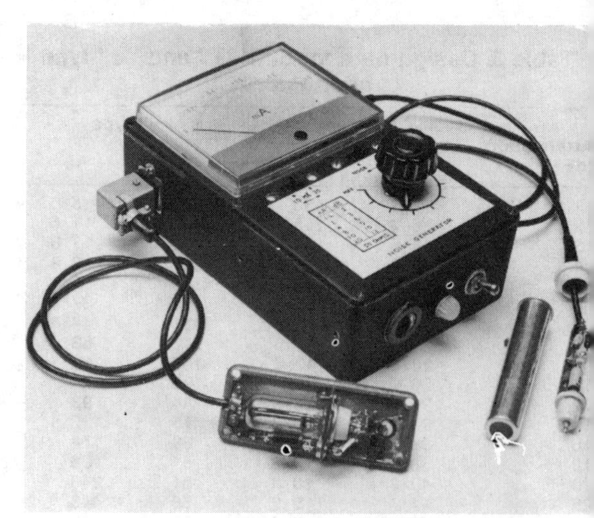

Noise generator head, power supply and rf probe

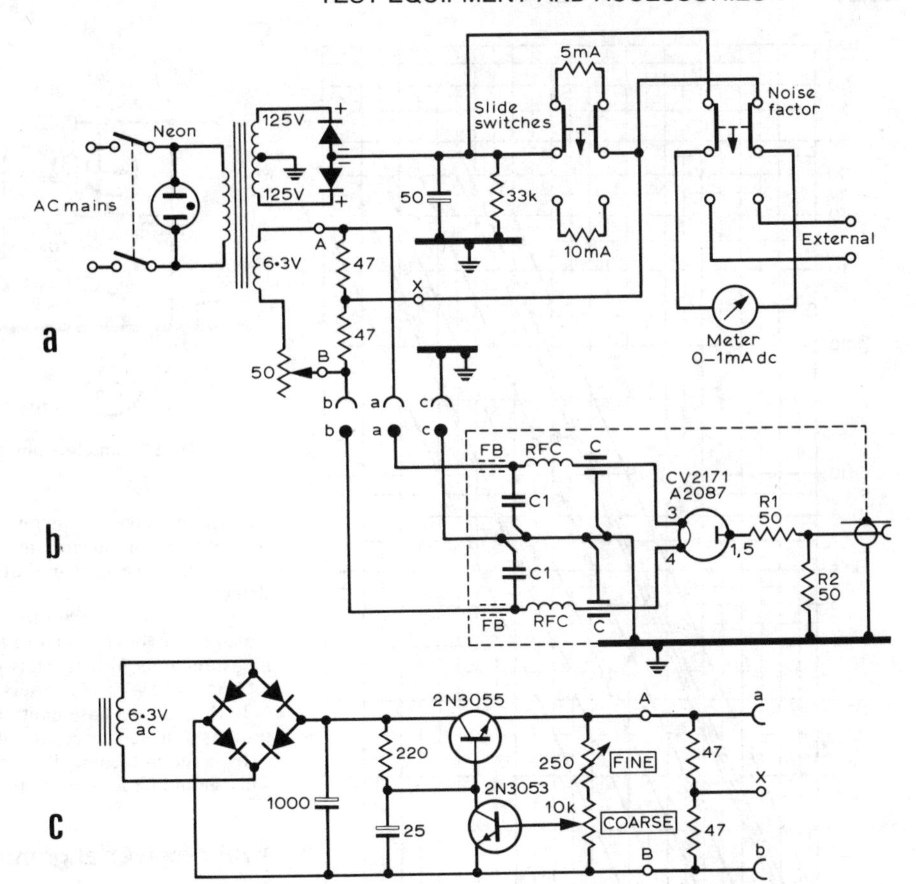

▮ 54. The practical noise nerator. (a) is the power sup- / with integral meter; (b) the ise diode head and (c) the rf probe

onstruction of a noise generator

he most convenient arrangement is to make the power supply nit in one box together with a large current meter, and put the :tual diode head into a small box of suitable size and shape for ugging directly into the input socket of the receiver or conver- r.

The need for a large meter may not be clear at first sight, but : low values of noise factor an error of ± 0·1mA becomes creasingly important.

To illustrate the problem numerically, if a current of, say, ·3mA is being read, an error of + 0·1mA will indicate 3·8dB, nd an error of −0·1mA will indicate 3·4dB—ie 0·4dB differ- nce. At lower currents the error can be even more serious. At a current of 1·5mA, the possible error amounts to 0·58dB, so it is clear from this that it is necessary for a meter which is both accurate and can be read to at least ±0·1mA.

Close-up view of noise generator head

Noise generators in use

The method of making measurements is to adjust the receiver gain controls until the amplified noise signal produced by the source resistance R_S and the receiver noise produce a suitable deflection on a meter connected to the output. This may conveniently take the form of an ac voltmeter connected across the loudspeaker. A suitable deflection might be 0·5V. This initial setting up is done with the diode filament switched off, and any agc in the receiver chain disabled.

Having set the zero conditions, the noise diode filament is switched on and slowly increased in temperature by reducing the variable resistance in its circuit until the output power of the receiver is doubled. If a voltmeter is being used as an indicator then the volts will need to rise by a factor of $\sqrt{2}$. Now the diode anode current needed for this operation should be read. The noise factor can be calculated from the following formula taking the normal room temperature as 290°K.

$$\text{NF (dB)} = 10 \log_{10} \frac{20\, I_d\, R_s}{1{,}000}$$

where I_d = diode anode current (mA)
R_s = source resistor (Ω)

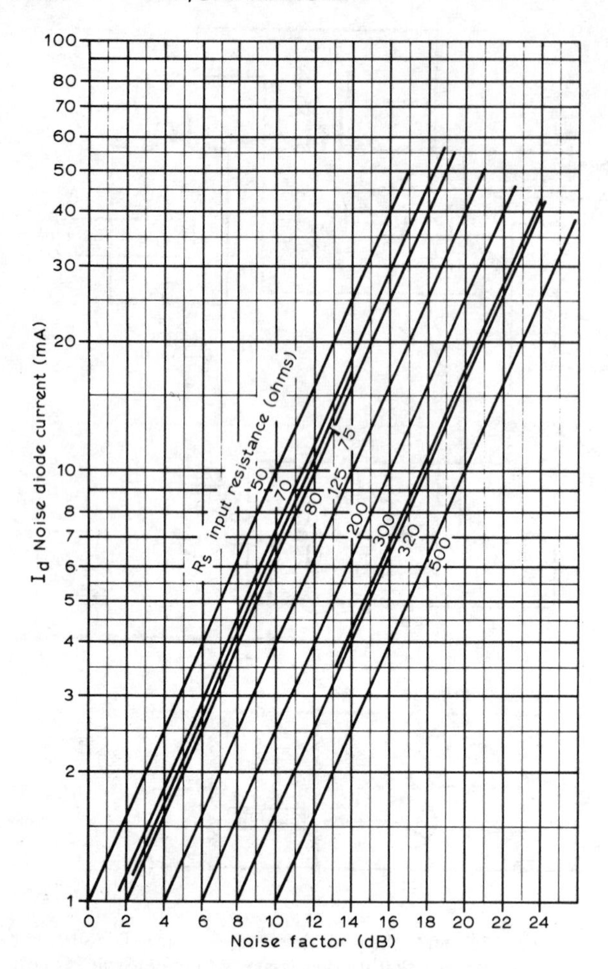

Fig 55. Chart showing noise factor for various values of source impedance

If the temperature is other than 290°K, this may be corrected by the formula:

$$\text{NF (at 290°K)} = \text{NF at different temperature} \times \frac{290 - T}{290}$$

The output indicator could be calibrated so that the meter M is scaled with 3dB (2-to-1 power) points. This will enable the output to be set at various points and if tests are made at several levels it will enable some assessment of the linearity of the receiver to be made. Care must be taken, though, that no

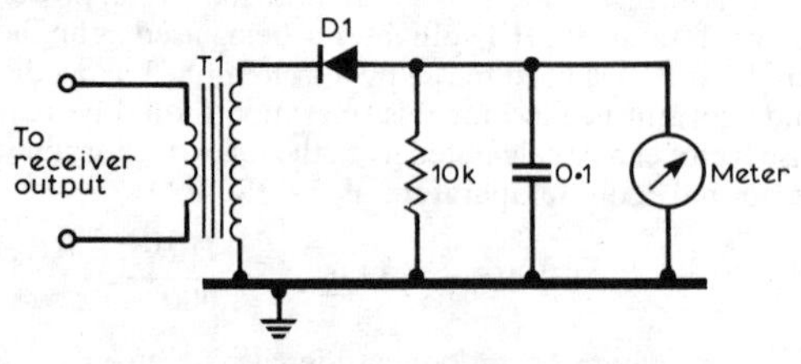

Fig 56. Circuit of a suitable output indicator. T1 is a small audio output transformer; CR1 is a 1N34 or equivalent

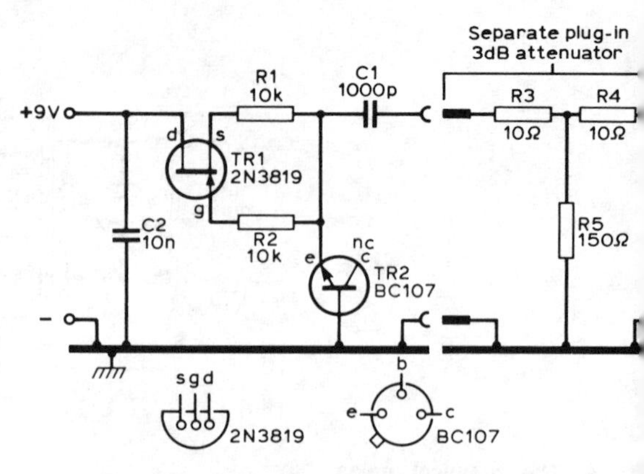

Fig 57. Simple semiconductor noise generator

overloading takes place anywhere in the receiver chain. So improvement in linearity may be obtained by switching on bfo as this sometimes improves performance of some types detector.

Fig 57 shows a circuit for a simple type of noise generat which is suitable for relative tests. It is not capable of accur measurements, although it is a useful check instrument for bo 144 and 432MHz converters.

In this unit the base-emitter function of a silicon transisto used as a noise source, and the noise is amplified by an fe

Included in the circuit diagram, Fig 57, is a 3dB attenuat This should be a separate plug-in unit.

VHF receiver alignment aid

The technique of alignment of the input circuits of a receiver converter for maximum signal/noise ratio, which rarely occ at the same point as that of maximum signal (gain), tends become a tedious operation.

A useful method which has become available recently is use an instrument that provides a continuous readout of difference between the audio output of the overall receiver w no rf input and the output when a wide-band noise generato connected to the input. In this instrument a meter indicates t ratio between the outputs under these conditions. The readi itself is not sensitive to variations in the mean level of the sig over quite wide limits. The meter has a logarithmic respor and may be calibrated in decibels (if required), though normal purposes this is not necessary.

A suitable circuit has been described by G4COM in *Rad Communication* January 1976 (Fig 58).

IC1 is used in a precision rectifier circuit which gives a output from ac inputs down to a very low level, unlike t conventional half-wave rectifier which requires some hundre of millivolts for satisfactory operation. The gain of the circui determined by R2/(R1 + RV1), while D2 and R3 prevent t op-amp from saturating on negative half cycles of the input. T output from the circuit is partially smoothed by R4 and C1, a is fed to IC2 which is connected as a logarithmic amplifier the use of TR1 in its feedback loop (the voltage across a silic transistor, base shorted to collector, is proportional to t logarithm of the current through the transistor).

This circuit is the "heart" of the instrument. It is fed alt nately with two voltages corresponding to the receiver no

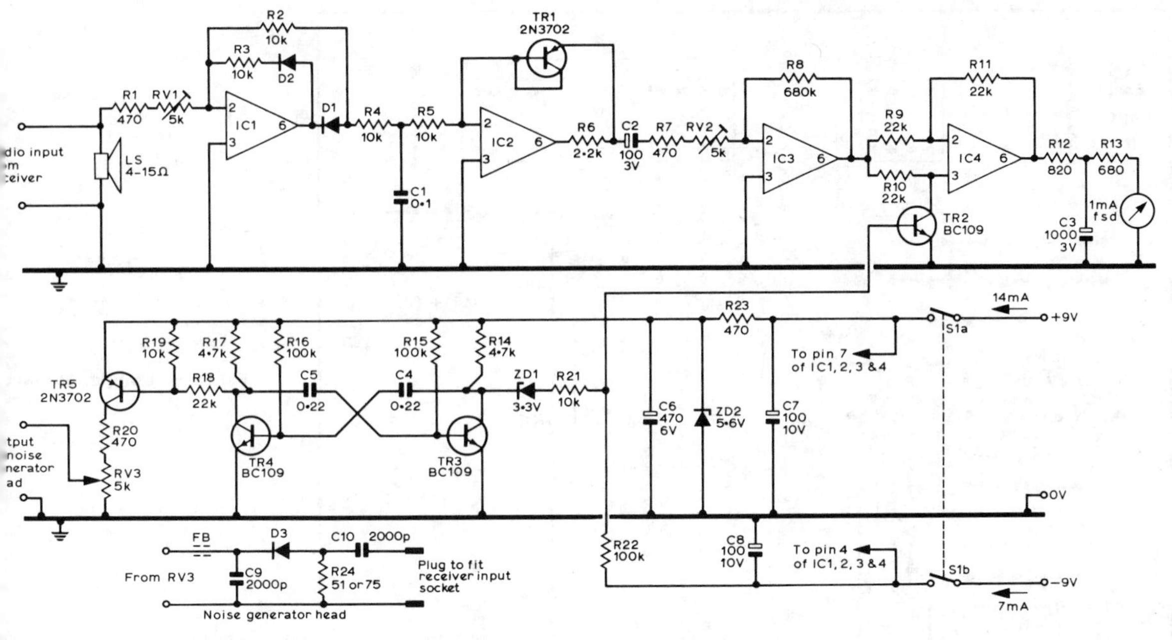

Fig 58. Circuit diagram of alignment aid

ıtput and the receiver signal-plus-noise output. The differ-ıce (in millivolts) between its output voltages under these two nditions is a function of the ratio between the two input ıltages, and this ratio is independent of the average input vel. Hence, provided that the various stages of the receiver ıd the circuit around IC1 are working within their linear nge, the ac output from the circuit around IC2 at the pulse equency employed will be dependent only on the overall s/n tio. Since the ac output of this circuit is only a small fraction of volt peak-to-peak, it is amplified by IC3 connected as a ıltage amplifier, having a gain R8/(R7 + RV2).

The output of IC3 is fed to IC4, a phase-sensitive detector of ity gain. The reference signal is provided by TR2 from the ılse generator TR3, TR4. A phase-sensitive detector is ideally ited to applications such as this, where an indication is quired of the magnitude of an ac signal which has a known equency and phase but a high accompanying noise level. In e present application, the psd gives a usable output when the gnal is accompanied by so much noise that it is undetectable ear or by examining an oscilloscope trace.

Full-scale deflection in the prototype was about 10dB (s + /n, with the scale reading linearly in decibels. IC4 has a low ıtput impedance adequate for driving a 1mA meter. R12, 13 and C3 are chosen to give adequate damping for the meter, hich otherwise would have a very erratic response due to the ndom nature of the noise inputs. The switching device TR2 is standard general-purpose bipolar transistor. In principle a fet ould be more suitable but this would require a larger peak--peak switching voltage than is conveniently available, and in actice the simple circuit shown here is quite adequate.

The pulse generator TR3, TR4 is a conventional astable ultivibrator operating at about 30Hz. Its output is amplified TR5 and fed to the noise diode via limiting resistor R20, the ode current being adjusted by RV3. The pulse generator also ovides the reference voltage for the psd. The noise generator rcuit is conventional and can be built into the body of a uhf plug. The power supply to the pulse generator and noise diode is roughly regulated by ZD1.

Components

Few of the component values are critical and 20 per cent tolerance will suffice. C2, 3, 6, 7 and 8 can be any convenient value not less than the values shown, while C2 only needs to be 2V working. D1 and D2 can be almost any germanium diode such as OA79, OA90 and OA81. The npn transistors can be any low-level audio or switching silicon types of minimum h_{fe} 100. The pnp transistors require a similar specification. Resistors can be rated $\frac{1}{4}$W.

In the noise generator head the resistor should be of metal film construction for minimum inductance, 51Ω or 75Ω as appropriate, and the capacitors small ceramic. The diode used in the prototype was a CV364 microwave mixer from the spares box. Alternatives are 1N21, 1N25, 1N32, 1N23 or, less suitably, 1N82A and 1N34; failing any of these, it may be worth while to try an assortment of signal, rectifier and zener diodes as available, in the hope of finding one having sufficient noise output over a wide frequency band.

Setting up

The unit requires little alignment, and even this can be done without test equipment. Switch on the receiver, plug in the noise diode and adjust the receiver tuning and audio controls to give an audible noise level. Switch on the alignment unit and adjust the diode current (RV3) to give an audible signal, a rough purring noise.

Connect the audio output of the receiver to the input of the unit. The meter should now give a fairly steady reading which can be varied by adjusting the diode current. Set RV1 so that the meter reading is constant over a wide range of receiver audio gain settings; set RV2 to give fsd on the meter at maximum diode current on the highest frequency band to be required. The unit is now ready for use.

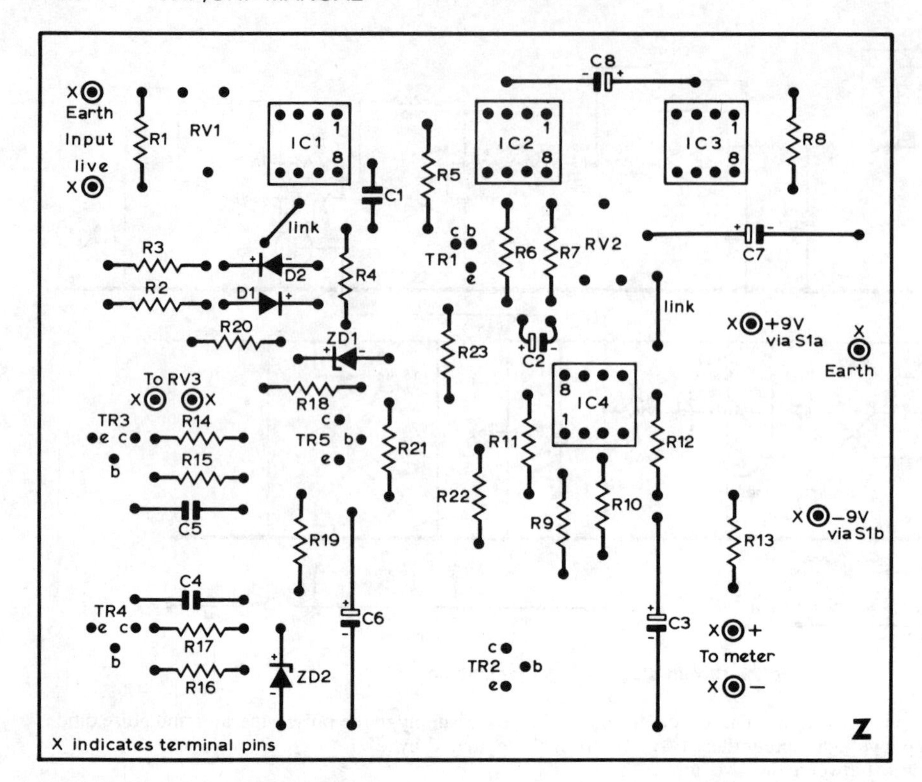

Fig 59(a). Component layo

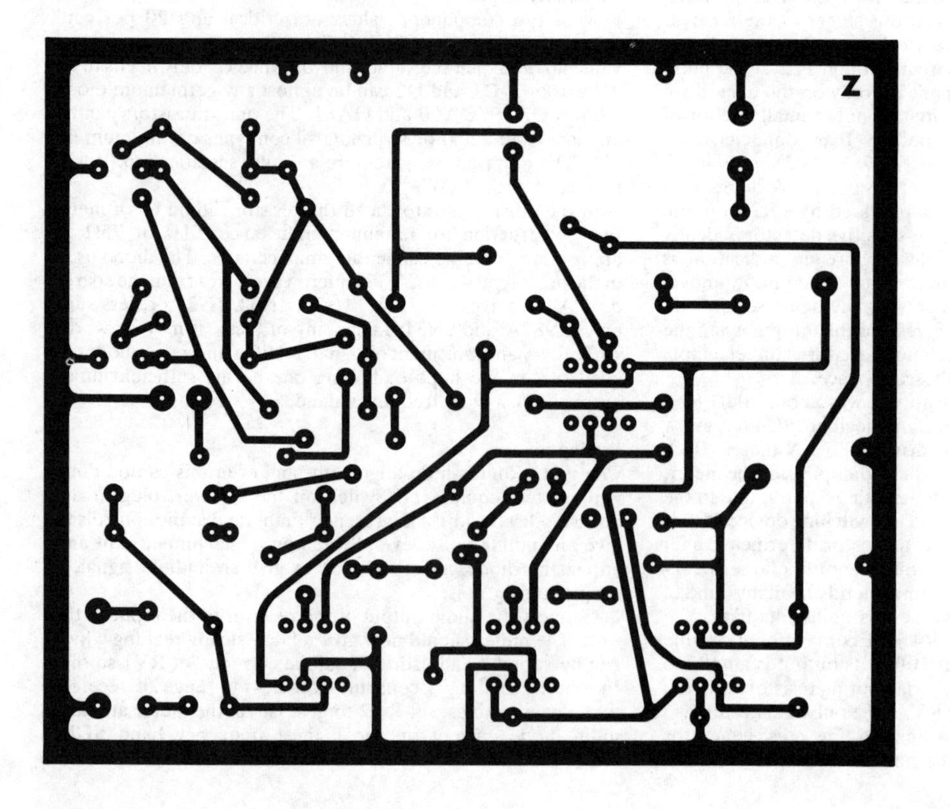

Fig 59(b). Underside of boa
showing foil pattern

Table 4. Components list

R1, 7, 20, 23	470Ω
R2, 3, 4, 5, 19, 21	10kΩ
R6	2·2kΩ
R8	680kΩ
R9, 10, 11, 18	22kΩ
R12	820Ω
R13	680Ω
R14, 17	4·7kΩ
R15, 16, 22	100kΩ
R24	51Ω or 75Ω to suit receiver
RV1, 2	5kΩ skeleton preset 0·1W horizontal
RV3	5kΩ carbon linear
C1	0·1μF polyester
C2	100μF 3V tantalum
C3	1,000μF 3V
C4, 5	0·22μF polyester
C6	470μF 6V
C7, 8	100μF 10V
C9, 10	2,000pF ceramic
FB	Ferrite bead
ZD1	3·3V 400mW zener diode
ZD2	5·6V 400mW zener diode
D1, 2	OA47, OA79, OA90 or similar
D3	See text
TR1, 5	2N3702, 2N3703, 2N4126 or similar
TR2, 3, 4	BC109, 2N2926 or similar
IC1, 2, 3, 4	741 eight-lead dil
LS	Replacement spkr 4-15Ω
S1	Switch dpst

Use

Connect up the unit as above and adjust RV3 for about half-scale deflection on the meter. Any adjustment of the receiver which results in an improved signal gain with no change in the noise figure, or a reduced noise figure with no change in signal gain, or both simultaneously, will result in an increased meter reading. Therefore by noting the meter reading at a given setting of RV3 the effects of various circuit changes in the receiver can be assessed. Although the unit is not especially sensitive to small changes in temperature or battery voltage, it is probably wise to switch on the unit 10min before it is required, and to ensure that the ambient temperature is reasonably constant and that the batteries are fresh before using the unit for periodic checks on receiver performance. As mentioned above, the principle of the instrument assumes reasonable linearity of the receiver. It is not suitable for fm alignment. Noise blankers and agc should be disabled before using the unit for testing.

It is recommended that a signal generator or off-air signal be used for initial alignment, as there is a risk that one or more of the front-end circuits may be peaked up to resonate at an image or other spurious frequency when a wide-band signal source is used.

Simple signal sources

A reliable signal source is very useful for setting up receivers or converters, particularly during the initial stages when a new item of equipment has been built. Once the signal has been found it is then better to do further trimming using a more remote signal such as one of the beacons.

Two simple circuits are given in Figs 60 and 61, but the output should be checked using an unambiguous absorption wavemeter to ensure that it is tuned to the correct frequency.

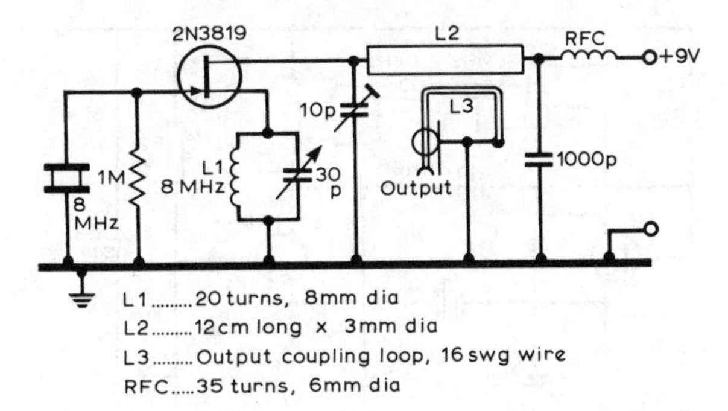

Fig 60. A simple signal source for 144MHz

The source tuned circuit should be tuned to the crystal frequency, which will normally be found at the point where the current falls about 3mA to 2mA.

The simple method may of course be applied to other bands using appropriate crystals and output tuned circuits.

In construction, it is desirable for the unit to be completely enclosed so that output is only obtained from the output socket, this will largely eliminate unwanted signals and also allow some control of the level. The battery should also be enclosed in the screened box.

Although relatively low frequency crystals are indicated in diagrams, there is obviously a distinct advantage in using higher frequencies such as 36 or 72MHz. This will provide greater assurance of the correct output frequency, especially if it is desired for use at 432MHz.

Dual output signal source

A useful signal source having outputs at 144 and 432MHz can be constructed readily using the familiar Butler crystal oscillator/multiplier circuit with a fifth overtone crystal of 103MHz.

The circuit arrangement (Fig 62) is a standard Butler oscillator with a series-resonant crystal, but the two different frequency output tuned circuits are connected to the respective collectors of the transistors, in order to obtain the maximum output from the 432·6MHz side. A series-resonant circuit tuned to 288·4MHz is connected in the emitter circuit. An output power of 30mW is obtainable on 144·2MHz and 10mW on 432·6MHz, for an input power of 120mW.

The outputs are inductively coupled and suitably supported

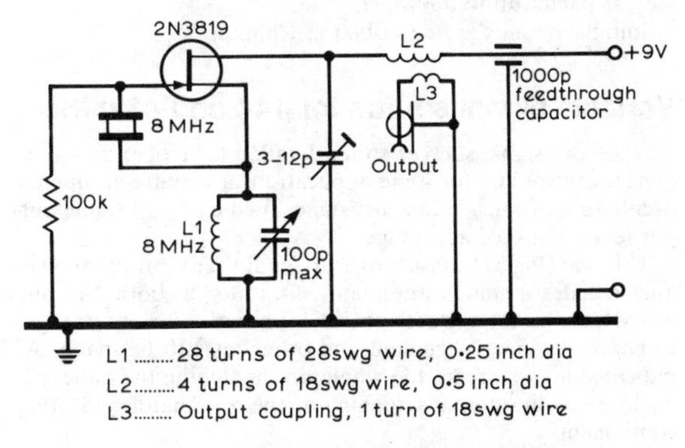

Fig 61. An alternative signal source design

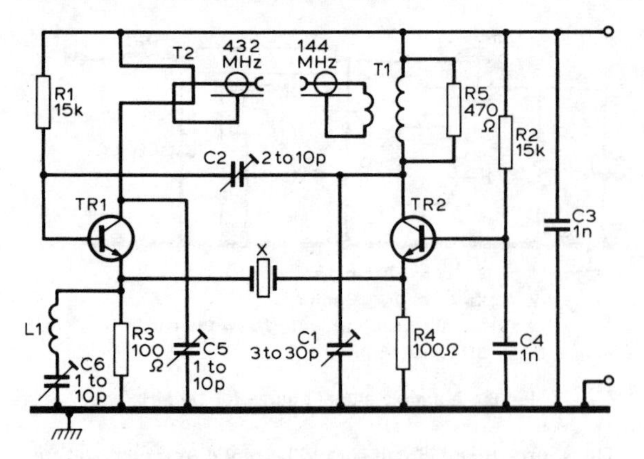

Fig 62. Circuit of dual-output signal source

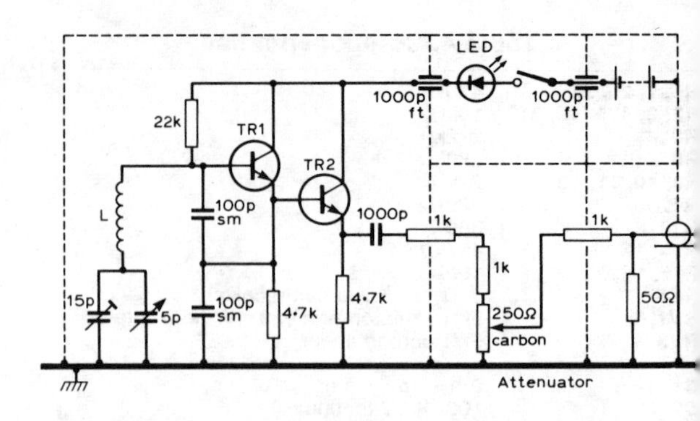

Fig 63. Variable signal source for 144–432MHz

and adjusted. The transformer T1 for 144·2MHz output consists of four turns of 0·5mm wire wound 7mm internal diameter, 9mm long, with a two-turn link output coil. T2, the 432·6MHz output circuit, consists of 4·3cm lengths of wire formed into suitable loops. The 288·4MHz idler circuit (L1, C6) is formed of a coil of three turns of 0·5mm wire, 6mm internal diameter, 10mm long, tuned by a 1–10pF trimmer.

The transistors used are BFY90 or equivalent; types such as BSX20 will also be satisfactory, although somewhat lower output will be achieved.

Medium power signal sources for 144MHz

There are many applications where a "clean" signal source of reasonably large output can be useful, such as for checking antennas, filters and output circuits of linear amplifiers. The latter would of course also require an impedance bridge.

Transistors as frequency doublers do not always give full output without very careful adjustment; usually there is a substantial amount of the fundamental (input) frequency included with the wanted output frequency.

An improvement can be obtained by using a pair of transistors in push-push. The CA3028A ic will give a better performance in this arrangement for frequencies up to 120MHz with its input fed in push-pull and outputs in parallel. In addition, to ensure that the signal is as clean as possible, link couplings between each stage can be used. A CA3049T ic can be used in a similar circuit up to 500MHz.

Suitable circuits are described in Chapter 5.

Variable signal source for 144 and 432MHz

The various signal sources so far detailed have been based on crystal control and for some applications a variable frequency oscillator is of considerable assistance, while an adjustable output level is also of advantage.

This unit (Fig 63) consists of a vfo feeding an emitter follower and includes a simple attenuator. Outputs on both 144 and 432MHz as harmonics of the oscillator are of sufficient strength to enable receiver alignment and other tests to be made. As indicated in the circuit, the whole unit including the battery is enclosed, with internal screening of the attenuator and other components.

The oscillator stability will be adequate for short-term tests. It may of course be made elaborate to provide suitable long-term stability and appropriate information in this respect can be found in the "Oscillator" section of Chapter 4.

Simple rf probe

For general rf measurements an rf probe is used in conjunction with an electronic voltmeter. The probe consists of an isolating capacitor, low-capacitance diode, and a series resistor, and is essentially a peak reading device, It is important that the input capacitor and diode leads are as short as possible. The diode will normally be a point-contact germanium type, with a typical capacitance of about 1pF. This type of diode is limited in its maximum reverse voltage and if voltages are likely to be high a number of diodes should be connected in series.

In Fig 64 the basic circuit if an rf probe is given. If the series resistor is made 4·7MΩ and with a 10MΩ input resistance electronic voltmeter the output voltage then becomes the rms value. Alternatively, for an rf voltage indicator, the resistor may be chosen to suit the meter (dc) to which it is to be connected. A 50 or 100μA fsd meter together with the probe described forms a useful device for setting up low-power exciter or local oscillator stages.

In Fig 65 details of the general arrangement of a simple rf probe are given. The construction may take any convenient form provided the essential points noted above and illustrated in Fig 64 are observed.

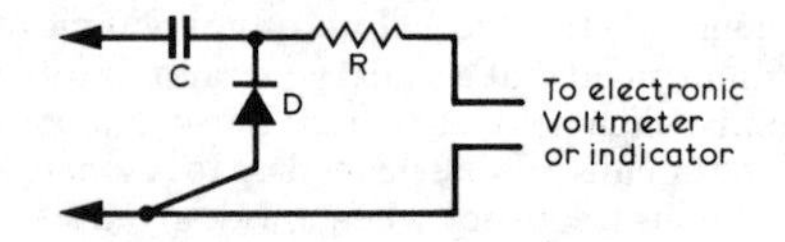

Fig 64. Basic rf voltmeter head

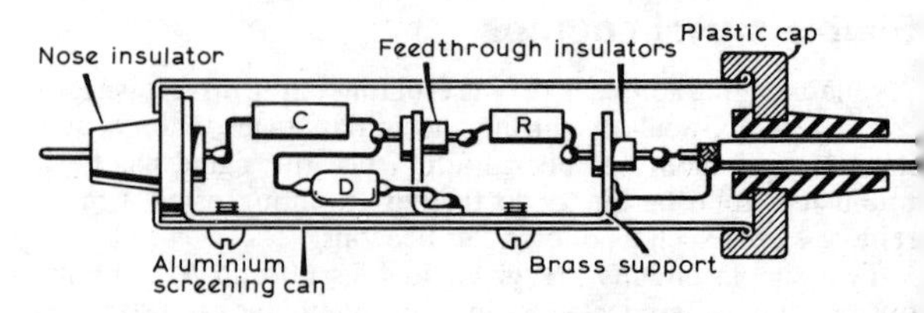

Fig 65. A practical rf probe

Coaxial relays

In most vhf and uhf installations, coaxial cable is employed for the transfer of rf power from the transmitter to the antenna, and from the antenna to the receiving system. For rapid changeover of the antenna between the receive and transmit modes, a relay is required which, ideally, should have been specifically designed to function with this type of cable. These are known as *coaxial relays.*

Coaxial relays are constructed so that they exhibit a characteristic impedance which matches that of the coaxial cable with which they operate. When the impedance of the relay and that of the cable are identical, no mismatch will be introduced into the transmission line to degrade the swr and produce reflections in the feed system. In practice, absolute perfection in matching is rarely, if ever, attained, due in the main to the fact that the impedance quoted for coaxial cable is normally a nominal figure and subject to some variation.

The relay to be described may be constructed for coaxial line impedance of 52, 50 or 75Ω, the impedance being determined by the dimensions of the cavity containing the switching arm and the size of the switching arm itself. Full dimensions are given, and while these are expressed in millimetres, they may be converted into inches by use of the following formula:

$$\text{Inches} = \frac{x}{25 \cdot 4}$$

where x is the dimension given in millimetres.

One particular feature of the relays is their good crosstalk damping level, and this is of special interest in receiving systems employing devices which can be easily damaged by excessive rf leakage during transmission periods. Specific information on the crosstalk level is given later.

The form of the relay is such that it can be mechanically linked to other contact sets and so be built up into a complete master control unit. When giving thought to such an arrangement, however, the possible need to arrange sequential switching should be remembered, and as will be seen, this is related to the rf power that the coaxial relay is expected to carry.

Mechanical description

Fig 66 shows the cross-section through the relay. Three coaxial sockets (3) (4) are fitted to a rectangular brass block which has been drilled out both horizontally and vertically to produce a cross-shaped cavity. Socket 3 (4) which is fitted to the right-hand end, carries a spring switching strip fitted with double contacts, these being positioned precisely in line with the stubs on sockets 1 and 2 (3). The stubs of sockets 1 and 2 (3) are fitted with contacts and these will mate with those on the spring arm.

The spring strip attached to socket 3 (4) is formed so that it is normally in contact with the stub of socket 1. Pressure on the actuating rod (6) will move the spring strip from its rest position in contact with socket 1, over to the contact on socket 2. The actuating rod (6) is powered by the solenoid (5) and its associated plunger. The extent of the movement of the plunger/actuating rod is shown as (h) on the drawing.

A second actuating rod (11) may be fitted opposite the primary actuating rod (6). This allows switching of other contact strips (10) which may be built on to the coaxial relay unit and employed for control switching purposes.

After the position of the spring switching strip, and the contact separation (a) have been adjusted, the front of the brass block (1) is closed by fitting the cover (2) and the leads from the solenoid terminated on the connecting block (7).

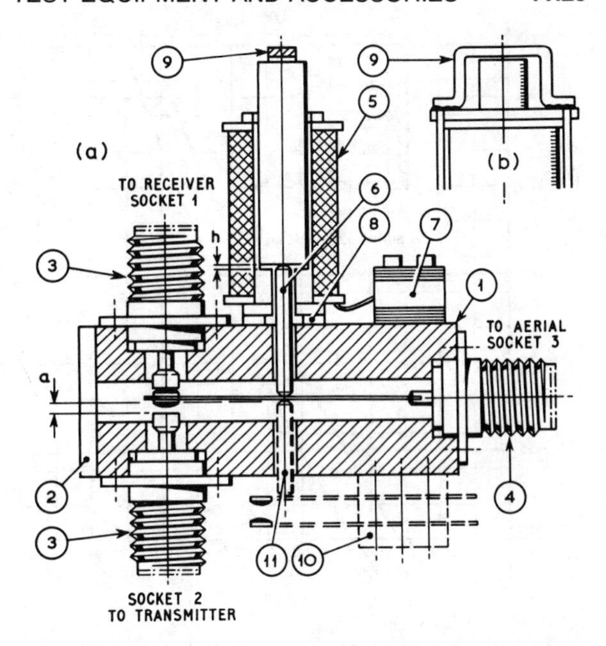

Fig 66. A general cross-section view of the assembled relay

Design impedance

Coaxial cable usually employed has an impedance of either 52, 60 or 75Ω. For the reasons already covered, the characteristic impedance of the relay, sockets and cable should all be the same, and this means that the relay must be designed to operate with the particular cable concerned in respect of its quoted impedance. The section of an asymmetrical hf conductor corresponding to the relay is shown in Fig 67.

The flat spring strip of width f and thickness s lies centrally in the circular conductor, this being formed by the horizontal bore through the block (1). The characteristic impedance Z with air dielectric ($K = 1$) can be calculated from the formula given in Fig 67 or derived from the graphs. The dimensions required to produce specific impedances are given in the table associated with Fig 68.

Coaxial sockets

The sockets shown in the description are types UG58A/U and UG58/U.

The normal hf coaxial sockets with a square mounting flange have, on their mounting side, one or more cylindrical steps. This means that the relay body (1) has to be counter-bored accordingly. As the dimensions of these steps differ according to the manufacturer, the dimensions of the counter-bore will have to be adjusted according to the exact type of socket employed. It is particularly important that the end of the outer conductor of the socket makes good electrical contact with the base of the counter-bored hole.

The N series is rated for use on frequencies up to 10GHz, but in practice is not generally used above 3GHz. The insulation may either be Teflon or polystyrene according to the manufacturer. They are waterproof and can handle up to 1,500V, and may be obtained for 70Ω impedance. The C series has the same characteristic and is available in 50 or 70Ω impedance.

Connectors are available for matching and interconnecting one series with another.

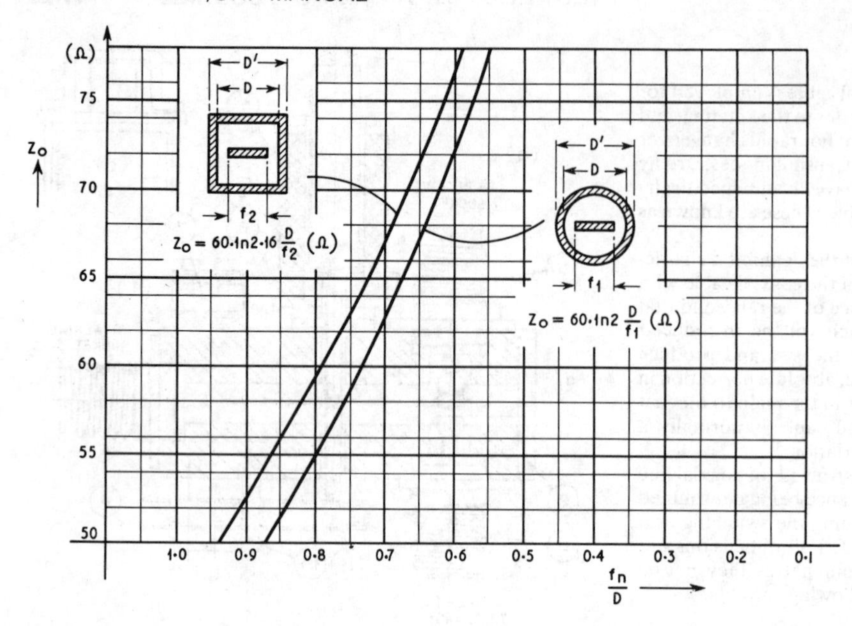

Fig 67. The characteristic impedance of a conductor having a circular or rectangular cross-section, assuming an air dielectric ($K = 1$)

The construction when N or C type sockets are employed can be simplified by ignoring the stepped shoulders on these sockets. The diameter of the cavity bore is made constant from one end of the block to the other. That is, the diameter (b) on the left-hand side of the section A–B is increased to the same as that of (c) on the right-hand side (Fig 67).

Making this bore a constant 9·5mm throughout its length will clear the shoulders of the sockets. If this course is adopted, the impedance of the relay is adjusted by correct selection of the size of the switching arm. This will be found in the table associated with Fig 69.

Ideally, the main cavity containing the switching arm should be drilled about 0·2mm under size, and then finished with a reamer. The final surface must be smooth and free from burrs, particularly at the intersections with cross drilled holes.

The hole (e) which accommodates the actuating rod should not exceed 3·2mm in diameter, and if it is required that the coaxial relay shall operate other contact sets driven by the same energizing system, then this hole should be drilled right through the block.

The main cavity bore housing the switching arm should be silver plated.

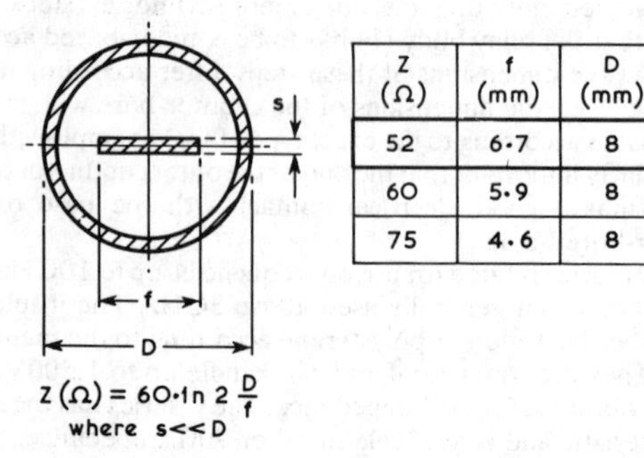

Z (Ω)	f (mm)	D (mm)
52	6·7	8
60	5·9	8
75	4·6	8

Fig 68. Conductor dimensions for different impedances

The solenoid is secured to the body of the relay by two countersunk brass screws which pass right through the body of the relay block, and this is illustrated in section X–Y in Fig 69, the screws being designated M3.

The solenoid specified has only a very small hole in its base, and this has to be increased to 3·2mm in order to accommodate the 3mm actuating rod. If it is made larger than 3·2mm, the performance of the solenoid will be affected.

Prior to plating the main cavity, the solenoid should be secured to the main block, and the alignment of the drilling of the base of the solenoid to that of the hole in the block which accommodates the actuating arm, checked. Any adjustments that are found to be required should be made before the cavity is plated.

After assembling the relay and checking the contacts, the wire loop (9 of Fig 70) is soldered to the magnet frame as shown in Fig 66(b) to prevent the plunger falling out of its housing.

The rod (6) shown in Fig 66 and in Fig 71(b) should be 25·5mm long, but if the solenoid is mounted on an angle piece (8) in Fig 72 and Fig 66 instead of being secured directly to the main body of the block, it will have to be increased to 27·5mm. The rod is made from 3mm diameter polystyrene stock as is that for coupling in other contact sets if they are fitted.

Assembly

Fig 73 provides details of the manner in which the contact is fitted to the spring arm, while Fig 71(c) illustrates how the contacts are prepared prior to being fitted.

The shaft of one of the contact rivets is removed, and the back filed flat. This rivet is then drilled centrally with a hole equal to the diameter of the shaft of the other rivet. A sandwich is made consisting of the stemmed rivet passing through the spring arm—previously drilled to take the stem shown in Fig 71(c)—and the drilled rivet head slipped over the stem. The shaft which protrudes through the drilled contact head is marked at about 0·3mm proud of the dome of the head and carefully cut at this point. The shaft is now dressed back with a light hammer until a hemispherical head is produced with the

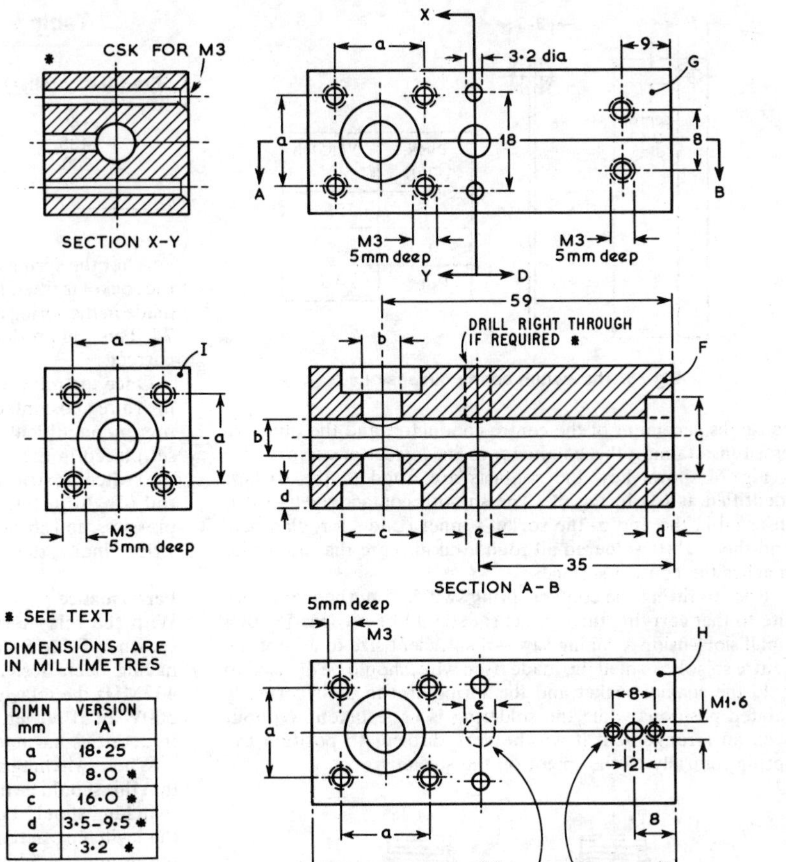

* SEE TEXT

DIMENSIONS ARE IN MILLIMETRES

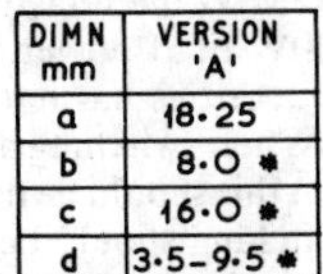

DIMN mm	VERSION 'A'
a	18·25
b	8·0 *
c	16·0 *
d	3·5–9·5 *
e	3·2 *

69. The relay body component parts. Dimension "e" should not exceed 3·2mm

ITEM 9 LOOP
14 swg COPPER WIRE
BENT TO SHAPE AS SHOWN

Fig 70. The plunger retaining loop

spring strip firmly clamped. Provided that the riveting has been correctly executed, soldering will not be necessary. Finally a small radius is filed on each corner of the spring strip adjacent to the contacts.

Before soldering either the spring arm or the contacts to the sockets, a plug should be mated with the socket concerned. Under the heat of soldering, the insulation may well soften and

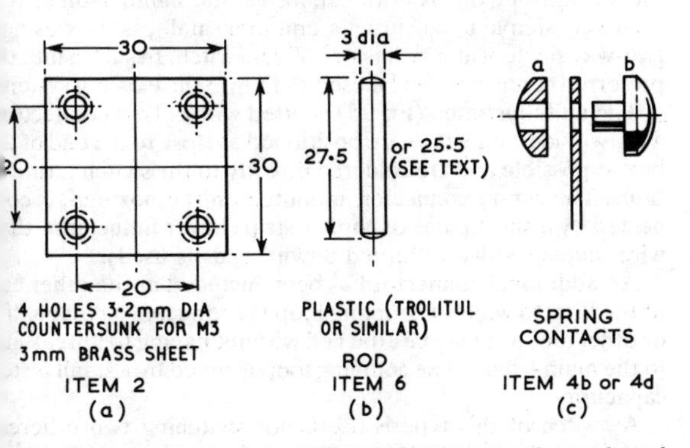

Fig 71. The relay body end plate, the plastic actuating rod, and the method of assembling the spring contacts

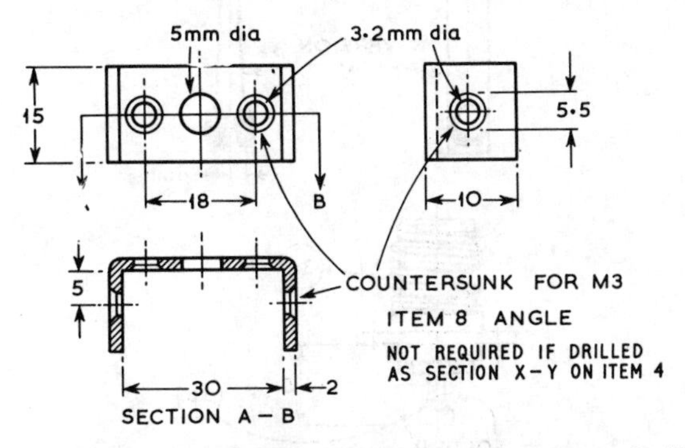

Fig 72. The U-support for the solenoid. This item is not required if the solenoid is mounted directly on the relay body

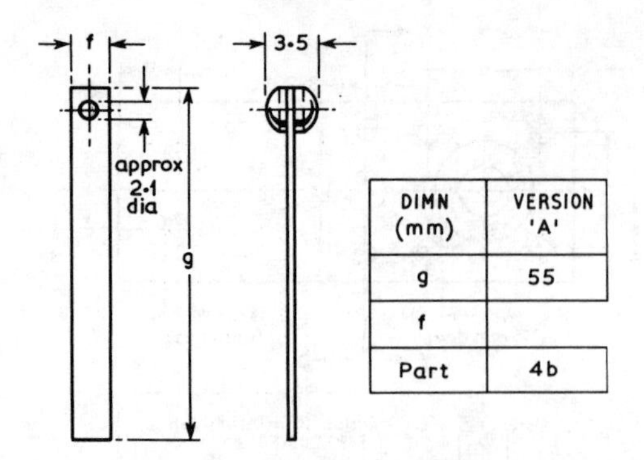

Fig 73. The switch spring dimensions

cause displacement of the centre conductor, and the plug will assist in retaining this conductor in its correct position.

Fig 74 shows how the contacts are fitted to the sockets identified as (3) in Fig 66. The smooth contact rivet (3b) is inserted in the end of the socket's inner conductor, clamped, and then lightly soldered all round, taking care that no solder reaches the contact surface.

Prior to fitting the contact spring switch arm, the end opposite to that carrying the contact set should be provided with a small slot—using a coping saw—of sufficient size to accept the centre spigot. A small jig, made from wire, should be devised to hold the coaxial socket and the spring arm in their correctly related positions while the soldering is undertaken. Without such an arrangement it will be very difficult to position the spring centrally to the spigot on the socket.

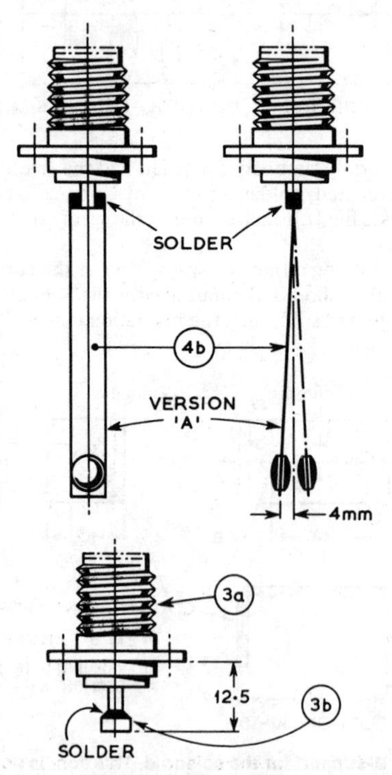

Fig 74. Sockets used at 3 and 4, Fig 66, showing contacts attached

Table 5. Coaxial relay performance

Frequency (MHz)	Reflected power (%)	Crosstalk level (dB)
145	0·1	−40
435	0·7	−32
600	1·0	−30
1,000	4·0	−23

After the spring arm has been fitted to the socket, but befc the socket is fitted to the body of the relay, a small set should made in the spring arm so that it deviates by about 4mm, see F 74. This will produce a contact pressure of about 50g, which correct.

Once the relay has been assembled, it is checked for conta pressure and contact register. The unenergized position shou present no difficulty since this is determined by the angle of t set placed in the arm. However, with the solenoid energize the switching strip should not be bowed too far by the actuati rod (6). Adjusting the length of this rod will vary the conta pressure, and consequently the amount of bow in the switchi strip. Finally, the cover (2) should be screwed into positior

Performance

With the relay terminated in a 60Ω impedance, the figur shown in Table 5 have been obtained, the relay itself, of cour having been designed for 60Ω operation. On 145MHz a 432MHz the relay proved itself capable of handling more th 200W of rf power. Its performance in this respect on high frequencies has not so far been checked.

When switching appreciable rf power it is not recommend that this should be done by the relay directly. Rather, sequent switching should be employed, the power being applied aft the switching action has taken place. Failure to observe t requirement could lead to flash-over and arcing with serio damage to the contact surfaces.

Coaxial switch

Although manually operated coaxial switches are availabl these are generally fitted with SO239/PL259 uhf type conne tors, whereas many station installations use type N, C or BN connections; units with these fittings are significantly mo expensive than those with the uhf fittings.

Of course adapters may be added to a commercial unit wi uhf fittings but this is both expensive and cumbersome. It relatively simple to construct a unit in a small cast box using two-way single-wafer switch or a slider switch. In such a unit t preferred connector can be used to fit into the existing system

The unit illustrated (Fig 75) is fitted with N type connecto The two side connectors are positioned as close to the end of t box as possible and are soldered directly to the switch termin tions. The centre connector, mounted on the box end, is co nected by a short piece of copper strip (lower inductance tha wire unless rod with "turned down" ends is used).

An additional connector has been included at the other e of the box, to which a coupling loop is connected so that a df or other monitor may be attached without having to "break-ir to the main circuit. The coupling loop is tuned by a small pisto capacitor.

A switch of this type is useful for switching two differe antennas or from antenna to dummy load.

The performance of the prototype, with all ports matched

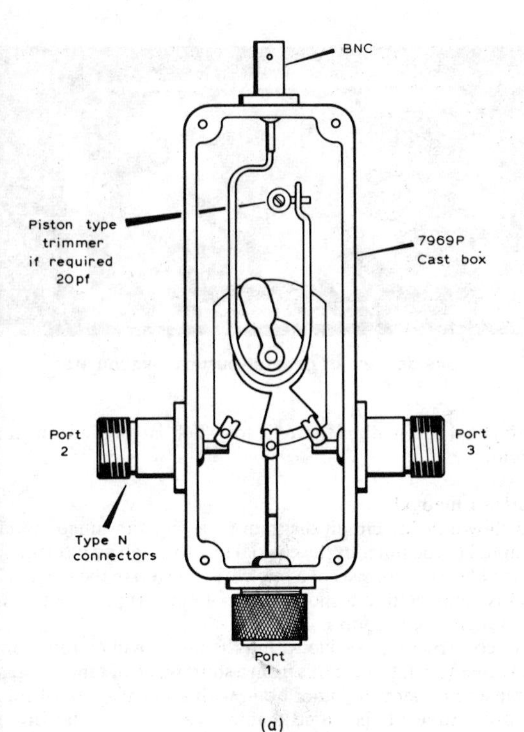

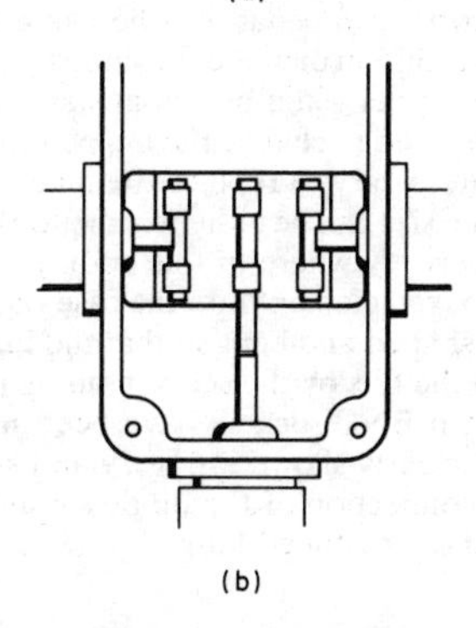

75. Coaxial switch using (a) rotary switch or alternatively (b) a slide switch

Coaxial switch showing coupling loop

Table 6. Performance of prototype coaxial switch

Frequency (MHz)	Insertion loss ports 1 to 2 (dB)	Isolation ports 2 to 3 (dB)	VSWR
70	less than 0·1	44	1·15
144	0·2	38	1·3
432	0·85	26	2·1

50Ω and the switch set to connect ports 1 and 2, is shown in Table 6.

Absorption wavemeters

One of the important uses of an absorption wavemeter is to enable the identification of the presence of harmonics in the output of a transmitter or transceiver. An absorption wavemeter provides an unambiguous frequency measurement and it is also a requirement of the amateur licence to check regularly the harmonic output.

Fortunately in the 144MHz band only the second harmonic is likely to cause any trouble; the third falls within the 432MHz band and any serious radiation in that band will soon be reported by other operators. On 70MHz both the second and third harmonics fall into other users' bands and therefore need some care and attention. The generation of the second harmonic by a 144MHz transmitter is all too easy. For example, it is often heard that by "twiddling" with the tuning adjustments a significant increase in output can be obtained—very often the majority of the apparent increase is second harmonic and very little increase in the fundamental.

A good absorption wavemeter should have at least a two-to-one frequency coverage, preferably without switching bands. With care this can readily be attained, although many commercial types do not tune above 250MHz.

Two designs are described for two different applications—one for general-purpose use, the other for insertion into the coaxial line. Both types cover a frequency range of 125–350MHz, and are sufficiently sensitive to obtain a reasonable indication of the fundamental frequency of an fet dip oscillator having an output of about 3–5mW at a distance of 4–5 in.

General-purpose wavemeter

In this design an edge-mounted meter has been used, which at first sight may seem odd. There is however some advantage in this method insofar as in use it is almost always necessary to "bend over" to be able to see the meter whereas with it in the end of the box direct observation is possible.

In order to obtain an adequate inductance for coupling to the circuit under test and still small enough to reach the top frequency, it is necessary to make the external loop and the connections to the tuning capacitor of material with low inductance per unit length. The external loop also needs to be mechanically rigid to avoid damage or calibration changes, and to avoid restriction of the top frequency the material used for mounting the external loop needs to be of low dielectric constant. The most suitable material for this purpose is ptfe or an equivalent.

The construction is shown in the diagrams and needs little further explanation.

The external loop is attached to the internal connections by 4BA brass cheesehead screws and the strip connections to the capacitor are soldered directly to the slots in the heads of the

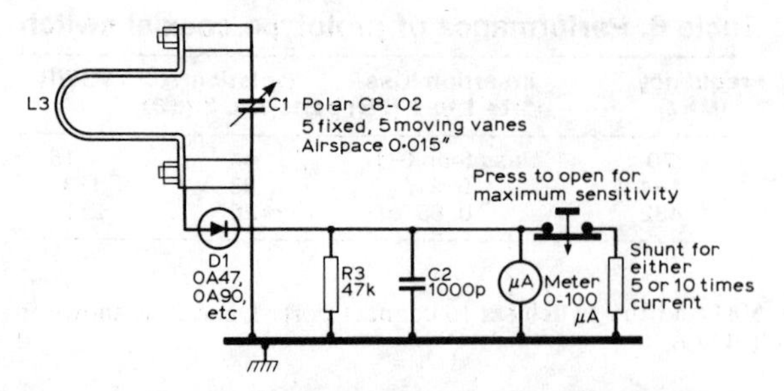

Fig 76. General-purpose (search) type wavemeter. An alternative capacitor is the Jackson C804. Plates should be removed as stated to give 50pF maximum capacitance

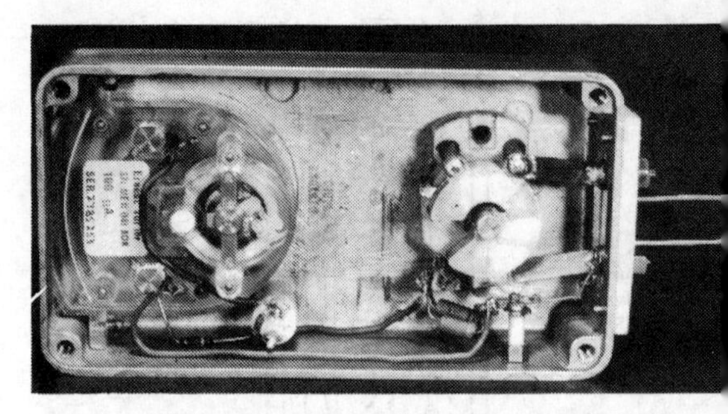

Inside view of general-purpose wavemeter

screws. The detector diode, an OA47, OA90, 1N60 or equivalent, is connected to one of the screws, thereby providing a tap-down of about 25 per cent of the total inductance and avoiding undue damping of the circuit.

Calibration can readily be carried out by use of a suitable dip oscillator, the actual frequency of which is verified by a dfm.

If it is desired to cover 70MHz and possibly 50MHz, then a substantially larger external inductance will be needed. This may take any convenient form—a suitable coil that covers 48·5 to 130MHz consists of four turns of $\frac{5}{8}$in id $\frac{1}{8}$in copper close wound with 1in tails.

With this much larger external inductance the tapping point of the diode detector will be very much lower down and therefore the full sensitivity of the indicating meter will be required.

Through-line type wavemeters

This type is intended for connection in the coaxial cable either between an exciter or the antenna feeder. In the latter case some care is needed to ensure that the unit is not damaged when used with a high-power amplifier. In this case it should be used with a "T" connector and a suitable terminating resistor.

The main element of this type of wavemeter is a short section of coaxial line within the unit to which is coupled the tu
circuit.

Indirect method

As shown in the circuit diagram (Fig 78), the tuned circui coupled to the inner of the coaxial line through an intermedi loop. The loop consists of a fine wire inserted in the coaxial l and is connected to a short length of more rigid wire to wh the tuned circuit loop is coupled.

In constructing the line within the unit it will be found m convenient to fabricate this from a short piece of semi-airspa cable and replace the outer braid with a short length of cop or brass tube of the same diameter as the original braid maintain the correct impedance. The cable used in the p totype had an insulation diameter of $\frac{1}{4}$in so that by use of a pi of $\frac{1}{4}$in standard copper water pipe a satisfactory element can made. If it is required to change the impedance, say, from 5(75Ω it is only necessary to replace the inner conductor wit thinner wire (the size can be either calculated or obtained fr the relevant chart elsewhere in this book.)

Fitting the coaxial element into the case requires the ends the tube to be shaped and bent so that the lugs thus produ can be fixed to the box by the screw holding the connector. the design shown BNC sockets have been used. Compon arrangement is clearly shown in Fig 79 and should present problems, the connection of the diode should be 20mm fr the ground end of the tuned loop.

Direct method

In this form, as mentioned earlier, the intermediate coupl loop is avoided, and there is direct coupling of the tuned circ to the inner conductor through a slot in the coaxial out

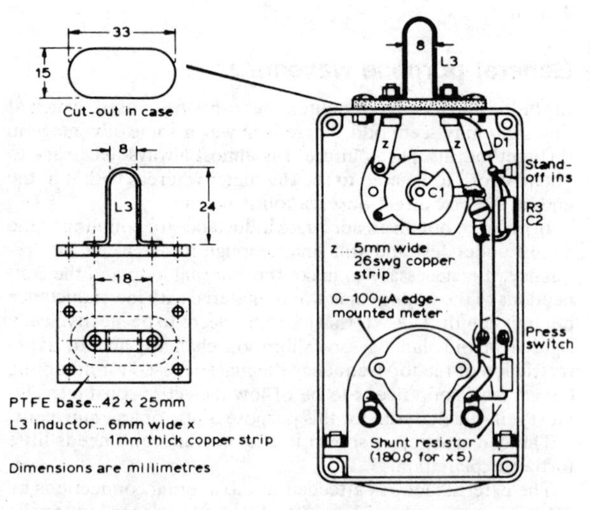

Fig 77. Arrangement of components of general-purpose wavemeter

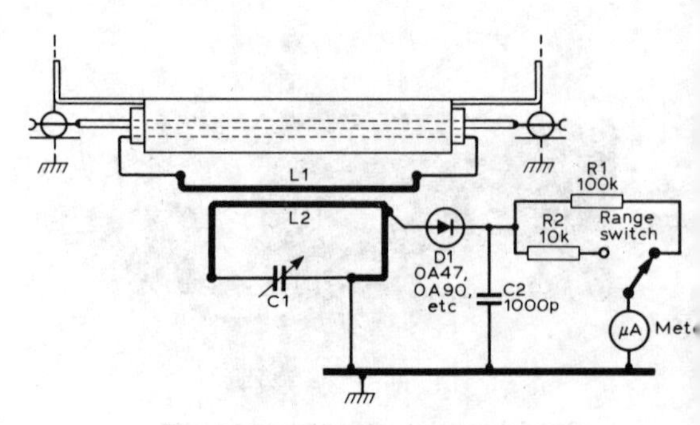

Fig 78. Indirect through-line wavemeter

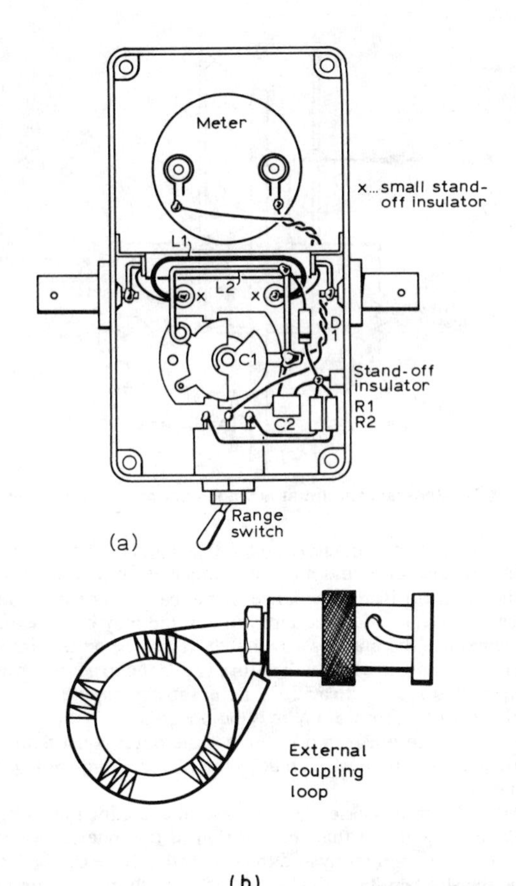

ig 79. (a) Arrangement of components of indirect through-line wavemeter. (b) External coupling loop

)etails of a suitable slotted line are given in Fig 81. The tuned ircuit inductance consists of a simple "U"-shaped piece of 8swg enamelled wire to which the detector diode is connected t a point 20mm from the earth end. Spacing the loop from the nner conductor is important and should be within the field of he outer of the coaxial line. To assist the alignment the slot is rranged to be vertical and this means that the fixing lugs of the ube forming the outer of the line must be at 45° to the slot to nable the line to be fixed by one the screws holding the coaxial ocket.

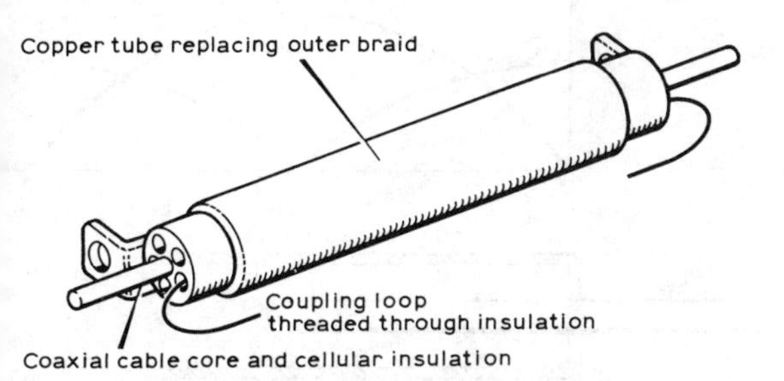

Fig 80. Coupling for through-line wavemeter

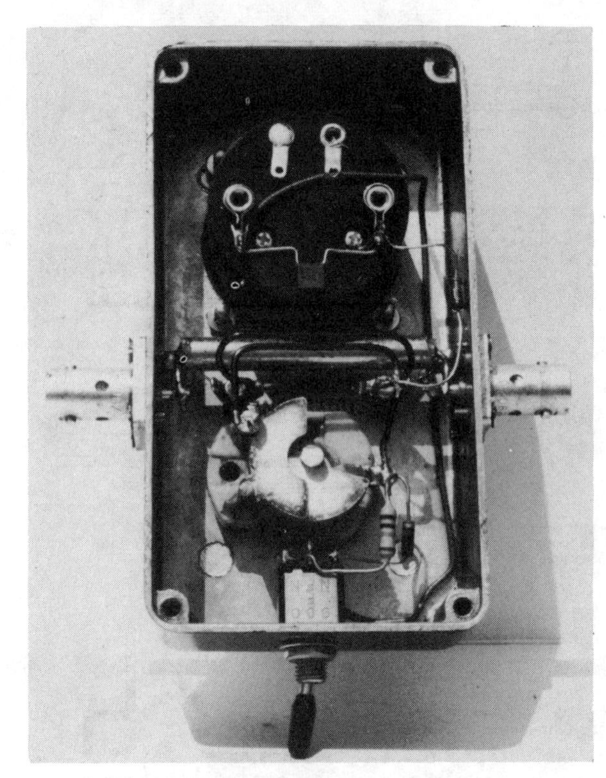

Inside view of indirect through-line wavemeter

Wide-range cavity wavemeter

Measurement of frequencies above 500MHz becomes difficult using conventional lumped-circuit wavemeters, so that it is an advantage to use a cavity design. These are often constructed to cover relatively small bands, but for amateur purposes it is desirable to cover several bands if possible, thus providing continuous coverage and allowing its use for second harmonics.

The wavemeter described has been designed to cover from

Inside view of direct through-line wavemeter

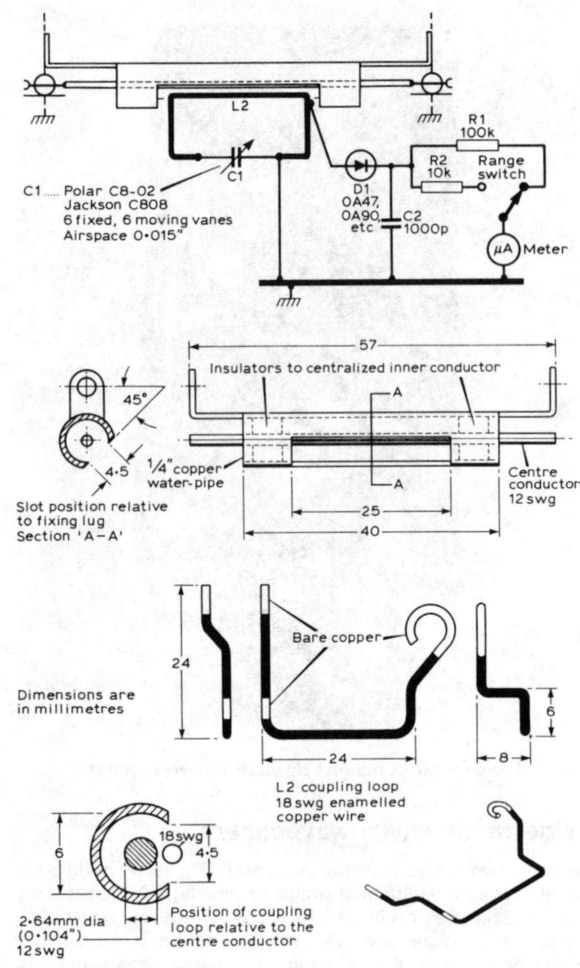

Fig 81. Direct through-line wavemeter

around 400MHz to 2·5GHz using a single cavity with an adjustable inner λ/4 element.

Basically the direct measurement of a λ/4 element represents the wavelength to which it is resonant. An equivalent circuit of the wavemeter is shown in Fig 82. It comprises an input coupling, resonant circuit and an indicator probe or circuit.

When a λ/4 circuit is energized, the current maximum will occur at the shorted end and a voltage maximum at the open end as shown in Fig 83.

A current resonance indicator must therefore be coupled to the low-impedance end of the circuit, that is as near as possible to the short circuit. Also, as the input will normally be the output of an oscillator or transmitter, this will be a low impedance, and should be coupled to the circuit near the short circuit.

Both these couplings should be relatively loose so as not to foreshorten the length of the inner conductor by capacitative loading and so that the mechanical length of the inner conductor is substantially the electrical length of λ/4. There will however be some apparent shortening of the inner conductor compared with the free space length, due to the stray field from its end to the continuing outer. This will be most noticeable at the highest frequencies, and may be as much as 4mm as 2·5GHz.

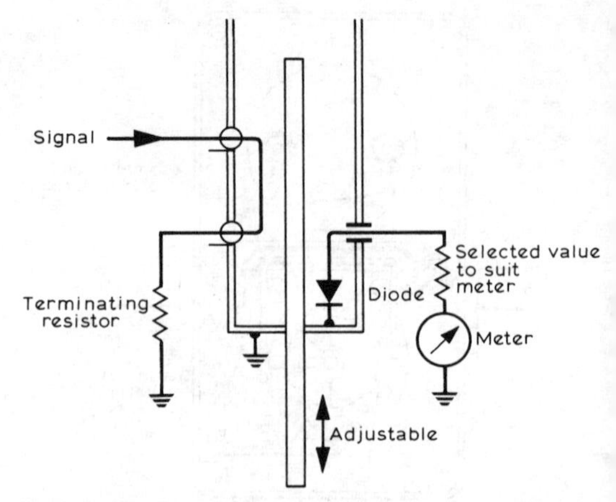

Fig 82. Generalized circuit arrangement of the wavemeter

The characteristic impedance of the cavity is of no significance in the case of a frequency meter and may be of a value convenient to the materials available. It may be either circular or square. The sensitivity will naturally depend to a large extent on the meter used. With a 50μA meter satisfactory indication at levels down to about 5mW may be observed.

In the design illustrated in Fig 84, the outer consists of 1in inside diameter tube with an adjustable inner conductor of ¼in diameter.

The outer in this case has a narrow slot running most of the outer tube length so that the position of the inner conductor may be observed directly and the calibration scale can be fixed along the slot (similar to a slotted line). An alternative method of fitting a calibration scale to the extension of the inner conductor outside the cavity is indicated in the diagram.

Construction

As mentioned, the precise dimensions of the cavity are not critical, though if materials permit it can be made for 50 or 75Ω, and may either be round or square in cross-section.

For convenience, the inner conductor should be ¼in diameter, the outer 1in inside diameter is suitable. The material may be copper or brass—the latter is more rigid and therefore preferable for the inner conductor. The outer may for preference be copper as this is more likely to be easily obtained in the form of water pipe.

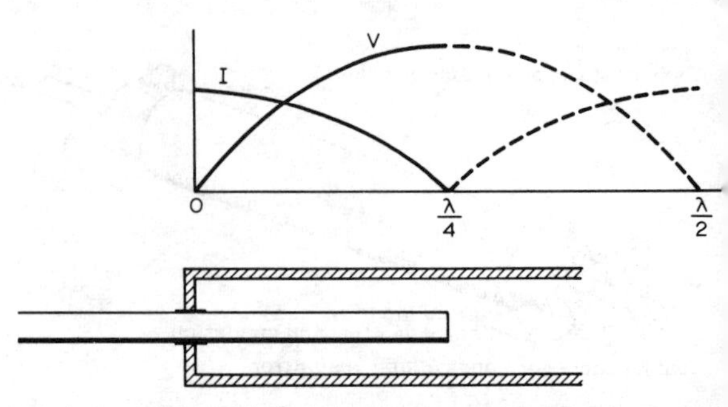

Fig 83. Current (*I*) and voltage (*V*) distribution in a λ/4 cavity

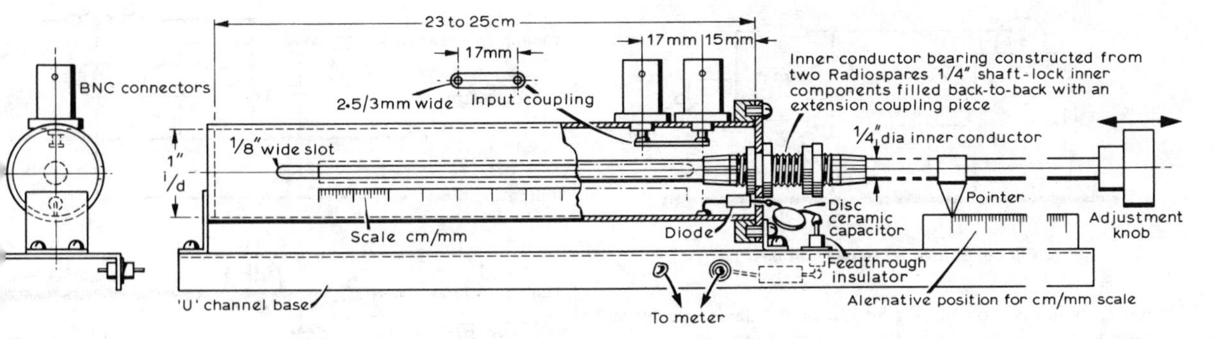

Fig 84. Layout of the wide-range cavity wavemeter

It is important to provide a reliable sliding contact for the inner conductor. If ¼in material is used, then two of the conventional shaft locks should be connected back to back, preferably with an extension tube between them to provide a long bearing.

The input coupling is arranged at the shorted end and consists of a strip drilled and soldered directly to the connectors.

For frequency measurement a terminating resistor of appropriate value should be fitted into a connector (or socket) for use as a load.

UHF trough line

A trough line is a simplified version of the slotted line (Fig 85). It is relatively easy to construct and may be used for the measure of frequency (in a similar manner to Lecher lines) and standing wave ratios. The length of the line section will determine the lowest frequency which can be measured.

It is necessary to be able to observe with sliding probe one maximum and one minimum quarter wavelength but it is better to be able to observe two maximum and one minimum half wavelengths. With a section length of 36 to 40in it may be used down to 145MHz provided that the input cable is adjusted to obtain the first maximum or minimum near the input end.

The characteristic impedance of the line section should be made the same as the normally used coaxial cable, 50 or 70Ω. The dimensions for any cross-sectional size may be calculated with the transmission line formula given for a wire parallel to two infinite planes (see Chapter 3). Typical cross-sectional dimensions for 50Ω are: inner conductor diameter 0·5in, spacing between walls 0·9in, height of walls 3½ to 4in, with inner conductor located centrally.

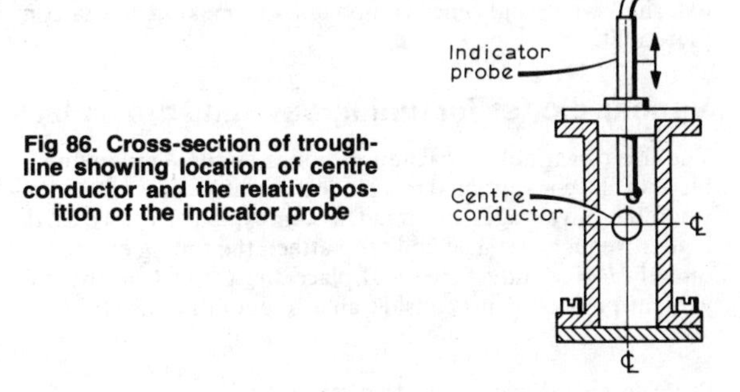

Fig 86. Cross-section of trough-line showing location of centre conductor and the relative position of the indicator probe

The insertion of the probe is made adjustable (Fig 86) and fixed in an appropriate position, the signal detecting diode being fitted inside the probe tube. The probe loop should be relatively small, and formed from the diode lead (Fig 87). The indicating meter should be a high-sensitivity 50 or 100μA type; alternatively if preferred an amplifier may be added so as to allow the use of a less-sensitive meter. A circuit of a simple

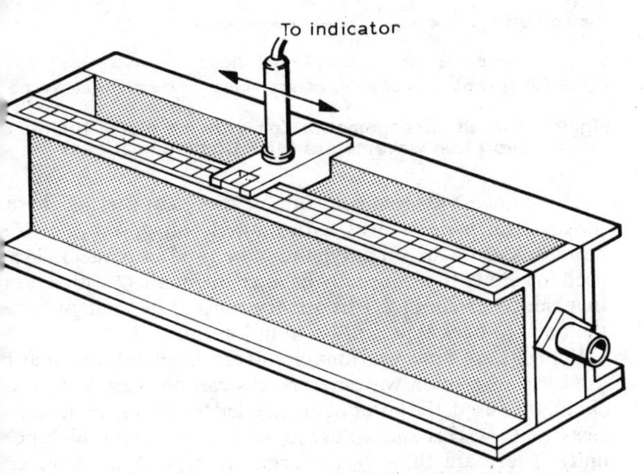

Fig 85. General arrangement of the troughline with scale in centimetres and millimetres

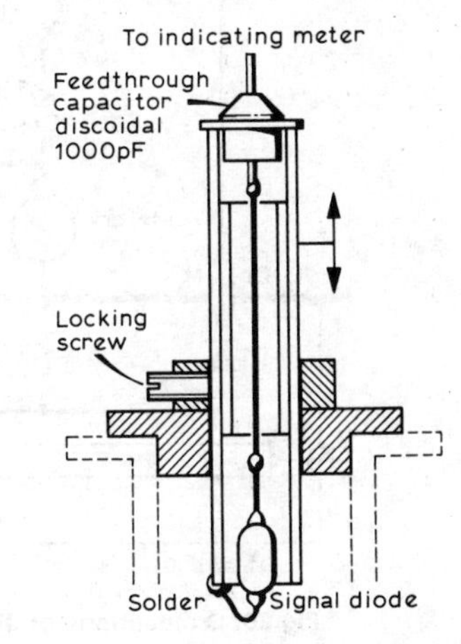

Fig 87. General arrangement of the indicator probe

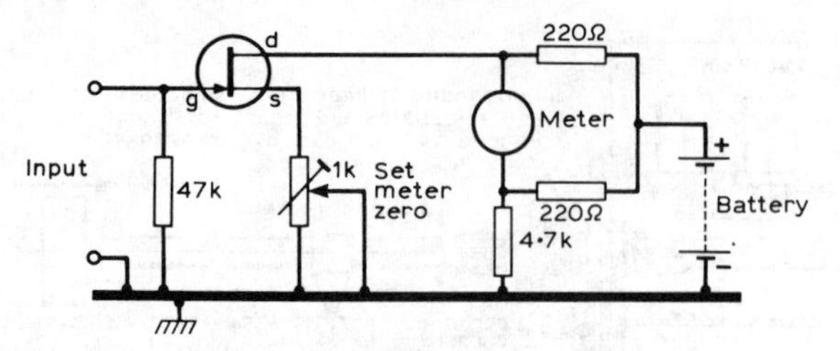

Fig 88. Simple fet meter amplifier

meter amplifier is shown in Fig 88; the actual device and component values can be adjusted to suit the requirements.

In addition to the trough line itself, using the cross-sectional dimensions a directional coupler can be constructed (Figs 89 and 90), with its indicating meter attached together with the external switch and other components to make it into a complete unit.

Varicap diodes for tuning wave and dip meters

The use of variable-capacitance diodes as tuning elements in place of the conventional mechanical variable units offers considerable advantages in circuit assembly, particularly at the higher frequencies. The ability to attach the tuning element(s) directly to the inductance and place the control in any convenient position gains considerable freedom in design.

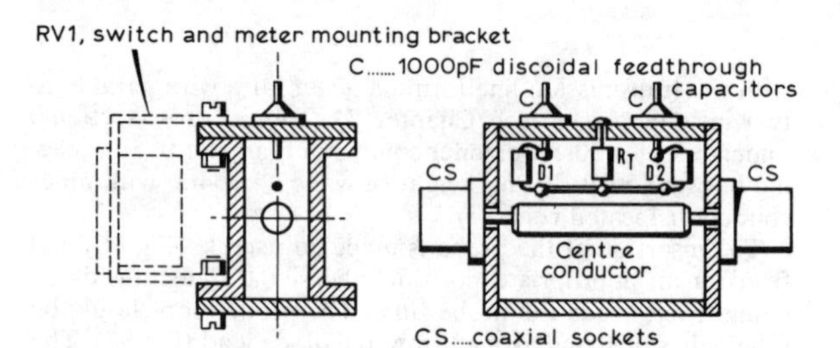

Fig 89. General arrangement of directional coupler

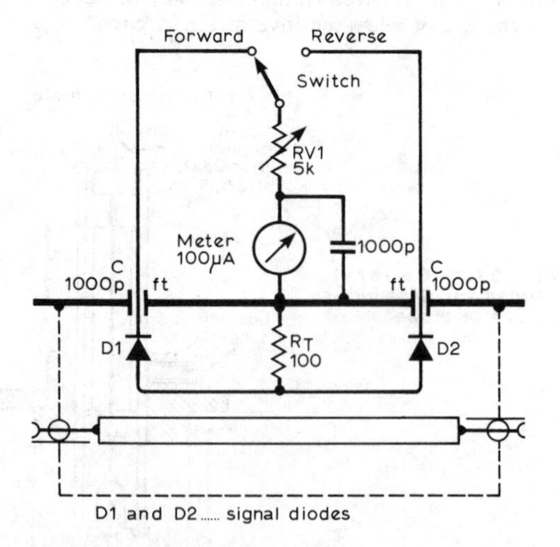

Fig 90. Connections of directional coupler

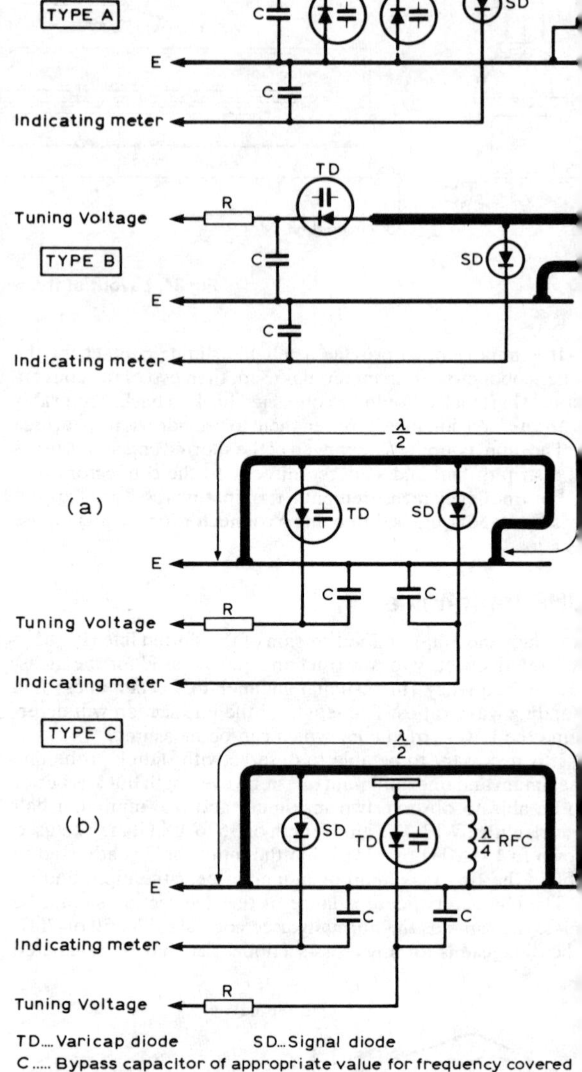

Fig 91. Circuit arrangements for varicap diode tuning o absorption wavemeters (VHF Communications)

There are a wide range of suitable diodes of varying characteristics; for wider ranges with limited voltage range two or more diodes of the same type may be used in parallel. Types used for uhf tv tuners usually have an adequate Q with a range that can cover about 2:1 frequency range. For some purposes the back-to-back type will be found useful.

In Fig 91 are shown various circuit arrangements that may be used for absorption wavemeters. As can be seen, $\lambda/4$ or $\lambda/$ circuits are used, the latter being needed for the higher frequencies (the 1·3GHz band is close to the upper limit for this type of unit). There are three basic forms. In type A a simple coil including a coupling loop and two diodes is appropriate for frequencies around 100MHz. Type B is the same $\lambda/4$ circuit bu

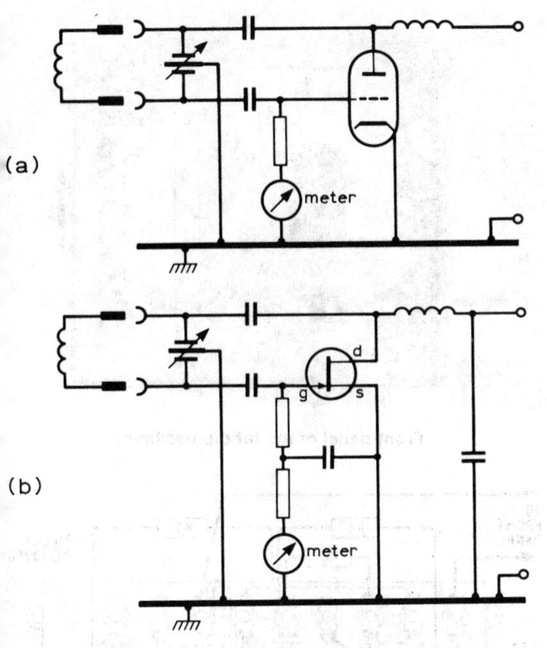

Fig 92. Basic dip oscillators: (a) valve type, (b) fet type

e inductor is formed of strip or heavy-gauge copper and can used up to around 500MHz. Above this frequency, type C (a 2 arrangement) becomes necessary.

A suitable power source is needed and may be either a mains it or a battery. The actual voltage range will depend on the odes and the frequency required. The variable control can efully employ a 10-turn potentiometer which would allow sy and accurate reading. At the lower end the voltage should t be allowed to go below about 10 per cent of the total ltage, and this can be fixed by use of a resistor connected at e lower end of the voltage control.

ip oscillators

dip oscillator is an essential tool for the construction of f/uhf equipment. In its simplest form (Fig 92), it consists of a nable oscillator covering a wide range of frequencies. epending on the actual range, the inductance will be cut to an propriate size and it will normally be a plug-in type. Some rm of indicator, such as a meter, is required to show when the p oscillator is tuned to the circuit under test.

Although a valve-type unit (grid dip oscillator—gdo) is tisfactory, such units need a mains power source which duces their flexibility and they also tend to be "high power" hich may in certain cases cause damage in transistor equip- ent. The indicator is usually connected in series with a grid ak, though it is possible to use an amplifier, either another alve or transistor, for an increased sensitivity (Fig 93).

For vhf and uhf dip oscillators, there is an advantage in using ts in a push-pull circuit. With circuits of this type oscillators r use up to 500MHz are practical with careful mechanical yout so that the connecting leads between the plug-in coil and e tuning capacitor are short and of as low inductance as ossible.

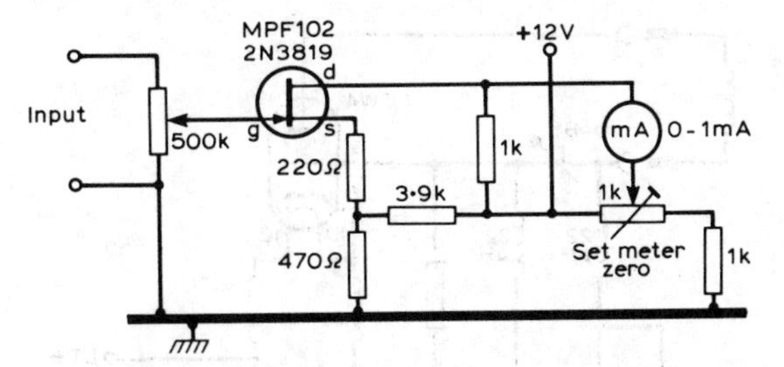

Fig 93. Meter amplifier suitable for application where a more sensitive indication is required

Plug-in coils for the higher frequencies are usually made of sufficiently substantial material to be self supporting. If, however, any support is needed, low-dielectric constant material such as ptfe should be used. Sockets for the coils should be mounted on similar material, and adequate clearance for the sockets from the box should be provided. These precautions assist in the attainment of the highest frequencies.

The indicator may be either a low-reading microammeter or a more robust instrument operated by a simple amplifier. The tuning control should for preference be driven by a slow-motion dial, although a large-diameter dial operated by the thumb has some merit in this type of instrument.

Two valve gdo designs are illustrated in Figs 94 and 95.

FET dip oscillator for 29 to 460MHz

This dip oscillator covers the vhf and part of the uhf region. In this circuit (Fig 96), the oscillator is the well-known Kalitron with a pair of TIS88 junction gate fets. A balanced diode detector is used (to avoid non-symmetrical loading) which feeds into the dc amplifier with a meter in its collector. A jack is included in the circuit to enable the unit to be used as a monitor.

Two switches are included. S1 is the on/off switch, and S2 allows the use of the unit as either a dip oscillator or as a sensitive wavemeter. The tuning capacitor, C1, is a standard

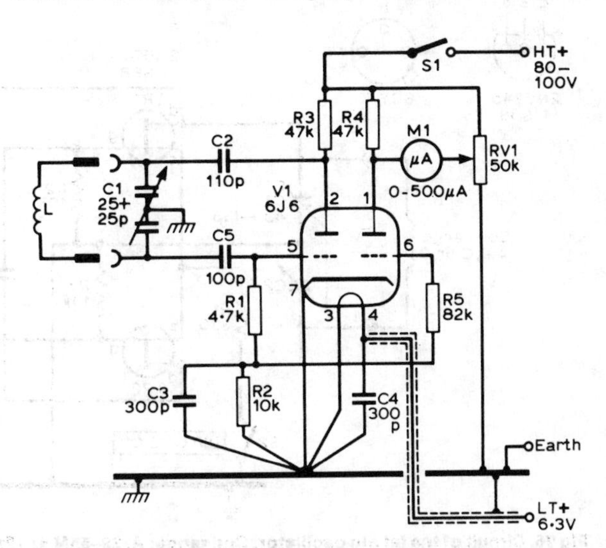

Fig 94. Valve-type gdo using a double triode, the second triode operating as an amplifier

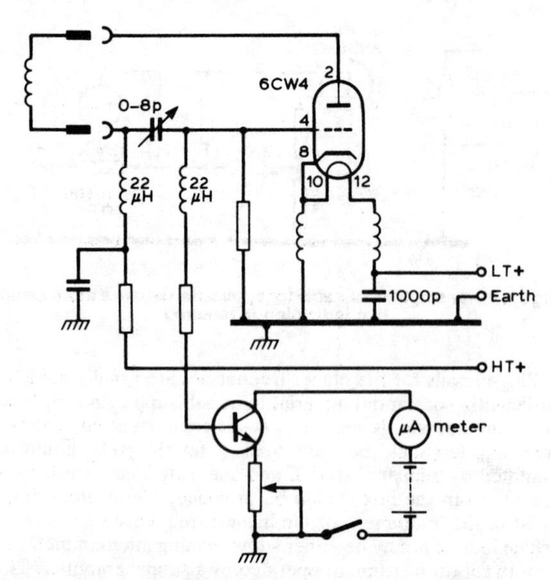

Fig 95. Valve-type gdo with transistor amplifier suitable for up to 700MHz. The tuning range for an individual coil will however be limited if the highest frequency is to be acheved

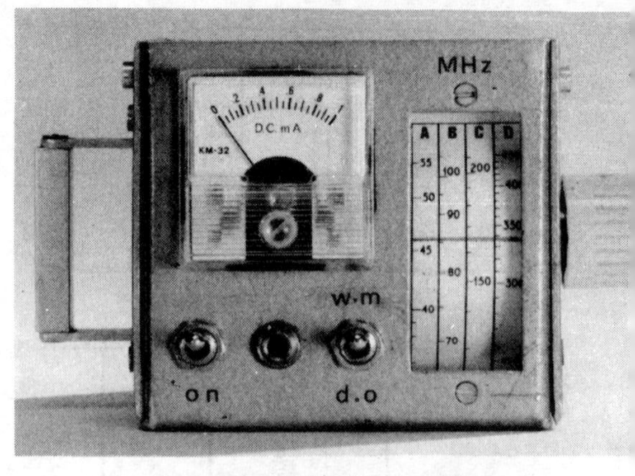

Front panel of the fet dip oscillator

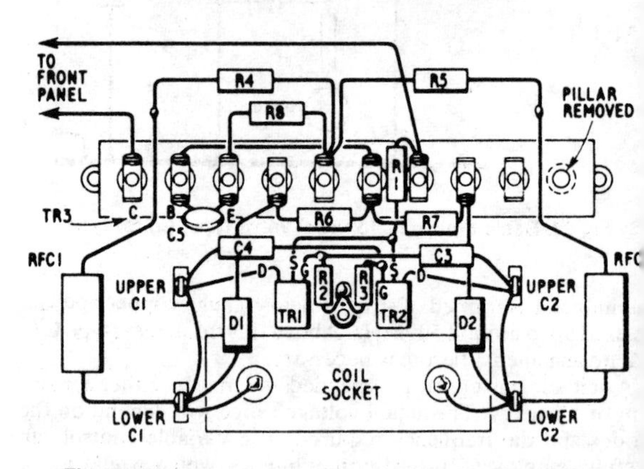

Fig 97. Component arrangement of the fet dip oscillator

split-stator type, 3·5 to 43pF per section (Jackson C808). The tuning scale is of a drum form with actual drive through a 6:1 ratio ball drive (Jackson 4511). All the components should be as small as possible. Most are mounted and arranged around a miniature terminal strip as shown in Fig 97.

The most important feature to ensure reaching the highest frequency is the use of copper strip connections to the rotor and stators of the tuning capacitator C1 and keeping all the rf circuit lead lengths to a minimum. In particular, the common source lead of TR1 and TR2 should not be more than ¼in long.

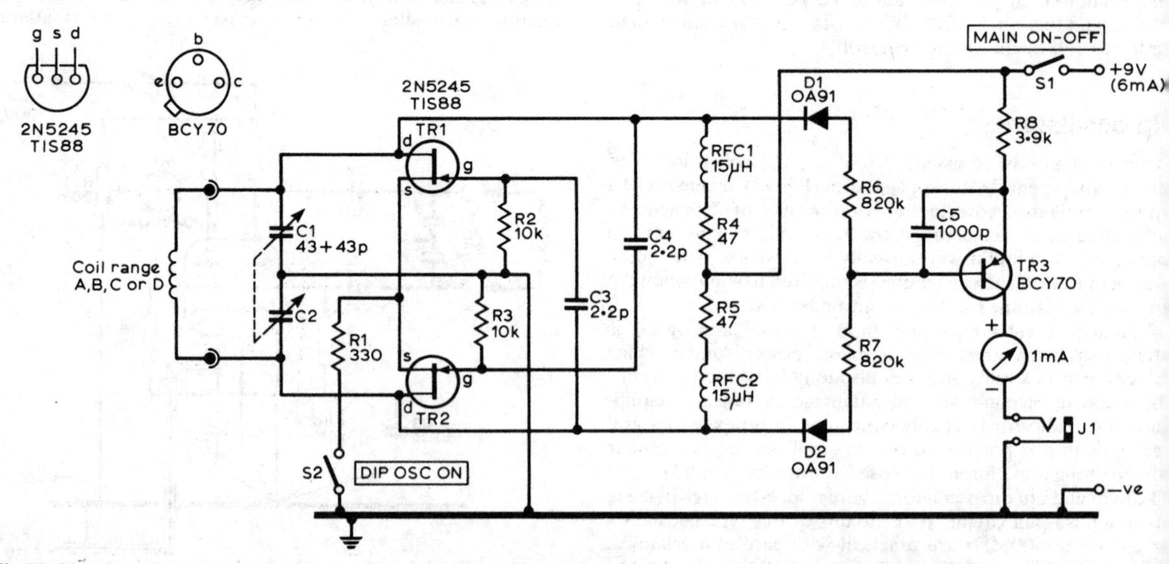

Fig 96. Circuit of the fet dip oscillator. Coil range: A, 29–55MHz 12t closewound 22swg ½in diam; B, 50–109MHz 8t closewound 13swg ⅜in diam; C, 97–220MHz ⅝in wide 2⅞in long 13swg; D, 190–460MHz $\frac{3}{16}$in wide $1\frac{1}{16}$in long 26swg strip. Coils A and B have 1¾in long 13swg legs as suppor*

Detail of the fet dip oscillator

The construction is clearly shown by the photograph and mponent arrangement given in Fig 97. The box in the original as a cube of 2in, but the size is largely a matter of personal oice and the size of the meter used.

To enable the tuning scale and the drive to be fitted after the nnections to the tuning capacitor, the side panel is made movable and the tuning capacitor itself mounted by brackets ed to the bottom of the box.

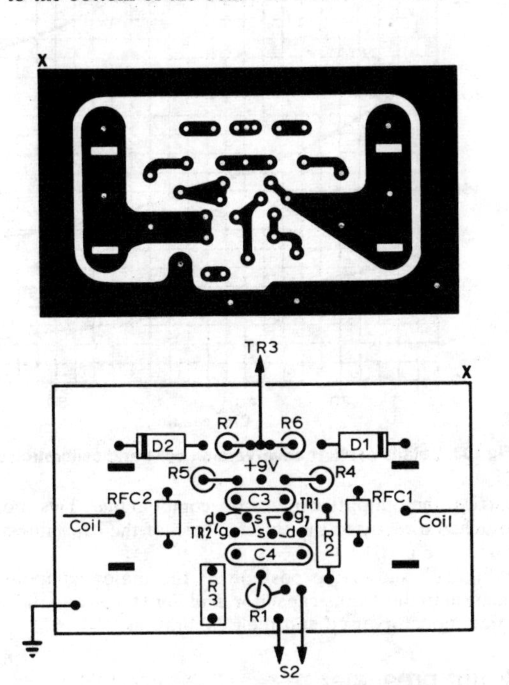

ig 98. Printed circuit board designed by G3XGP for the fet dip oscillator

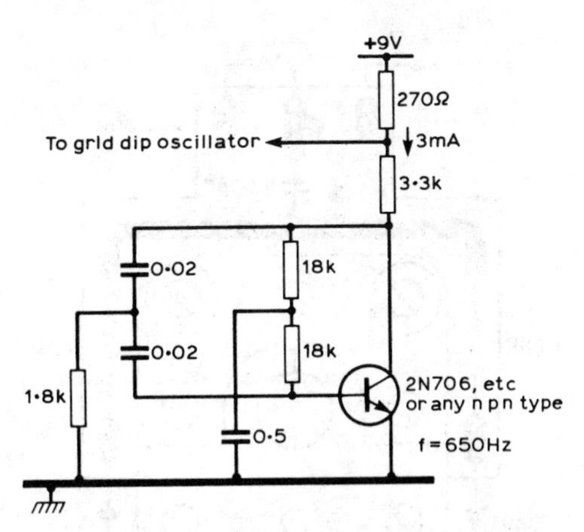

Fig 99. Twin-T audio oscillator as a modulator

Increased sensitivity as a wavemeter is easily met by substituting a 100μA meter for the 1mA meter and putting a 1–5kΩ potentiometer across the meter as an external sensitivity adjustment.

The inclusion of modulation in a dip oscillator is an advantage, allowing easier identification of the signal. This can be achieved by adding the circuit shown in Fig 99.

Alternative method of construction

In this design, the circuit and components are the same except that the tuning capacitor is an Eddystone split-stator capacitor and the inductors (only three are used) are of course changed to suit. One small addition is an led connected in series with the supply which, although passing only 4·5 to 5mA, gives enough light to show when the unit is on without increasing the battery drain.

The construction is based on two die-cast boxes without lids, fixed together by drilling fixing holes right through with a 4BA clearance drill.

The circuit is assembled in two parts. One board carries the oscillator components as shown in Fig 100 and is made of ptfe—desirable because of its low dielectric constant, thus giving minimum shunt capacitance across the inductor sockets.

The second board is an ordinary printed-circuit type and

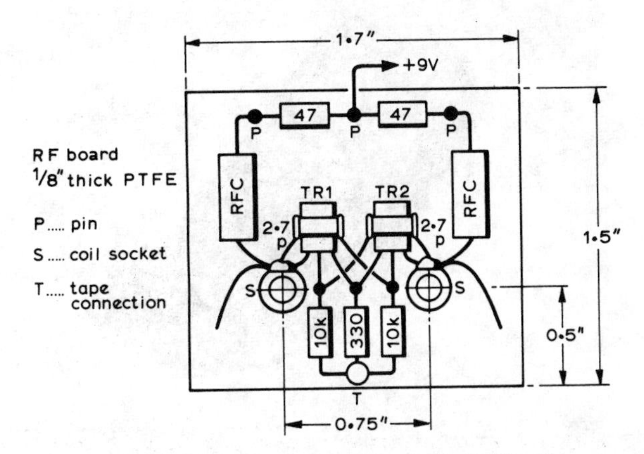

Fig 100. RF section of alternative version of the gdo

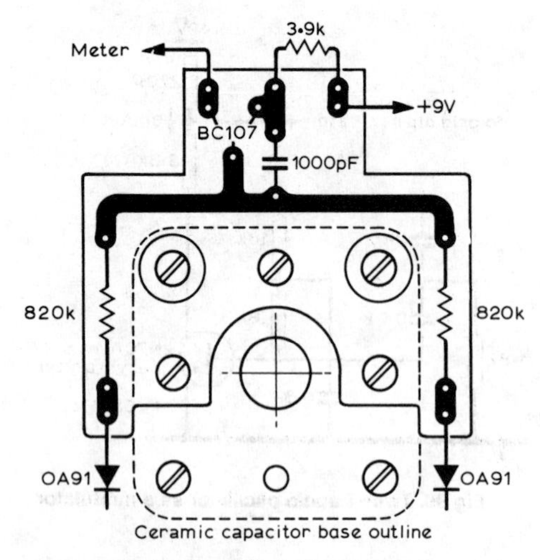

Fig 101. Amplifier indicator board

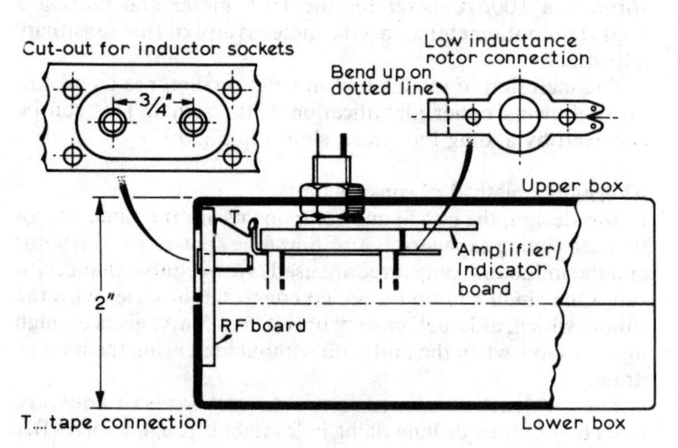

Fig 102. Layout of major components

One half of the case removed

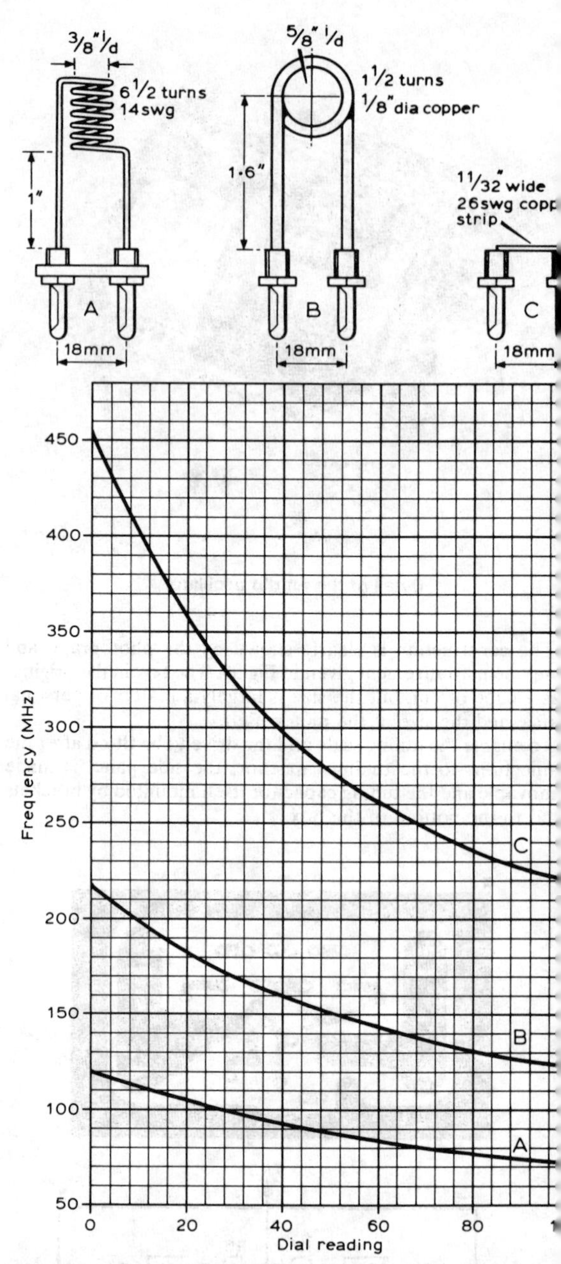

Fig 103. Details of alternative-version coils and calibration curv

carries the amplifier/indicator components. This board attached directly to the ceramic base of the capacitor as in cated in Fig 101.

Fig 102 shows the position of the major components relation to the tuning capacitor, and Fig 103 gives details of three inductors used and their calibration.

A uhf prescaler

A useful prescaler to extend frequency counters to cover up

The completed alternative-construction version

e 1·3GHz band was described in *Ham Radio* December 78. It uses a divide-by-four ic (MC1697) which will operate to 1·5GHz with an input signal of 1mW (Fig 104). "Chip" pacitors are preferred but silver mica may be used. Any ndency to self-oscillation can be overcome by connecting a kΩ resistor between pins 4 and 5 of the ic.

tation monitor for fm transmissions

ansmission of fm is less easily monitored than other forms of odulation which can be checked by a simple diode demodator or meter indicators. With fm it is necessary to use some rm of élementary receiver including a suitable discriminator.

In Fig 106 are shown the essential units of a basic, lownsitivity monitor-receiver. The construction of such a

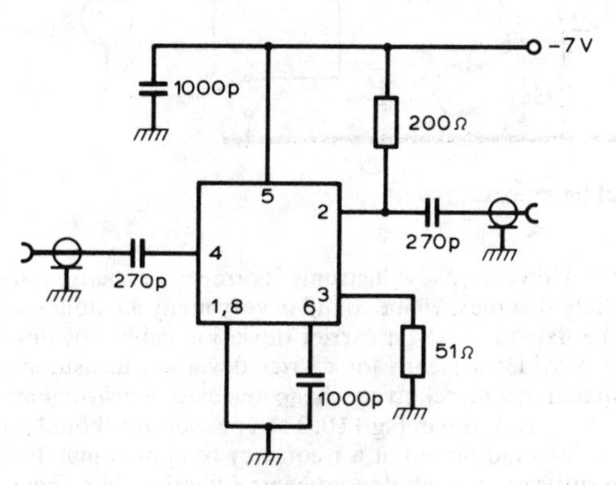

Fig 104. UHF prescaler

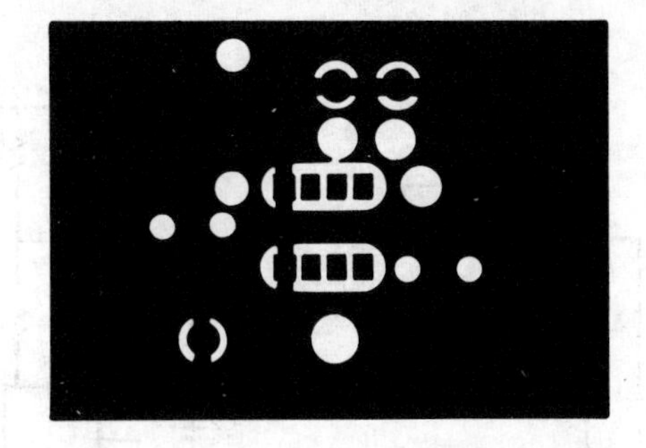

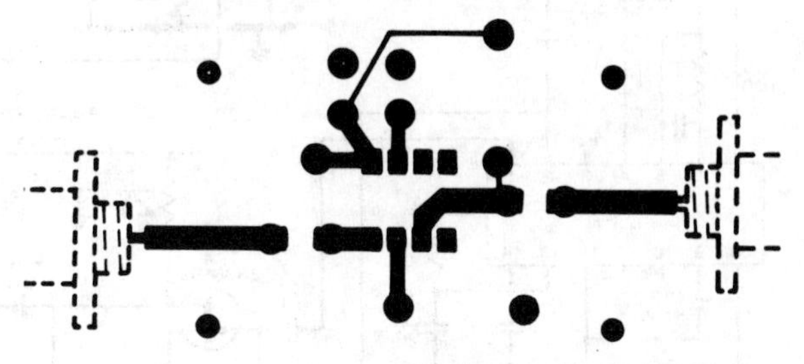

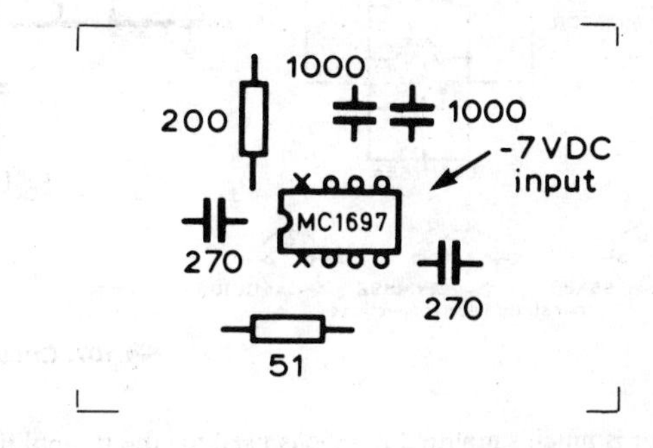

Fig 105. The top and bottom sides of the prescaler pcb are shown in (a) and (b) respectively. In the layout, C, C1 and C2 are installed on the top of the board if glass or mica capacitors are used; if chip ceramics are used they are mounted on the foil side. The leads marked "X" are to be soldered on the ground-plane side

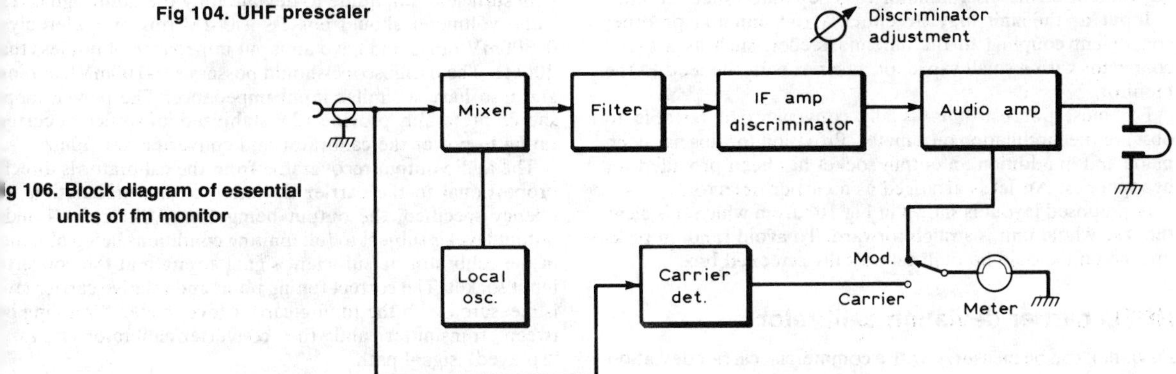

g 106. Block diagram of essential units of fm monitor

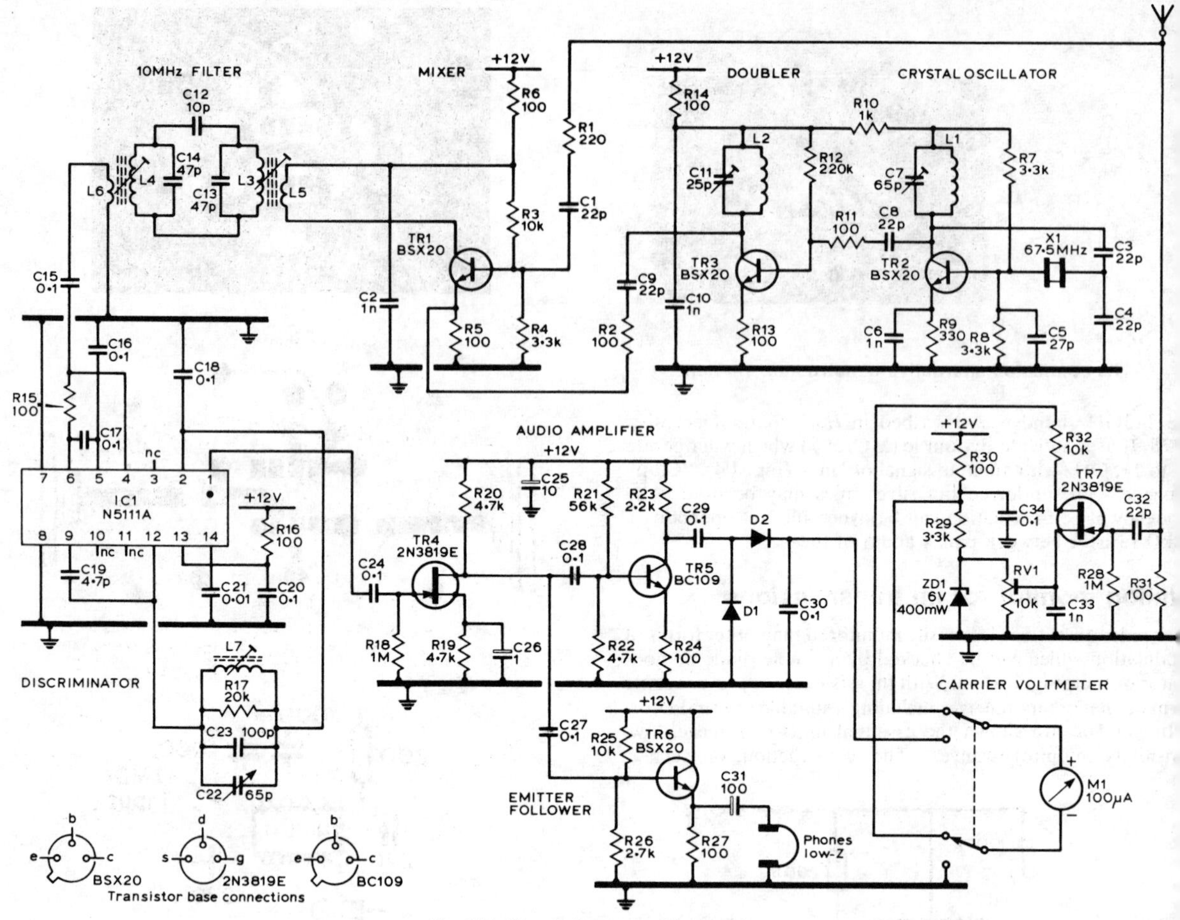

Fig 107. Circuit diagram of fm monitor

receiver is much simplified if an ic is used for the if amplifier-discriminator.

The complete circuit is shown in Fig 107. The input is to a single transistor mixer (any other suitable form of mixer may be used if preferred) with a crystal-controlled local oscillator. The output from the mixer is passed through a reasonably wide-band filter, to feed into the if amplifier. Provision is made for adjustment of the discriminator by a separate tuned circuit.

Input to the unit may be either a rod antenna or other convenient coupling to the antenna feeder, such as a "tee" connector with a small capacitor in series with the lead to the monitor.

For most purpose it is usually convenient to be able to observe the modulation on a meter. Provision for this has been made and in addition an output socket has been provided for headphones. An fet is arranged as a carrier detector.

A proposed layout is shown in Fig 108 from which it is clear that the whole unit is straightforward. To avoid random pick-up, the unit should be built into a fully screened box.

NBFM carrier deviation calibrator

Deviation can be measured with a commercial carrier deviation meter. However, these instruments are very expensive and it unlikely that they will be found in very many amateur station

The narrow-band fm carrier deviation calibrator describ here provides a means for carrier deviation measurement conjunction with relatively cheap and simple instruments. T test set up is shown in Fig 110. The af generator should provi an undistorted output at a frequency of approximately 1kH with sufficient amplitude to deviate fully the nbfm signal. T audio voltmeter should possess a 0–1V rms or preferably 0–300mV range and have an input impedance of not less th 200kΩ. The oscilloscope should possess a 0–100mV/cm ran and also have a similar input impedance. The power supp should preferably provide 12V stabilized, of sufficient curre rating to power the calibrator and converter, say 50mA.

The audio output recoverable from the calibrator is direct proportional to the carrier deviation at the modulation fr quency specified, the output being 100mV/kHz. This aud output level is subject to full limiting conditions being obtaine in the calibrator, ie sufficient signal strength at the convert input socket. The correct tuning point and relative carrier lev is measured with the tuning/carrier level meter. Coupling b tween transmitter and the converter/calibrator is by "sprayed" signal path.

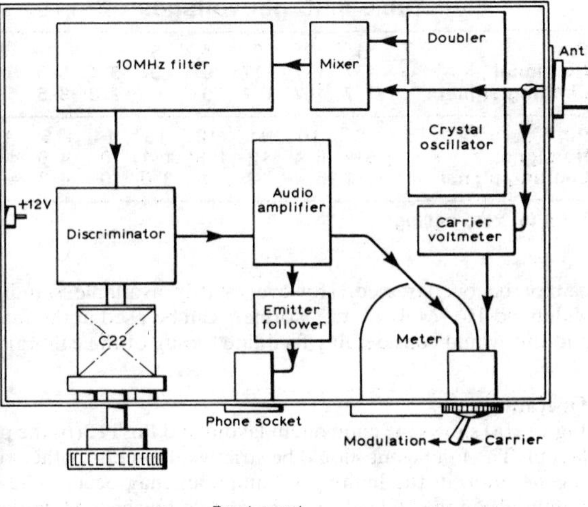

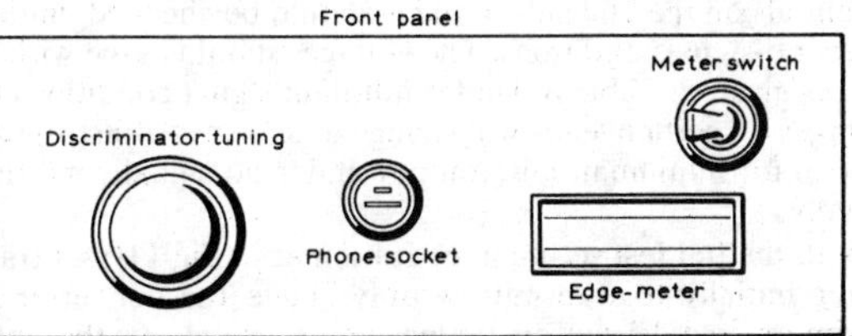

g 108. Typical layout of various units—width 7in, height 2½in, depth 5in.

Table 7. Components list

1, 3, 4,		R1	220Ω
9, 32	22pF	R2, 5, 6,	
2, 6, 10,		11, 13, 14,	
3	1nF	15, 16, 24,	
5	27pF	27, 30, 31	100Ω
7	65pF trimmer	R3, 25	
11	25pF trimmer	32	10kΩ
12	10pF	R4, 7, 8,	
13, 14	47pF	29	3·3kΩ
15, 16,		R9	330Ω
, 18, 20,		R10	1kΩ
, 27, 28,		R12	220kΩ
, 30, 34	0·1μF	R17	20kΩ
19	4·7pF	R18, 28	1MΩ
21	0·01μF	R19, 20,	
22	65pF variable	22	4·7kΩ
23	100pF	R21	56kΩ
25	10μF electrolytic	R23	2·2kΩ
26	1μF electrolytic	R26	2·7kΩ
31	100μF electrolytic	RV1	10kΩ preset
1, 2	silicon	S1	dpdt
1	Signetics N5111A	TR1, 2,	
1	6t ¼in dia	3, 6	BSX20
2	3t ¼in dia	TR4, 7	2N3819E
3, 4	20t 7mm dia slug tuned	TR5	BC109
		X1	67·5MHz
5, 6	4t 7mm dia slug tuned	ZD1	zener diode 6V 400mW
7	19t 4mm dia slug tuned		
1	meter 100μA		
nones	low Z		

All the 0·1μF capacitors were 63V ceramic plates. Apart from the electrolytics, the remainder were low voltage ceramic plates.

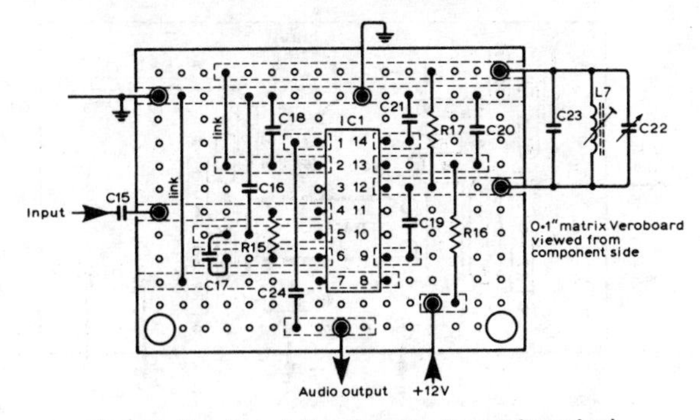

Fig 109. Veroboard discriminator layout (top view)

Design

The design of the calibrator is based upon the CA3089E (RCA). (The SGS-Ates TDA1200 is identical.) The circuit of this ic is complex, but essentially its functions are limiting i.f. amplifier, double balance quadrature detector, level detector and meter drive, mute squelch drive, afc and audio amplifier and internal voltage regulation. Fig 111 shows the external circuit requirements. All the functions of the ic are used except for afc facility. The crystal in the quadrature detector is centred on 10·7MHz, the exact frequency being dependent on the

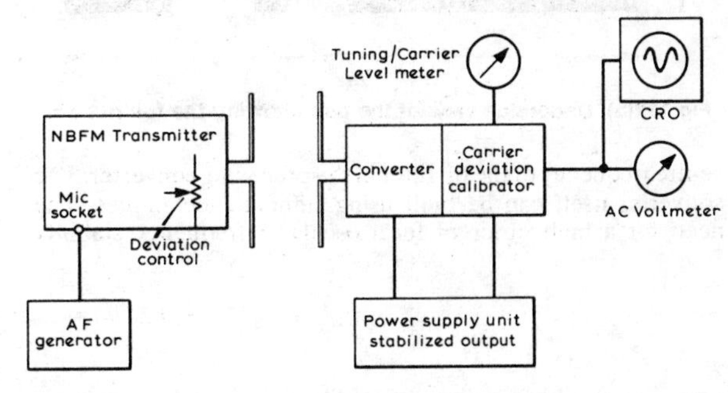

Fig 110. How the carrier deviation calibrator is arranged for nbfm measurements

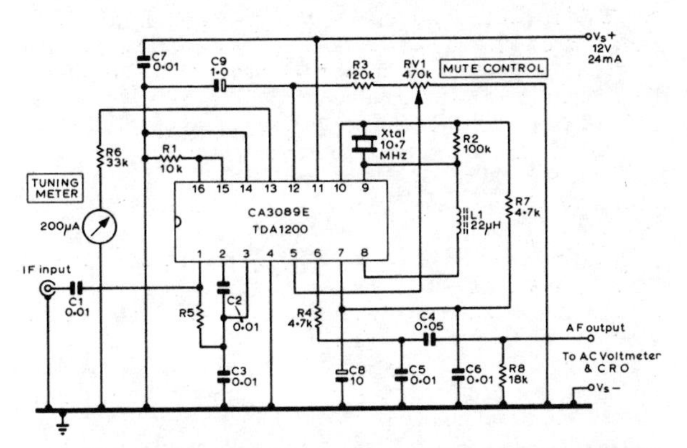

Fig 111. Circuit diagram of the carrier deviation calibrator using the RCA 3089E or the equivalent SGS-Ates TDA1200. The value of R5 depends on the preceding i.f. filter. If in doubt use 47Ω. The voltages on the ic pins are shown in Table 8

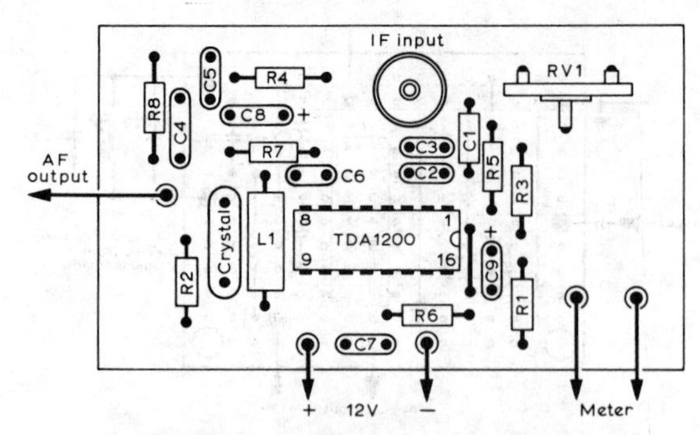

Fig 112(a). Component layout, top view

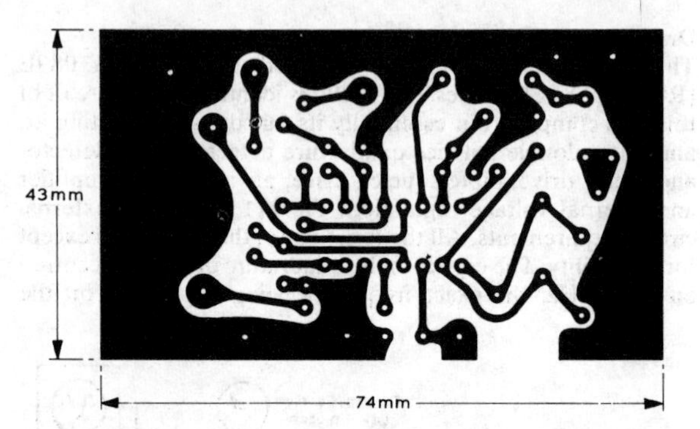

Fig 112(b). Underside view of the pcb showing the foil pattern

centre frequency of the i.f. filter in the preceding converter. The converter itself can be built using standard techniques. The need for a high order of local oscillator frequency stability

Table 8. IC pin voltages

Pin	1	2	3	4	5	6	7	8
No signal	1·7	1·7	1·7	0	0	5·1	5·3	5·
Limiting signal	1·7	1·7	1·7	0	0	7·3	6·6	5·

Pin	9	10	11	12	13	14	15	16
No signal	5·2	5·4	12	1·8*	1·1	0	4·6	4·
Limiting signal	5·2	5·4	12	0	3·0	0	4·3	4·

* Set for zero muting.

cannot be overstressed. However, easily available standai wideband 10·7MHz i.f. transformers can be used in the filte and this would considerably facilitate tuning of the calibrato

Operation

Fig 112(a) shows the component layout and Fig 112(b) the pc layout. The foil layout should be strictly adhered to, otherwis regeneration in the limiting i.f. amplifier may occur. The potentials on the 16 leads of the ic should be checked, initial under no-signal conditions. The voltages should agree with th figures given in Table 8. Under full-limit signal conditions th voltages on certain leads will change as shown. Adjust squelc control for minimum noise output under no-signal conditio initially.

With the full test set-up in operation as in Fig 110 set tran mitter initially to transmit cw only. Tune the converter f maximum signal level on tuning meter, switch on the audi generator and adjust audio gain/deviation control to give reading of 300mV on audio voltmeter, corresponding to pea deviation of (±) 3kHz of transmitter carrier. Adjust th attenuator or oscilloscope for a satisfactory waveform heigh and note the peak-to-peak deflection. Disconnect audi generator and replace with a microphone. Under norma speech conditions ensure that the peak-to-peak deflection do not exceed the deflection with a constant 1kHz tone.

PENDIX

ata

mponent colour codes

e electrical parameters of fixed resistors and capacitors are ally indicated by colour codes. The same colour code is netimes used to indicate the type numbers of semi- iductors.

Standard colour code

lour	Significant figure	Decimal multiplier	Tolerance (per cent)
ck	0	1	—
wn	1	10	± 1
d	2	100	± 2
ange	3	1,000	± 3
llow	4	10,000	+100, −0
een	5	100,000	± 5
e	6	1,000,000	± 6
let	7	10,000,000	—
ey	8	0·01	
ite	9	0·1	—
d	—	—	± 5
ver	—	—	±10
colour	—	—	±20

Marking of resistors

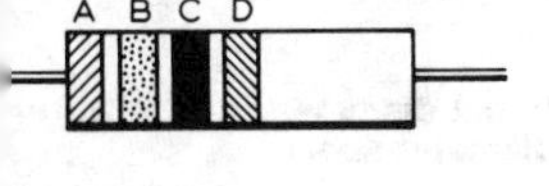

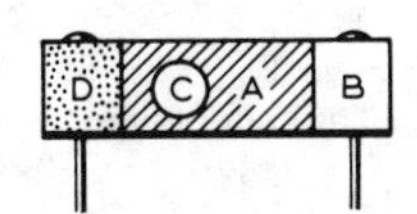

ial leads	Colour indicates	Radial leads
and A	First significant figure of value in Ω	Body A
and B	Second significant figure	End B
and C	Decimal multiplier	Dot C
and D	Tolerance	B and D

S 1852 Resistor Code

esistor value

47Ω	marked R47
00Ω	marked 1R0
7Ω	marked 4R7
·0Ω	marked 10R
·0Ω	marked 47R
0·0Ω	marked 100R
Ω	marked 1K0
KΩ	marked 10K
Ω	marked 1M0
MΩ	marked 10M

Tolerance suffix

F	± 1 per cent
G	± 2 per cent
J	± 5 per cent
K	± 10 per cent
M	± 20 per cent

Examples

R33M	= 0·33Ω	± 20 per cent
4R7K	= 4·7Ω	± 10 per cent
390RJ	= 390Ω	± 5 per cent
6K8F	= 6·8kΩ	± 1 per cent
68KK	= 68kΩ	± 10 per cent
4M7M	= 4·7MΩ	± 20 per cent

Marking of fixed ceramic capacitors

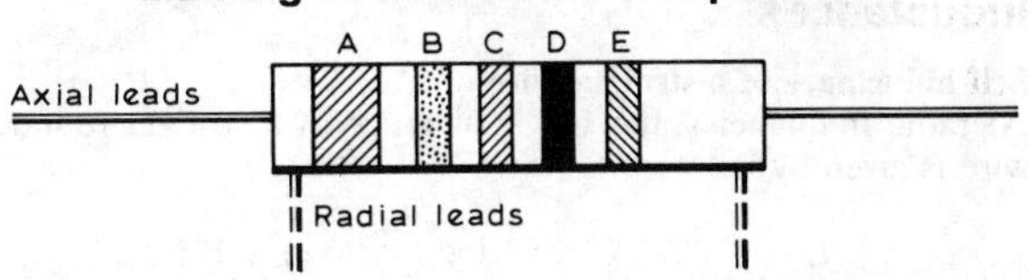

The standard colour code applies to Bands B–E inclusive, Band A has the following significance

Colour	Temperature coefficient (parts/million/°C)
Black	0
Brown	− 30
Red	− 80
Orange	−150
Yellow	−220
Green	−330
Blue	−470
Violet	−750
Grey	+ 30
White	+100 to −750

Band or stripe A—Temperature coefficient
Band or stripe B—First significant figure
Band or stripe C—Second significant figure
Band or stripe D—Decimal multiplier
Band or stripe E—Tolerance

Marking of tantalum capacitors

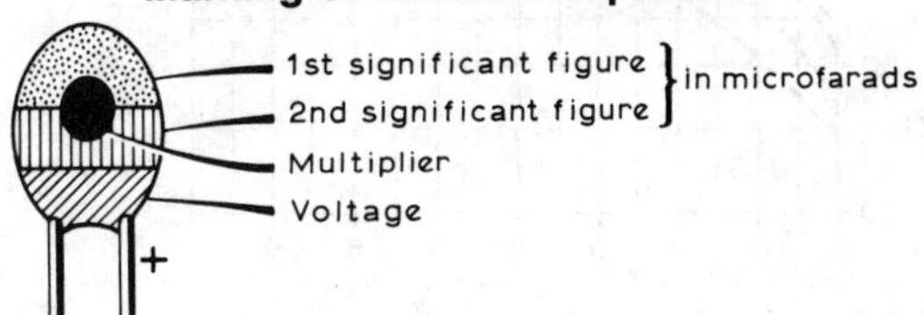

The standard colour code applies except for voltage

Colour	Voltage (V)
Yellow	6·3
Green	16
Blue	20
Grey	25
White	3
Black	10
Pink	35

Marking of polyester capacitors

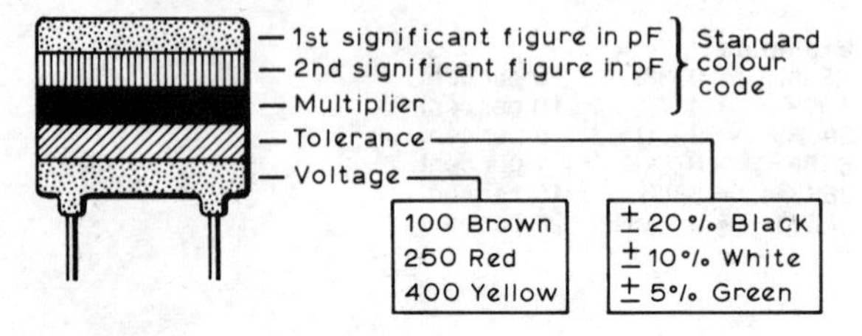

Inductances

Self inductance of a straight wire

At radio frequencies, the self inductance of a straight round wire is given by

$$L = 0{\cdot}0021\,(2{\cdot}303 \log_{10} \frac{4l}{d} - 1)\ \mu\text{H}$$

where l = length in centimetres
d = dia in centimetres

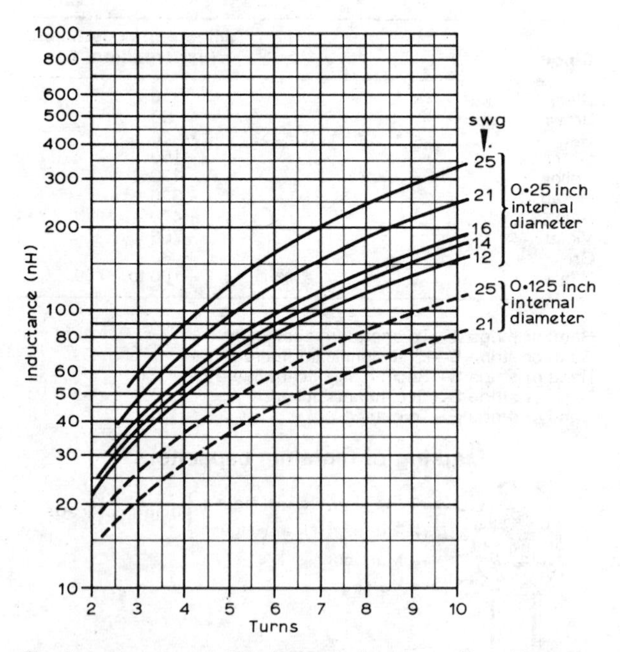

The inductance of 0·25in internal diameter coils with turns spaced one diameter apart

Inductance of a single-layer coil

The inductance of a single-layer coil of length at least equal its radius is given by

$$L = \frac{N^2r^2}{9r + 10l}\ \mu\text{H}$$

where r = radius of coil (in)
l = length of coil (in)
N = number of turns

This applies to both close-wound and spaced-turn coils. C respondingly, the number of turns for a given inductance i

$$N = L\sqrt{\frac{9r + 10l}{r^2}}$$

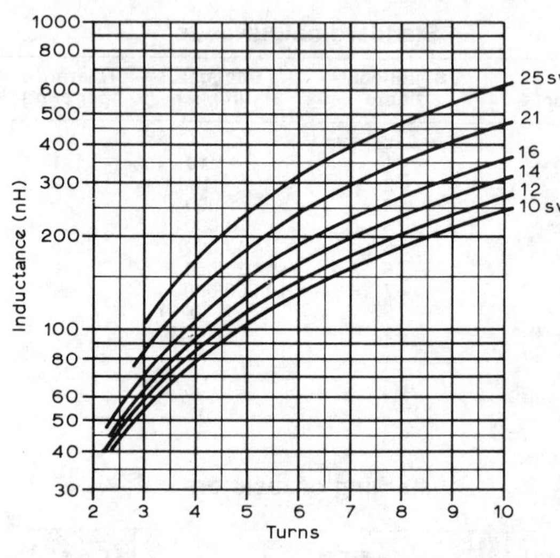

The inductance of 0·375in internal diameter coils with tur spaced one diameter apart

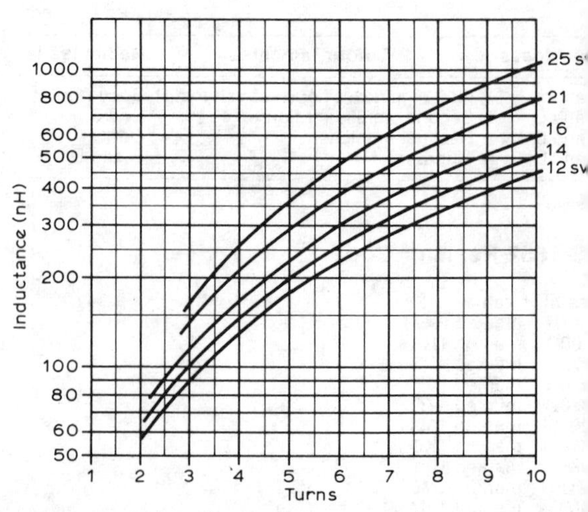

The inductance of 0·5in internal diameter coils, with tur spaced one diameter apart

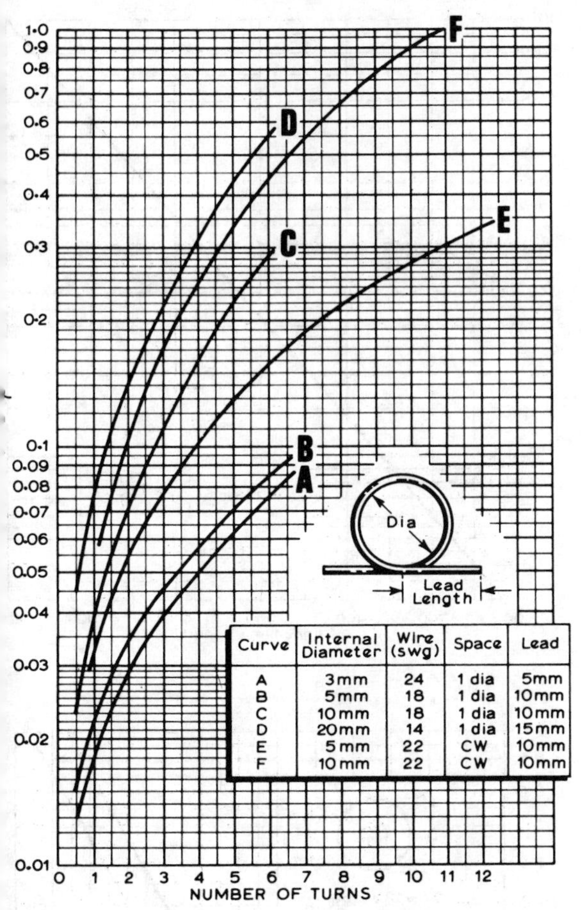

Curve	Internal Diameter	Wire (swg)	Space	Lead
A	3mm	24	1 dia	5mm
B	5mm	18	1 dia	10mm
C	10mm	18	1 dia	10mm
D	20mm	14	1 dia	15mm
E	5mm	22	CW	10mm
F	10mm	22	CW	10mm

Characteristics of small inductors

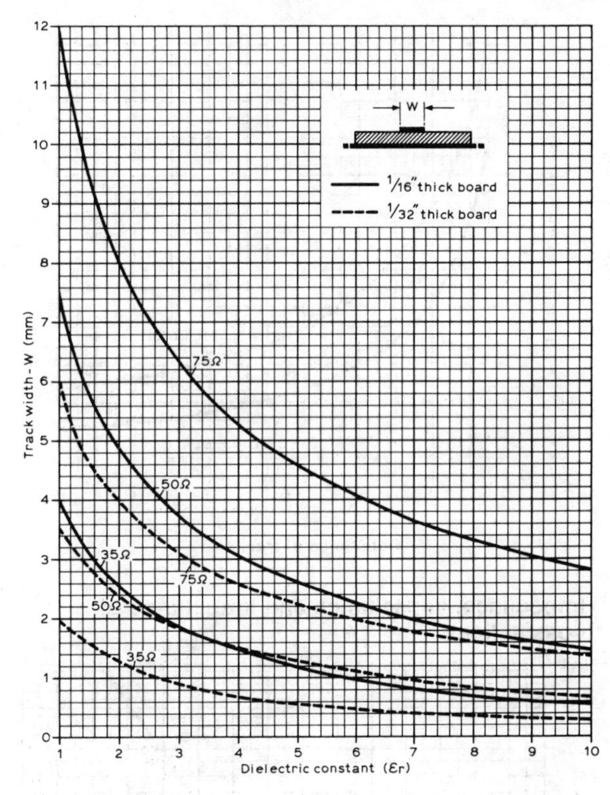

Characteristic impedance of tracks on double-sided boards

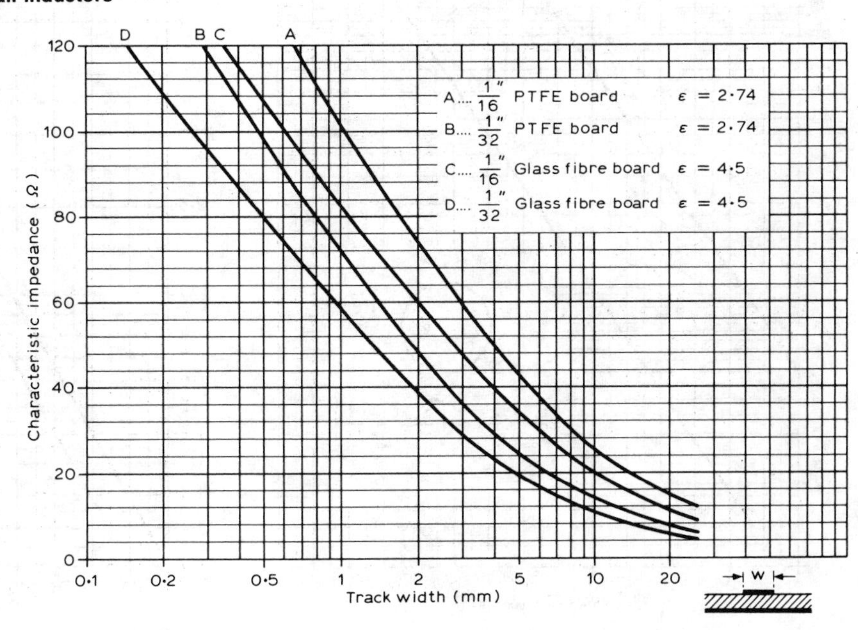

haracteristic impedance of racks on double-sided boards

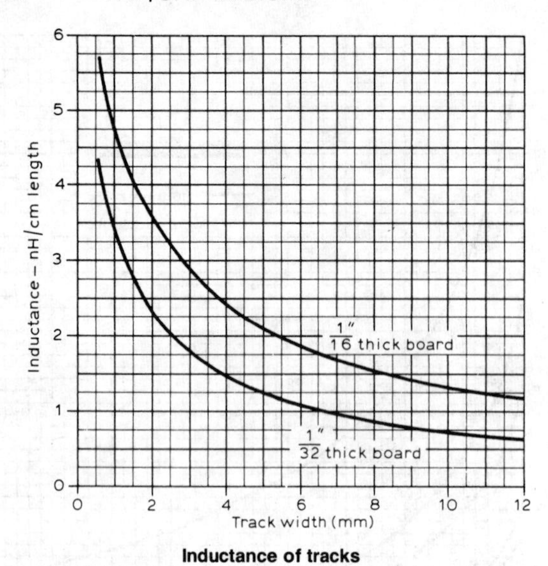

Inductance of tracks

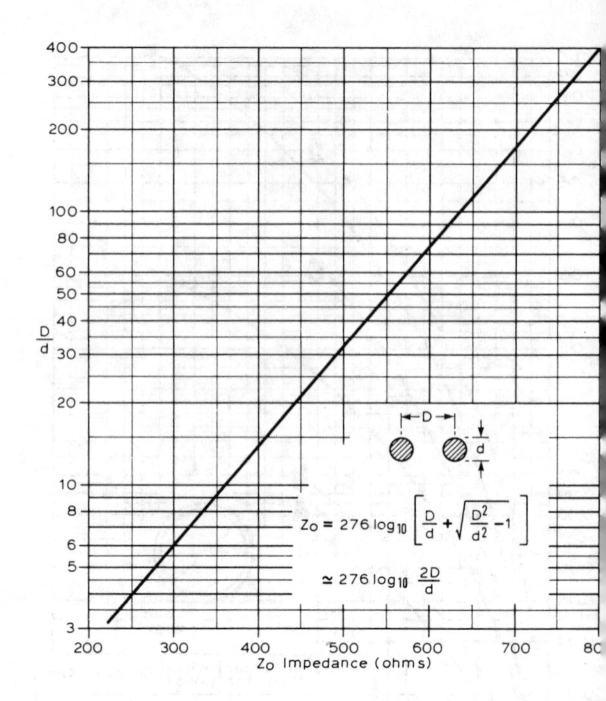

D/d
$Z_O = 276 \log_{10}\left[\frac{D}{d} + \sqrt{\frac{D^2}{d^2} - 1}\right]$
$\simeq 276 \log_{10} \frac{2D}{d}$
Z_O Impedance (ohms)

Impedance, capacitance and inductance of coaxial lines

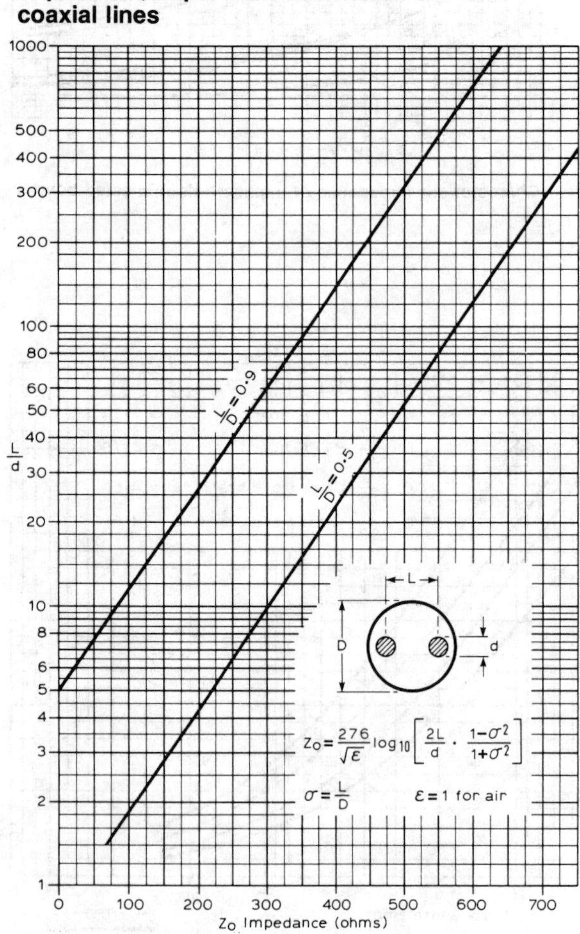

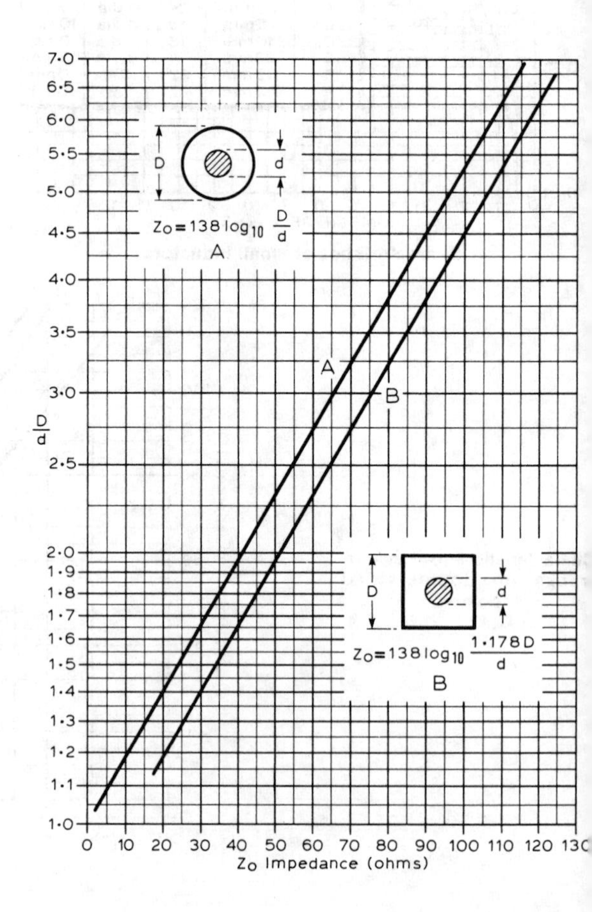

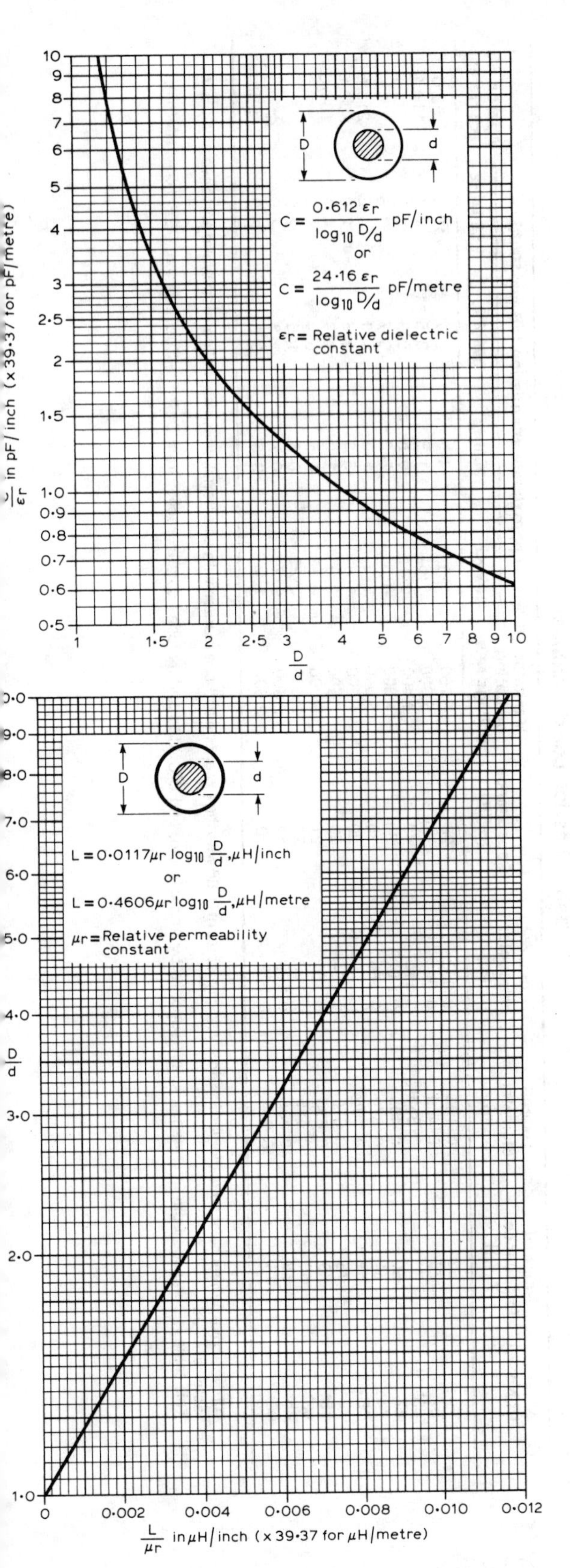
D
d
$C = \frac{0\cdot612\,\varepsilon_r}{\log_{10} D/d}$ pF/inch
or
$C = \frac{24\cdot16\,\varepsilon_r}{\log_{10} D/d}$ pF/metre
ε_r = Relative dielectric constant
$\frac{C}{\varepsilon_r}$ in pF/inch (x 39·37 for pF/metre)
$\frac{D}{d}$
$L = 0\cdot0117\mu_r \log_{10} \frac{D}{d}$, μH/inch
or
$L = 0\cdot4606\mu_r \log_{10} \frac{D}{d}$, μH/metre
μ_r = Relative permeability constant
$\frac{L}{\mu_r}$ in μH/inch (x 39·37 for μH/metre)

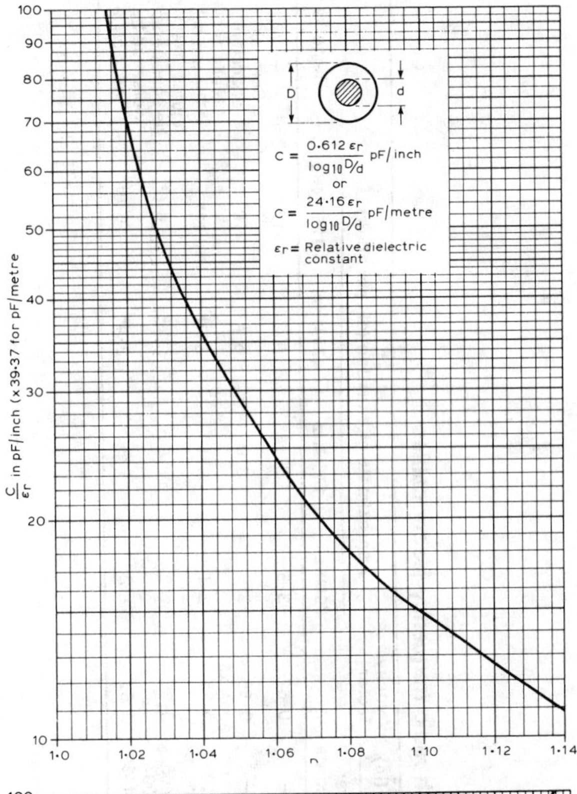
D
d
$C = \frac{0\cdot612\,\varepsilon_r}{\log_{10} D/d}$ pF/inch
or
$C = \frac{24\cdot16\,\varepsilon_r}{\log_{10} D/d}$ pF/metre
ε_r = Relative dielectric constant
$\frac{C}{\varepsilon_r}$ in pF/inch (x 39·37 for pF/metre

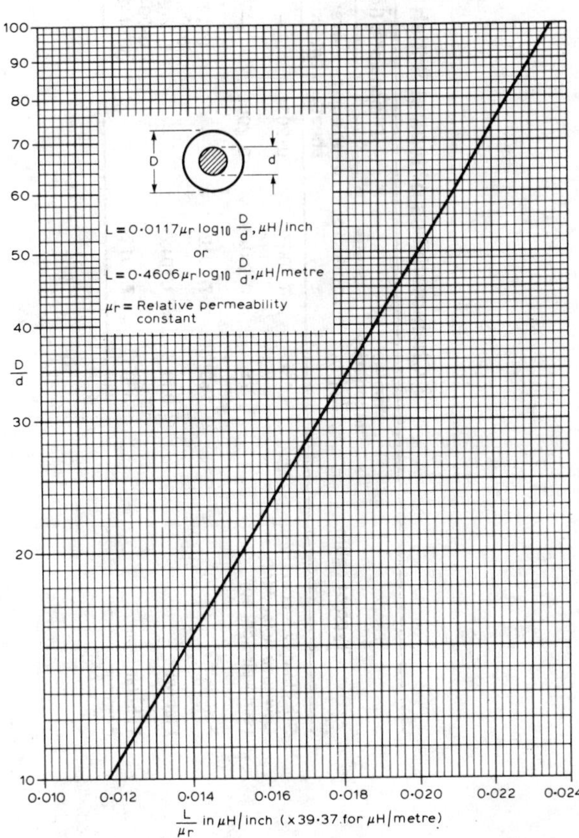
D
d
$L = 0\cdot0117\mu_r \log_{10} \frac{D}{d}$, μH/inch
or
$L = 0\cdot4606\mu_r \log_{10} \frac{D}{d}$, μH/metre
μ_r = Relative permeability constant
$\frac{D}{d}$
$\frac{L}{\mu_r}$ in μH/inch (x 39·37 for μH/metre)

Characteristics of typical British radio frequency feeder cables

Type of cable	Nominal impedance Z_0 (Ω)	Centre conductor	Dimensions (in) over outer sheath	Dimensions (in) over twincores	Velocity factor	Approximate attenuation (dB per 100ft) 70Mhz	145MHz	430MHz	1250MHz	Remarks
Standard tv feeder	75	7/·0076	0·202	—	0·67	3·5	5·1	9·2	17	—
Low-loss tv feeder (semi-air spaced)	75	0·048	0·290	—	0·86	2·0	3·0	5·4	10	Semi-air spaced or cellular
Flat twin	150	7/·012	—	0·18 0·09	approx. 0·71	2·1	3·1	5·7*	11*	*Theoretical figures, likely to be considerably worsened by radiation
Flat twin	300	7/·012	—	0·405 0·09	0·85	1·2	1·8	3·4*	6·6*	
Tubular twin	300	7/·012	—	0·446	0·85	1·2	1·8	3·4*	6·6*	

British UR series coaxial cables

UR No	Nominal impedance Z_0 (Ω)	Overall diameter (in)	Inner conductor (in)	Capacitance (pF/ft)	Maximum operating voltage rms	Approximate attenuation (dB per 100ft) 10MHz	100MHz	300MHz	1,000MHz	Approx RG. equivalent
43	52	0·195	0·032	29	2,750	1·3	4·3	8·7	18·1	58/U
57	75	0·405	0·044	20·6	5,000	0·6	1·9	3·5	7·1	11A/U
63*	75	0·853	0·175	14	4,400	0·15	0·5	0·9	1·7	
67	50	0·405	7/0·029	30	4,800	0·6	2·0	3·7	7·5	213/U
74	51	0·870	0·188	30·7	15,000	0·3	1·0	1·9	4·2	218/U
76	51	0·195	19/0·0066	29	1,800	1·6	5·3	9·6	22·0	58C/U
77	75	0·870	0·104	20·5	12,500	0·3	1·0	1·9	4·2	164/U
79*	50	0·855	0·265	21	6,000	0·16	0·5	0·9	1·8	
83*	50	0·555	0·168	21	2,600	0·25	0·8	1·5	2·8	
85*	75	0·555	0·109	14	2,600	0·2	0·7	1·3	2·5	
90	75	0·242	0·022	0	2,500	1·1	3·5	6·3	12·3	59B/U

All the above cables have solid dielectric with a velocity factor of 0·66 with the exception of those marked with an asterisk which are helical membrane and have a velocity factor of 0·96.

This table is compiled from information kindly supplied by Aerialite Ltd, and BICC Ltd and includes data extracted from Defence Specification, DEF-14-A (HMSO).

USA RG series coaxial cables

Cable No.	Nominal impedance Z_0 (Ω)	Cable outside diameter (in)	Velocity factor	Approximate attenuation (dB per 100ft)					Capacitance (pF/ft)	Maximum operating voltage (rms)
				1MHz	10MHz	100MHz	1,000MHz	3,000MHz		
RG-5/U	52·5	0·332	0·659	0·21	0·77	2·9	11·5	22·0	28·5	3,000
RG-5B/U	50·0	0·332	0·659	0·16	0·66	2·4	8·8	16·7	29·5	3,000
RG-6A/U	75·0	0·332	0·659	0·21	0·78	2·9	11·2	21·0	20·0	2,700
RG-8A/U	50·0	0·405	0·659	0·16	0·55	2·0	8·0	16·5	30·5	4,000
RG-9/U	51·0	0·420	0·659	0·16	0·57	2·0	7·3	15·5	30·0	4,000
RG-9B/U	50·0	0·425	0·659	0·175	0·61	2·1	9·0	18·0	30·5	4,000
RG-10A/U	50·0	0·475	0·659	0·16	0·55	2·0	8·0	16·5	30·5	4,000
RG-11A/U	75·0	0·405	0·66	0·18	0·7	2·3	7·8	16·5	20·5	5,000
RG-12A/U	75·0	0·475	0·659	0·18	0·66	2·3	8·0	16·5	20·5	4,000
RG-13A/U	75·0	0·425	0·659	0·18	0·66	2·3	8·0	16·5	20·5	4,000
RG-14A/U	50·0	0·545	0·659	0·12	0·41	1·4	5·5	12·0	30·0	5,500
RG-16/U	52·0	0·630	0·670	0·1	0·4	1·2	6·7	16·0	29·5	6,000
RG-17A/U	50·0	0·870	0·659	0·066	0·225	0·80	3·4	8·5	30·0	11,000
RG-18A/U	50·0	0·945	0·659	0·066	0·225	0·80	3·4	8·5	30·5	11,000
RG-19A/U	50·0	1·120	0·659	0·04	0·17	0·68	3·5	7·7	30·5	14,000
RG-20A/U	50·0	1·195	0·659	0·04	0·17	0·68	3·5	7·7	30·5	14,000
RG-21A/U	50·0	0·332	0·659	1·4	4·4	13·0	43·0	85·0	30·0	2,700
RG-29/U	53·5	0·184	0·659	0·33	1·2	4·4	16·0	30·0	28·5	1,900
RG-34A/U	75·0	0·630	0·659	0·065	0·29	1·3	6·0	12·5	20·5	5,200
RG-34B/U	75	0·630	0·66		0·3	1·4	5·8		21·5	6,500
RG-35A/U	75·0	0·945	0·659	0·07	0·235	0·85	3·5	8·60	20·5	10,000
RG-54A/U	58·0	0·250	0·659	0·18	0·74	3·1	11·5	21·5	26·5	3,000
RG-55/U	53·5	0·206	0·659	0·36	1·3	4·8	17·0	32·0	28·5	1,900
RG-55A/U	50·0	0·216	0·659	0·36	1·3	4·8	17·0	32·0	29·5	1,900
RG-58/U	53·5	0·195	0·659	0·33	1·25	4·65	17·5	37·5	28·5	1,900
RG-58C/U	50·0	0·195	0·659	0·42	1·4	4·9	24·0	45·0	30·0	1,900
RG-59A/U	75·0	0·242	0·659	0·34	1·10	3·40	12·0	26·0	20·5	2,300
RG-59B/U	75	0·242	0·66		1·1	3·4	12		21	2,300
RG-62A/U	93·0	0·242	0·84	0·25	0·85	2·70	8·6	18·5	13·5	750
RG-74A/U	50·0	0·615	0·659	0·10	0·38	1·5	6·0	11·5	30·0	5,500
RG-83/U	35·0	0·405	0·66	0·23	0·80	2·8	9·6	24·0	44·0	2,000
*RG-213/U	50	0·405	0·66	0·16	0·6	1·9	8·0		29·5	5,000
†RG-218/U	50	0·870	0·66	0·066	0·2	1·0	4·4		29·5	11,000
‡RG-220/U	50	1·120	0·66	0·04	0·2	0·7	3·6		29·5	14,000

* Formerly RG8A/U † Formerly RG17A/U ‡ Formerly RG19A/U

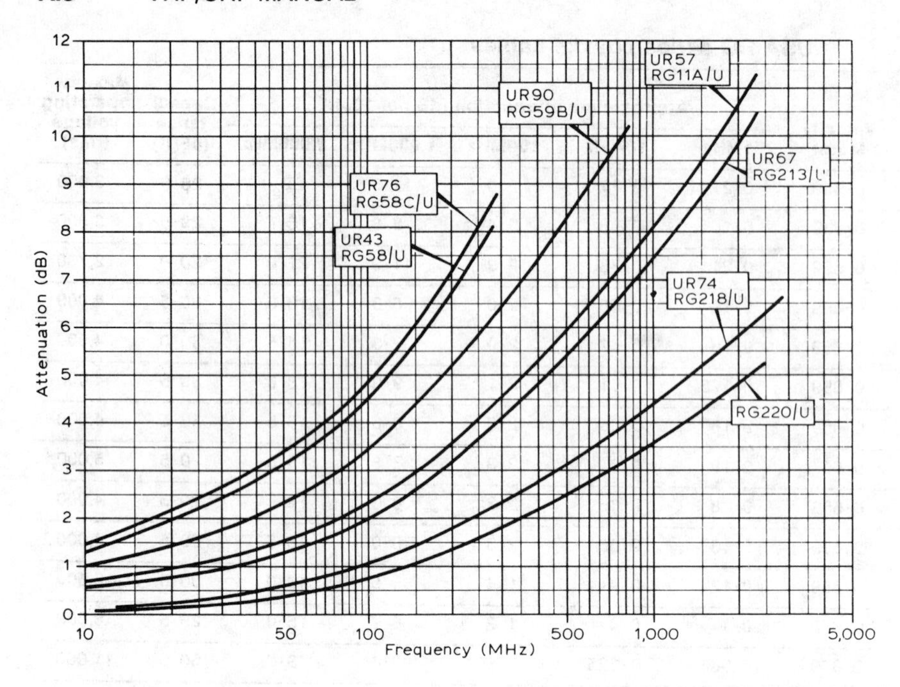

Attenuation of various cables

Waveguide sizes

Frequency (GHz)	Wavelength (cm)	WG Internal dimensions (in)	WG Internal dimensions (cm)	RCSC British WG No	British Inter-Services Ref No: Brass 70/30	British Inter-Services Ref No: Aluminium	EIA WR ( )	IEC R ( )	NATO NWG (1 or 2)*	JAN Type RG ( ): Copper or brass	JAN Type RG ( ): Aluminium	JAN Type RG ( ): Silver	Cut-off Frequency
0·32– 0·49	93·68–61·18	23·80 ×11·5	58·420 ×29·210	00			2300	3	01				0·26
0·35– 0·53	85·65–56·56	21·0 ×10·5	53·34 ×26·670	0			2100	4	02				0·28
0·41– 0·625	73·11–47·96	18·0 × 9·0	45·72 ×22·86	1			1800	5	03		201		0·32
0·49– 0·75	61·18–39·97	15·0 × 7·5	38·1 ×19·65	2			1500	6	04		202		0·39
0·64– 0·96	46·84–31·23	11·5 × 5·75	29·210 ×14·605	3			1150	8	05		203		0·51
0·75– 1·12	39·95–26·76	9·75 × 4·875	24·765 ×12·3825	4			975	9	06		204		0·605
0·96– 1·45	31·23–20·67	7·7 × 3·85	19·558 × 9·779	5			770	12	07		205		0·76
1·12– 1·70	26·76–17·63	6·5 × 3·25	16·510 × 8·255	6		012–0037	650	14	08	69	103		0·90
1·45– 2·20	20·67–13·62	5·1 × 2·55	12·954 × 6·477	7			510	18	09				1·15
1·70– 2·60	17·63–11·53	4·3 × 2·15	10·922 × 5·461	8	083–0144	083–0144	430	22	10	104	105		1·372
2·20– 3·30	13·63– 9·08	3·4 × 1·7	8·636 × 4·318	9A	012–0040	012–0042	340	24	11	112	113		1·76
2·60– 3·95	11·53– 7·59	2·84 × 1·34	7·2163× 3·403	10	083–0068	083–0069	284	32	12	48	75		2·07
3·30– 4·90	9·08– 6·12	2·29 × 1·145	5·8166× 2·909	11A	012–0045	012–0047	229	40	13				2·57
3·95– 5·85	7·95– 5·12	1·872× 0·872	4·7549× 2·2149	12	083–0077	083–0078	187	48	14	49	95		3·15
4·90– 7·05	6·12– 4·25	1·59 × 0·795	4·0486× 2·0193	13	083–0146	083–0147	159	58	15				3·71
5·85– 8·20	5·12– 3·66	1·372× 0·622	3·4849× 1·58	14	083–0081	083–0082	137	70	16	50	106		4·30
7·05– 10·00	4·25– 2·99	1·122× 0·497	2·880 × 1·2624	15	083–0086	083–0087	112	84	17	51	68		5·25
8·20– 12·40	3·66– 2·42	0·90 × 0·40	2·286 × 1·016	16	083–0097	083–0099	90	100	18	52	67		6·557
10·00– 15·00	2·99– 2·00	0·75 × 0·375	1·9050× 0·9525	17	———		75	120	19				2·868
12·40– 18·00	2·42– 1·66	0·622× 0·311	1·58 × 0·790	18	083–0101		62	140	20	91		107	9·426
15·00– 22·00	2·00– 1·36	0·510× 0·255	1·295 × 0·6477	19			51	180	21				11·574
18·00– 26·50	1·66– 1·13	0·420× 0·170	1·0668× 0·4318	20	Precision		42	220	22	53	121	66	14·047
22·00– 33·00	1·36– 0·91	0·340× 0·170	0·8636× 0·4318	21			34	260	23				17·328
26·50– 40·00	1·13 –0·75	0·280× 0·140	0·7112× 0·3556	22	083–1500		28	320	24			96	21·081
33·00– 50·00	0·91– 0·60	0·224× 0·112	0·5659× 0·2845	23	083–1501		22	400	25			97	26·342
40·00– 60·00	0·75– 0·50	0·188× 0·94	0·4775× 0·2388	24	083–1502		19	500	26				31·357
50·00– 75·00	0·60– 0·40	0·148× 0·074	0·3759× 0·1880	25	083–1503		15	620	27			98	39·863
60·00– 90·00	0·50– 0·33	0·122× 0·061	0·3098× 0·1550	26	083–1504		12	740	28			99	48·350
75·00–100·00	0·40– 0·27	0·100× 0·050	0·2540× 0·1270	27	083–1505		10	900	29				59·010
90·00–140·0	0·33– 0·22	0·080× 0·040	0·2032× 0·1016	28	083–1506		8	1200	30				73·80
140·00–220·0	0·22– 0·14	0·051× 0·025	0·1295× 0·0635										116·80

Note: (1) Aluminium. (2) Copper based alloy.

The cut-off wavelength of a rectangular waveguide, the wide dimension of which is *a* cm given by $\lambda_{co} = 2a$.

For a waveguide $\frac{1}{\lambda^2} + \frac{1}{\lambda_{co}^2} = \frac{1}{\lambda_o^2}$

where λ = waveguide wavelength, λ_{co} = waveguide cut-off wavelength, and λ_o = free space wavelength.

Standing wave ratio charts

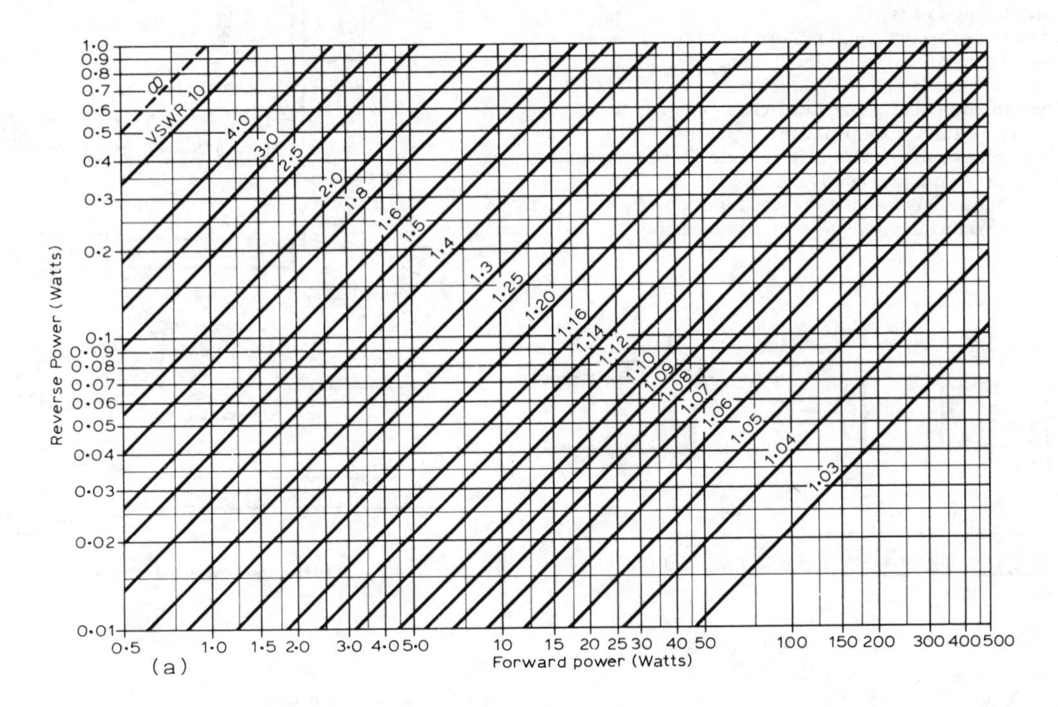

(a)

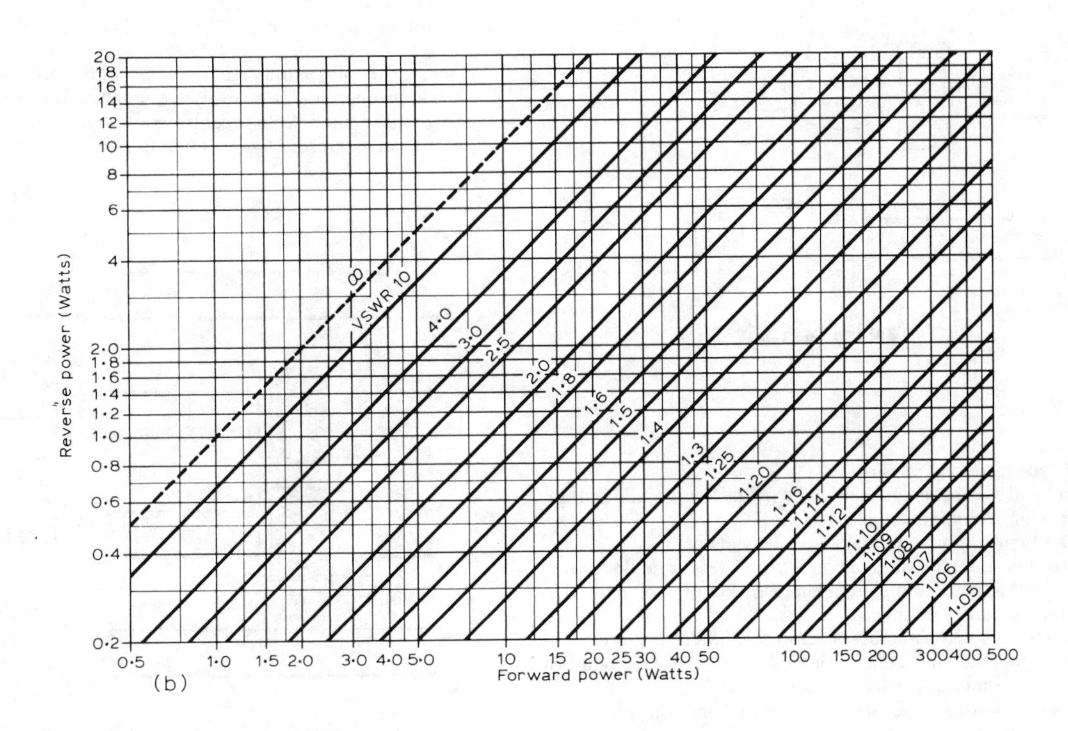

(b)

Coaxial plug assembly

Standard Belling Lee type

1. Cut end of cable even and remove $\frac{7}{8}$in of outer sheath.
2. Remove $\frac{5}{8}$in of dielectric without damaging the inner conductor. Tin lightly end of conductor.
3. Slide cap and collet clamp over cable and slightly clench collet in position. Comb out the braid and fan out over collet. Solder cable centre conductor to tip of plug centre conductor. Avoid overheating.
4. Push sub-assembly into the body as far as possible. Gently screw cap on to the body to complete assembly.

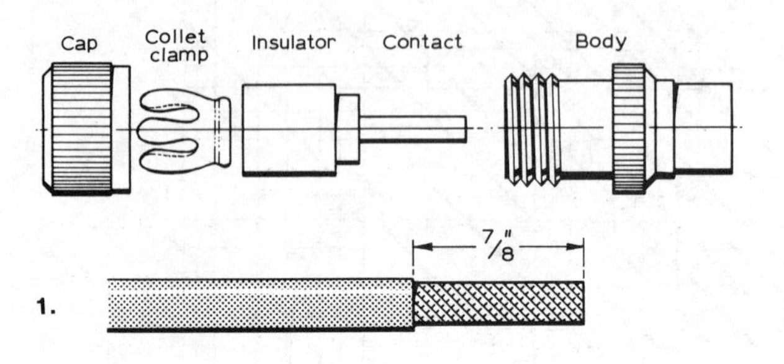

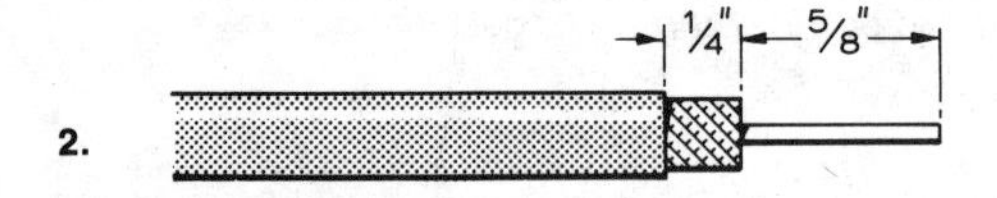

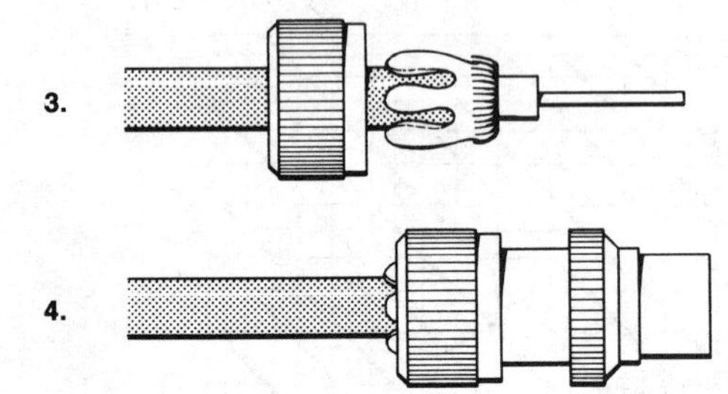

Belling Lee type

UHF type (clamped screen)

1. Cut end of cable even. Remove vinyl jacket $\frac{3}{4}$in. Slide coupling ring and adapter on cable.
2. Fan braid slightly and fold back as shown.
3. Position adapter to dimension shown. Press braid down over body of adapter and trim to $\frac{3}{8}$in. Bare $\frac{5}{8}$in of conductor. Tin exposed centre conductor.
4. Screw plug sub-assembly on adapter. Solder braid to shell through solder holes. Use enough heat to create bond of braid to shell. Solder conductor to contact.
5. For final assembly, screw coupling ring on plug sub-assembly.

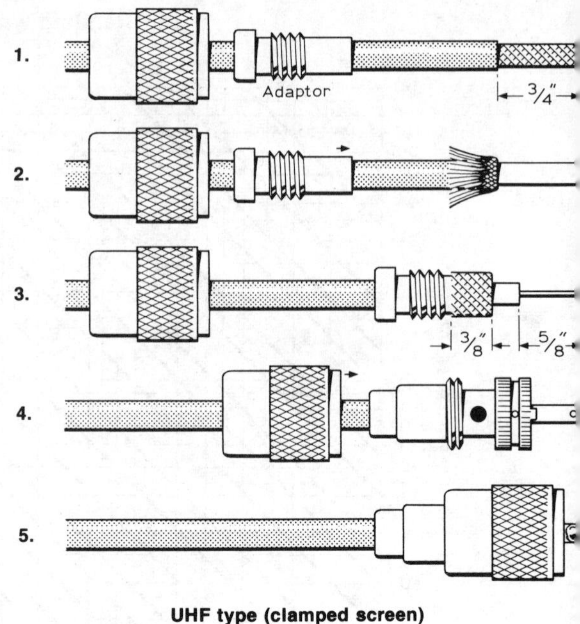

UHF type (clamped screen)

UHF type (soldered screen)

1. Cut end of cable even. Remove vinyl jacket $1\frac{1}{8}$in.
2. Bare $\frac{5}{8}$in of centre conductor. Trim braided shield. Slid coupling ring on cable. Tin exposed centre conductor an braid.
3. Screw the plug sub-assembly on cable. Solder assembly t braid through solder holes. Use enough heat to create bon to braid to shell. Solder centre conductor to contact.
4. For final assembly, screw coupling ring on plug subassem bly.

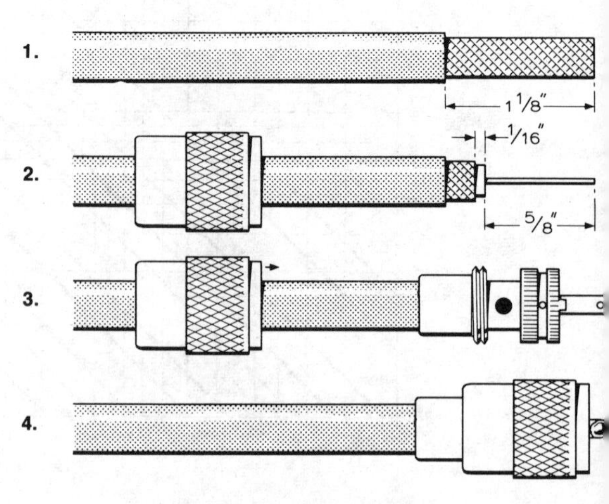

UHF type (soldered screen)

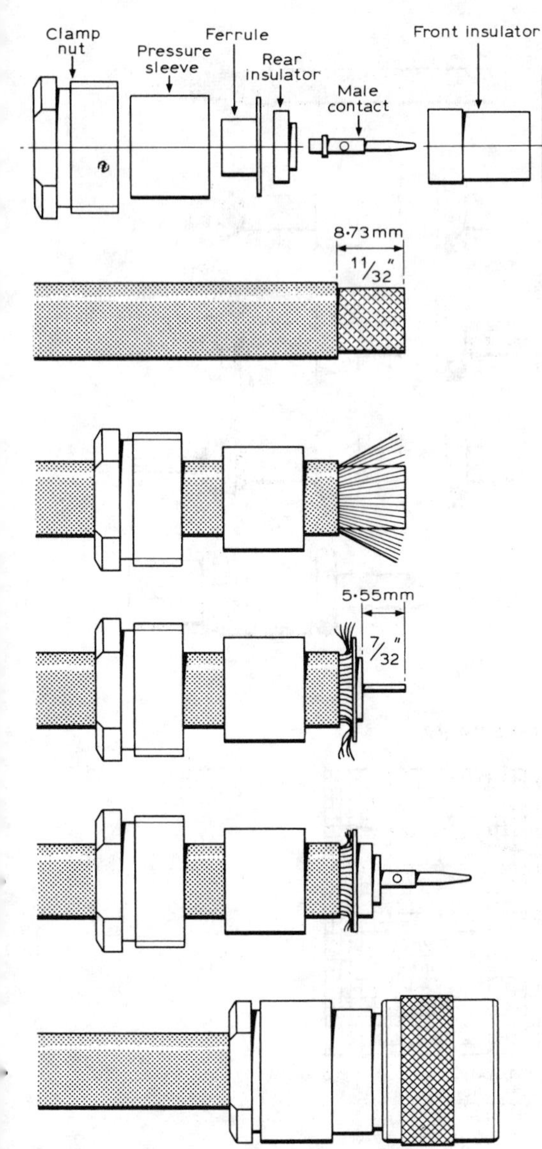

N type

N type

1. Cut end of cable even and remove 8·73mm ($\frac{11}{32}$in) of outer sheath.
2. Slide the clamp nut and pressure sleeve over cable. Comb out the braid.
3. Fold the braid back. Insert the ferrule between braid and dielectric. Trim off excess braid. Remove 5·55mm ($\frac{7}{32}$in) of the dielectric without damaging the inner conductor. Tin end of conductor.
4. Slide rear insulator over conductor and position against end of dielectric. Slide the contact over conductor until the shoulder of the contact is pressed hard against the rear insulator. Solder the contact to the conductor but avoid over-heating.
5. Fit front insulator in body and push sub-assembly into the body as far as possible. Slide pressure sleeve into body and screw in the clamp nut tightly to clamp cable.

BNC type (male contact)

1. Cut end of cable even and remove 7·93mm ($\frac{5}{16}$in) of outer sheath.
2. Slide the clamp nut and pressure sleeve over cable. Comb out the braid.
3. Fold the braid back. Insert the ferrule between braid and dielectric. Trim off excess braid. Remove 5·16mm ($\frac{13}{64}$in) of the dielectric without damaging the inner conductor. Tin end of conductor.
4. Slide rear insulator over conductor and locate shoulder of insulator inside recess in ferrule. Slide the contact over conductor until the shoulder of the contact is pressed hard against the rear insulator. Solder contact to the conductor but avoid over-heating.
5. Fit front insulator in body and push sub-assembly into the body as far as possible. Slide pressure sleeve into body and screw in the clamp nut tightly to clamp cable.

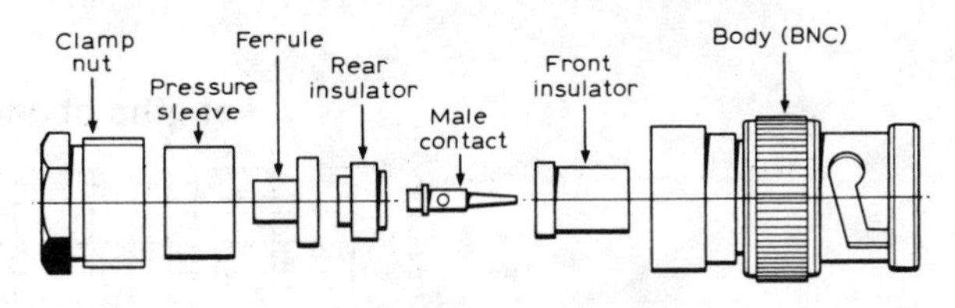

1.

5/16"
7·93mm

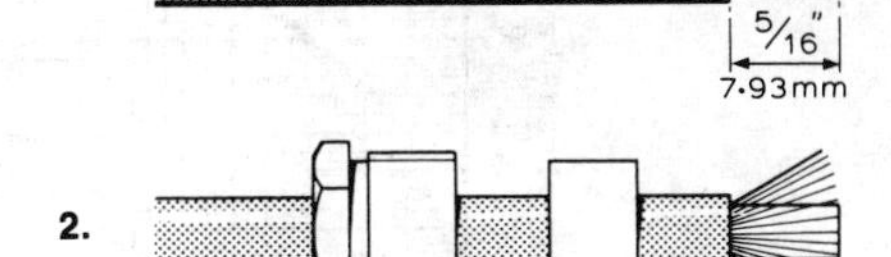

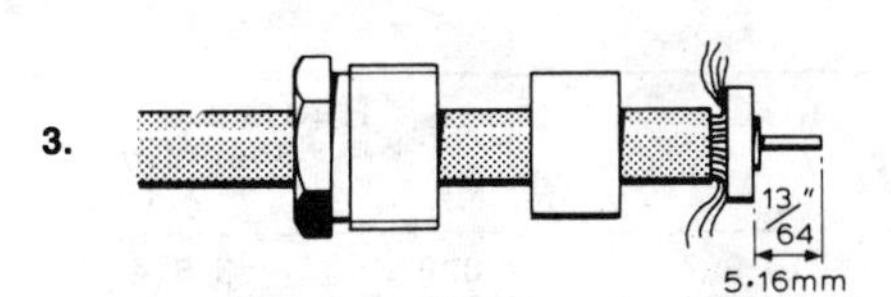

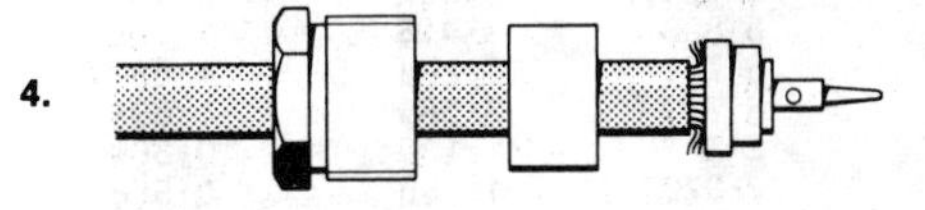

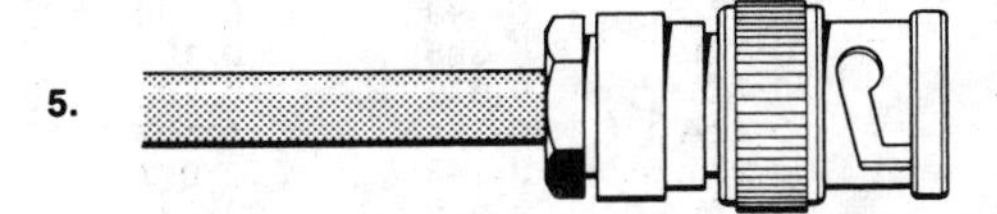

BNC type (male contact)

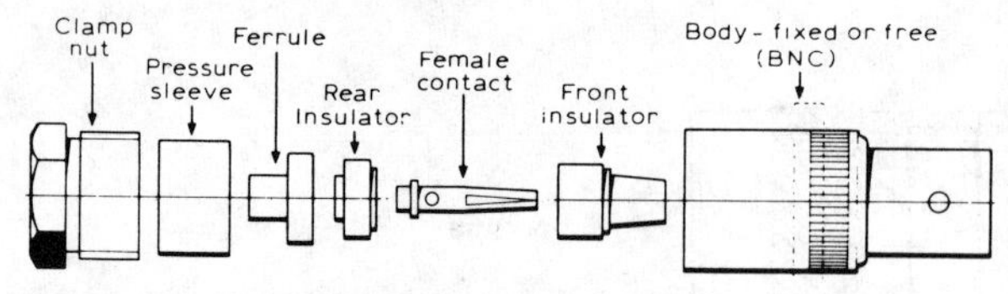

BNC type (female contact)

1.
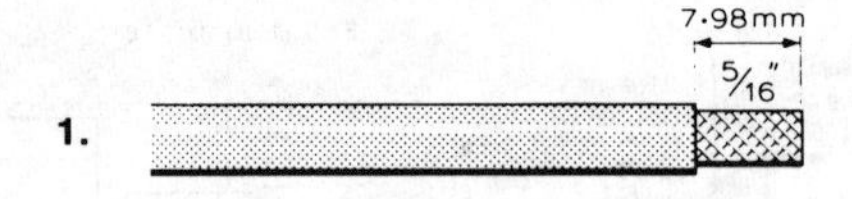

2.
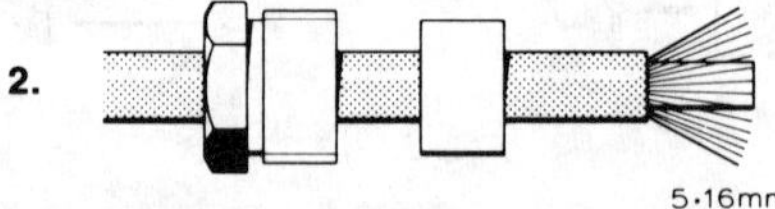

3.
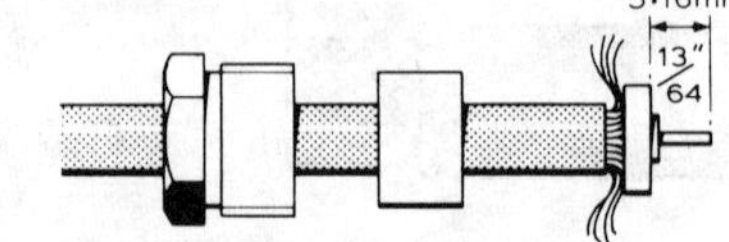

4.
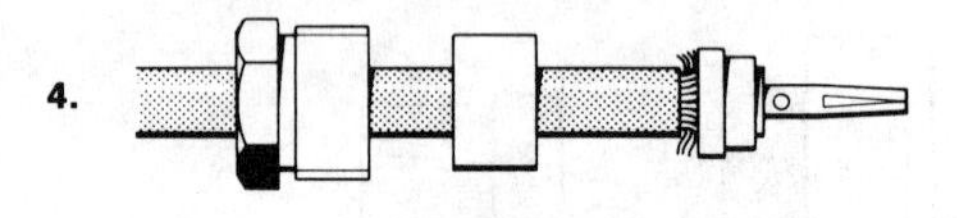

5.
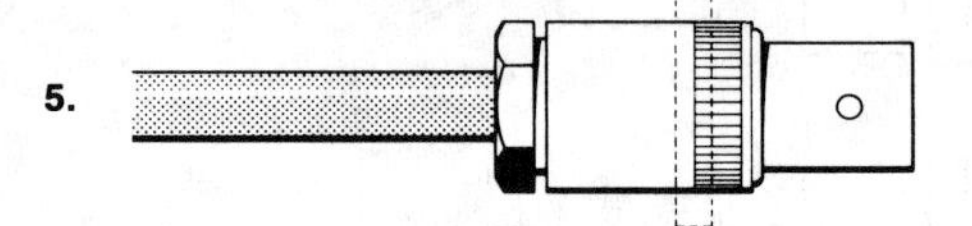

BNC type (female contact)

1. Cut end of cable even and remove 7·93mm ($\frac{5}{16}$in) of outer sheath.
2. Slide the clamp nut and pressure sleeve over cable. Comb out the braid.
3. Fold the braid back. Insert the ferrule between braid and dielectric. Trim off excess braid. Remove 5·16mm ($\frac{13}{64}$in) of the dielectric without damaging the inner conductor. Tin end of conductor.
4. Slide rear insulator over conductor and locate shoulder of insulator inside recess in ferrule. Slide the contact over conductor until the shoulder of the contact is pressed hard against the rear insulator. Solder contact to the conductor but avoid over-heating.
5. Fit front insulator in body and push sub-assembly into the body as far as possible. Slide pressure sleeve into body and screw in the clamp nut tightly to clamp cable.

Lengths of antenna elements

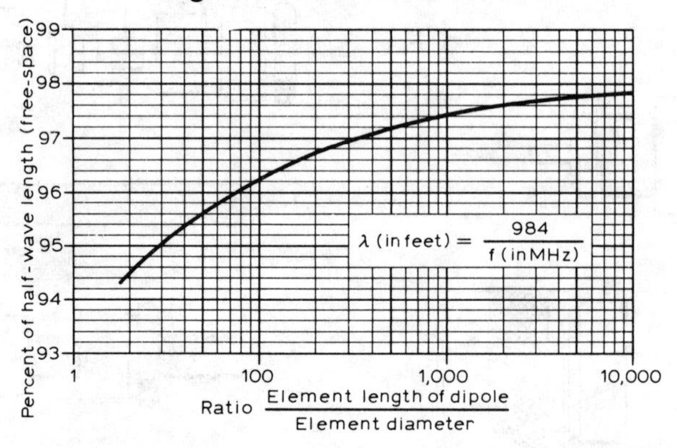

f (MHz)	Free space wavelength (ft) λ	λ/2	λ/4	λ/4 (in)	Corrected λ/4 (in) element diameter ⅛ in	¼ in	½ in
70	14·057	7·028	3·514	42·168	41·02	40·9	40·69
70·7	13·924	6·962	3·481	41·77	41·64	40·39	40·30
144	6·833	3·416	1·708	20·49	19·87	19·72	19·67
145	6·788	3·394	1·697	20·37	19·76	19·65	19·55
146	6·779	3·389	1·694	20·33	19·72	19·62	19·52
432	2·277	1·138	0·569	6·83	6·57	6·54	6·49
433	2·272	1·136	0·568	6·82	6·56	6·53	6·47
434	2·267	1·133	0·567	6·80	6·54	6·51	6·46
1,250	0·787	0·393	0·196	2·352	2·24	2·218	–
1,275	0·771	0·385	0·192	2·304	2·19	2·173	–
1,296	0·759	0·379	0·189	2·268	2·16	2·139	–
2,304	0·427	0·214	0·107	1·284	1·216	–	–
3,456	0·285	0·143	0·071	0·852	0·797	–	–
5,750	0·171	0·085	0·043	0·516	0·4798	–	–
10,350	0·095	0·0475	0·0237	0·284	0·2613	–	–

Ratings of some commonly used pa valves

ype	Base	Heater (V)	(A)	P_a (W)	V_a	V_{G_2}	F_{max} full rating (MHz)	$P_o$max (W)	Socket
ET22 DO3-10	Disc seal	6·3	0·4	10	350	—	100	2·4	Special
ET29	Disc seal	6·3	0·5	10	450	—	2,300	3·5	Special
ET24 DO4-20	Disc seal	6·3	1·0	20	400	—	600	23	Special
QV02-6*	B9A	6·3 12·6	0·8 0·4	2 × 3	275	200	500	5	B9A
QV03-10* 360	B9A	6·3 12·6	0·8 0·4	2 × 5	300	200	225	12·5	B9A
QV03-20A* 252	B7A	6·3 12·6	1·3 0·65	2 × 10	600	250	200 600	48 20	B7A
QV06-40A* 894	B7A	6·3 12·6	1·8 0·9	2 × 20	750	250	200 475	90 60	B7A
QV07-50*	B7A	6·3 12·6	2·5 1·25	2 × 25	750 600	250 250	180 470	130 69	B7A
X150A V1-150A	B8F Special	6·0	2·6	150	1,250	200	165 500	195 140	2m SK600A 70cm SK620A
C39A 289 CX100A5	Disc seal	6·3	1·05	100	1,000	—	2,500	40 17	500MHz Special 2,500MHz
CX250B E61-250 V2-2506	B8F Special	6·0	2·6	250	2,000	400	500	300 (AB1) 390 (C)	2m SK600A 70cm SK620A
CX250R 580W	Special	6·0	2·6	250	2,000	400	500	330 (AB1) 420 (C)	2m SK600A 70cm SK620A
CX350A 321	Special	6·0	2·9	350	2,500	450	150	400 (AB1)	2m SK600A
CX350FJ 904	Special	26·5	0·65	350	2,500	450	150	400 (AB1)	2m SK600A
874 875		6·3	3·0	400	2,200	—	500	500	Special
930	B8F Special	6·0	2·6	350	2,400	450	500	350 (AB1) 450 (C)	SK646
CX100U7 961	Disc seal	6	3	100	1,250	—	1,200	225 (C)	Special
122	11-pin	13·5	1·3	400	2,200	400	500	380 (AB1)	11-pin special
877 CX1500A7		6	3	1,500	4,000	—	250	1,500 (AB1) 2,000 (C)	

Double tetrode

Ratings of some commonly used power transistors

Type	V_{cbo} (V)	V_{ceo} (V)	I_c max (A)	P_d max (W)	P_o (W)	f (MHz)	P_g (dB)	V_{cc} (V)
BLX68	36	18	4	10	7·8	470	5·9	13·8
BLX69A	36	18	10	50	20	470	>4	13·8
BLX95	65	30	10	75	40	470	>4·5	28
BLY33	66	33	1·5	5	2	175	8	13·8
BLY34	40	20	1·5	5	3	175	8	13·8
BLY83	66	33	7·5	12	7	175	13	13·8
BLY85	40	20	3	10	>4	175	>10	13·8
BLY88A	36	18	7·5	32	15	175	7·5	12·5
BLY89A	36	18	10	62	25	175	>6	12·5
BLY90	36	18	20	113	50	175	>5	12·5
BLY93A	65	36	9	62	25	175	>9	28
2N3375	65	40	1·5	11·6	>3	400	—	28
2N3553	65	40	1	7	>2·5	175	—	28
2N3632	65	40	3	23	13·5	175	—	28
2N3866	55	30	0·4	5	1	175	10	13·5
2N4427	40	20	0·4	3·5	1	175	10	13·5
2N5590	—	—	—	—	10	175	5·2	13·5
2N5591	36	18	4	70	25	175	4·4	13·5
2N5944	36	16	0·4	5	2	470	9	12·5
2N5945	36	16	0·8	15	4	470	8	12·5
2N5946	36	18	2	37·5	10	470	6	12·5
2N6080	36	18	1·5	12	4	175	12	12·5
2N6081	36	18	2·5	31	15	175	6·3	12·5
2N6082	36	18	4	65	25	175	6·2	12·5
2N6083	36	18	4	65	30	175	5·7	12·5
2N6084	36	18	6	80	40	175	4·5	12·5
C1-12	36	15	0·25	5	1	470	10	12·5
C3-12	36	17	1	10	4	470	6	12·5
C12-12	36	17	2	25	12	470	—	12·5

Characteristics of some double-balanced diode mixers

Maker	Relcom	Anzac	MCL	MCL	MCL	MCL	Olektron	Olektron	Olektron	Olektron	Olektron
Model	MSF	MD108	SRA-1	SRA-1H	RAY-1	MA-1	CDB-198	CDB-110	CDB-112	CDB-114	CDB-185§
Frequency range lo (MHz)	2–500	5–500	5–500	5–500	5–500	1–2,500	0·002–50	0·01–100	0·2–200	1–500	5–1,000
RF input (MHz)	2–500	5–500	5–500	5–500	5–500	1–2,500	0·002–50	0·01–100	0·2–200	1–500	5–1,000
I.F. output (MHz)	DC–500	DC–500	DC–500	DC–500	DC–500	1–1,000	DC–50	DC–100	DC–200	DC–500	DC–800
Conversion loss (dB)	9	7·5‡	6·5†	6·5†	7·5†	8·0†	8·0‡	6·5‡	7·5‡	6†	7†
Isolation lo/rf (dB)	35–40	40*	45†	45†	40†	40†	45	45	35	35	20
Isolation lo/i.f. (dB)	25–35	35*	40†	40†	40†	40†	40	40	20	30	15
Power input (total) (mW)	50	400	500	500	1,000	50	40	40	30	35	15
Power lo (dBm)	+7	+7	+7	+17	+23	+10	—	—	—	—	—
(mW)	5	5	5	50	200	10	—	—	—	—	—
Signal 1dB compression level (dBm)	—	—	+1	+10	+15	+7	+7 to +13	+7 to +13	+7 to +13	+7 to +13	+7 to +13
Impedance, all ports (Ω)	50	50	50	50	50	50	50	50	50	50	50

‡Max *Min †Typical §May be used with lo power + 4dBm.

Ratings of other semiconductor power devices

ype	V_{ds} (V)	I_c max (A)	P_d Max (W)	P_o (W)	f (MHz)	P_g (dB)	V_{cc} (V)
			Power fets				
R66AJ	60	2	25	10	200	10	24
V2820S	65	2	40	20	175	10	28
V2840S	65	4	80	40	175	10	28
V2880U	65	8	160	80	175	10	28
			Broadband modules (cascade amplifiers)				
GY32	—	—	—	18	68–88	100mW	12·5
GY35	—	—	—	18	132–156	100mW	12·5
GY36	—	—	—	18	148–174	100mW	12·5
HW709	—	—	—	7·5	400–470	18·8	12·5
HW710	—	—	—	13	400–512	19·4	12·5
HW601	—	—	—	13	146–174	21·0	12·5
HW602	—	—	—	20	146–174	20·6	12·5

Wire sizes

ire No.	SWG (in)	SWG (mm)	AWG (in)	AWG (mm)	BWG (in)	BWG (mm)	Std metric (ref to swg) (mm)
000	0·40	10·16	0·460	11·68	0·454	11·53	
000	0·372	9·45	0·409	10·41	0·425	10·80	
00	0·348	8·84	0·365	9·27	0·380	9·65	
0	0·324	8·23	0·325	8·25	0·340	8·64	
1	0·300	7·62	0·289	7·35	0·300	7·62	
2	0·276	7·01	0·258	6·54	0·283	7·21	
3	0·252	6·40	0·229	5·83	0·259	6·58	
4	0·232	5·89	0·204	5·19	0·238	6·05	
5	0·212	5·38	0·182	4·62	0·220	5·59	
6	0·192	4·88	0·162	4·11	0·203	5·16	
7	0·176	4·47	0·144	3·66	0·179	4·57	
8	0·160	4·06	0·128	3·26	0·164	4·19	
9	0·144	3·66	0·114	2·90	0·147	3·76	
10	0·128	3·25	0·102	2·59	0·134	3·40	
11	0·116	2·95	0·091	2·30	0·120	3·05	
12	0·104	2·64	0·081	2·05	0·109	2·77	
13	0·092	2·34	0·072	1·83	0·095	2·41	
14	0·081	2·03	0·064	1·63	0·083	2·11	
15	0·072	1·83	0·057	1·45	0·072	1·83	
16	0·064	1·63	0·051	1·29	0·065	1·65	
17	0·056	1·42	0·045	1·15	0·058	1·47	1·5
18	0·048	1·22	0·040	1·02	0·049	1·24	1·25
19	0·040	1·02	0·036	0·91	0·042	1·07	1·00
20	0·036	0·92	0·032	0·81	0·035	0·89	
21	0·032	0·81	0·028	0·72	0·031	0·81	0·8
22	0·028	0·71	0·025	0·64	0·028	0·71	0·71
23	0·024	0·61	0·023	0·57	0·025	0·64	
24	0·023	0·56	0·020	0·51	0·023	0·56	0·56
25	0·020	0·51	0·018	0·45	0·020	0·51	0·5
26	0·018	0·46	0·016	0·40	0·018	0·46	
27	0·016	0·41	0·014	0·36	0·016	0·41	0·4
28	0·014	0·38	0·013	0·32	0·0135	0·356	
29	0·013	0·35	0·011	0·29	0·013	0·33	
30	0·012	0·305	0·010	0·25	0·012	0·305	0·315
31	0·011	0·29	0·009	0·23	0·010	0·254	
32	0·0106	0·27	0·008	0·20	0·009	0·299	
33	0·010	0·254	0·007	0·18	0·008	0·203	0·25
34	0·009	0·229	0·0063	0·16	0·007	0·178	0·224
35	0·008	0·203	0·0056	0·14	0·005	0·127	0·2
36	0·007	0·178	0·0050	0·13	0·004	0·102	
37	0·0067	0·17	0·0044	0·11			
38	0·006	0·15	0·0040	0·10			
39	0·005	0·127	0·0035	0·08			

WG = Standard wire gauge; AWG = American wire gauge; BWG = Birmingham wire gauge. Diameters in millimetres are derived from riginal inch sizes.

Power and voltage ratios in decibels

Power and voltage ratios are normally expressed in decibels where

$$N\ (\text{dB}) = 10 \log_{10} \frac{P_2}{P_1}$$

where P_1 and P_2 are the power ratios being compared. On the assumption of constant impedance, the corresponding voltage ratios V_2 and V_1 may be used,

$$N\ (\text{dB}) = 20 \log_{10} \frac{V_2}{V_1}$$

A value in decibels only has absolute meaning if the reference level is stated. The expressions dBm and dBW are frequently used to express decibels with respect to 1mW and 1W respec tively. The table below gives the decibel equivalents of a wide range of voltage and power ratios.

Relationship between dBm and voltage

A power level of 1mW into a 600 or 50Ω resistance has becom a standard for comparative purposes. It is the datum 0dBm Signal levels above and below this datum are expressed i ± dBm; they correspond to finite voltage (or current levels—not ratios.

0dBm into a 600Ω resistance corresponds to 0·775V
0dBm into a 50Ω resistance corresponds to 0·225V

Decibel table

← Voltage ratio (equal impedance)	Power ratio	− dB +	Voltage ratio (equal impedance) →	Power ratio
1·000	1·000	**0**	1·000	1·000
0·989	0·977	**0·1**	1·012	1·023
0·977	0·955	**0·2**	1·023	1·047
0·966	0·933	**0·3**	1·035	1·072
0·955	0·912	**0·4**	1·047	1·096
0·944	0·891	**0·5**	1·059	1·122
0·933	0·871	**0·6**	1·072	1·148
0·923	0·851	**0·7**	1·084	1·175
0·912	0·832	**0·8**	1·096	1·202
0·902	0·813	**0·9**	1·109	1·230
0·891	0·794	**1·0**	1·122	1·259
0·841	0·708	**1·5**	1·189	1·413
0·794	0·631	**2·0**	1·259	1·585
0·750	0·562	**2·5**	1·334	1·778
0·708	0·501	**3·0**	1·413	1·995
0·668	0·447	**3·5**	1·496	2·239
0·631	0·398	**4·0**	1·585	2·512
0·596	0·355	**4·5**	1·679	2·818
0·562	0·316	**5·0**	1·778	3·162
0·531	0·282	**5·5**	1·884	3·548
0·501	0·251	**6·0**	1·995	3·981
0·473	0·224	**6·5**	2·113	4·467
0·447	0·200	**7·0**	2·239	5·012
0·422	0·178	**7·5**	2·371	5·623
0·398	0·159	**8·0**	2·512	6·310
0·376	0·141	**8·5**	2·661	7·079
0·355	0·126	**9·0**	2·818	7·943
0·335	0·112	**9·5**	2·985	8·913
0·316	0·100	**10**	3·162	10·00
0·282	0·0794	**11**	3·55	12·6
0·251	0·0631	**12**	3·98	15·9
0·224	0·0501	**13**	4·47	20·0
0·200	0·0398	**14**	5·01	25·1
0·178	0·0316	**15**	5·62	31·6
0·159	0·0251	**16**	6·31	39·8
0·141	0·0200	**17**	7·08	50·1
0·126	0·0159	**18**	7·94	63·1
0·112	0·0126	**19**	8·91	79·4
0·100	0·0100	**20**	10·00	100·0
$3·16 \times 10^{-2}$	10^{-3}	**30**	$3·16 \times 10$	10^{3}
10^{-2}	10^{-4}	**40**	10^{2}	10^{4}
$3·16 \times 10^{-3}$	10^{-5}	**50**	$3·16 \times 10^{2}$	10^{5}
10^{-3}	10^{-6}	**60**	10^{3}	10^{6}
$3·16 \times 10^{-4}$	10^{-7}	**70**	$3·16 \times 10^{3}$	10^{7}
10^{-4}	10^{-8}	**80**	10^{4}	10^{8}
$3·16 \times 10^{-5}$	10^{-9}	**90**	$3·16 \times 10^{4}$	10^{9}
10^{-5}	10^{-10}	**100**	10^{5}	10^{10}
$3·16 \times 10^{-6}$	10^{-11}	**110**	$3·16 \times 10^{5}$	10^{11}
10^{-6}	10^{-12}	**120**	10^{6}	10^{12}

Relationship between dBm and voltage

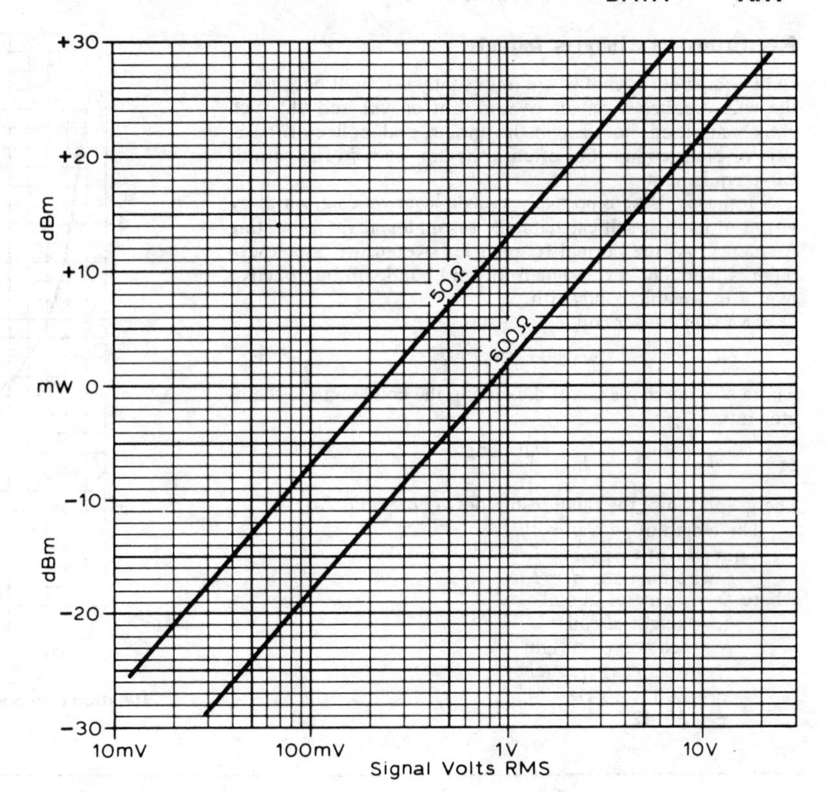

"T" attenuators (50Ω)

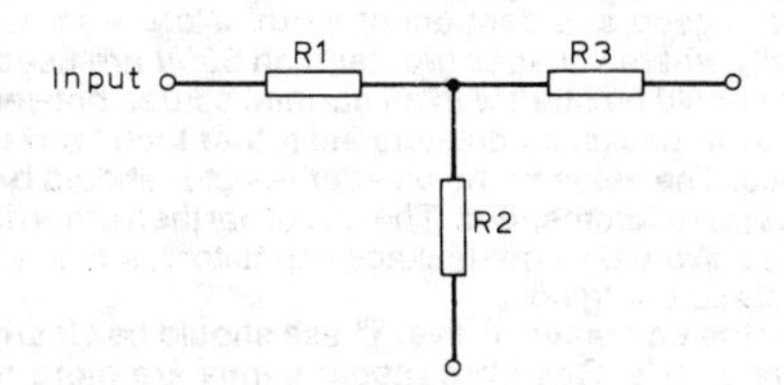

Attenuation (dB)	R1 Resistance (Ω)	R1 Dissipation (mW)	R2 Resistance (Ω)	R2 Dissipation (mW)	R3 Resistance (Ω)	R3 Dissipation (mW)	Total dissipation (mW)
1	2·875	57	433·3	102	2·875	46	205
2	5·731	114	215·2	180	5·731	72	360
3	8·55	171	141·9	242	8·55	87	446
4	11·31	226	104·8	285	11·31	90	520
5	14·01	280	82·24	314	14·01	88	682
6	16·61	332	66·93	332	16·61	83	747
7	19·12	387	55·80	341	19·12	76	804
8	21·53	430	47·31	343	21·53	68	841
0	25·97	519	35·14	328	25·97	52	899
2	29·92	598	26·81	300	29·92	38	936
5	34·9	710	18·36	235	34·9	21	966
0	40·91	818	10·10	168	40·91	10	996
5	44·67	894	5·641	98	44·67	5	997
0	46·9	938	3·165	59	46·9	1	998
5	48·25	970	1·779	29	48·25	<1	999
0	49·01	980	1·000	20	49·01	<1	1,000

Dissipations based on 1W input with a 50Ω termination.

Resonant rf chokes for vhf

In hf equipment rf chokes are not usually resonant because of the wide frequency range covered, but on vhf and uhf such chokes are used, not only in the anode, grid, collector, base, gate or drain circuits but often in heater leads in the case of valve equipment.

A resonant choke is normally a single-layer winding, which by virtue of its own self-capacitance, resonates at the operating frequency. At the normal frequencies over which the equipment is used, chokes designed for mid band will be effective over a reasonable bandwidth.

For a single-layer coil

$$\text{wavelength} = NL$$

where N is the shape factor depending the coil length to diameter ratio

or $$L = \frac{\text{wavelength}}{N}$$

The graph shows the relationship between N and L/D

The length of wire $L = c/fD$

number of turns $n = L/\pi D$

wire diameter $d = L/N$

where D = diameter of coil

L = length of coil

N = see curve on right

f = operating frequency

$c = 300 \times 10^6$Hz

$\pi = 3 \cdot 142$

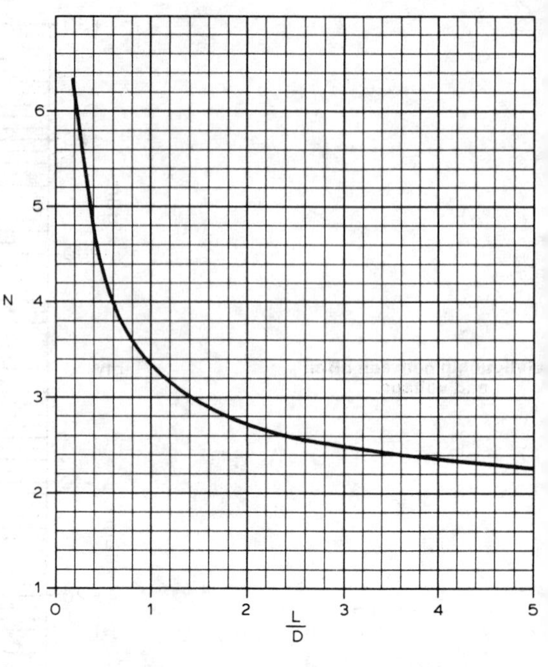

Relationship between shape factor and length/diameter ratio

Safety recommendations for the amateur radio station

1. All equipment should be controlled by one master switch, the position of which should be well known to others in the house or club.
2. All equipment should be properly connected to a good and permanent earth. (*Note A.*)
3. Wiring should be adequately insulated, especially where voltages greater than 500V are used. Terminals should be suitably protected.
4. Transformers operating at more than 100V rms should be fitted with an earthed screen between the primary and secondary windings.
5. Capacitors of more than 0·01μF operating in power packs, modulators etc (other than for rf bypass or coupling) should have a bleeder resistor connected directly across their terminals. The value of the bleeder resistor should be low enough to ensure rapid discharge. A value of 1/C Megohms (where C is in microfarads) is recommended. The use of earthed probe leads for discharging capacitors in case the bleeder resistor is defective is also recommended. (*Note B*). Low-leakage capacitors, such as paper and oil-filled types, should be stored with their terminals short-circuited to prevent static charging.
6. Indicator lamps should be installed showing that the equipment is live. These should be clearly visible at the operating and test positions. Faulty indicator lamps should be replaced immediately. Gas-filled (neon) lamps are more reliable than filament types.
7. Double-pole switches should be used for breaking mains circuits on equipment. Fuses of correct rating should be connected to the equipment side of each switch. (*Note C*). Always switch off before changing a fuse. The use of ac/dc equipment should be avoided.
8. In metal enclosed equipment install primary circuit breakers, such as micro-switches, which operate when the door or lid is opened. Check their operation frequently.
9. Test prods and test lamps should be of the insulated pattern.
10. A rubber mat should be used when the equipment is installed on a floor that is likely to become damp.
11. Switch off before making any adjustments. If adjustments must be made while the equipment is live, use one hand only and keep the other in your pocket. Never attempt two-handed work without switching off first. Use good-quality insulated tools for adjustments.
12. Do not wear headphones while making internal adjustments on live equipment.
13. Ensure that the metal cases of microphones, morse keys etc are properly connected to the chassis.
14. Do not use meters with metal zero-adjusting screws in high-voltage circuits. Beware of live shafts projecting through panels, particularly when metal grub screws are used in control knobs.
15. Antennas should not, under any circumstances, be connected to the mains or other ht source. Where feeders are connected through a capacitor which may have ht on the other side, a low-resistance dc path to earth should be provided (rf choke).

Note A. Owing to the common use of plastic water main and sections of plastic pipe in effecting repairs, it is no longer safe to assume that a mains water pipe is effectively connected to earth. Steps must be taken, therefore, to ensure that the earth connection is of sufficiently low resistance to provide safety in the event of a fault. Checks should be made whenever repairs are made to the mains water system in the building.

Note B. A "wandering earth lead" or an "insulated earthed probe lead" is an insulated lead permanently connected at one end to the chassis of the equipment; at the other end a suitable length of bare wire is provided for touch-contacting the high potential terminals to be discharged.

Note C. Where necessary, surge-proof fuses can be used.

Battery data

ze	Ever-Ready	IEC	Shape	Length diam	Width	Height	Contact type	Current range (mA)	Weight (g)	Voltage
AA*	HP16	R03	Round	10·5	—	45·0	Cap and base	0–1,000	8·5	1·5
A	HP7	R6	Round	14·5	—	50·5	Cap and base	0–75	16·5	1·5
A	C7	R6	Round	14·5	—	50·5	Cap and base	0–75	16·5	1·5
	SP11	R14	Round	26·2	—	50·0	Cap and base	20–60	45·0	1·5
*	HP11	R14	Round	26·2	—	50·0	Cap and base	0–1,000	45·0	1·5
	C11	R14	Round	26·2	—	50·0	Cap and base	0–5	45·0	1·5
	SP2	R20	Round	34·2	—	61·8	Cap and base	25–100	90·0	1·5
*	HP2	R20	Round	34·2	—	61·8	Cap and base	0–2,000	90·0	1·5
	AD28	3R25	Block	101·6	34·9	67·0	Socket	30–300	453·6	4·5
	PP8	4F100-4	Block	65·1	51·6	200·0	Stud	20–150	1·1kg	6
	PJ996	4R25	Block	67·0	67·0	102·0	Spring	30–300	581	6
	991		Block	135·7	72·2	125·4	Screws	30–500	1·47kg	6
	PP3-P	6F22	Block	26·5	17·5	48·5	Stud	0–50	39	9
	PP3-C	6F22	Block	26·5	17·5	48·5	Stud	0–50	39	9
	PP3	6F22	Block	26·5	17·5	48·5	Stud	0–10	38	9
	PP4	6F20	Round	25·5	—	50·0	Stud	0–10	51	9
	PP6	6F50-2	Round	36·0	34·5	70·0	Stud	2·5–15	142	9
	PP7	6F90	Round	46·0	46·0	61·9	Stud	5–20	198	9
	PP9	6F100	Round	66·0	52·0	81·0	Stud	5–50	425	9
	PP10	6F100-3	Round	66·0	52·0	226·0	Socket	15–150	1·25kg	9
	MN1300‡	LR20	Round	34·2	—	61·5	Cap and base	0–2,000	123	1·5
*	MN1400‡	LR14	Round	26·2	—	50·0	Cap and base	0–1,000	65	1·5
A*	MN1500‡	LR6	Round	14·5	—	50·5	Cap and base	0–250	23	1·5
AA	MN2400‡	LR03	Round	10·5	—	44·5	Cap and base	0–100	13	1·5

Suitable for motor equipment, recorders etc; ‡Manganese alkaline

VHF/UHF MANUAL

Errata

Page 3.5 (5th panel from top). Revised formula.
Page 3.5 (7th panel from top). Revised formula.
Page 4.43 (halfway down LH col), to read 3N204, not 2N204.
Page 5.4 (Fig 7) Earth connection added to lower end of L8.
Page 7.3 (LH col) to read one eighth of an inch, not seven eighths.
Page 5.71 (Fig 148). Revised drawing
Page 5.72 (Fig 149). Revised drawing
Page 5.74 (Tables 18 and 19). Revised data below.
Page A.4 (square coaxial chart) Revise formula as per 3.5 above.
Page A.6 (British UR chart) UR90 capacitance pF/ft shown as 0, should read 21.
Fig 148: C35 5 to 60p should be C35 7 to 100p. RH C20 should be C21.

Page 5.74 (Table 18). See revised items below. Items not listed remain unchanged

C1	18pF
C2,10,11,14	5-65pF 2222 808 32659 film dielectric Mullard.
C5,7,21,17,25,33	10nF
C13	delete
C36,37	delete

Add the following items:

D1,2,3	1N4001
C27,29	5-60pF high temperature type 2222 809 07011
C35	7-100pF high temp type 2222 809 07015

Note: Both type 2222s are Mullard film dielectric.

Page 5.74 (Table 19). See revised items below

Inductor	Turns	swg	ID(mm)	Other detail
L1	1	20	0.25(6mm)	--
L2	3	20	0.25(6mm)	0.25(6mm) long
L3	2	18	0.40(10mm)	0.25(6mm) long
L4,5	1	18	0.40(10mm)	0.2(4mm) lead length
L6,7	2	20	0.25(6mm)	0.25(6mm) long
L8,9	3	18	0.375(4.5mm)	0.2(4mm) long 0.25(6mm) lead

ndex